The Birds of Zambia

An atlas and handbook

by

Robert J. Dowsett,
Dylan R. Aspinwall †
and
Françoise Dowsett-Lemaire

2008

Tauraco Press and Aves a.s.b.l.
Rue Fusch 3, B-4000 Liège, Belgium (www.aves.be)

First edition 2008

ISBN 2-87225-005-0

Dépôt légal D/2008/6838/06

Cover photos: Central Bearded Scrub Robin (Mutinondo Wilderness, Warwick Tarboton); inselberg rising from a sea of miombo woodland, with Lake Lusiwashi in the background (Phil Berry, 2004).

Design by R.J. Dowsett & F. Dowsett-Lemaire

Typeset by R.J. Dowsett

Colour preparation by Aves a.s.b.l. and Ginko

Printed in France by Imprimerie Chirat, Saint Just la Pendue

Available from the Natural History Book Service Ltd, 2-3 Wills Road, Totnes, Devon TQ9 5XN, United Kingdom
Internet: www.nhbs.com

Contents

PREFACE

This is the sixth in a series of documentations of the Zambian avifauna, which started 70 years ago. The first pioneering faunal survey by Charles Pitman (1934) was followed by periodic updates by ornithologists resident in the country: Jack Winterbottom (1939), Charles White and Winterbottom (1949), Con Benson and White (1957), Benson with Richard Brooke, Bob Dowsett and Michael Irwin (1971). The present revision continues this tradition, and I have been especially fortunate to have known and worked with all these predecessors.

The presentation of successive checklists has developed, and in the new *Birds of Zambia* we have in particular expanded the use of species distribution maps started in 1971, and at the same time added much information on subjects such as breeding seasons and migrations, which have been studied here in recent years. Our aim is to present a synthesis of all that is known about birds in Zambia, as a firm basis for future research and conservation.

Zambian ornithology has benefited from the presence of a number of keen, long-term residents, supplemented by shorter-term contract workers and the occasional professional research scientist. The base on which this is constructed is narrow, however, and there have inevitably been periods of limited activity (through paucity of observers or security restrictions on travel). In analysing changes of status over time we have tried to take the factor of uneven observer effort into account, and although a large proportion of the fieldwork described here took place some time ago, attention has been paid to including the results of recent monitoring.

There is now a great body of data available to the student of Zambian birds, much of it published. My own studies were full-time over 20 years, while variously game ranger and then ornithologist (1962-79 resident in the country, then 1979-82, when Françoise and I lived in Malawi, but worked on the Nyika Plateau). We undertook similar fieldwork elsewhere in Malawi during several years, to 2002. Dylan Aspinwall used the school holidays for extensive surveys throughout Zambia, from 1971 to 1995, and during several years was able to cover much of the country professionally, as Inspector of French. Françoise Lemaire's commitment to African ornithology started in Zambia in 1976.

We have enjoyed the friendship and cooperation of a network of correspondents (acknowledged elsewhere), and have benefited from observations documented in the Zambian Ornithological Society's *Bulletin* (1969-84), *Newsletter* (1971 to date) and *Zambia Bird Report* (1997-99).

Responsibility for assembling these data has ultimately been my own, but up to the time of his tragic disappearance at the end of 1995 Dylan and I had agreed on our treatment of the distributional and migration data, on which species records at that time were sufficiently well documented to be included, and on the basic format of this work. The present documentation and analysis is the joint effort of Françoise and myself. For anyone needing to investigate the status of any species in more detail than the synthesis presented here, attention is drawn to the *Tauraco Research Report* no. 9 (Dowsett in press), which documents many unpublished observations, and the references therein.

R.J. Dowsett

INTRODUCTION

1. Physical features

Geography

Zambia is a land-locked country situated on the Central African plateau, at the south-western end of the Great Rift Valley, between latitudes 8° and 18°S and longitudes 22° and 33°E. It is bordered to the north by Zaire (at present called République Démocratique du Congo), north-east by Tanzania, to the east by Malawi, south-east by Mozambique, south by Zimbabwe, south-west by Botswana and Namibia, and to the west by Angola. The country is some 1350 km at its widest (from north-east to south-west), and 270 km at its narrowest (south of the "Congo pedicle"), with a land area of some 753,000 km². The physical features of Zambia were well documented in *Zambia in maps* (Davis 1971), some maps relevant to the discussion that follows being repeated by Ansell (1978). The country is served by a good set of maps at 1:250,000. Zambia has at present nine provinces (**Fig. 1**) divided into 72 districts.

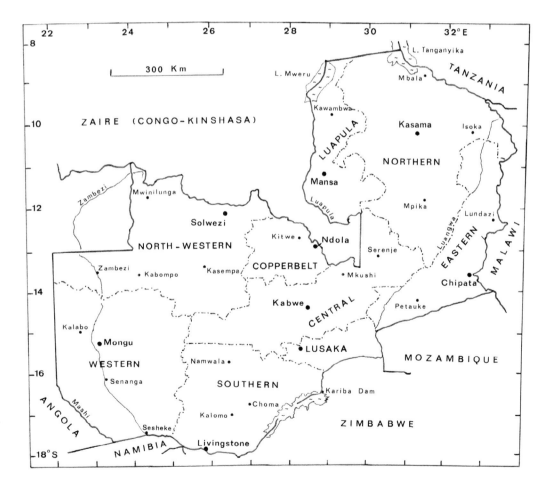

Figure 1. Map of Zambia, showing Provinces, Provincial headquarters (large dots) and some important towns or localities (small dots).

The Rift is represented by the Luangwa River, which rises in the Mafinga Mts and drains the north-eastern part of the country; it flows through a broad valley at 500-700 m, joining the Zambezi at Feira (now called Luangwa town), at an altitude of 330 m, the lowest point in the country (**Fig. 2**). The Zambezi River too rises in Zambia, the source of the Zambezi being in northern Mwinilunga District at 1490 m. After crossing the great Barotse Floodplain, the Zambezi forms the southern boundary in an immense arc, from Sesheke to Luangwa town. Other major rivers are the Luapula (rising in Lake Bangweulu, and flowing into the Congo system in Zaire), the Chambeshi (rising near the Tanzanian border, and draining into Lake Bangweulu) and the Kafue (a tributary of the Zambezi, with its source on the border with Zaire).

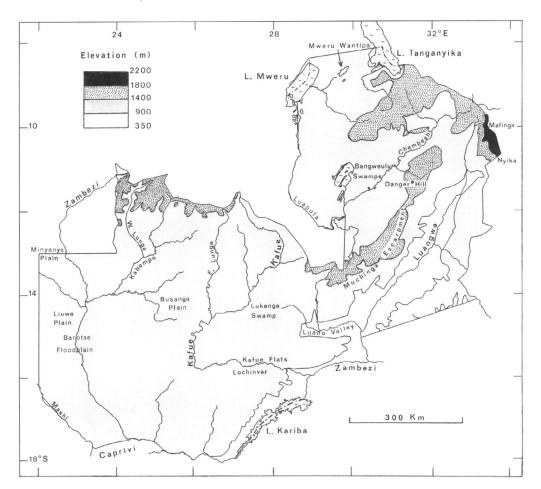

Figure 2. Topography of Zambia, with some important geographical features.

Most of Zambia is occupied by the Central African peneplain at 900-1400 m, above which a few hills and high plateaux rise in the north-east to 1800-2300 m – notably the Mafinga Mts (peak at *c.* 2290 m), the Makutu Plateau (2119 m) and the Nyika Plateau (2200 m, reaching 2606 m on the far more extensive Malawi side). The relief of these mountains is rather gentle, the slopes rising gradually from the woodlands below. A few parts of the Zambian plateau, while not montane in character today, do reach 1400-1700 m and the avifauna (and locally the botany) provide evidence of a "southern montane route" between the highlands of East and West Africa. Well-known examples are Bwingimfumu Hills (Danger Hill), Mutinondo Wilderness and Musense, all along the Muchinga Escarpment. A conspicuous feature of the Muchingas (forming the northern edge of the Luangwa Valley) and the Middle Zambezi escarpment is the presence of large rock faces, while inselbergs (koppjes) occur locally on the Eastern Province plateau.

The main geological features of the Zambian plateau are Sandveld, replaced by Kalahari Sands from 25°E westwards. The escarpment areas of the north-east, east and south are a mixture, including rocks of the Mafingi System, chiefly quartzites, schists and phyllites, with local intrusions of granite, syenite and pyroxenite. In the north-east the most important intrusion is the large granite mass which forms most of the Nyika Plateau. The Rift Valley floor is occupied by soft sedimentary rocks of Karoo and post-Karoo age – shales, mudstones, sandstones – and more recent alluvial deposits, as are the Bangweulu and Lukanga Swamps, the Kafue Flats and the Barotse Floodplain. The different soil types are mapped in Ansell (1978: Map D), and a detailed geological bibliography was presented by Guernsey (1954).

The map (**Fig. 2**) shows major rivers and lakes. The Upper Zambezi, Kafue, and Chambeshi Rivers and Lake Bangweulu are lined with permanent wetlands in places, some very large. All are bordered by large seasonal swamps and floodplain grassland. Where it meets Lake Mweru, the Luapula River is flanked by dense Papyrus swamp; otherwise most of its course is narrow and rocky.

Climate

Zambia has a tropical continental climate, without the maritime influences from the Mozambique Channel that are a feature of the weather in neighbouring Malawi to the east. There is a cool dry season from May to August, then an increasingly hot, dry one, until late October or November, followed by the warm rainy season through to March or April. Past climatological data are available for a wide scattering of places throughout the country (Anon. 1971). Typical rainfall patterns are shown in **Fig. 3** for two extreme localities, Mwinilunga (heavy rainfall) and Livingstone (light rainfall) – for the position of these localities, see **Fig. 1**. Similarly, seasonal variations in temperature are shown for two extreme areas, Mbala (moderate winter and summer temperatures) and Livingstone (low winter and high summer peaks).

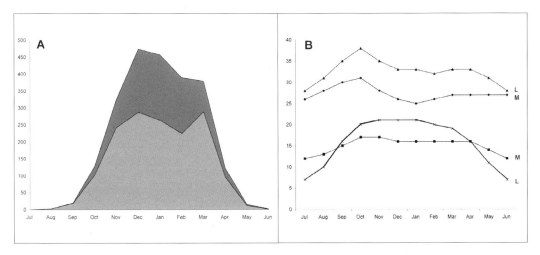

Figure 3. (A) Mean monthly rainfall (mm) at Mwinilunga (black) & Livingstone (grey), 1941-1991. (B) Mean monthly minimum and maximum temperatures (°C) at Mbala (M) & Livingstone (L).

Temperatures vary considerably with altitude as well as time of year, the hottest part of the country being the Middle Zambezi and Luangwa Valleys where daily maxima may exceed 38°C while the higher levels of the plateau may have frost during the dry season. Mean annual temperatures vary from 25-26°C at 330 m, to 20-22°C at 950-1250 m, 18-20°C at 1250-1450 m and <19°C above 1600 m. Night frosts occur occasionally on 2-4 days per year in many parts of the country (to as low as Livingstone), in the colder months of May to July – with an average of 7-10 days a year at Serenje and Mwinilunga (at *c.* 1350-1400 m alt.). The rainy season lasts from November to about March in the south, starting a month earlier and finishing a month later at places in the north such as Mwinilunga.

Mean annual rainfall varies greatly in different parts of the country, from *c.* 700 mm to just under 1400 mm. The least rainfall is on the plateau from Lusaka south-westwards, in the Luangwa Valley, and the low-lying country between lakes Mweru and Tanganyika in the far north (Map C in Ansell 1978). The most is in the north, from a line Mwinilunga-Samfya-Mbala. During the first half of the rains (October to December) precipitation is normally marked (mean > 400 mm) in a limited area, north of 13°S and west of 31°E. The second half (January to March) usually sees heavy rain (> 550 mm) in most of the country north of 14°S, including now the east.

In recent years there have been series of drought years with rainfall well below average, and a few years when it was well above. However, what is most noticeable is the extreme variation – within one season southern parts of the country may experience a drought, while the north or east witnesses serious flooding. Even in one area a rainy season may start abnormally late, with drought followed by extensive floods. However, the overall tendency in much of the country is not a decrease in annual rainfall. Of nine sites analysed in detail (for their location, see **Fig. 1**), mean annual rainfall increased in four (Lusaka, Mwinilunga, Kasama, Mbala) in the period 1971-2000, compared to the previous 30 years, by 2-5%. There was a significant decrease in three areas in the south and south-west, Livingstone (-5%), Choma and Mongu (-8% each). In these areas drought conditions resulted not only from rather fewer days with rain (e.g. at Mongu a decrease from 102 days p.a. to 90), but in particular significantly less rain from February onwards. At Chipata and Mpika there was no significant change.

In the country as a whole, the 35 years 1966-2000 saw eight seasons with much reduced rainfall (1967, 1972, 1981-83, 1986-87, 1993), and eight with significantly more (1973-74, 1980, 1984-85, 1988, 1996, 1998), but the situation is complicated by regional variation. Detailed annual rainfall data are available from the Choma area for the 57 years 1950/51 to 2006/07 (**Fig. 4**).

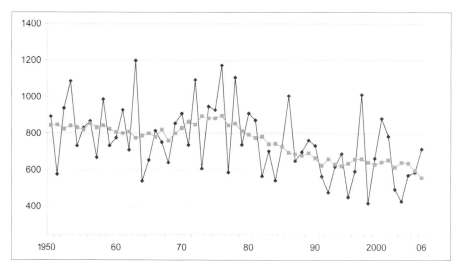

Figure 4. Annual rainfall (mm) at Choma, 1950-2006 (with 10-year rolling mean).

In the Choma farming area "January has been the most reliable month with the rolling average peaking at about 225 mm in the late 1960s and just dropping below 150 mm recently – up to 2000 it did not fall below 175 mm per month. December shows the biggest, steadiest decline from 250 mm in 1960 to less than 150 mm now" (B. Danckwerts *in litt.* 2007).

Of the four years in which there were significant influxes of Grey-backed Sparrow-Larks *Eremopterix verticalis* to southern Zambia, three were in the cold winters preceding failed rains (1964, 1982 and 1992, in which there fell only 476-566 mm of rain, the exception being 1970). Increasing drought in the south-west has apparently influenced the recent arrival of such species as Kori Bustard *Ardeotis kori* (since 1977), Burchell's Sandgrouse *Pterocles burchelli* and Scaly-feathered Finch *Sporopipes squamifrons* (since 1992).

Human population

The majority of Zambia's estimated population of 9-10 million people live in urban or semi-urban areas. Population density varies therefore from fewer than $10/km^2$ in many rural areas to more than $250/km^2$ in large urban centres along "line of rail" (i.e. the main rail/road linking Livingstone and the Copperbelt, via Lusaka), with some large concentrations too in the Luapula Valley and parts of the Eastern Province plateau. Probably no more than 30% of the land is cultivated – with maize (or cassava locally in the north) as the main subsistence crop, tobacco the most important cash crop. In most places the natural vegetation has been affected by man, even though the system of "chitemene" or shifting cultivation enabled old gardens to regenerate. Fire has had considerable influence and it has been shown in places that either miombo or "chipya" woodland is an extremely fire-hardy climax which has replaced evergreen forest. Locally there has been extensive clearing of protected forests, especially in Mwinilunga District and parts of Eastern Province. The best hope for preserving large tracts of indigenous vegetation in the long term is the national park system, forest reserves being far more vulnerable – see under Conservation.

Zambia has had for many years an economy based principally on mineral exploitation, with agriculture generally underachieving. In the 1980s and 90s the collapse of the copper market coincided with a considerable decline in agricultural production, although more recently the world demand for copper has grown. There has been an increase in commercial agricultural exploitation in the past few years, with an influx of government-encouraged farmers from Zimbabwe and South Africa. Resulting land clearance will have a serious effect on the conservation of the woodlands of the Zambian plateau.

2. Vegetation and major bird habitats

Biogeographically, Zambia lies within the Zambezian regional centre of endemism (or Zambezian region), dominated by various types of woodland or dry forest. In addition there is a localized pocket of Afromontane vegetation in the small area of highlands of the north-east on the Malawi border, and an enclave of Guineo-Congolian forest vegetation in the Mwinilunga area, on the borders with Zaire and Angola. There is also a diffuse Afromontane and Guineo-Congolian influence through the moister types of evergreen forest in the higher-rainfall regions of the north, and a dry Kalahari influence in the extreme south-west.

  At low altitudes (mainly below 900 m) in the Luangwa and Middle Zambezi Valleys the dominant woodland type is mopane (with some thicket), which gives way to miombo on the escarpments and almost throughout the central plateau, whereas on Kalahari sands of the south-west (Senanga, Sesheke) and west (Kabompo, Lukulu) respectively, dry deciduous forest (*Baikiaea*) and evergreen forest (*Cryptosepalum*) replace miombo; undifferentiated woodland occupies other sections of the south-west and some of the Kafue, Bangweulu and Chambeshi basins, and grows alongside mopane in the low-lying valleys. Open grasslands and swamps also occupy significant areas in Zambia: extensive grasslands are to be found in the Upper Zambezi and in the floodplains of the Kafue, Chambeshi and Bangweulu basins; important permanent swamps, from north to south, include Mweru Wantipa, Bangweulu, Lukanga and parts of the Kafue Flats. Moist evergreen forest is very localized and fragmented, occurring in small patches mainly in the higher-rainfall belt of the northern half; above 1800 m larger patches of montane rain forest intersected with montane grassland are to be found in the north-eastern highlands.

  The terms used in this book to designate the different vegetation types largely follow the definitions of White (1983a: 46):

forest is a continuous stand of trees at least 8-10 m high, their crowns interlocking;
woodland is an open stand of trees at least 8 m tall with a canopy cover of 40% or more. The field layer
   is usually dominated by grasses;
transition woodland is intermediate between forest and woodland and usually consists of a deciduous
   canopy and evergreen understorey;
wooded grassland (or wooded savanna) is an open stand of trees with a canopy cover of between 10
   and 40%;
grassland is land covered with grasses and other herbs, either without woody plants or the latter not
   covering more than 10% of the ground;
thicket is a closed stand of bushes usually 3-8 m tall;
shrubland (or bracken-briar) is an open or closed stand of shrubs up to 2-3 m.

A map showing the main vegetation types in Zambia is presented on **page 14**; it has been adapted from the vegetation map of White (1983a).

1. Zambezian woodland

Zambezian woodland is normally deciduous for parts of the dry season; in miombo leaf flush occurs just before the onset of the rains, and a little later in mopane (at the start of the rains).

1.1. Miombo or *Brachystegia* woodland

Widespread in the Zambezian region from Angola across to Tanzania and Mozambique, miombo represents (or used to occupy) about 80% of woodland cover in Zambia. It is usually dominated by species of *Brachystegia, Isoberlinia* and *Julbernardia*, but after cultivation or on shallow soils it can be dominated by *Uapaca* species; *Uapaca* and *Protea* species are also characteristic of the ecotone at dambo edges. Normally with a light canopy 15-20 m high, more stunted on poor soils, in some areas it becomes so dense that it would be more appropriately called miombo forest (as in parts of Kasempa District). Termite mounds and rocky outcrops encourage the development of thickets. In higher-rainfall areas (as on the Copperbelt) patches of miombo protected from fire have reverted to dry evergreen forest or transition woodland on deep soils, but on the shallowest soils miombo has maintained itself (Trapnell 1959, White 1983a). Epiphytic vegetation is well developed only in the wetter regions.

Miombo is normally absent from the valley floor of the Luangwa but appears on small hills at about 600-700 m; it is completely dominant at intermediate elevations (between 900 and 1700 m); in the north-eastern highlands tall miombo ascends the drier, western slopes up to 2000-2100 m (as in the Mafingas). On the Nyika tall miombo extends up to 2050 m on the Malawi side of the border and is rather more stunted on the steep Zambian escarpment (as below the Manyenjere ridge). Miombo woodland has been cleared in large areas for subsistence cultivation, commercial crops (especially maize and tobacco) or felled for firewood. However, very extensive stands remain on private land, as well as in several of the National Parks – especially Kafue N.P., where it covers some three-quarters of the 22,400 km² (Mitchell 1963) – and many Forest Reserves.

The avifauna of miombo woodland contains a mixture of species endemic to this vegetation type (and indeed to the Zambezian region as a whole) and others with a wider ecological niche, and/or more widely distributed in the Afrotropics. A list of the most characteristic or conspicuous species encountered should include at least the following: Schalow's Turaco *Tauraco schalowi*, Striped Kingfisher *Halcyon chelicuti*, Racket-tailed Roller *Coracias spatulatus*, Red-billed Wood Hoopoe *Phoeniculus purpureus*, Scimitarbill *P. cyanomelas*, Pale-billed Hornbill *Tockus pallidirostris*, Anchieta's Barbet *Stactolaema anchietae* and Whyte's Barbet *S. whytii* (largely allopatric), Yellow-fronted Tinkerbird *Pogoniulus chrysoconus*, Miombo Pied Barbet *Tricholaema frontata*, Bennett's Woodpecker *Campethera bennettii*, Golden-tailed Woodpecker *C. abingoni*, Cardinal Woodpecker *Dendropicos fuscescens*, Bearded Woodpecker *Thripias namaquus*, Long-billed Pipit *Anthus similis*, Striped Pipit *A. lineiventris* (near rocks), Black Cuckoo-shrike *Campephaga flava*, White-breasted Cuckoo-shrike *Coracina pectoralis*, Miombo Rock Thrush *Monticola angolensis*, Kurrichane Thrush *Turdus libonyana*, Central Bearded Scrub Robin *Erythropygia barbata*, White-browed Scrub Robin *E. leucophrys*, Arnot's Chat *Myrmecocichla arnotti*, Green-capped Eremomela *Eremomela scotops*, Black-collared Eremomela *E. atricollis*, Yellow-bellied Eremomela *E. icteropygialis*, Red-capped Crombec *Sylvietta ruficapilla*, Yellow-bellied Hyliota *Hyliota flavigaster*, Southern Hyliota *H. australis*, Neddicky *Cisticola fulvicapilla*, Trilling Cisticola *C. woosnami*, Miombo Barred Warbler *Camaroptera undosa*, Pallid Flycatcher *Bradornis pallidus*, Böhm's Flycatcher *Muscicapa boehmi*, Chinspot Batis *Batis molitor*, Miombo Grey Tit *Parus griseiventris*, Rufous-bellied Tit *P. rufiventris*, Grey Penduline Tit *Anthoscopus caroli*, Spotted Creeper *Salpornis spilonotus*, Red-and-blue Sunbird *Anthreptes anchietae*, Violet-backed Sunbird *A. longuemarei*, Black Sunbird *Nectarinia amethystina*, Miombo Double-collared Sunbird *N. manoensis*, Yellow White-eye *Zosterops senegalensis*, African Golden Oriole *Oriolus auratus*, Eastern Black-headed Oriole *O. larvatus*, Sousa's Shrike *Lanius souzae*, Brubru *Nilaus afer*, Southern Puffback *Dryoscopus cubla*, White Helmet Shrike *Prionops plumatus*, Retz's Red-billed Helmet Shrike *P. retzii*, Fork-tailed Drongo *Dicrurus adsimilis*, Lesser Blue-eared Starling *Lamprotornis chloropterus*, Amethyst Starling *Cinnyricinclus leucogaster*, Yellow-throated Petronia *Petronia superciliaris*, Chestnut-mantled Sparrow-weaver *Plocepasser rufoscapulatus*, Bar-winged Weaver *Ploceus angolensis* (local in the wetter types), Red-headed Weaver *Anaplectes melanotis*, Red-backed Mannikin *Spermestes bicolor*, Black-eared Seedeater *Serinus mennelli*, Stripe-breasted Seedeater *S. reichardi*, Golden-breasted Bunting *Emberiza flaviventris* and Cabanis's Bunting *E. cabanisi*; in addition to various raptors, doves, parrots (mainly Meyer's *Poicephalus meyeri*), cuckoos (especially Red-chested *Cuculus solitarius* and African Grey *C. gularis*), owls (e.g. African Scops *Otus senegalensis*), nightjars (especially Pennant-winged *Macrodipteryx vexillarius*) and bee-eaters (Swallow-tailed *Merops hirundineus*). Most of the insectivorous species feed in mixed parties. The great majority of species are resident; a few are intra-African migrants (Pennant-winged Nightjar) or have shorter-distance but complex movements (Swallow-tailed Bee-eater, Amethyst Starling).

Altitudinal zonation of miombo species has not been studied in as much detail as in Malawi; there is little doubt that the avifauna is richest in mature miombo at medium elevations (above 1000 m). Few species reach the highest levels (as in the Mafingas) where the following ascend to the upper limit of woodland at about 2000 m or slightly higher: Golden-tailed and Cardinal Woodpeckers, Miombo Rock Thrush, Green-capped Eremomela, Red-capped Crombec, Yellow-bellied Hyliota (1950 m), Trilling Cisticola, Southern Black Flycatcher *Melaenornis pammelaina,* Chinspot Batis, Miombo Grey and Rufous-bellied Tits, Black and Miombo Double-collared Sunbirds, helmet shrikes *Prionops* spp. (1950 m), Yellow-throated Petronia (1950 m), Black-eared Seedeater, Golden-breasted and Cabanis's Buntings.

Miombo is the favoured wintering habitat of at least one Palaearctic migrant, Collared Flycatcher *Ficedula albicollis*, and Tree Pipit *Anthus trivialis* is frequent on the north-central plateau.

1.2. Mopane woodland

Mopane woodland has an open canopy 6-20 m high, with *Colophospermum mopane* pure or almost so. It is found in the valleys of the Luangwa (almost to its source), Luano, Kafue as far north as the Nanzhila area (Kafue N.P.), Zambezi west to Katima Mulilo and the Mashi to just north of the Sesheke-Senanga border. Its altitudinal range in Zambia is mainly 400-900 m, but in the upper Luangwa mopane woodland ascends to the plateau at the unusual altitude of 1200 m in Chama District, while on the Southern Province plateau there are small pockets near Choma at about 1300 m. Mopane is often inter-rupted by clumps of *Acacia nigrescens, Combretum imberbe, Kirkia acuminata* and Baobab thickets (latter usually on termite mounds). Most of the mopane is protected within national parks, especially in the Luangwa Valley.

A few bird species are largely confined to mopane in Zambia: Three-banded Courser *Rhinoptilus cinctus,* Lilian's Lovebird *Agapornis lilianae,* Southern Long-tailed Starling *Lamprotornis mevesii* and White-browed Sparrow-weaver *Plocepasser mahali.* The following are characteristic of mopane woodland and *Acacia* savanna: Black-cheeked Lovebird *Agapornis nigrigenis,* Double-banded Sandgrouse *Pterocles bicinctus,* Senegal Kingfisher *Halcyon senegalensis,* Red-billed Hornbill *Tockus erythrorhynchus,* Long-billed Crombec *Sylvietta rufescens,* Southern Black Tit *Parus niger,* Southern White-bellied Sunbird *Nectarinia talatala,* Southern Grey-headed Sparrow *Passer diffusus* and Red-billed Buffalo Weaver *Bubalornis niger.* Many of the unspecialized woodland species found commonly in miombo occur also in mopane (such as various woodpeckers and wood hoopoes, Kurrichane Thrush, Chinspot Batis, Southern Puffback, helmet shrikes, Fork-tailed Drongo, Yellow-throated Petronia etc.) but quite a few miombo specialists are absent from mopane (e.g. Anchieta's and Whyte's Barbets, Miombo Rock Thrush, Central Bearded Scrub Robin, Black-collared Eremomela, Red-capped Crombec, hyliotas, Böhm's Flycatcher, Red-and-blue Sunbird, Sousa's Shrike, Bar-winged Weaver, Black-eared and Stripe-breasted Seedeaters). Winterbottom (1938b, 1956a) carried out some censuses in the mopane of the Luangwa and Middle Zambezi: White-browed Sparrow-weaver was each time the most numerous species, followed by the ubiquitous Cape Turtle Dove *Streptopelia capicola.* Some of the Zambezian endemics are more commonly distributed in mopane than miombo, including Racket-tailed Roller and Arnot's Chat. The localized White-winged Starling *Neocichla gutturalis* occurs in both miombo and tall mopane mixed with miombo.

1.3. Undifferentiated woodland or wooded grassland

This type is floristically rich but more easily defined by the absence of miombo and mopane dominants. In the lower-lying valleys and the dry south-west species of *Acacia*, *Combretum* and *Terminalia* are usually characteristic and *Adansonia* (Baobab), *Albizia*, *Borassus* and *Hyphaene* palms, *Erythrophleum*, *Lonchocarpus*, *Pterocarpus*, *Sclerocarya* etc. also occur. On the Kalahari sands of Barotseland broad-leaved woodland or wooded grassland has various dominants (with local variants), including *Burkea africana*, *Combretum* spp., *Erythrophleum africanum*, *Terminalia sericea*. *Baikiaea plurijuga* may occur in the southern variants, and *Brachystegia* spp., *Cryptosepalum pseudotaxus* and *Julbernardia paniculata* in the northern variants. Much of this woodland is clearly secondary and derived from *Cryptosepalum* and *Baikiaea* forest, respectively (see below).

Finally, "chipya" woodland is a very open, tall woodland (often 20 m or more) with a dense grass layer; its constituent tree species are extremely fire-resistant. It is most extensively developed on the alluvial soils of lake basins, especially Lake Bangweulu and Chambeshi River, and is clearly derived from dry evergreen forest modified by fire and cultivation (White 1983a: 96). Characteristic large tree species include *Albizia antunesiana*, *Burkea africana*, *Erythrophleum africanum*, *Parinari curatellifolia*, *Pericopsis angolensis* and *Pterocarpus angolensis*.

The avifauna of chipya woodland or wooded grassland is fairly similar to that of miombo; in addition, the important grass layer also harbours a number of species absent from mature miombo, e.g. Red-necked Francolin *Francolinus afer*, Kurrichane Buttonquail *Turnix sylvaticus*, Little Bee-eater *Merops pusillus*, Flappet Lark *Mirafra rufocinnamomea*, Tawny-flanked Prinia *Prinia subflava*, cisti-colas, tchagras *Tchagra* spp., bishops *Euplectes* spp., pytilias *Pytilia* spp., firefinches *Lagonosticta* spp. and parasitic widows *Vidua* species. In general, wooded grassland with its more open tree cover is attractive to various species avoiding closed woodland, such as Lilac-breasted Roller *Coracias caudatus*, Black-eyed Bulbul *Pycnonotus barbatus* and Greater Blue-eared Starling *Lamprotornis chalybaeus*.

Many unspecialized woodland species occur; some are more common in *Acacia-Combretum* than in other types, e.g. Pearl-spotted Owlet *Glaucidium perlatum*, Grey Lourie *Corythaixoides concolor*, Long-billed Crombec and Southern Black Tit (these are also well represented in mopane and dry thickets). A few species are essentially confined to *Acacia*-dominated savanna: African Mourning Dove *Streptopelia decipiens*, Southern Yellow-billed Hornbill *Tockus leucomelas*, Acacia Pied Barbet *Tricholaema leucomelas* (in the south-west), Spot-flanked Barbet *T. lacrymosa* (in the north-east), Chestnut-vented Tit-babbler *Sylvia subcaerulea*, Burnt-necked Eremomela *Eremomela usticollis* (par-tial to the canopy of large *Acacia*), Marico Flycatcher *Bradornis mariquensis*, Marico Sunbird *Nectarinia mariquensis*, Crimson-breasted Bush Shrike *Laniarius atrococcineus*, Magpie Shrike *Urolestes melanoleucus*, Cape Glossy Starling *Lamprotornis nitens*, Burchell's Starling *L. australis* (partial to Camelthorn *A. erioloba* (=*giraffae*)), Black-cheeked Waxbill *Estrilda erythronotos*, Violet-eared Waxbill *Uraeginthus granatinus* (which also penetrates into thickets in dry forest) and Shaft-tailed Widow *Vidua regia*.

A few species are somewhat dependent on the presence of *Borassus* and *Hyphaene* palms, especially Dickinson's Kestrel *Falco dickinsoni*, Red-necked Falcon *F. chicquera* and African Palm Swift *Cypsiurus parvus* (as nesting support), and Collared Palm Thrush *Cichladusa arquata*. The bamboo *Oxytenanthera abyssinica* is locally common in dry (riparian) thickets in undifferentiated woodland and drier forms of miombo: one bird that is almost entirely dependent on it for food is Pied Mannikin *Spermestes fringilloides*. Open parkland savanna with a preponderance of *Ficus sycomorus* is favoured by Chaplin's Barbet *Lybius chaplini*.

A few Palaearctic warblers are partial to *Acacia* canopy, namely Icterine Warbler *Hippolais icterina* and Olive-tree Warbler *H. olivetorum*.

2. Deciduous forest and thicket

2.1. *Baikiaea* deciduous forest

Baikiaea forest (or "mutemwa") is dominant in the low-rainfall areas of the south-west and is almost restricted to Kalahari sands: it occurs in an arc running from Namwala through Kalomo and Sesheke to Senanga District; there are small relics in Mongu and Zambezi Districts. Fanshawe (1969) gives a particularly detailed account of this forest type. *Baikiaea plurijuga* forms a closed or open canopy (9-20 m or more) with *Pterocarpus antunesii*; *Entandrophragma caudatum* is a local emergent. *Pterocarpus antunesii* reoccurs further east on suitable sites in the Zambezi and Luangwa Valleys. The shrub layer forms a well-defined deciduous thicket 5-8 m tall, with impenetrable *Acacia ataxacantha* and broad-leaved *Baphia, Bauhinia, Combretum, Dalbergia* etc. Near Livingstone *Baikiaea* is more open and gets mixed with miombo species: this is where Miombo Pied Barbet comes into contact with Acacia Pied Barbet. Bradfield's Hornbill *Tockus bradfieldi* is virtually confined to *Baikiaea*, otherwise many of the species of dry miombo woodland in southern Zambia also occur in *Baikiaea*, including (where it is not too dense) Zambezian endemics like Miombo Barred Warbler, Miombo Grey Tit, Rufous-bellied Tit, Shelley's Sunbird *Nectarinia shelleyi* and Black-eared Seedeater.
     Various thicket species inhabit the understorey.

2.2. Other dry thicket or forest

The most extensive patch is the *Itigi* thicket in the north, in the depression between Lake Mweru Wantipa and Lake Tanganyika. It is 3-5 m high, completely thornless and characterized by the emergents (6-12 m) *Baphia massaiensis, Burttia prunoides* and *Bussea massaiensis*. At the other extreme, in the dry south-west, patches of thicket on the edge of dambos resemble the understorey of *Baikiaea* forest, and some include dwarf specimens of *Baikiaea*; further north in Kalabo District thicket dominated by dwarf *Brachystegia bakerana* occurs in similar situations. Many other types of thicket occur in the country, particularly on termite mounds (in any woodland) where they are floristically rich, and more extensive patches are to be found on the Karoo sands of the lower Luano, Luangwa and Zambezi Valleys. Further north on the Copperbelt there are patches of semi-deciduous forest where the common emergent trees are mainly evergreen whereas the understorey is deciduous.
     Characteristic bird species include Crested Francolin *Francolinus sephaena*, Red-billed Francolin *F. adspersus* (extreme south-west) and Natal Francolin *F. natalensis*, Crested Guineafowl *Guttera pucherani*, Purple-crested Turaco *Tauraco porphyreolophus*, Barred Long-tailed Cuckoo *Cercococcyx montanus* (very local), Wood Owl *Strix woodfordii*, Narina's Trogon *Apaloderma narina*, African Broadbill *Smithornis capensis*, African Pitta *Pitta angolensis*, Sombre Bulbul *Andropadus importunus*, Yellow-bellied Bulbul *Chlorocichla flaviventris*, Terrestrial Bulbul *Phyllastrephus terrestris*, White-throated Nicator *Nicator gularis*, Red-capped Robin *Cossypha natalensis*, Eastern Bearded Scrub Robin *Erythropygia quadrivirgata*, Yellow-breasted Apalis *Apalis flavida*, Bleating Bush Warbler *Camaroptera brachyura*, Black-throated Wattle-eye *Platysteira peltata*, Livingstone's Flycatcher *Erythrocercus livingstonei*, Collared Sunbird *Anthreptes collaris*, Tropical Boubou *Laniarius aethiopicus*, Green-winged Pytilia *Pytilia melba*, Red-throated Twinspot *Hypargos niveoguttatus* and Jameson's Firefinch *Lagonosticta rhodopareia*. Some of the species confined to *Acacia* thicket in the south-west (derived from *Baikiaea* forest) have been cited above.
     Deciduous thickets when in leaf harbour locally very large numbers of Palaearctic migrants, in particular Thrush Nightingale *Luscinia luscinia* and Marsh Warbler *Acrocephalus palustris*.

3. Evergreen forest

It is useful to recognize the following categories:

dry evergreen forest (including *Cryptosepalum*);
moist evergreen (including swamp forest);
riparian forest;
Afromontane rain forest.

3.1. Dry evergreen forest

The most extensive remnants are to be found on Kalahari sands in the west: canopy dominants are restricted to *Cryptosepalum pseudotaxus* and *Guibourtia coleosperma* in the lower-rainfall areas of Zambezi, Kabompo and Kaoma, but associated with *Marquesia acuminata, M. macroura, Parinari excelsa* and *Syzygium guineense* ssp. *afromontanum* in the higher-rainfall region of Mwinilunga. There is a total lack of surface water. *Cryptosepalum* forest (or "mavunda") is sufficiently extensive to have been mapped by White (1983a) on a continental scale (see **p. 14**). The canopy is about 20 m high, locally less, and fairly broken; it is underlain by a thicket layer of shrubs and lianes and mosses predominate on the forest floor (Trapnell & Clothier 1957). *Cryptosepalum* forest is surrounded by and intermingles with *Brachystegia* woodland (in which *Cryptosepalum* trees also occur); fire cannot penetrate the forest, but its destruction through cultivation will lead to invasion by *Brachystegia* and other woodland species. Large expanses of dry forest are, however, reasonably intact and some are protected within the West Lunga N.P. Towards its southern limits, *Cryptosepalum* forest is gradually replaced by *Baikiaea* dry forest.

      The avifauna of *Cryptosepalum* forest has been well studied (Benson & Irwin 1965a, Oatley 1969, Bowen 1980e) and the area much visited by numerous ornithologists. White-chested Tinkerbird *Pogoniulus makawai*, known from the unique type specimen collected at Mayau in 1964 and never found again, is at present considered as perhaps an aberrant individual of Golden-rumped Tinkerbird *P. bilineatus*; *P. bilineatus* is abundant and the woodland Yellow-fronted Tinkerbird also occurs common-ly in the canopy. The avifauna includes a mixture of woodland species (present in the canopy) and forest/thicket elements; in Zambia Gorgeous Bush Shrike *Malaconotus viridis* is confined to the under-storey of this forest type. Other forest and thicket species are widespread in other formations and include Crested Guineafowl, Golden-rumped Tinkerbird, African Broadbill, Purple-throated Cuckoo-shrike *Campephaga quiscalina,* Yellow-bellied Bulbul, Cabanis's Bulbul *Phyllastrephus cabanisi,* Margaret's Batis *Batis margaritae* (very common), Red-capped Robin, Yellow-breasted Apalis, Bleating Bush Warbler, Tropical Boubou, Many-coloured Bush Shrike *Malaconotus multicolor,* Collared Sunbird, Olive Sunbird *Nectarinia olivacea,* Dark-backed Weaver *Ploceus bicolor,* Red-throated Twinspot and Black-tailed Grey Waxbill *Estrilda perreini.*

      Smaller patches of dry evergreen forest are scattered across much of northern Zambia; some of the more widespread large trees are *Marquesia acuminata, M. macroura, Parinari excelsa* and *Syzygium guineense* ssp. *afromontanum.* A 30-m tall formation has been described for the Kawambwa District (Luapula) and, interestingly (at 1300 m a.s.l.), the montane *Podocarpus latifolius* is a locally abundant species (Lawton 1964). The patches of *Parinari-Syzygium* forest occurring near Ndola also belong here. Benson & Irwin (1965c) described a short type of *Marquesia* forest (or thicket, as it is only 10-12 m high) from Mwinilunga District; they found it impoverished bird-wise, no doubt due to the very small size and low height of the forest fragments they looked at. In general, the avifauna of tall *Marquesia-Parinari-Syzygium* forest of northern Zambia does not differ from that of moister evergreen forest (including swamp forest) dealt with below.

3.2. Moist evergreen forest

The distinction between dry and moist evergreen forest is not necessarily clear-cut; with a tall canopy, the presence of emergents and large woody climbers, some patches of evergreen forest in northern Zambia can be classified as rain forest relics. Swamp forest (or "mushitu") is a widespread variant of moist evergreen forest, to be found throughout the northern half of the country: it is restricted to the seepage area around stream heads and locally along sluggish watercourses and in the middle of dambos. It becomes flooded for at least part of the year and can merge into better-drained riparian forest. The canopy is 20-27 m high with an open understorey, and dominant tree species are of Guineo-Congolian affinity (*Mitragyna stipulosa, Syzygium owariense, Xylopia aethiopica, X. rubescens, Uapaca guineensis*, the latter three with characteristic stilt-roots). The Afromontane species *Ilex mitis* is frequent in the understorey; *Syzygium cordatum* is common on the fringes and is also one of the dominant trees of riparian strips in dambos, with the palm *Raphia farinifera*.

The forest patches of northern Mwinilunga constitute an enclave of Guineo-Congolian vegetation: they are at the southern limit of a few Guineo-Congolian endemic trees such as *Klainedoxa gabonensis* and the liane *Tetracera alnifolia*. These forests are not effectively protected, and the future of several bird species within Zambia is in jeopardy. Near Mbala some patches of forest with *Aningeria altissima* and *Trichilia prieuriana* are also of Guineo-Congolian affinity.

Characteristic bird species of moist or dry evergreen forest include at least the following: African Goshawk *Accipiter tachiro,* Schalow's Turaco, Lady Ross's Turaco *Musophaga rossae,* Green Coucal *Ceuthmochares aereus* (uncommon), Wood Owl, Narina's Trogon, Golden-rumped Tinkerbird, Black-backed Barbet *Lybius minor,* African Broadbill, Purple-throated Cuckoo-shrike, Little Greenbul *Andropadus virens,* Yellow-throated Leaflove *Chlorocichla flavicollis,* Cabanis's Bulbul, Grey-olive Bulbul *Phyllastrephus cerviniventris,* West African Thrush *Turdus pelios,* Bocage's Robin *Sheppardia bocagei,* Red-capped Robin, Evergreen Forest Warbler *Bradypterus lopezi,* Laura's Warbler *Phylloscopus laurae,* Grey Apalis *Apalis cinerea,* Margaret's Batis (local), Black-throated Wattle-eye, Blue-mantled Flycatcher *Trochocercus cyanomelas,* Collared and Olive Sunbirds, Green-headed Sunbird *Nectarinia verticalis,* Many-coloured Bush Shrike, Square-tailed Drongo *Dicrurus ludwigii,* Splendid Starling *Lamprotornis splendidus,* Dark-backed Weaver, Red-throated Twinspot and Black-tailed Grey Waxbill. A small number of species is confined to the extreme north-west in Mwinilunga (e.g. White-spotted Flufftail *Sarothrura pulchra,* Afep Pigeon *Columba unicincta,* Olive Long-tailed Cuckoo *Cercococcyx olivinus,* White-bellied Kingfisher *Alcedo leucogaster,* Honeyguide Greenbul *Baeopogon indicator,* African Bristlebill *Bleda syndactylus,* Rufous Ant Thrush *Stizorhina fraseri,* Buff-throated Apalis *Apalis rufogularis,* Sooty Flycatcher *Muscicapa infuscata,* Red-bellied Paradise Flycatcher *Terpsiphone rufiventer,* Bates's Sunbird *Nectarinia batesi* and Green-throated Sunbird *N. rubescens*). One species (Joyful Greenbul *Chlorocichla laetissima*) appears marginally in the extreme north of Luapula, and a handful are shared between Mwinilunga and the north of Luapula Province (Bamboo Warbler *Bradypterus alfredi,* Grey-winged Robin *Cossypha polioptera,* Cassin's Grey Flycatcher *Muscicapa cassini* and Spotted Thrush Babbler *Ptyrticus turdinus*). Black-bellied Seedcracker *Pyrenestes ostrinus* is typically a species of ecotone of swamp or riparian forest and moist grassland; White-chinned Prinia *Prinia leucopogon* is another ecotone species of rank growth, often near water.

Madge (1972b) described the avifauna of the Forestry plots near Ndola which regenerated into (dry) evergreen forest (from miombo woodland); most of the typical forest bird species have recolonized them, including Bocage's Robin, Laura's Warbler and Margaret's Batis.

3.3. Riparian forest

Riparian forest consists of a narrow strip of trees, usually evergreen, growing on the banks of watercourses. Almost completely evergreen in the northern half of the country, riparian forest contains an increasing proportion of deciduous tree species in the south (including *Acacia* spp.), but some large evergreen trees occur throughout the country, such as *Diospyros mespiliformis* and *Trichilia emetica*.

In addition to a number of unspecialized forest birds, water-dependent species whose survival requires the presence of good vegetation cover include White-backed Night Heron *Gorsachius leuconotus*, African Finfoot *Podica senegalensis*, Pel's Fishing Owl *Scotopelia peli* and Half-collared Kingfisher *Alcedo semitorquata*. Among widespread forest passerines, Grey-olive Bulbul prefers riparian situations. Palm-nut Vulture *Gypohierax angolensis* feeds to a large extent on fruits of *Raphia farinifera*, and the distribution of the species largely reflects that of its food plant; the Oil Palm *Elaeis guineensis* is known from two localities in the north (Kilwa Island in Lake Mweru and near Mbete on Lake Tanganyika: Peters 1953). Its nuts are much sought after by the vulture in Central Africa; whether this is so in Zambia has not been documented.

Several species occur in riparian forest in association with adjacent miombo woodland, notably Little Spotted Woodpecker *Campethera cailliautii*, Whyte's Barbet, Black Saw-wing *Psalidoprocne pristoptera*, Lead-coloured Flycatcher *Myioparus plumbeus* and White-tailed Blue Flycatcher *Elminia albicauda*.

3.4. Afromontane rain forest

Afromontane rain forest is confined to the small area of highlands in the extreme north-east, with the best developed patches occurring on the south-western slopes of the Nyika Plateau (Chowo and Manyenjere measuring 90 and 75 ha at 2090-2200 and 1970-2070 m respectively); the largest single patch on the Mafingas is Mulangale forest (40 ha) at 1950 m; the Makutu Plateau has several patches of broad (100-300 m) riparian forest around 2100 m. The floristic composition of the Nyika forests has been studied in detail (Dowsett-Lemaire 1985b), but that of the Mafingas and Makutu remains undescribed! The various collections mentioned in White (1962) from the Mafingas were in fact obtained from the eastern (and wetter) escarpment on the Malawi side (F. White pers. comm.). On the Nyika, the forests have a tall, closed canopy (25-30 m high) with emergents reaching 35-40 m (*Aningeria adolfi-friederici*, *Entandrophragma excelsum*, *Olea capensis*); *Afrocrania (Cornus) volkensii*, *Croton macrostachyus*, *Podocarpus latifolius*, *Polyscias fulva* are important fruit trees, in addition to *Olea*, for various bird species including Rameron Pigeon *Columba arquatrix*. Tall *Parinari excelsa* occur in forest as well as some way outside in secondary grassland as their bark is extremely fire-resistant.

The avifauna of the highlands has been overall well studied (Dowsett 1971h for the Makutu Plateau, Dowsett & Stjernstedt 1973, Aspinwall 1976b, Leonard *et al.* 2001a for the Mafingas, Dowsett-Lemaire 1983c & 2006a for the Nyika). The forest avifauna includes a significant proportion of Afromontane endemic or near-endemic species, of which the following all breed on the south-western scarp of the Nyika: Rameron Pigeon, Cinnamon Dove *Aplopelia larvata*, Scarce Swift *Schoutedenapus myoptilus*, Bar-tailed Trogon *Apaloderma vittatum*, Moustached Green Tinkerbird *Pogoniulus leucomystax*, Eastern Mountain Greenbul *Andropadus nigriceps*, Yellow-streaked Bulbul *Phyllastrephus flavostriatus* (*alfredi*), White-chested Alethe *Alethe fuelleborni*, Starred Robin *Pogonocichla stellata*, Sharpe's Akalat *Sheppardia sharpei*, Olive-flanked Robin *Cossypha anomala*, Orange Thrush *Zoothera gurneyi*, Olive Thrush *Turdus olivaceus*, Evergreen Forest Warbler, Chestnut-headed Apalis *Apalis chapini*, Bar-throated Apalis *A. thoracica*, Grey Apalis, Cape Batis *Batis capensis*, White-tailed Crested Flycatcher *Elminia albonotata*, African Hill Babbler *Pseudoalcippe abyssinica*, Fülleborn's Black Boubou *Laniarius fuelleborni*, Waller's Starling *Onychognathus walleri*, Eastern Double-collared Sunbird *Nectarinia mediocris* and Red-faced Crimsonwing *Cryptospiza reichenovii*. Not all of these can be found in the smaller or more isolated patches of the Mafingas and Makutu (Scarce Swift, Olive-flanked Robin, African Hill Babbler, Fülleborn's Black Boubou, Waller's Starling and Red-faced Crimsonwing are missing from both Makutu and Mafinga), but Cabanis's Bulbul (race

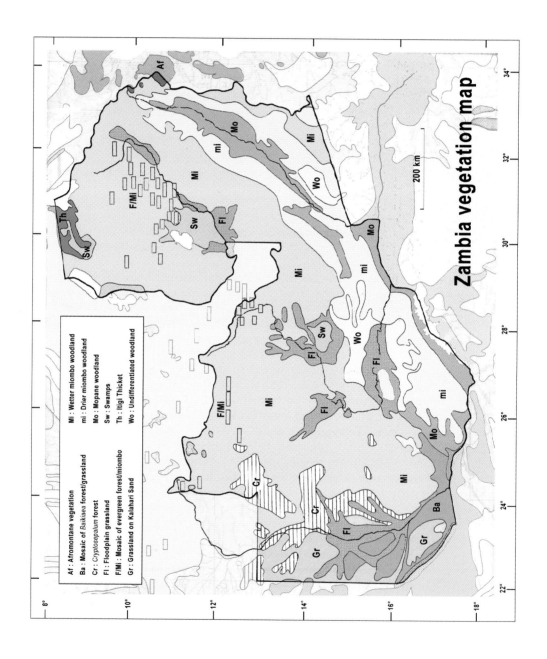

Zambia vegetation map

Af : Afromontane vegetation
Ba : Mosaic of *Baikiaea* forest/grassland
Cr : *Cryptosepalum* forest
Fl : Floodplain grassland
F/Mi : Mosaic of evergreen forest/miombo
Gr : Grassland on Kalahari Sand

Mi : Wetter miombo woodland
mi : Drier miombo woodland
Mo : Mopane woodland
Sw : Swamps
Th : Itigi Thicket
Wo : Undifferentiated woodland

200 km

Mopane woodland in fresh foliage, Luangwa Valley (Phil Berry)

The Black-cheeked Lovebird (here at a nest in the Ngwezi area) has a restricted range in the mopane woodlands of southern Zambia (Louise Warburton)

Lilian's Lovebirds are locally numerous in the Luangwa Valley (Juliet Shenton)

placidus) and Yellow-throated Warbler *Phylloscopus ruficapilla* have been found on the Mafingas and not surprisingly are widespread elsewhere in the highlands of Malawi. In addition to montane species, a number of ecological and chorological transgressors are also found commonly in Afromontane forest, e.g. Crowned Eagle *Stephanoaetus coronatus,* Tambourine Dove *Turtur tympanistria,* Schalow's Turaco, Wood Owl, Crowned Hornbill *Tockus alboterminatus,* Scaly-throated Honeyguide *Indicator variegatus,* African Broadbill, Little Greenbul, Olive Sunbird, Yellow White-eye and Southern Puffback. Olive Woodpecker *Mesopicos griseocephalus* is the most characteristic and common wood-pecker of Afromontane forest and, although widespread in evergreen forest at medium elevations in northern Zambia, ranges mainly in the highlands elsewhere on the continent.

Small patches of Afromontane forest can also be found near the top of the Muchinga escarp-ment (Mpika District) at *c.* 1800 m: Afromontane tree species collected there (mostly from White 1962) include *Croton machrostachyus, Ficalhoa laurifolia, Ocotea usambarensis, Olea capensis, Podocarpus latifolius* and *Polyscias fulva.* Further north, around Danger Hill (Bwingimfumu Hills, Chinsali District), similar small patches exist (or existed, as they were receding fast through bush fires), with also *Ocotea, Olea, Podocarpus, Olinia rochetiana* and *Rapanea melanophloeos* (Fanshawe 1960). A small community of Afromontane bird species occurs there too: Rameron Pigeon (perhaps only in the off-season), Cinnamon Dove, Bocage's Robin (more typically sub-Afromontane, see next Chapter), Evergreen Forest Warbler, Bar-throated Apalis, Grey Apalis, White-tailed Crested Flycatcher and the ecotone species Swee Waxbill *Estrilda melanotis.* Small patches of montane forest occur near Mbala (e.g. Sizya forest, at about 1800 m) with Evergreen Forest Warbler, White-tailed Crested Flycatcher and African Citril *Serinus citrinelloides*; the area has been visited by Rameron Pigeon and Pink-breasted Turtle Dove *Streptopelia lugens.* A handful of montane birds inhabit some patches of moist evergreen forest elsewhere in the north (as do some montane trees); this is discussed in more detail in the bio-geography chapter.

A few stenotypic forest birds undertake migratory movements on a large scale: Scarce Swift is an intra-African migrant and large numbers of Rameron Pigeon disappear after breeding; Starred Robin is a well-known partial altitudinal migrant.

One montane warbler, Brown Warbler *Sylvia lugens*, feeds exclusively in the canopy of *Acacia abyssinica* – a montane tree growing at forest edges or forming small riparian groves; the bird and its tree are found on the Nyika, Mafinga and Muchinga escarpment. Afromontane or upland forest is the main wintering habitat of a Palaearctic warbler, Blackcap *Sylvia atricapilla.*

4. Evergreen shrubland or bracken-briar

This vegetation type occurs within the Afromontane zone and is part of the forest regeneration (or degeneration) process. It is usually 2-4 m tall and is most floristically diverse and developed on the Nyika Plateau. Next to ecological and chorological transgressors (among them Hildebrandt's Francolin *Francolinus hildebrandti,* Grass Owl *Tyto capensis,* coucals *Centropus* spp., Speckled Mousebird *Colius striatus,* Stonechat *Saxicola torquatus,* Broad-tailed Warbler *Schoenicola platyurus,* African Yellow Warbler *Chloropeta natalensis,* Singing Cisticola *Cisticola cantans,* Tropical Boubou, Marsh Tchagra *Tchagra minutus,* Yellow-bellied Sunbird *Nectarinia venusta,* Red-collared Whydah *Euplectes ardens,* Blue-billed Firefinch *Lagonosticta rubricata* and Bully Canary *Serinus sulphuratus*) the Nyika shrublands hold a rich assemblage of montane species, with Cape Robin *Cossypha caffra,* Cinnamon Bracken Warbler *Bradypterus cinnamomeus,* Mountain Yellow Warbler *Chloropeta similis,* Black-lored Cisticola *Cisticola nigriloris,* Greater Double-collared Sunbird *Nectarinia afra* (*whytei*), Red-tufted Malachite Sunbird *N. johnstoni,* Bronze Sunbird *N. kilimensis* and Streaky Seedeater *Serinus striolatus.* Baglafecht Weaver *Ploceus baglafecht* and Bertram's Weaver *P. bertrandi* occur in shrubs with scat-tered trees and other ecotone forest/grassland species are Pink-breasted Turtle Dove, Mountain Nightjar

Caprimulgus poliocephalus, White-headed Saw-wing *Psalidoprocne albiceps,* Slaty Flycatcher *Melaenornis chocolatinus,* Swee Waxbill, Cape Canary *Serinus canicollis* and African Citril. *Protea* spp. are common locally among rocks (with *Erica* (ex-*Philippia*)) or in montane grassland (*Protea* wooded grassland); they are an important habitat for Yellow-tufted *Nectarinia famosa* and Red-tufted Malachite Sunbirds.

Some of these montane endemics reach the Mafingas – Black-lored Cisticola (very rare), Slaty Flycatcher, Yellow-tufted Malachite Sunbird (rare), Cape Canary, African Citril (and beyond), Streaky Seedeater (very rare) – and a few both the Mafinga and Makutu highlands (Mountain Nightjar, White-headed Saw-wing, Cape Robin, Bronze Sunbird, Bertram's Weaver, Swee Waxbill). The bracken-briar habitat of the Mafingas deserves further study, as Red-tufted Malachite Sunbird was observed once on the Malawi border (Dowsett-Lemaire 2006b) and a *Bradypterus* sp. occurs but appears very scarce and has not yet been properly identified (Leonard *et al.* 2001a).

5. Grassland

Dry, watershed grassland is extensive on the Kalahari sands of western Zambia; a similar type of dry grassland reappears on the montane massifs of the Nyika (most of it on the Malawi side) and Mafinga. Elsewhere edaphic grassland is mainly associated with floodplains, or drainage lines on water-logged soils (dambos).

5.1. Montane grassland

Montane grassland on the Nyika is to some extent fire-maintained and forest will regenerate where bracken-briar is strictly protected from fires; much forest regeneration took place on the south-western slopes of the Nyika from 1953 to the early 1980s until the fire protection policy broke down. On thinner soils the grassland is dominated by *Andropogon schirensis, Loudetia simplex* and *Monocymbium ceresiiforme.* Bracken *Pteridium aquilinum* is extremely fire-resistant and may invade some areas also as a result of soil impoverishment and recurrent fires.

The Nyika grasslands are inhabited by a number of montane endemics as well as more widespread species, characteristic species being Red-winged Francolin *Francolinus levaillantii* (the endemic race *crawshayi*), Common Quail *Coturnix coturnix,* Red-tailed Flufftail *Sarothrura affinis,* Wattled Crane *Grus carunculatus,* Denham's Bustard *Neotis denhami,* Rufous-naped Lark *Mirafra africana* (*nyikae*, a race endemic to Nyika and part of southern Tanzania), Banded Martin *Riparia cincta,* Grey-rumped Swallow *Pseudhirundo griseopyga,* Blue Swallow *Hirundo atrocaerulea,* Angola Swallow *H. angolensis,* Richard's Pipit *Anthus richardi,* Ayres's Cisticola *Cisticola ayresii,* Wailing Cisticola *C. lais* and Churring Cisticola *C. njombe.* Dambos and moist grassland near streams hold good numbers of Mountain Marsh Whydah *Euplectes psammocromius* – like Churring Cisticola, found here at its southern limit of distribution from Tanzania.

The montane Slender-billed Starling *Onychognathus tenuirostris* feeds largely in grassland (also on the edge of forest) but breeds on rock faces by waterfalls; it is probably confined to the Nyika area in Zambia (there is an unconfirmed record from the Mafingas) as also is Red-breasted Sparrowhawk *Accipiter rufiventris*, a montane hawk feeding mostly in open country. None of the montane grassland endemics seems to reach the Mafingas but more exploration is needed, particularly in the rainy season.

Most species are resident, but all the swallows are intra-African migrants; several non-breeding visitors include Buffy Pipit *Anthus vaalensis,* Capped Wheatear *Oenanthe pileata* (both intra-African migrants), and the Palaearctic Pallid Harrier *Circus macrourus,* Corn Crake *Crex crex* and Northern Wheatear *Oenanthe oenanthe.*

Miombo woodland near Kundalila Falls, Serenje District (FD-L, 1977)

Miombo woodland, Kasanka National Park (Phil Berry)

White-winged Starling at nest, Vwaza Marsh (in neighbouring Malawi, Jack Clark)

Rufous-bellied Tit (left) and Red-and-blue Sunbird (right), two Zambezian endemics confined to
miombo woodland (Mutinondo, Johann Grobbelaar)

5.2. Watershed grassland

This type is a short wiry grassland most extensively developed on the Kalahari sands of the Upper Zambezi basin west of the Zambezi River in Barotseland; it occupies the wide, virtually flat, interfluves between the tributary rivers. The most widespread grasses are *Loudetia simplex, Monocymbium ceresiiforme* and *Andropogon schirensis* (as in montane areas); it becomes seasonally water-logged. There are also some smaller grass plains in Mwinilunga District (e.g. Chitunta and Mundwiji).

Characteristic species of dry watershed plains include Black-shouldered Kite *Elanus caeruleus,* Secretary Bird *Sagittarius serpentarius,* Greater Kestrel *Falco rupicoloides,* White-throated Francolin *Francolinus albogularis* and Red-winged Francolin (race *momboloensis*) (the last two restricted to plains west of the Zambezi), Denham's Bustard, Red-crested Korhaan *Eupodotis ruficrista,* White-bellied Bustard *E. senegalensis,* Temminck's Courser *Cursorius temminckii,* Crowned Plover *Vanellus coronatus,* Yellow-throated Sandgrouse *Pterocles gutturalis,* Natal Nightjar *Caprimulgus natalensis,* various larks (Rufous-naped, Red-capped *Calandrella cinerea*, Chestnut-backed Sparrow-Lark *Eremopterix leucotis*, with Fawn-coloured *M. africanoides,* Clapper *M. apiata,* Pink-billed Lark *Spizocorys conirostris* and Grey-backed Sparrow-Lark all centred on the Kalahari sands of Barotseland), Banded Martin, Grey-rumped Swallow, Richard's, Buffy and Short-tailed Pipit *Anthus brachyurus,* Capped Wheatear, Sooty Chat *Myrmecocichla nigra,* Fan-tailed Cisticola *Cisticola juncidis,* Desert Cisticola *C. aridulus,* African Quail Finch *Ortygospiza atricollis,* with also Black Crow *Corvus capensis* (centred on the plains west of the Zambezi). Cloud Cisticola *C. textrix,* localized in short grassland of the Upper Zambezi, is replaced in similar watershed grassland further north (Mwinilunga) by Ayres's Cisticola, a montane relic; three other localized species of the north-western plains are Angola Lark *Mirafra angolensis,* Red-and-blue Swallow *Hirundo nigrorufa* and Black-tailed Cisticola *Cisticola dambo.* Some of the larks are subject to irruptive movements and Yellow-throated Sandgrouse is a dry-season breeding visitor. A few Palaearctic species (Caspian Plover *Charadrius asiaticus,* Black-winged Pratincole *Glareola nordmanni*) are abundant transients on southward passage through the Liuwa Plain and (the plover) Kafue Flats.

5.3. Floodplain grassland and dambos

The most extensive areas of floodplain grassland are in the Upper Zambezi, Kafue Flats, Chambeshi Valley and in the Mweru Wantipa and Bangweulu basins. Species of *Andropogon, Loudetia, Monocymbium, Setaria* and *Themeda* grasses prevail in the better-drained areas; the principal grasses of the wetter types include *Acroceras macrum, Echinochloa* spp., *Leersia hexandra, Oryza longistami-nata, Panicum* spp., *Sacciolepsis africana* and *Vossia cuspidata.*

Bird species typical of extensive (seasonally) wet grassland are African Marsh Harrier *Circus ranivorus,* Wattled Crane, Southern Crowned Crane *Balearica regulorum,* Blue Quail *Coturnix chinensis,* Streaky-breasted Flufftail *Sarothrura boehmi,* African Crake *Crecopsis egregia,* Lesser Moorhen *Gallinula angulata,* Ethiopian Snipe *Gallinago nigripennis,* Senegal Wattled Plover *Vanellus senegallus,* Long-toed Plover *V. crassirostris* (in the wetter sections), Common Pratincole *Glareola pratincola,* African Black Coucal *Centropus grillii,* Marsh Owl *Asio capensis,* Natal Nightjar, White-cheeked Bee-eater *Merops variegatus,* Banded Martin, Cape Wagtail *Motacilla capensis,* longclaws *Macronyx* spp., Greater Black-backed Cisticola *Cisticola galactotes,* Yellow-crowned Bishop *Euplectes afer,* Yellow-mantled Whydah *E. macroura,* Red-headed Quelea *Quelea erythrops,* Common Waxbill *Estrilda astrild,* Zebra Waxbill *Amandava subflava,* Locust Finch *Paludipasser locustella* and Pin-tailed Widow *Vidua macroura.* Flooded grasslands on the periphery of swamps are visited by various Ardeidae (including the Zambezian Slaty Egret *Egretta vinaceigula*), Threskiornithidae, Ciconiidae and Anatidae (e.g. Egyptian Goose *Alopochen aegyptiaca* and Spur-winged Goose *Plectropterus gambensis*). The largest complex of flooded grassland, the Kafue Flats, spreads along 240 km from west to east as the river meanders in an easterly direction; the flats, at 975 m a.s.l., are widest (40-50 km) in the middle. Remarkable concentrations of waterbirds have been counted over past decades, reaching tens of thousands in the case of Openbill Stork *Anastomus lamelligerus,* Fulvous Tree Duck *Dendrocygna bicolor,* Spur-winged Goose, Knob-billed Duck *Sarkidiornis melanotos,* Red-billed Teal *Anas ery-throrhyncha* and Common Pratincole. It is estimated that over 1000 pairs of Wattled Crane breed in the Kafue, with large numbers present also on the Liuwa Plain and Bangweulu.

Dambos constitute the most widespread type of edaphic grassland in the Zambezian region as they occur throughout the woodland belt in shallow depressions wherever drainage is sluggish. They are subject to seasonal flooding and parts may remain boggy throughout the year. The soil is normally acid and the vegetation forms a dense mat of grasses (*Andropogon, Hyparrhenia, Loudetia, Setaria, Trachypogon* etc.); Cyperaceae are also present in the wetter sections, where they can be dominant. Dambos are inhabited by various crakes, especially Streaky-breasted Flufftail, Long-toed Flufftail *Sarothrura lugens* (in the deep, large dambos of the north), and Red-chested *S. rufa* (resident in the central wet sections); other characteristic species include African Marsh Harrier, Hottentot Buttonquail *Turnix hottentotus,* Blue Quail, both cranes, Ethiopian Snipe, Grass Owl, Banded Martin, Red-breasted Swallow *Hirundo semirufa,* Plain-backed Pipit *Anthus leucophrys* (short-grass dambos), longclaws, Stonechat, Broad-tailed Warbler, Pale-crowned *Cisticola cinnamomeus* and Fan-tailed Cisticolas, Croaking Cisticola *C. natalensis*, Stout Cisticola *C. robustus,* Marsh Tchagra, Yellow-mantled Whydah, Marsh Whydah *Euplectes hartlaubi,* Fawn-coloured Waxbill *Estrilda paludicola,* Locust Finch and Black-chinned Quail Finch *Ortygospiza gabonensis*. There is evidently a certain amount of overlap between the avifaunas of grassy floodplains and of short-grass dambos, although a few species of dense, deep, matted grass are confined to the large moist dambos of the north and do not penetrate floodplains (such as Long-toed Flufftail and Marsh Whydah): some of the crakes (Streaky-breasted Flufftail and Lesser Gallinule *Porphyrula alleni*) and swallows are seasonal breeding migrants.

Extensive moist grassland and large dambos attract a number of migratory species in the rains, e.g. White Stork *Ciconia ciconia*, Abdim's Stork *C. abdimii*, Eurasian Marsh Harrier *Circus aerugi-nosus,* Pallid Harrier, Montagu's Harrier *C. pygargus,* Lesser Kestrel *Falco naumanni,* Eastern Red-footed Falcon *F. amurensis,* Ruff *Philomachus pugnax* (wintering in their tens of thousands in Barotseland, Bangweulu and Kafue Flats), Great Snipe *Gallinago media* and Blue-cheeked Bee-eater *Merops persicus*. White-throated Swallow *Hirundo albigularis* is a locally abundant dry-season visitor of floodplains and open grasslands.

6. Swamps

The most extensive permanent swamps are located in the Lake Bangweulu basin, home to a large breed-ing population of Shoebill *Balaeniceps rex*; the species probably bred also in Mweru Wantipa, but the recent construction of a dam there has increased the water level and the ecological impact of the dam has not yet been studied. The Lukanga Swamp is another important area but remains badly under-explored. Finally, some dense Papyrus marsh flanks the lower Luapula, while significant areas of permanent swamp (with *Cyperus papyrus, Typha* and *Phragmites*) occur in the centre of the Kafue Flats, where however the surface area of floodplain grassland is much more important.

Many small slow-flowing streams, drainage lines, pools and dams are lined with wet herbage, sedges and reedbeds, the home of Purple Heron *Ardea purpurea,* African Water Rail *Rallus caerulescens,* Black Crake *Amaurornis flavirostra*, Red-chested Flufftail and other crakes, Coppery-tailed Coucal *Centropus cupreicaudus,* Little Rush Warbler *Bradypterus baboecala* and Lesser Swamp Warbler *Acrocephalus gracilirostris* (also the Palaearctic Sedge Warbler *A. schoenobaenus*). Dense reedbeds are the nesting support for various weavers including Spotted-backed Weaver *Ploceus cucullatus,* Southern Brown-throated Weaver *P. xanthopterus* (in the south-west), Yellow-backed

Grove of *Acacia albida* in a seasonal lagoon, Luangwa Valley (Phil Berry)

Chaplin's Barbet, endemic to southern Zambia, is partial to dry, park-like country
(Muckle Neuk, Claire Spottiswoode)

Fire-trimmed edges of dry evergreen forest, Mwinilunga District (RJD, 1973)

Crytosepalum forest near Mayau (RJD, 1973); this is the type locality
of the unique specimen of White-chested Tinkerbird *Pogoniulus makawai*

P. melanocephalus (far north) and Thick-billed Weaver *Amblyospiza albifrons*, and bishops (Red Bishop *Euplectes orix* and Red-shouldered Whydah *E. axillaris*). The Palaearctic Eurasian Swallow *Hirundo rustica* and Eurasian Sand Martin *Riparia riparia* both roost in reedbeds. The permanently wet centres of dambos (where Cyperaceae are dominant) and bogs are home to Lesser Black-backed Cisticola *Cisticola tinniens*, whereas Chirping Cisticola *C. pipiens* occupies a wide range of taller herbaceous vegetation in permanent swamps or dambo centres. Clumps of Papyrus are the favoured breeding habitat of a handful of species, especially Greater Swamp Warbler *Acrocephalus rufescens* (as other habitats are occupied by Lesser Swamp Warbler). Papyrus beds are most extensive in some swamps of the north, as on the lower Luapula River to its mouth at Lake Mweru, where White-winged Warbler *Bradypterus carpalis* and Papyrus Yellow Warbler *Chloropeta gracilirostris* can be found in some numbers. The habitat of the localized Swamp Flycatcher *Muscicapa aquatica* consists of the edge of thicket and Papyrus (the bird reaching its southern limit of distribution in the Kafue Flats), although further north in Africa this species is widespread on the edge of gallery forest. A couple of ducks (White-backed Duck *Thalassornis leuconotus* and African Pygmy Goose *Nettapus auritus*) and both jacanas frequent ponds and lakes with emergent or floating vegetation.

7. Open waters and mud-flats

Zambia has several large lakes and dams (from Lake Tanganyika to Kariba Dam), as well as numerous seasonal pans; the shallow water of pools and the margin of lakes attract fish-eating species such as cormorants *Phalacrocorax* spp., African Darter *Anhinga rufa*, pelicans *Pelecanus* spp., African Fish Eagle *Haliaeetus vocifer* and Pied Kingfisher *Ceryle rudis*; muddy shores are used by Palaearctic waders and some local species (e.g. Blacksmith Plover *Vanellus armatus*, Kittlitz's Plover *Charadrius pecuarius* and Three-banded Plover *C. tricollaris*). Several species have benefited from the creation of artificial dams and sewage ponds, most notably Little Grebe *Tachybaptus ruficollis*, several ducks (e.g. Yellow-billed Duck *Anas undulata* and Southern Pochard *Netta erythrophthalma*), Common Moorhen *Gallinula chloropus* and Red-knobbed Coot *Fulica cristata*.

  Some species of open waters are widespread in the country but breed only very locally: thus White Pelican *Pelecanus onocrotalus* has bred only in Mweru Wantipa and the Kafue Flats, Pink-backed Pelican *P. rufescens* also in the Kafue Flats and once at Mongu, while Whiskered Tern *Chlidonias hybrida* has been confirmed to breed only on the Liuwa. Neither flamingo occurs in large numbers and local conditions of salinity appear unsuitable for breeding, with the notable exception of one attempt by Lesser Flamingo *Phoeniconaias minor* in Mweru Wantipa in 1955. This last was the only saline swamp in Zambia (White 1983a: 267), but conditions have been altered by hydrological engineering (a dam and various channels), in part to eliminate conditions suitable for the breeding of Red Locusts.

  Seasonal ponds with a ring of vegetation attract quite a few Ardeidae and other waterbirds – e.g. Dwarf Bittern *Ixobrychus sturmii*, an intra-African migrant. Most of the Palaearctic ducks are of rare and irregular occurrence, except (in some years) Garganey *Anas querquedula*; there are moderate numbers of White-winged Black Terns *Chlidonias leucopterus*, and Gull-billed Terns *Sterna nilotica* may be on the increase.

8. Rivers

The larger rivers support fair numbers of waterbirds, especially where floodwaters fill adjacent lagoons. Rocky, fast-flowing rivers with well-wooded banks are the favoured habitat of African Black Duck *Anas sparsa* and Long-tailed Wagtail *Motacilla clara*, whereas Rock Pratincole *Glareola nuchalis* (an intra-African migrant) breeds on emerged rocks at the end of the dry season. Species associated with sandy shores of rivers and lakes include Egyptian Goose, Water Dikkop *Burhinus vermiculatus,* White-fronted Sand Plover *Charadrius marginatus,* White-crowned Plover *Vanellus albiceps* and African Skimmer *Rynchops flavirostris*. Others breed in holes within sand cliffs (Giant Kingfisher *Megaceryle maxima,* Pied Kingfisher, White-fronted Bee-eater *Merops bullockoides,* Southern Carmine Bee-eater *M. nubicoides,* Horus Swift *Apus horus* and African Sand Martin *Riparia paludicola*). The sandy Luangwa River holds the largest breeding populations of the more specialized species such as African Skimmer, Southern Carmine Bee-eater and Horus Swift (this last using bee-eater holes).

Osprey *Pandion haliaetus* is a regular Palaearctic visitor to large rivers, lakes and dams.

9. Cliffs and boulders

Rocky hills, cliffs and escarpments are not as widespread as in adjacent, mountainous Malawi, and are essentially confined to the eastern half of the country: from Kalambo Falls down the Muchinga and Zambezi escarpments to the Livingstone gorges, including the koppjes of the Eastern Province plateau. Most of the bird species associated with these habitats have a well-defined range corresponding to the eastern half of the country as defined above, including Black Eagle *Aquila verreauxii,* Augur Buzzard *Buteo augur,* Black Stork *Ciconia nigra,* White-necked Raven *Corvus albicollis* and African Red-winged Starling *Onychognathus morio*; even Rock Cisticola *Cisticola aberrans* shows this pattern, even though the scrub and long grass it favours in thin, rocky miombo does extend to some hills further west. A few species indeed extend a little further west, to the Copperbelt hills and with also small isolated populations in Mwinilunga (Freckled Rock Nightjar *Caprimulgus tristigma,* African Rock Martin *Hirundo fuligula,* Striped Pipit and Mocking Chat *Myrmecocichla cinnamomeiventris*). Lanner *Falco biarmicus* and Peregrine Falcon *F. peregrinus* both breed on cliffs but may wander a long way from breeding habitat and the more adaptable Lanner also breeds in trees. Whereas Lanner is dominant over Peregrine at nesting sites, the latter is dominant over Taita Falcon *F. fasciinucha*, which may in part explain the more restricted range of the Taita (from the Muchingas to Livingstone). Other localized species are Mottled Swift *Apus aequatorialis* and African Black Swift *A. barbatus*; Boulder Chat *Pinarornis plumosus* and Cape Bunting *Emberiza capensis* favour the bare rocks and scrub of large inselbergs, to be found only in the small south-eastern corner of the country.

10. Large mammals

Both oxpeckers *Buphagus* spp. feed on ticks taken from various ungulates and (especially Red-billed *B. erythrorhynchus*) from cattle: thus the latter is more widespread. Populations of both must have been affected by the decrease of wild game populations and also by cattle dipping wherever it has taken place, but they remain common in the major national parks. Much the same can be said about specialized carrion feeders (such as the larger vultures). More catholic scavengers such as Bateleur *Terathopius ecaudatus* remain extremely widespread.

11. Man-made habitats

Artificial dams have already been mentioned as having benefited some waterbirds. Other forms of man-made habitats are listed below.

Bocage's Robin is widespread in the forests of the north, up to the Mafinga Mountains (Mutinondo, Johann Grobbelaar)

Mosaic of montane grassland and forest at the source of the Luangwa River, Mafinga Mountains (Phil Berry, 2002)

Manyenjere forest, Nyika Plateau (FD-L, 1981)

A temporary river (the Mutinsase) running down the Muchinga escarpment into the Luangwa
(Serenje District, Phil Berry)

11.1. Human habitations and bridges

Several species of swifts (Little *Apus affinis,* African White-rumped *A. caffer*) and swallows (Mosque *Hirundo senegalensis,* Lesser Striped *H. abyssinica,* African Rock Martin, Wire-tailed Swallow *H. smithii,* Angola Swallow) regularly use brick buildings and bridges as nesting support. Red-breasted Swallow has taken advantage of culverts and Red-throated Cliff Swallow *H. rufigula* (a localized species of the Copperbelt and Mwinilunga) today nests predominantly on bridges and dam walls; populations of this and other species have likely increased in recent decades.

      African Pied Wagtail *Motacilla aguimp* and Northern Grey-headed Sparrow *Passer griseus* commonly breed on brick houses and House Sparrow *P. domesticus* exclusively so, having spread through the more populated areas since the 1960s.

11.2. Airfields and bare ploughed ground

Several species of short, dry grassland have adapted to airfields, earth roads and ploughed land. These include Temminck's Courser, Crowned Plover, Red-capped Lark, sparrow-larks, Richard's and Buffy Pipits, Grey-rumped Swallow and Capped Wheatear. African Quail Finch is also found on airfields and cattle pastures. Spotted Eagle Owl *Bubo africanus* and nightjars commonly feed around earth roads, and various raptors are attracted to them for their improved visibility, while doves and francolins may pick some small food items and grit; dikkops *Burhinus* and coursers *Rhinoptilus* spp. may feed on them at night.

11.3. Cultivation and exotic plantations

Various species of rank herbaceous growth thrive in neglected cultivation, particularly Red-necked Francolin, Swainson's Francolin *Francolinus swainsonii,* and some doves. Several passerines have adapted well to overgrown fields and fallow land, e.g. Tawny-flanked Prinia, Fiscal Shrike *Lanius collaris* (with some tall trees or telegraph poles used as perches), Tropical Boubou, Black-crowned Tchagra *Tchagra senegalus,* Red-collared Whydah, Yellow-rumped Bishop *Euplectes capensis,* Black-winged Bishop *E. hordeaceus,* Common Waxbill and Pin-tailed Widow. Red-billed Quelea *Quelea quelea* thrives on annual grass seeds, whether natural or planted, and it may be a pest in rice-growing areas.

      Exotic plantations of eucalyptus or pines are of minor importance in Zambia (unlike adjacent Malawi), and their use by the avifauna has not been examined. 85% of exotic plantations are to be found on the Copperbelt. Near villages, eucalyptus plots have encouraged the nesting of some commensal species (Pied Crow *Corvus albus*). Normally, neglected plantations where some natural undergrowth is allowed to grow can be inhabited by some species of thicket or shaded woodland understorey. Similarly, a number of unspecialized thicket birds thrive in well-wooded gardens, e.g. Heuglin's Robin *Cossypha heuglini,* African Paradise Flycatcher *Terpsiphone viridis,* Arrow-marked Babbler *Turdoides jardineii,* and various sunbirds are attracted to the flowers of introduced plants.

3. Biogeography

1. Biogeographical concepts and definitions

The distribution patterns of a large number of landbird species in Africa are closely correlated to those of vegetation zones of high floristic distinctness – or phytochoria. A review of the arrangements followed by various ornithological workers since the pioneer study of Chapin (1932, especially pp. 83-264) has been discussed by Dowsett-Lemaire & Dowsett (2006). In 1989 Dowsett-Lemaire (1989b) presented a zoogeographical analysis of the forest avifauna of Malawi based closely on the phytochoria of White (1983a), and in *The Birds of Malawi* (2006) we have developed these ideas for the avifauna of that country as a whole.

Lists of biome-restricted species may differ slightly between different workers according to taxonomic treatment, precise delineation of biome boundaries and the definition of what represents a biome endemic or (especially) a near-endemic species. We have followed White closely in his definition of Afromontane and Zambezian regions. An endemic taxon is entirely confined to a stated area; when a species belongs overwhelmingly to one region but is also feebly represented elsewhere – either in neighbouring transition zones or in more distant satellite populations – it is referred to as a "near-endemic" (in the meaning of White 1979).

Other factors influencing the distribution of birds are also examined, such as the Luangwa Rift.

In this discussion, and throughout the book, we revert to the terms Zaire and Congo-Brazzaville for the countries currently called République Démocratique du Congo and République Populaire du Congo, to avoid the confusion of having two Congos. Similarly we refer to Katanga Province – also known as Shaba.

2. The Zambezian region

Zambia lies entirely within this region, which extends from Angola and south-eastern Zaire to Tanzania and Mozambique, south to the north of Namibia, Botswana, the whole of Zimbabwe and most of the Transvaal (Fig. 4 in White 1983a). The region corresponds to the combined African range of miombo and mopane woodlands.

2.1. Zambezian bird species

We recognize 64 species as being endemic (44) or near-endemic (20) to the Zambezian region. This list differs little from that (of 67 species) presented by Fishpool & Evans (2001: 1103-1104) – the species "missing" from ours are mainly the result of different taxonomic considerations, and we have excluded White-throated Robin *Cossypha humeralis* as being too widely represented in another region (Eastern). We also exclude Black-lored Babbler *Turdoides melanops*, which is instead a Kalahari-Highveld near-endemic. On the other hand, we have added Slaty Egret, a full Zambezian endemic (inadvertently omitted by Fishpool & Evans) and a few more near-endemics that occur marginally in neighbouring regions, particularly transition zones. **Table 1** shows the distribution of these 64 species within the Zambezian region and also in two of the neighbouring transition zones to the north: the Guineo-Congolian/Zambezian transition zone (represented in the table by southern Gabon and Congo-Brazzaville) and the Lake Victoria regional mosaic (with Rwanda and Burundi).

The northern limit of the Guineo-Congolian/Zambezian transition zone as shown on White's map crosses Bas-Zaire; in the years preceding White (1983a) the vegetation of southern Congo-Brazzaville was very poorly documented and F. White (pers. comm.) agreed later that the transition zone should be extended northwards to include the savannas and gallery forests of the whole of the

Montane *Protea* grassland on the western edge of the Nyika Plateau
(FD-L), and a Red-winged Francolin, of the race *crawshayi* endemic to
the Nyika (Alex Paul)

Aerial view of Liuwa Plain, with a pan. The black dots in the sparse
vegetation are Wildebeest (Richard Beilfuss, 2001)

A large dambo in miombo
woodland, Lavushi Manda
National Park (Phil Berry)

Rosy-breasted
Longclaw,
a typical dambo bird
(Bangweulu, Kasanka
Trust)

Dambo at Kundalila Falls,
with a clump of *Raphia
farinifera* (FD-L)

Table 1. Zambezian bird species and their distribution in the Zambezian region and transition zones to the north (Gabon/Congo; Rwanda/Burundi); * designates near-endemics. Key to columns: 1 = Gabon & Congo-Brazzaville; 2 = Zaire; 3 = Rwanda & Burundi; 4 = Tanzania; 5 = Angola; 6 = Zambia; 7 = Malawi; 8 = Mozambique; 9 = Namibia; 10 = Botswana; 11 = Zimbabwe & South Africa.

Species	1	2	3	4	5	6	7	8	9	10	11
Slaty Egret	-	-	-	-	?	x	-	-	x	x	x
Dickinson's Kestrel	-	x	-	x	x	x	x	x	x	x	x
Lilian's Lovebird	-	-	-	x	-	x	x	x	-	-	x
Black-cheeked Lovebird	-	-	-	-	-	x	-	-	?	?	?
Red-crested Turaco	-	-	-	-	x	-	-	-	-	-	-
Coppery-tailed Coucal	-	x	-	x	x	x	x	-	x	x	x
Red-backed Mousebird	-	x	-	-	x	-	-	-	-	-	-
Böhm's Bee-eater	-	x	-	x	-	x	x	x	-	-	-
Racket-tailed Roller*	-	x	-	x	x	x	x	x	-	x	x
Bradfield's Hornbill	-	-	-	-	x	x	-	-	x	x	x
Pale-billed Hornbill	-	x	-	x	x	x	x	x	-	-	-
Anchieta's Barbet	-	x	-	-	x	x	-	-	-	-	-
Whyte's Barbet	-	-	-	x	-	x	x	x	-	-	x
Miombo Pied Barbet*	x	x	-	x	x	x	x	-	-	-	-
Chaplin's Barbet	-	-	-	-	-	x	-	-	-	-	-
Black-backed Barbet*	x	x	x	x	x	x	x	-	-	-	-
Stierling's Woodpecker	-	-	-	x	-	-	x	x	-	-	-
Angola lark	-	x	-	x	x	x	-	-	-	-	-
Red-throated Cliff Swallow*	x	x	-	-	x	x	-	-	-	-	-
Black-and-rufous Swallow	-	x	-	-	x	x	-	-	-	-	-
Fülleborn's Longclaw*	-	x	-	x	x	x	-	-	x	-	-
Grimwood's Longclaw	-	x	-	-	x	x	-	-	-	-	-
Miombo Rock Thrush*	-	x	x	x	x	x	x	x	-	x	x
Kurrichane Thrush*	-	x	x	x	x	x	x	x	x	x	x
Boulder Chat	-	-	-	-	-	x	x	x	-	x	x
Collared Palm Thrush*	-	x	x	x	-	x	x	x	-	-	x
Central Bearded Scrub Robin	-	x	x	x	x	x	x	x	-	-	-
Arnot's Chat	-	x	x	x	x	x	x	x	x	x	x
Black-collared Eremomela	-	x	-	-	x	x	-	-	-	-	-
Red-capped Crombec*	x	x	-	x	x	x	x	x	-	-	x
Laura's Warbler	-	x	-	x	x	x	-	-	-	-	-
Black-tailed Cisticola*	x	x	-	-	x	x	-	-	-	-	-
Tinkling Cisticola*	x	x	-	-	x	x	x	-	x	x	x
Slender-tailed Cisticola*	-	x	-	-	x	-	-	-	-	-	-
Chirping Cisticola	-	x	x	x	x	x	-	-	x	x	x
Miombo Barred Warbler*	-	x	x	x	x	x	x	x	x	x	x
Böhm's Flycatcher	-	x	-	x	x	x	x	-	-	-	-
Margaret's Batis	-	x	-	-	x	x	-	-	-	-	-
White-tailed Blue Flycatcher*	-	x	x	x	x	x	x	x	-	-	-
Miombo Grey Tit	-	x	-	x	x	x	x	x	-	-	x
Rufous-bellied Tit*	x	x	-	x	x	x	x	x	x	x	x
Red-and-blue Sunbird	-	x	-	x	x	x	x	x	-	-	-
Bannerman's Sunbird	-	x	-	-	x	x	-	-	-	-	-
S. White-bellied Sunbird*	-	x	-	x	x	x	x	x	x	x	x
Oustalet's White-bellied Sunbird	-	-	-	x	x	x	x	-	-	-	-

Table 1 (contd). Zambezian bird species and their distribution in the Zambezian region and transition zones to the north.

Species	1	2	3	4	5	6	7	8	9	10	11
Miombo Double-collared Sunbird	-	x	-	x	x	x	x	x	-	?	x
Shelley's Sunbird	-	x	-	x	?	x	x	x	-	-	x
Bocage's Sunbird	-	x	-	-	x	-	-	-	-	-	-
Sousa's Shrike*	x	x	x	x	x	x	x	x	x	x	-
Sharp-tailed Starling	-	x	-	x	x	x	-	-	x	x	-
S. Long-tailed Starling	-	-	-	-	x	x	x	x	x	x	x
White-winged Starling	-	-	-	x	x	x	x	-	-	-	-
Chestnut-mantled Sparrow-weaver	-	x	-	-	x	x	x	-	-	-	-
Bocage's Weaver	-	x	-	-	x	x	-	-	-	-	-
Kilombero Weaver	-	-	-	x	-	-	-	-	-	-	-
Lake Tanganyika Weaver	-	x	-	x	?	x	-	-	-	-	-
Bar-winged Weaver	-	x	-	-	x	x	-	-	-	-	-
Olive-headed Weaver	-	-	-	x	-	x	x	x	-	-	-
Golden-backed Bishop	-	-	-	-	x	-	-	-	-	-	-
Red-throated Twinspot*	-	x	x	x	x	x	x	x	x	-	x
Green Indigobird	-	-	-	-	-	x	x	-	-	-	x
Broad-tailed Paradise Widow*	-	x	?	x	x	x	x	x	x	x	x
Black-faced Canary*	x	x	x	-	x	x	-	-	-	-	-
Black-eared Seedeater	-	x	-	x	x	x	x	x	-	x	x
Totals	**9**	**48**	**12**	**39**	**50**	**57**	**37**	**28**	**17**	**19**	**26**

Note: For scientific names see systematic list and index.

Téké Plateau (in Congo-Brazzaville and Gabon): Miombo Pied Barbet, Black-backed Barbet, Red-throated Cliff Swallow, Red-capped Crombec, Black-tailed Cisticola, Tinkling Cisticola *Cisticola rufilatus,* Rufous-bellied Tit, Sousa's Shrike and Black-faced Canary *Serinus capistratus* occur mainly in the Zambezian region but extend into this transition zone to the north. Some of these species are characteristic of the northern, more humid Zambezian region (Black-backed Barbet and Black-faced Canary at forest edges, Black-tailed Cisticola in rank grass). Those species usually confined to *Brachystegia* woodland in Zambia-Malawi such as Rufous-bellied Tit and Red-capped Crombec occur in Congo-Brazzaville in more open *Hymenocardia acida* wooded grassland but are rather rare, although the crombec is found all the way to Odzala on the Equator. Sousa's Shrike and Tinkling Cisticola are, within the Zambezian region, partial to light miombo woodland and (the cisticola) secondary formations; Tinkling Cisticola is particularly common in the wooded grasslands of Congo-Brazzaville and Gabon, which are in structure very similar to the secondary, short-canopied woodland favoured by the species in countries to the south. There is, in fact, no *Brachystegia* woodland in the savannas of Gabon and Congo-Brazzaville, contrary to the claim in Urban *et al.* (1997: 325); indeed the northern limit of the Zambezian region as defined by White (1983a) corresponds to the northern limit of miombo woodland through northern Angola and southern Zaire.

Other Zambezian near-endemics reach the Lake Victoria regional mosaic, e.g. Miombo Rock Thrush, Kurrichane Thrush, Collared Palm Thrush, Miombo Barred Warbler, White-tailed Blue Flycatcher and Red-throated Twinspot. The palm thrush and twinspot also penetrate marginally into the Eastern region in Kenya. Near-endemics which, on the other hand, are predominantly Zambezian but

Aerial views of the Kafue Flats, showing above the extensive flooded grassland (RJD, 1970)
and below an area of permanent marsh (Richard Beilfuss, 2001)

Chambeshi River, on the edge of Bangweulu Swamps (Richard Beilfuss, 2001)

Shoebill, photographed at one of its breeding strongholds, the Bangweulu Swamps (Geneviève Renson)

Slaty Egret, a rare species endemic to Zambezian swamps (Warwick Tarboton)

extend a little beyond to the south-east (into the Eastern region) include Racket-tailed Roller and Southern White-bellied Sunbird.

Of the 64 species (near-)endemic to the Zambezian biome, no fewer than 57 occur in Zambia, more than in any other country. Those lacking are species known from further west in Angola (though Bocage's Sunbird *Nectarinia bocagii* should be sought for in western Zambia), Stierling's Woodpecker *Dendropicos stierlingi* (which seems not to range further west than Malawi, for reasons that are not evident) and Kilombero Weaver *Ploceus burnieri* (known only from a limited area of southern Tanzania, with its affinities perhaps further north). Overall, Zambia with adjacent southern Zaire and parts of Angola hold the largest number of Zambezian species (62 of 64); from this centre of Zambezian diversity there is general impoverishment southwards and eastwards, with 37 species present in Malawi and fewer still in Zimbabwe and Mozambique (Table 1). In their analysis of *Brachystegia* avifaunas (leaving out Zambezian species of other woodland types) Benson & Irwin (1966c) have shown similar trends of species richness and impoverishment across the miombo belt (their Table 1). The rich woodlands and forest patches of the high plateaux of the northern half of Zambia are the most diverse in birdlife, and it is possible that many of the Zambezian miombo endemics are derived from forest forms. The dry forests of western Zambia (evergreen with *Cryptosepalum*, deciduous with *Baikiaea*) have almost certainly a Guineo-Congolian origin. Miombo woodland is essentially a fire climax and on the deeper soils the woodland returns to evergreen forest when protected from fire.

At least two species have their closest relatives among Afromontane species: Margaret's Batis is very closely related to Cape Batis (and more distantly to Ruwenzori Batis *B. diops*) and Laura's Warbler belongs to a genus which in Africa is otherwise montane. In Angola they both occur in Afromontane forest; in Zambia Laura's Warbler reaches the forest patches of the Muchinga escarpment (at 1800 m) while Margaret's Batis is centred at medium elevations in the north-west. They both occur alongside several Afromontane near-endemics of the "southern migratory track" on the Congo-Zambezi watershed (see below) and, given their distribution in upland Angola they could marginally have been classified as Afromontane instead of Zambezian species.

Other Zambezian endemics show a preference for drier types of woodland and thicket and must have completely different origins: for instance Chaplin's Barbet is most closely related to White-headed Barbet *Lybius leucocephalus* of the northern tropics and eastern Africa, of which it represents a relict population (as also another small population in south-western Angola). Chestnut-mantled Sparrow-weaver of tall, dry miombo woodland (and marginally mopane) has its closest relative in the dry woodlands of the Sudanian region (Chestnut-crowned Sparrow-weaver *P. superciliosus*); Southern Long-tailed Starling *Lamprotornis mevesii* of mopane woodland is represented in the dry woodlands of the Sudanian region by a close relative, the Northern Long-tailed Starling *L. caudatus*.

Oustalet's White-bellied Sunbird *Nectarinia oustaleti* of dry, secondary miombo, presents a somewhat anomalous distribution, being confined to north-eastern Zambia and reappearing in south-western Angola; in this case, competition with the (southern Zambezian) Southern White-bellied Sunbird may explain the discontinuity in range (Benson & White 1960). In the case of White-winged Starling (confined to tall mature woodland in the north-east of the Zambezian region and reappearing in Angola), the present distribution is difficult to explain, as the species has no obvious close relative.

Floristically the Zambezian centre of endemism is one of the two richest regions on the continent, with over 8500 species of phanerogamic species (the Guineo-Congolian region having about 8000); of those about 54% are endemic (with endemism reaching 80-90% in the Guineo-Congolian region: White 1979, 1983a). Within the Guineo-Congolian region about 80% of the forest birds present are (near-)endemic species (Dowsett-Lemaire & Dowsett 1998), a very high proportion similar to that observed among plants. Quite surprisingly the proportion of endemic birds present in Zambezian woodland, dry forest and thicket is much less, under 20% of the whole avifauna.

2.2. Other species present in Zambezian vegetation

Among the numerous species that inhabit Zambezian vegetation (but are not Zambezian endemics), some occur within just one more phytochorion or region, such as Eastern: Purple-crested Turaco, Bat-like Spinetail *Neafrapus boehmi*, Rosy-breasted Longclaw *Macronyx ameliae*, Southern Brown-throated Weaver and Black-tailed Grey Waxbill. A dozen belong to both the Zambezian and Kalahari-Highveld regions: Red-billed and Swainson's Francolins, Double-banded Sandgrouse, Bennett's Woodpecker, Monotonous Lark *Mirafra passerina*, Pink-billed Lark, Burnt-necked Eremomela, Marico Flycatcher, Crimson-breasted Bush Shrike, Violet-eared Waxbill and Shaft-tailed Widow. A species like Bennett's Woodpecker is widespread in the dry woodlands of both regions, but several of the others (in Zambia) are confined to the dry *Acacia* savannas of the south-west and are more extensively distributed in the Kalahari-Highveld region. Some other species restricted to similar habitats reappear in eastern Africa (e.g. Magpie Shrike, Marico Sunbird, Black-cheeked Waxbill). One species, Schalow's Turaco, is a Zambezian/Afromontane species (equally common in miombo woodland and evergreen forest including Afromontane) and another is a Zambezian/Guineo-Congolian species (Long-toed Flufftail of large dambos and moist forest regrowth).

The following six species extend their range a little too far into neighbouring phytochoria to be considered as Zambezian near-endemics, but they are still predominantly Zambezian (at least 80% of their range): Crested Barbet *Trachyphonus vaillantii*, Eastern Least Honeyguide *Indicator meliphilus*, Green-capped Eremomela, Southern Black Tit, Retz's Red-billed Helmet Shrike and Yellow-throated Petronia.

Of particular interest are those species confined to *Brachystegia* woodland in Zambia (and elsewhere in the Zambezian region) which nevertheless inhabit other vegetation types beyond the Zambezian region, e.g. Coqui Francolin *Francolinus coqui*, Striped Pipit and Rock Cisticola (the last two both on rocky substrate), Groundscraper Thrush *Psophocichla litsitsirupa*, Yellow-bellied and Southern Hyliotas, Trilling Cisticola, Violet-backed Sunbird, Stripe-breasted Seedeater and Cabanis's Bunting. Some of them (Yellow-bellied Hyliota, Violet-backed Sunbird, Cabanis's Bunting) are widespread in the deciduous woodlands of the Sudanian region, the populations north and south of the Equator somewhat connecting via the transition zone of the Lake Victoria basin. These northern deciduous woodlands, especially those dominated by *Isoberlinia* spp., are physiognomically similar to miombo woodland and other bird species shared between Sudanian and Zambezian woodlands (but also occurring marginally in other phytochoria) include White-breasted Cuckoo-shrike and Spotted Creeper. Floristically the Sudanian woodlands have much in common also with Zambezian woodlands (White 1965) but are considerably impoverished, both in total number of species and in endemism (White 1983a).

Three species are represented by other races outside the Zambezian region: Groundscraper Thrush by the isolated race *simensis* in Ethiopia and Eritrea; Southern Hyliota by two very isolated forest races to the north of the Zambezian region (*usambara* and *slatini*) whose taxonomic status requires further study, and the single specimen of an immature supposedly of this species collected in Cameroon is perhaps another species. Finally, the race *striatipectus* of Stripe-breasted Seedeater in north-east Africa appears to be specifically distinct (Zimmerman *et al.* 1996), in which case *Serinus reichardi sensu stricto* should become a Zambezian endemic.

3. The Afromontane region

The small highlands of the north-east (Makutu, 2119 m, Mafinga, 2290 m and the south-western section of the Nyika Plateau, peak at 2606 m on the Malawi side) and the higher sections of the Muchinga escarpment are an integral part of the more extensive montane complex of northern Malawi. In addition,

The Luangwa River just south of Mfuwe (Phil Berry)

Fishing party (mainly Yellow-billed Storks) in a lagoon, with *Trichilia* riparian forest,
South Luangwa National Park (Phil Berry)

A bend in the Luangwa River (Phil Berry)

Carmine Bee-eaters breed colonially in sand cliffs along the Luangwa (Kerri Rademeyer) and (below) a congregation of Crowned Cranes, a common sight in the Valley (Phil Berry)

the mid-altitude plateaux of northern Zambia (at 1200-1600 m) are still inhabited by a handful of montane trees and birds and provide evidence of a linking route between the mountains of East and West Africa in the not so distant past.

3.1. Afromontane bird species

The Afromontane region is very rich in endemic species, taking second place only after the Guineo-Congolian region (Dowsett-Lemaire & Dowsett 1998, 2001). We recognize some 230 endemic and near-endemic species, of which over 160 are forest elements (listed in appendix in Dowsett-Lemaire & Dowsett 2001). Altogether 55 Afromontane species occur in Zambia (**Table 2**), of which two are Sub-Afromontane as defined below, plus a well-marked race of Yellow-streaked Bulbul (*alfredi*). Sharpe's Starling *Cinnyricinclus sharpii* is a vagrant, and is not included in the total.

Table 2. Afromontane bird species occurring in Zambia. * designates near-endemics and bold those endemic to the Tanzania-Malawi regional group.

Red-breasted Sparrowhawk*, Red-tailed Flufftail*, Rameron Pigeon*, Pink-breasted Turtle Dove, Cinnamon Dove*, Mountain Nightjar, Scarce Swift, Bar-tailed Trogon, Moustached Green Tinkerbird, White-headed Saw-wing*, Blue Swallow, Eastern Mountain Greenbul, Joyful Greenbul*, Cabanis's Greenbul*, Olive Thrush*, Orange Thrush, White-chested Alethe, Starred Robin, **Sharpe's Akalat**, **Olive-flanked Robin**, Cape Robin*, Cinnamon Bracken Warbler, Evergreen Forest Warbler*, Mountain Yellow Warbler, Yellow-throated Warbler, Brown Parisoma, Ayres's Cisticola*, Wailing Cisticola, **Churring Cisticola**, **Black-lored Cisticola**, Bar-throated Apalis*, Grey Apalis*, **Chestnut-headed Apalis**, Slaty Flycatcher, Cape Batis*, White-tailed Crested Flycatcher, African Hill Babbler, Greater Double-collared Sunbird*, Eastern Double-collared Sunbird, Yellow-tufted Malachite Sunbird*, Red-tufted Malachite Sunbird, Bronze Sunbird, Fülleborn's Black Boubou, Waller's Starling, Slender-billed Starling, Sharpe's Starling (*vagrant*), Baglafecht Weaver*, **Bertram's Weaver**, **Mountain Marsh Whydah**, Red-faced Crimsonwing, Swee Waxbill*, Cape Canary*, African Citril*, Streaky Seedeater.

Sub-Afromontane: Bocage's Robin, Bamboo Warbler.

Our concept of near-endemics is broader than that of Fishpool & Evans (2001) as we follow White's (1979, 1981, 1983a) definition more closely. Like White, we include as Afromontane near-endemics species which are predominantly Afromontane but also survive today in small satellite populations at intermediate elevations. Of the 27 montane birds found in both Cameroon and eastern Zaire, nine are also found in relict populations away from the mountains, mainly in mid-altitude forest along the Congo-Zambezi watershed and on some hills in Lower Guinea between Cameroon and Angola. These stepping stones show a connecting route very similar to the "southern migratory track" of a number of Afromontane trees (White 1981, 1983b). Typical examples of montane trees with relict populations in northern Zambia are mapped in White (1981, 1983b) and White *et al.* (2001), among them *Agauria salicifolia, Alangium chinense, Ficalhoa laurifolia, Nuxia congesta, Olea capensis, Podocarpus latifolius* and *Rapanea melanophloeos*. These can all be found in small forest patches in Mwinilunga, at an altitude of 1200-1300 m, and in a few other places on the Congo-Zambezi watershed. Most of these satellite populations are on the banks of rivers or in sheltered situations among rocks. *Ilex mitis*, the most widespread Afromontane tree in northern Zambia, is usually in the under-storey of swamp forest, but locally *Podocarpus latifolius* has been found thriving in the understorey of *Marquesia acuminata* dry evergreen forest, a long way away from water, as in Luapula Province at the altitude of only 1300 m, and *Olea capensis* occurs in the canopy (Lawton 1964). It is not difficult to imagine that, in climatic conditions only slightly cooler than those of today, Afromontane communities were much more widespread on the northern Zambian plateau.

Some of the Afromontane bird species which we have classified as "near-endemics" are well represented on the African mountains and also have residual populations along the "southern migratory track" of White (1981, 1983b): the more widespread in northern Zambia are Cinnamon Dove, Cabanis's Bulbul, Evergreen Forest Warbler and Grey Apalis. Two races of Grey Apalis (*grandis* and *alticola*) occur in the highlands of Angola, which suggests that *A. cinerea s.l.* (represented in Zambia today by the race *alticola*) has crossed the gap between the mountains of Angola and East Africa on more than one occasion. Associated with the highlands of the Sudan/Kenya group and the Albertine Rift, Joyful Greenbul reaches its southern limit of range in the extreme north of Zambia, at the altitude of no more than 1500 m. Another localized Afromontane relic is the Mwinilunga population of Ayres's Cisticola (present on the watershed plains at 1200-1460 m), a species otherwise characteristic of short montane grassland in the highlands of Angola and eastern Africa south to South Africa. Although several populations and races of Red-winged Francolin are strictly montane (including *crawshayi* on the Nyika), the race *momboloensis* inhabits watershed grasslands in eastern Angola and western Zambia at medium altitudes (950-1150 m); possibly this population is also a relic of colder climes.

Rameron Pigeon is one of the most characteristic Afromontane species across the continent as well as a highly specialized frugivore and disperser (Dowsett-Lemaire 1988b); it has never been recorded breeding away from Afromontane forest, but undergoes regular migrations or long-distance movements. In Zambia the few records of this bird away from the north-eastern highlands are of off-season wanderers, and they come mostly from Mwinilunga. Unfortunately we have no direct observations of which fruit species the bird was after on such occasions, but it is probably no coincidence that most of the Afromontane near-endemic trees surviving in satellite populations in northern Zambia are among its favourite fruit plants (e.g. *Olea capensis, Podocarpus* and *Polyscias*).

Some bird species, absent from lowland forest as such, occur on the lower slopes of mountains or generally at medium elevations, i.e. below the level of typical Afromontane species. It is useful to recognize for these the category of Sub-Afromontane species, as has been done for woody plants (Dowsett-Lemaire 1988a, 1989a, White *et al.* 2001). Most of the bird species endemic to the Angola scarp fit into this category, and overall we have identified 16 Sub-Afromontane species in Africa (listed in Dowsett-Lemaire & Dowsett 2001). In Zambia Bocage's Robin and Bamboo Warbler fit into this category. Fishpool & Evans (2001) have not retained this subdivision, and have replaced most of those semi-montane species into the Guineo-Congolian biome, with one exception (Bamboo Warbler) which they have inserted in the Afromontane list. Bocage's Robin is typically Sub-Afromontane: in the Cameroon highlands it occurs on the lower slopes of mountains (mostly from 1000-1500 m); in Angola it is found on the Gabela escarpment (like most of the Angolan Sub-Afromontane endemics) and in Afromontane forest higher up (to at least 2100 m); in Zambia its altitudinal range is mostly 1100-1800 m, with feeble penetration into the Mafinga highlands at 1950 m. Its scarcity in the Mafingas may be related to the local presence there of Sharpe's Akalat, also at the limit of its range.

Based on faunistic similarities and patterns of local endemism, the mountains of Africa have been grouped into seven regional systems independently by Carcasson (1964) and Moreau (1966). North-eastern Zambia is part of the "Tanzania-Malawi" group, and the local endemics which reach Zambia are listed in **Table 2**; the race *alfredi* of Yellow-streaked Bulbul also belongs here. Several more widespread Afromontane species reach their southern limit of distribution on the Nyika: Pink-breasted Turtle Dove, Mountain Yellow Warbler, Red-tufted Malachite Sunbird and Baglafecht Weaver. Cape Batis reaches its northern limit of range in the Mafinga and Makutu Mountains; otherwise the montane avifaunas of Malawi and adjacent Zambia have far more in common with mountains to the north than to the south (Dowsett-Lemaire 1989b). Notwithstanding these varying patterns of local endemism, one of the most striking characteristics of Afromontane flora and fauna alike is the wide distribution of many species across the continent: Rameron Pigeon and Scarce Swift are present in all seven regional

The larger rivers of Zambia hold an important population of African Skimmer (Phil Palmer)

The Zambezi River in the gorges below Victoria Falls (FD-L)

A nest site of Taita Falcon in "Gorge 5" below Victoria Falls – now deserted, probably through excessive disturbance by tourists and overflights (FD-L, Dalena Mostert)

Over centuries severe bush fires have altered Zambezian vegetation, for instance turning some of the dry evergreen forest into miombo or "chipya" woodland (RJD)

groups, African Hill Babbler in six of them and Bar-tailed Trogon in five (including Cameroon and Angola). Although the first two are migrants, most montane species are sedentary, with limited inter-montane movements (Dowsett-Lemaire 1989b). The presence of relict or satellite populations of some montane species along the "southern migratory track" in northern Zambia leads to the speculation that, in climatic conditions not very different from those of today, stenotypic montane birds could have reached the highlands of Cameroon and Angola without resorting to long-distance migration.

3.2. Other species present in Afromontane vegetation

Montane grassland on the Nyika Plateau is also inhabited by a number of widely distributed, azonal species including Wattled Crane, Denham's Bustard, Rufous-naped Lark and Richard's Pipit. Similarly, montane shrubland attracts generalists such as Stonechat which (like Broad-tailed Warbler, African Yellow Warbler and Marsh Tchagra) prefer moister habitats at lower altitudes. In the montane forests of the south-western Nyika Plateau (2000-2200 m) more than 60% of the constituent species are Afromontane; non-montane bird species on the Nyika and elsewhere include forest species that are well represented in the Guineo-Congolian region (e.g. Little Greenbul, Olive Sunbird, Green-headed Sunbird), ecological transgressors (e.g. Southern Puffback, Yellow White-eye) and one Zambezian/Afromontane species (Schalow's Turaco). Dusky Flycatcher *Muscicapa adusta* is common in both mid-altitude miombo woodland and at the edges of montane forest; outside the Zambezian region this flycatcher is largely confined to highlands. Olive Woodpecker is very common in the frag-mented forests of the Nyika and other highlands; it is so widespread elsewhere in Zambia (in evergreen forest) that it is difficult to consider it as an Afromontane near-endemic species, but again outside the Zambezian region it is basically restricted to highlands.

4. The Guineo-Congolian enclave in Mwinilunga

The small forest patches of northern Mwinilunga are clearly of Guineo-Congolian origin but constitute an enclave within the Zambezian region (as the northern boundary of the Zambezian region falls well north of Mwinilunga). Of some 250 Guineo-Congolian endemic and near-endemic forest-associated bird species (listed in Dowsett-Lemaire & Dowsett 2001) 17 near-endemics reach Mwinilunga: White-spotted Flufftail, Afep Pigeon, Olive Long-tailed Cuckoo, White-bellied Kingfisher, Brown-eared Woodpecker *Campethera caroli,* Honeyguide Greenbul, African Bristlebill, Rufous Ant Thrush, White-chinned Prinia, Buff-throated Apalis, Sooty Flycatcher, Cassin's Grey Flycatcher, Shrike Flycatcher *Megabyas flammulatus,* Chestnut Wattle-eye *Dyaphorophyia castanea,* Red-bellied Paradise Flycatcher, Bates's and Green-throated Sunbirds. Most species are reasonably common but two appear very rare (Shrike Flycatcher and Chestnut Wattle-eye) and the survival of this special guild in Zambia is at risk from intensive deforestation. Cassin's Grey Flycatcher and White-chinned Prinia are the only Guineo-Congolian species to have been located elsewhere in northern Zambia (in Luapula Province) but some of the forest patches of that region deserve further exploration.

Another two species present in Mwinilunga forests (Blue-breasted Kingfisher *Halcyon malimbica* and Shining Blue Kingfisher *Alcedo quadribrachys*) have their main range centred on the Guineo-Congolian region but extending north into Sudanian galleries. Other forest birds include some belonging to "Circum-Congo" transition zones (especially Grey-winged Robin, Spotted Thrush Babbler and Orange-tufted Sunbird *Nectarinia bouvieri*), a few species highly characteristic of Guineo-Congolian forest but also widespread in evergreen forest elsewhere (e.g. Little Greenbul and Olive Sunbird), a few montane elements (e.g. Cabanis's Bulbul, Bamboo Warbler and Evergreen Forest Warbler) and a number of ecological and chorological transgressors.

5. Representatives of other marginal zoochoria

5.1. The Guineo-Congolian/Zambezian transition zone

Black-collared Bulbul *Neolestes torquatus* of wooded grassland is the only representative of the Guineo-Congolian/Zambezian transition zone to have reached Zambia; this transition zone (mapped in White 1983a) has not been retained by Fishpool & Evans (2001) as the number of bird species confined to it is rather low. It includes the special Téké avifauna of the plateau grasslands of northern Angola to southern Gabon and Congo-Brazzaville (Finsch's Francolin *Francolinus finschi*, Congo Moor Chat *Myrmecocichla tholloni* and Black-chinned Weaver *Ploceus nigrimentus*) and the little-known Angola White-headed Robin *Cossypha heinrichi*. Other species characteristic of wooded grassland of Mwinilunga include Red-throated Wryneck *Jynx ruficollis*; like the *Neolestes*, it is locally very common in the open woodlands of the Téké Plateau, but its distribution elsewhere in Africa is largely montane. It reappears on the other side of the miombo/forest belt in central, eastern and South Africa. Whistling Cisticola *Cisticola lateralis*, of rank growth at forest edges, is widespread in the Guineo-Congolian and Circum-Congo transition zones.

5.2. The Lake Victoria regional mosaic

This is a complex area of transitional character, at the margin of several regions (Guineo-Congolian, Afromontane, Somalia-Masai, Sudanian and Zambezian) and rather poor in endemics, both in plants (White 1983a) and birds. We consider that no more than nine species qualify for this category; Fishpool & Evans (2001: 1097) list 12, but some (Ring-necked Francolin *Francolinus streptophorus*) extend far beyond the region. Several of the endemics or near-endemics are restricted to large Papyrus swamps. The region itself does not reach Zambia but two of its Papyrus near-endemics have satellite populations in the extreme north: White-winged Warbler (discovered only in 1996) and Papyrus Yellow Warbler.

5.3. The Eastern (forest) region

White's (1983a) concept of this region was treated differently in some of his other publications and was redefined by Dowsett-Lemaire (1988a: Mulanje), see also Dowsett-Lemaire & Dowsett (1998, 2006). Briefly the Eastern region encompasses the two regional mosaics of Eastern (coastal) elements (the Zanzibar-Inhambane and Tongaland-Pondoland regions of Fig. 4 in White 1983a) and extends inland along riparian formations or in the foothills of mountains, penetrating into the eastern half of the Zambezian region and marginally into the Lake Victoria basin. The main vegetation type is forest or thicket. Dowsett-Lemaire & Dowsett (2006: 54) list 45 endemic and near-endemic species; our concept of near-endemics differs somewhat from that of Fishpool & Evans (2001) who present a shorter list, but who have included a few species which are clearly both Eastern and Zambezian (such as Brown-headed Parrot *Poicephalus cryptoxanthus* and Mozambique Batis *Batis soror*, both widespread in typical Zambezian woodland in Malawi and elsewhere).

Naturally the number of Eastern species decreases from east to west, and Zambia has only six as opposed to 20 in Malawi. These are: Sombre Bulbul, Grey-olive Bulbul, White-throated Nicator, Eastern Bearded Scrub Robin, Livingstone's Flycatcher and Blue-mantled Flycatcher. The status of a seventh, Mangrove Kingfisher *Halcyon senegaloides*, requires further investigation.

A few species behave like Eastern elements in parts of their range (as in Zambia) and are montane elsewhere: Barred Long-tailed Cuckoo is a typical example. Silvery-cheeked Hornbill *Bycanistes brevis* ascends the mountains to high altitudes in various parts of its range and is also probably best considered as a species linking the Afromontane and Eastern regions. Many Eastern species have their closest relatives in lowland vegetation elsewhere in Africa, especially in the Guineo-Congolian region:

for example White-throated Nicator and Blue-mantled Flycatcher are members of superspecies with the Guineo-Congolian Western Nicator *Nicator chloris* and Blue-headed Crested Flycatcher *Trochocercus nitens* respectively; other examples are discussed in Dowsett-Lemaire & Dowsett (2006).

5.4. The Kalahari-Highveld transition zone

The Kalahari-Highveld region is very poor in endemics, thus best considered a transition zone (White 1983a). Only 14 species belong here (i.e. the 13 species listed by Fishpool & Evans 2001: 1104, plus Black-lored Babbler). There are only two in Zambia: Burchell's Sandgrouse *Pterocles burchelli* and Burchell's Starling *Lamprotornis australis*. The latter extends rather widely into the Zambezian region and could equally be treated as a Kalahari/Zambezian species. Several other species with a south-western centre of distribution in Zambia are classified as Kalahari/Zambezian (see p. 37).

6. The "*Brachystegia* interval" in species distribution

The *Brachystegia* belt which occupies most of Zambia is an obvious barrier to the distribution of species of drier woodland or steppes. This subject has been discussed in detail by Benson & White (1960), who gave numerous examples of species occurring on both sides of the belt in southern and eastern Africa, some of them missing Zambia altogether (e.g. Pygmy Falcon *Polihierax semitorquatus* and white-crowned shrikes *Eurocephalus* spp.). Among those reaching south-western Zambia, we may cite Ostrich *Struthio camelus* (with past records only), Greater Kestrel, Kori Bustard, Red-crested Korhaan, Yellow-throated Sandgrouse, Fawn-coloured Lark, Magpie Shrike and Black-cheeked Waxbill. Some of these extend into the Luangwa Valley (e.g. Double-banded Sandgrouse, Red-billed Hornbill, Red-billed Buffalo Weaver) or reappear in the extreme north-east of Zambia (Marico Sunbird). It is not difficult to suppose that in climatic conditions slightly drier than those of today, many species would have been connected through the low-lying valley of the Luangwa. In some cases, speciation has occurred in the different habitat types: Miombo Pied Barbet has evolved in the miombo belt from a common stock that includes Acacia Pied Barbet in the dry south-west and Red-fronted Barbet *Tricholaema diademata* in eastern Africa. There is a similar story with Miombo Grey Tit of the miombo belt and the Ashy and Northern Grey Tit *Parus cinerascens-P. thruppi* superspecies of the drier *Acacia* woodlands on either side, and with Miombo Barred Warbler (with Southern Barred Warbler *Camaroptera fasciolatus* and Grey Wren Warbler *C. simplex* to the south-west and north-east respectively).

The miombo belt has also apparently acted as a barrier in the case of a number of forest birds that occur in the Guineo-Congolian region and reappear in the Eastern forest region. One species that comes close to the Zambian border (Mwinilunga) but skips the country altogether is Black-and-white Flycatcher *Bias musicus*. Delegorgue's Pigeon *Columba delegorguei* (*sensu lato*) occurs in the Mwinilunga forests but does not reappear within the same latitudes before Thyolo Mtn in southern Malawi; we need to know more about the bird's feeding requirements to understand why it is absent from other forest patches in northern Zambia and why it is so local in Malawi (being confined to a fig-dominated forest).

The case of the Gorgeous Bush Shrike is particularly interesting, as the *quadricolor* population of eastern Africa is sometimes considered specifically distinct and occurs with certainty no nearer to western Zambia than in the thickets of Lengwe in southern Malawi and in the Middle Zambezi (Zimbabwe). Nominate *viridis* in Zambia is confined to the thickets underlying the open canopy of *Cryptosepalum* forest on Kalahari sands; *Cryptosepalum* is replaced by drier *Baikiaea* as rainfall decreases southwards. The floristic composition of the thickets underlying *Baikiaea* forest in the south-west resembles rather closely that of the Lengwe thickets. *Pterocarpus antunesii* is often a codominant of *Baikiaea* and occurs more or less throughout the thickets of the Middle Zambezi, Gwembe and Luangwa Valleys, all the way to the Lower Zambezi and Lower Shire Valley in Lengwe (where it is a dominant canopy tree). There is little doubt that the Zambezi Valley is the connecting route of the past between the Malawian and Zambian populations of Gorgeous Bush Shrike, as suggested by recent records from the Middle Zambezi in Zimbabwe (in Harrison *et al.* 1997).

7. The Luangwa Rift

The Luangwa River rises in the Mafinga Mountains near the Malawi border, and drops gently from *c.* 1000 m to 330 m along 600 km from its head in Isoka District to its confluence with the Zambezi. The Valley is as much as 60 km wide in many places; the predominant vegetation type is mopane wood-land, with some *Acacia*, whereas the adjacent, wetter plateaux to the east and west are clothed in miombo woodland. It is enclosed by a high escarpment wall, reaching an altitude of 1800 m up the western side in Mpika District. The biogeographical importance of this rift fault has been discussed in detail by Benson *et al.* (1962).

Several species approach the Rift from the western side in various habitats but have not crossed it and indeed are not recorded from Malawi, among them: Lady Ross's Turaco, Cape Wagtail, Purple-throated Cuckoo-shrike, Yellow-throated Leaflove, West African Thrush, Sooty Chat, Black-collared Eremomela, Pale-crowned, Stout, Chirping and Lesser Black-backed Cisticolas, White-rumped Babbler *Turdoides leucopygia,* Marsh Whydah, Brown Firefinch *Lagonosticta rufopicta* and Fawn-breasted Waxbill. Square-tailed Drongo and Dark-backed Weaver are absent from eastern Zambia as well as north-central Malawi, reappearing only in the forests and thickets of southern Malawi, even though there is suitable habitat further north. A few species pairs occur on either side, including Fülleborn's Longclaw *Macronyx fuelleborni* (west) and Yellow-throated *M. croceus* (east), Bar-winged Weaver and Olive-headed Weaver *Ploceus olivaceiceps,* and the races (among others) of Cabanis's Bulbul, *Phyllastrephus c. cabanisi* and *P. c. placidus.* Lesser Seedcracker *Pyrenestes minor* replaces Black-bellied Seedcracker in Malawi but has never been recorded from south-eastern Zambia (which may be too dry).

4. A History of Ornithology in Zambia (ex-Northern Rhodesia)

The Portuguese were the first explorers to travel extensively here, and they had reached the Zambezi/Kafue confluence by the end of the 17th century. Dr Francisco José Maria de Lacerda e Almeida [d. 1798], newly appointed Governor of the Tete District of Mozambique, travelled in 1798 to Kazembe on the Luapula, on a route already used by Indian traders. His aim was to open communications between Mozambique and Angola, but he died of fever at or near Kazembe. By 1836 Portuguese explorers had reached the Upper Zambezi from Angola, and that area was visited by Antonio Francisco Ferreira da Silva Porto [1817-1890] in 1848. Unfortunately none of the early Portuguese explorers appears to have produced any collections of birds. This is the more striking as elsewhere in Africa ornithological discovery was well advanced by the end of the 18th century, and some 540 of the 753 species of birds now on the Zambian List were already known to science by 1850.

The ornithological record in Zambia dates only from the early 1850s. In 1853 Dr David Livingstone [1813-1873] first visited the Upper Zambezi, travelling through the Barotse Valley. He revisited this area from Angola in 1855, and after leaving Linyanti on 3 November, went down the Zambezi by boat, and on 16 November became the first European to see the Victoria Falls. He reached the Kafue River on 18 December, and then went on to Quelimane, on the Mozambique coast (Clark & Clay 1963). In 1858 he was a member of the expedition led by William Cotton Oswell [1818-1893], which could ascend the Zambezi no further than the rapids of Cabora Bassa (Mozambique). From the natural history viewpoint these expeditions were unimportant, but they led to another expedition to central Africa in 1858-59 on which Livingstone was accompanied by his brother Rev. Charles [1821-1873] and the physician and botanist Dr John Kirk [1832-1922]; they visited Victoria Falls in August 1860. Both Charles Livingstone and John Kirk made important natural history collections, including birds (Kirk 1864), although little within what is now Zambia. In 1866 David Livingstone went via Lake Nyasa to Lake Tanganyika, and he discovered Lake Bangweulu in 1868. His travels included a visit to Shiwa Ngandu: he called the lake "Chitane's water" after his dog, but it was later called Lake Young, after an early administrator "Bobo" Young (Gore-Browne 1953). David Livingstone's few bird observations from 1866 until his death, some of which are still of interest, were summarized by Clay (1943), with additional comment by Benson (1978).

During the period 1872-87 the Czech Dr Emil Holub [1847-1902], based as a doctor in Kimberley, South Africa, came north to Zambia. During a first expedition (1872-77) he explored as far north as the Zambezi, studying the local people and collecting birds and other objects of natural history (Spohr 1979). During a later expedition he and his wife were attacked by villagers, but did manage to save part of the bird collection (which is now in various museums).

Dr Benjamin Bradshaw [*c.* 1844-1903?] resided in the Panda Matenga (Botswana)-Victoria Falls area from 1874 to 1883 (Sampson 1956), but his collection of specimens was dispersed upon his death, and no complete account was ever published. Sharpe (1881) gave Victoria Falls as a locality, but very few specimens seem to have been obtained there by anyone (Sclater 1905).

In 1890 Harry Johnston [1858-1927], Commissioner of Nyasaland, sent Alfred Sharpe [1853-1935] to explore parts of what is now north-eastern Zambia. Sharpe visited Lake Mweru and Mweru Wantipa (Anon. 1957), and again in 1892 he travelled to Lake Mweru and the Luapula, including the recently established station of Rhodesia (Chiengi) (Anon. 1965, Brelsford 1955, Sharpe 1893). Sharpe collected a number of specimens "from the east side of Lake Mweru" (Shelley & Sclater 1901). Details of loci were given in that paper by John McClounie [1870-?], Chief of the Scientific Staff at Zomba: Ikawa (near Fife), Karungwesi (Kalungwizi) River, Kikomba (Kwikomba) – plateau between Lakes Nyasa and Tanganyika – and Lake Mweru. He gave the wrong localities for Mambwe and Mbara (both of which were in Northern Rhodesia, and not Nyasaland as stated). No dates were provided for these specimens (which went to the British Museum). It seems probable that the first new taxon to be described from this country was obtained on this trip, the race *alfredi* of Mottled Swift (Shelley 1900: 345) from "Mbaro" (Mbala, presumably from Kalambo Falls). Shelley & Sclater (1901) included the first record of Garganey (listed in error as Cape Teal *Querquedula capensis*) from Mbala.

In 1897 the country became known as Northern Rhodesia. Between July and September 1898, collectors belonging to the scientific staff at Zomba (Nyasaland) were attached to the Commission for the Delimitation of the Anglo-German Boundary, under the control of Lt-Col. William Manning [1863-1932] (Deputy Commissioner). Although the hunters employed by Alfred Sharpe (who succeeded Johnston as Commissioner) operated usually in the Nyasaland Protectorate, this time they travelled from Karonga, thence northwards from Fort Hill (now Chitipa, Malawi), to Fife, an African Lakes Company post on the Stevenson's Road, west of Mwenzo Mission. Most of their bird specimens were obtained at Ikawa and Luchinde in what is now Isoka District. These included type material of Black-backed Barbet (race *macclounii*), Grey Apalis (race *alticola*) and Many-coloured Bush Shrike (race *manningi*). The collection (which went to the British Museum) was detailed by Shelley (1899a,b) and the geographical part of the expedition by Boileau (1899).

Boyd Alexander

In 1899 the country was divided into North-Western and North-Eastern Rhodesia. At about the same time that the Boundary Commission's collections were being made, Lieut. Boyd Alexander [1873-1910] left Chindi on the coast on 18 July 1898 for an expedition up the Zambezi River, with his sole aim the collection of natural history material. This proved to be the most important 19th century collection from Northern Rhodesia (Dowsett 1988b). Boyd Alexander was accompanying Col. James Stevenson-Hamilton [1867-1957] on an expedition led by Major Alfred St Hill Gibbons, the aim of which was geographical exploration and hunting (Alexander 1899-1900, Carruthers 2001). Among the 258 species recorded was the first specimen of a new sunbird from the Middle Zambezi, to be named *Nectarinia shelleyi* (Alexander 1899).

William Lutley Sclater [1863-1944], together with his wife and a taxidermist, visited the Victoria Falls in September 1904 (Sclater 1905). He was at the time Director of the South African Museum in Cape Town, and they travelled on the recently-opened railway between Bulawayo and the Falls. From the Zambian point of view the most interesting observation was the first report here of Three-banded Courser, between Livingstone and the Sinde River.

At the same time, but independently, Dr A.H.B. Kirkman collected the first specimen of a new species of lovebird on the Ngwezi River, in September 1904, while on a hunting trip. It was Sclater who named and described the new species as *Agapornis nigrigenis* (Sclater 1906), the type being in the South African Museum. We know nothing of Kirkman's travels or of any other specimens he may have obtained.

The next serious ornithologist to collect was the gifted naturalist Sheffield Airey Neave [1879-1961], with whose name is associated Dr Frederick Otto Stoehr [1871-1946] – see Stoehr & Sclater 1906) and the accounts by Benson *et al.* (1970) and Crook (1970). Neave's collections in 1905 and 1908 were especially thorough and important (Neave 1906, 1907, 1909, 1910). Among no fewer than 11 taxa new to science from Zambia were two species, Locust Finch (from Bangweulu) and Green Indigobird *Vidua codringtoni* (the Luangwa Valley). In the Luangwa Valley he went north in the first half of 1905 to Mirongo station, which existed from 1895-1904 or 1905 to stop the Arab slave traffic (Jones 1964). His collection of some 750 specimens went mainly to the British Museum. In June 1908 Neave was in

Stevenson Clarke

Col. Stephenson Robert Clarke [1862-1948] visited the southern Kafue Flats on a hunting expedition in 1920. On 30 August, in what was evidently the Maala area (Dowsett 1980b), he collected the type of a new species of barbet, which he named Chaplin's Barbet *Lybius chaplini*, after the Administrator of the Rhodesias, Sir Drummond Chaplin [1866-1933] (Clarke 1920, 1921). This species is strictly endemic to Zambia.

Charles Pitman

the Luena area of the Bangweulu Swamps, Luena station being "a most unhealthy and mosquito-ridden place", opened in 1901 and closed sometime after 1907 (Jones 1964). His second expedition yielded some 850 bird specimens.

Ernest C. Chubb [1884-1972], then at Bulawayo Museum, visited the country in 1909 with Rev. F.A. Rogers, and they collected the type of the race *chubbi* of Red-capped Crombec, probably at Broken Hill, now Kabwe (Ogilvie-Grant 1910).

In 1911 the country again became a single unit, Northern Rhodesia. Between August and November, Leofwyn Beresford Mouritz [1888-1915], an Australian mining engineer, explored parts of the Katanga, including the Luapula Valley (Brooke 1970, Mouritz 1914).

Jack Vincent & Hubert Lynes (early 1930s)

An important contribution was made by Rear Adm. Hubert Lynes [1874-1942] and Col. Jack Vincent [1904-1999], who spent some time in the north of the country during the Lynes-Vincent tour of 1930-31 (Lynes & Sclater 1933-34). In their selective collection of specimens (the emphasis being on elucidating the species limits and habits of *Cisticola* species) were six new taxa.

Capt. Charles Robert Senhouse Pitman [1890-1975], Game Warden of Uganda, was invited to carry out a faunal survey of the country with a view to recommending conservation measures. Apart from his own fieldwork 1931-32, he collated information on a variety of relevant topics; his very thorough report

Jack Winterbottom

(1934) included the first bird checklist, containing no fewer than 481 confirmed species.

John Miall Winterbottom [1903-1984] was the first ornithologist to attempt quantitative surveys in the country (e.g. Winterbottom 1938c). He arrived in Northern Rhodesia from the Gold Coast in 1931, and his first publication here was Winterbottom (1932). In his update of Pitman (1934) – the second checklist – he listed an additional 25 species for the country (Winterbottom 1939a). By 1949 he and White were able to list a further 81 species in the third checklist (White & Winterbottom 1949), bringing the total known to 587. A member of the Education Department, he travelled extensively, in particular in the Eastern Province and much of the west. He returned home to South Africa in 1950, but in a final fieldtrip in 1952, in the extreme south-west, he found four species new to the country (Smithers 1956).

Charles Matthew Newton White [1914-1978] lived in the country from 1938-65. He came out as a cadet in the Provincial Administration, and being already an active ornithologist (Dowsett 1978d) he was soon documenting the birds of his various postings (e.g. White 1945-46). He was himself responsible for adding at least 29 species to the country list between 1938 and 1951, especially from Mwinilunga and Balovale

Charles White

(now Zambezi) Districts. His collector, Kabali Muzeya, discovered a further three. He was a naturalist of many interests, entomological as well as ornithological, and whose *Revised Check List of African Birds* (1960-65) has provided a firm foundation for modern African ornithology.

T.G.C. Vaughan-Jones [1907-1986] joined the Provincial Administration in 1929, and developing the recommendations of Pitman's report, he submitted plans for a game department and the necessary legislation in 1938-39. The Game Department was formally established in 1942, and in 1945 "V.J." became the first Director (Ansell 1987). As such he did much to establish the firm basis on which is built the present protected areas system, so important for the conservation of the country's avifauna. In consultation with Reay Smithers he also encouraged research.

In 1938 Arthur M. Champion collected a few specimens at Mwenzo, now mostly in the National Museum of Kenya in Nairobi, including the first Oustalet's White-bellied Sunbird for the country (Williams 1955b).

John Awdry Cottrell [1904-1997], of the Education Department, came to Northern Rhodesia in 1930, and in 1948 became Director of African Education. He was a keen oologist, and discovered Red-throated Cliff Swallow nesting in Kabompo District (White 1949b). Part of his collection is in the National Museum of Zimbabwe (James 1970).

William Vernon Brelsford [1907-1980], who came to Northern Rhodesia as a cadet in the Administration in 1930, first published in 1941 and documented in particular the avifauna of the Bangweulu region. He also did much to further knowledge of the history of the country, through the Northern Rhodesia Society.

Gervas Charles Robert Clay [1907-?], recruited to the Provincial Administration, went to Northern Rhodesia in the same year as Brelsford, 1930, and was present until 1964. His interest initially was in game bird shooting, but after encouragement from Winterbottom and White, he paid more attention to birds in general. He was deaf to bird song, the result of too much quinine taken as malarial prophylactic, but touring (frequently by bicycle) he discovered much of interest in the Isoka region (Clay 1953). He was the first to explore the eastern highlands in Zambia, and in October 1942 and 1943 found no fewer than 10 species new to the country's avifauna there (especially in the Mafingas).

Errol Lancelot Button [1913-?], also in the Provincial Administration, lived in Northern Rhodesia 1937-66. He was personally responsible for the addition of 20 species to the country's avifauna, in particular between 1947 and 1951 when he was the first to investigate in some detail the forests of the south-western (Zambian) Nyika. He provided proof of the occurrence of Common Snipe *Gallinago gallinago* in the country (Button 1973). He also supervised Jali Makawa when he visited the lower slopes of the Makutu Plateau in 1948, and the Zambian Nyika in 1952, adding a further 10 species to the country list.

Major Edward L. Haydock published on the birds of the Luanshya area, starting in 1949. He was the first to report African White-rumped Swift reliably, on the Copperbelt (Haydock 1949a). He was also the first to ring birds in the country, and a Yellow-billed Kite *Milvus migrans parasitus* marked at Luanshya in 1948 was found later near Bulawayo, Zimbabwe (Appendix 1).

Reay Henry Noble Smithers [1907-1987] was Assistant Director (later Director) of the National Museums of Southern Rhodesia from 1947, and made a unique contribution to Zambian ornithology by encouraging, sponsoring and curating important collections from various parts of the country. Not only are the most important series of Zambian specimens held in Bulawayo Museum, but they formed the basis of the detailed studies of Benson and his close collaborator M.P.S. Irwin. Reay Smithers had the agreeable gift of remembering and telling stories that show the human side of many of the African ornithologists he knew; of particular interest to the student of Zambian birds are Smithers (1984, 1985). Smithers recalled that an interest in natural history was encouraged by the then Governor of Northern Rhodesia as preferable to "women and the bottle". For an appreciation of Reay Smithers himself, see Irwin (1988).

Reay Smithers

Major William Eustace Poles [1902-1990] was a game warden with a particular interest in falconry. After a distinguished period of war service in Burma, he joined the Northern Rhodesian Game Department in 1946 and was given charge of a huge area, including the Luangwa Valley and Bangweulu. Encouraged by Reay Smithers, Poles organized the training of skinners at Mpika. During his explorations he made valuable observations and collections, and was the first to find Laura's Warbler in Zambia (the race named after him, *eustacei*). Poles and Ian Grimwood discovered the ornithological importance of the Bwingimfumu submontane forests on the Muchinga escarpment (Grimwood in Smithers 1952: 104-107). Poles retired in 1957, and for a short time managed Blue Lagoon (then a ranch). For an obituary see *The Daily Telegraph* (15 August 1990, p. 17).

William Frank Harding Ansell [1923-1996], mammalogist, after war service in Burma, lived in Zambia from 1947 to 1974. During his long career in the Game Department he provided enormous encouragement to colleagues to undertake serious studies of the country's natural history. Frank collaborated closely with Benson and Dowsett in collecting expeditions throughout the country. Dowsett

(1997) gave details of the contribution made by Frank Ansell to Zambian zoology and conservation.

Jali Makawa (Mafinga Mts, 1971)

Con Benson (Bulawayo, 1970)

Constantine Walter Benson [1909-1982] came to Northern Rhodesia in 1952 from neighbouring Nyasaland. As a biologist in the Game Department he travelled extensively and encouraged colleagues to collect specimens and record their observations. He published a great deal, essentially dealing with the topics of taxonomy and distribution. Benson joined White as co-author of the fourth checklist (Benson & White 1957), and with 80 additional species they brought the Zambian list to 667. He made some especially interesting discoveries of Guineo-Congolian species in the forests of northern Mwinilunga (Benson 1958b). The further revision in 1971 (the fifth checklist: Benson *et al*. 1971a) listed 45 more species, the total now being 712 (699 were listed, but taxonomic changes and some subsequent confirmations have increased this number). During his time in the country Con Benson was responsible for finding at least 30 species new to the avifauna, alone or (especially) in collaboration with Jali Makawa. From 1962-65 Benson spent his final years in Zambia on secondment to the Livingstone Museum, where he started to build up a representative collection of zoological study specimens, and documented breeding data in south-central Africa (Benson *et al*. 1964). In this he was helped by Clayton S. Holliday [b. 1930] and as taxidermist by Aaron Muchindu [1939-2002], as well as Jali. Among the obituaries of Con Benson should be mentioned those of two close collaborators (Brooke 1982 and Irwin 1983b).

Jali Makawa [d. 1995] was Benson's personal collector, and undoubtedly one of the most able anywhere in Africa. He was responsible for more than 31 additions to the country list, alone or in association with Benson, Traylor and others. He was a very selective collector, and would usually restrict himself to target species, which Carl Vernon recalls were described to him by Con Benson in a mixture of English, scientific and local Chinyanja names. The Broad-tailed Warbler was "Mbalami wa India" (Indian bird), because Con had told Jali it also occurred in India. Jali had an exceptional ear, and could mimic or otherwise call up a great many of the trickier species. Accounts of Jali's life will be found in Benson (1970), Dowsett (1975d) and Irwin (1996).

One of Con Benson's colleagues was Ian Robert Grimwood [1912-1990], a biologist in the Game Department (later Assistant Director), 1948-60. In the early 1950s Grimwood added no fewer

**(L to R) Bernard Carp, Reay Smithers
& Ian Grimwood (Nangweshi, 1949)**

than 11 species to the Zambian avifauna, especially a number of forest birds from the north-west (e.g. White & Grimwood 1954), including a species new to science, Grimwood's Longclaw. As a member of the expedition organized by Bernard Carp [1901-1966] to the south-west in 1952, he added a further five species in collaboration with Reay Smithers. He went on to contribute greatly to international wildlife conservation (see obituary in *The Times* of 30 January 1991).

Other members of the Game and Fisheries Department made important contributions to ornithological knowledge in the 1950s and 1960s. Roelf I.G. Attwell [b. 1917], was in Zambia 1950-64 and as Chief Wildlife Research Officer did much to encourage young game rangers with no formal zoological training. Peter Ian Rupert Maclaren [1919-1956], fisheries officer, had a special interest in waders (Benson *et al.* 1955); he was killed by a crocodile tragically young – his interest in natural history was continued actively by his sister, Margaret Bruce-Miller. Norman Carr [1912-1997] made a unique contribution to conservation in Zambia, especially in the Luangwa Valley.

Special mention should be made of J.M.C. Uys [1926-1973], another who died too young, killed by an elephant in Zimbabwe. Johnny Uys was the rare example of a naturalist of exceptional and broad talent who had received almost no formal education. He was a gifted student of mammals and botany, and no mean ornithologist too. Above all, as Game Warden (later Chief Wildlife Warden) he greatly encouraged his younger colleagues to be more than just law enforcers.

Johnny Uys

Robert Jack Dowsett [b. 1942] arrived in Northern Rhodesia early in 1962, and after a spell as a Government accountant he transferred to the Game Department as ranger involved in studies of various large mammals in the Kafue and Luangwa Valley National Parks. After a year in Nigeria in 1968 he returned to Zambia to concentrate on ornithological research for the Wildlife Conservation Society, based on the Kafue Flats. In 1971 he became head of the Natural History department at Livingstone Museum, where he spent eight years before moving to adjacent Malawi in 1979. In addition to fieldwork while living in the Luangwa Valley, at Lochinvar, Livingstone and the Nyika, he undertook a number of expeditions, to north-eastern and north-western Zambia. When he left the Museum, the collection there consisted of some

Bob Dowsett & Aaron Muchindu (R) (Mafinga Mts, 1971)

10,000 specimens, covering the great majority of Zambian species. In 1969 he took over as Chairman of the Zambian Ornithological Society from its first Chairman, Johnny Uys. At the same time he started the society's *Bulletin* (which presented articles on the country's ornithology up to 1984, before its production ceased). He was co-author of the fifth account of the Zambian avifauna and direct predecessor of this book, *The Birds of Zambia* (Benson *et al.* 1971a), a landmark in the history of the country's ornithology. For this work Zambian residents Benson and Dowsett were joined by two Zimbabwean colleagues with whom they had long collaborated, Michael Stuart Irwin [b. 1925] and Richard Kendall Brooke [1930-1996]. These two brought with them knowledge of the collection of Zambian birds housed in Bulawayo and a broad expertise in southern African ornithology.

Others who were active ornithologically in the 1960s and early 1970s, and who published their observations, included Leslie D.E.F. Vesey-Fitzgerald [1909-1974], an ecologist working largely in Tanzania, who made useful observations of the birds of northern Zambia; Anthony John Tree [b. 1937], a keen student of migration (e.g. Tree 1962b, 1969); Vivian John Wilson [b. 1932], who was employed in the Tsetse Control Department in Eastern Province (Wilson 1972a); Peter Leslie Britton [b. 1943] and his wife Hazel Ann [b. 1944], who studied the birds of Balovale 1964-67 (Britton 1970). S. Graham Madge [1920-2002] was the leading Copperbelt ornithologist 1970-73, drawing particular attention to the Ndola forestry plots (Madge 1972b). He also found the first breeding evidence in Zambia for Great

Richard Brooke

Michael Irwin (Bulawayo, 1970)

Norman Carr & Phil Berry (Mfuwe, 1969)

Crested Grebe *Podiceps cristatus* and African Cuckoo Hawk *Aviceda cuculoides* (Madge 1971b, d). Philip S.M. Berry [b. 1942], another member of the Game Department, and still active in the Luangwa Valley after more than 45 years, has done much to encourage and document observations in this permanently inhabited wildlife area (e.g. Berry 1981a). Phil was in the party that discovered Sharpe's Starling in the Mafingas (Dowsett *et al.* 2003). Robert Stjernstedt [b. 1941] has been resident in various parts of Zambia since 1969, and is especially known for his recordings and documentation of Zambian bird vocalisations (Stjernstedt 1989, 1996).

Much of the impetus at this time was encouraged by the publication of *The Birds of Zambia*, and that would not have been possible without the active interest of the Critchleys. Zambian ornithology has benefited not only from those with a direct involvement in field and museum studies, but from the healthy cooperation that existed with conservationists, foremost of whom were Lt-Col. Ronald Asheton Critchley [1905-1999] and his wife Erica [1910-1976]. Their contribution includes the establishment of Blue Lagoon National Park (their home for many years, and one of which many of us have very happy memories), the active role of the Wildlife Conservation Society, sponsoring the publication of *The Birds of Zambia* in 1971 (aided by the good offices of the Anglo-American Corporation), and their excellent relationship with the then President of Zambia, Kenneth Kaunda, which saw the gazetting of no fewer than 18 national parks in 1971. For a fascinating obituary of Ronnie Critchley, see *The Times* of 29 September 1999.

Ronnie Critchley (Blue Lagoon)

Erica Critchley (Blue Lagoon)

Among visiting ornithologists who have published important papers involving Zambian birds, mention should be made of the following. Major Melvin A. Traylor Jnr [b. 1915] made a valuable collection in Barotseland October-December 1971 (helped by Jali Makawa), including no fewer than four additions to the Zambian list (Traylor 1965b). G. Stuart Keith [1937-2003] and Carl J. Vernon [b. 1939] collected the first Eurasian Rock Thrush *Monticola saxatilis* and were the first to recognize Scarce Swift on the Nyika Plateau (Keith & Vernon 1969), while the latter also published an interesting paper on the ecology of Nyika cisticolas (Vernon 1964). Carl had been posted temporarily to Kasama 1958-59, where he studied martins and swifts (Brooke & Vernon 1961a,b), and he subsequently made a number of field trips north of the Zambezi, usually in collaboration with Con Benson. Terence Barry Oatley [b. 1934] wrote a valuable account of the birds of some of the forests in the north-west of the country (Oatley 1969). Robert B. Payne [b. 1938] has paid several long visits to Zambia, where he and his students have done much to elucidate the life history of parasitic Viduidae and their hosts (Payne 1980a,b, 1987).

Dylan Aspinwall (Muckle Neuk, 1973)

The 1970s saw a great increase in the number of people actively looking at birds in the field, and foremost of these was Dylan Richard Aspinwall [1942-1995]. Dylan came to Zambia in 1966, but it was not until the early 1970s that he began to take an interest in birds. His employment as a secondary school teacher (initially of French, later English) meant that he had long holidays in which to travel around the country, and when he was appointed Inspector of French he was able to travel widely as part of his official duties too. He had an exceptionally good ear, and between 1972 and 1994 he found no fewer than 10 species for the first time in Zambia, and helped confirm two others. Dylan entered enthusiastically into the mapping project initiated by Bob Dowsett in 1975, and at the time of his tragic disappearance had almost reached his aim of 200 species confirmed in each atlas square (a large percentage of the likely total in each square, necessary for the maps to reflect actual distribution).

Clide Carter, Huw Penry, Barry Taylor and others based on the Copperbelt travelled widely atlassing, and added half a dozen vagrants to the Zambian list in the late 1970s and 1980s. Professional ornithologists active then included Timothy O. Osborne [b. 1944], resident 1967-76, who studied the birds of Liuwa Plain and Lochinvar National Parks, and paid particular attention to raptors (e.g. Osborne 1978, 1981). The Kafue Flats also benefited from the waterfowl research of Robert J. Douthwaite (e.g. Douthwaite 1977, 1978), including the continuation of a ringing station established by Bob Dowsett and staff of the Livingstone Museum.

During the 1970s Zambian ornithology had the pleasure of the direct and enthusiastic involvement of the late Paddy and Margaret Bruce-Miller at Muckle Neuk, Choma. Not only did they themselves travel to many parts of the country in search of birds, but above all they made Muckle Neuk a warm second home for all their birdy friends.

Oology has received the attention of several ornithologists in the past, such as Cottrell, but the most important contribution by far has been made by Major John Frederick Robert Colebrook-Robjent [b. 1935]. John Robjent has lived in Zambia from 1966 to date, and has farmed in the Choma District since 1969.

Françoise Lemaire (Victoria Falls, 1976)

Françoise Lemaire [b. 1952] first visited Zambia in 1976, to study the migratory European Marsh Warbler *Acrocephalus palustris*, in particular its incorporation of the vocalisations of other species into its own song (Dowsett-Lemaire 1979). From 1979 to 1982 she and her husband Bob Dowsett studied intensively the avifauna, especially forest populations, on the Nyika Plateau (Dowsett 1985a, Dowsett-Lemaire 1983c, 1985a), whose vegetation she documented (Dowsett-Lemaire 1985b).

Since the death of Dylan Aspinwall Zambian ornithology has depended on a few keen people, notably Carl Beel, Fil Hide, Stuart Norman, Bob Stjernstedt, Rod Tether, Paul Van Daele, and especially Pete Leonard. Peter M. Leonard [b. 1972] lived in Zambia between 1994 and 2003, during which time he was instrumental in five additions to the Zambian list, most notably White-winged Warbler in the Luapula Valley (Leonard & Beel 1999). Pete is a school teacher, and he also studied intensively the birds of the two places where he taught (Kafue Fisheries and Muckle Neuk, Choma), and resurrected the *Bulletin of the Zambian Ornithological Society* in a much improved format, as the *Zambia Bird Report*. Three issues appeared (1997-99), but regrettably the publication died with his departure from Zambia. Pete has produced an excellent account of Zambian Important Bird Areas (Leonard 2005), discussed in the Conservation section.

The 124 type specimens from Zambia are in the collections of the Natural History Museum, Tring (NHM, ex-BM, 45), Bulawayo Museum (NMZB, 29), New York (AMNH, 7), Oxford (OUM, 7), Livingstone (NMZL, 5), Chicago (FMNH, 4), Cape Town (SAM, 3), Pretoria (TMP, 3) and Durban (DM, 2). No fewer than 18 type specimens (mostly from the private collection of C.M.N. White) cannot be traced, and one specimen in the museum at Budapest was destroyed in the Soviet invasion of 1956. Although the great majority of collections from Zambia are now in NHM and NMZB, large numbers are housed in some other institutions, e.g. some 2973 Zambian specimens in FMNH (2007). In addition to its reference collection of bird skins, the Livingstone Museum also holds an important ornithological library.

The Zambian Ornithological Society produces a Newsletter (an invaluable source of records since 1971) and supports conservation in Zambia, especially through its schools education programme and the Important Bird Areas project (www.wattledcrane.com & zos@zamnet.zm).

5. The composition of the avifauna

Table 3. The composition of the Zambian avifauna in 2007.

Resident	553	(504 with definite breeding records)
Intra-African migrants	105	(73 have definitely bred)
Intra-African vagrants	18	
Palaearctic migrants	96	(of which 64 winter in Zambia; including 14 vagrants)
Nearctic vagrants	3	

In **Table 3** five species included in the total of Palaearctic migrants also have local African populations (see p. 63). A number of breeding species have double status (part-resident, part-migratory) and several of the resident species see their breeding population augmented by an influx of seasonal visitors (e.g. Hoopoe *Upupa epops*, African Black Swift). Many species classified as resident are subject to at least local movements, wandering or post-breeding concentrations (e.g. various waterbirds, sunbirds and orioles). Brown-necked Parrots and African Green Pigeons have movements clearly related to fruiting seasons of certain food plants (as on the Nyika Plateau, Dowsett-Lemaire 2006a).

The number of species known when the previous account of the Zambian avifauna was published (Benson *et al.* 1971a) was 712 (699 were listed, but some in square brackets are now accepted, and there have been some taxonomic splits). The total number of species on the Zambian List is currently 752 (excluding one extinct). Most of the 40 species added since are vagrants, but a number are members of the resident, breeding population: Brown-eared Woodpecker and Chestnut Wattle-eye (northern Mwinilunga); Silvery-cheeked Hornbill, Sharpe's Akalat and Yellow-throated Warbler (forests in the eastern highlands); White-winged Warbler and Spot-flanked Barbet (north-eastern plateau); Fischer's Sparrow-Lark *Eremopterix leucopareia* and Olive-headed Weaver (Eastern Province); Scaly-feathered Finch (south-west). In addition, Slaty Egret (wetlands) and Barred Long-tailed Cuckoo (valley thickets) have occurred regularly, and are likely to be found breeding in time, as might two recent arrivals: Spur-winged Plover *Vanellus spinosus* (northern wetlands) and Speckled Pigeon *Columba guinea* (Southern Province).

The following (in systematic order) are the 20 species present in most squares (291 squares or more, i.e. >95%): Bateleur, Cape Turtle Dove*, Red-eyed Dove *Streptopelia semitorquata**, Emerald-spotted Wood Dove *Turtur chalcospilos**, Meyer's Parrot, Yellow-fronted Tinkerbird, Cardinal Woodpecker, Eurasian Swallow*, Black-eyed Bulbul*, Heuglin's Robin*, White-browed Scrub Robin, Tawny-flanked Prinia*, Chinspot Batis, African Paradise Flycatcher*, Southern Puffback*, Black-crowned Tchagra*, Eastern Black-headed Oriole*, Fork-tailed Drongo*, Yellow-throated Petronia and Yellow-eyed Canary *Serinus mozambicus**. The 13 species marked with an asterisk are also among the 20 most widespread species in neighbouring Malawi. Only two of the Malawi "Top 20" are significantly less widespread in Zambia: African Pied Wagtail (75%, cf. 93% in Malawi) and Yellow-rumped Bishop (52%, cf. 87%).

Migration and movements

Of 100 or so **Palaearctic migrants**, over 60 have a significant proportion wintering, and the following 15 are known from more than 50% of squares: Common Buzzard *Buteo buteo*, Eurasian Hobby *Falco subbuteo*, Greenshank *Tringa nebularia*, Wood Sandpiper *T. glareola*, Common Sandpiper *Actitis hypoleucos*, Eurasian Swift *Apus apus*, Blue-cheeked Bee-eater, Eurasian Bee-eater *Merops apiaster*, Eurasian Sand Martin, Eurasian Swallow, Eurasian House Martin *Delichon urbicum*, Willow Warbler *Phylloscopus trochilus*, Spotted Flycatcher *Muscicapa striata*, Red-backed Shrike *Lanius collurio* and Lesser Grey Shrike *L. minor*. The last is numerous on passage; all others have both wintering and transient populations. For some of these, Zambia's woodlands and floodplains are a major wintering destination and the numbers involved must be considerable – especially for several waders (cited above), both bee-eaters, Eurasian Swift and Swallow (roosts of Eurasian Swallows may contain tens of thousands or more), Spotted Flycatcher, some of the warblers and (more locally) Tree Pipit. At the peak of the rains Palaearctic swifts and swallows outnumber local species. Similarly some of the warblers, especially Sedge and Marsh Warblers (with 45% and 28% of square coverage respectively) reach densities far in excess of their African congeners.

    Zambia's floodplains and wetlands are home to large numbers of visiting or wintering waders: for instance many thousands of Ruff winter in flooded grassland, and tens of thousands of Caspian Plover may be counted on southbound stop-over in the Kafue Flats, in the drier grasslands. In recent years, the Kafue Flats have seen the arrival of Black-tailed Godwit *Limosa limosa*, now wintering in their thousands. Of the wader species that winter mainly on the coasts of the African continent (e.g. Turnstone *Arenaria interpres*, Sanderling *Calidris alba*, Bar-tailed Godwit *L. lapponica*) the limited passage recorded through Zambia is essentially or exclusively southbound (cf. Dowsett 1980a).

    In many Palaearctic species higher numbers cross Zambia than remain to winter, and passage is sometimes concentrated. Thus for Common Buzzard it is not unusual to see hundreds in a day heading north in February or March in the east of the country, as also (more occasionally) in Lesser Spotted Eagle *Aquila pomarina* and Steppe Eagle *A. nipalensis*. Conversely, other species follow a narrow route on southward migration, the most spectacular being Black-winged Pratincole, with hundreds of thousands flying over the Liuwa Plain in mid-November – whether this phenomenon is annual is unknown due to irregular coverage in the far west. Some species undergo a loop migration within Zambia and adjacent Malawi: thus large numbers of Lesser Grey Shrike cross the western half of Zambia in late October and November (to winter further, in arid south-western Africa) whereas northbound migration is displaced to the east, mostly through Malawi (Dowsett 1971f). A similar pattern is apparently followed by Red-backed Shrike, although the latter is more widespread and does winter in some numbers.

    Table 4 presents the arrival and departure dates of those Palaearctic migrants for which there are good samples. No mean departure dates can be given for three waders, as wintering populations are small or non-existent. Excluded are species for which there are significant numbers of observations during the Palaearctic breeding season (particularly waders, but also Eurasian Swallow). Not taken into account in the Table are the few examples of species that are clearly out of season.

    Species migrating to Zambia exhibit two extremes, those that appear to fly in directly, arriving usually in August or September (e.g. Eurasian Bee-eater, Willow Warbler), and those that spend time in north-eastern Africa before moving southwards (e.g. Thrush Nightingale, Marsh Warbler), arriving as the first rains produce prodigious plant growth and insect life. The two-step movements of these and other species, with delayed crossing of the Equator, are well shown by studies of migration in eastern Kenya (Pearson & Backhurst 1976). In between these two extremes, many species do not arrive before October or early November, which implies a leisurely movement south.

    Three **Nearctic vagrants** have occurred (Lesser Yellowlegs *Tringa flavipes*, Solitary Sandpiper *T. solitaria* and Franklin's Gull *Larus pipixcan*); all have appeared in January and February, in contrast to the preponderance of similar Palaearctic vagrants, which are on passage September to

Table 4. Chronology of Palaearctic migrants in Zambia (1971-2002).

Species	First arrivals			Last dates		
	Mean	SD	n years	Mean	SD	n years
Honey Buzzard	Oct 22	11.8	19	Apr 1	20.4	20
Pallid Harrier	Oct 29	15.2	26	Mar 7	15.7	19
Montagu's Harrier	Nov 2	16.0	26	Mar 10	21.8	23
Common Buzzard	Oct 5	10.7	29	Apr 6	18.6	28
Lesser Spotted Eagle	Oct 27	17.3	29	Mar 18	18.1	25
Steppe Eagle	Oct 27	15.3	27	Mar 27	16.7	25
Lesser Kestrel	Oct 26	9.0	27	Mar 31	14.8	25
Eastern Red-footed Falcon	Nov 13	13.6	20	Mar 24	13.8	21
Eurasian Hobby	Oct 15	13.8	30	Mar 30	10.4	28
Ringed Plover	Sep 19	12.3	28	-	-	-
Caspian Plover	Aug 27	10.7	26	-	-	-
Green Sandpiper	Sep 19	18.1	27	Mar 28	11.6	19
Turnstone	Sep 21	14.7	20	-	-	-
Eurasian Swift	Oct 1	13.6	28	Mar 25	20.0	26
Blue-cheeked Bee-eater	Nov 4	12.1	26	Apr 18	12.0	28
Eurasian Bee-eater	Sep 4	9.1	29	Apr 21	7.1	29
Eurasian Roller	Nov 9	10.9	28	Apr 7	14.8	21
Eurasian Sand Martin	Sep 28	14.6	27	May 5	14.5	26
Eurasian House Martin	Sep 27	10.5	29	Apr 29	12.9	28
Yellow Wagtail	Oct 7	9.4	29	Apr 29	15.2	22
Tree Pipit	Nov 1	12.9	25	Mar 24	12.5	22
Thrush Nightingale	Dec 15	10.6	24	Mar 13	11.8	28
Whinchat	Nov 16	15.4	17	Feb 27	22.1	14
Sedge Warbler	Nov 7	13.8	25	Apr 26	8.1	24
Marsh Warbler	Dec 14	13.8	21	Apr 8	11.5	22
Great Reed Warbler	Nov 20	10.3	24	Apr 4	8.8	25
Willow Warbler	Sept 24	6.9	24	Apr 27	11.6	22
Garden Warbler	Oct 7	9.6	26	Apr 3	12.8	24
Common Whitethroat	Nov 14	12.8	19	Apr 8	10.1	24
Spotted Flycatcher	Oct 5	10.0	24	Apr 18	10.5	23
Eurasian Golden Oriole	Oct 22	17.9	28	Mar 24	18.0	16
Red-backed Shrike	Oct 24	8.3	29	Apr 22	7.6	26
Lesser Grey Shrike	Oct 20	5.4	28	Apr 16	5.5	26

November (e.g. Dowsett 1980a). This suggests they are birds that have crossed the Atlantic earlier, per-haps to western Europe, before wandering southwards into Africa.

Of some 105 **intra-African migrants**, the majority arrive in the late dry season or early rains to breed locally – i.e. in the austral summer. Typical examples include Dwarf Bittern, several crakes and quails, cuckoos of the genera *Clamator*, *Cuculus* and *Chrysococcyx*, Pennant-winged Nightjar, Broad-billed Roller *Eurystomus glaucurus*, Senegal Kingfisher and Pygmy Kingfisher *Ceyx pictus*, several swifts and swallows, African Pitta and African Paradise Flycatcher. A few waterbirds are present year-round but with an obvious influx of immigrants in the rains, such as Knob-billed Duck, known from ringing recoveries to be a trans-equatorial migrant. Fulvous Tree Duck is also known to cross the Equator, but in the Kafue Flats the timing of peak numbers has fluctuated with the regime of floods, and has changed since the construction of dams.

Several species of open country favour the dry season, some to breed, others not. The complexity and diversity of intra-African migration are well illustrated by the example of the Hirundines. All migratory swallows exhibit somewhat different patterns: the montane Blue Swallow is the most clearcut, breeding in the summer rains then leaving completely from May to August, to winter quarters to the north. The White-headed Saw-wing follows a similar pattern but a few may linger in the cold months. The Red-breasted Swallow arrives earlier, being most frequent July to March and breeding in the early rains; the Red-throated Cliff Swallow arrives in April-June to breed before the rains and most leave before December. In the Angola Swallow some birds may be resident (Copperbelt) but in the north-west it is most numerous in March-September and on the Nyika from May to January – with breeding records overall from May to December. In Banded Martin and Grey-rumped Swallow, breeding activity peaks in August, but movements are complex and probably involve different populations, as Banded Martins are in fact more numerous and widespread in the rains, but the opposite is true of Grey-rumped. Finally, White-throated Swallow is a non-breeding visitor (from the south), at times numerous (early and late dry seasons), while small numbers of Greater Striped Swallow *Hirundo cucullata* and South African Cliff Swallow *H. spilodera* cross western Zambia en route to their winter quarters to the north. Several other swallows generally considered as resident have at least local movements, or Zambian populations may be augmented by an influx of visitors in the cold season (e.g. Lesser Striped Swallow).

Table 5 presents the average dates of arrival and departure of a number of migrants with a large sample of observations. Abdim's Stork and Alpine Swift *Apus melba* are non-breeding visitors which nest, respectively, in northern and southern Africa. The rest breed in Zambia and the majority (in all probability trans-equatorial migrants) arrive to nest just before or during the rains. Two, however, Dusky Lark *Pinarocorys nigricans* and Capped Wheatear, breed on dry ground and leave before the rains to spend the off-season south of Zambia. Other typical dry-ground nesters, with significant numbers arriving in the early dry season, include Bronze-winged Courser *Rhinoptilus chalcopterus*, Swallow-tailed Bee-eater, Red-capped Lark and Buffy Pipit.

The movements of Splendid Glossy Starling (**Table 5**) may be influenced by the seasonality

Table 5. Selected Intra-African migrants, with first and last dates (1971-2002).

Species	(extreme dates)	First arrivals			Last dates		
		Mean	SD	n (y)	Mean	SD	n (y)
Abdim's Stork	(Oct 10-Jun 16)	Oct 24	8.8	30	Apr 21	7.2	14
Wahlberg's Eagle	(Jul 25-Apr 28)	Aug 11	7.8	28	Apr 17	10.0	29
African Crake	(Nov 27-Jul 1)	Dec 10	9.5	29	Apr 17	11.5	16
Jacobin Cuckoo	(Sep 25-May 17)	Oct 10	7.3	19	Apr 12	12.8	22
Striped Crested Cuckoo	(Aug 22-Jun 28)	Oct 10	12.9	26	May 9	26.6	28
Red-chested Cuckoo	(Aug 1-May 1)	Aug 26	14.4	29	Mar 16	23.5	24
Black Cuckoo	(Aug 17-May 19)	Sep 5	12.2	27	Apr 1	20.0	26
African Grey Cuckoo	(Jul 31-May 6)	Sep 2	14.6	25	Apr 11	12.6	23
Pennant-winged Nightjar	(Aug 1-Mar 31)	Aug 23	14.3	28	Mar 7	10.9	20
Alpine Swift	(Mar 29-Nov 30)	Apr 22	18.5	12	-	-	-
Pygmy Kingfisher	(all months)	Oct 4	18.4	27	Apr 20	17.7	22
Senegal Kingfisher	(all months)	Oct 4	17.7	23	Apr 27	14.9	22
Dusky Lark	(all months)	Apr 28	15.3	24	-	-	-
Capped Wheatear	(all months)	May 16	18.5	29	Nov 29	18.0	28
Splendid Glossy Starling	(May 28-Jan 17)	Aug 5	34.4	26	Dec 14	21.1	21
Red-headed Quelea	(Sep 11-May 20)	Dec 11	16.2	17	Apr 10	19.0	21

of fruiting: two other frugivorous species, the Afep Pigeon (in Mwinilunga) and Rameron Pigeon (in the highlands of the east) also leave the country largely in December, and in the case of the Rameron this is clearly induced by the end of fruiting of favoured fruit trees (Dowsett-Lemaire 1988b). Some aspects of intra-African migration are discussed by Benson (1982) and Dowsett (1988a).

Of five species with both Afrotropical and Palaearctic populations, four are represented by a local race that breeds – Little Bittern *Ixobrychus minutus*, Yellow-billed Kite, Rock Kestrel *Falco tinnunculus* and African Reed Warbler *Acrocephalus scirpaceus* (*baeticatus*) – whereas White Storks are shown by ringing recoveries to come essentially from the Palaearctic, with a few also from the small South African population. It is possible that some Booted Eagles *Hieraaetus pennatus* and Eurasian Bee-eaters also come from the southern African breeding population, but this remains as yet unproven.

Breeding birds

There being a single rainy season in Zambia, the **seasonality of breeding** by most birds is in relation to this, to coincide with food supplies (e.g. the burst of insect life just before and during the early rains in the Zambezian woodlands), or to avoid adverse nesting conditions (e.g. the necessity of open ground-nesters to avoid the heavy rains). **Table 6** presents some of the larger samples available of nesting records of Zambian species. As samples for waterbirds are rather small, they are not shown here, but overall duck and crake species of seasonal marsh and shallow water breed in the rains and early dry season, as do also several herons and storks.

Table 6. Breeding seasons of some common Zambian species (number of egg-laying records per month, with bold for months with at least 50% of total).

Species	Jan	Feb	Mar	Apr	May	Jun	Jul	Aug	Sep	Oct	Nov	Dec	Total
Woodland													
Yellow-billed Kite	0	0	0	0	0	0	0	53	**84**	16	1	0	154
Shikra	0	0	0	0	0	0	0	0	**76**	41	2	2	121
Lizard Buzzard	0	0	0	0	0	0	0	1	32	**130**	13	1	177
Wahlberg's Eagle	0	0	0	0	0	0	0	4	**192**	119	4	1	320
Fiery-necked Nightjar	0	0	0	0	0	0	1	14	**49**	**52**	13	0	129
Pennant-winged Nightjar	0	0	0	0	0	0	0	6	57	**147**	44	0	254
Chestnut-bellied Kingfisher	1	1	0	0	0	0	0	0	21	**56**	28	4	111
Black-collared Barbet	7	5	3	0	0	0	0	0	**54**	**62**	31	9	171
Kurrichane Thrush	1	0	2	2	0	0	0	2	**67**	**59**	43	10	186
Long-billed Crombec	3	5	4	1	0	0	0	1	**81**	**68**	58	15	236
Neddicky	**41**	31	10	1	0	0	0	0	0	3	27	**48**	161
Pallid Flycatcher	0	0	0	0	0	0	0	2	**65**	**59**	21	10	157
Southern Black Flycatcher	1	0	0	0	0	0	0	1	**83**	50	40	4	179
Chinspot Batis	1	0	0	0	0	0	0	6	**94**	57	8	2	168
Black Sunbird	3	8	5	1	0	0	0	2	**40**	**39**	14	11	123
African Golden Oriole	0	0	0	0	0	0	0	0	**96**	**114**	10	0	220
Sousa's Shrike	0	0	0	0	0	0	0	1	**48**	28	20	4	101
White Helmet Shrike	0	0	2	4	0	1	0	4	**50**	40	14	3	118
Fork-tailed Drongo	1	0	0	0	1	0	0	4	**340**	234	93	2	675
Amethyst Starling	0	0	0	0	0	0	0	0	2	**62**	27	2	93
Red-headed Weaver	0	0	0	0	0	0	0	5	**56**	35	24	5	125
Golden-breasted Bunting	7	4	1	0	1	0	0	0	21	**49**	**33**	19	135

Table 6. Breeding seasons of some common Zambian species (number of egg-laying records per month) (contd).

Species	Jan	Feb	Mar	Apr	May	Jun	Jul	Aug	Sep	Oct	Nov	Dec	Total
Forest													
Starred Robin	2	0	0	0	0	0	0	0	4	39	**89**	70	204
Cape Batis	6	3	0	0	0	0	0	0	32	**51**	41	40	173
Yellow White-eye	5	1	0	1	0	0	0	11	34	**75**	32	12	171
Thicket													
Yellow-bellied Bulbul	**22**	8	0	0	0	0	0	0	1	15	23	27	96
Terrestrial Bulbul	**35**	5	2	1	0	0	0	0	1	5	11	**61**	121
Heuglin's Robin	**27**	20	0	0	1	0	0	0	9	22	12	**32**	123
Bleating Bush Warbler	**26**	15	3	0	1	0	0	0	0	1	6	**43**	95
African Paradise Flycatcher	11	2	1	0	0	0	0	1	5	58	**68**	43	189
Arrow-marked Babbler	6	**18**	**18**	7	4	1	1	1	26	22	16	5	125
Tropical Boubou	**26**	17	4	0	0	1	0	1	17	17	24	**44**	151
Open dry ground													
Bronze-winged Courser	0	0	0	0	1	2	1	10	**48**	33	1	0	96
Temminck's Courser	0	0	0	0	1	5	12	24	**31**	30	13	0	116
Kittlitz's Plover	1	0	0	2	5	13	23	42	**53**	22	4	0	165
Crowned Plover	0	0	0	3	5	11	20	32	**35**	25	1	0	132
Buffy Pipit	0	0	0	0	0	1	3	20	**27**	24	7	0	82
Riverine													
Rock Pratincole	1	0	0	0	0	0	0	8	**64**	24	22	11	130
African Skimmer	0	0	0	0	5	8	**67**	48	43	22	0	0	193
(Wooded) Grassland													
Little Bee-eater	0	0	0	0	0	0	1	5	33	**123**	28	2	192
Rufous-naped Lark	11	8	5	0	0	0	0	4	6	**18**	23	12	87
Fan-tailed Cisticola	38	**42**	**46**	34	5	1	0	0	0	0	7	21	194
Rattling Cisticola	**54**	45	21	5	0	0	0	0	0	0	14	34	173
Red-faced Cisticola	66	**68**	23	4	0	0	0	0	0	0	0	15	176
Tawny-flanked Prinia	348	**351**	135	21	5	0	0	0	2	0	7	92	961
Fiscal Shrike	2	0	2	2	0	1	0	11	**40**	37	20	8	123
Brown-headed Tchagra	17	8	4	4	0	1	0	8	**39**	31	28	19	159
Black-crowned Tchagra	11	11	5	1	1	2	1	2	35	**84**	48	13	214
Seed-eaters													
Large Golden Weaver	55	**65**	20	2	0	0	0	1	17	30	13	16	219
African Masked Weaver	**172**	134	22	0	0	0	0	1	17	19	55	71	491
Spotted-backed Weaver	63	**272**	42	0	0	0	0	0	35	47	12	4	475
Red Bishop	**402**	304	114	15	0	0	0	0	0	0	0	23	858
Yellow-rumped Bishop	**158**	120	38	13	0	0	0	0	0	0	0	20	349
Green-winged Pytilia	6	31	**50**	17	12	0	0	0	0	1	0	2	119
Blue Waxbill	41	35	**60**	33	3	1	0	0	0	0	0	7	180
Yellow-eyed Canary	37	**19**	17	4	0	0	0	6	2	0	0	13	98

Table 6. Breeding seasons of some common Zambian species (number of egg-laying records per month) (contd).

Species	Jan	Feb	Mar	Apr	May	Jun	Jul	Aug	Sep	Oct	Nov	Dec	Total
Various/Commensal													
Wire-tailed Swallow	1	9	**22**	7	2	4	6	**43**	19	17	0	0	130
African Pied Wagtail	0	2	7	7	3	2	11	**16**	29	18	12	6	113
Black-eyed Bulbul	49	21	2	2	0	0	1	12	88	**127**	109	62	473
Scarlet-chested Sunbird	4	2	2	2	1	0	1	12	**53**	45	12	4	138
House Sparrow	3	2	12	10	13	2	**13**	**22**	19	29	11	8	144
Scavengers													
Marabou Stork	0	0	0	1	18	**53**	58	23	4	0	0	0	157
White-backed Vulture	0	0	1	11	**57**	33	10	4	0	0	0	0	117

Seasonality of breeding is particularly well marked in insectivorous birds of woodland (including small raptors like Lizard Buzzard *Kaupifalco monogrammicus*), with egg-laying usually centred around September-October. In miombo woodland leaf flush associated with an evident increase in arthropod food usually happens in October (just before the rains) and about a month later in mopane. Thus feeding conditions are optimal from October to December. The Neddicky lays noticeably later than other species (**Table 6**), as conditions for this understorey warbler improve during the rains.

The narrow peak of breeding records in the great majority of woodland birds suggests single-broodedness. This aspect was studied in more detail in montane forest birds of the Nyika Plateau (Dowsett & Dowsett-Lemaire 1984, Dowsett-Lemaire 1985a), where the short breeding seasons (two to four months in most species) are indeed associated with single-broodedness, as proven by the observation of individually colour-ringed birds. Some birds may lay again after the first attempt failed and for instance the few late January-February clutches of Cape Batis are known to be repeats after one or two breeding failures. The termination of breeding in montane species is probably controlled by the necessity to moult in the second half of the rains, before the cold weather starts in May, and birds that successfully breed early waste no time in starting moult.

Overall, thicket birds breed later than woodland species. Those that inhabit primarily deciduous thickets (e.g. Terrestrial Bulbul) find optimal conditions only after these come into leaf (with the early rains), with most egg-laying taking place in December-January. With two peaks of laying the cooperative Arrow-marked Babblers appear to be double-brooded.

Generalist sunbirds like Black and Scarlet-chested *Nectarinia senegalensis* have a long breeding season; the unspecialized Greater Double-collared Sunbird on the Nyika can raise up to three broods in a year (Dowsett-Lemaire 1989c). By contrast, the larger, longer-billed Malachite Sunbirds have a more restricted feeding niche and are almost certainly single-brooded.

Coursers, various plovers and pipits of short, dry grassland lay before the rains, in the hot dry season. Likewise, Rock Pratincole and African Skimmer nest along rivers in the late dry season, the first on emerged rocks, the second on sand beaches, before the rise in water levels is likely to flood their broods.

The majority of insectivorous birds of rank grass and low bush breed in the rains (e.g. Cisticola warblers). Tchagra bush shrikes have an extended season, from September to the middle of the rains. Among species of wooded grassland, exceptions to this pattern include Fiscal Shrike (whose feeding technique is most efficient before the grass gets too long) and several bee-eaters which nest in earth or sand banks before the ground gets too soggy.

Examples of seed-eating species shown in **Table 6** come from a variety of habitats, but all tend to breed mainly in the rains, grass or other seeds being most abundant towards the end of the rains. A number of adaptable and semi-commensal species have extensive seasons, most of all the wholly commensal House Sparrow, which can lay in any month and is indeed known to be multiple-brooded (A.J. Scott in Dowsett in press a).

The larger raptors have a long breeding cycle and patterns of egg-laying are more difficult to interpret. Two medium-sized intra-African migrants, Yellow-billed Kite and Wahlberg's Eagle *Aquila wahlbergi*, have a very concentrated laying season (mainly in September), breeding as soon as they arrive. Resident scavengers like White-backed Vultures *Gyps africanus* lay in the early dry season: feeding conditions for young birds should improve when increasing drought and bush fires not only clear the ground but also kill a certain amount of potential prey. A scavenger from another family, the Marabou Stork *Leptoptilos crumeniferus*, shows the same trend.

There is now a large body of **clutch-size** data from Zambia (**Table 7**), considerably larger overall than those published from other parts of the continent. Smaller samples published for Zimbabwe (in Benson *et al.* 1964) and Natal-Zululand (Dean 1971) show a similar dominance of C/2 and/or C/3 in passerines and most small non passerines. Some species tend to lay bigger clutches with increasing latitude, for instance Black-eyed Bulbul, Chinspot Batis, Black-crowned Tchagra, Tropical Boubou

Table 7. Clutch-size data for some common Zambian birds (clutch-sizes representing more than 50% of total in bold).

Species	C/1	C/2	C/3	C/4	C/5	C/6	Total
Yellow-billed Kite	20	**87**	21	0	0	0	128
Lizard Buzzard	16	**125**	8	0	0	0	149
Wahlberg's Eagle	**230**	6	0	0	0	0	236
Crowned Plover	4	37	59	2	0	0	102
Fiery-necked Nightjar	15	**95**	0	0	0	0	110
Pennant-winged Nightjar	20	**161**	1	1	0	0	183
Little Bee-eater	6	21	17	**38**	20	0	102
Black-collared Barbet	4	25	**46**	29	3	0	107
Terrestrial Bulbul	15	**81**	15	0	0	0	111
Black-eyed Bulbul	33	**195**	78	0	0	0	306
Kurrichane Thrush	1	37	**96**	1	0	0	135
Long-billed Crombec	24	**176**	1	0	0	0	201
Fan-tailed Cisticola	5	15	**46**	**61**	18	0	145
Rattling Cisticola	0	16	**112**	28	1	0	157
Tawny-flanked Prinia	26	161	**381**	145	0	0	713
Pallid Flycatcher	3	**66**	49	0	0	0	118
Southern Black Flycatcher	1	31	**77**	2	0	0	111
Chinspot Batis	10	**110**	0	0	0	0	120
Black-crowned Tchagra	6	**120**	6	1	0	0	133
Tropical Boubou	9	**106**	10	0	0	0	125
African Golden Oriole	13	**103**	68	0	0	0	184
Fork-tailed Drongo	20	189	**286**	9	0	0	504
White-browed Sparrow-Weaver	**52**	**52**	8	0	0	0	112
African Masked Weaver	41	139	162	13	0	0	355
Red Bishop	38	247	**351**	59	3	0	698
Blue Waxbill	4	7	23	**33**	42	13	123
Golden-breasted Bunting	15	**80**	8	0	0	0	103

(and its close relative Southern Boubou *Laniarius ferrugineus*) and Golden-breasted Bunting. In Black-eyed Bulbul there is already a significant difference in the breeding output of Zambian birds (with a dominance of C/2, 64% of 306 clutches) compared to those of Zimbabwe (with a dominance of C/3, 53% of 338 clutches). Moreau (1944) also found that clutches near the Equator tend to be smaller on average than in southern Africa, but his samples were extremely small. However, a full analysis is beyond the scope of this book and will have to wait until the large amount of more recent data from southern Africa gets into print, an opportunity unfortunately not fulfilled by the revised edition of "Roberts Birds of Southern Africa" (Hockey *et al*. 2005): not all available data have been included, and where large samples are produced, they have usually been lumped for the whole subregion.

There is a complete annual moult of the plumage (and in a few species a second, partial moult). In most species this is probably post-breeding, as has been found in montane birds (Dowsett & Dowsett-Lemaire 1984). In nine forest passerines on the Nyika it was measured to last from three to four months. Information on moult of other Zambian birds remains very incomplete (e.g. Dowsett in press a).

6. Conservation

The conservation situation in Zambia, especially as it concerns birds, has been very well documented by Leonard (2005), in his review of the Important Bird Areas, and it remains here merely to make some additional points.

Zambia is a large country which has been able to establish a considerable area as protected wildlife estate (19 national parks, totalling nearly 64,000 km², or 8.5% of the country). Most of these reserves are difficult of access, in areas with low human densities and unattractive for development (e.g. poor agricultural land, prevalence of tsetse fly). Consequently, most of these national parks form the core of a protected area system for bird species. Unfortunately the same confidence cannot exist as regards forest reserves, or private or other public lands, such areas not providing a certain long-term protection. Of the 626 species known or likely to breed in Zambia, 587 occur within the national parks system (Dowsett & Leonard in press b). **Table 8** lists those 39 that do not.

Table 8. Species that are members of the Zambian breeding avifauna (or which might well breed), which are not known from any one of the network of 19 national parks.

Great Crested Grebe *Podiceps cristatus*, White-throated Francolin *Francolinus albogularis*, White-spotted Flufftail *Sarothrura pulchra*, Shining-blue Kingfisher *Alcedo quadribrachys*, White-bellied Kingfisher *A. leucogaster*, Spot-flanked Barbet *Tricholaema lacrymosa*, Western Least Honeyguide *Indicator exilis*, Brown-eared Woodpecker *Campethera caroli*, Angola Lark *Mirafra angolensis*, Grimwood's Longclaw *Macronyx grimwoodi*, Honeyguide Greenbul *Baeopogon indicator*, Joyful Greenbul *Chlorocichla laetissima*, African Bristlebill *Bleda syndactylus*, Black-collared Bulbul *Neolestes torquatus*, Rufous Ant Thrush *Stizorhina fraseri*, Boulder Chat *Pinarornis plumosus*, White-winged Warbler *Bradypterus carpalis*, Papyrus Yellow Warbler *Chloropeta gracilirostris*, Yellow-throated Warbler *Phylloscopus ruficapilla*, Cloud Cisticola *Cisticola textrix*, Black-tailed Cisticola *C. dambo*, Whistling Cisticola *C. lateralis*, White-chinned Prinia *Prinia leucopogon*, Buff-throated Apalis *Apalis rufogularis*, Sooty Flycatcher *Muscicapa infuscata*, Shrike Flycatcher *Megabyas flammulatus*, Chestnut Wattle-eye *Dyaphorophyia castanea*, Red-bellied Paradise Flycatcher *Terpsiphone rufiventer*, Spotted Thrush-Babbler *Ptyrticus turdinus*, Bates's Sunbird *Nectarinia batesi*, Bannerman's Sunbird *N. bannermani*, Green-throated Sunbird *N. rubescens*, Orange-tufted Sunbird *N. bouvieri*, Slender-billed Weaver *Ploceus pelzelni*, Bocage's Weaver *P. temporalis*, Lake Tanganyika Weaver *P. reichardi*, Compact Weaver *P. superciliosus*, Orange-cheeked Waxbill *Estrilda melpoda*, Cape Bunting *Emberiza capensis*.

Many of these species occur only in a few forests in the extreme north and north-west of the country, especially in northern Mwinilunga District. Some of the latter are to be found in one Important Bird Area in particular, Hillwood (IBA #1 in Leonard 2005); at present this is an excellently-run private sanctuary, which has been protected by the Fisher family for over a century. One must hope that this will continue, without forgetting what has happened to private property in some other African countries. One of the most important small forests in Mwinilunga was Isombu (Lisombo), frequently mentioned in the species accounts that follow; it has been almost completely destroyed. The only really satisfactory long-term protection would be provided by a national park, which would at the same time confirm the Zambian Government's will to protect the natural environment. But this has been urged by conservationists and scientists in Zambia since the 1970s (Ansell 1978), and it is probably too late now to identify a single viable area, as the forests there are fragmented and under increasing pressure by clearance for subsistence cultivation (Leonard & Van Daele 1999a). A hydro-electric power station being built at Zambezi Rapids is believed by the Zambian Ornithological Society, which is monitoring the situation, not to present any important threat to the local avian environment.

Table 9. Globally threatened species and their threat level in Zambia. EN = Endangered; VU = Vulnerable; NT = Near threatened (BirdLife International 2000, 2004a).

Species	2000	2004	Status	N° squares (%)	Threat level
Madagascar Squacco Heron *Ardeola idae*	VU	EN	AMW	8 (3)	Low
Slaty Egret *Egretta vinaceigula*	VU	VU	R	36 (12)	Medium
Shoebill **Balaeniceps rex**	**NT**	**VU**	**RB**	**18 (6)**	**High**
Lesser Flamingo **Phoeniconaias minor**	**NT**	**NT**	**AM (B)**	**23 (8)**	**High**
Cape Vulture *Gyps coprotheres*	VU	VU	AM	5 (2)	Low
Lappet-faced Vulture *Torgos tracheliotus*	VU	VU	RB	103 (34)	Medium
Pallid Harrier *Circus macrourus*	NT	NT	PW	64 (21)	Low
Lesser Kestrel *Falco naumanni*	VU	VU	PW	95 (31)	Low
Taita Falcon *Falco fasciinucha*	NT	NT	RB	5 (2)	Medium
Corn Crake *Crex crex*	VU	NT	PW	42 (14)	Low
Wattled Crane **Grus carunculatus**	**VU**	**VU**	**RB**	**131 (43)**	**High**
Denham's Bustard *Neotis denhami*	NT	NT	RB	85 (28)	Medium
Great Snipe *Gallinago media*	NT	NT	PW	78 (26)	Low
African Skimmer *Rynchops flavirostris*	NT	NT	RB	82 (27)	Medium
Lilian's Lovebird *Agapornis lilianae*	-	NT	RB	27 (9)	Medium
Black-cheeked Lovebird **Agapornis nigrigenis**	**VU**	**VU**	**RB**	**10 (3)**	**High**
Chaplin's Barbet **Lybius chaplini**	**NT**	**NT**	**RB**	**27 (9)**	**High**
Blue Swallow *Hirundo atrocaerulea*	VU	VU	AMB	3 (1)	Low
Papyrus Yellow Warbler *Chloropeta gracilirostris*	VU	VU	R (B)	3 (1)	Medium
Olive-headed Weaver **Ploceus olivaceiceps**	**NT**	**NT**	**RB**	**6 (2)**	**High**
Locust Finch *Paludipasser locustella*	-	NT	RB	106 (35)	Low

Table 9 details the 21 globally threatened species that occur in Zambia. Four of these are Palaearctic migrants (PW), none of which is apparently affected detrimentally by environmental change in the country; indeed, increased deforestation tends to produce more secondary growth favourable for a species such as Corn Crake.

Of the six resident breeding species (RB) or intra-African migrant (AM) for which the threat level in Zambia is judged to be high, two wetland birds (Shoebill and Wattled Crane) are potentially vulnerable to changes in landscape management. The Shoebill is additionally trapped illegally for foreign aviculturalists, but recent aerial surveys do suggest the Bangweulu population is larger than once believed, with some 500 birds (Roxburgh *et al.* 2006). The Black-cheeked Lovebird (almost endemic to Zambia) has been the subject of detailed study by Warburton (e.g. Warburton 2002, Warburton & Perrin 2006); in the past it has been heavily exploited for the cagebird trade, and it is an occasional pest in subsistence cultivation. Chaplin's Barbet (endemic to southern Zambia) is apparently disappearing from parts of its traditional range, and this is probably connected to its dependence on fig trees (especially *Ficus sycomorus*) which are dying or being felled in some key areas. Olive-headed Weaver too is highly endangered in Zambia (where it occurs only marginally) through felling of much miombo woodland for cultivation or firewood. The sixth species with a high threat level is Lesser Flamingo, which bred once in Mweru Wantipa, in 1953-54. It seems unlikely ever to breed again in Zambia with the changes to the water levels in the area, although it still occurs in numbers at times on nearby Lake Tondwa. The extent to which the construction of a dam and water channels affected the ecology and abundance of waterfowl (including the endangered Shoebill) has not been investigated.

The Kafue Flats constitute another, and much larger, wetland greatly affected by an artificial change of flood regime. In natural conditions an extensive area of grassland was flooded gradually in the rains, with peak floods occurring from March-May. In 1971 the Kafue Gorge Dam (downriver from the Flats) was completed (Sayer & van Lavieren 1975), and the Itezhi-Tezhi Dam (upriver) in 1975 (Mwima 2001), as part of a hydro-electric project. Regulation has decreased the extent and volume of flooding, while raising minimum water levels. The timing of flooding has been much less regular, with sometimes two peaks (February-March and May-June); the change in timing has doubtless affected waterfowl chronology. In some years water levels have risen towards the end of the dry season, destroying many nests (Leonard 2005: 85). Invasive plants (*Mimosa pigra*, Water Hyacinth *Eichhornia crassipes*) have spread dramatically, to the detriment of natural habitats.

Acknowledgements

During the time he spent in Zambia RJD was employed as biologist by the Zambian Government (Dept of National Parks and Wildlife), Wildlife Conservation Society of Zambia and National Museums Board of Zambia. These organisations did much to encourage and facilitate ornithological research, and to them and his colleagues RJD is greatly indebted. FD-L's fieldwork in the 1970s was funded by a PhD grant through the University of Liège, Belgium, and our joint research on the Nyika Plateau (Malawi/Zambia) 1979-82 by the "Fonds National de la Recherche Scientifique" in Belgium (1979-81) and the National Geographic Society (Washington, U.S.A., 1979). DRA's fieldwork was undertaken while he was employed by the Ministry of Education.

Many friends and colleagues have added to knowledge of the birds of this country since the publication of Benson *et al.* (1971a, *The Birds of Zambia*). They are too numerous for us to name all here, but some of the more important contributions have come from:

Nikki Ashley, Angela Aspinwall, John Atkins, Jim Auburn, Carl Beel, Dirk Berkvens, Phil Berry, Bruce Bolnick, Paul Bourdin, Gus Bowden, Phil Bowen, Paddy & Margaret Bruce-Miller, Clide Carter, Roger Casalis de Pury, John Colebrook-Robjent, Pete Conant, Bruce Danckwerts, Bob Douthwaite, William Dunlop, Dave Francis, David Grant, Tony Green, Dean Greenberg, John Harvey, Penny Harvey, Fil Hide, Gordon Holtshausen, Nigel Irving, John Johnson, Kate Knox, Pete Leonard, Rory Macdougall, Graeme Madge, Deidre Major, Jali Makawa, Jorg Mellenthin, Joy Miles, Stuart Norman, Tim Osborne, Huw & Sue Penry, Wouter Peters, Robin Pope, Dave Richards, Peter Robinson, Lizanne Roxburgh, Tom Savory, Alister Scott, Roger Smith, Derek Solomon, Bob Sternstedt, Jim Sweetman, Barry Taylor, Rod Tether, Esther Townsend, John Tucker, Paul van Daele, Walter Winkelhuysen.

John Colebrook-Robjent's expertise in matters concerning oology, and his generosity in making available his unequalled body of breeding data (most of it hitherto unpublished), warrant special thanks. We are particularly grateful to Pete Leonard for reading through and commenting on a draft of the species accounts, and for forwarding records from a number of observers in Zambia. Selected species accounts were also read in draft by Tim Osborne and Huw Penry, whom we thank. Chris Brewster, Anthony Cizek and Chris Hines have commented on extralimital records. Christophe Collas and Louis Bronne (Aves) competently undertook the colour preparation, and David Coumans (Ginko) and Marie-Françoise Gonot kindly helped prepare some of the illustrations.

Photographs

We thank those who have generously allowed use of their colour photographs: Rich Beilfuss, Phil Berry, Jack Clark, Edmund Farmer (Kasanka Trust), Johann Grobbelaar, Dalena Mostert, Phil Palmer, Alex Paul, Kerri Rademeyer, Geneviève Renson (who is preparing a book on the Shoebills of Bangweulu), Juliet Shenton, Claire Spottiswoode, Warwick Tarboton and Louise Warburton.

Sources of black and white illustrations are: B. Alexander (Alexander B. 1907. *From the Niger to the Nile*. London: Edward Arnold); S. Clarke (*Ibis* 1949, 91: opp. p. 354); J. Vincent & H. Lynes (Brain C.K. 1998. *Austin Roberts. A lifelong devotion to South Africa's birds and beasts*. Cape Town: John Voelcker Bird Book Fund); C.R.S. Pitman (*Ibis* 1968, 110: opp. p. 367); J.M. Winterbottom (*Ostrich* 1984, 55: 107); C.M.N. White (*Ibis* 1979, 121: opp. p. 234); R.H.N. Smithers (*Transvaal Mus. Bull.* 1984, 20: 4); C.W. Benson (Peter Steyn, *Bokmakierie* 1972, 24: 62); B. Carp, R.H.N. Smithers & I.R. Grimwood (*Transvaal Mus. Bull.* 1984, 20: 5); J.M.C. Uys (*Black Lechwe* 1973, 11 (3): 10); N.J. Carr & P.S.M. Berry (Astle W.L. 1999. *A history of wildlife conservation and management in the mid-Luangwa Valley, Zambia*. Bristol: British Empire & Commonwealth Museum); R.K. Brooke (*Bokmakierie* 1972, 24: opp. p. 24); M.P.S. Irwin (Peter Steyn, *Bokmakierie* 1972, 24: opp. p. 24); R.A. Critchley (*Black Lechwe* 1972, 10 (1): 7); Mrs E. Critchley (*Black Lechwe* 1976, 12 (3): 4); D.R. Aspinwall (T.O. Osborne). All others by R.J. Dowsett.

SYSTEMATIC LIST

Sequence and nomenclature

English names are mostly those in current use in Zambia (e.g. Leonard 2005), except that we prefer Eurasian rather than European as a prefix for those species whose breeding range extends beyond eastern Europe. We believe that English names should reflect established local usage and we do not think it wise to introduce new names – e.g. the International Ornithological Congress's World list (Gill & Wright 2006) – until such time as they have received wide acceptance. We note that the American Ornithologists' Union has declined to follow the I.O.C. list, in order to maintain stability (American Ornithologists' Union 2007). Even though most authors are using "widow" for *Euplectes* and "whydah" for *Vidua*, we feel justified in keeping whydah for *Euplectes* as it is based on the historical fact that Whidah (Ouidah), in Benin, was the type locality of *E. macroura* (the type species of the genus).

The sequence and scientific nomenclature generally follow those of the *Checklist of Birds of the Afrotropical and Malagasy Regions* (Dowsett & Forbes-Watson 1993); changes since *The Birds of Zambia* (Benson *et al.* 1971a) and *The Birds of Malawi* (Benson & Benson 1977) were explained in a companion volume (Dowsett & Dowsett-Lemaire 1993). A limited number of modifications are adopted here (and documented in the species' accounts), including: the Black-breasted Snake Eagle *Circaetus pectoralis* regains full species status, following Clark (1999), although we believe it is very closely-related to the Short-toed Eagle *C. gallicus* of Europe; the African Green Pigeon *Treron calvus* is split from the Malagasy species *Treron australis* (following general opinion and our own observations in Madagascar); Scimitarbill becomes again *Phoeniculus cyanomelas* (rather than *Rhinopomastus*), as in most recent works; the Broad-tailed Warbler is returned to the larger concept of *Schoenicola platyurus* (following general usage supported by our field experience in India). *Cisticola cinnamomeus* is split from *C. brunnescens* (mainly north of the Equator), following Urban *et al.* (1997). The family attribution of *Nicator* spp. is still matter for speculation (e.g. Keith in Fry *et al.* 2000) but on present DNA evidence it is not a bush shrike Malaconotidae (Dowsett *et al.* 1999) nor a bulbul Pycnonotidae (Moyle & Marks 2006). For practical purposes, however, we have kept it at the end of the Pycnonotidae.

At the family level and higher there is much continuing activity by molecular biologists which will doubtless prove substantial changes to be necessary to the sequence of higher avian taxa until now most often followed. But we do not think the time is yet ripe to produce new sequences of families in a work such as this, which can only be confusing to the reader used to a traditional order of families. Regional avifaunas which have introduced new sequences in recent years have already been overtaken by the most recent research in several instances. Genera and species limits are also being questioned by molecular research, and we have drawn attention to relevant recent publications.

Arising from recent research, mainly grammatical re-assessment of the Latin and Greek origins of names (especially by David & Gosselin 2002a, 2002b), the ending or spelling of the following specific names has to change, and they become: Green-backed Heron *Butorides striata*, Egyptian Goose *Alopochen aegyptiaca*, Kurrichane Buttonquail *Turnix sylvaticus*, Hottentot Buttonquail *T. hottentottus*, Black Crake *Amaurornis flavirostra*, Whiskered Tern *Chlidonias hybrida*, Lilac-breasted Roller *Coracias caudatus*, Racket-tailed Roller *C. spatulatus*, Purple Roller *C. naevius*, Eurasian House Martin *Delichon urbicum*, African Bristlebill *Bleda syndactylus*, Groundscraper Thrush *Psophocichla litsitsirupa*, Stonechat *Saxicola torquatus*, Yellow-throated Warbler *Phylloscopus ruficapilla*, Red-winged Warbler *Heliolais erythropterus*, Neddicky *Cisticola fulvicapilla*, White-rumped Babbler *Turdoides leucopygia*, Marsh Tchagra *Tchagra minutus* and Black-crowned Tchagra *T. senegalus*.

We continue to consider the African Reed Warbler as a race of the Eurasian *Acrocephalus scirpaceus* (cf. Dowsett-Lemaire & Dowsett 1987a), a decision that has received further support recently from DNA studies (Parkin *et al.* 2004).

The status of species in Zambia is abbreviated using one or more of the following symbols:

R   Resident
AM   Intra-African migrant (migrant within Africa south of the Sahara; this category also includes a few visitors from Madagascar or the Indian Ocean; not included are those species with purely local movements)
B   Species proven to breed; **(B)** likely to breed
V   Vagrant (no more than six records)
P   Palaearctic migrant; **NV** Nearctic vagrant
W   wintering species (i.e. present in the non-breeding season)

Species whose occurrence in the country is not adequately proven or previously accepted but now rejected are inserted in square brackets, as are some known from immediately neighbouring countries. One introduced species (*Columba livia*) is in square brackets, as there is no proof of a feral population.

Presentation of species accounts

A species's name is followed by the number used in *Birds of Zambia* (Benson *et al.* 1971a), and status abbreviations (as above). The species accounts are presented under the following series of subheadings.

Distribution. The chorological status is given first, with a summary of the general distribution outside Zambia. The distribution in Zambia follows, with (where possible) an indication of abundance and as many details as are needed to interpret the map. Records are plotted by 30 x 30 minute squares, using the programme DMAP (http://www.dmap.co.uk/). The default (normal) plot is a blue square; where applicable a special symbol is used for showing breeding sites of colonial or otherwise localized species, winter records in altitudinal migrants, irregular vagrants or records of a distinctive race. Altitudinal limits are given for all species: this topic had not received much attention from Zambian workers, except for the extremes of the eastern highlands and the influences of valleys on distribution. Doubtless this is a reflection of the supposed relative uniformity of the Zambian topography (in fact, of the 800 or so loci in the Gazetteer, 95% are within the range 400-1700 m). We have included altitudes for nearly every locality in the Gazetteer. Altitudes are indicated on the maps by shading: < 900 m (white), 900-1800 m (pale grey), > 1800 m (dark grey).
       The abundance scale adopted follows that used by Dowsett-Lemaire & Dowsett (2006):
Rare: rarely seen. Breeding species in very small numbers, or occasional/irregular visitor.
Scarce: irregularly and infrequently seen in preferred habitat.
Uncommon: usually, but not frequently, encountered in preferred habitat.
Common: encountered frequently in preferred habitat.
Abundant: encountered in large numbers or high densities in preferred habitat.
       The Middle Zambezi Valley is taken as the section from Feira (Luangwa town) up to the Victoria Falls Gorges (including what is known as the Lower Zambezi N.P.); the river above Livingstone becomes the Upper Zambezi.

Ecology. Includes a description of the habitat and also of feeding behaviour and specific food items taken when this subject has been studied in Zambia, and nest sites. Botanical terms such as miombo woodland and dambo are explained in Chapter 2. Most species breed solitarily (i.e. as territorial pairs), and this is not specified except where it constitutes the exception to the rule or when some members of a family do one thing and others behave differently (as in Timaliidae). Association with other species and ecological distinction from close relatives may also be mentioned. In the case of vagrant species, **Distribution** and **Status** are combined (and a separate **Ecology** section has not been retained).

Status. Includes details of movements if any, whether migratory, nomadic or local, their extent and timing; the numbers encountered in congregatory and colonial species; ringing recoveries and longevity where known, and examples of site fidelity proven by ringing. "Wintering", for both Palaearctic and Afrotropical migrants, refers to the non-breeding season. "Over-summering" in the case of Palaearctic migrants refers to birds spending the local winter (i.e. Palaearctic summer) in Zambia.

Conservation. Zambia is a large country with (for the moment) relatively limited pressure on natural habitats overall, thus the majority of bird species are under no threat. Unlike *Birds of Malawi* (Dowsett-Lemaire & Dowsett 2006) this section has therefore not been used for every species. We detail under the species account birds listed as Globally Threatened by BirdLife International (2000, 2004a), and others considered to be seriously endangered elsewhere in southern Africa. There are also some birds of local distribution within Zambia which are affected by clearance of forest habitat (especially in Mwinilunga District), hydrological or agricultural schemes.

Breeding. The breeding season is indicated as number of clutches started in each month: a large proportion of records consists of collected clutches, but some are based on back-dating of observations of the feeding of nestlings or fledglings. For these calculations the duration of incubation and nestling periods has been taken from the Roberts's handbook (Maclean 1993) and other published and unpublished sources.

The size of clutches is given as C/x and broods as N/x in which the observed size is presumed or known to be x. Note that C/1 may often be incomplete, but in few cases can this be known for certain and so no attempt is made usually to identify incomplete clutches. Localities or altitudes from which breeding data are available may be given for a few rare or local species, or for which the data are scanty. For some species with a well-marked breeding dress (e.g. *Euplectes* and *Vidua*), the information on breeding seasons is complemented by observations on the duration of breeding plumage worn by males. Seasonality of song may also be given here, where it supplements significantly limited breeding data. Where information is available on the timing of replacement of flight feathers in Zambia, based on examination of birds caught for ringing, this is given in a *Moult* sub-section; for non-breeding visitors this appears at the end of the **Status** section.

Taxonomy. This section deals with subspecific variation and other taxonomic and nomenclatural aspects where appropriate, including the citation for the 124 taxa of which Zambia is the type locality. The museums which house type material (where known) are detailed on p. 58. The subspecific taxonomy follows mainly the detailed comparative studies by C.W. Benson and M.P.S. Irwin (incorporated in Benson *et al.* 1971a) and R.J. Dowsett's research while based at the Livingstone Museum (1971-79). References are given to any significant departure from the treatment by Benson *et al.* (1971a) and to subsequent re-assessment of species' relationships. The detailed information we now have on the almost continuous distribution of many species within their Zambian ranges suggests that much morphological variation is likely to be clinal, and many recognized subspecies of doubtful validity, were sufficient series of specimens to be available for study. Personalities after whom birds have been named are mentioned in some detail, except where they are treated fully in Chapter 4. A few plumage abnormalities observed in Zambia are noted here, but this aspect is not treated exhaustively.

References. A supra-numbering system has been used in the text, with references listed at the end of each account by alphabetical and date order.

Abbreviations. Months are abbreviated to the first three letters. Protected areas are designated by N.P. (National Park), F.R. (Forest Reserve, both National and Local).

Sources of data

The maps include 81,141 species-square records from the 303 30 x 30 minute squares (each of which was visited at least once). Some border squares very largely outside Zambia produced few records, but 23 squares have more than 400 species (maximum 487-488 from Kitwe, Lusaka and Kafue town areas). The level of coverage achieved by the year 2007 is shown in **Fig. 5**; the mean number of species per square is 267.

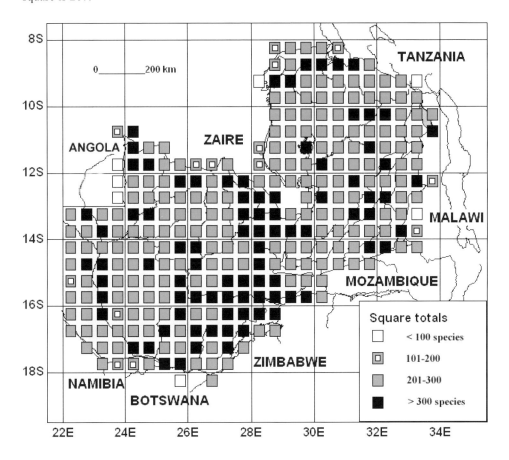

Figure 5. Atlas coverage to 2007 (number of species recorded per 30 x 30 minute square).

     An Atlas scheme was started by Dowsett in 1975. The principal contributor of records has been Dylan Aspinwall, whose aim was at least 200 species in each square, and this was achieved for all but 21 squares (largely marginal). Many records have also been obtained by Dowsett and a keen team of 20 or more observers, some of whom remain active in Zambia. Most key areas have been visited up to the present day, e.g. in connection with the ongoing surveys of Important Bird Areas (Leonard 2005). Indeed, all published and unpublished observations up to December 2007 have been taken into account. For the great majority of bird species and their distribution limits the maps and associated text reflect the current status. We draw attention to the few areas where a species is now (or may be) no longer present, often the result of habitat changes (e.g. the forests of N. Mwinilunga). In such a large country, with few observers, it was not possible to analyse the data on a quantitative or seasonal basis.

We think it important in a work such as this that the historical record be taken into account as much as possible. For this reason the species texts include both recent and older published references. With very few exceptions the numerous references that formed the basis of the earlier checklists (Pitman 1934 to Benson *et al.* 1971a) have been rechecked by the senior author. All recent literature has been consulted, including general bird records presented in the local journals and newsletter *Bull. Zambian Orn. Soc.* (1969-84), *Zambia Bird Report* (1997-1999) and *Zambia Orn. Soc. Newsletter* (1971 to date); in the case of the last, where records are usually not vetted, more important observations have been verified with the observer concerned. Whenever we have felt that the source of an unpublished record needed to be given, we are presenting the details and observers' names in a parallel publication (Dowsett in press a,b, Dowsett & Leonard in press a). This applies to changes to the range limits given in Benson *et al.* (1971a), numbers and dates of arrival and departure of migrating species, unusual breeding records and other relevant observations which can only be summarized in this book.

To the 7938 dated records of egg-laying (for 495 species) that appeared in Benson *et al.* (1971a) have been added a further 21,207 records, bringing the total to 29,145 (of 572 species). For some 40 species which certainly breed we still have no record that can be back-dated with certainty to month of egg-laying (including a few fairly widespread birds, such as Bushveld Pipit and Singing Cisticola). This body of data is largely the result of the tireless efforts of John Colebrook-Robjent since 1966, mostly in Southern Province. More than 1000 records are available from the Nyika Plateau (Dowsett & Dowsett-Lemaire 1984). We also present in this book the details of clutch-sizes known for each species (a total of more than 15,800 records). Clutch-size data were not included in Benson *et al.* (1971a) and the majority have never been published (the original data being in the papers of the late Con Benson). It has not been possible to examine his files for unpublished details of clutch-sizes and nest sites.

Information on moult comes from a few published works (e.g. Dowsett & Dowsett-Lemaire 1984 for the Nyika, Traylor 1965b from W. Zambia) and unpublished data (e.g. Dowsett in press a).

Appendices

Ringing recoveries affecting Zambia have been published periodically, and an update was presented by Dowsett & Leonard (2001), including the longevity data referred to under various species accounts in this book. In **Appendix 1** we summarize recoveries of birds ringed in Zambia (foreign recoveries and the more striking local ones), and those of birds ringed abroad and found in this country. Maps show a selection of foreign recoveries.

A **Gazetteer** (**Appendix 2**) gives coordinates for practically all localities mentioned in the text; very few remain untraced. Most coordinates and altitudes were collected over the years by RJD and DRA from the set of 1:250,000 and 1:50,000 maps printed by the Government Department of Surveys and from various gazetteers (including Google Earth), with some use of GPS in recent years. As the boundaries and names of districts have changed a great deal since Independence, we have as far as possible avoided referring in the species accounts to "districts" in describing distribution, as when taken from an old reference this could be misleading. However, we have tried to indicate the current district in which localities that are not in national parks are located. The spelling of some localities has changed in the years since Independence in 1964; we have tried to respect these changes, but where there might be confusion over names used in the ornithological literature, we have given the more important alternative spellings in the gazetteer.

We have throughout this book used the name Zaire for the country which is currently known officially as the Democratic Republic of Congo; this is to avoid the confusion (evident in much that has been published on African zoology) with Congo-Brazzaville (the Popular Republic of Congo).

Struthionidae

[Ostrich *Struthio camelus*   B1 **Extinct**

Distribution *Afrotropical* (*Mauritania to South Africa*). Extinct, possibly since about 1912, certainly by the middle of the 20th century. Ostriches were reported as having formerly occurred in small numbers west of the Zambezi[7,8]. By the 1950s local bushmen could obtain Ostrich eggs only on the Mashi River or further west, in Angola[2]. Although suggested as a possible straggler to W. Kalabo Dist.[1], local people were unaware of any there by 1961[6]. The former range and status are therefore uncertain, although apparently suitable habitat exists on several plains in the west. The reasons for extinction are not known, but the use of eggs as ornaments or objects of barter, and the custom of wearing Ostrich feathers as adornments in Barotseland, may have contributed.

Ostriches still occur just south of the Zambezi in Zimbabwe (in Zambezi N.P. and on Nampini ranch[3]), and in Botswana north to Gokora Pan and even further north[4,5]. It is less certain that the species may have been present early in the 20th century on the Zambian/Tanzania border at about 32°30'E[1]. It has in recent years been introduced into parts of Zambia for commercial exploitation.

Breeding No records.

Taxonomy No specimens, but the subspecies would have been *S. c. australis*.

References [1]Benson *et al.* (1971a); [2]Clark (1951); [3]Irwin (1981a); [4]Irwin *et al.* (1969); [5]Penry (1994); [6]Traylor (1965b); [7]White (1945-6); [8]Winterbottom (1942a).]

Podicipedidae

Little Grebe (Dabchick) *Tachybaptus ruficollis*   B2 **RB**

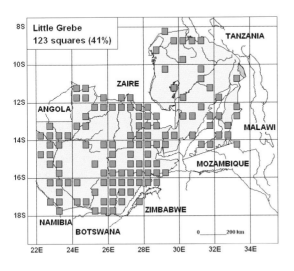

Distribution *Old World* (*in the Afrotropics, Mauritania to South Africa*). Through much of the country, but sparse in the north-east. Unknown in the Luapula above Nchelenge, and in the Middle Zambezi reported only rarely[1]. Scarce generally at low altitude, but has bred in the Luangwa Valley. *Alt.* 370-1800 m (Uningi Pans), usually above 950 m (and to 2300 m on the Malawi side of the Nyika Plateau).

Ecology Pools and lakes, usually with fringing vegetation. Largest numbers occur on sewage ponds, and the species has undoubtedly benefited from the increase in man-made waters (although on many it may be present only as a non-breeding visitor). New dams, fish ponds etc. are colonized soon after filling.

Status Resident on permanent waters, with local movements – numbers peak in the dry season, when there are fewest on man-made waters. At several artificial sites maximum numbers occur Oct-Dec (up to 600 at Lusaka), possibly an influx before breeding.

Breeding[2]

	Dec	Jan	Feb	Mar	Apr	May	Jun	Jul	Aug
(n=101)	10	35	19	19	6	2	5	4	1

Clutch: C/1 (2); C/2 (5); C/3 (6); C/4 (5); C/5 (4).

Moult: there is no evidence for a complete, simultaneous moult of flight feathers: for example, a year-round study at Kitwe did not report flightless birds[2].

Taxonomy *T. r. capensis.*

References [1]Dowsett (in press a); [2]Penry (1975e).

[Black-necked Grebe *Podiceps nigricollis*

Old and New Worlds (in the Afrotropics, scattered populations breed Ethiopia to South Africa). A single sight record has been claimed, of a bird in non-breeding dress at Chipata 8 Nov-6 Dec 1984[1]. Although this record was not proven satisfactorily, the species might be expected to occur as an irregular non-breeding visitor from Botswana to SW Zambia. **References** [1]Dowsett & Leonard (in press a).]

Great Crested Grebe *Podiceps cristatus*   B3 **RB**

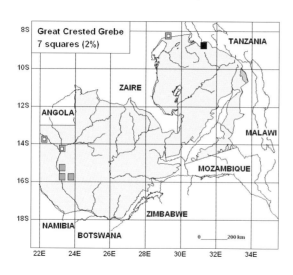

Distribution *Old World (in the Afrotropics, breeds Ethiopia to South Africa)*. Known to have bred only at Uningi Pans near Mbala[5] (black square). A single bird at Kabendwe in Jul[1] (open square) may have wandered from Uningi. However, it probably nests too in W. Zambia, in the mosaic of pans and lakes either side of the Zambezi between Lakes Makapaela and Silita, as there are records for most months[3,6]. Local reports suggest it may range north into W. Zambezi Dist. (open squares)[4]. *Alt.* 1020-1100 m, and at 1660-1800 m in the Mbala area.

Ecology Pans in woodland, subject to seasonal fluctuations in water level.

Status Was resident, but present status uncertain. Up to 42 birds have been recorded at L. Chila (near Mbala), but numbers in W. Zambia may be smaller, no more than 8 being reported from any one lake there[4].

Conservation Since 1983 a series of droughts has affected lakes such as Makapaella; they used to hold water year-round, but do so now for only a few months of the year. Surveys in 1999 failed to find any *P. cristatus* in the area[7,8] (where last reported in 1986). In recent years the species appears to have deserted Uningi pans (the last report was in 1994), at least temporarily, possibly also because of changes in seasonal water levels. It seems possible this bird is presently extinct as a breeding species in Zambia. In Kenya too populations have declined greatly[2].

Breeding   Feb   Mar

(n=3)   1   2   In addition, nest-building has been reported in Sep.

Clutch: C/2 (1); C/4 (1).

Taxonomy *P. c. infuscatus.*

References [1]Aspinwall (1978a); [2]Bennun & Njoroge (1999); [3]Bruce-Miller & Dowsett (1977); [4]Dowsett (in press a); [5]Madge (1971b); [6]Madge & Sitters (1973); [7]Van Daele & Leonard (2001); [8]Van Daele & Stjernstedt (2001b).

Phalacrocoracidae

White-breasted Cormorant *Phalacrocorax carbo*   B6 **RB**

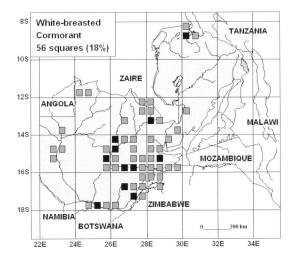

White-breasted
Cormorant
56 squares (18%)

Distribution *Almost Cosmopolitan* (*in the Afrotropics, Mauritania to South Africa*). Locally common on permanent waters, but very few records in NE Zambia away from L. Tanganyika, and in particular it appears to be absent from the Luangwa and Luapula River systems, for reasons that are not clear but presumably related to fish stocks or water turbidity. It is numerous in the Kafue drainage, where 2000 or more have been counted in the Itezhi-Tezhi area since the formation of that lake in 1975. Conversely, since the flooding of L. Kariba (in the late 1950s) numbers in the Middle Zambezi Valley have been reduced[4]. There may have been some spread on the Southern Province plateau in recent years, although breeding was already known from a dam on the Copperbelt in the 1950s[3]. Breeds colonially (black squares), the largest colony being of 500 nests on the Kafue Flats[1]. *Alt.* 950-1400 m, rarely as low as 370 m.

Ecology Larger dams and rivers, and more extensive floodplains, where it feeds in relatively deep water. Nests in isolated clumps of *Acacia, Syzygium* and other large trees (often with other species).

Status Mainly resident. The large numbers reported in the Kafue basin Oct-May may represent just a local, post-breeding dispersal. It is usually during this same period that small numbers (up to 80) occur on smaller waters on the Copperbelt and at Lusaka. However, a ringing recovery of one marked as a nestling in South Africa (Appendix 1) shows that some longer-distance movements occur.

Breeding	Jan	Feb	Mar	Apr	May	Jun	Jul	Aug	Sep
(n=111)	1	4	30	19	28	4	15	5	5

Most young would be on the wing as water levels drop, and fishing is thus relatively easy during their first months. *Clutch*: C/2 (1); C/3 (2); C/4 (6).

Moult: in contrast to *P. africanus*, none of 13 adults examined in Jun was in moult[2].

Taxonomy *P. c. lucidus*. Considered a distinct species by some.

References [1]Benson & Pitman (1956-57); [2]Dowsett (in press a); [3]Haydock (1956); [4]Hustler *et al.* (1986).

Reed Cormorant *Phalacrocorax africanus*   B7 **RB**

Distribution *Afrotropical* (*Mauritania to South Africa*). Occurs commonly on almost any water, even the smallest, but notably scarce in the low-lying Luangwa Valley (whence there are no breeding records). Breeds widely (black squares) in small to large colonies (often with herons), up to 4000 nests on the Kafue Flats[1]. *Alt.* 330-1800 m (Uningi Pans).

Ecology Any area of water (except the smallest mountain streams), from farm dams (and even puddles in woodland) to floodplains and large lakes. Nests in reeds and bushes. A survey in Bangweulu and L. Mweru[2] showed that some 50% of the fish taken by *P. africanus* were species of commercial value (most commonly Mormyridae *Gnathonemus spp.* and *Marcusenius spp.* and the catfish *Schilbe mystus*).

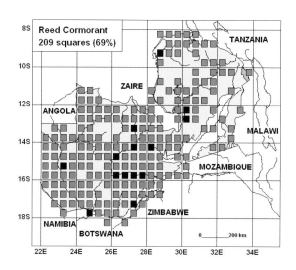

However, fish stocks at that time were considered to be excessive, and the 280 short tons of fish taken by some 10,000 cormorants was in fact of benefit to the fisheries. In 65 bird stomachs examined on the Kafue Flats[3], the main fish species were *Schilbe mystus* (in 22 samples) and the squeaker *Synodontis macrostigma* (12). Both of these small fish are abundant in the Kafue[5], but there is little commercial demand for them there[4].

Status During a 2-year survey its presence was greater Sep-Apr than May-Aug. Numbers increase in the non-breeding season, when flocks of 2000 or more occur on larger areas of water. At small dams too an influx is often noticed at this time, probably post-breeding dispersal from colonies not far distant. A nestling ringed in South Africa Mar was recovered in Zambia in Oct, 16 years later (Appendix 1).

Breeding

	Dec	Jan	Feb	Mar	Apr	May	Jun	Jul	Aug	Sep
(n=134)	2	5	8	26	22	7	16	44	3	1

Clutch: C/2 (2); C/3 (9); C/4 (5); C/5 (2).

Moult: in Bangweulu all birds (adults and juveniles) had moulted into black body plumage by the end of May[2]. On the Kafue Flats active primary moult was mainly Apr-Jun and Oct-Nov (little or no active moult in samples in Dec, Feb and Mar)[3].

Taxonomy *P. a. africanus*.

References [1]Benson & White (1957); [2]Bowmaker (1963); [3]Dowsett (in press a); [4]Everett (1971); [5]Jackson (1961).

Anhingidae

African Darter *Anhinga rufa*   B8 **RB**

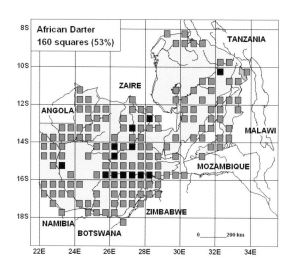

Distribution *Mainly Afrotropical (Mauritania to South Africa)*. Almost as widespread as *Phalacrocorax africanus*, and the more common in the Luangwa Valley, but unrecorded from the Luapula River. Most often on larger rivers and floodplains (locally frequent), less common at dams, and rarely at sewage ponds. Consequently, scarce on the Copperbelt and in much of North-Western Province. Most colonies (black squares) are of up to 25 nests, but reported abundant in a colony on the Lufupa River[1]. *Alt.* 330-1660 m, rarely to 1800 m (Uningi Pans).

Ecology Most areas of water, but especially where there is fringing vegetation, including riparian forest, nesting in reedbeds or trees.

Stomach contents examined on the Kafue Flats showed a wide range of small fish, particularly the cichlids *Tilapia andersonii* and *Haplochromis* spp.[2] (the former perhaps the most important species commercially in that area)[3].

Status Usually singly or in small groups, with no evidence of any movements.

Breeding	Jan	Feb	Mar	Apr	May	Jun	Jul	Aug	Sep	Oct	Nov	Dec
(n=291)	7	56	102	34	32	7	14	5	10	14	5	5

Clutch: C/1 (1); C/2 (1); C/3 (8); C/4 (3). *Moult*: noted only in Nov[2].

Taxonomy *A. r. rufa*; Afrotropical birds and the Oriental *A. melanogaster* are closely related[4], but here treated as separate species.

References [1]Benson & Pitman (1963); [2]Dowsett (in press a); [3]Jackson (1961); [4]Snow (1978).

Pelecanidae

White Pelican *Pelecanus onocrotalus*   B4 **RB**

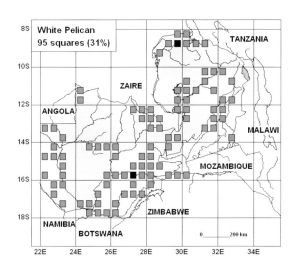

White Pelican
95 squares (31%)

Distribution *Old World (in the Afrotropics, Mauritania to South Africa)*. Has bred (black squares) only in Mweru Wantipa (over 1500 young reported in 1954, when water levels in N. Zambia were remarkably low)[1,2] and on the Kafue Flats (up to 20 pairs, on several occasions, most recent evidence in 1975)[4]. Occurs on shallow waters, in the Luangwa Valley and on the large floodplains of Bangweulu, the Kafue Flats, Liuwa Plain and also L. Itezhi-Tezhi. Rare on L. Kariba. *Alt.* 330-1700 m.

Ecology Open areas of shallow water, whether pans in the major valleys or extensive floodplains. Breeds in colonies, on the ground. Stomachs of 10 were examined on the Kafue Flats: four contained cichlids *Tilapia* spp.[4]. Elsewhere it has been seen to feed on *Barbus* spp. in lagoons when water levels are low.

Status Some may be resident, although numbers are significantly greater in the dry season (Jul-Nov), when there is a large influx, presumably from breeding colonies largely outside Zambia. Annual in flocks of up to 400 or so in the dry season at pans in the Luangwa Valley. On the Kafue Flats numbers at Lochinvar have exceeded 6000 in Oct-Nov, and large numbers still occur (e.g. 2800 in Jul 2006)[4]. Thousands were present in Bangweulu in Oct 1943[3] (this species, and not *P. rufescens* as originally reported), and 3-5000 in Mweru Wantipa, Dec 1993. On smaller waters wanderers can occur at any season, usually no more than 20 but exceptionally 100 once at Ndola (Aug 1984)[4].

Conservation Vulnerable to human and other predators when nesting; the fact that breeding has occurred but rarely may reflect a conservation problem, but this is not certain.

Breeding	Apr	May	Jun	Nov
(n=18)	12	1	3	2

Clutch: C/2 (12).

Moult: birds in moult Nov-Dec included two in breeding condition[4].

Taxonomy No races recognized.

References [1]Benson (1956e); [2]Benson (1960a); [3]Brelsford (1947); [4]Dowsett (in press a).

Pink-backed Pelican *Pelecanus rufescens*   B5 **RB**

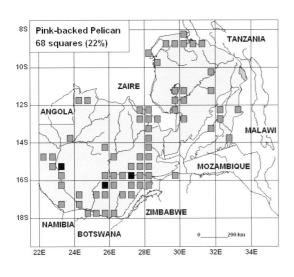

Distribution *Afrotropical* (*Mauritania to South Africa*). Can occur on any shallow waters between about 950 and 1800 m (Uningi Pans); rarely to 550 m, and usually nowhere as common as *P. onocrotalus* (with which it is only rarely in association). Usually fewer than 100 although exceptionally 300-500 have been reported from Lochinvar and Liuwa.

Ecology Dams, pans and floodplains. Nests in colonies, in trees. Fish in a sample of 21 stomachs on the Kafue Flats included pike *Hepsetus odoe* and the cichlid *Tilapia macrochir*, species caught commercially[2].

Status Unlike *P. onocrotalus*, a survey (1981-83) showed that the presence of this species was more frequent in the rains (Dec-May), even on small artificial waters (as at Lusaka and Luanshya)[2]. Most breeding may perhaps be outside Zambia, during the dry season.

Breeding Has attempted to breed in only three areas (black squares), but in no case was the outcome monitored in detail: Lochinvar in Aug 1969 (20 nests)[1], Mongu in Mar 1974 (*c.* 6 nests) and Nanzhila (100 nests) in the dry season of 1994 and on occasions up to 2006[2]. *Clutch*: no data.

Moult: noted Nov-Dec and Mar-Jun[2].

Conservation No evidence of any persecution, but it might be considered a threat by fishermen.

Taxonomy No races recognized.

References [1]Benson *et al.* (1970); [2]Dowsett (in press a).

[Fregatidae

Greater Frigatebird *Fregata minor*

Pan-tropical, breeds Indian Ocean. A vagrant was photographed on L. Kariba (1628D), just within Zimbabwe, 29 Aug 2001[1]. **References** [1]Riddell (2004b).]

Ardeidae

Common Bittern *Botaurus stellaris*   B9 **R(B)**

Distribution *Afrotropical and Palaearctic* (*probably breeds in Africa from Angola to South Africa*). Very few records, from scattered localities between about 900 and 1330 m altitude. Occurs in the area of Mweru Wantipa to Sumbu, the Kabonde Swamp, and especially in the L. Bangweulu region (whence comes the only specimen record, from Matongo Is. on 28 Nov 1937)[6]. There are irregular records from Itawa Swamp, Ndola, where it has occasionally been seen or heard over several months at a time. Further south in the Kafue drainage there are very few acceptable records, though it has been heard in the Lukanga Swamp[4] and on the northern edge of the Kafue Flats at Blue Lagoon[3]. On the Zambezi Floodplain there are acceptable local reports from Sitoya, south to L. Ilowa[4]. [There are also possible sight and sound records from the southern edge of the Kafue Flats (open squares). One reported seen in a small area of reeds near Livingstone 26 Nov ("?" on map), if correct, could have been no more than a vagrant, perhaps from the Upper Zambezi[4]. Sight records from the Luangwa Valley[1] were certainly

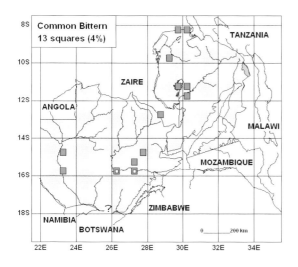

errors of identification; they have not been repeated in recent years and there is no suitable habitat. Similarly, a report from Chinsali[2] cannot be accepted without question, confusion with juvenile *Nycticorax nycticorax* occurring quite often[4].] Easily overlooked.

Ecology Extensive reedbeds, particularly in floodplains such as Bangweulu.

Status There are acceptable reports for most months, even at Ndola whence records are spasmodic. The seasonality of booming, and population sizes, require investigation.

Breeding No records. Booming has been reported most months in the north and at Ndola (especially Mar-Sep)[4]; egg-laying in southern Africa is Sep-Jan[5].

Taxonomy *B. s. capensis.*

References [1]Benson (1956d); [2]Brelsford (1942); [3]Dowsett (1965c); [4]Dowsett (in press a); [5]Dean in Hockey *et al.* (2005); [6]Kinnear (1938).

Little Bittern *Ixobrychus minutus*   B10 **RB/PW**

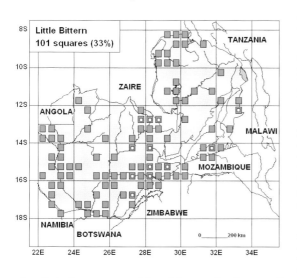

Distribution *Old World* (*in the Afrotropics, the race* payesii *occurs from The Gambia to South Africa; Palaearctic birds nominate* minutus *winter Senegal to Zambezian region*). Probably in reeds almost throughout; unrecorded from most of the low-lying Luangwa and Middle Zambezi Valleys, where reedbeds generally absent[1]. *Alt.* 330-1660 m, very scarce below 880 m.

Ecology Reedbeds, even quite small ones by dams, as well as the larger floodplains. Feeds on small fish and insects, the latter taken either from the ground or at varying levels.

Status Two populations. One is resident, widespread and breeds. The other is a Palaearctic migrant, recorded between 11 Nov and 22 Apr in ones and twos (up to 4 occasionally), from scattered localities on the Eastern Province plateau and "line of rail" south to near Choma (12 open squares)[2]. The two are sometimes present at the same locality[3].

Breeding   Mar   Apr   Jun   Jul
(n=6)   3   1   1   1   *Clutch*: C/2 (1).

Moult: *I. m. payesii* were in fairly fresh plumage Nov-Feb[1].

Taxonomy The resident subspecies is *I. m. payesii*, the Palaearctic migrant *I. m. minutus* (differing in being longer-winged and with paler neck).

References [1]Dowsett (in press a); [2]Dowsett (in press b); [3]Miles (1977).

Dwarf Bittern *Ixobrychus sturmii*   B11 **AMB**

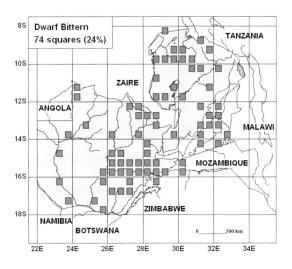

Distribution *Afrotropical* (*Mauritania to South Africa*). Widespread by shallow waters, but so far not known west of the Zambezi, where it occurs from Mumbeji to Kalobolelwa[2]. On the Eastern Province plateau not known north of the Chipata area[4], but in the Luangwa Valley occurs to at least as far north as Luambe[2]. *Alt.* 330-1700 m.

Ecology Typically in seasonally inundated grassy pans, but by any pool when on passage. Nests in small trees, occasionally reeds.

Status An intra-African migrant[1,2], arriving to breed in the rains, records falling between 11 Oct and 28 May. First arrivals may be from the end of the first week of Nov, but are often not before mid-Dec and in some years of reduced rainfall few if any may be noted before mid-Jan. Regularly present in numbers to late Apr, with the occasional one in early May. The odd bird has been reported Jun to mid-Sep (suggesting some may over-winter)[2], while a very young bird near Lusaka 24 Nov suggests some Zambian birds may have bred further north[3].

Breeding   Dec   Jan
(n=2)   1   1   *Clutch*: C/4 (1).

Taxonomy No races recognized.

References [1]Benson & Irwin (1966d); [2]Dowsett & Leonard (in press a); [3]Leonard (1999a); [4]Winterbottom (1936).

Black-crowned Night Heron *Nycticorax nycticorax*   B12 **RB**

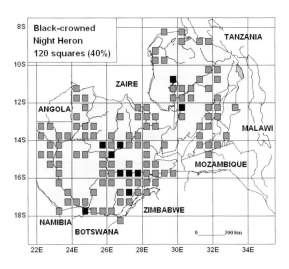

Distribution *Cosmopolitan* (*in the Afro-tropics, Mauritania to South Africa*). Widespread in most wetlands, but there are few records west of the Zambezi south of the Kalabo area. In the Luapula Valley unrecorded upstream of Chabilikila[1], and on Eastern Province plateau reported north only to Lundazi[4]. Breeds colonially (black squares), the largest colony known is of over 250 nests (Bangweulu)[2], although sometimes only a few pairs nest together[1]. *Alt.* 330-1700 m.

Ecology Generally in reeds and Papyrus, less commonly on the edge of riparian forest or lagoons. Nocturnal and crepuscular, resting in cover during the day. One colony was in *Syzygium* trees, all others in reedbeds, usually with other species[1].

Status Commonly post-breeding roosts of up to 20, exceptionally 60-100 (Oct-Jan)[1]. There is no evidence of any regular migration, although Palaearctic birds might be expected to reach Zambia on occasion; whereas Western European birds migrate to West Africa, one ringed in Romania reached Mozambique. A South African-ringed nestling recovered in Katanga, Zaire[3] suggests that some Zambian birds may be of southern origin.

Breeding   Jan   Feb   Mar   Apr   Jun   Aug
(n=13)   2   1   2   3   1   4   *Clutch*: C/3 (10); C/4 (1).
Moult: one juvenile started Jan[1].
Taxonomy *N. n. nycticorax*.
References [1]Dowsett (in press a); [2]Mwenya (1973); [3]Underhill *et al.* (1999); [4]Winterbottom (1937).

White-backed Night Heron *Gorsachius leuconotus*   B13 **RB**

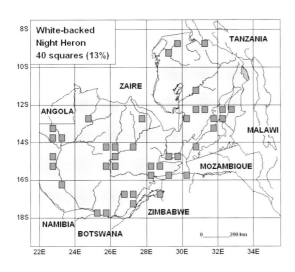

Distribution *Afrotropical* (*Senegal to South Africa*). Very sparse (though easily over-looked). Inhabits the larger, well-wooded river systems, throughout the Zambezi and Kafue basins (except absent from the largely treeless Kafue Flats), and the Luangwa up to about the Mwaleshi[1]. In the extreme north it is known from Kundabwika Falls[3], Mweru Wantipa[5] and Mpulungu[2]. It is unknown in NW Zambia between Fitula Dambo near Chingola and the West Lunga River[5]. *Alt.* 330-1300 m (Fitula Dambo).

Ecology On the edge of and within riparian cover by permanent water, particularly the larger rivers. Nocturnal and crepuscular. Nest-sites described have been trees overhanging water (2) and a pile of driftwood (1)[5].

Status Apparently does not assemble in any more than small, perhaps family, groups (in contrast to the large roosts of *Nycticorax nycticorax*). Probably sedentary, with no more than local wandering.

Breeding   Jan   Mar   Apr   Sep   Oct
(n=9)   2   2   1   2   2   There is a case of re-laying a month after a clutch
was destroyed in Sep[4]. *Clutch*: C/2 (2); C/3 (3).
Taxonomy[6] *G. l. natalensis*.
References [1]Benson (1962a); [2]Benson & Pitman (1956-57); [3]Benson & White (1957); [4]Berry & Robinson (1979); [5]Dowsett (in press a); [6]Irwin & Benson (1967b).

Madagascar Squacco Heron *Ardeola idae*   B15 **AM/W**

Distribution *Breeds in the Malagasy region* (*some migrating to eastern and central Africa, especially Zaire, in the off-season*). Known from a number of localities in the eastern half of the country (perhaps annual in the Luangwa Valley)[3], west to Lochinvar[1]. Separation of the species from *A. ralloides* in non-breeding dress requires care, and a few sight records have not been accepted. *Alt.* 550-1650 m.

Ecology By any water with fringing vegetation, at times in more wooded situations than *A. ralloides* (though often alongside that species).

Status Non-breeding visitor from the Malagasy region, with at least 11 acceptable records (3 of them

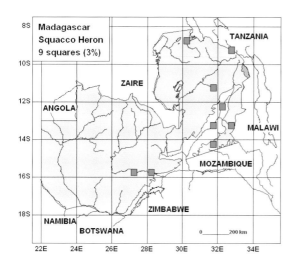

specimens[1]), of up to 3 birds together, 2 May to 10 Oct (towards the end some birds showing traces of breeding dress)[3]. [There are also sight records claimed for immatures in Nov, Jan and Feb and examination of specimens showed that some immatures remain during the breeding season in Zaire[4]; but they would be difficult to separate from any Palaearctic *A. r. ralloides* that might occur.]

Conservation Classified as "Endangered"[2], but not threatened in its winter quarters.

Taxonomy No races recognized.

References [1]Benson & Dowsett (1969); [2]BirdLife International (2004a); [3]Dowsett & Leonard (in press a); [4]Prigogine (1976).

Common Squacco Heron *Ardeola ralloides* B14 **RB/P?**

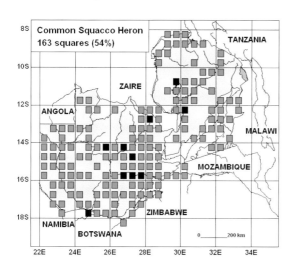

Distribution *Afrotropical (breeds Mauritania to South Africa) and Palaearctic (wintering north of the Equator)*. Locally common throughout the country, by any marsh-fringed water. *Alt.* 330-1800 m (Uningi Pans).

Ecology Feeds in floating vegetation and on the muddy edge of dams, pans and floodplains, or in shallow water, avoiding only well-wooded rivers and lakesides. Feeds largely on invertebrates, amphibians and small fish. Nests colonially (black squares) in reedbeds, up to 300 pairs in one colony (Lochinvar)[4], often with other species.

Status There is no unequivocal proof that Palaearctic migrants occur as far south as Zambia (see Taxonomy); the most southerly recovery is of a Russian-ringed bird near the Equator, on L. Albert[5]. Usually in small numbers, but concentrations of 100 or more at times[4].

Breeding

	Jan	Feb	Mar	Apr	May	Aug	Sep	Oct
(n=69)	6	2	45	12	1	1	1	1

Clutch: C/1 (1); C/3 (5); C/4 (1).

Moult: birds examined in May, Jun, Oct and Dec showed no sign of moult[4].

Taxonomy[1,2] *A. r. paludivaga* (type locality Luapula River mouth; *NMZB*)[3] is recognisable as the local breeding form. It is possible that the paler nominate *A. r. ralloides* occurs in Zambia as a Palaearctic migrant[3], but it would be very difficult to separate with certainty on plumage characters.

References [1]Benson (1962a); [2]Benson *et al.* (1970); [3]Clancey (1968a: 3); [4]Dowsett (in press a); [5]Prigogine (1975).

Rufous-bellied Heron *Ardeola rufiventris*   B18 **RB**

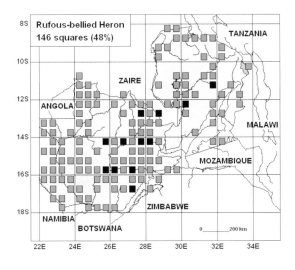

Distribution *Afrotropical* (*breeds Zaire to South Africa*). Small numbers in wetlands practically throughout the country. Breeds colonially (black squares); a colony of 400 nests has been reported from Bangweulu[2], but usually only up to 60[1]. *Alt.* 370-1800 m (Uningi Pans).

Ecology Reedbeds in dams, edge of lagoons, inundated dambos and floodplains. Colonies have been mostly in *Phragmites mauritianus*, also in *Typha*[2,3].

Status Resident, with probably no more than local movements to areas that are seasonally flooded (e.g. almost solely a rains visitor to the Luangwa Valley)[1]. Usually singly or in small, scattered groups, when not breeding.

Breeding[3] Dec   Jan   Feb   Mar   Apr   May   Jun   Aug
(n=124)   1   7   3   83   13   3   13   1
Clutch: C/1 (5); C/2 (23); C/3 (28); C/4 (6).
Taxonomy No races recognized.
References [1]Dowsett (in press a); [2]Mwenya (1973); [3]Uys & Clutton-Brock (1966).

Cattle Egret *Bubulcus ibis*   B16 **AM/W**

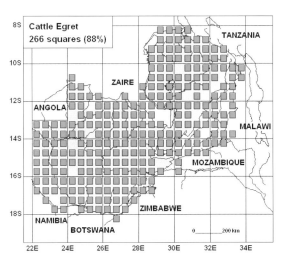

Distribution *Cosmopolitan; throughout the continent, but there are large areas where it does not breed, including most of south-central Africa.* Most numerous in the floodplains of S. and central Zambia, and in areas of extensive farming. Sparse in the well-wooded plateau areas of N. and NW Zambia. *Alt.* at all levels (330-2200 m), but scarce above 1600 m.

Ecology Feeds in any grassland, dry or moist, frequently accompanying cattle and wild ungulates, to take insects disturbed. In the dry season mostly in areas that remain moist, such as floodplains or irrigated agricultural land.

Status Present throughout the year, but greatest numbers by far are from Nov-Mar, fewest Apr-Oct. At their peak roosts may be of 10,000 or more. In parts of N. Zambia, present almost only on passage, Nov-Dec and Feb-Apr. Numbers build up in Dec or earlier (with the first main rains), and remain high until mid-Mar when they start to decrease (and passage becomes evident)[1]. 13 birds ringed as nestlings in South Africa between Nov and Feb have been recovered in Zambia, mostly Apr-May and Aug-Dec (Appendix 1). The oldest of these was nearly 12 years of age. These are very possibly on passage to winter in equatorial Africa, as there are recoveries at that season from Zaire, Uganda etc[4].

Breeding No confirmed record, although increasing numbers are nesting in Zimbabwe, and the first records occurred in Malawi in 2000[2]. Breeding in southern Africa is often in areas of low rainfall, and drought conditions may be favouring its spread at present. Breeding dress noted in Zambia from mid-Sep to Dec as a rule (breeding in southern Africa is mainly Dec-Feb), but one such bird in Dec had worn flight feathers, suggesting it was not a local breeder[1].

Taxonomy *B. i. ibis.* Apparently grey morphs reported from Kitwe[3] and Kafue Fisheries[1].

References [1]Dowsett & Leonard (in press a); [2]Dowsett-Lemaire (2006b); [3]Penry (1976c); [4]Underhill *et al.* (1999).

Green-backed Heron *Butorides striata* B17 **RB**

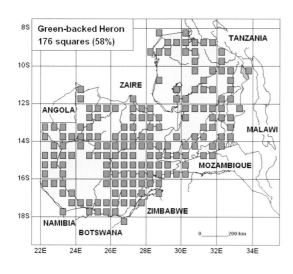

Green-backed Heron
176 squares (58%)

Distribution *Mainly Pantropical (in the Afrotropics, Mauritania to South Africa).* Occurs in small numbers wherever there are suitable wooded wetlands. *Alt.* 330-1800 m (in the north-east).

Ecology Any dam, lagoon, river or stream with wooded banks, rarely on open flood-plains and sewage ponds (in the rains)[1].

Status Solitary, and certainly resident.

Breeding	Jan	Feb	Mar	Apr	May
(n=44)	8	5	5	3	1
	Jun	Aug	Sep	Oct	Nov	Dec
	1	6	5	5	1	4

Clutch: C/1 (2); C/2 (4); C/3 (1); C/4 (5).

Taxonomy *B. s. atricapilla.*

References [1]Dowsett (in press a).

Slaty Egret *Egretta vinaceigula* B - **R(B)**

Distribution *A Zambezian species of restricted range in south-central Africa, centred on N. Botswana and adjacent S. Zambia*[5]. First identified in 1969. Confined mainly to the swamps of the Upper Zambezi, the Kafue Flats[5], and Bangweulu[3], where occasionally rather common. In the Zambezi it occurs from the Lutembwe/Lungwebungu area south to about Livingstone, and in the Kafue from the Busanga Swamps. Wanderers have been noted in West Lunga N.P., Solwezi, on the Copperbelt at Luanshya and Chililabombwe, at Lusaka, and it is even reported from Chiawa in the Middle Zambezi[7]. In the north it has occurred at Shiwa Ngandu, and even at Kabendwe on the border with Zaire[1], the most northerly record of the species. *Alt.* 950-1400 m, rarely down to 370 m.

Ecology Seasonally flooded grassland and pans in floodplains, also at times on small dams where there is shallow water. Unlike *E. ardesiaca* it does not fish by using its wings as an umbrella shade.

Status Occurs in small groups as a rule (up to 6 birds), although larger concentrations have been reported (Jun-Sep) of more than 30 (Liuwa and Kafue Flats) and "very numerous" in Bangweulu (end Jun 1981)[7]. Numbers fluctuate locally, and it almost certainly wanders greatly, thus no population figure is available for Zambia.

Conservation Considered "Vulnerable"[4], this species needs to be investigated in detail. It certainly has a very small population, with few known breeding colonies. It is potentially highly vulnerable to changing flood regimes (such as through the Kafue hydro-electric schemes) and even direct human pillaging of nesting sites.

Breeding No record yet from Zambia, but "one very young bird with a short bill" seen in Lochinvar N.P. 9 Mar 1998[7] (and see under *E. ardesiaca*). In Botswana it nests in small groups in inundated clumps of *Ficus verruculosa*[6], reeds *Phragmites* and at one site in palms *Phoenix reclinata*[8].
Moult: two adults in S. Zambia were in worn plumage early Oct[7].

Taxonomy No races recognized. Formerly thought to be a colour phase of *E. ardesiaca*, but it is a good species[2].

References [1]Aspinwall (1978a); [2]Benson *et al.* (1971b); [3]Berry (1974); [4]BirdLife International (2000, 2004a); [5]Dowsett (1971c); [6]Dowsett (1981); [7]Dowsett (in press a); [8]Tyler (2005).

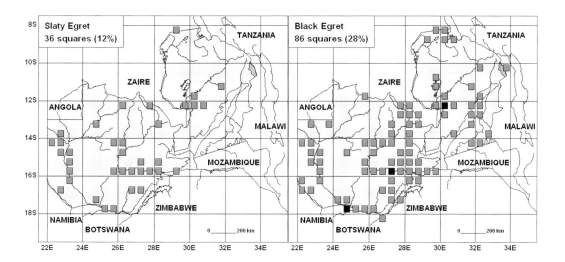

Black Egret *Egretta ardesiaca*   B19 **RB**

Distribution *Afrotropical (Mauritania to South Africa).* Through most of the wetlands, except unrecorded from the Luapula basin and the extreme north-west. Nests colonially (black squares); usually up to 50 nests in a colony, but possibly as many as 250 at a Bangweulu site[3]. Nests reportedly of this species in two colonies near the Machile/Zambezi River confluence in 1963 and earlier years[1] may (with hindsight) have included at least some *E. vinaceigula*. The third known nesting area is Lochinvar[2]. *Alt.* 950-1600 m, rarely down to 370 m.

Ecology Pans, lagoons and floodplains. Nests with other herons, in bushes or dense reeds (2-3 m above water).

Status Present throughout the year, with no significant seasonal differences, except that most large concentrations (up to 300) are present Jan-Apr[2]. A total of 1500 was estimated at Lochinvar, Jan 1994[4]. A nestling ringed in Bangweulu (Aug) was recovered in Zimbabwe (Jan) (Appendix 1).

Breeding   Feb   Mar   Apr   May   Jun
(n=7)   1   1   2   1   2   *Clutch*: C/3 (2); C/4 (1).

Taxonomy No races recognized.

References [1]Benson & Irwin (1967b); [2]Dowsett (in press a); [3]Mwenya (1973); [4]Taylor & Rose (1994).

Little Egret *Egretta garzetta*   B22 **RB**

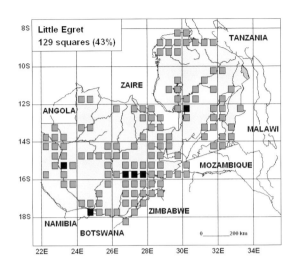

Distribution *Old World* (*in the Afrotropics, Mauritania to South Africa*). Almost throughout, except there are so far no records from the Mashi River, the Luapula or parts of the lower Luangwa. Only a vagrant to North-Western Province[2]. Colonies (black squares) are known on the Upper Zambezi, the Kafue and in Bangweulu, the largest (at the Machile/Zambezi River confluence) being of 100 nests[1]. *Alt.* 330-1800 m (Uningi Pans).

Ecology Shallow water at the edge of lagoons, floodplains and dams, or on rivers, where it feeds on small fish, amphibians and insects. Most nests have been in reedbeds, but also in bushes by water.

Status Although present in all months, a survey showed its presence to be rather more frequent Nov-Apr than May-Oct[2]. Usually singly or in small, loose groups, up to 285 together[2].

Breeding   Feb   Mar   Apr   May   Jun   Jul
(n=14)   1   2   2   3   5   1   *Clutch*: C/3 (3); C/4 (2).

Taxonomy *E. g. garzetta*. Birds in an aberrant dark grey plumage have twice been reported[2].
References [1]Benson & Irwin (1967b); [2]Dowsett (in press a).

Western Reef Heron *Egretta gularis*   B - **AV**

Distribution and Status *Old World Tropics* (*in the Afrotropics, coastal West and East Africa and the Indian Ocean islands, wandering rarely inland*). A single vagrant (possibly immature) was present (photographed) 3 Feb to mid-Feb 2006 at Kafunta (1331B), on the edge of the Luangwa River[1,2].
Taxonomy *E. g. schistacea*, the form of eastern Africa and the Indian sub-continent.
References [1]Dowsett & Leonard (in press a); [2]Poole (2006).

Yellow-billed Egret *Egretta intermedia*   B21 **RB**

Distribution *Old World Tropics* (*in the Afrotropics, Mauritania to South Africa*). Recorded throughout the country, but most commonly on floodplains in the south (Kafue Flats) and west (Liuwa Plain). Breeds in small, mixed colonies (up to 50 pairs) on the Upper Zambezi, in the Kafue basin, L. Kariba and Bangweulu (black squares)[4]. *Alt.* 330-1800 m (Uningi Pans).
Ecology Feeds principally on invertebrates (e.g. crickets) on dry floodplains near water, or in the shallows. It shares this niche in part with the smaller *Bubulcus ibis* and the larger *Egretta alba*. Nests have been in trees, including *Syzygium*.
Status Usually singly, but flocks of many hundreds on the Liuwa in Apr and concentrations at Lochinvar of up to 500+ late Dec to late Apr are indicative of movements. At Ndola numbers peaked in Jul and declined from Sep[4]. A nestling ringed in the Cape in Nov was recovered in W. Zambia in late May (this species, and not *Bubulcus ibis* as originally reported)[1] (Appendix 1).

Breeding[2,3] Feb   Mar   Apr   Aug   Sep
(n=39)   10   10   7   3   9   *Clutch*: C/2 (1); C/3 (3); C/4 (1).
Moult: adults in May-Jun were in worn plumage[4].
Taxonomy *E. i. brachyrhyncha*.
References [1]Benson *et al.* (1971a); [2]Benson & Pitman (1963); [3]Benson & Pitman (1964); [4]Dowsett (in press a).

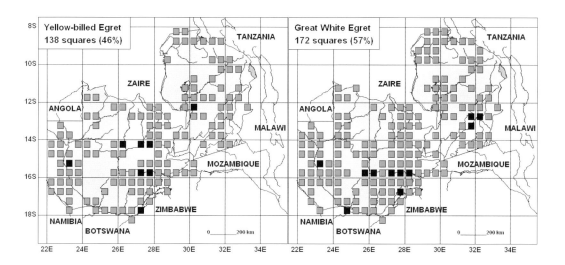

Great White Egret *Egretta alba*   B20 **RB**

Distribution *Cosmopolitan* (*in the Afrotropics, Mauritania to South Africa*). Throughout the country, common by any water, although known to nest in only a few places (black squares). The two main breeding colonies in the Luangwa Valley total some 400 nests (one of 250 nests); they have been known since the 1950s[4] and are still occupied annually[3]. Other important colonies include two on the Kafue Flats[1,2]. *Alt.* 330-1800 m (Uningi Pans).
Ecology Feeds in shallow or fairly deep water, thus frequents dams, the larger rivers and floodplains. The major breeding colonies are in *Acacia albida* trees in small, seasonally flooded, lagoons[4]. Feeds on insects, amphibians and a variety of small fish (the catfish *Schilbe mystus*, cichlids such as *Tilapia* spp.)[3].
Status Mainly resident. Usually singly, although concentrations do occur at times outside the breeding season, groups of up to 55 at Lochinvar (a favoured site, in Oct), with a total of over 500 in Blue Lagoon N.P. (Jul 1997)[3], and 2000 as a whole on the Kafue Flats (Jul 1993)[5].
Breeding   Dec   Jan   Feb   Mar   Apr   May   Jun   Aug   Sep
(n=16)   2   3   2   1   4   1   1   1   1   *Clutch*: C/3 (1).
Moult: adults in worn plumage Nov, in Mar fresh[3].
Taxonomy *E. a. melanorhynchos*.
References [1]Benson & Pitman (1958-59); [2]Benson & Pitman (1963); [3]Dowsett (in press a); [4]Feely (1964); [5]Taylor & Rose (1994).

Purple Heron *Ardea purpurea*　　　　　　　　　B26 **RB**

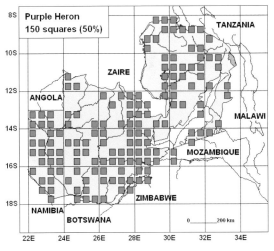

Distribution *Old World* (*in the Afrotropics, Mauritania to South Africa*). Almost throughout the country, wherever there are reedbeds (thus scarce in the Luangwa Valley, but resident at low altitude elsewhere). Common only in the larger marshes. Although there are definite nesting records from few places, it probably breeds widely. Colonies of 50-100 nests are known[2,3]. *Alt.* 330-1800 m (Uningi Pans).

Ecology Reedbeds, especially on the larger dams, rivers and floodplains (suitable reeds are usually absent from sewage ponds). Nests in reeds usually about 2 m above water level[1]. Feeds in fairly deep water, essentially on fish (*Schilbe mystus* and cichlids *Tilapia spp.* on the Kafue Flats)[3].

Status Appears to be resident (there is no evidence that Palaearctic birds, indistinguishable, occur any further south than West Africa, whence there are many ringing recoveries). Not usually gregarious outside the breeding season.

Breeding　　Jan　Feb　Mar　Apr　Jun　Jul　Aug
(n=37)　　　　20　　5　　3　　6　　1　　1　　1
Clutch: C/1 (1); C/2 (3); C/3 (14); C/4 (1).
Moult: an adult in Nov starting moult[3].
Taxonomy *A. p. purpurea.*
References [1]Benson & Pitman (1963); [2]Benson & White (1957: 157); [3]Dowsett (in press a).

Grey Heron *Ardea cinerea*　　　　　　　　　B23 **RB**

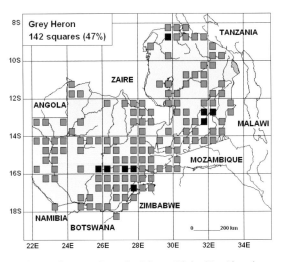

Distribution *Old World* (*in the Afrotropics, Mauritania to South Africa*). Through most of the country, by any water. Scarce in well-wooded areas, and irregular in Mwinilunga. Most colonies (black squares) are small (max. 50 nests). *Alt.* 330-1800 m (Uningi Pans).

Ecology Dams, rivers, lakes and floodplains, in fact by almost any patch of water. Feeds on a variety of small fish (including a pike *Hepsetus odoe* of 280 g)[2]. Nests are placed in thorn trees (often with other species)[1].

Status Present in all months, with no significant fluctuations, and presumably resident, although in Mwinilunga most records are in the dry season[2]. Usually singly or in small, loose groups, but there are dry season concentrations of up to 50 on the Liuwa Plain (Apr)[1] and even of 150 at Blue Lagoon (Oct)[2]. A nestling ringed on the Kafue Flats (May) has been recovered in Zimbabwe (Sep) (Appendix 1). There is no evidence that Palaearctic birds occur further south than West Africa.

Breeding   Feb   Apr   May   Jun   Jul   Aug   Sep   Oct   Nov   Dec
(n=59)   4   38   3   5   1   1   1   2   1   3

Clutch: C/2 (1); C/3 (2); C/4 (1); C/5 (1).

Moult: in Nov and Apr, while a female about to breed in Oct had interrupted moult[2].

Taxonomy *A. c. cinerea.*

References [1]Benson & Pitman (1958-59); [2]Dowsett (in press a).

Black-headed Heron *Ardea melanocephala*   B24 **RB**

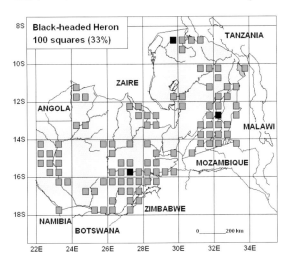

Distribution *Afrotropical* (*Mauritania to South Africa*). In plains and river basins, except for the Luapula basin. Commonest on the Upper Zambezi, in the Kafue drainage and the Luangwa Valley. Nesting is known from only three areas (black squares). *Alt.* 370-1700 m.

Ecology Often by water, but usually in a variety of dry situations nearby, such as grassland, cultivation and even near villages. Colonies are very small (fewer than 10 nests) and in natural situations – i.e. not near villages as in Malawi[2], although in Jul 2007 a "heronry" was reported, without details, in the grounds of State House, Lusaka[1].

Status Recorded in all months, but a survey showed that its presence was reported significantly more often Oct-Mar than Apr-Sep[1]. The dry season is when the species breeds, and these differences may reflect no more than local dispersal. Small groups, up to 30, even 50, in any month.

Breeding   Mar   Apr   Aug   Sep
(n=13)   4   2   1   6   *Clutch*: C/1 (2); C/3 (4); C/4 (1).

In addition, egg-laying started in Nov in one colony.

Taxonomy No races recognized.

References [1]Dowsett (in press a); [2]Dowsett-Lemaire & Dowsett (2006).

Goliath Heron *Ardea goliath*   B25 **RB**

Distribution *Mainly Afrotropical* (*Mauritania to South Africa*). Occurs sparsely in extensive wetlands through much of the country, although so far unknown from the extreme south-west, and occurs no nearer the north-west than the Matebo area[2]. Commonest in the low-lying Middle Zambezi and Luangwa Valleys, and between L. Tanganyika and Mweru Wantipa. Known nesting localities plotted as black squares[2]. *Alt.* 330-1800 m (Uningi Pans).

Ecology Most often on large rivers and the more extensive floodplains. Nests (usually in trees or reedbeds) either singly or in small colonies (20 nests on the ground on Katema Is. in 1951)[1].

Status Resident, usually singly or pairs.

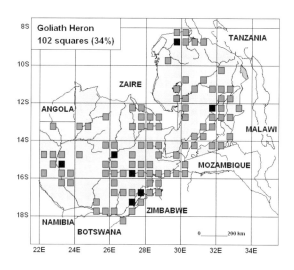

Breeding	Jan	Feb	Mar	Apr
(n=71)	6	5	9	5
	May	Jun	Jul	Aug
	4	9	13	11
	Sep	Oct	Nov	Dec
	2	1	2	4

Clutch: C/2 (6); C/3 (9); C/4 (6).
Taxonomy No races recognized.
References [1]Berwick (1954); [2]Dowsett (in press a).

Scopidae

Hamerkop *Scopus umbretta*   B28 **RB**

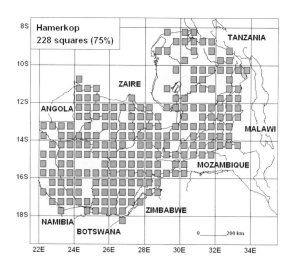

Distribution *Afrotropical* (*Mauritania to South Africa*). Occurs practically throughout the country, including the north-west[1], although there are few records from the Luapula drainage (as is the case with many other species). *Alt.* 330-1900 m.
Ecology Generally along smaller rivers where there are rocks and pools, and also on the muddy edges of lagoons and small pans, even at puddles on tracks. Scarce in large wetlands. Its enormous nest is placed in a tree near permanent or seasonal water. Feeds on amphibians, small fish and large invertebrates.
Status Recorded all months, and although it may be slightly more noticeable in the rains, there may be no more than local wanderings[1].

Breeding	Jan	Feb	Mar	Apr	Jun	Jul	Aug	Sep	Oct	Dec
(n=30)	1	5	6	2	2	5	5	2	1	1

Clutch: C/2 (1); C/4 (2); C/5 (4); C/6 (2).
Taxonomy *S. u. umbretta*.
References [1]Dowsett (in press a).

Ciconiidae

Yellow-billed Stork *Mycteria ibis*   B36 **RB**

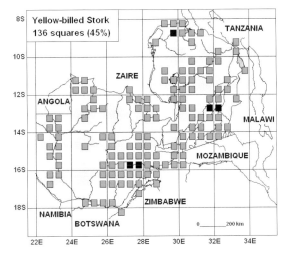

Distribution *Afrotropical (Mauritania to South Africa)*. Occurs through most of the country, commonest in Mweru Wantipa, the Luangwa Valley and on the Kafue Flats, where breeds (black squares), colonies in the Luangwa being of up to 150 pairs[2,3]. *Alt.* 330-1800 m (Uningi Pans).

Ecology Edges of swamps and lagoons, floodplains and on sand beaches on the larger rivers. Feeds tactily in shallow water, on small fish, frogs etc. The Luangwa colonies are in large *Acacia albida* trees in lagoons[3], but on Katema Is. (Mweru Wantipa) nests were in bushes, only 2 m above the ground[1].

Status There is no evidence of any real movement other than purely local, to small dams (at any time of year). Occurs in flocks of up to 50 in its strongholds when not breeding (even 300 at times)[2].

Conservation The three known nesting areas are all within national parks.

Breeding	Feb	Mar	Apr	May	Jun	Jul	Aug	Sep	Oct
(n=23)	2	3	3	1	4	4	2	3	1

Clutch: C/2 (4); C/3 (4).

Taxonomy No races recognized.

References [1]Benson & Pitman (1956-57); [2]Dowsett (in press a); [3]Feely (1964).

Openbill Stork *Anastomus lamelligerus*   B34 **AMB**

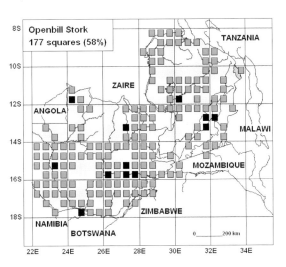

Distribution *Afrotropical (breeds Sierra Leone to South Africa)*. Widespread, locally numerous, in large floodplains. Most colonies (black squares) are of 100-150 pairs, but one on the Kafue Flats covered an area of several hectares, and one at Blue Lagoon held some 5000 nests[2]. It also nests on the Zimbabwe side of L. Kariba[3]. *Alt.* 330-1800 m.

Ecology Feeds on dry land or in shallow water, on bivalve molluscs and snails, and thus occurs mainly on floodplains and large lagoons.

Status Present throughout the year, but generally more often observed Jan-Jun (flocks totalling thousands at times) than during the rest of the year. In Nov 1970 an aerial survey showed there to be some 500,000 birds on the Kafue Flats alone[1]. While it seems probable that at least part of the population consists of long-distance migrants, the only firm evidence for this is the recovery of a nestling ringed at Lochinvar (Jul) in Namibia (the following Jan) (Appendix 1).

Conservation Colonies occur both in nominally protected areas and outside them. There is no evidence of persecution, but detailed investigation is desirable, for Zambia holds one of the largest breeding populations of this species.

Breeding   Feb   Mar   Apr   Jun
(n=16)   2   6   5   3   *Clutch*: C/3 (2); C/4 (3).

Taxonomy *A. l. lamelligerus.*

References [1]Dowsett (1971e); [2]Dowsett & Leonard (in press a); [3]Sparrow (1993).

Black Stork *Ciconia nigra* B30 **RB**

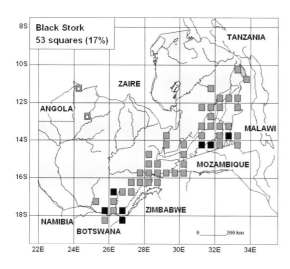

Distribution *Afrotropical* (*breeds in south-central Africa*), *and Palaearctic* (*wintering Senegal to Tanzania*). Closely associated with the rocky hills along the Muchinga and Zambezi escarpments and on the Eastern Province plateau (known breeding sites are black squares). In addition to local movements when not breeding (see below), wanderers have occurred west to Ngwezi, to the Copperbelt at Ndola and the Northern Province plateau at Shiwa Ngandu. Accepted sight records in the Upper Zambezi (Sakeji, Sep[1] and West Lunga N.P., 28 Oct[3], open squares) suggest an overlooked population in Zaire or Angola. *Alt.* 330-2000 m (Makutu Plateau)[2].

Ecology Feeds in shallow water and moist grassland, usually not far from rocky hills or escarpments, where it breeds. When not nesting it does wander to not too distant rivers and even dams.

Status Subject to at least local movements. Birds that occur regularly on the Luangwa River and its tributaries (mostly Jun-Oct) are probably from the Eastern Province plateau or the Muchinga escarpment. However, there are few records during the rains, and there may be some movement out of the country, perhaps southwards[3,4]. Usually in pairs or small family groups, even up to 13 together (Chipata, 2 Mar)[3].

Breeding   May   Jun
(n=15)   6   9   *Clutch*: N/2 (3); N/3 (5); N/4 (1); N/5 (1).

Taxonomy No races recognized.

References [1]Benson & White (1957); [2]Dowsett (1971h); [3]Dowsett (in press a); [4]Leonard (1999a).

Abdim's Stork *Ciconia abdimii* B31**AMW**

Distribution *Afrotropical* (*breeding Mauritania to Uganda; wintering mainly Zambezian region to South Africa*). Can be expected almost anywhere, but there are no records from L. Mweru and the lower Luapula, while west of the Zambezi it is reported only from the Imusho area[1] (the last, and the scarcity in general in NW Zambia, suggesting that most storks avoid migrating across the Central

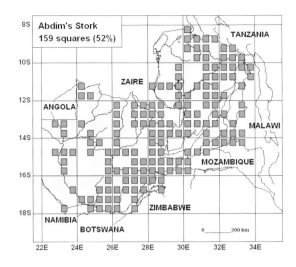

African forest). *Alt.* 330-2200 m (Nyika).

Ecology In floodplain, dambos or any open grassland (including irrigated farm land).

Status A non-breeding intra-African migrant, recorded from 10 Oct to 16 Jun (Aug, Sep and some Jun records may have been misidentified *C. nigra*). The average first date over 30 years was 24 Oct, the average last (in 14 years) 21 Apr[1]. The great majority are on passage, as only small numbers remain during the rains, and then mostly in S. and SE Zambia. During peak passage (early Nov to mid-Dec and again mid-Feb to early Mar) flocks of hundreds occur (up to 1000), and daily totals at places in the eastern half of the country can surpass 5000[1].

Conservation The species is as numerous now as in the past. Apart from the menace of pesticides, there is some danger from hunting (a bird with an arrow in its flank had probably been the target of a hunter further north in Africa).

Taxonomy No races recognized.

References [1]Dowsett & Leonard (in press a).

Woolly-necked Stork *Ciconia episcopus*   B32 **RB**

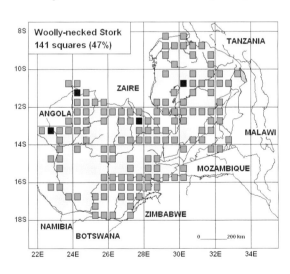

Distribution *Old World Tropics (in Africa breeds Sierra Leone to South Africa).* Although it is known to breed only in the forests of the north (black squares), it has been recorded widely, in the south especially in the Luangwa Valley and the Kafue Flats. *Alt.* 330-1600 m.

Ecology When breeding it is normally associated with riparian forest or mushitu, but feeds in any open grassland, especially near water. The one nest examined in detail was at Makuwa Kuwa (Zambezi Dist.), 30 m up in small riparian mushitu[3]. A solitary breeder.

Status In the south, where it may not breed, large flocks (up to 45) are reported only Nov-Apr. In the north of the country there are observations for all months, but too few for any clear pattern to emerge[1].

Breeding   Jul

(n=1)   1   In addition, a nest was occupied in Aug at Matipa (Chilubi Dist.), while nest-building was reported in that month in N. Mwinilunga[1] and in Sep in the Lukolwe area[2] and near Chingola[1]. *Clutch*: N/1+ (1).

Taxonomy *C. e. microscelis.*

References [1]Dowsett (in press a); [2]Leonard (1998b); [3]Van Daele (1999c).

White Stork *Ciconia ciconia* B29 **PW/AV**

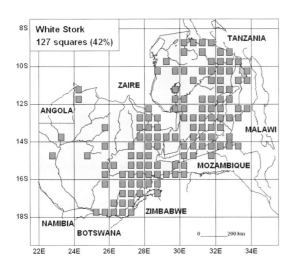

8S White Stork
127 squares (42%)
TANZANIA
10S
ZAIRE
12S
ANGOLA
MALAWI
14S
MOZAMBIQUE
16S
ZIMBABWE
18S
NAMIBIA
BOTSWANA
0   200 km
22E   24E   26E   28E   30E   32E   34E

Distribution *Palaearctic* (*winters Mauritania to South Africa, with also a tiny population breeding in the Cape Province, South Africa*). Most records are from the eastern half of the country[2], with very few west of "line of rail" (there being just a scattering of observations along the Zambezi, to Mwinilunga[3]). It seems certain that this species largely avoids the Congo forest block, depending as it does on suitable conditions for soaring. *Alt.* all levels (330-2200 m).

Ecology Any open grassland, pasture or flood-plain.

Status A Palaearctic migrant and winter visitor. Most birds occur on passage, flocks of over 200 being reported only between 15 Nov and 25 Dec (southward passage, max. 500) and from 9 Feb to 28 Apr (northwards, max. 3320, but otherwise up to 1000)[4]. Very few are present during Jan (groups up to 12, once 70 on 31st), but serious passage starts the second half of Feb, mostly through to mid-Apr. A few are present during the austral winter (May-Sep, groups of up to 30), from the Copperbelt south to the Central Province plateau, very rarely elsewhere[4].

There are at least 66 recoveries in Zambia of birds ringed as nestlings in the Palaearctic (the oldest *c.* 10 years old). The 63 such recoveries for which exact ringing localities are known are from the main part of the species's breeding range, except that there is one from Spain, from where the population usually migrates to West Africa. The majority of recoveries fall between Nov and Mar, but there have been several in other months: most of the ringed birds recovered between May and Sep were a year old, thus not returning to Europe in their first year (Appendix 1). There have also been two recoveries of birds from the South African breeding population (one of them a satellite-tracked bird, en route to Rwanda)[1].

Conservation Birds are occasionally killed by man, but this appears to be opportunistic and never on a large scale. The species is to a great extent insectivorous, and thus potentially vulnerable to chemical spraying (e.g. in tsetse fly control or to eliminate agricultural pests), though reported cases of deaths in this way are few. Numbers on passage through Zambia are still considerable at times[5], and appear not to have diminished greatly over the years.

Breeding No records (an old claim being in error)[4].

Taxonomy *C. c. ciconia.*

References [1]Avian Demography Unit (2001); [2]Benson (1967); [3]Bowen (1980c); [4]Dowsett (in press b); [5]Lister (1998).

Saddlebill (Saddle-billed Stork) *Ephippiorhynchus senegalensis* B33 **RB**

Distribution *Afrotropical* (*Senegal to South Africa*). Known breeding sites are few but widely scattered, and it has been found sparsely through most of Zambia (but for much of the Luapula Valley). *Alt.* 330-1800 m (Uningi Pans).

Ecology Usually on larger floodplains, lagoons and the major rivers, less often in moist dambos or at dams.

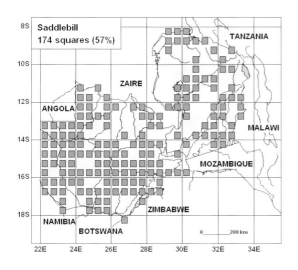

Status Resident, usually in territorial pairs or family parties. However, in the non-breeding season large groups sometimes occur, with up to 30 not infrequent on the Liuwa Plain and Kafue Flats (mostly Oct-Mar)[2], and an exceptional concentration of 84 was at a lagoon in the Luangwa Valley mid-Oct 1983[1].

Breeding[3]

(n=25)	Jan	Feb	Mar	Apr
	2	5	5	7
	May	Jun	Aug	
	3	2	1	

Clutch: No data. Usually 1-2 juveniles together, one record of 3[2].

Taxonomy No races recognized.

References [1]Berry (1984); [2]Dowsett (in press a); [3]Pitman (1965b).

Marabou Stork *Leptoptilos crumeniferus*   B35 **RB**

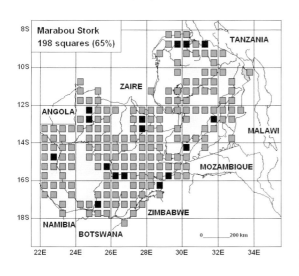

Distribution *Afrotropical* (*Mauritania to South Africa*). Occurs almost throughout, especially in areas where it can benefit from fish or the carcasses of dead animals. Locally very numerous in big-game and floodplain areas such as the Liuwa Plain, Kafue Flats, Zambezi and Luangwa Valleys (nest sites shown as black squares). *Alt.* 330-1800 m.

Ecology In a variety of open habitats, especially feeding on burnt ground, by lagoons, rivers and floodplains, or at abattoirs. Scarce in well-wooded areas such as the Copperbelt and NW Zambia. Most nests are in trees in forest or dry savanna[3], but it does nest on cliffs, e.g. at Kalambo Falls[4] and a precipice 30 m high on the Kalaye escarpment, overlooking L. Chishi[2]. This last had 30 nests in 1952. Largest colony of 164 nests, Maala, Jul 1974[3].

Status Wanders a great deal, probably opportunistically, judging by the occurrence of flocks of up to 50 at any time of the year in the Lusaka area, though most often in the rains[1]. The only recovery of a ringed bird showed movement of only 40 km (after 3 years) (Appendix 1).

Breeding

(n=157)	Apr	May	Jun	Jul	Aug	Sep
	1	18	53	58	23	4

Clutch: C/1 (4); C/2 (14); C/3 (21); C/4 (3).

Taxonomy No races recognized.

References [1]Aspinwall (1975b); [2]Benson & Pitman (1956-57); [3]Dowsett (in press a); [4]Jones (1946).

Balaenicipitidae

Shoebill *Balaeniceps rex*   B27 **RB**

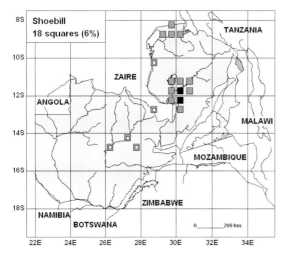

Distribution *Afrotropical (breeding in scattered localities from S. Sudan to N. Zambia).* Although known to breed only in Bangweulu[1,4,8], it may do so (or have done so in the past) in Mweru Wantipa[5], where it is known from several places, from L. Kako in the east, north to Choma and west to near Musombwe[3]. Present in any numbers only in Bangweulu; it is widely distributed there, with breeding known in the southern part, between Ncheta Is. and south of Chikuni (black squares). The species is also known from Kasanka N.P.[3,5,6]. Wanderers (open squares) have occurred to Kampemba on the Luapula[3], Ndola (at least twice)[3,7], the Lufupa/Kafue River confluence (two together) and Lukanga Swamp (twice, the most southerly records of the species)[3,10]. *Alt.* 950-1300 m.

Ecology Papyrus swamps, feeding in clearings of shorter, more open vegetation. Feeds on fish (especially barbel) and frogs.

Status Resident, with some wandering (see above). Usually singly or in pairs.

Conservation Classed as "Vulnerable"[2]. There is evidence of nests destroyed and birds being killed in Bangweulu by fishermen, and there are reports of birds being captured for foreign zoos (and even shot by foreigners!)[8]. The Zambian population is one of the most important, and needs to be monitored regularly. An aerial survey in 2006 (transects of 488 km) suggests some 250-500 birds in Bangweulu[9]. Its status in Mweru Wantipa is not clear.

Breeding   Apr   May   Jul
(n=11)   1   9   1

Clutch: C/1 (2); C/2 (5) & N/2 (1). A nest mid-Jul contained two young, but the smaller was dead by the end of the month, and probably only one young usually survives.

Taxonomy No races recognized.

References [1]Benson (1961d); [2]BirdLife International (2004a); [3]Burton & Benson (1961); [4]Buxton *et al.* (1978); [5]Dowsett (in press a); [6]Farmer (1992); [7]Madge (1971c); [8]Renson (1998); [9]Roxburgh *et al.* (2006); [10]van Lavieren (1973).

Threskiornithidae

Sacred Ibis *Threskiornis aethiopicus*   B37 **AMW/RB**

Distribution *Old World Tropics (in Africa breeds Mauritania to South Africa).* Common locally in most wetlands, but absent or very scarce in well-wooded areas, whether at low levels (lower Luangwa) or plateau (Mwinilunga Dist.). There are few records in Katanga (Zaire), and none from Kasaji[5]. Absent from much of the Luapula drainage, where the narrow, rocky river offers little suitable habitat. Breeding sites shown as black squares. *Alt.* 330-1800 m (Uningi Pans).

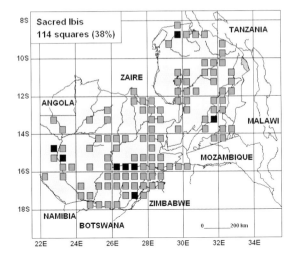

Ecology By almost any water, whether large rivers with sand beaches, extensive flood-plains or small farm dams. Breeds colonially (up to 100 nests in Lochinvar), often with herons and storks.

Status Present in all months, but rather more frequently observed Aug-Jan. In addition to breeding birds, a large number of birds bred in southern Africa spend the off-season here, especially in the west. Of 57 recoveries of nestlings ringed in South Africa (between late Sep and early Mar), all but four have been found in Zambia between late Mar and late Oct[1,2]. The oldest of these was more than 9 years old (Appendix 1). Overall, numbers are significantly higher Aug-Jan[3]. Usually in groups of up to 50, but at times in hundreds (max. 1-2000 at Lochinvar in Jan)[3].

Breeding[4]   Mar   May   Jun   Jul   Aug   Sep

(n=17)   3   1   3   3   4   3   *Clutch*: C/1 (3); C/2 (4); C/3 (5).

Taxonomy *T. a. aethiopicus*.

References [1]Dowsett (1969c); [2]Dowsett & Leonard (2001); [3]Dowsett & Leonard (in press a); [4]Feely (1964); [5]Schouteden (1971).

Glossy Ibis *Plegadis falcinellus*   B39 **RB/AM**

Distribution *Cosmopolitan (in the Afrotropics breeds locally in West Africa, and Kenya to South Africa).* Breeding is known from three areas on the Kafue Flats and Zambezi Floodplain (black squares), but it can turn up almost anywhere, and it is at times numerous in the larger wetlands. *Alt.* 330-1800 m (Uningi Pans).

Ecology Extensive swamps and floodplains, rarely on small dams. Breeds colonially.

Status Usually scarce, but thousands have been observed at Blue Lagoon in Oct and Dec, while at both Lochinvar and the Liuwa Plain flocks of hundreds have been noted between Feb and Apr[1]. These are suggestive of long-distance movements, and there is a recovery of a nestling ringed in South Africa in Nov, found in W. Zambia in Aug (Appendix 1).

Breeding   Jun   Jul

(n=6)   2   4   *Clutch*: C/3 (5); C/4 (1). *Moult*: a first-year bird started late Apr[1].

Taxonomy *P. f. falcinellus*.

References [1]Dowsett (in press a).

Hadada Ibis *Bostrychia hagedash* B38 **RB**

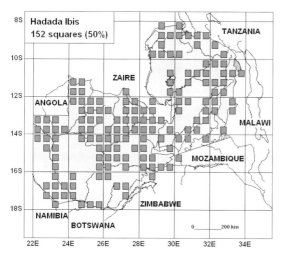

Distribution *Afrotropical* (*Mauritania to South Africa*). Recorded in small numbers almost throughout the country; this non-colonial species nests only in well-wooded wetlands, and so it is especially scarce in places like the Kafue Flats[1]. *Alt.* 370-1800 m, wandering even to 2150 m (Nyika Plateau)[2].

Ecology Rivers and lagoons with well developed riparian forest, rarely wandering onto open floodplains.

Status Resident, usually in pairs or presumed family groups, in parties of up to 25 at times[1].

Breeding (n=16)	Jul	Aug	Sep	Oct
	1	1	1	1
	Nov	Dec	Jan	Mar
	5	3	2	2

Clutch: C/2 (5); C/3 (2).

Taxonomy *B. h. brevirostris*.
References [1]Dowsett (in press a); [2]Dowsett-Lemaire (2006a).

African Spoonbill *Platalea alba* B40 **RB**

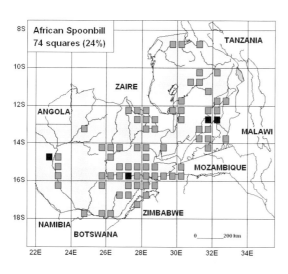

Distribution *Afrotropical* (*Mauritania to South Africa*). Breeding sites are few (black squares), but this species occurs in most major wetlands (except the Luapula Valley), though in the Zambezi drainage it is not known north of the West Lunga N.P. Only at all common on Liuwa Plain (groups of up to 35), the Kafue Flats (100+) and Luangwa Valley (up to 23 together)[2]. Only small colonies are known, up to 30 nests in the Liuwa area[1], except for one of 100 nests at Lochinvar[2]. *Alt.* 330-1660 m.

Ecology Large lagoons or pans, less often on dams (and then never numerous). Feeds on small organisms, occasionally quite large fish.

Status Perhaps resident in breeding areas, elsewhere wandering in any month in small groups (but with concentrations of 100 or more on the Kafue Flats, and 700 estimated in all at Lochinvar; Jan 1994)[2,3]. There is a recovery in Sep in W. Zambia of a young bird ringed in South Africa the previous Oct (Appendix 1).

Conservation Most of the colonies known are in nominally protected areas.

Breeding (n=6)	Apr	May	Jun	Jul
	2	1	1	2

Clutch: C/2 (1); C/3 (1); C/4 (1).

Taxonomy No races recognized.
References [1]Benson & Irwin (1967b); [2]Dowsett (in press a); [3]Taylor & Rose (1994).

Phoenicopteridae

Greater Flamingo *Phoenicopterus roseus*   B41 **AM**

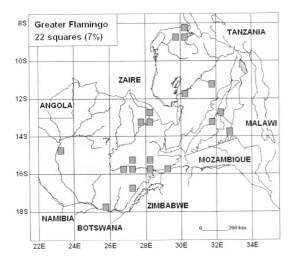

Distribution *Old World; in the Afrotropics, breeds Mauritania, Senegal and Kenya to South Africa.* Records are mostly in the eastern half of the country, west to the Copperbelt, Blue Lagoon and Lochinvar[1], and the Zambezi near Livingstone, except for a report from Tiger camp north of Mongu. The few flamingo records from the well-watched Luangwa Valley are in the majority this species, that from Luangwa town (Feira) uncertain (as is that from the Busanga)[3] ("?" on map). *Alt.* 370-1400 m.

Ecology Floodplains and larger pans, only rarely on small dams. Feeds on small invertebrates.

Status Occurs most years as a non-breeding visitor, records being fairly evenly distributed throughout the year. It is most frequently found at Lochinvar, with parties often in double figures, max. 54 mid-Sep (1980)[3].

Breeding No records (it was present in the Mweru Wantipa colony of *Phoeniconaias minor* in 1955, but apparently there was no attempt to nest)[2].

Taxonomy *P. roseus.* Formerly treated as a race of the New World *P. ruber*[4].

References [1]Benson *et al.* (1970); [2]Brown (1957); [3]Dowsett & Leonard (in press a); [4]Knox *et al.* (2002).

Lesser Flamingo *Phoeniconaias minor*   B42 **AM(B)**

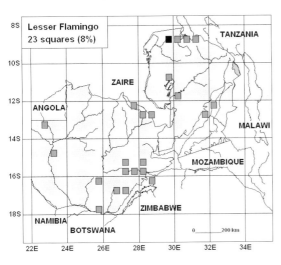

Distribution *Afrotropical (most breeding Kenya to South Africa) and Oriental (to India).* Apart from a massive, but failed, attempt to nest in Mweru Wantipa (the "lake of mud") in 1955 (black square)[3], this species has occurred only as a non-breeding visitor to most parts of the country. *Alt.* mainly 950-1700 m.

Ecology As for *Phoenicopterus roseus*, non-breeding birds occur on floodplains or large pans, much less often on dams or at sewage ponds. To breed, however, particular conditions of water salinity and level would be needed for the proliferation of their food (blue-green algae), and it seems unlikely that the species can nest in Zambia under current conditions.

Status Even allowing for some records that could not be attributed with certainty to either species, this flamingo appears to be the less frequent of the two, and not of annual occurrence (though at times the more numerous). Records are scattered throughout the year, and groups rarely exceed 20 away from N. Zambia (max. 60 at Lochinvar in Sep 1964)[4]. Larger numbers are occasionally reported from the general area of Mweru Wantipa, exceptional being 1500 at L. Tondwa in Nov 1976 and Jan 1977[5].

Conservation Classed as "Near-threatened"[1]. The year the species nested in Mweru Wantipa (1953-54) rainfall was very low; at times the marsh dried up completely, at others it was a large lake[2,3], thus there was much variation in salinity[6]. Attempts have been made to stabilise water levels there, in part to prevent breeding by locusts in drought years; a dam has been built, which means that the marsh is now a permanent lake. Whereas breeding attempts could only be irregular in the past, they are now likely to be impossible.

Breeding   Jan   Feb
(n=640)   250   390   *Clutch*: all nests were reported to contain C/1.

Taxonomy No races recognized.

References [1]BirdLife International (2000, 2004a); [2]Brelsford (1955); [3]Brown (1957); [4]Dowsett (1966b); [5]Dowsett & Leonard (in press a); [6]Macrae (1956).

Anatidae

Fulvous Tree (Whistling) Duck *Dendrocygna bicolor*   **B43 AMB**

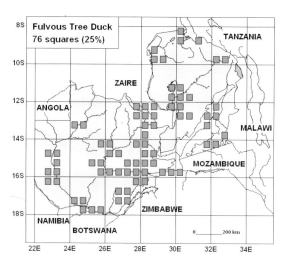

Fulvous Tree Duck
76 squares (25%)

Distribution *Pantropical* (*in the Afrotropics, breeds Mauritania to South Africa*). Occurs through much of the country, and especially numerous on the Kafue Flats, but unknown in the north-west beyond the Copperbelt and the Lusongwa River[5]. *Alt.* 330-1660 m.

Ecology In perennial and seasonal swamps. On the Kafue Flats it occupies the meander belt near the river during the rains, moving onto lagoons as water levels fall. It feeds principally on seeds (e.g. *Nymphoides indica*), obtained mainly by diving rather than dabbling[2].

Status On the Kafue Flats it was an abundant dry season visitor in some years. At Lochinvar usually most numerous Jun-Oct, when annually in the 1970s between 15,000 and 30,000[2,3]; very scarce or absent at low flood. An overall count of more than 58,000 was claimed for Lochinvar in Jan 1994[4], which suggests that the changes in timing of flooding (result of the hydro-electric dams on the Kafue) may have affected waterfowl chronology. Numbers fluctuate greatly over a few days, apparently depending on the availability of fruits of *Echinochloa stagnina* and seeds of *Nymphaea capensis* and *Nymphoides*[2]. At Chisenga Is. 4000 were seen early Oct 1954[1]. One ringed at Lochinvar in Dec was recovered in Sudan in Jul (Appendix 1).

Breeding   Feb   Mar   May   Jul
(n=14)   6   2   3   3   *Clutch*: C/8 (2).

Moult: hundreds, sometimes thousands, were flightless at Lochinvar, mid-Apr to mid-Jul (especially Jun)[2,3].

Taxonomy No races recognized.
References [1]Benson (1963); [2]Douthwaite (1977); [3]Dowsett & Leonard (in press a); [4]Taylor & Rose (1994); [5]White (1945-46).

White-faced Tree (Whistling) Duck *Dendrocygna viduata*   B44 **RB**

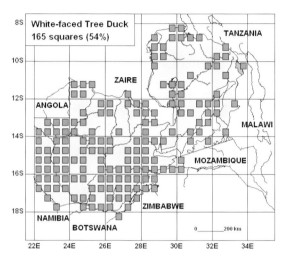

Distribution *Afrotropical (Mauritania to South Africa) and Neotropical.* Almost throughout and locally abundant, but scarce in the better wooded regions, such as most of the Northern Province plateau. *Alt.* 330-1800 m (Uningi Pans).

Ecology In a wide variety of wetlands, including small dams. On the Kafue Flats much less on lagoons than *D. bicolor*, making more use of the meander belt and the floodplain itself in most months. During the rains, when grasses are tall, it moves to areas trampled flat by Lechwe or Hippopotamus. It feeds principally on seeds, obtained mainly by upending or dabbling, rather than by diving[1].

Status On the Kafue Flats numbers increase most years during the dry season, to peak in Sep (up to 24,000 counted in 1971), although it has also been noted as abundant in Mar. In the Luangwa Valley, on the other hand, it is an abundant breeding visitor during the rains (Nov-May), with few in the dry season, and on the Liuwa Plain too it is abundant during the rains. Elsewhere, mostly resident, some dispersing at times to small plateau wetlands[2]. There are 5 ringing recoveries to or from Zimbabwe (in the latter country in Oct, Dec, Feb and Mar, and in Zambia May, Jun, Sep and Dec) (Appendix 1).

Breeding   Dec   Jan   Feb   Mar   Apr   May   Jun
(n=77)   6   27   28   11   2   2   1
Clutch: C/2 (1); C/4 (1); C/6 (1); C/8 (1); C/11 (3); C/12 (1).
Moult: several hundreds moult on the Kafue Flats in some years, May to Jul[1].
Taxonomy No races recognized.
References [1]Douthwaite (1977); [2]Dowsett (in press a).

White-backed Duck *Thalassornis leuconotus*   B58 **RB**

Distribution *Afrotropical (most breeding Kenya to South Africa).* Widespread on vegetated lagoons and locally numerous, but sparse on the Eastern Province plateau, in the Luapula drainage and generally at low altitude. In the far north, common a times in the Uningi pans[5] and L. Tondwa area[4], as on the Kafue Flats. There are a few records from the Luangwa Valley (especially at Frank's Lakes), but on Eastern Province plateau it is reported only from Katete and Lundazi[3]. In the Middle Zambezi Valley known only from Zibamenda pan, Gwembe[1]. *Alt.* 500-1800 m (Uningi Pans), but rare below 950 m.
Ecology A bird of lagoons, pans and small ponds and dams with surface vegetation, rather than open rivers or floodplains. It feeds principally on seeds, obtained by diving.
Status Subject to at least local movements. On the Kafue Flats up to 500 were counted in some years, May-Jun. Otherwise, groups of between 20 and 50 birds have been reported from several sites, from

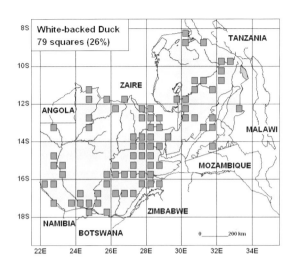

White-backed Duck
79 squares (26%)

Liuwa Plain and L. Silita, to Lusaka and Chembe on the Copperbelt, and Uningi Pans[3]. A bird ringed at Lochinvar in Jul was recovered 180 km NE in the Lukanga Swamp in May (Appendix 1).

Breeding Dec Jan Feb Mar Apr
(n=52) 2 6 7 2 9
  May Jun Jul Aug
  6 13 4 3

Clutch: C/1 (1); C/2 (1); C/6 (1); C/7 (1) & N/7 (4).

Moult: a few moult on the Kafue Flats Jun-Jul, but most are thought to do so elsewhere[2].

Taxonomy *T. l. leuconotus*.

References [1]Berry (1972); [2]Douthwaite (1977); [3]Dowsett (in press a); [4]Heery (1974); [5]Madge (1971a).

Egyptian Goose *Alopochen aegyptiaca* B45 **RB**

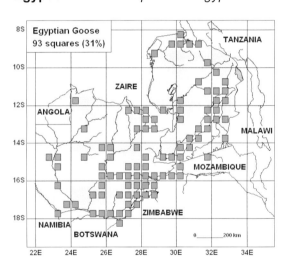

Egyptian Goose
93 squares (31%)

Distribution *Afrotropical* (*Mauritania to South Africa; formerly S. Palaearctic*). Mostly a bird of the large sandy rivers, the Luangwa and the Middle Zambezi, but numbers have increased noticeably since the 1970s on the Kafue Flats. Has bred throughout the range shown, except that it appears (on present evidence) to be merely a non-breeding wanderer to the Upper Zambezi (even to the Nyidi Plain in Mwinilunga[2]), more regularly to the Copperbelt, but only rarely on the Eastern Province plateau (at Chipata and, once, a dambo in Petauke Dist.)[4]. *Alt.* 330-1660 m, but common only below 1000 m.

Ecology Most commonly on the larger sandy rivers and associated lagoons. Nests have been found in the nests of *Scopus umbretta* and on a rocky ledge on the top of Katema Is.[1]. The increasingly large population on the Kafue Flats grazes on short grasslands above the floodline, on such vegetable matter as the leaves of *Panicum repens* and the ripening seeds of *Panicum subalbidum*[3]. In farming areas they have been seen to feed on germinating wheat, and so may become a pest locally[4].

Status On the Kafue Flats present all months (up to 30), but since the late 1960s there has been an annual influx of some 700-850 between Jan and Sep[3], with even 3500 estimated in the 1990s and with maxima in Apr and May[4]. Resident in the Luangwa and Middle Zambezi Valleys.

Breeding Jan Feb Mar Apr May Jun Jul Aug Sep Oct Nov Dec
(n=93) 1 3 7 5 7 16 13 22 8 8 2 1

Clutch: C/5 (1); C/6 (1); C/8 (2); C/9 (1); C/11 (1); C/14 (1).

Moult: flightless birds in moult occur annually at Lochinvar Feb to mid-May[3].

Taxonomy No races recognized.
References [1]Benson & Pitman (1956-57); [2]Bowen (1983i); [3]Douthwaite (1978); [4]Dowsett (in press a).

Spur-winged Goose *Plectropterus gambensis*   B46 **RB**

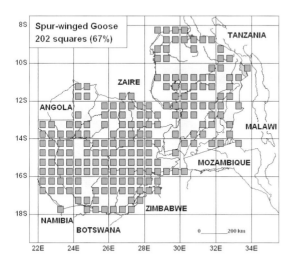

Distribution *Afrotropical* (*Mauritania to South Africa*). Probably throughout the country, locally abundant on large floodplains. *Alt.* 330-1700 m.

Ecology Feeds in shallowly flooded or damp grassland, and at drying pools, by grazing and foraging, on grass leaves during the rains, and at other times on a variety of grass seeds (*Panicum coloratum, Echinochloa colonum* etc.), rhizomes of the sedge *Cyperus usitatus*, winged termites and much else[1]. In farming areas they have been reported feeding on sprouting maize[2].

Status At Lochinvar a few thousand immigrants during the rainy season, up to Mar, augment the resident population (estimated to be 200-300). Exceptionally, in the dry season of 1973 there were some 60,000 to 90,000 in the central Kafue Flats[1]. The species is also extremely abundant on Liuwa Plain Nov-Feb[2], but numbers elsewhere in the country appear to be much smaller.

Breeding	Sep	Oct	Nov	Dec	Jan	Feb	Mar	Apr	May
(n=71)	1	2	4	5	24	18	11	2	4

Clutch: C/6 (1); C/8 (1); C/9 (1).
Moult: on the Kafue Flats several thousands moult (and are flightless) May-Jul[1], one as late as Nov[2].
Taxonomy No races (*P. g. niger* is doubtfully recognizable).
References [1]Douthwaite (1978); [2]Dowsett (in press a).

Knob-billed Duck *Sarkidiornis melanotos*   B47 **AMB**

Distribution *Pantropical* (*in Africa, Mauritania to South Africa*). Throughout, and locally abundant. *Alt.* 330-1800 m.

Ecology The shallow water of lakes and pools. On the Kafue Flats males feed mainly in lagoons or flooded grassland, whereas the smaller females tend to do so on the shoreline or in drier grassland away from the shoreline. In wet periods most food taken was the seeds of the grass *Brachiaria xantholeuca*, but in drier spells they fed near the floodline, mainly on the seeds of *Echinochloa colonum*[1].

Status Present all months, but greatest numbers by far are recorded overall Nov-Apr[2]. On the Kafue Flats the species is most abundant in the latter part of the rains and early dry season (Jan-Jul), with marked passage Apr-Jul. Total numbers at Lochinvar are over 4000 in some years, with more than 20,000 estimated there in Jan 1994[3]. In the Luangwa Valley this bird is abundant during the rains, when it breeds, much less common Jun-Oct. Outside its favoured areas, peak numbers are probably at time of passage, e.g. 500 near Choma in Nov and 200 at Mufulira Apr[2]. As with most waterfowl, there is some dispersal to smaller bodies of water (e.g. dams)[2]. Three birds ringed in Zimbabwe (Nov, Mar) have been recovered in Zambia (Nov, Jan, Apr) (Appendix 1), and others from there have reached Zaire,

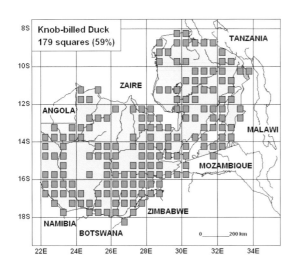

Chad and Sudan[4].

Breeding

	Nov	Jan	Feb	Mar	Apr
(n=53)		1	24	22	5	1

Clutch: C/4 (1). Also N/14 (two broods?). *Moult*: in some years numbers moult on the Kafue Flats Mar-Jul, mostly May (mainly males)[1].

Taxonomy *S. m. melanotos*.

References [1]Douthwaite (1978); [2]Dowsett & Leonard (in press a); [3]Taylor & Rose (1994); [4]Underhill *et al.* (1999).

Pygmy Goose *Nettapus auritus*   B48 **RB**

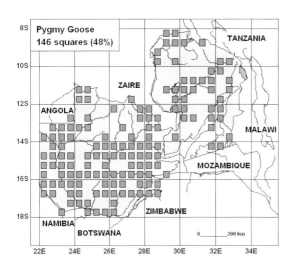

Distribution *Afrotropical* (*Mauritania to South Africa*). On vegetated lagoons almost throughout; absent from the lower Luangwa and Middle Zambezi Valleys, between Mfuwe and the Chiawa area (where suitable lagoons are lacking)[3]. *Alt.* 370-1800 m (Uningi Pans), but sparse below 650 m.

Ecology Lagoons with emergent vegetation, where they feed on the surface by grazing or filtering, principally the seeds of the water-lily *Nymphaea capensis*[2]. Nests may be on the ground, or in a hole in a tree[4] (presumably to avoid flooding).

Status Resident, with seasonal concentrations. At Lochinvar, numbers increase Mar-May, and are thought to be immatures or non-breeding adult moult migrants. Transects on the Kafue Flats in Apr-May 1972 suggested a population of 10,000 to 15,000[2]. At low altitude most records occur when water levels are high (e.g. Gwembe[1], Luangwa Valley Mar-Jun), and at Kabwe numbers peak in Jun[3]. A bird ringed at Lochinvar in May was recovered 180 km NE in the Lukanga Swamp in early Mar (Appendix 1).

Breeding

	Sep	Nov	Dec	Jan	Feb	Mar	Apr
(n=47)	2	2	5	13	14	10	1

Clutch: C/2 (1); C/6 (1); C/8 (1).

Taxonomy No races recognized.

References [1]Benson (1963); [2]Douthwaite (1978); [3]Dowsett (in press a); [4]Traylor & Hart (1965).

[Mallard *Anas platyrhynchos*
An adult male photographed in the Luangwa Valley 28 Oct 1999 was almost certainly an escape from captivity; this Holarctic species is not known to migrate south of the Equator, but is often present in waterfowl collections (e.g. at State House, Lusaka, in the past)[1]. **References** [1]Leonard (2001a).]

African Black Duck *Anas sparsa*   B49 **RB**

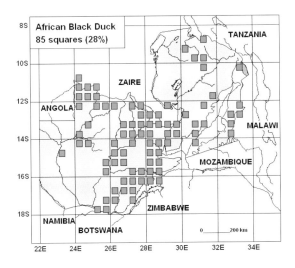

Distribution *Afrotropical* (*most breeding Ethiopia to South Africa*). On well-wooded rivers and dams over much of N. and central Zambia, but curiously unrecorded from most of the Luapula Valley. Absent from the floor of the lower Luangwa and Middle Zambezi Valleys, until Kariba is reached (where rare). In the Upper Zambezi ranges south to Tiger camp, but immediately above Victoria Falls is known only as far as the Kazungula area[1]. *Alt.* 950-1900 m (Makutu), once 580 m (Kariba)[1]. **Ecology** Rocky rivers and secluded, wooded dams as a rule, although does occasionally turn up at sewage ponds. **Status** Resident in pairs or small family groups.

Breeding	Jan	Feb	Apr	May	Jun	Jul	Aug	
(n=26)	1	1	1	3	5	13	2	*Clutch*: C/5 (1).

Taxonomy *A. s. sparsa.*
References [1]Dowsett (in press a).

Yellow-billed Duck *Anas undulata*   B51 **RB**

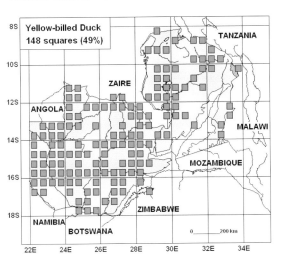

Distribution *Afrotropical* (*mainly Ethiopia to South Africa*). Common on most of the Zambian plateaux wetlands, but absent from the floor of the Luangwa Valley, and in the Middle Zambezi reported only (once) from Siavonga[5]. Above the Victoria Falls[4] to Mwandi[1] scarce, but commoner on the floodplains of the west, from Lupuka and Kaungo northwards[5]. *Alt.* 950-1800 m (Uningi Pans), once down to 550 m (Siavonga). **Ecology** Pools in floodplains and dams. On the Kafue Flats almost exclusively in the meander belt near the river in the dry season, moving onto part of the peripheral floodplain as waters rise. It appears to feed principally on seeds, obtained mainly by dabbling[3].

Status Subject to local movements. On the Kafue Flats very locally distributed in all months, and reported in numbers only Feb-Apr each year (up to 400 counted)[5]. In Bangweulu huge numbers were reported in Aug-Nov in particular[2], with over 600 estimated in Jul 1993[6]. Smaller numbers in the north-west (e.g. up to 50 at L. Ndungu in Nov)[5]. Large numbers have been ringed in South Africa, so the single recovery of one ringed in Oct in South Africa, found in Aug in Zambia (Appendix 1), suggests there may not be a significant influx from the south.

Breeding	Jan	Feb	Mar	Apr	May	Jun	Sep	Oct	Nov
(n=24)	3	2	1	6	2	3	2	2	3

Clutch: C/1 (1); C/7 (1). Also N/9.
Moult: a few on the Kafue Flats in Jul[3].
Taxonomy *A. u. undulata*.
References [1]Benson *et al.* (1971a); [2]Brelsford (1946); [3]Douthwaite (1977); [4]Dowsett (1973f); [5]Dowsett (in press a); [6]Taylor & Rose (1994).

Cape Teal *Anas capensis*   B50 **AM/R?(B)**

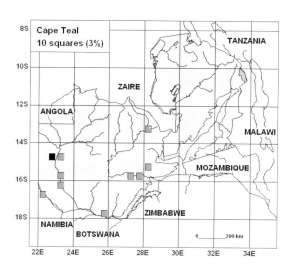

Cape Teal
10 squares (3%)

Distribution *Afrotropical, but with a discontinuous distribution* (*largely absent from south-central Africa, between SW Tanzania and SW Zambia*). The sole breeding evidence is from the Liuwa Plain[1] (black square), and there are a few other records in the west, south to Lupuka, but no evidence that it is likely to be resident there. Elsewhere wanderers have occurred as far as Luanshya[3], Lusaka and Livingstone, less rarely on the Kafue Flats[2]. *Alt.* 1000-1260 m.
Ecology In W. Zambia has occurred on pans, but wanderers may turn up on any dam or floodplain.
Status The great majority of records fall between 3 Apr[2] and 13 Nov[1]. Almost annual in the 1970s away from the Liuwa, usually in small groups (up to 6), but very few records anywhere since 1981[2]. It is possible these are wanderers from southern Africa, like the much rarer *Anas smithii*; one such bird stayed 3 months at Lusaka[2]. On the Liuwa a group of as many as 13 was present in Jul 1964[1].

Breeding	Jun
(n=2)	2

Clutch: no data.
Taxonomy No races recognized.
References [1]Benson & Pitman (1966); [2]Dowsett & Leonard (in press a); [3]Taylor (1982a).

Pintail *Anas acuta*   B52 **PW**

Distribution *Holarctic* (*in the Afrotropics, wintering usually Senegal to Tanzania*). A rare visitor, almost exclusively from the Copperbelt to Lochinvar[6], with one reported at Chipata[3]. *Alt.* 1000-1330 m.
Ecology Floodplains and dams.

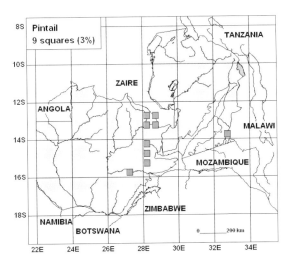

Status Palaearctic migrant, not of annual occurrence, and there have been very few reports since the mid-1980s. Birds have been recorded between 12 Nov and 5 Mar only, mostly Dec-Feb[3]. Usually up to 3 birds together, but in 1979-80 numbers built up to 37 at Luanshya in Jan[1], it was exceptionally widespread that season in Zambia and East Africa, and the first report from Malawi was in Mar 1980[4]. It has been suggested this species occurs as far south as Zambia only in years of drought in its normal wintering areas further north[2,5]. Males in moult to breeding dress have been recorded during Dec.

Taxonomy *A. a. acuta.*

References [1]Casalis de Pury & Taylor (1980); [2]Clark (1977); [3]Dowsett (in press b); [4]Dowsett-Lemaire & Dowsett (2006); [5]Irwin (1974); [6]Penry (1975a).

Red-billed Teal *Anas erythrorhyncha*   B53 **AMW/RB**

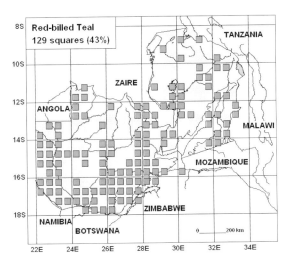

Distribution *Afrotropical (Ethiopia to South Africa)*. Practically throughout and locally common (even on small dams), although there are few records from the Luangwa and Middle Zambezi Valleys. *Alt.* 330-1800 m (Uningi Pans), but scarce below 900 m.

Ecology Mainly lakes and ponds. On the Kafue Flats it occupies a variety of habitats, particularly lagoons during the dry season, and the floodplain once water levels rise. It feeds principally on seeds, but other vegetable matter is important too, obtained by dabbling[1].

Status Present throughout the year, but on the Kafue Flats greatest numbers occur late Apr to Sep (peak 29,000 at Lochinvar in Aug 1971)[1], declining as water levels drop. On artificial waters, as many as 2000 at Lusaka sewage ponds in mid-Nov 1981[4]. The origin of some of these birds is shown by 26 foreign recoveries of Zambian-ringed birds, and the recovery here of 14 ringed to the south (Appendix 1). Most of these were in southern Africa Sep-Apr[2], in Zambia Mar-Nov[4]. The oldest bird recovered was at least 24 years old[3].

Breeding	Dec	Jan	Feb	Mar	Apr	May	Jun
(n=50)	2	10	23	7	2	3	3

Clutch: C/4 (1); C/5 (1); C/6 (1); C/8 (1). *Moult*: early Apr to early Oct (especially May-Jun) as many as 10,000 to 20,000 may be temporarily flightless at Lochinvar[1].

Taxonomy No races recognized.

References [1]Douthwaite (1977); [2]Dowsett (1966d); [3]Dowsett & Leonard (2001); [4]Dowsett & Leonard (in press a).

Hottentot Teal *Anas hottentota*   B54 **RB/AMW**

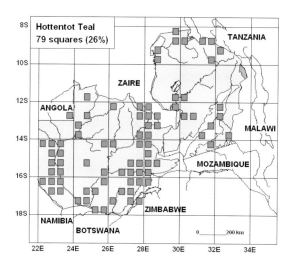

Distribution *Afrotropical (S. Niger and Nigeria to South Africa).* Less widespread than the larger *A. erythrorhyncha*, but locally common, except irregular at lower levels. *Alt.* 500-1700 m, but rare below 900 m.

Ecology On lakes and pools. On the Kafue Flats, in contrast to *A. erythrorhyncha,* in the dry season it dabbles in the meander belt, and at all seasons seeks shallow water. It feeds principally on invertebrates, although seeds are also important, obtained by dabbling[1].

Status[2] Present in all months, with no clear pattern to the seasonality of distribution, except that on the Kafue Flats peak numbers each year are reported in the rains, Dec-Mar (up to 500 counted at Lochinvar)[1]. Two birds ringed at Lochinvar in Oct were recovered in Botswana (Jan and Mar) (Appendix 1). The oldest local recovery is of a bird 7 years old[4].

Breeding   Dec   Jan   Feb   Mar   Apr   May   Jun   Aug
(n=14)   1   2   2   2   2   1   3   1   *Clutch*: no data.

Moult: of 62 birds examined on the Kafue Flats (mostly Feb-May), most were in very fresh plumage[3]; it has been suggested moult may take place Aug-Sep[1].

Taxonomy No races recognized.

References [1]Douthwaite (1977); [2]Dowsett (1966c); [3]Dowsett (in press a); [4]Dowsett & Leonard (2001).

Garganey *Anas querquedula*   B55 **PW**

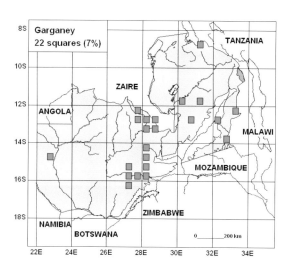

Distribution *Palaearctic (in the Afrotropics, winters usually Senegal to Zambezian region).* Most frequent from the Copperbelt to Monze[4]. But known too from Mbala[1] southwards, on the Eastern Province plateau at Lundazi[3] and Chipata, and once in the Luangwa Valley at Chibembe. Has been reported once in the west, on Liuwa Plain[2]. *Alt.* 550-1660 m, but few records below 1000 m.

Ecology Most common on the larger flood-plains, although it does also occur on sewage ponds and dams (regularly so at Luanshya and Lusaka).

Status A Palaearctic winter visitor, annual to the end of the 1980s. Extreme dates are 9 Oct and 21 Apr [unconfirmed was one in female dress reported at Luanshya 4 Sep 1987], but first arrivals are usually in the second half of Nov, and often there are none remaining after early Mar[2]. Although numbers fluctuate during any season, there is no evidence of onward passage southwards.

Usually in groups of 1-5, but up to 27 at sewage ponds, and even more on the Kafue Flats. In 1974 there were unprecedented numbers at Lochinvar, with at least 100, perhaps as many as 500, in Feb and Mar. But there were very few reports in the 1990s[2] (when observer coverage of the Copperbelt decreased).
Taxonomy No races recognized.
References [1]Benson *et al.* (1970); [2]Dowsett (in press b); [3]Grimwood (1957); [4]White (1943e).

Northern Shoveler *Anas clypeata*   B56 **PW**

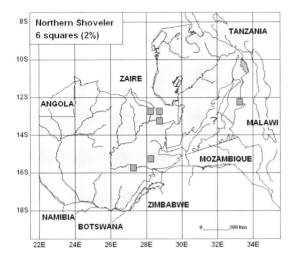

Distribution *Holarctic (in the Afrotropics, winters mainly Senegal to Tanzania).* There are several records (including a specimen) from the Copperbelt to Lochinvar. The species has also occurred once at Lundazi[3]. A sight record claimed from Mfuwe in the Luangwa Valley[1] ("?" on map) cannot be attributed with certainty to this species or to *A. smithii* (and the date, 19 Apr, would be the latest for *A. clypeata* by several weeks)[2]. *Alt.* 1000-1300 m.
Ecology Can occur on any dam or floodplain.
Status Rare Palaearctic migrant, with a dozen records (but none since 1981), usually of singles, though once up to 4 (at Kitwe, Dec 1973)[4]. Extreme dates 12 Nov and 27 Feb[2].
Taxonomy No races recognized.
References [1]Berry (1981a); [2]Dowsett (in press b); [3]Grimwood (1957); [4]Penry (1975a).

Cape Shoveler *Anas smithii*   B p.56 **AM**

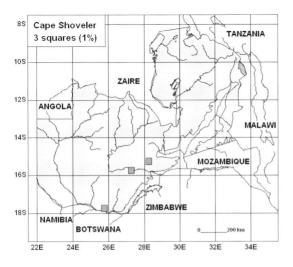

Distribution *Afrotropical (breeds southern Africa only).* Since the first in 1969, there have been six acceptable records (including photographs), from three localities: Livingstone (once)[2], Lochinvar (three times)[1] and Lusaka (twice)[3]. *Alt.* 900-1260 m.
Ecology Has occurred on dams, floodplain and the Zambezi River.
Status A rare visitor from southern Africa, usually singly, but once 3 birds together. Extreme dates are 23 Feb to 20 Apr and 29 Aug to 18 Nov (the period during which one bird stayed at Lusaka)[2].
Breeding No records.
Taxonomy No races recognized. In the past, considered a race of *A. clypeata*.
References [1]Benson *et al.* (1970); [2]Dowsett & Leonard (in press a); [3]Dowsett *et al.* (1999a).

Southern Pochard *Netta erythrophthalma* B57**AMB**

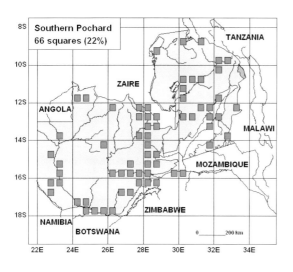

Southern Pochard
66 squares (22%)

Distribution *Afrotropical (breeds Kenya to South Africa) and Neotropical.* Can occur on any open water, but scarce at low altitude in the Luangwa Valley[3], and not known from the Middle Zambezi further upriver than Chirundu[4]. *Alt.* 330-1800 m (Uningi Pans).

Ecology Deep water (even sewage ponds). On the Kafue Flats this diving duck inhabits particularly the lagoons as water levels recede in the dry season. It feeds principally on seeds, although other vegetable matter is taken, obtained mainly by diving, but also by upend-ing[2].

Status Since the construction of the dams on the Kafue River, the timing of maximum numbers on the Kafue Flats has changed. Previously there was an annual influx mid-May, building up to some 3000 by Sep, with numbers declining thereafter. Maximum numbers were 6550 in Jun 1973. Since then, maximum counts at Lochinvar have been some 2000 (Oct 1997) and 3000 (Jan 1998)[3]. Six birds ringed in South Africa have been recovered in Zambia in the months of Apr, Jun-Aug and Oct, suggesting an origin for the dry season influx (Appendix 1). Birds ringed in South Africa have also reached East Africa. Elsewhere, while there are records throughout the year, the species is reported most often, and significantly most abundant overall, Oct-Apr. Large numbers have included 1000 at Chisenga Is. early Oct 1954[1], and on artificial waters hundreds or thousands at Lusaka Nov, with 500+ there late Mar[3].

Breeding	Dec	Jan	Feb	Mar	Apr	May	Jun	Jul	Aug
(n=18)	1	1	3	4	3	1	2	2	1

Clutch: C/4 (1); C/6 (1).

Moult: up to 300 flightless birds have been noted at Lochinvar May-Jul[2].

Taxonomy *N. e. brunnea.*

References [1]Benson (1963); [2]Douthwaite (1977); [3]Dowsett & Leonard (in press a); [4]Smith (1950).

Accipitridae

African Cuckoo Hawk *Aviceda cuculoides* B97 **RB**

Distribution *Afrotropical (breeds Sierra Leone to South Africa).* Widespread, but uncommon in the north, and more frequent in drier woodlands in the south and west (e.g. the Shangombo area)[2]. Unrecorded from sparsely-wooded plains, as west of Zambezi town (Balovale)[1]. *Alt.* 450-1700 m.

Ecology Any woodland and thicket, especially the drier types, and often in mopane. Nests may be in quite small, relatively bare trees[4].

Status Present in all months, although the possibility of movements has been suggested[3]. Up to 6 birds have been seen together, undertaking what appeared to be display flights in Apr[2].

Breeding	Sep	Oct	Nov	Dec	Jan	Feb
(n=17)	2	7	2	2	2	2

Clutch: C/1 (2); C/2 (12).

Taxonomy *A. c. verreauxii.*

References [1]Aspinwall (1979b); [2]Dowsett (in press a); [3]Leonard (1999a); [4]Madge (1971d).

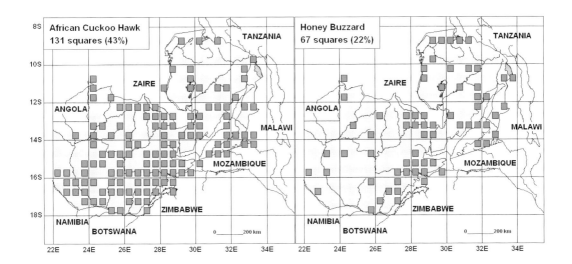

Honey Buzzard *Pernis apivorus* B96 **PW**

Distribution *Palaearctic* (*the whole population winters Senegambia to South Africa*). Likely to occur throughout the country, although there are few records from the low-lying valleys, and it is known west of the Zambezi only from the South Lueti River[2] and Lupuka[1]. *Alt.* 550-2200 m, mostly above 950 m.
Ecology Any woodland.
Status A Palaearctic migrant with small numbers (up to 6 together) on passage, and singles wintering. The species has been recorded between 4 Oct (average first date over 19 years is 22 Oct) and 1 May (but mean last date in 20 years is 1 Apr, and some sightings later in May are possibly misidentifications)[1].
Taxonomy No races recognized.
References [1]Dowsett (in press b); [2]Traylor (1965b).

Bat Hawk *Macheiramphus alcinus* B99 **RB**

Distribution *Old World Tropics* (*in Africa, Senegal to South Africa*). Throughout the country, wherever there are bat colonies (which may be in hollow trees, caves or buildings), except so far unrecorded in the south-west between Mongu[7] and Kazungula[3]. *Alt.* 370-1660 m, wandering up to 2150 m on the Nyika Plateau[4].
Ecology Feeds not only on bats, usually hunting singly at dusk, but also on small, diurnal birds[1,3]. Nests in large trees[2,6].
Status Resident. The same nests were used in successive years at Victoria Falls Gorges and Choma, and at the latter site the same female was thought to be involved[2,3].

Breeding   Sep   Oct
(n=15)   8   7   Display has been noted as early as the end of Mar, and nest-building in Jun. *Clutch*: C/1 (8).
Taxonomy[5] *M. a. anderssoni*.

References [1]Black *et al.* (1979); [2]Colebrook-Robjent (1975b); [3]Dowsett (in press a); [4]Dowsett-Lemaire (2006a); [5]Irwin & Benson (1967a); [6]Madge (1972c); [7]Winterbottom (1942a).

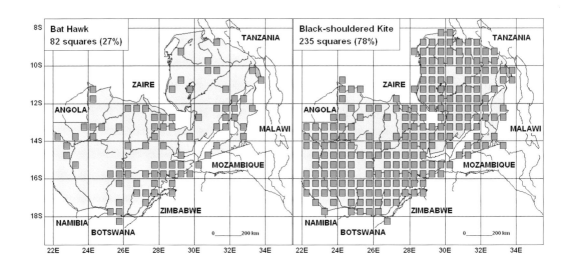

Black-shouldered Kite *Elanus caeruleus*   B98 **RB/AM?**

Distribution *Old World* (*in the Afrotropics, Mauritania to South Africa*). Practically throughout. *Alt.* 370-2200 m, mostly above 600 m.

Ecology Any open country with isolated trees or bushes.

Status Although present all months, it is more in evidence in the dry season (mid-May to early Nov), and most records Dec-Feb are from S. Zambia[1], with numbers increasing as early as Mar in some years. Feeds to a great extent on rodents, and occurrence and opportunistic breeding of the kite are likely to be influenced by population cycles of rodents. An origin for some of these birds is suggested by the recovery of South African-ringed birds in Malawi (Aug) and Uganda (Oct)[2].

Breeding	Jan	Feb	Mar	Apr	May	Jun	Jul	Aug	Sep	Oct	Nov	Dec
(n=113)	1	2	20	37	17	5	4	12	6	2	2	5

Clutch: C/2 (7); C/3 (29); C/4 (34); C/5 (3); C/6 (1).

Taxonomy *E. c. caeruleus*.

References [1]Dowsett (in press a); [2]Oatley *et al.* (1998).

Eurasian Black Kite *Milvus m. migrans*   B95 (part) **PW**

Distribution *Palaearctic* (*wintering Mauritania to South Africa*). Recorded throughout the country, especially along "line of rail" (a reflection of greater observer effort there). *Alt.* 370-2200 m.

Ecology Any light woodland or open country.

Status[1] Palaearctic migrant with extreme dates 3 Oct and 15 Apr, first arrivals being usually second half Oct, and latest usually third week of Mar. Relatively few birds remain during the rains (there are few Jan records), the great majority being on passage[2]. In the past large numbers have been reported on northward passage, in flocks of up to 50 (exceptionally up to 1000 in a day mid-Feb at Danger Hill[3]), but since 100+ over Chipata 3 Mar 1989 there have been remarkably few at any time in Zambia[2].

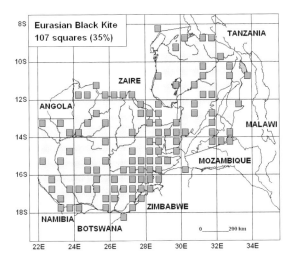

Conservation Allowing for a reduction in the numbers of active observers in Zambia, there does nevertheless appear to have been a notable decline in the numbers of *M. m. migrans* since the 1980s (in some years there have been no reports of Palaearctic kites at all)[2].

Taxonomy *M. m. migrans* (bill black in adults, and head contrastingly grey).

References [1]Brooke (1974b); [2]Dowsett (in press b); [3]Tree (1961).

Yellow-billed Kite *Milvus migrans parasitus*   B95 (part) **AMB**

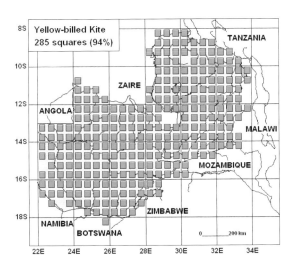

Distribution *Afrotropical (populations of* M. migrans *breed Mauritania to South Africa).* Until recently one of the commonest raptors throughout. *Alt.* 330-2200 m.

Ecology Any light woodland or open country. Usually an opportunist scavenger, one has been seen to kill a *Merops nubicoides*[7]. Nests in trees in woodland or on the edge of forest. The species is less associated with towns in Zambia than in some other countries where public hygiene is less evident, but it is numerous in association with fishing settlements.

Status A breeding migrant, with the great majority present Jul-Mar, and very few recorded Apr-Jun. Many are on passage, and even breeding birds seem to move away promptly, which means that there are relatively few observations Dec-Jan in most years. Hundreds have been noted on passage on dates between 24 Sep and 2 Nov[2] (presumably some are moving further south to breed). Return passage northwards (peaking at 2000 or more a day) has been noted late Jan to mid-Mar. There have been two recoveries of *M. m. parasitus* ringed in Zambia, in Angola (Oct) and Zimbabwe (Dec) (Appendix 1); a juvenile ringed in Namibia was killed in Burundi (Jun)[5].

Conservation Since the 1990s there appears to have been a marked reduction in the numbers of this species[3], and although no cause for this is known, it is potentially vulnerable to pesticide utilisation.

Breeding[6]   Aug   Sep   Oct   Nov
(n=154)   53   84   16   1   *Clutch*: C/1 (20); C/2 (87); C/3 (21).

Taxonomy The local breeding form is *M. m. parasitus* (bill yellow in adults); it is not clear if it should be treated as a species distinct from the Eurasian bird (e.g. as *M. aegyptius*)[4].

References [1]Bowen (1977b); [2]Bowen (1980a); [3]Dowsett & Leonard (in press a); [4]Johnson *et al.* (2005); [5]Oatley *et al.* (1998); [6]Penry (1975b); [7]Taylor (1977).

African Fish Eagle *Haliaeetus vocifer* B94 **RB**

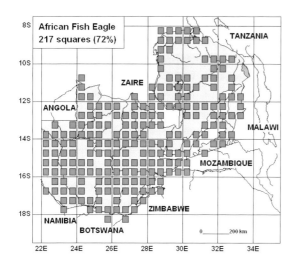

Distribution *Afrotropical* (*Mauritania to South Africa*). Almost throughout, and locally numerous. *Alt.* 330-1660 m.

Ecology Around any large areas of water, rivers and even quite small dams, being especially numerous on rivers with high fish densities (such as the Kafue and the Luangwa). Scarcest on heavily-wooded rivers, as in most of NW Zambia[1]. Feeds mainly on fish (alive or dead), often robbing *Ardea goliath* of its catch. Has also been seen eating an antelope carcass[1].

Status Resident, with much local wandering to small bodies of water (farm dams etc.). Although usually in pairs, loose groups of 10 or more are not infrequent in areas such as the Kafue Flats[2].

Breeding	Feb	Mar	Apr	May	Jun	Jul	Aug	Sep	Oct
(n=93)	3	8	16	26	24	10	4	1	1

Clutch: C/1 (4); C/2 (16); C/3 (7).
Taxonomy No races recognized.
References [1]Benson *et al.* (1970); [2]Dowsett (in press a).

Palm-nut Vulture *Gypohierax angolensis* B64 **RB**

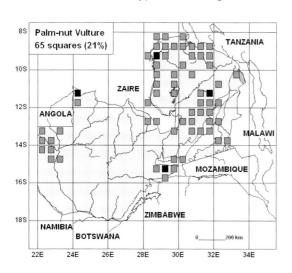

Distribution *Afrotropical* (*Senegal to South Africa*). Although known to breed at only four localities (black squares), it may do so widely north of 13°S. In the west, ranges from N. Mwinilunga to Chitunta Plain, reappearing west of the Zambezi, south to Liuwa Plain[5] and Sitoya. In the north-east it occurs throughout the Luapula, east to the Katumba stream on the upper Luangwa, wandering rarely to the Copperbelt at Kitwe and Ndola[3]. Further south in the east there are scattered observations from Chipata west to Chongwe and Chalimbana[1], where *Raphia* palms are locally common (e.g. at Talabuku[2]) and there is a small breeding population, south to Chiawa[3]. [Sight records of Egyptian Vulture *Neophron*

percnopterus[4] are now believed to refer to *Gypohierax angolensis*; they fit in well with what is known of the distribution of wandering birds.] *Alt.* 330-1800 m (Uningi Pans), mostly above 900 m.

Ecology Usually associated with riparian forest where *Raphia* palms are numerous. Also scavenges (especially for dead fish, but even on the carcasses of two Wild Dogs *Lycaon pictus* killed by traffic)[3].

Status Usually resident, singly or in pairs, but probable wanderers have occurred in areas where it is unlikely to breed, May-Aug.

Breeding　　Jun　Jul　Aug
(n=4)　　　　　1　　1　　2　　*Clutch*: C/1 (2) & N/1 (1).

Taxonomy No races recognized.

References [1]Aspinwall (1977h); [2]Atkins (1977); [3]Dowsett (in press a); [4]Dowsett & Tree (1964); [5]Osborne (1978).

Hooded Vulture *Necrosyrtes monachus*　　　　　　　　B63 **RB**

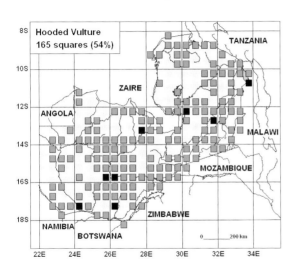

Distribution *Afrotropical* (*Mauritania to South Africa*). Almost throughout, and although so far unrecorded from the far west, along the Angolan border, it is quite common along the major rivers in NW Zambia. Black squares are known nesting areas. *Alt.* from 370 m up to 2200 m on the Zambian Nyika[5] (where it breeds).

Ecology Usually associated with open woodland or riparian forest (not the commensal bird it is in West Africa). Feeds on a variety of small items, scavenging as a minor member of vulture groups at large carcasses, but also on dead fish, flying termites, and apparently flamingo eggs[3]. At carcasses it is the first to arrive and to start feeding, for once the larger vultures are there, it has little opportunity[1]. Nests in large trees.

Status Resident. Not usually numerous, larger groups observed in the major big game areas (Kafue, Lochinvar and Luangwa Valley N.P.) being 6-7[4]. [An exceptional report of a group of some 300 at a massive termite emergence in Kafue N.P.[2] is best disregarded as a possible misidentification.]

Conservation Not normally associated with human habitation, and the wild population is not known to have suffered any significant decline in recent years.

Breeding　　May　Jun　Jul
(n=11)　　　　3　　5　　3　　*Clutch*: C/1 (2).

Taxonomy *N. m. pileatus.*

References [1]Attwell (1963); [2]Benson *et al.* (1971a); [3]Brown (1957); [4]Dowsett (in press a); [5]Dowsett-Lemaire (2006a).

African White-backed Vulture *Gyps africanus*　　　　　　B62 **RB**

Distribution *Afrotropical* (*Mauritania to South Africa*). Occurs throughout (and breeds widely: black squares), except for well-wooded areas (with limited populations of large game animals) in the north-

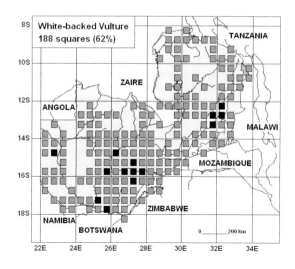

west, north of about Ntambu[3], or much of the Luapula Valley. *Alt.* from 370 m up to 2200 m on the Zambian Nyika[5] (higher on the Malawi side).

Ecology Any open country with large mammal populations. There is a great deal of intra-specific aggression at carcasses, but *G. africanus* usually gives way to *Torgos tracheliotus*. Nests in the tops of tall trees[2].

Status Resident, with local wandering. In most big game areas this is the most abundant vulture, forming over 85% of the vulture population[1]. Maximum congregations of this species in the major national parks are: Kafue (80), Lochinvar (70) and Luangwa (150 or more)[3]. Usually much less numerous in farming areas, but 40 were at a dead bull at Katete (in 1963)[3]. A bird ringed as a nestling was recovered 86 km distant[4].

Conservation Populations outside the national parks have apparently declined considerably in recent decades, perhaps largely as a result of the use of poisonous cattle dips. However, within the protected areas populations remain healthy[3], and there is no evidence so far of the disease that is decimating numbers of *Gyps* vultures in the Indian sub-continent and elsewhere.

Breeding Mar Apr May Jun Jul Aug
(n=116)   1   11   57   33   10   4

A record is also claimed (without details) for Jan. *Clutch*: C/1 (33).

Taxonomy No races recognized. Forms a superspecies with the Indian *G. bengalensis*.

References [1]Attwell (1963); [2]Benson & Pitman (1956-57); [3]Dowsett (in press a); [4]Dowsett & Leonard (2001); [5]Dowsett-Lemaire (2006a).

Cape Vulture *Gyps coprotheres*   B - **AM**

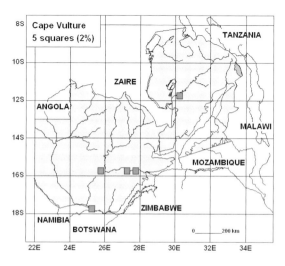

Distribution *Afrotropical* (*breeds in southern Africa only*). First reported in 1974, vagrants (twice photographed) have wandered to as far north as the Bovu River, Ngoma, Lochinvar[2,6], Mazabuka[5] and Chikuni (Bangweulu)[3]. *Alt.* 1000-1160 m.

Ecology Likely to turn up almost anywhere where there are large carcasses, especially in S. Zambia.

Status There are so far eight acceptable records, usually of singles, but once two adults together. Extreme dates are 12 Mar and 26 May, once 8 Oct[3] (in South Africa lays May-Jun)[4].

Conservation This species is considered "Vulnerable" in southern Africa[1].

Taxonomy No races recognized.

References [1]BirdLife International (2000, 2004a); [2]Dowsett (1979a); [3]Dowsett & Leonard (in press a); [4]Piper in Hockey *et al.* (2005); [5]Leonard & Peters (1998); [6]Osborne & Scott (1976).

## Rüppell's Vulture *Gyps rueppellii*					B - **AV**

Distribution and Status *Afrotropical (Mauritania to Tanzania).* An adult was well seen in the Nsefu sector of the South Luangwa N.P. (1231D), on 1 Aug 1998 (not 1999)[3]. A common species in East Africa which, in recent years, has wandered as far south as Zimbabwe[2] and N. South Africa[1].
Taxonomy No specimen, but most probably the nominate race.
References [1]Mills in Hockey *et al.* (2005); [2]Mundy (1998); [3]Pope *et al.* (1999).

## Lappet-faced Vulture *Torgos tracheliotus*					B60 **RB**

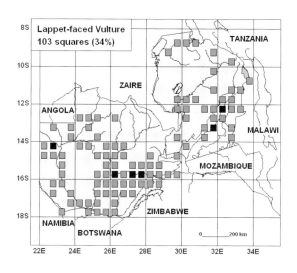

Distribution *Mainly Afrotropical (Mauritania to South Africa).* Almost confined to the big game areas of the south and east of the country, breeding from Liuwa Plain east to the Luangwa (black squares). In the west, no further north than West Lunga N.P. and south of Solwezi, and in the central areas north only occasionally to Lusaka and Chisamba[4] (there is no record from the Copperbelt). In the north, there is a large area with no records from Lusenga Plain N.P.[2] south to Bangweulu (where it is scarce). Wanders onto the Eastern Province plateau south (rarely) to Chipata. Numerous on the Kafue Flats (up to 25 together at Lochinvar, at times the most numerous vulture at carcasses of Lechwe)[4], and not uncommon on the Liuwa Plain, Nyika Plateau and elsewhere (concentrations of up to 8 in the Luangwa Valley, 15 in Kafue N.P.). Most breeding records are from Lochinvar (in several successive years up to five active nests examined), but similar concentrations of nests are known from the Liuwa Plain[2]. Breeds regularly in the Luangwa Valley, but its present status in other areas where it has bred is not known. *Alt.* from 370 m up to 2200 m on the Zambian Nyika[5] (higher on the Malawi side).
Ecology Any open habitat with large game mammal populations, scarce in the plateau miombo woodlands (e.g. Kasanka N.P.). This huge bird usually dominates and has the respect of the far more abundant *Gyps africanus* at any carcass[1], but it can allow the small *Necrosyrtes monachus* to feed alongside it. A young bird raised in captivity even prevented two Lions from taking its bones[7]. Nests are usually high in flat-topped trees, such as *Acacia* spp. and Baobab. Feeds only on large carcasses, and not recorded killing smaller prey for itself.
Status Seems to be essentially resident, but a bird ringed as a nestling in South Africa in Nov was seen in the Luangwa Valley in Oct of the next year (Appendix 1). A second bird from the Kruger N.P. reached Fothergill Is. (1628D) on the Zimbabwe side of L. Kariba[6]. Usually in ones and twos, but see above.
Conservation Considered Vulnerable[3], this vulture is now very rarely recorded outside the major big game areas. Although in several national parks it remains common (groups of up to 25 still recorded at

Lochinvar in the 1990s)[4], and there is no overall cause for concern regarding its status in Zambia, it is a species that ought to be monitored.

Breeding   Mar   Apr   May   Jun   Jul   Aug

(n=74)   1   2   36   25   8   2   *Clutch*: C/1 (51) & N/1 (17).

Taxonomy *A. t. tracheliotus*.

References [1]Attwell (1963); [2]Benson & White (1957); [3]BirdLife International (2000, 2004a); [4]Dowsett (in press a); [5]Dowsett-Lemaire (2006a); [6]Oatley *et al.* (1998); [7]Shenton (1961).

White-headed Vulture *Trigonoceps occipitalis*   B61 **RB**

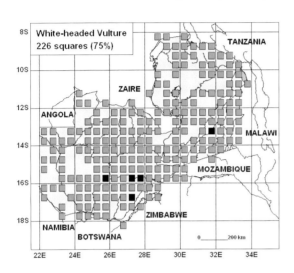

8S   White-headed Vulture
226 squares (75%)

Distribution *Afrotropical* (*Mauritania to South Africa*). Throughout, the most widespread of all vultures. *Alt.* 330-2200 m (Nyika, higher on the Malawi side, where it breeds)[3].

Ecology Any woodland or savanna, but scarce in the more heavily-wooded areas or near centres of population, such as the Copperbelt. Feeds on a very wide range of items, and is not wholly dependent upon carcasses of large mammals. It has been observed eating reptiles (including monitor lizards *Varanus* spp.), fish and insects, and perhaps even killing such prey as snakes and a mongoose itself[1].

Status Resident. Usually no more than 3 or 4 together at a carcass, maximum recorded being 6 (Luangwa Valley)[2].

Conservation In southern Africa there are fears that this species is becoming rare away from "pristine" habitats, as a result largely of the use of pesticides. This has not been monitored in Zambia, but some observers believe there has been a decline in numbers in farming areas around Choma[2]. Still widespread, although no doubt less common with increasing deforestation for farming.

Breeding   May   Jun   Jul   Aug   Oct

(n=28)   1   13   8   5   1   *Clutch*: C/1 (9).

Taxonomy No races recognized.

References [1]Attwell (1963); [2]Dowsett (in press a); [3]Dowsett-Lemaire (2006a).

Black-breasted Snake Eagle *Circaetus pectoralis*   B70 **RB**

Distribution *Afrotropical* (*Sudan to South Africa*). Practically throughout, and locally common. *Alt.* 330-2200 m (Nyika).

Ecology Open woodland and wooded or grass plains are favoured, where it hunts mainly by hovering, though at times by pouncing. It feeds principally on reptiles, especially snakes.

Status Present throughout the year, but greatest numbers are noted in the dry season (Mar-Oct)[2]. Often up to 6 seen at once, while dry season roosts of 21 and 43 birds have been noted in S. Zambia[4,5].

Breeding   Feb   Mar   Apr   May   Jun   Jul   Aug   Sep

(n=38)   1   3   9   5   9   6   4   1   *Clutch*: C/1 (16).

Taxonomy No races recognized. Forms a superspecies with the Palaearctic *C. gallicus* and Afrotropical

C. beaudouini[1] (and considered conspecific by some authorities)[3].
References [1]Clark (1999); [2]Dowsett (in press a); [3]Dowsett & Dowsett-Lemaire (1993); [4]Naylor (1974); [5]Osborne (1975b).

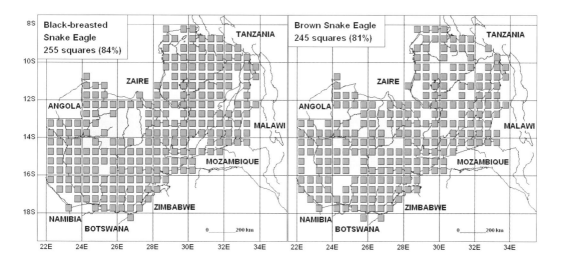

Brown Snake Eagle *Circaetus cinereus*   B71 **RB**

Distribution *Afrotropical* (*Senegal to South Africa*). Throughout the country, but not numerous, and rather sparse in well-wooded areas such as the north-west. *Alt.* usually 330-1800 m, but rarely wanders in the cold weather up to 2150 m on the Nyika Plateau[2].
Ecology Any woodland and dry forest, much less often on open plains than *C. pectoralis*. Usually hunts from a perch.
Status There is no evidence of anything other than local fluctuations in frequency of observations[1] (although a bird ringed as a nestling in South Africa has been recovered in Zaire)[3]. Usually solitary, and never in concentrations like those of *C. pectoralis*.
Breeding   Dec   Jan   Feb
(n=9)   1   5   3   *Clutch*: C/1 (6) & N/1 (1).
Taxonomy No races recognized.
References [1]Dowsett (in press a); [2]Dowsett-Lemaire (2006a); [3]Oatley *et al.* (1998).

Western Banded Snake Eagle *Circaetus cinerascens*   B72 **RB**

Distribution *Afrotropical* (*Senegal to South Africa*). Widespread and locally quite common, along the larger, well-wooded river systems; thus rather scarce in parts of the dry Kalahari sand woodlands of the west. *Alt.* 330-1600 m.
Ecology Usually in riparian forest (even the drier types in the Luangwa Valley[2] and elsewhere) and on the edge of mushitu in higher-rainfall areas. Still-hunts from a perch, feeding on reptiles (snakes, lizards and even a tortoise) and insects.
Status Resident, with no evidence of more than local wandering.

Breeding[1,3] Dec
(n=1)   1   Juvenile food-begging has been reported Sep-Oct. Noisy display flights occur between Jan and Jul. *Clutch*: C/1 (1).
Taxonomy No races recognized.
References [1]Colebrook-Robjent & Aspinwall (1986); [2]Dowsett (in press a); [3]Madge (1972a).

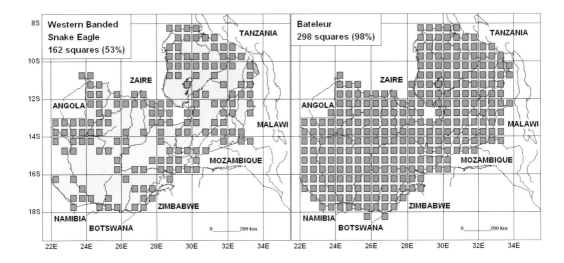

Bateleur *Terathopius ecaudatus*   B69 **RB**

Distribution *Afrotropical* (*Mauritania to South Africa*). Throughout and generally common. *Alt.* 330-2200 m (Nyika, higher on the Malawi side).
Ecology Any woodland, wooded grassland or open plain, avoiding only the more densely-wooded areas. It feeds especially on reptiles, but also small mammals and anything that is killed by bush fires. Often the first to notice carcasses, arriving before vultures to remove the eyes.
Status Most often reported during the dry (non-breeding) season, mainly Jul-Dec, such a pattern especially noticeable in higher-rainfall areas. Most likely this is the result of it becoming less conspicuous when nesting, and there is no evidence of any regular movements. Often there are several birds in view quartering the sky at the same time, and at termite emergences or by water large concentrations may occur (up to 21 together in the Choma area in 1973)[2].
Conservation This eagle is especially sensitive to human disturbance when nesting. In settled areas it has certainly become scarce in recent years, perhaps also as a result of the use of pesticides. Most abundant now in such national parks as Kafue, Lochinvar and the Luangwa Valley, and remote areas with low human density (e.g. parts of the west)[2].
Breeding[1,3] Nov   Dec   Jan   Feb   Mar   Apr   May   Jul   Aug
(n=48)   2   3   12   17   7   4   1   1   1   *Clutch*: C/1 (12).
Taxonomy No races recognized. Of the two colour phases, the chestnut-backed is usually more common that the cream-backed one.
References [1]Danckwerts (1979); [2]Dowsett (in press a); [3]Osborne (1982b).

Gymnogene *Polyboroides typus*   B68 **RB**

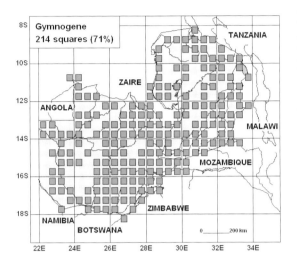

Distribution *Afrotropical* (*Mauritania to South Africa*). Probably throughout and locally common. *Alt.* 330 to 1950 m (in the Mafingas[4]), and wandering rarely to 2200 m on the Nyika[1].

Ecology Any woodland or forest, often near water. It feeds on a variety of prey, but it is especially inclined to take young weavers (Ploceidae) from nests.

Status Resident, with local wandering.

Breeding (n=98)	Jul	Aug	Sep
	1	33	47
	Oct	Nov	Dec
	12	4	1

Clutch: C/1 (15); C/2 (70); C/4 (1).

The C/4 was probably laid by two females[2].

Taxonomy No races recognized (but closely related to the Madagascan *P. radiatus*[3], and they have in the past been treated as conspecific).

References [1]Carter (1975); [2]Dowsett (in press a); [3]Dowsett & Dowsett-Lemaire (1993); [4]Dowsett & Stjernstedt (1973).

Eurasian Marsh Harrier *Circus aeruginosus*   B67 (part) **PW**

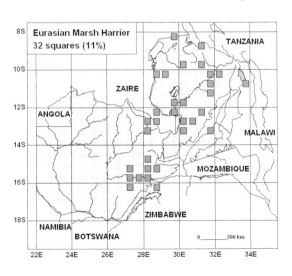

Distribution *Palaearctic* (*winters mainly Senegal to Zambezian region*). Occurs fairly widely in the eastern half of the country, although there is but one record of a vagrant from the Luangwa Valley (Mfuwe[1]) and none at all from Eastern Province plateau. Ranges south and west to the Monze area[2]. *Alt.* 550-2200 m, but rarely below 950 m.

Ecology Over dry grassland, floodplain, dambos and marshes.

Status A Palaearctic migrant and winter visitor, recorded between 15 Sep and 14 Apr, but mostly from mid-Nov or Dec to mid-Mar. Usually singly, it is here near the southern limit of its normal wintering range, and numbers seem to vary annually[2]. However, identification of this species is sometimes difficult through confusion with *C. ranivorus*.

Taxonomy *C. a. aeruginosus*. The separation of the African *ranivorus* as a full species is now generally accepted[3].

References [1]Benson *et al.* (1970); [2]Dowsett (in press b); [3]Dowsett & Dowsett-Lemaire (1980).

African Marsh Harrier *Circus ranivorus* B67 (part) **RB**

Distribution *Afrotropical* (*Sudan to South Africa*). Throughout the country and locally quite common, but scarce in drier areas, such as the low-lying Luangwa and Middle Zambezi Valleys (where it does not breed). *Alt.* 370-1800 m, mostly above 650 m (occasionally as high as 2200 m on the Nyika, and it has bred higher on the Malawi side)[4].

Ecology Unlike *C. aeruginosus*, almost always in wet situations, especially *Phragmites* reedbeds and *Typha*, moist dambos and floodplains. Feeds on rodents and small birds, even to the size of a female *Philomachus pugnax*[1].

Status Resident, with several pairs nesting in favoured areas. In the Choma farming area it has become very rare during the 1990s, where once common[2].

Breeding   Dec   Jan   Feb   Mar   Apr   May   Jun   Jul   Aug
(n=73)   1   9   11   18   17   12   3   1   1
Clutch: C/1 (1); C/2 (9); C/3 (15); C/4 (9).
Moult: an adult male was half-way through moult end Nov[2].
Taxonomy No races. Forms a superspecies with *C. aeruginosus*[3].
References [1]Benson *et al.* (1970); [2]Dowsett (in press a); [3]Dowsett & Dowsett-Lemaire (1980); [4]Dowsett-Lemaire (2006a).

Pallid Harrier *Circus macrourus* B65 **PW**

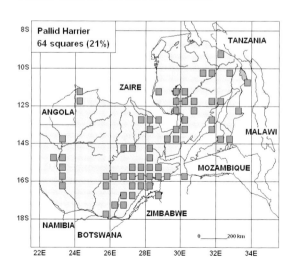

Distribution *Palaearctic* (*winters Mauritania to South Africa*). Occurs through most of the country, west to Liuwa Plain N.P., except that unrecorded from north of a line from Chozi to the Mansa area. On the whole somewhat less frequently reported than *C. pygargus*, although locally more common in favoured areas such as the Nyika Plateau and the Kafue Flats. *Alt.* 330-2200 m (higher on the Malawi side of Nyika).

Ecology Any open grassland including dambos, which it quarters in search of rodents and small birds.

Status A Palaearctic migrant and winter visitor. Extreme dates are 9 Oct and 11 May, but first arrivals are usually the second half of Oct (mean date over 26 years, 29 Oct), and most have left by mid-Mar (mean last date in 19 years is 7 Mar)[3]. [Records in Jul and Sep may well have

been misidentifications[2,4], although over-summering may be expected to occur rarely.]
Conservation Considered "Near Threatened"[1]; but no evidence of any decline in numbers in Zambia.
Taxonomy No races recognized.
References [1]BirdLife International (2000, 2004a); [2]Brelsford (1947); [3]Dowsett (in press b);
[4]Winterbottom (1939b).

Montagu's Harrier *Circus pygargus*   B66 **PW**

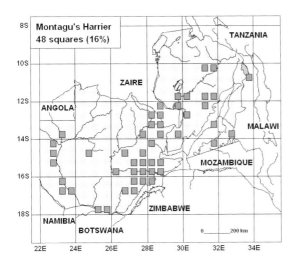

Distribution *Palaearctic* (*winters Mauritania to South Africa*). Distribution much as for *C. macrourus*, but unrecorded from the whole of the north-west, beyond the Copperbelt and Zambezi town (Balovale)[2], and rare at low altitude. A favoured wintering area is the Bangweulu Swamps. So far unrecorded north of Kasama[1]. In parts of the country more frequently reported than *C. macrourus*. *Alt.* 650-2200 m.
Ecology As for *C. macrourus*, any open grassland and floodplain, which it quarters in search of rodents and small birds.
Status A Palaearctic migrant and winter visitor, present from 6 Oct to 12 Apr, but in some years first arrivals are nearer mid-Nov (mean date 2 Nov over 26 years), and most have left by mid-Mar (average last date in 23 years is 10 Mar)[3]. The odd one remains, as at Zambezi town (Balovale) on 25 Jun[2] and one thought to be this species at Lochinvar 23 Sep. Often loose concentrations of up to 6, and as many as 50 were noted over an area of floodplain in Bangweulu (in Feb 1991)[3]. There is no sign of any diminution of numbers wintering in Zambia.
Taxonomy No races recognized.
References [1]Benson (1956d); [2]Britton (1970); [3]Dowsett (in press b).

[**Pale Chanting Goshawk** *Melierax canorus*
Afrotropical (*Ethiopia to South Africa*). Reported to occur in the Caprivi Strip adjacent to SW Zambia, and ranges north to Savuti in Botswana[1] and Kazuma Pan in Zimbabwe[2]; the species may possibly occur north of the Zambezi, therefore. **References** [1]Dowsett *et al.* (in prep.); [2]Irwin (1981a).]

Dark Chanting Goshawk *Melierax metabates*   B79 **RB**

Distribution *Mainly Afrotropical* (*Mauritania to South Africa*). Occurs practically throughout the country, commonest in the south, but scarce in the Luangwa Valley[2]. *Alt.* 330-1800 m, but mostly above 600 m.
Ecology On the edge of woodland (especially miombo) or in wooded grassland; often at bush fires. It feeds on reptiles, rodents and small birds, caught by still-hunting. A nest was near the top of a 13 m high *Brachystegia* tree[1].

Status Resident, with only local wandering[2].
Breeding   Aug   Sep   Oct
(n=80)   20   53   7   *Clutch*: C/1 (16); C/2 (21).
Taxonomy *M. m. mechowi.*
References [1]Benson & Pitman (1956-57); [2]Dowsett (in press a).

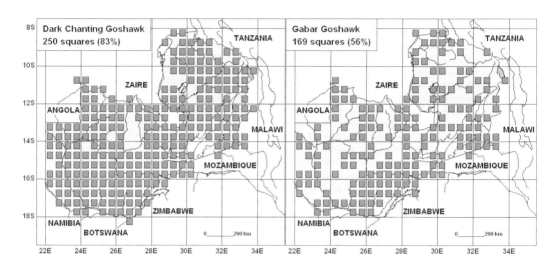

Gabar Goshawk *Melierax gabar*   B80 **RB**

Distribution *Afrotropical* (*Mauritania to South Africa*). There are records from the whole of Zambia, but it is overall scarce, and rare in the Middle Zambezi Valley[1]. *Alt.* 330-1700 m.
Ecology In drier woodland types overall, cultivation in miombo and gardens. Hunting technique similar to that of *Accipiter* spp.
Status Resident, with some local wandering.
Breeding   Jul   Aug   Sep   Oct
(n=48)   1   19   23   5   *Clutch*: C/1 (2); C/2 (8); C/3 (23); C/4 (2).
Taxonomy[2] No races recognized. The black phase is very much rarer than the grey one.
References [1]Dowsett (in press a); [2]Irwin & Benson (1966b).

Black Goshawk *Accipiter melanoleucus*   B73 **RB**

Distribution *Afrotropical* (*Senegal to South Africa*). Through most of the country, except no further west than Sihole[4]. *Alt.* 550-2200 m (on the Nyika, where it breeds, and higher on the Malawi side[5]), but never common, especially below 900 m.
Ecology Usually in rich miombo and evergreen forest in the higher-rainfall areas, and rare in drier riparian at low altitude (as in the Luangwa[3] and Middle Zambezi Valleys[4]). Nests reported in trees over a perennial river[1], in *Brachystegia* woodland[2] and in montane forest[5].
Status Apparently resident.
Breeding   Jul   Aug   Sep   Oct   Nov
(n=55)   9   17   20   8   1   *Clutch*: C/1 (2); C/2 (9); C/3 (24); C/4 (2).
Taxonomy *A. m. melanoleucus.*

References [1]Benson & Pitman (1956-57); [2]Benson & Pitman (1961); [3]Berry (1981a); [4]Dowsett (in press a); [5]Dowsett-Lemaire (2006a).

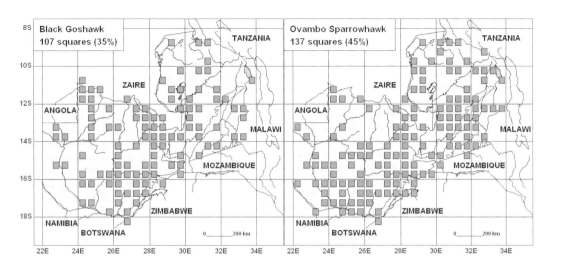

Ovambo Sparrowhawk *Accipiter ovampensis*   B75 **RB**

Distribution *Afrotropical* (*breeds mainly Zambia to South Africa*). Almost throughout the country, but much scarcer than other sympatric *Accipiter* hawks. *Alt.* 330-1700 m.

Ecology The drier woodlands, including dry evergreen forest on the Copperbelt, and regular at low levels (as in the Luangwa Valley). One nest was 20 m up in an evergreen tree[1].

Status Present in all months, though less often noted during the rains (Nov-Feb). It has often been considered a trans-equatorial migrant, in view of its being seasonally present in West Africa, with little evidence of breeding there. This may well be a result of its scarcity further north, and the relative lack of observers, and there is no evidence at present of any substantial movement involving Zambian birds[2].

Breeding   Aug   Sep   Oct   Nov
(n=30)   1   17   10   2   *Clutch*: C/1 (2); C/2 (8); C/3 (14) & N/3 (1).

Taxonomy No races recognized. Melanistic birds have been reported occasionally (e.g. Mporokoso[1], several Copperbelt localities, Choma and Livingstone)[2]. Records of this species (even specimens) have at times been attributed erroneously to *A. rufiventris*[3].

References [1]Benson & Pitman (1956-57); [2]Dowsett (in press a); [3]Irwin *et al.* (1982).

Red-breasted Sparrowhawk *Accipiter rufiventris*   B74 **R(B)**

Distribution *Afromontane near-endemic* (*Ethiopia to South Africa*). Known only from the Nyika Plateau, where not uncommon. *Alt. c.* 2000-2200 m (higher on the Malawi side)[2]. [Earlier records from a scattering of lowland localities have been shown to refer to *A. ovampensis*[3].]

Ecology Edge of forest and plantation and open grassland. Flies low, often along roads, hunting small birds (up to the size of a young francolin)[1] and rodents.

Status Resident.

Breeding No records (but known to breed Malawi side of Nyika[2]).

Taxonomy *A. r. rufiventris*.
References [1]Dowsett (1977d); [2]Dowsett-Lemaire (2006a); [3]Irwin *et al.* (1982).

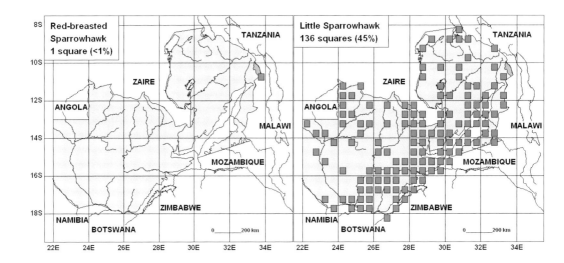

Little Sparrowhawk *Accipiter minullus* B78 **RB**

Distribution *Afrotropical* (*Ethiopia to South Africa*). Through most of Zambia, except that in the extreme south-west known only from the Sinjembela area[2]. Generally scarce, but easily overlooked. *Alt.* 370-1660 m.
Ecology Thickets, dense woodland and dry riparian forest. Occurs in gardens, but much less often than *A. badius*. A nest was 8 m up in a tall *Acacia* tree, 70-150 m from occupied nests of *A. ovampensis* and *Kaupifalco monogrammicus*[1]. Has been observed feeding on roosting *Hirundo rustica*[2].
Status Resident.
Breeding   Aug   Sep   Oct   Nov
(n=39)   1   9   24   5   *Clutch*: C/1 (1); C/2 (30); C/3 (1).
Moult: an adult was half-way through moult in Dec[2].
Taxonomy *A. m. minullus*.
References [1]Benson & Pitman (1956-57); [2]Dowsett (in press a).

African Goshawk *Accipiter tachiro* B76 **RB**

Distribution *Afrotropical* (*Senegal to South Africa*). Throughout the country, especially in well-wooded areas. More easily located than other *Accipiter* spp. from its noisy aerial display. *Alt.* 330-2200 m (Nyika, higher on the Malawi side)[2].
Ecology Evergreen forest (including *Cryptosepalum*), deciduous forest, thicket and dense woodland types (in dry as well as moist situations)[1].
Status Resident.
Conservation Samples from this species in the Zambezi Valley have shown high levels of DDT, the result of spraying against Tsetse fly[3]; this is likely to be a problem that affects other raptors, but remains to be investigated.

Breeding   Oct   Nov   Dec
(n=30)   15   8   7   *Clutch*: C/2 (23); C/3 (2) & N/3 (1).
Taxonomy[4] *A. t. sparsimfasciatus.*
References [1]Dowsett (in press a); [2]Dowsett-Lemaire (2006a); [3]Hartley & Douthwaite (1994); [4]Irwin & Benson (1966b).

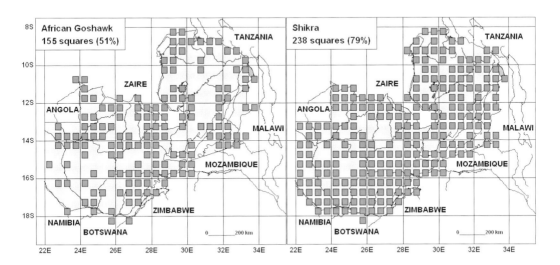

Shikra *Accipiter badius*   B77 **RB**

Distribution *Old World Tropics* (*in Africa, Mauritania to South Africa*). Very widespread and one of the commonest small raptors. *Alt.* 330-1900 m, rarely wandering up to 2150 m on the Nyika in winter (Jul)[2].
Ecology Any woodland, plantations, wooded grassland and gardens. Feeds on small birds and lizards[1].
Status Resident. Up to 5 at a roost of *Quelea quelea* in Aug[1].
Breeding   Sep   Oct   Nov   Dec
(n=121)   76   41   2   2   *Clutch*: C/1 (3); C/2 (44); C/3 (48).
Taxonomy *A. b. polyzonoides.*
References [1]Dowsett (in press a); [2]Dowsett-Lemaire (2006a).

Lizard Buzzard *Kaupifalco monogrammicus*   B81 **RB**

Distribution *Afrotropical* (*Senegal to South Africa*). The commonest small raptor, everywhere. *Alt.* 330-2150 m (visitors to the Nyika Plateau)[3].
Ecology In any woodland (common in miombo), edges of thicket, plantations and gardens. Feeds mainly by still-hunting for reptiles, rodents and insects (in contrast to the more active hunting in flight usually undertaken by the *Accipiter* hawks).
Status Resident. Local movements have been noted in the dry season[2], most notably a few going to the high Nyika in the austral winter (up to 2350 m on the Malawi side)[3].
Breeding   Aug   Sep   Oct   Nov   Dec
(n=177)   1   32   130   13   1   Display noted from May onwards[2].

Clutch: C/1 (16); C/2 (125); C/3 (8) & N/3 (1).
Taxonomy No races recognized[1].
References [1]Benson *et al.* (1970); [2]Dowsett (in press a); [3]Dowsett-Lemaire (2006a).

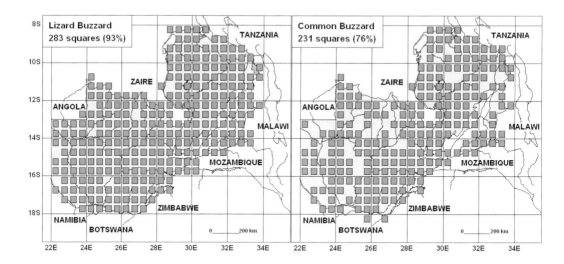

Common (Steppe) Buzzard *Buteo buteo*   B84 **PW**

Distribution *Palaearctic* (*winters mainly Ethiopia to South Africa*). Passes throughout the country, with main concentrations of migrants in the east. *Alt.* 350-2200 m, mostly above 600 m.
Ecology Any open woodland or wooded grassland, often alongside roads. It has been recorded feeding on lizards, rodents and a small passerine bird.
Status A Palaearctic migrant and winter visitor, recorded between 28 Aug and 15 May. Most are passing through, with only small numbers staying during the rains (when usually seen singly). First arrivals are often late Sep (average date 5 Oct in 29 years), but main passage is from mid-Oct into Nov (with 500 passing in an hour at Mbala at times). Return passage is mostly during the first half of Mar, and can be even heavier, with up to 800 in a day frequently at some places in the east of the country (e.g. Chipata and Mbala)[1], and some 2330 moving north at Danger Hill on 10 Mar 1960[2]. Average last date over 28 years was 6 Apr[1]. [Possible records in Jun and early Aug are considered uncertain, although occasional over-summering cannot be ruled out.] Two Finnish-ringed birds were recovered in E. Zambia (Oct, Dec) (Appendix 1).
Taxonomy *B. b. vulpinus*.
References [1]Dowsett (in press b); [2]Tree (1961).

[Long-legged Buzzard *Buteo rufinus*   B82
A Palaearctic species of which some migrate to NE Africa, south to Kenya. It has been claimed to occur further south, including a specimen reported previously from Zambia[1] which has disappeared from the British Museum collection, and so cannot be confirmed. These records are believed all to be based on misidentifications[2]. **References** [1]Benson (1948a); [2]Dowsett & Kemp (1988).]

[Forest Buzzard *Buteo oreophilus*

Afromontane endemic: occurs in the montane forests of Africa as two distinct populations, oreophilus *in eastern Africa (south to Tanzania and Malawi) and* trizonatus *in South Africa (sometimes treated as a distinct species).* This species occurs on the eastern, Malawi side of the Nyika Plateau[2], but was not observed on the Zambian side during nearly 3 years' residence[3], and there is not enough forest for a breeding population. There is a single-observer sight record, but confirmation is required before it can be admitted to the Zambian avifauna[1]. An old specimen claimed for Zambia cannot be accepted[4].
References [1]Dowsett (in press a); [2]Dowsett & Dowsett-Lemaire (1979c); [3]Dowsett *et al.* (1999a); [4]Dowsett & Kemp (1988).]

Augur Buzzard *Buteo augur*   B83 **RB**

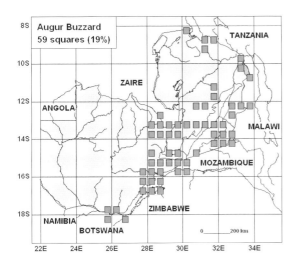

8S Augur Buzzard
59 squares (19%)

Distribution *Afrotropical (breeds mainly Ethiopia to Zimbabwe).* Common around the rocky hills associated with the Muchingas, the Zambezi escarpment and the Eastern Province kopjes. Thus from Kalambo Falls and to the north of Sumbu, south-westwards to the Copperbelt (mostly as a wanderer from nearby hills). [The suggestion that the species might have once been shot further west in hills near Solwezi[5] has never been confirmed.] Then along much of the Middle Zambezi to the Victoria Falls, and also up the Kafue River to Kafue Gorge and the Munali Hills[1]. *Alt.* 450 to 1950 m in the Mafingas[3], and 2200 m on the Nyika (higher on the Malawi side)[4].
Ecology Associated with rocky hills and escarpments, hunting in open country, where it feeds in particular on reptiles, small mammals and birds.
Status Apart from some local wandering, wholly resident.
Breeding   Jun   Jul   Aug   Sep   Oct
(n=9)   1   3   1   3   1   *Clutch*: C/1 (2); C/2 (2).
Taxonomy *B. a. augur.* Forms a superspecies with the southern African *B. rufofuscus,* in the past considered conspecific[2]. Birds with the underside wholly black are rarely seen on the Nyika (and once at Munali Pass)[1].
References [1]Dowsett (in press a); [2]Dowsett & Dowsett-Lemaire (1993); [3]Dowsett & Stjernstedt (1973); [4]Dowsett-Lemaire (2006a); [5]White (1945-46).

Wahlberg's Eagle *Aquila wahlbergi*   B93 **AMB**

Distribution *Afrotropical (Senegal to South Africa).* The most widespread and common eagle in Zambia. *Alt.* 330-2000 m (scarce at both low levels and high altitude), wandering up to 2200 m.
Ecology Any woodland (especially common in miombo), but even in dry, open mopane (although less common as a breeding bird in low-lying valleys such as the Luangwa). It feeds on small mammals (rodents, but even mongooses), birds, amphibians and reptiles, and has been reported following the plough[2,5].

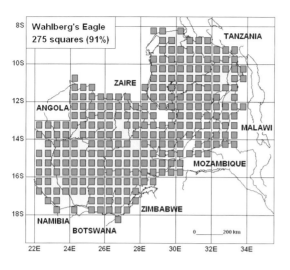

Status An intra-African migrant, breeding in Zambia, then moving north towards the Equator. Acceptable records fall between 25 Jul and 28 Apr[2]. [A handful of records outside this period, in May and early Jul may not have been correctly identified. There is certainly no evidence to support the idea that some birds remain and even breed at that time[1].] First arrivals each year are almost consistently in the first half of Aug (average first date 11 Aug over 28 years)[2], and birds display and start to breed within a day or two. There is some evidence of onward passage at this season, e.g. many passing south over the Luangwa Valley 20 Aug[2]. [A report of over 100 passing over Leopardshill as late as mid-Nov[7] is difficult to explain.] Return passage north is well-marked in the south and east of the country, starting late Feb, with daily peaks of up to 35 moving north, especially in the first week of Apr. Mean last date is 17 Apr (over 29 years)[2]. An adult ringed in South Africa (Nov) was recovered in Zambia mid-Mar (Appendix 1). Birds ringed in southern Africa have been recovered in Sudan and Zaire (Apr and Aug-Sep)[4], and trans-equatorial migration to Nigeria has also been shown by a satellite-tracked bird[3].

Breeding[5,6]

	Aug	Sep	Oct	Nov	Dec
(n=320)	4	192	119	4	1

Clutch: C/1 (230); C/2 (6).
13 young were raised at 21 active sites in S. Zambia in 1974[5]. Single-brooded[2]. [A juvenile specimen from Zambezi town (Balovale), dated 6 Jul 1943 and back-dated to an egg probably laid in Mar[1], is so unusual that one must wonder if it was correctly labelled. This specimen was not mentioned by White[8], although he was based at Balovale at the time.]

Taxonomy No races recognized.

References [1]Brooke (1972a); [2]Dowsett & Leonard (in press a); [3]Meyburg *et al.* (1995a); [4]Oatley *et al.* (1998); [5]Osborne & Colebrook-Robjent (1975); [6]Pitman (1935a); [7]Tree (1962b); [8]White (1945-46).

Lesser Spotted Eagle *Aquila pomarina*   B92 **PW**

Distribution *Palaearctic and Oriental (in Africa, winters almost entirely in the southern third).* Almost throughout, though so far unrecorded north-west of a line from Shangombo on the Mashi to Jivundu on the Kabompo River[3]. *Alt.* 330-2200 m.

Ecology Any open woodland or wooded grassland. Often feeding at termite alate swarms, and stomach contents have also included a frog[2].

Status A Palaearctic migrant and winter visitor. Most birds are on passage from mid-Oct to the third week of Nov, and from mid-Feb to the third week of Mar. Some stay during the rains, especially in the south and east. Extreme dates are 29 Sep and 30 Apr (apart from an exceptional report of one on 9 Sep), with average first date 27 Oct (over 29 years) and last 18 Mar (25 years)[3]. Southward passage is in small groups, and rarely as many as 100 in a day, whereas in the flight northwards flocks are much more in evidence, and as many as 360 passed over Chipata in mixed groups on 2 Mar. In W. Zambia there is some southward passage, but none northwards[1]. Five European-ringed birds have been recovered in Zambia (27 Oct to early Mar) (Appendix 1), and others have been tracked by satellite across the country[4], including two that wintered in N. Namibia[5]. It is possible that populations have declined in the

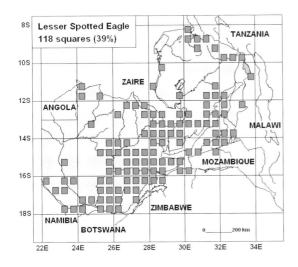

past few years, only small numbers being reported during the 1990s, but this could be the result of thinner observer coverage.

Taxonomy *A. p. pomarina.*

References [1]Bowen (1983h); [2]Brooke *et al.* (1972); [3]Dowsett (in press b); [4]Meyburg *et al.* (1995b); [5]Meyburg *et al.* (2001).

[**Greater Spotted Eagle** *Aquila clanga*   **B -**

Palaearctic (*winters usually south to Kenya*). A satellite-tracked eagle (from Poland) wintered two years running (1996-7, 1997-8), extreme dates 3 Dec to 11 Mar, in the Luangwa Valley, not far from Nsefu (1331B). It had been tracked across the North Luangwa N.P. en route[3,5]. The bird was not seen, as the area frequented was flooded and inaccessible. A second such bird (both were adult males) was reported from Zambia later[6]. There is a later unconfirmed sight record[2]. However, one cannot rule out the possibility that these were hybrids with *A. pomarina* (as known from central Europe[4]), south of the normal quarters of *A. clanga* in East Africa. *A. clanga* is classified as "Vulnerable"[1]. **References** [1]BirdLife International (2000, 2004a); [2]Dowsett (in press b); [3]Dowsett *et al.* (1999a); [4]Helbig *et al.* (2005); [5]Leonard (1998a); [6]Meyburg & Meyburg (2005).]

Tawny Eagle *Aquila rapax*   **B91 RB**

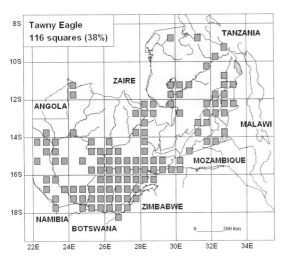

Distribution *Old World Tropics and SW Palaearctic* (*in the Afrotropics, Mauritania to South Africa*). Mostly in the open woodlands of the south and west, the Luangwa Valley and the Chambeshi drainage. Common in large game and cattle areas. In the west the only records north of the Kabompo area are from the Mwinilunga Dist., where it is a rare straggler[3]. It is scarce on the Eastern Province plateau, rare on the Copperbelt, and north of the Chambeshi reported only from Musombwe (Mweru Wantipa)[2] and near Mbala[4]. *Alt.* 330-1660 m, scarce above 1400 m.

Ecology Dry, more open woodlands and wooded grassland. Feeds on a variety of small and medium-sized prey, and up to 3 have been recorded scavenging together at large mammal carcasses[1].

Status Resident, with local dispersal. A nestling ringed at Lochinvar was recovered in Zimbabwe in Aug, 4 years later (Appendix 1).

Breeding[7]   Apr   May   Jun   Jul   Aug   Sep

(n=143)   32   77   24   6   2   2   *Clutch*: C/1 (14); C/2 (51); C/3 (1).

Taxonomy *A. r. rapax*, with probably *A. r. belisarius* (darker, less tawny brown) in NE Zambia[6] (there is a specimen in neighbouring Malawi)[5].

References [1]Attwell (1963); [2]Benson (1956f); [3]Bowen (1983j); [4]Dowsett (in press a); [5]Dowsett-Lemaire & Dowsett (2006); [6]Irwin & Benson (1966b); [7]Osborne (1982a).

Steppe Eagle *Aquila nipalensis*   B p.69 **PW**

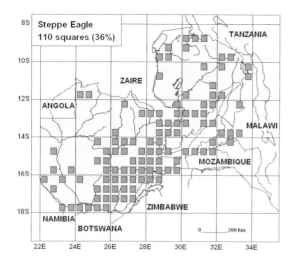

Distribution *Palaearctic* (*winters Ethiopia to South Africa*). Through much of the plateau of S. and central Zambia, but very scarce at low altitude, with few records from the Luangwa and Middle Zambezi Valleys[5]. In the west there is an area north of the Liuwa Plain whence there is as yet no record, and it is rare in Mwinilunga[1]. *Alt.* 370-2200 m.

Ecology Open woodland, wooded grassland and floodplain. Frequently in mixed raptor groups at termite swarms[4], and one had also eaten a small rodent (*Praomys natalensis*)[2].

Status A Palaearctic migrant and winter visitor, with all reports falling between 29 Sep and 30 Apr. First arrivals each year are usually in the third week of Oct (average first date over 27 years is 27 Oct), with groups of up to 50 (exceptionally up to 200) passing. Northward passage is similar, and last dates each year are usually about the first week of Apr (mean 27 Mar over 25 years)[5]. There is no evidence for any change in numbers in Zambia.

Taxonomy Variation is clinal, eastern birds ("*A. n. orientalis*") being only marginally larger[3].

References [1]Bowen (1983h); [2]Brooke *et al.* (1972); [3]Clark (2005); [4]Dowsett (1970b); [5]Dowsett (in press b).

Black Eagle *Aquila verreauxii*   B90 **RB**

Distribution *Mainly Afrotropical* (*Mauritania to South Africa*). Occurs sparsely in several areas of rocky hills (black squares are breeding sites). Present at Kalambo Falls[7] and seen once in the Mafingas[5], then down the Muchinga escarpment from Shiwa Ngandu to near Kapiri Mposhi and the Luano Valley[1]. Occasionally seen in the Middle Zambezi Valley and Kafue Gorge, more frequent along the escarpment bordering L. Kariba[5], to the gorges below Victoria Falls[6] (although traditional nest sites have been unoccupied in recent years)[5]. There is a small population on the Eastern Province plateau in the area from Nyanje to Chadiza[3], wandering as far as Kukwe Hill near Chipata[5]. [Sight records from elsewhere in Northern Province, and even at Solwezi, have not been confirmed, and were rejected[2].] *Alt.* 330-2000 m (Mafingas), mostly 750-1800 m.

Ecology Rocky hills, gorges and escarpments. It appears to feed almost exclusively on hyraxes

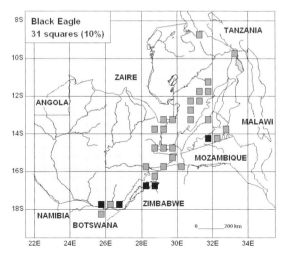

Dendrohyrax brucei (plus *Procavia capensis* in Eastern Province), although has been seen to kill a Cattle Egret *Bubulcus ibis*[8].

Status Resident, with local dispersal; usually singly or in pairs.

Conservation In recent years it has stopped nesting in the gorges in the vicinity of Victoria Falls, probably as a result of disturbance by tourists (including over-flights)[5].

Breeding[4] May   Jun
(n=7)   4   3   *Clutch*: C/2 (1).

Taxonomy No races recognized.

References [1]Benson (1959c); [2]Benson & Irwin (1967b); [3]Colebrook-Robjent (1975b); [4]Colebrook-Robjent & Osborne (1973); [5]Dowsett (in press a); [6]Dowsett & Robjent (1972); [7]Irwin & Benson (1966b); [8]Wyatt (1965).

African Hawk Eagle *Hieraaetus spilogaster*   B88 **RB**

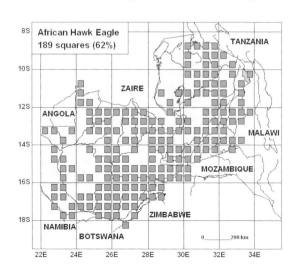

Distribution *Afrotropical (Mauritania to South Africa)*. Through much of Zambia, except so far unrecorded from parts of the extreme west, along the Angolan border, and from the lower Luapula[2] below Mansa Dist. and west of Sumbu[1]. *Alt.* 330-1770 m (Danger Hill).

Ecology In any open woodland and dry riparian forest, nesting in large trees. It has been observed eating a squirrel[4], Vervet Monkey *Cercopithecus aethiops*, game birds including *Numida meleagris*, and Python *Python sebae*[2]. Common only in areas where game birds remain numerous.

Status Resident, although a bird ringed in South Africa moved 800 km to Victoria Falls (Zimbabwe)[3].

Breeding   May   Jun   Jul
(n=36)   12   19   5   *Clutch*: C/1 (6); C/2 (7).

Taxonomy No races recognized. DNA studies suggest that *Hieraaetus* eagles may be best considered congeneric with *Aquila*[5].

References [1]Benson & White (1957); [2]Dowsett (in press a); [3]Oatley *et al.* (1998); [4]Robinson (1973b); [5]Sangster *et al.* (2005).

Booted Eagle *Hieraaetus pennatus*

B p.68 **PW/AMW?**

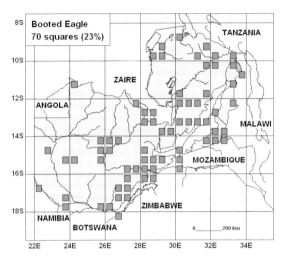

Distribution *Mainly Palaearctic* (*wintering Senegal to Malawi*), *with an isolated population breeding in the Cape and Namibia.* Fairly widespread, except very scarce in the northwest (where known only from the Mwinilunga area)[1]. *Alt.* 330-2200 m, most often above 1000 m.

Ecology In open country including forest-grassland mosaic, light woodland, rocky hills and escarpments.

Status A Palaearctic migrant and winter visitor. Extreme dates of most records are 29 Sep and 28 Apr. There are half-a-dozen observations (all of single birds) outside this period, perhaps indicating the presence of South African birds[2,3]. Usually singly, but up to 7 seen daily on passage over the Nyika mid-Mar[4]. Dark phase birds are perhaps marginally commoner than pale phase, although most observers find pale birds easier to identify.

Breeding No records. In southern Africa, as elsewhere, it is usually a cliff-nester, and suggestions that it might have bred in a tree in W. Zambia probably result from misidentifications[3].

Taxonomy No specimen but presumably *H. p. pennatus.*

References [1]Bowen (1983h); [2]Dowsett (1978b); [3]Dowsett (in press b); [4]Dowsett-Lemaire (2006a).

Ayres's Hawk Eagle *Hieraaetus ayresii*

B89 **RB**

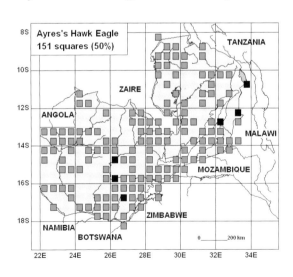

Distribution *Afrotropical* (*Senegal to South Africa*). Almost throughout Zambia; not encountered often, but this may be because it is discreet, with no conspicuous song-flights, rather than actually rare. Black squares denote sites where breeding attempted. *Alt.* 370-1700 m, rarely to 2200 m on the Nyika Plateau[1], where it has bred[4].

Ecology In evergreen and deciduous forest, and dense woodland (especially miombo); occasionally hunting in more open country as around human settlements. Preys on medium-sized birds, including doves and a *Coracias*[4]. Overall in denser vegetation than its congener *H. spilogaster.*

Status Resident on the Copperbelt; in parts of S. Zambia it is said to be absent in the cold winter months (e.g. May-Sep)[5], but this may simply be because this discreet eagle is breeding then[4].

Breeding   May   Jul   Sep
(n=8)   5   1   2   *Clutch*: C/1 (4) & N/1 (2); C/2 (1). The C/2 was from near Lundazi,

and the male adult collected[2]. Four records are from Choma.
Taxonomy No races recognized. Formerly known as *H. dubius*[3].
References [1]Aspinwall *et al.* (1973); [2]Benson (1952a); [3]Brooke & Vernon (1981); [4]Dowsett (in press a); [5]Leonard (1999a).

Long-crested Eagle *Lophaetus occipitalis*   B85 **RB**

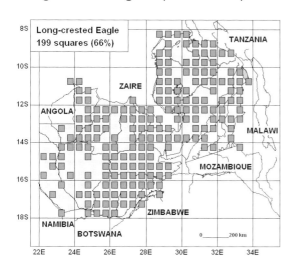

Distribution *Afrotropical (Mauritania to South Africa).* Through most of the country, locally not uncommon; scarce west of the Zambezi (between Kalabo-Mapungu[1] and Kaungo), as in much of the lower Luangwa and Middle Zambezi Valleys[2]. *Alt.* 370-2200 m, commonest above 600 m.

Ecology Typically an ecotone species, e.g. in tall riparian vegetation close to dambos, patches of woodland or large trees next to swamps. Still-hunts in clearings along the margins of forest or woodland, from tall trees.

Status Resident.

Breeding (n=36)	Jan	Feb	Mar	Jun	Jul
	1	1	1	1	4
	Aug	Sep	Oct	Nov	Dec
	5	12	2	6	3

Clutch: C/1 (10); C/2 (14).
Taxonomy No races recognized.
References [1]Benson & Irwin (1967b); [2]Dowsett (in press a).

Crowned Eagle *Stephanoaetus coronatus*   B86 **RB**

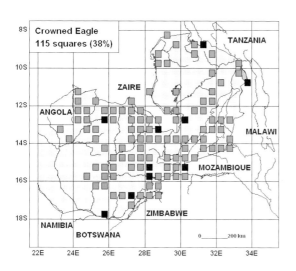

Distribution *Afrotropical (Senegal to South Africa).* Through most of Zambia, except for the south-west, where it reaches the Victoria Falls Gorges[2], Kataba (Kazungula Dist.)[1] and the Kakeka area. In the past it was supposed to be confined to the northern evergreen forests, but whether this is a real extension of range, or whether the species was overlooked before, is not clear[3]. It is not uncommon even on the Copperbelt[5]. *Alt.* 330-2200 m (Nyika, higher on the Malawi side)[4], but sparse at lower levels. Black squares are breeding sites.

Ecology Widely distributed in evergreen and deciduous forest, rich miombo, and generally in dense riparian vegetation. Two pairs breeding on the Zambian Nyika, 4 km from each other (in Chowo and Manyenjere) were often seen flying off a long way over the wooded escarpment to hunt[4]. Prey: mostly monkeys, hyraxes *Dendrohyrax* and game birds, although in one case a small child was attacked[6]. Nests in very large trees.

Status Resident.

Breeding   Jun   Jul   Aug   Sep   Oct   Nov   Dec
(n=20)   1   1   6   6   4   1   1   *Clutch*: C/1 (2); C/2 (1).

Taxonomy No races recognized.

References [1]Bruce-Miller & Dowsett (1977); [2]Colebrook-Robjent (1973); [3]Dowsett (in press a); [4]Dowsett-Lemaire (2006a); [5]Robinson (1973d); [6]Stjernstedt (1975).

Martial Eagle *Polemaetus bellicosus*   B87 **RB**

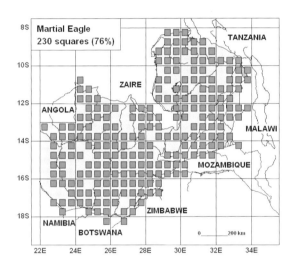

Martial Eagle
230 squares (76%)

Distribution *Afrotropical* (*Mauritania to South Africa*). Throughout the country (further exploration of the Angola border area will doubtless extend its range), and locally not uncommon (e.g. Kafue Flats). *Alt.* 330-2200 m (on the Nyika, higher on the Malawi side)[3].

Ecology In any open country, nesting in large trees. Attacks medium-size mammals (up to the size of juvenile Impala *Aepyceros melampus*)[1] and birds.

Status Resident, with local wandering. A bird ringed as a nestling was recovered after more than 21 years[2] (some 80 km distant).

Breeding   Mar   Apr   May   Jun   Jul
(n=53)   5   14   19   9   6
Clutch: C/1 (32); C/2 (1).

Taxonomy No races recognized.

References [1]Dowsett (in press a); [2]Dowsett & Leonard (2001); [3]Dowsett-Lemaire (2006a).

Pandionidae

Osprey *Pandion haliaetus*   B100 **PW**

Distribution *Almost Cosmopolitan, birds in tropical Africa being essentially of Palaearctic origin* (*wintering Mauritania to South Africa*); *very rarely breeds in sub-Saharan Africa*. Through most of the country, except rare in the south-west (with no records from the Mashi). *Alt.* 330-1650 m.

Ecology On lakes, rivers and dams, including suburban locations (e.g. the Copperbelt), wherever there are suitable fish stocks.

Status A Palaearctic migrant, mostly Sep-Apr, but some staying all year[1]. Usually seen singly. A nestling ringed in Sweden was recovered in Zambia in Jan, nearly 17 years later (Appendix 1).

Breeding No records.

Taxonomy *P. h. haliaetus*.

References [1]Dowsett (in press b).

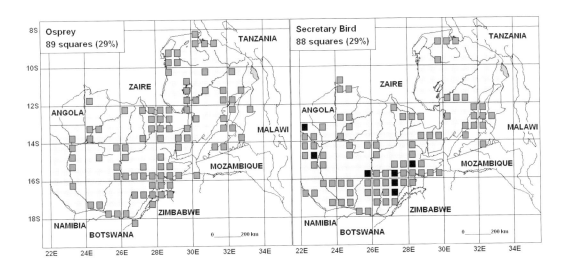

Sagittariidae

Secretary Bird *Sagittarius serpentarius*   B59 **RB**

Distribution *Afrotropical* (*Mauritania to South Africa*). Patchily distributed, with most records from the large floodplains of the Kafue Flats and west of the Zambezi[5]. In Northern Province, north of Bangweulu, known only from the area between L. Tanganyika and Mweru Wantipa[2], with one observation from the Kalungwishi plateau[7]. Wanders occasionally down to the Luangwa and Middle Zambezi Valleys[1,5], but on the Eastern Province plateau known only from vagrants near Katete[4] and in Lukusuzi N.P.[2]. In the Kariba area reported only once, from Sinazongwe[3]. *Alt.* 370-1600 m, but only wanderers below 900 m[5]. Has occurred on the Malawi side of the Nyika[6].
Ecology Drier margins of large dambos and floodplains and abandoned cultivation. Feeds on a variety of prey killed on the ground, especially reptiles, but also tortoises, young birds etc[5].
Status Resident, with local wandering.

Breeding	Jan	Mar	Apr	May	Jul	Aug	Sep	Oct	Nov	Dec
(n=24)	2	1	5	3	2	1	2	3	4	1

Clutch: C/1 (2); C/2 (8); C/3 (1).
Taxonomy No races recognized.
References [1]Allen & Ansell (1966); [2]Benson (1956d); [3]Benson (1959c); [4]Benson *et al.* (1970); [5]Dowsett (in press a); [6]Dowsett-Lemaire (2006a); [7]Neave (1910).

Falconidae

Lesser Kestrel *Falco naumanni*   B110 **PW**

Distribution *Palaearctic* (*the whole population winters Senegal to South Africa*). Passes almost throughout in more open country, though there are as yet no records from the area north of Liuwa Plain, and few observations from Mwinilunga[2,4]. Most frequently reported from the Kafue Flats and Southern

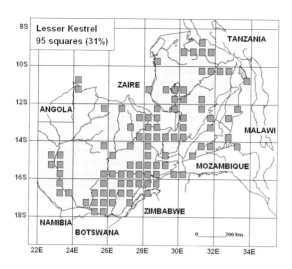

Province plateau. *Alt.* 330-2200 m.

Ecology Birds feed over any grassland (especially floodplains and dambos) and cultivation.

Status A Palaearctic migrant and winter visitor. Records all fall between 10 Oct (mean first date 26 Oct in 27 years) and 27 Apr (mean last 31 Mar in 25 years)[3], but rather few winter. Most are on passage in Nov and (especially) Mar, when groups of up to 150 (though usually up to 25) may occur in the western half of the country, especially at Lochinvar[3].

Conservation Classed as "Vulnerable"[1], but no evidence of a decline in numbers or of persecution in Zambia.

Taxonomy No races recognized.

References [1]BirdLife International (2000, 2004a); [2]Bowen (1983h); [3]Dowsett (in press b); [4]White (1945-46).

Rock (Common) Kestrel *Falco tinnunculus*   B111 **RB/PV**

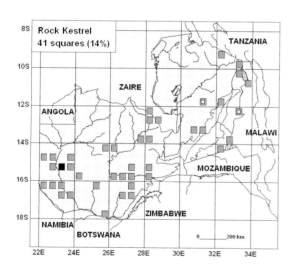

Distribution *Old World* (*in the Afrotropics, breeds from parts of West Africa to South Africa; Palaearctic birds winter mainly Senegal to Tanzania*). No regular breeding sites are known, but it has nested at Mongu[3] (black square) and probably does so in the Mafingas. Associated with plains in the south and west, north to Nasilele, Kaba Hill[6] and the Busanga[10]. In the eastern and central parts of the country more a bird of rocky hills and escarpments (absent from the valleys), so far unknown north-west of Chozi and Mpika[2]. The Mpika record and that from Lundazi[5] (open squares) are specimens of the Palaearctic nominate race. *Alt.* 950 to 2000 m in the Mafingas[7], wandering rarely to 2100 m on the Nyika (near Manyenjere).

Ecology Hunts over any open country. The one known nest (at Mongu) was on a building[3], but birds behaving as if breeding were around rocky outcrops on the Mafingas[6].

Status[1] Probably resident in the extreme east and west, but although there are records for all months, most are May to Oct and many may be wanderers from further south. Usually singly, but up to 4 together. The species is not recorded in most years, and influxes may be irregular and influenced by particularly cold winters (as with other species, such as the sparrow-lark *Eremopterix verticalis*)[6]. Dates of the two Palaearctic specimens are 8 Jan and 18 Mar[5].

Breeding   Aug/Sep
(n=1)   1

Birds on the Mafingas appeared to be territorial in Oct. *Clutch*: C/3 (1).

Taxonomy[9] *F. t. rupicolus* has been collected in W. Zambia, during a dry season irruption[4], and is also likely to be the local breeding form. *F. t. tinnunculus* (paler and larger) has occurred as a migrant from the Palaearctic. Molecular studies suggest these two taxa may be different species[8].
References [1]Aspinwall (1977a); [2]Benson (1956d); [3]Benson (1959c); [4]Benson & Irwin (1967b); [5]Benson *et al.* (1970); [6]Dowsett (in press a); [7]Dowsett & Stjernstedt (1973); [8]Groombridge *et al.* (2002); [9]Irwin & Benson (1966b); [10]Pitman (1934).

Greater Kestrel *Falco rupicoloides* B112 **AMB**

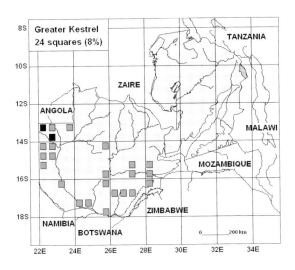

Distribution *Afrotropical (disjunct populations, Somalia to South Africa).* Known to breed (black squares) only in the far west, on the Minyanya, Mitashi and South Kashiji Plains[1]. Wanders further in some years, east to the Busanga Plain, the Lusaka area, Batoka plateau[2] and Livingstone[3]. *Alt.* 950-1300 m.
Ecology Its breeding habitat is watershed grass plains, but wanderers can occur over any grassland. Utilises the old nests of *Corvus capensis*[1]. Prey has included a variety of invertebrates, and a Pygmy Mouse *Mus minutoides*[3].
Status An intra-African migrant and breeding visitor. Records fall between 30 Apr and 8 Jan (away from the breeding area not after 1 Nov), so most if not all are probably dry season visitors, presumably from further south. However, possibly resident in the far west (lack of permanent observers means that its status there during the rains is unknown). When not breeding seen in ones and twos usually, but 8 together at Lochinvar 28 Aug 1964[3], a year when other southern species invaded Zambia.
Breeding[4]   Aug   Sep
(n=10)   1   9   *Clutch*: C/1 (2); C/2 (2); C/3 (2); C/4 (4).
Taxonomy *F. r. rupicoloides.*
References [1]Aspinwall (1979b); [2]Benson (1956d); [3]Dowsett & Leonard (in press a); [4]Osborne & Colebrook-Robjent (1982).

Dickinson's Kestrel *Falco dickinsoni* B107 **RB**

Distribution *Zambezian endemic (Zaire to South Africa).* Almost throughout, but few records west of the Zambezi (e.g. Luachi River[6] and Imusho[1]), and sparse on the Eastern Province plateau[3]. *Alt.* 330-1800 m, wandering exceptionally to 2150 m (Nyika Plateau[4]).
Ecology Hunts in lightly wooded country or grassland. Is much attracted to grass fires (including the bird which appeared on the Nyika Plateau in Jun-Jul 1980)[4]. Nests studied were in dead *Hyphaene* palm stumps, with their crowns broken off, 7-18 m high. Also nests in *Borassus* palms. Food given to chicks included small lizards, chameleons, grasshoppers and other invertebrates, small amphibians, a rat and a small insectivorous bat[2]. Adults are largely insectivorous, but have been recorded feeding on most of

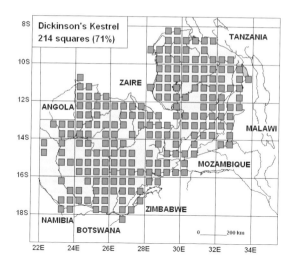

the items given to chicks, as well as snakes and birds (e.g. one was seen to try to catch a lark and another *Prinia subflava*)[3,5].

Status Resident, but there may be a post-breeding dispersal, in part altitudinal, as frequency rates are noticeably lower Nov-Jan. Usually singly when not breeding, but groups of up to 9 are reported[3].

Breeding

	Sep	Oct	Nov
(n=54)	19	33	2

Also "breeding" Jul[7].

Clutch: C/1 (5); C/2 (12); C/3 (31); C/4 (2).

Taxonomy No races recognized.

References [1]Benson & Irwin (1967b); [2]Colebrook-Robjent & Tanner (1978); [3]Dowsett (in press a); [4]Dowsett-Lemaire (2006a); [5]Robinson (1973c); [6]Traylor & Hart (1965); [7]Winterbottom (1939a).

[Grey Kestrel *Falco ardosiaceus*

Afrotropical (*Mauritania to W. Tanzania; virtually allopatric with* F. dickinsoni). There is a single-observer sight record from Chana Chamuhina Plain (1024C) in N. Mwinilunga, on 5 and 6 Nov 1998[5]. This may have been correctly identified (it is necessary to rule out the possibility of such similar species as *F. dickinsoni* and *F. concolor,* and even *Melierax gabar* has been confused in the past). However, confirmation in the form of a film or specimen is desirable. One among several sightings from Sumbu (0830C) on L. Tanganyika[1] may also have been correct, although others from there were certainly misidentified. There are two Feb and Mar specimens from Kasaji[4], and at least one specimen from SE Zaire (although another seems to be a hybrid *F. ardosiaceus x F. dickinsoni*[2], which shows the care needed to identify this species). *F. ardosiaceus* ranges to the Rukwa Valley in SW Tanzania, and has also been collected once (15 May) in N. Malawi[3], an extreme vagrant. **References** [1]Jones (1974a); [2]Louette (1989); [3]Nhlane (1989); [4]Schouteden (1971); [5]Van Daele (1999b).]

Western Red-footed Falcon *Falco vespertinus*   B108 **P(W)**

Distribution *Palaearctic* (*its main wintering range is in Botswana and N. Namibia*). Commonest in the western half of the country, although does occur east to Mbala and (rarely) the Nyika Plateau[3]. Unknown from the Eastern Province plateau [records from Chassa[5] were in fact of *F. amurensis*[4]]. *Alt.* 800-2200 m.

Ecology In open country; may associate with other falcons (*F. naumanni* and *F. amurensis*), feeding on flying termites.

Status A Palaearctic migrant and (in part) winter visitor. The species is recorded between 30 Sep and 7 Apr (either this species or *F. amurensis* on 12 Apr)[2]. Very few stay during the rains, and return movements north are small. Flocks of up to 50 are noted mostly on southward passage, Oct-Dec[2]. Exceptionally up to 2000 were present in Mwinilunga 7-8 Oct 1978, after the first rains on 6th[1]. Through lack of regular coverage in W. Zambia, we do not know if numbers have decreased in recent years.

Taxonomy No races recognized.

References [1]Bowen (1979g); [2]Dowsett (in press b); [3]Dowsett-Lemaire (2006a); [4]Garcia (1975); [5]Taylor (1979a).

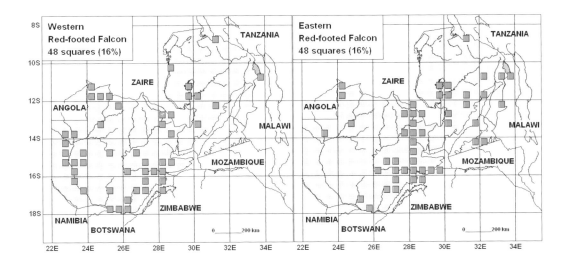

Eastern Red-footed (Amur) Falcon *Falco amurensis*   B109 **PW**

Distribution *Palaearctic* (*the whole population winters in southern Africa*)[3]. Mainly in the central and eastern parts of Zambia, being very scarce in the west[2], to Mwinilunga[4], Zambezi town (Balovale)[1,4] and Livingstone[2]. *Alt.* 550-2200 m.

Ecology Feeds over grassland and cultivation, eating essentially insects (such as locusts and flying termites).

Status A Palaearctic migrant and winter visitor, with extreme dates 9 Oct and 18 Apr. Occurs mostly from mid-Nov (mean first date 13 Nov in 20 years) to the third week of Mar (mean last 24 Mar in 21 years)[2]. Present throughout the rains, usually in small groups of up to 50, sometimes 200-300 (Dec-Jan in S. Zambia). In some recent years very large numbers have roosted on passage in the Choma area (thousands at Nkanga, Feb 2007, with few remaining early Apr)[2]. Certainly more often encountered than *F. vespertinus*. Rarely numerous in Zambia, and when large numbers occur, this may reflect displacement of roosts from elsewhere in southern Africa.

Taxonomy No races recognized. In the past has been considered conspecific with *F. vespertinus*.

References [1]Britton (1970); [2]Dowsett (in press b); [3]Mendelsohn in Harrison *et al.* (1997); [4]White (1945-46).

Red-necked Falcon *Falco chicquera*   B106 **RB**

Distribution *Old World Tropics* (*in Africa, Mauritania to South Africa*). Apart from Mbesuma on the Chambeshi, its northern distribution is essentially the country between Lakes Tanganyika and Mweru and the Luapula Valley, wandering as a vagrant to Ndola[6] and the slopes of the Nyika[3] (open squares). It is present in the central and upper Luangwa Valley, from Chama, and throughout the lower Kafue basin to the Lukanga River confluence[3]. Probably throughout the Upper Zambezi, but there are so far no records from the extreme south-west between Senanga and Barker's[3], nor from the Gwembe Valley.

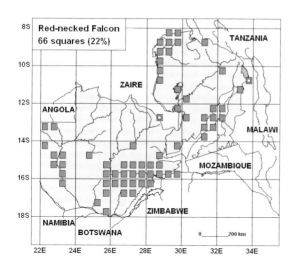

Alt. 500-1660 m.

Ecology[2] Often associated with *Borassus* and *Hyphaene* palms (used for nesting), hunting in lightly-wooded country, grassland (of flood-plains, dambos) and cultivation. They also use other birds' nests, especially those of crows *Corvus albus*[7] and *C. capensis*[1]. Their main prey consists of birds (98% of prey in the Luangwa Valley, especially *Agapornis lilianae*, which are abundant there) and bats[4]. Locally common in breeding areas, with 8 nests in 44 sq. km on the Kafue Flats[2,8].

Status Resident.

Breeding[2,6]   Aug   Sep
(n=88)   52   36

Clutch: C/1 (3); C/2 (11); C/3 (27); C/4 (31).

Taxonomy[5] *F. c. ruficollis*.

References [1]Aspinwall (1979b); [2]Colebrook-Robjent & Osborne (1974); [3]Dowsett (in press a); [4]Guhrs & Osborne (1988); [5]Irwin & Benson (1966b); [6]Jones (1974b); [7]Osborne (1981); [8]Osborne (1984).

Eurasian Hobby *Falco subbuteo*   B105 **PW**

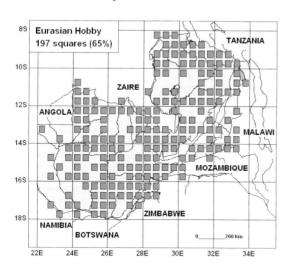

Distribution *Palaearctic (in the Afrotropics, winters mainly Ivory Coast to South Africa).* Widespread throughout the rains in small numbers, the sparseness of records in the far west probably a reflection of insufficient observer coverage. *Alt.* 330-2200 m.

Ecology Over any woodland, wooded grass-land, forest-grassland mosaic, also in subur-ban situations. Singles or often in small groups (as when catching flying termites, or even birds).

Status A Palaearctic migrant and winter visi-tor, with extreme dates 22 Sep and 23 Apr. First arrivals in the north are often early Oct (mean date 15 Oct over 30 years), but main passage south seems influenced by the arrival of heavy rains (when sometimes associated with flocks of *Hirundo rustica*). Parties of up to 30 or even 50 are regular on passage with maxima of *c.* 100 mid-Dec and 50+ mid-Mar (few after that date: mean last date 30 Mar, sample 28 years)[3]. [A record claimed for Aug[1] seems to have been in error[3].] A nestling ringed in Holland was recovered in Zambia in Nov, 10 years later (Appendix 1).

Taxonomy[2] *F. s. subbuteo*, but it is possible the race *jugurtha* (if valid) also occurs (whiter below, with narrower streaking). A partial albino was seen at Kitwe[4].

References [1]Bowen (1979a); [2]Clancey (1974a); [3]Dowsett (in press b); [4]Tree (1963a).

African Hobby *Falco cuvierii* B104 **AMB**

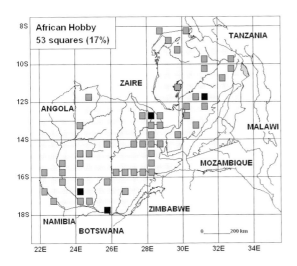

Distribution *Afrotropical (Senegal to South Africa).* A bird confined to plateau areas, being absent from the Eastern Province plateau and Luangwa Valley [but known in the Middle Zambezi Valley, associated with palms, from Kariba (1628D) down to the Dande area (1630A), Zimbabwe[6,7]]. It ranges throughout much of N. Zambia, westwards to Mundwiji Plain[8], Manyinga and Simuhanga[4], and south to Sesheke and Livingstone[2] (nest sites are black squares). In the north-east it is unknown in the Luapula Valley between L. Mweru and Samfya, but otherwise ranges east to the Isoka area[3] (there are few if any authentic records from Malawi). *Alt.* 950-1700 m.

Ecology Typically in or near open country, especially plains with light woodland, where it hunts small birds such as swallows *Hirundo* spp. The Oct/Nov breeding record is based on an occupied nest (probably of *Corvus albus*) at Mpika, high in a tall eucalyptus tree[1]. A pair was present early Nov at "a big old-looking stick nest at a height of 10-15 m in the fork of a *Guibourtia coleosperma*"[4]. It has also attempted to breed in a *Haliaeetus vocifer* nest[9].

Status Apparently an intra-African breeding visitor, with all records between 5 Aug and 9 Mar, except for three sightings of single birds between 26 Apr and 23 Jun[4]. In southern Africa most records are Sep-Apr[5]. The timing of its presence is very similar to that of an established intra-African migrant, *Milvus migrans parasitus*. No report of more than 3 together.

Breeding Oct Oct/Nov
(n=2) 1 1 *Clutch:* C/3 (1).

Taxonomy No races recognized.

References [1]Benson (1956d); [2]Brooke (1969); [3]Clay (1953); [4]Dowsett & Leonard (in press a); [5]Mendelsohn in Harrison *et al.* (1997); [6]Howells (1985); [7]Hustler (1987); [8]Leonard & Peters (1999); [9]Penry (1978b).

Sooty Falcon *Falco concolor* B - **P(W)**

Distribution *Saharo-Sindian (E. Sahara to Arabian Peninsula), migrating mostly to Madagascar, with a small population also regularly visiting the coast of KwaZulu-Natal.* Since 1976 there have been several acceptable sight records (including a photograph)[3], from Kasaba Bay and Homani, west to Kitwe and Mwinilunga, and south to Choma and Livingstone[2]. *Alt.* 1100-1350 m.

Ecology In any open woodland, even gardens.

Status[1,2] A Palaearctic migrant. The 20 or so acceptable records all fall between 4 Oct and 28 Apr. Most are on passage, but it is clear that an occasional bird winters. All but one have been singles, once two together.

Taxonomy No races recognized.

References [1]Dowsett (1979a); [2]Leonard & Colebrook-Robjent (2001); [3]Penry (1979a).

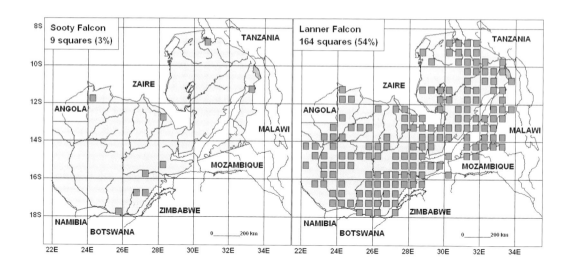

Lanner Falcon *Falco biarmicus*   B101 **RB**

Distribution *S. Palaearctic and Afrotropical (Mauritania to South Africa)*. Possibly throughout: the gaps in parts of Northern and Luapula Provinces may reflect scarcity in higher-rainfall areas, or else inadequate exploration. *Alt.* 330-2200 m (Nyika).

Ecology Nests on cliffs (locally on quite small rocky hills), but also often in abandoned raptors' nests in trees[1]. Hunts in open country; mainly birds up to the size of *Tockus nasutus*[5]. Not uncommon near habitation, frequently taking poultry. In many rocky areas it replaces *F. peregrinus*, and active confrontation between the two has been observed (to the detriment of Peregrine)[1].

Status Mostly resident. The recovery in Zambia (in Jun) of a bird ringed in South Africa (as an adult in Mar, Appendix 1) matches a similar example in Malawi (an adult ringed in South Africa in Mar recovered in May)[2]; this suggests a small influx of birds in the dry season from the arid south-west of southern Africa (where the species is a partial migrant[3]).

Breeding[4]   Jun   Jul   Aug   Sep

(n=41)   2   26   9   4   *Clutch*: C/1 (1); C/2 (3); C/3 (6); C/4 (10).

Taxonomy *F. b. biarmicus*.

References [1]Dowsett (in press a); [2]Dowsett-Lemaire & Dowsett (2006); [3]Jenkins in Harrison *et al.* (1997); [4]Osborne & Colebrook-Robjent (1984); [5]Tree (1963c).

Peregrine Falcon *Falco peregrinus*   B102 **RB**

Distribution *Almost Cosmopolitan (in the Afrotropics, breeds Sahel to South Africa, with Palaearctic migrants rarely reaching southern Africa)*. Mostly associated with rocky areas in the eastern half of the country, west to the Copperbelt[2], Itezhi-Tezhi and the Victoria Falls Gorges[1] (black squares are nest sites). It has also been seen occasionally west to Mwinilunga Dist. It wanders at times to floodplains (the Kafue Flats and Busanga, for example). The species is unrecorded from the Luapula region, west of Sumbu N.P. and Samfya. There is no certain record of the Palaearctic race, but Peregrines thought to possess the characters of *calidus* include birds seen at known or probable breeding sites (Livingstone and Mulungushi Dam)[1]. *Alt.* 370-2200 m.

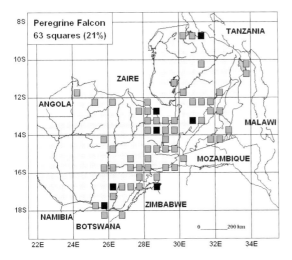

Ecology Hunts in any type of wooded country, escarpments and gorges, breeding on cliffs. Observations of birds in floodplains a long way away from cliffs (e.g. Lochinvar) may refer to the Palaearctic race, but are as likely to be resident birds.

Status Resident, with local wandering.

Breeding

	Jun	Jul	Aug	Sep
(n=15)	1	3	10	1

Clutch: C/2 (2); C/3 (6) & N/3 (2).

Taxonomy *F. p. minor* is the breeding form, while *F. p. calidus* (larger and paler) may occur as a Palaearctic migrant.

References [1]Dowsett (in press a); [2]Robinson (1975a).

## Taita Falcon *Falco fasciinucha*					B103 **RB**

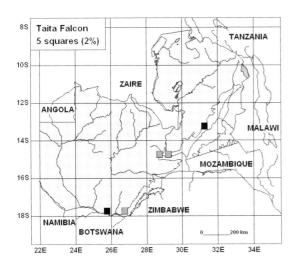

Distribution *Afrotropical (Ethiopia to N. South Africa)*. Very sparse, known from scattered localities along the Muchinga and Zambezi escarpments (doubtless overlooked in a habitat very difficult of access). From the Masase area[1], Wonder Gorge, Devil's Gorge (opposite the Gwaai River mouth)[8] and along the gorges below the Victoria Falls[2,4,6]. Black squares denote known breeding areas (there are others on the Zimbabwe side of the Middle Zambezi Valley). *Alt.* 880-1500 m.

Ecology Nests in holes and on sheltered ledges on cliff faces in rocky gorges. In the Victoria Falls Gorges in 1984 sites of 3 nests were some 3 km apart, while the overall density in part of the Gorges was one pair per 6 km[9]. Preys predominantly on small birds, up to the size of *Pycnonotus barbatus*[4]. It was suggested that the choice of a "less than optimal" breeding site on the Muchinga escarpment was the result of competition with the larger *F. peregrinus*, also present[9].

Status Resident, wandering only a few km from nesting areas.

Conservation Classed as "Near Threatened"[3]. Can no longer be found readily in its best known area, the Victoria Falls Gorges, possibly as a result of tourist disturbance (e.g. over-flights) or competition with the two larger *Falco, F. biarmicus* and *F. peregrinus*[7]. On the other hand, most of its habitat is extremely difficult of access, and there is no reason to worry about the population as a whole. Several nest sites are known along the Muchinga escarpment[5].

Breeding[4]

	Jul	Aug	Sep
(n=16)	2	4	10

Clutch: C/3 (7); C/4 (1).

Taxonomy No races recognized.

References [1]Benson (1961c); [2]Benson & Smithers (1958); [3]BirdLife International (2000, 2004a); [4]Dowsett (1983); [5]Dowsett (in press a); [6]Holliday (1965b); [7]Leonard (2005); [8]Thomson (1969); [9]Weaver *et al.* (2002).

Phasianidae

Coqui Francolin *Francolinus coqui* B114 **RB**

Distribution *Afrotropical* (*Niger to South Africa*). Throughout the Zambian plateau, absent from the low-lying Luangwa and Middle Zambezi Valleys, except marginally in the latter near Kariba and in the Gwembe area[3]. *Alt. c.* 550 m (Kariba) to 1800 m (eastern highlands).
Ecology Common in miombo woodland (with good grass cover), less so in mopane, wooded grassland and edges of plains.
Status Resident.
Breeding

	Jul	Aug	Sep	Oct	Nov	Dec	Jan	Feb	Mar	Apr	May
(n=75)	1	3	5	7	11	10	12	12	3	5	6

Clutch: C/1 (2); C/2 (2); C/3 (4); C/4 (7); C/5 (10); C/6 (2).
Taxonomy *F. c. coqui*, replaced by *F. c. vernayi* (males paler, more sandy grey on the mantle) in the Kalahari sand woodlands of the west (Kabompo south to Sesheke), and by *F. c. angolensis* (crown darker chestnut, whole plumage more saturated) in the north-west (intergrading with *vernayi*)[1]. Some authors place it in the genus *Peliperdix*[2].
References [1]Benson & Irwin (1967b); [2]Crowe *et al.* (1992); [3]Dowsett (in press a).

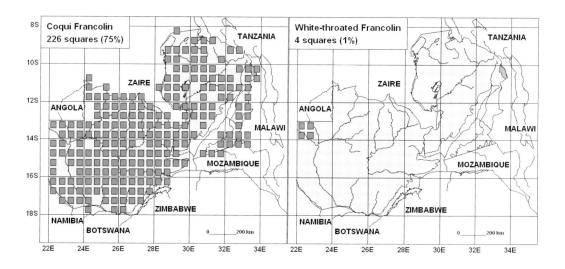

White-throated Francolin *Francolinus albogularis* B113 **R(B)**

Distribution *Afrotropical* (*Senegal to Angola and Zambia*). Enters Zambia in the extreme west, in Zambezi Dist. west of the river. Known only from plains centred on the North Kashiji River: Minyanya[1], east to the Lukolwe River[3], south to Kumanu Plain (where first found by K. Muzeya in 1943[4]; the most southerly records of the species). Quite common on Minyanya, with 10-15 heard calling early morning Aug-Sep[1]. *Alt.* 950-1150 m.

Ecology On dry grass plains, locally with carpets of suffrutex (*Parinari capensis*). Fly onto small wooded islands when disturbed (and roost in them). Feeds on termites, ants, beetles, grass seeds etc[1]. Slightly smaller than *F. coqui*, which occurs in more wooded situations.

Status Resident, in small, doubtless family, groups (5 or more)[1].

Breeding No records.

Taxonomy *F. a. meinertzhageni* (type locality Kumanu Plain; *NHM*)[4], named for Richard Meinertzhagen [1878-1967], ornithologist and explorer. Some authors place it in the genus *Peliperdix*[2].

References [1]Aspinwall (1979b); [2]Crowe *et al.* (1992); [3]Dowsett (in press a); [4]White (1944d:7).

Crested Francolin *Francolinus sephaena*   B115 **RB**

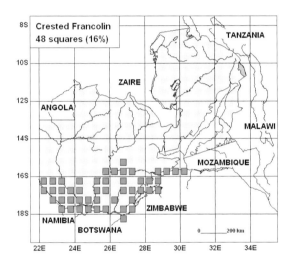

Distribution *Afrotropical* (*Ethiopia to South Africa*). Locally quite common in the southern third of Zambia, north in the west to some 45 km north of Shangombo[1], in the Kafue basin to the Mumbwa-Nalusanga road[4], and along the Zambezi, east to Luangwa town (Feira)[4,5]. *Alt.* 330-1200 m.

Ecology Common in thickets (including in *Baikiaea* forest) and dry riparian vegetation.

Status Resident.

Breeding (n=15)	Oct	Nov	Dec
	1	1	8
	Jan	Feb	Mar
	3	1	1

Clutch: C/2 (1); C/3 (5); C/4 (1); C/5 (1); C/6 (2).

Taxonomy *F. s. zambesiae*[5], with some tendency towards nominate *sephaena* (less red above, a paler, creamy buff below) in the Kazungula area[2]. Sometimes placed in the genus *Dendroperdix*[3].

References [1]Benson & Irwin (1967b); [2]Clancey (1968c); [3]Crowe *et al.* (1992); [4]Dowsett (in press a); [5]Irwin & Benson (1967b).

Shelley's Francolin *Francolinus shelleyi*   B116 **RB**

Distribution *Afrotropical* (*Zaire to South Africa*). Sparse, in rocky woodlands in much of N. and south-central Zambia. In the north, west to Nsama, and to Mupemba (Mansa Dist.)[2]. In the west of the country reaches the Mwinilunga area[9], the Luena River[1] and on the Zambezi to near Livingstone[9]. In the Luangwa and Middle Zambezi Valleys the species is present only along the rocky escarpments[5]. *Alt.* 330 to 1950 m in the Mafingas[6] and Nyika[7].

Ecology Mainly in light miombo woodland, also mopane, with a preference for hills with rocky or stony terrain.

Status Resident.

Breeding (n=26)	Feb	Mar	Apr	May	Jun	Sep	Oct	Nov	Dec
	2	1	3	3	1	9	5	1	1

Clutch: C/2 (1); C/3 (1); C/4 (1); C/5 (3); C/6 (4); C/7 (1).

Taxonomy[3] *F. s. shelleyi* E. and S. Zambia, replaced by *F. s. whytei* (type locality Nyika Plateau, Malawi)[8] elsewhere. Some authors recognize the genus *Scleroptila*[4].

References [1]Benson & Irwin (1967b); [2]Benson & White (1957); [3]Benson *et al.* (1971a); [4]Crowe *et al.* (1992); [5]Dowsett (in press a); [6]Dowsett & Stjernstedt (1973); [7]Dowsett-Lemaire (2006a); [8]Neumann (1908); [9]White & Winterbottom (1949).

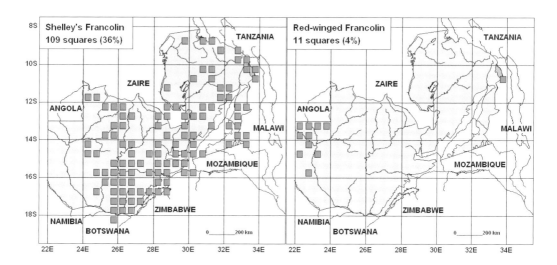

Red-winged Francolin *Francolinus levaillantii*   B117 **RB**

Distribution *Afrotropical* (*Uganda to South Africa*)*; montane in many parts of its range, including NE Zambia.* There are two distinct populations, one in the eastern highlands (confined to the Nyika plateau, where common[5]), the other coming into the western plains, east to Konkano Plain[8] and the Luena Flats[2], south to Lushushwa[4]. *Alt.* 1000-1150 m in the west, 1950-2200 m on the Nyika (higher on the Malawi side)[5].

Ecology Montane grassland (common above 2100 m) in the east, dry watershed grasslands in the west.

Status Resident.

Breeding

	Oct	Nov	Dec	Jan	Mar	Apr	Jul	Aug	Sep
(n=13)	2	1	2	1	1	1	1	2	2

All records Oct-Apr are from the Nyika, all Jul-Sep from W. Zambia.

Clutch: C/4 (1). Also one group of 8 chicks on the Nyika.

Taxonomy *F. l. crawshayi* on the Nyika Plateau (type locality Nchenachena on the Malawi side)[6], and *F. l. momboloensis* (nom. nov. for *benguellensis*) (blacker, less rufous above) in the west[1] (syn. *F. l. clayi* type locality Kajilisha[7]; *type specimen lost*, named for G. Clay). Some authors recognize the genus *Scleroptila*[3].

References [1]Benson & Irwin (1967b); [2]Benson & White (1957); [3]Crowe *et al.* (1992); [4]Dowsett (in press a); [5]Dowsett-Lemaire (2006a); [6]Ogilvie-Grant (1896); [7]White (1944b: 50); [8]White (1946b).

[Orange River Francolin *Francolinus levaillantoides*

Somalia-Masai and Kalahari (*Sudan to Kenya and Angola to South Africa*). This species has been mapped as occurring in the Caprivi Strip adjacent to SW Zambia (1723D, 1724C)[4], but this may be a misidentification[3]. It is also reported as far north as Moxico in Angola[1], but this is in error, and far from the normal range of the species[2,5]. **References** [1]Dean (2000); [2]Dean *et al.* (2002); [3]Dowsett *et al.* (in prep.); [4]Little & Allan in Harrison *et al.* (1997); [5]Pinto (1983).]

Red-billed Francolin *Francolinus adspersus*   B118 **RB**

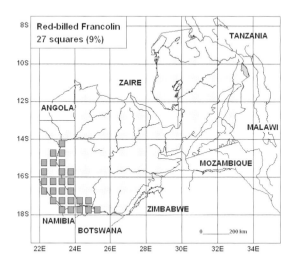

Distribution *Kalahari/Zambezian (Angola to South Africa).* Confined to the south-west, where at the edge of its range, but locally common (and the most numerous francolin in Sioma-Ngwezi N.P.). Ranges up the Zambezi to the Lukulu area[5], and eastwards to Kazungula[1]. *Alt.* 950-1050 m.

Ecology Most often in thickets near water, especially on floodplains (where it retreats a short distance to higher ground at peak floods). Occasionally in thicket in *Baikiaea* away from water.

Status Resident.

Breeding   Dec   Jan   Mar
(n=3)   1   1   1

Clutch: C/4 (1); C/5 (1).

Taxonomy[2,3] *F. a. mesicus.* May be placed in the genus *Pternistis*[4].

References [1]Benson & Irwin (1967b); [2]Clancey (1968c); [3]Clancey (1996); [4]Crowe *et al.* (1992); [5]Dowsett (in press a).

Natal Francolin *Francolinus natalensis*   B119 **RB**

Distribution *Afrotropical (Zambia to South Africa).* Ranges in thicket from just above 13°S in the upper Luangwa Valley (Julius and the Nsefu area)[4], down through the Luano and Middle Zambezi Valleys, west to the Mulobezi area and to between Masese and Sesheke[6]. It does not range west of the Zambezi (and is unknown from the whole of Angola). Throughout the Southern Province plateau (where common), to the north side of the Kafue Flats and up the Kafue to the Kafue/Lufupa River confluence[7] and Mswebe. It occurs locally in some plateau areas, as at Mkushi River (Chalata)[6]. [There are reports near Chipata and Nyanje in Eastern Province, not mapped, as the possibility of confusion with *F. hildebrandti* cannot be ruled out[6]. It is unknown from the Malawi side of the border.] *Alt.* 330-1400 m (Chalata).

Ecology Dense deciduous thickets principally, dry riparian forest and in places cover on rocky hillsides (as at Itezhi-Tezhi). It occurs locally alongside *F. sephaena* and even *F. afer*, where that species is in thicker vegetation. But it is not known from the same localities as *F. hildebrandti*. Feeds on a variety of invertebrate and vegetable matter[1,2].

Status Resident.

Breeding   Jan   Mar   Apr   May   Jul   Aug
(n=18)   1   2   7   3   3   2   *Clutch*: C/7 (1).

Taxonomy *F. n. neavei* (type locality near Old Petauke; *NHM*)[5,7], named for S.A. Neave, doubtfully separable from *F. n. natalensis*. This species and *F. hildebrandti* are very closely related (the males are impossible to separate in the field), and they replace each other in the Luangwa Valley. The range

limits of each are poorly known, and the possibility of hybridisation has not been investigated. Some authors would place it in the genus *Pternistis*[3].
References [1]Benson (1960b); [2]Benson (1963); [3]Crowe *et al.* (1992); [4]Dowsett (1969a); [5]Dowsett (1980b); [6]Dowsett (in press a); [7]Mackworth-Praed (1920: 140).

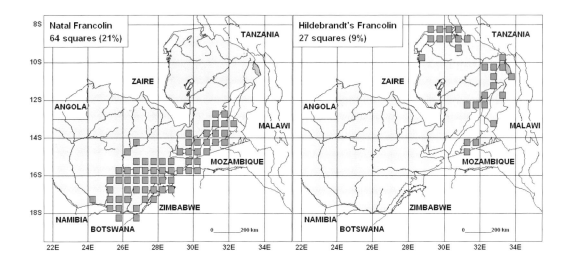

Hildebrandt's Francolin *Francolinus hildebrandti*   B120 **RB**

Distribution *Afrotropical* (*Kenya to Malawi*). This species and *F. natalensis* are essentially allopatric. *F. hildebrandti* occurs in the low-lying area between Lakes Tanganyika and Mweru, south to Kapweshi in the Luapula basin[1]. From the top of the Luangwa Valley it ranges south at low altitude to the Mwaleshi[5] and Lundazi Rivers[7], and on the Muchingas at Kungulu Hill[5]. On Eastern Province plateau, south to Kalikali[3], reappearing in the Nyanje-Petauke area (where not uncommon), to Katayauchi Hill on the upper Mvuvye River[5]. *Alt.* 650 m to 1950 m in the Mafingas[6] and to 2200 m on the Nyika.
Ecology In dense deciduous thicket (e.g. Itigi), edges of evergreen forest, and bracken-briar (especially on rocky hills).
Status Resident.
Breeding   Jun   Jul   Aug   Sep
(n=5)   1   2   1   1   *Clutch*: no data.
Taxonomy *F. h. hildebrandti*, although it is possible that birds of the race *johnstoni* (females lack the black mottling on hind neck and breast) are those occurring in parts of the Eastern Province plateau[2]. Some authors would place it in the genus *Pternistis*[4].
References [1]Aspinwall (1974); [2]Benson *et al.* (1970); [3]Benson & Irwin (1964b); [4]Crowe *et al.* (1992); [5]Dowsett (in press a); [6]Dowsett & Stjernstedt (1973); [7]Meyer de Schauensee (1951).

[Scaly Francolin *Francolinus squamatus*
Guineo-Congolian/Afromontane species (*Nigeria and Ethiopia to Malawi*). Occurs in riparian forest at Kasaji in Katanga[2]. There is one, tentative and unconfirmed, sound record from N. Mwinilunga[1].
References [1]Dowsett (in press a); [2]Schouteden (1971).]

Red-necked Francolin *Francolinus afer*   B121 **RB**

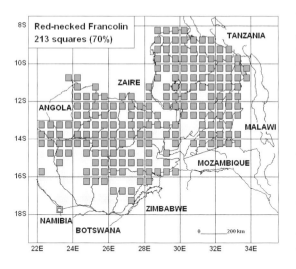

Red-necked Francolin
213 squares (70%)

Distribution *Afrotropical* (*Kenya to South Africa*). Locally abundant throughout the northern two-thirds of the country, though in the Luangwa Valley not known south of about the Mvuvye River[6]. West of the Zambezi south to some 55 km north of Shangombo[1], and exceptionally in the Imusho area (open square)[3], and in the Kafue basin to the upper Machile. Very scarce in the Kafue Flats area, but ranges locally in parts of Southern Province plateau to the Zambezi escarpment in the Masuku area[3]. *Alt.* 550 m to 1950 m in the Mafingas[4] and to 2150 m on the Nyika.

Ecology In any rank grass (thus found in all types of open woodland), abandoned cultivation, clearings in *Cryptosepalum* forest, maize fields, montane grassland and scrub, edges of thickets and mushitu. Where it occurs with *F. swainsonii* it is often in thicker vegetation, but both may mix in the same flock.

Status Resident; large groups may congregate in optimal situations.

Breeding

	Nov	Dec	Jan	Feb	Mar	Apr	May	Jun	Jul	Aug
(n=135)	3	4	4	32	30	33	23	3	2	1

Clutch: C/4 (1); C/7 (1). *Moult*: late Jun-Nov[3,7].

Taxonomy The following races occur: *F. a. cranchii*, replaced by *F. a. loangwae* (type locality Old Petauke; *NHM*)[5] in E. Zambia (down to the Lower Zambezi N.P.), which differs in having the abdomen black with white streaking, rather than with chestnut-brown streaks. Intermediates between these two occur in the Mafingas[4]. *F. a. mackenziei* (type locality Nguvu; *type specimen lost*)[8], named for E.K. Mackenzie [1904-?], Game & Tsetse Control Officer, is a synonym of the first; and *F. a. aylwinae* (type locality Mwase Lundazi; *NHM*)[9] of the second (named for the wife of E.L. Button). Some authors would place it in the genus *Pternistis*[2].

References [1]Benson & Irwin (1967b); [2]Crowe *et al.* (1992); [3]Dowsett (in press a); [4]Dowsett & Stjernstedt (1973); [5]Grant & Mackworth-Praed (1934: 17); [6]Neave (1907); [7]Traylor (1965b); [8]White (1945b: 40); [9]White (1947b: 72).

Swainson's Francolin *Francolinus swainsonii*   B122 **RB**

Distribution *Zambezian/Kalahari* (*Angola to South Africa*). Locally abundant in the dry woodlands of the southern half of the country, north up the Zambezi to some 35 km north of Shangombo and Nasiongo[1]. In the Kafue drainage north to the Kabwe area, and throughout the Middle Zambezi and Luangwa Valleys to about Chiwale. A sight record from Kasanka N.P. (open square) is exceptional[3]. *Alt.* 330-1600 m.

Ecology Rank grass in mopane and other open woodlands, also cultivation and thicket. Food includes a variety of invertebrates, seeds and bulbs.

Status Resident, often assembling in large concentrations where feeding is optimal.

Breeding

	Jan	Feb	Mar	Apr	May	Jun	Jul	Aug	Sep	Oct	Nov	Dec
(n=113)	3	21	30	20	11	11	6	3	3	1	1	3

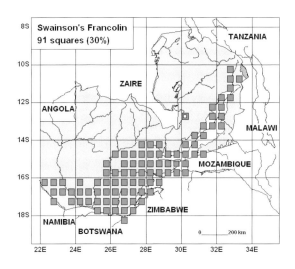

Clutch: C/5 (8); C/6 (3).

Moult: adults moult May-Aug[3].

Taxonomy *F. s. lundazi* (type locality Lupamadzi River; *type specimen lost*)[4]. Some authors would place it in the genus *Pternistis*[2].

References [1]Benson & Irwin (1967b); [2]Crowe *et al.* (1992); [3]Dowsett (in press a); [4]White (1947b: 72).

Common Quail *Coturnix coturnix*   B123 **R(B)/AM**

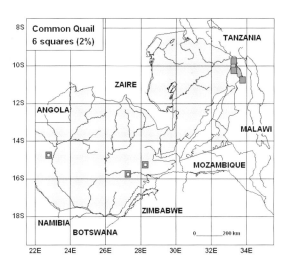

Distribution *Old World (breeding populations from Ethiopia to South Africa are essentially montane; Palaearctic birds winter north of the Equator)*. As a breeding resident only on the Nyika Plateau (where common)[4], and the Mafingas[5]. As an irregular invasive visitor from southern Africa in winter (open squares), recorded in the west on Liuwa Plain and in the Kafue basin at Lochinvar[2]. There are also convincing records from Lusaka[1]. *Alt.* montane populations at 2000-2200 m (higher Malawi side of Nyika)[4], others from 1000-1160 m.

Ecology In montane grassland as a breeding bird, in dry short grass plains as a migrant.

Status Resident on the Nyika, and presumably Mafingas. Migrants very irregular elsewhere (between 23 Apr and 8 Oct), perhaps only in very cold winters (as in 1964, when *Eremopterix verticalis* also arrived in the south of the country)[3]. The situation is confused by difficulties of identification. Reported to have occurred in large numbers in some years in the 1950s by European sportsmen, 27 reportedly shot on one day (20 May)[1].

Breeding No records in Zambia, but on the Malawi side of the Nyika egg-laying reported Feb-Mar (and song from Nov-Mar)[4].

Taxonomy The breeding form in the eastern highlands is *C. c. erlangeri*, while *C. c. africana* irrupts into the south-west on occasion.

References [1]Benson (1963); [2]Benson & Irwin (1966a); [3]Dowsett (in press a); [4]Dowsett-Lemaire (2006a); [5]Leonard *et al.* (2001a).

Harlequin Quail *Coturnix delegorguei* B124 **AMB**

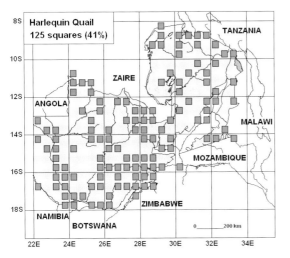

Distribution *Afrotropical (breeds Ethiopia to South Africa).* Probably throughout the country, but scarce in the low-lying Luangwa and Middle Zambezi Valleys. *Alt.* 330-1700 m.

Ecology Floodplain, grassland with scattered bushes or trees, also in cultivation.

Status Essentially a rains visitor, although there are records for all months. Observations are significantly more frequent Nov-May than Jun-Oct[4]. Passage is suggested by records of concentrations of up to 50 in Luangwa (Feira) Dist. in Apr[1], and one caught at night in a block of flats in Lusaka, 5 Dec[2].

Breeding Oct Feb Mar Apr
(n=8) 1 1 5 1
Clutch: C/3 (1); C/7 (1) − laid in one nest by two females[3]. *Moult*: one in mid-Mar[3].

Taxonomy *C. d. delegorguei.*
References [1]Benson (1956f); [2]Benson *et al.* (1970); [3]Dowsett & Leonard (in press a).

Blue Quail *Coturnix chinensis* B125 **AMB**

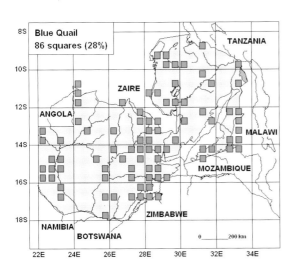

Distribution *Old World Tropics (in Africa breeds Liberia to southern Africa).* Occurs uncommonly in most moister grasslands, but there are some striking gaps. There are few records in the area between Lakes Tanganyika and Mweru, and between the Copperbelt and Mwinilunga. In the Luangwa Valley known only from Frank's Lakes[2], and equally rarely in the Gwembe Valley at Manchamvwa and Matinangala. Occurs rarely south to Livingstone, and further west to the area of the Matabele Plain[3]. *Alt.* 550-1670 m.

Ecology Mainly in dambos, more occasionally rank grass in secondary or lightly-wooded situations. Stomach contents have included grass seeds and grit[1].

Status Most records are during the rains, but a few remain during the dry season[3].

Breeding Jan Feb Apr
(n=8) 2 5 1 *Clutch*: C/3 (1); C/4 (1).
Taxonomy *C. c. adansonii* (sometimes treated as a species distinct from Oriental birds).
References [1]Benson & Pitman (1956-57); [2]Bourdin (1996); [3]Dowsett & Leonard (in press a).

Numididae

Crested Guineafowl *Guttera pucherani*   B127 **RB**

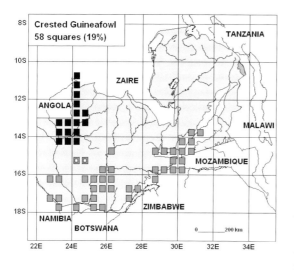

Distribution *Afrotropical (Guinea-Bissau to South Africa)*. Locally common in thicket country: from N. Mwinilinga[6] south to Luena[3], and west to the Zambezi (race *kathleenae*, black squares). Reappears (open squares, race unrecorded) to the south in the Kamando area, and at the Lufupa/Kafue River confluence (*edouardi*)[2] and near Natukoma (west of the Zambezi). It ranges south to the Mulobezi and Katombora areas, and even to Chundu (near Livingstone)[8], then locally along the Zambezi escarpment, through the Middle Zambezi and Luano Valleys, to 3 km below the Mkuzye/Luangwa River confluence[5]. It perhaps occurs in the Sumbu area ("?") in the far north, and local reports suggest it may also be in Mweru Wantipa[8] (although earlier reports were considered unproven[1]). [Similarly, old reports from the upper Kafue basin and Kasempa Dist. were rejected[4], but it remains possible that further pockets of this species will be found[8].] *Alt.* 330-1370 m.

Ecology Generally in thicket, deciduous and evergreen forest (including *Cryptosepalum* forest); common only locally, but at times in quite thin vegetation. Food includes numerous invertebrates (e.g. flying termites), seeds and tubers[11].

Status Resident; occasionally recorded in flocks of up to 30 (Chongwe/Zambezi River confluence, Jul 1969), even once of 70 in Ngoma forest, Kafue N.P. (Aug 1985)[8].

Conservation Although perhaps reduced in numbers through hunting in small forest patches in NW Zambia, and probably now extinct around Pemba and Choma, in most areas it holds its own (and it occurs in several national parks).

Breeding   Nov   Dec   Jan   Feb
(n=17)   5   9   1   2   *Clutch*: no data; groups of 6 and 8 chicks have been seen.

Taxonomy *G. p. edouardi*, replaced in NW Zambia[4] by *G. p. kathleenae* (type locality Kansoko; *type specimen not traced*); named for the sister of C.M.N. White[7,10]. *G. p. kathleenae* has the skin on the throat and neck scarlet (not blue-grey)[9].

References [1]Benson (1956f); [2]Benson (1960c); [3]Benson & Irwin (1965a); [4]Benson & Irwin (1967b); [5]Berry (1983); [6]Bowen (1980e); [7]Dowsett (1980b); [8]Dowsett (in press a); [9]Shenton (1963); [10]White (1943b: 19); [11]Wilson (1965).

Helmeted Guineafowl *Numida meleagris*   B126 **RB**

Distribution *Mainly Afrotropical (Mauritania to South Africa)*. Throughout the country and locally abundant, although sparse in the more densely-vegetated parts of Northern and North-Western Provinces. *Alt.* 330-1800 m.

Ecology[1] In all woodland types, wooded savannas, thickets, edges of cultivation and plantations; does

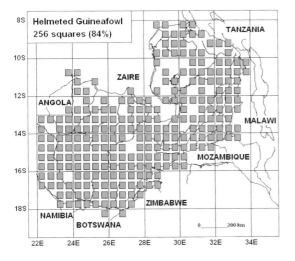

not penetrate evergreen forest in high-rainfall areas. Feeds on vegetable matter and insects[1].

Status Resident. Seasonally in large concentrations of 100 or more (e.g. in the Luangwa Valley and parts of Southern Province plateau)[5].

Breeding	Oct	Nov	Dec	Jan
(n=92)	13	22	27	18
	Feb	Mar	May	
	8	3	1	

Clutch: C/7 (2); C/9 (1); C/11 (1); C/12 (3); C/14 (1); C/15 (2); C/16 (2); C/28 (1).

The large clutches are presumably laid by more than one female in the same nest.

Taxonomy *N. m. marungensis* in N. Zambia, *N. m. mitratus* in the south and east[4] (the latter having the casque buffy, not orange, tapering and angular, rather than rounded and swollen)[2,3]. The two intergrade widely.

References [1]Angus & Wilson (1964); [2]Benson (1962a); [3]Benson *et al.* (1971a); [4]Benson & Irwin (1967b); [5]Dowsett (in press a).

Turnicidae

Kurrichane Buttonquail *Turnix sylvaticus*   B128 **RB**

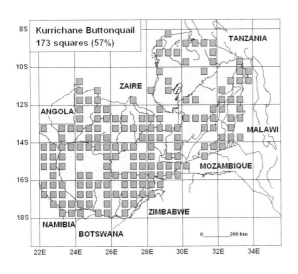

Distribution *Old World (in the Afrotropics, Mauritania to South Africa).* Almost throughout, except unrecorded from parts of the Luangwa Valley and a large area of Northern and Luapula Provinces, perhaps to some extent a reflection of inadequate exploration. *Alt.* 370-2150 m (Nyika)[2].

Ecology In any light woodland or wooded savanna with grass cover, also cultivation, dambos and pasture; occasionally seen on dirt roads.

Status Present throughout the year, with perhaps no more than local movements; rarely reported in some areas when grass is longest during the rains, Feb-Apr[1].

Breeding	Jan	Feb	Mar	Apr	May	Jun	Jul	Aug	Sep	Oct	Nov	Dec
(n=86)	2	4	12	24	9	4	5	5	2	9	9	1

Clutch: C/3 (9); C/4 (11).

Taxonomy *T. s. lepurana.*

References [1]Dowsett (in press a); [2]Dowsett-Lemaire (2006a).

Hottentot (Black-rumped) Buttonquail *Turnix hottentottus*   B129 **AMB**

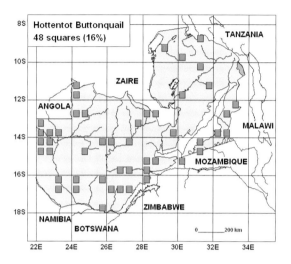

8S Hottentot Buttonquail
48 squares (16%)

Distribution *Afrotropical* (*breeds Ivory Coast to South Africa*). The plateau dambos of the country, in the north-east to the Kalungwishi and Mbala[1], and east to Shiwa Ngandu[3]. On the Eastern Province plateau, southwards from Mwase Lundazi. There is a gap in distribution between the Copperbelt and Mwinilunga (where it has probably been overlooked), but it occurs commonly south to the Liuwa Plain. There is a concentration of records from Matabele Plain to the Njoko River[3], and a few on the Southern Province plateau, to Livingstone[2]. *Alt.* 950-1670 m.

Ecology Generally in moister and shorter grassland than *T. sylvaticus*, in more open situations such as dambos, floodplain and edges of marsh. Densities estimated at one/ha on Liuwa Plain[3].

Status An intra-African migrant, mostly from mid-Sep to late Apr, when locally quite common (e.g. Liuwa Plain, as above). There are very few acceptable records outside this period (the situation confused by difficulties in separating this species in the field from others, in particular female *Coturnix chinensis*), but a few do remain during the dry season in some years[3].

Breeding   Oct   Dec   Jan   Feb
(n=6)   1   1   3   1   *Clutch*: C/3 (2).

Taxonomy *T. h. nanus*. Treated as a distinct species by some authors.

References [1]Benson (1956d); [2]Benson & Irwin (1967b); [3]Dowsett & Leonard (in press a).

Rallidae

White-spotted Flufftail *Sarothrura pulchra*   B139 **R(B)**

Distribution *Guineo-Congolian near-endemic* (*Senegal to W. Kenya, south to Zambia*). Known from several evergreen forest patches in N. Mwinilunga, especially in the Salujinga area[1], south to Jimbe Bridge (where locally not uncommon)[2]. These are the most southerly records for the species. *Alt.* 1160-1430 m.

Ecology On or near the ground inside riparian and other evergreen forest (not necessarily near water), feeding on ants, beetles etc.[1].

Status Resident.

Conservation Like most of the forest birds of N. Mwinilunga, its habitat there is greatly threatened by deforestation (riparian forest is often less than 100 m in width). However, it is an abundant species in most of Central and West Africa.

Breeding No records. Calling (during the day) has been noted early Oct to Nov, and late Mar, but visits to the area have been irregular.

Taxonomy *S. p. centralis*[3].

References [1]Benson & Irwin (1965b); [2]Dowsett (in press a); [3]Keith *et al.* (1970).

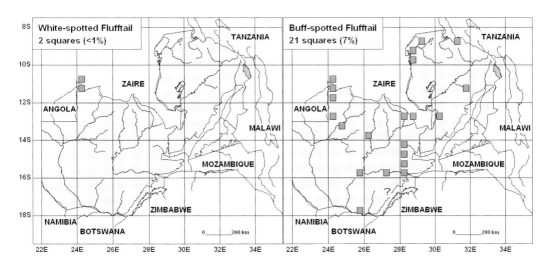

Buff-spotted Flufftail *Sarothrura elegans*   B140 **AM?(B)**

Distribution *Afrotropical* (*breeds Cameroon to South Africa*). Known from scattered localities in moist thickets, from Mbala[1] and N. Mwinilunga south to Livingstone[2], and west to Ngoma[4] and Mayau[3]. [There is a possible sight record from Muckle Neuk ("?" on map)[5]; the suggestion that it might occur in forest at Machile[7] has not yet been confirmed.] No record from the Luangwa and Middle Zambezi Valleys (where thickets perhaps too dry) nor from the Eastern Province plateau. *Alt.* 900-1660 m (Mbala).

Ecology Feeds on the ground in deciduous or evergreen thickets and forest, including *Cryptosepalum* (scarce). Most often located by its call, which is uttered mainly at night (by day when weather conditions overcast), and certainly much under-recorded.

Status Appears to be at least partly migratory, witness one attracted to a lighted window at night on 26 Dec at Mbala[1]. However, most records are based on birds heard, and vocal activity is apparently seasonal, confined to the breeding season. In South Africa there are several records in the non-breeding season[6]; thus, even though all Zambian reports fall between 4 Oct and 22 Mar[5], it remains to be proven whether it is resident here too or not.

Breeding No records. Song has been noted Oct to Mar.

Taxonomy[6] *S. e. elegans.*

References [1]Benson (1957); [2]Benson (1962a); [3]Benson & Irwin (1965a); [4]Brooke (1966c); [5]Dowsett & Leonard (in press a); [6]Keith *et al.* (1970); [7]White & Winterbottom (1949).

Red-chested Flufftail *Sarothrura rufa*   B141 **RB**

Distribution *Afrotropical* (*Sierra Leone to South Africa*). In any swampy situation, throughout the country and locally common, though very few records from low-lying areas (where suitable habitat largely lacking), and it appears to be genuinely absent from the Rift Valley in Malawi[6]. Occurs near streams on the slopes of the Nyika[5]. Although stated to be absent from the south-west[3], it is in fact known from Lupuka[2] and several other localities[4]. *Alt.* 370-2000 m (Nyika)[5].

Ecology Any permanent marsh where there is fairly tall and dense herbaceous cover, such as *Typha*

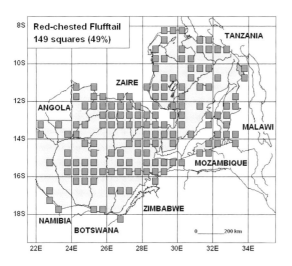

reedbeds and Papyrus, also wet dambos. Feeds on invertebrates such as ants and even small snails.

Status Generally resident, although a bird captured in unsuitable habitat at Chibembe (Luangwa Valley)[4] suggests there may be some local wandering. Easily overlooked when not calling, but use of a tape recording can prompt it to respond, even in marginal habitat as at Chingombe in the lower Luangwa[4].

Breeding Jan
(n=1)   1   *Clutch*: no data, this one record being based on a collected female, about to lay, at Nsombo. Two other females examined in Jan were in breeding condition[1]. "Calling" has been reported in all months, but this is a territorial or contact call and the song is more seasonal (being noted mainly late Jan to early May). *Moult*: one completing moult to adult plumage early Dec[8].

Taxonomy[7] *S. r. rufa.*

References [1]Benson (1956d); [2]Benson & Irwin (1967b); [3]Benson *et al.* (1971a); [4]Dowsett (in press a); [5]Dowsett-Lemaire (2006a); [6]Dowsett-Lemaire & Dowsett (2006); [7]Keith *et al.* (1970); [8]Traylor (1965b).

Long-toed Flufftail *Sarothrura lugens* B142 **RB**

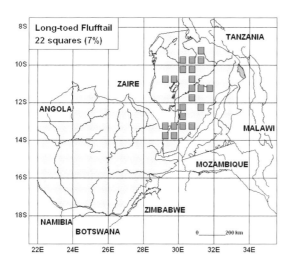

Distribution *Guineo-Congolian/Zambezian (Cameroon to central Zambia)*. Its distribution is based mainly on dambos in the Chambeshi drainage. Known from the Senga Hill area[3] and Ngitwa (where common)[1,6] south to Mkushi River (Chalata)[2] and Musofu[3], and east to Shiwa Ngandu[2]. *Alt.* 1310-1600 m.

Ecology At Ngitwa inhabits rank grass 0.5-1 m high, with patches of sedge, in the central, wetter part of the dambo (water up to 8 cm deep)[6]. Studied at only one place (Ngitwa), but found to be common there, with 5 or 6 birds calling within a radius of some 450 m[6].

Status Probably resident (records scattered throughout the year).

Breeding Mar
(n=1)   1   *Clutch*: no data, the breeding record being based on 2 very small, black chicks in Apr[1]. Song has been noted between 25 Dec and 20 Apr, and "calling" mid-Jul.

Taxonomy[5] *S. l. lynesi* (type locality Nsombo; *NHM*)[4]; named for Hubert Lynes.

References [1]Benson (1956d); [2]Benson (1959c); [3]Dowsett (in press a); [4]Grant & Mackworth-Praed (1934: 17); [5]Irwin & Benson (1966b); [6]Keith & Vernon (1969).

Streaky-breasted Flufftail *Sarothrura boehmi* B143 **AMB**

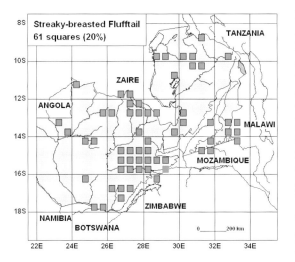

Distribution *Afrotropical* (*breeds Zaire to Zimbabwe*). Widespread in dambos in the higher-rainfall areas of N. Zambia, and locally on some dambos and inundated grasslands in the south. Ranges west to Kashima stream[3] and Kabompo Dist. in the Upper Zambezi, and to Bwina and near Livingstone further south. Largely absent from the low-lying Luangwa (except rarely in the Mfuwe area during floods) and Middle Zambezi Valleys (one on passage 9 Oct at Chiawa)[1], where dambos are missing, and W. Zambia (usually avoiding the larger floodplains). Locally very numerous, e.g. possibly 100 calling on Ipumbu Plain[1]. *Alt.* 950-1670 m, rarely down to 370 m.

Ecology Seasonally inundated short grassland (shorter and less dense than that inhabited by *S. rufa*) of dambos and the smaller floodplains, a habitat which is usually burnt off in the dry season. Nests (like all *Sarothrura*) on or near the ground in a tuft of dense vegetation.

Status Far more noticeable in wet rather than dry years, and appears to be a definite migrant, with extreme dates 8 Dec and 1 May, though often not noted before Jan and few after end Mar[1]. Specimen records confirm this pattern, being all Jan-Mar[2].

Breeding Jan Feb Mar
(n=40) 21 17 2 Calling has been noted in all the months this flufftail is present, the song mostly Jan-Mar.

Clutch: C/1 (4); C/2 (2); C/3 (11); C/4 (16); C/5 (4). The C/1 and C/2 were doubtless incomplete.

Taxonomy No races recognized.

References [1]Dowsett & Leonard (in press a); [2]Keith *et al.* (1970); [3]White (1945-46).

[White-winged Flufftail *Sarothrura ayresi*

Afrotropical (*definitely known only from Ethiopia, Zimbabwe and South Africa*)[3]. Two records have been claimed for this enigmatic species, from 27 km west of Chingola on the road to Solwezi (5 Nov 1962)[1] and Greystone, Kitwe (13 Feb 1981)[2]. The 1962 sighting was in "march grass" in a pan, that of 1981 in a dambo with grass no more than knee height and water ankle deep. Greystone is a well-known locality, and there is no other suggestion that *S. ayresi* occurs there. Sightings were brief and in neither case was the possibility of albinism in another species ruled out. But the occurrence of this bird is possible, as it has been reported rarely on the central watershed in Zimbabwe[4]. **References** [1]Brooke (1964); [2]Dowsett (in press a); [3]Taylor in Harrison *et al.* (1997); [4]Hopkinson & Masterson (1984).]

Red-tailed Flufftail *Sarothrura affinis* B144 **R(B)**

Distribution *Afromontane near-endemic* (*S. Sudan to South Africa*). Recorded only in the grasslands of the high Nyika Plateau, where common[1]. *Alt.* 2050-2200 m (higher on the Malawi side).

Ecology Normally in rank grass and bracken-briar, away from wet drainage channels. Even at times

inside montane forest, though never far from the edge, moving into dambos in the dry season[1].
Status Resident, recorded all months but Jul[1].
Breeding No records. Singing Nov to mid-Mar.
Taxonomy *S. a. antonii.*
References [1]Dowsett-Lemaire (2006a).

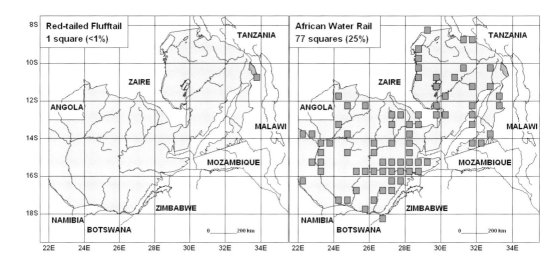

African Water Rail *Rallus caerulescens*   B132 **RB**

Distribution *Afrotropical* (*breeds Ethiopia to South Africa*). Throughout much of Zambia in better watered areas, with some obvious gaps (very rare in the largely dry, low-lying Luangwa Valley)[2] and some less easy to explain (perhaps overlooked in Mweru Wantipa). *Alt.* rarely down to 550 m, mostly 950-1670 m.
Ecology Dense rank growth and reedbeds in permanently wet swamps, marshy streams or lagoons. Locally not uncommon at farm dams in Southern Province and on the Kafue Flats.
Status Resident.
Breeding[1]   Jan   Aug   Oct
(n=3)   1   1   1
Calling birds have been reported Jan-Jun, being especially noisy in Jan. *Clutch*: C/7 (1).
Moult: an immature completing moult into adult plumage, early Dec[3].
Taxonomy No races recognized.
References [1]Benson & White (1957: 158); [2]Dowsett (in press a); [3]Traylor (1965b).

Corn Crake *Crex crex*   B133 **PW**

Distribution *Palaearctic* (*migrating entirely to Africa, wintering mainly Zambia southwards*)[6]. Probably throughout, this discreet bird has been noted mainly in rank grassland in higher-rainfall areas, from the Nyika to the Copperbelt and Zambezi town (Balovale)[3]. *Alt.* 550 (usually higher) to 2200 m.
Ecology Tussocky, drier grasses (0,3-2 m tall) or herbaceous growth in swamps, dambos or uplands. Avoids very wet areas or very sparse grass[8]. Usually solitary; estimated densities of one bird per 4-9 ha at Ndola[8].

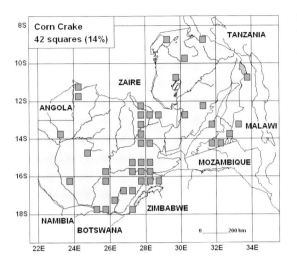

Status A Palaearctic migrant and winter visitor. Not uncommon and annual in NW Zambia[2,9], Ndola, the Nyika and Kafue Flats (though in years of very high rainfall may arrive late on the Copperbelt, and not stay long, perhaps because high water levels are less suitable). Extreme dates are 21 Oct (Mwinilunga) and 19 Apr (Lochinvar), but first arrivals are usually early Dec, and most have left by the end of Mar[3]. There is a partial, pre-nuptial moult of body plumage in Africa[5], noted in Zambia from late Jan[8].

Conservation Its status has been reduced from "Vulnerable" to "Near Threatened" as it is clear that Palaearctic breeding populations had been greatly underestimated in the past[1]. Moreover, it is probably no less common now in Zambia than it was in the 1940s, and its favoured habitat is one that human land abuse greatly augments (as is the case for many other Palaearctic migrants to Africa). On the other hand, it is heavily hunted in North Africa[7], and in Malawi numbers have declined (though not through hunting locally)[4].

Taxonomy No races recognized.

References [1]BirdLife International (2004a,b); [2]Bowen (1983h); [3]Dowsett (in press b); [4]Dowsett-Lemaire & Dowsett (2006); [5]Ginn & Melville (1983); [6]Stowe & Becker (1992); [7]Stowe & Green (1997); [8]Taylor (1984); [9]White (1945-46).

African Crake *Crecopsis egregia*   B134 **AMB**

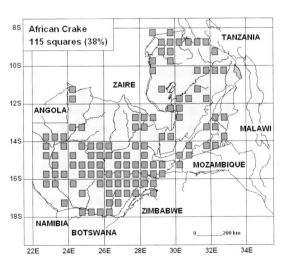

Distribution *Afrotropical (breeds Sierra Leone to South Africa)*. Occurs in grassland throughout the country (except at the highest levels), locally very common, but scarce in the Middle Zambezi Valley. *Alt.* 370-1660 m (Mbala).

Ecology Inhabits dambos (the short grassed edges), flooded grassland and rank growth generally, also in dry situations. Overlaps to some extent with *Crex crex*, but the latter is never in the wetter situations[3]. An estimate was made of one pair per 5 ha at Ndola[4], and it is abundant during the rains on floodplains such as the Kafue Flats and Busanga.

Status The great majority are migrants[2]: first arrivals are usually mid-Dec (in some years quite numerous from the first week of Dec, with first records often late Nov, earliest 27 Nov), and most have departed by the second half of Apr, with stragglers regularly to early May[3]. The average first date over 29 years was 10 Dec, the average last (in 16 years) 17 Apr[3]. There are a few records of single stragglers to 1 Jul, but most suitable habitat is burnt off each year during the dry season. Three flew into a lighted window at night near

Mbala, 26 Dec[1], and the species is very vocal at night on passage[3].

Breeding   Dec   Jan   Feb   Mar
(n=54)   4   14   32   4   Song has been noted from late Nov to mid-Apr[3].
Clutch: C/1 (1); C/2 (2); C/3 (1); C/4 (2); C/5 (2); C/6 (5); C/7 (5); C/8 (2).
C/3 and less doubtless incomplete.
Taxonomy No races recognized.
References [1]Benson (1957); [2]Benson (1964g); [3]Dowsett & Leonard (in press a); [4]Taylor (1985).

Black Crake *Amaurornis flavirostra*   B138 **RB**

Distribution *Afrotropical (Mauritania to South Africa)*. Throughout the country in most wetlands (especially those that are permanent), where usually very common; at all but the highest altitudes. *Alt.* 330-1800 m.
Ecology Wherever there is vegetation on water, including *Typha* reedbeds, water-lilies, and even grass banks.
Status Often in small concentrations. Mainly resident, with no more than local wandering to some seasonal wetlands[1].

Breeding   Jan   Feb   Mar   Apr   May   Jun   Jul   Aug   Sep   Oct   Nov   Dec
(n=37)   2   12   3   1   1   2   1   1   2   2   3   7
Clutch: C/1 (2); C/2 (2); C/3 (6); C/4 (6); C/6 (1).
Taxonomy No races recognized.
References [1]Dowsett (in press a).

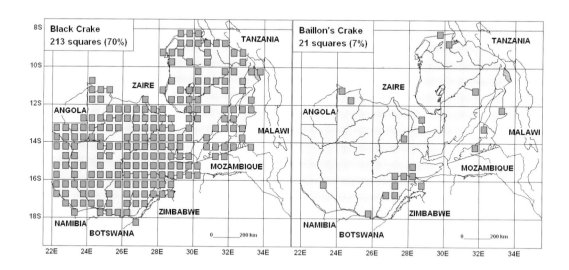

Baillon's Crake *Porzana pusilla*   B135 **R(B)**

Distribution *Old World (in the Afrotropics, breeds Ethiopia to South Africa)*. This skulking species has been found at a scattering of wetland sites throughout the country, from Mwawe in the north[1] to Nasiongo in the south-west[5], and Muckle Neuk and Livingstone in the south[3]. *Alt.* 420 (Nyamuomba)[4] to 1400 m.

Ecology Short sedges and grasses (45 cm high and dense), on mud or in shallow water, moving to taller reedbeds by permanent water when ground dries out.
Status The majority of records are in the rains (Oct-Jan), but there are several in the dry season[4], including one at Lusaka 12 Aug to 7 Oct[6], so it is probably resident. Usually singly, up to 4 together at times.
Breeding No records[2]. Song noted late Sep to mid-Dec[4].
Taxonomy[2] *P. p. intermedia.*
References [1]Benson (1956d); [2]Benson (1964b); [3]Dowsett (1974a); [4]Dowsett (in press a); [5]Smithers (1956); [6]Tucker (1973).

[Little Crake *Porzana parva*

Palaearctic (winters Mauritania to Ethiopia, rarely Uganda). A male was reported seen on three dates between 1 and 13 Mar 1980 at Itawa Swamp, Ndola[1]. This record may well be correct, but it was a single-observer sighting of a bird far to the south of its hitherto known winter range, and so we believe it cannot be accepted unconditionally. **References** [1]Taylor (1980e).]

Spotted Crake *Porzana porzana* B136 **PW**

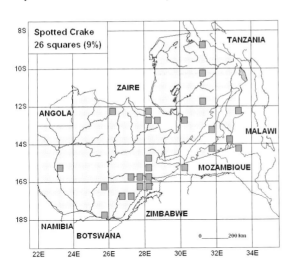

Distribution *Palaearctic (in Africa, winters mainly Senegal to Zimbabwe).* Reported from small areas of water at scattered localities throughout the country, south to Choma Dist.[1] and Livingstone[3], west to Sefula[4]. Only twice at low altitude, in the Luangwa Valley[2,3]. *Alt.* 1000-1670 m, exceptionally down to 450 m.
Ecology Unspecialized, in or close to reeds and similar cover on dams and pans, feeding on the muddy edge or floating vegetation, and also in swampy grassland (dambos). There are local movements as areas dry out[5].
Status A Palaearctic migrant and winter visitor. Sparse and difficult to find, but annual (in varying numbers) in one well-studied area, Ndola[5]. Arrives late, extreme dates being late Nov and 16 Apr[3]. Usually singly, but up to 4 together on occasion. *Moult*: body plumage only, Dec-Apr[2].
Taxonomy No races recognized.
References [1]Benson (1962a); [2]Brooke (1974a); [3]Dowsett (in press b); [4]Greenberg (1976); [5]Taylor (1987).

Striped Crake *Aenigmatolimnas marginalis* B137 **AMB**

Distribution *Afrotropical (breeds Ghana to southern Africa).* Recorded in seasonally inundated grassland at scattered localities throughout the country, at low and medium altitude. There are records in the Middle Zambezi and Luangwa Valleys for Dec and Apr, but also one from the latter area in Feb[1,6], which suggests some may breed at low altitude. A little-known species, perhaps not uncommon at

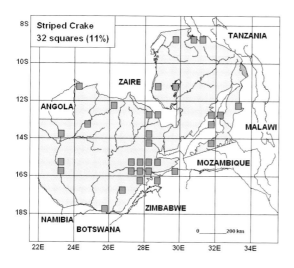

times, but easily overlooked. *Alt.* 370-1660 m.
Ecology Usually in dambos or other flooded grassland, less often on the edge of dams. As in the case of *Crecopsis egregia*, this is a habitat that is often burnt during the dry season. Nests in thick clumps of fine grasses in dambo with water 10-20 cm deep[2,8].

Status An intra-African migrant[4], with extreme dates 22 Nov and 7 May (both Livingstone), mostly late Dec to Mar[7]. [A specimen record from Lundazi supposedly 2 Sep was in fact 9 Feb, the label having been misread[7].] Birds have been attracted to lighted windows at Mbala, Kasaba Bay and elsewhere (23 Dec, 31 Mar and 11 Apr)[3,5], presumably on passage.

Breeding   Jan   Feb
(n=10)   7   3   *Clutch*: C/1 (2); C/2 (1); C/3 (1); C/4 (5).
Taxonomy No races recognized.
References [1]Aspinwall (1972a); [2]Aspinwall (1978c); [3]Benson (1957); [4]Benson (1964g); [5]Benson *et al.* (1970); [6]Berry (1981a); [7]Dowsett & Leonard (in press a); [8]Pitman (1965a).

Purple Gallinule *Porphyrio porphyrio*   B147 **RB**

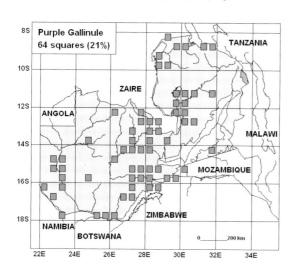

Distribution *Old World* (*in the Afrotropics, Mauritania to South Africa*). Especially in larger marshes (locally common), thus very rare in Eastern Province (reported only from Chassa)[3], NW Zambia and at low altitude. First appeared at Livingstone in 2003, when suitable habitat became available at the local sewage ponds[2]. *Alt.* mostly 950-1600 m, exceptionally down to 370 m.
Ecology *Typha* and Papyrus in extensive swamps, floodplains or (occasionally) reedbeds on large dams.
Status Resident[1]. Concentrations of up to 100 have been noted on the Kafue Flats mid-Mar to late Jul[2].

Breeding	Oct	Dec	Jan	Mar
(n=17)	1	1	1	3
	Apr	May	Jun	Jul
	6	2	1	2

Clutch: C/1 (1); C/2 (1); C/3 (3); C/4 (1).
Taxonomy *P. p. madagascariensis* (sometimes treated as a separate species).
References [1]Benson & Pitman (1966); [2]Dowsett (in press a); [3]Garcia (1975).

Lesser Gallinule *Porphyrula alleni* B148 **AMB**

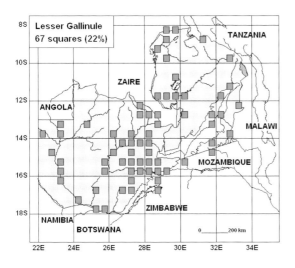

Distribution *Afrotropical (breeds Sierra Leone to South Africa).* In suitable wetlands throughout, at low and medium altitudes (breeding at all levels, even in the Luangwa Valley)[2]. Absent from some well-wooded areas in the north and north-west. Locally common to abundant on some floodplains, such as the Kafue Flats and the Zambezi above Katombora[5]. *Alt.* 370-1670 m.

Ecology Dense vegetation in seasonal wet-lands (especially sedges, also reedbeds or flooded grassland), occasionally farm dams or temporary pools.

Status On the whole, a wet season breeding visitor, usually from mid-Dec to late Apr (with some during Nov and May)[1]. There are only a handful of acceptable dry season records (Jun-Sep)[3]. Often in large concentrations, with 50 at Lochinvar as late as 18 May[3].

Breeding	Dec	Feb	Mar	Apr
(n=7)	1	3	1	2	*Clutch*: C/4 (2).

Taxonomy No races recognized. Tentatively removed from the genus *Porphyrio*[4].

References [1]Benson & Pitman (1966); [2]Berry & Robinson (1979); [3]Dowsett & Leonard (in press a); [4]Dowsett & Dowsett-Lemaire (1993); [5]Meiklejohn (1940).

Common Moorhen *Gallinula chloropus* B146 **RB**

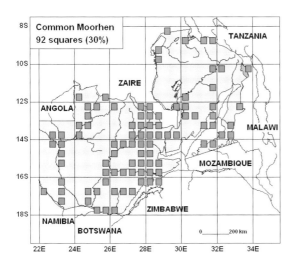

Distribution *Nearly Cosmopolitan (in the Afrotropics, Mauritania to South Africa).* Throughout the country on well vegetated waters, and locally not uncommon (though discreet). *Alt.* locally as low as 530 m, but mostly 950-1700 m.

Ecology Occurs on small, generally perma-nent, reed-fringed waters (especially small lagoons and dams).

Status Resident[1].

Breeding	Jan	Feb	Mar	Apr
(n=32)	3	8	2	3
	May	Jun	Jul	Aug
	2	5	1	3
	Sep	Oct	Nov	Dec
	1	1	1	2

Clutch: C/1 (1); C/2 (1); C/3 (3); C/4 (1); C/5 (2).

Taxonomy *G. c. meridionalis.* A partial albino has been noted[2].

References [1]Dowsett (in press a); [2]Meyer de Schauensee (1951).

Lesser Moorhen *Gallinula angulata*   B145 **AMB**

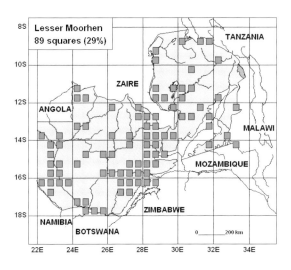

Distribution *Afrotropical* (*Senegal to South Africa*). Throughout Zambia, wherever there are extensive, seasonally inundated wetlands (thus very few records from the Luangwa and Middle Zambezi Valleys). During the rains abundant throughout the Kafue basin and much of the Upper Zambezi, as well as locally on the Copperbelt. *Alt.* locally as low as 530 m, mostly 950-1800 m (Uningi Pans).

Ecology Temporarily inundated grasslands and vegetated pans (habitats that are often burnt during the dry season), as well as permanent waters such as dams.

Status Mainly an intra-African migrant[1], although there are records throughout the year. First arrivals are usually late Nov/early Dec, with large numbers locally from the end of the year to Mar. In some years still numerous throughout Apr, and quite exceptionally there were still 1000+ at Lochinvar to 21 Jun (in 1975)[2]. One killed flying into a wall on 4 Apr may have been on passage[1]. There are otherwise records during the dry season (perhaps in most years) from scattered localities, especially between the Copperbelt and Choma[2], where most observers live.

Breeding   Nov   Dec   Jan   Feb   Mar
(n=35)   1   2   14   14   4   *Clutch*: C/2 (3); C/3 (5); C/4 (2); C/6 (3).
Taxonomy No races recognized.
References [1]Benson & Irwin (1965i); [2]Dowsett & Leonard (in press a).

Red-knobbed Coot *Fulica cristata*   B149 **RB**

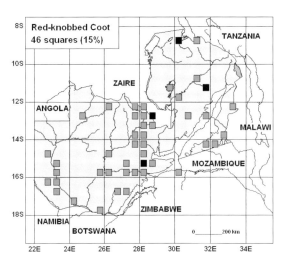

Distribution *SW Palaearctic and Afrotropical* (*Ethiopia to South Africa*). Occurs unevenly on the Zambian plateau, on artificial and natural wetlands, with few known breeding sites (black squares). Commonest from the Copperbelt to the Kafue Flats and Upper Zambezi Floodplain[8]. Absent from North-Western Province, except in West Lunga N.P. Said in error to be absent from Western (Barotse) Province[1], there are recent[3] and older records showing it to be common there at times[8]. At lower levels there are just records of vagrants in the Luangwa Valley[6], but it has colonized (the Zimbabwe side of) L. Kariba since the 1980s[5,7]. *Alt.* 950-1800 m (Uningi Pans, breeding at 2300 m on the Malawi side of the Nyika), vagrants down to 330 m.

Ecology Dams, sewage ponds, pans and floodplains. Does not usually nest on artificial waters such as sewage ponds; even though common in such habitat at Lusaka, nesting in the area is known only from small ponds on the golf course (where there is suitable fringing vegetation).

Status Present in all months, but in very large numbers at times, so some movements may be extensive. At artificial waters numbers increase during the rains (from Sep onwards), but on floodplains they are usually greatest mid-Jun to mid-Oct, when flocks of 200-250 are regular. Before the dams stabilized water levels, numbers on the Kafue Flats fluctuated (e.g. in the 1970s peaking at 5000 at Lochinvar in early Jul)[2], but numbers seem less variable now[3]. The two valley records are for Sep (Luambe) and Nov (Feira, now Luangwa town)[3]. As in South Africa this species may be an opportunistic breeder[4], and movements in Zambia may involve some birds from South Africa (although the thousands ringed there have produced no Zambian recoveries).

Breeding	Jan	Feb	Apr	May	Jun	Jul	Aug	Sep	Oct	Nov	Dec
(n=25)	1	3	1	1	6	3	3	4	1	1	1

Clutch: C/3 (1); C/6 (1).

Taxonomy No races recognized.

References [1]Benson *et al.* (1971a); [2]Douthwaite (1978); [3]Dowsett (in press a); [4]Taylor in Harrison *et al.* (1997); [5]Hustler & Eriksson (1985); [6]Stoehr & Sclater (1906); [7]Williams (1989); [8]Winterbottom (1942a).

Gruidae

Wattled Crane *Grus carunculatus*   B130 **RB**

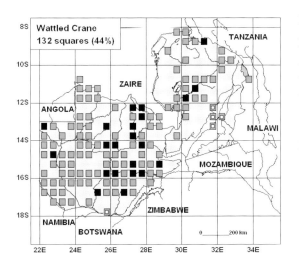

Distribution *Afrotropical* (*breeds Ethiopia to South Africa*). The map distinguishes known breeding squares (black) and non-breeding wanderers (open squares); the Luangwa Valley birds aside, perhaps, most of the remainder are from areas where breeding could occur. Present as a breeding bird in grasslands through much of the Zambian plateau, although so far no confirmed nest records from the extreme north-west or Luapula. Wanders rarely to the Luangwa Valley but there is no record from the Middle Zambezi. One on an island in the Zambezi, Victoria Falls area, Zimbabwe[15] might have been from the small population at Kazuma Pan, Zimbabwe[12]. *Alt.* as a breeding bird 950-1750 m, but occasionally down to 530 m (and breeds above 2200 m on the Malawi side of the Nyika)[7].

Ecology Floodplains and dambos, feeding both in shallow water and on dry land. In the past, the natural flood regime on the Kafue Flats (whence come most of the breeding records) was a peak about Apr, followed by dropping water levels which then gave the cranes the chance to nest. Since the construction of the Kafue Hydro-electric Scheme in the 1970s flooding has been much less regular, with sometimes two peaks (Feb-Mar and May-Jun), the latter possibly flooding nests or obliging birds to breed later[11]. The tubers of the sedge *Eleocharis angulata* form a major part of the diet, and the change in flooding regime has reduced the tuber production. Several pairs may breed in favoured areas, and young later form crèches of up to 60.

Status Pre-breeding concentrations have reached over 1800 in Mar (1973) at Lochinvar[5]. In Bangweulu flocks of 300 or so are regular, and counts in Jan 1992 suggested as many as 780 were present[13]. Even during the peak months for breeding large flocks of non-breeders may occur. One or two adults wander occasionally down to the Luangwa Valley (Apr-Jul), but probably not annually[6]. There is no evidence of any migration, but satellite-tracking should be carried out to determine the extent of seasonal movements.

Conservation Classed as "Vulnerable"[3]. Surveys on the Kafue Flats have suggested totals of 2500 (Nov 1987)[8] to some 3200 birds (Oct 1983)[9], with an estimated breeding population of 300 pairs in the 1970s[5]. Extrapolation of a partial survey of Bangweulu in Oct 1983 showing over 1700 birds there[9] requires confirmation. In 1993 aerial counts suggested a possible population in Zambia of some 5000[6] (out of an estimated world total for the species of 12,000). There is no indication that overall numbers have changed significantly during the past 40 years or so, but some breeding areas have almost certainly been lost through the control of the flooding regime on the Kafue Flats with the building of two large dams. Most *Grus carunculatus* in Zambia occur outside protected areas, and their status needs to be assessed thoroughly and regularly.

Breeding[1,10,14]

	Dec	Jan	Feb	Mar	Apr	May	Jun	Jul	Aug	Sep	Oct
(n=81)		1	1	2	6	10	20	14	18	4	3	2

Clutch: C/1 (15); C/2 (16). Rarely is more than one chick raised.

Moult: birds are flightless Jan-Apr[2,5].

Taxonomy No races recognized. Some authors place it in the monotypic genus *Bugeranus*[4], considering it to be closer to *Anthropoides* than to *Grus,* but it has also been considered close to the Siberian Crane *G. leucogeranus,* so for now we prefer to retain it in *Grus.*

References [1]Benson & Pitman (1964); [2]Benson *et al.* (1970); [3]BirdLife International (2000, 2004a); [4]Archibald & Meine in del Hoyo *et al.* (1996); [5]Douthwaite (1974); [6]Dowsett (in press a); [7]Dyer (1992); [8]Howard (1989); [9]Howard & Aspinwall (1984); [10]Macartney (1968); [11]Malambo & Chabwela (1992); [12]Mundy *et al.* (2001); [13]Perennou (1992); [14]Pitman (1935b); [15]Pollard (1991a).

[Blue Crane *Anthropoides paradiseus*

Afrotropical (*known with certainty only from Namibia, Botswana and South Africa*). Mapped as occurring in the Caprivi Strip (1724C), adjacent to SW Zambia[2], but this is probably a misidentification, and the species is unlikely so far north in that area[1]. **References** [1]Dowsett *et al.* (in prep.); [2]Allan in Harrison *et al.* (1997).]

Southern Crowned Crane *Balearica regulorum* B131 **RB**

Distribution *Afrotropical* (*Kenya to South Africa*). Mostly on the larger floodplains and in the upper Luangwa Valley, where it ranges throughout, south to Chilongozi[2], and on the Eastern Province plateau once to Chipata[6]. It reappears in the Middle Zambezi, from Luangwa town (Feira)[1] to Mutulanganga[2], thence throughout the Kafue basin north to the Lufwanyama River[4]. In the Upper Zambezi occasionally in the Kazungula area and Kambe Plain, but more especially in an area centred on the Liuwa Plain[2]. North of Zambezi town (Balovale)[5] it has been reported once on Chitunta Plain[2]. In Northern Province there are large populations in the Bangweulu Swamps, and in the area between Lakes Mweru and Tanganyika, and a few in the upper Chambeshi. Known to breed (black squares) only on the Liuwa Plain, Kafue Flats, the Kalungu River and (especially) in the Luangwa Valley, where locally common[2]. *Alt.* 330-1700 m.

Ecology In large dambos and floodplains, grassy shores of lakes, oxbow lagoons in low-lying valleys.

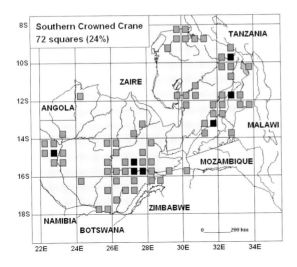

Status In small flocks of up to 50 outside the breeding season, with 150-200 on the Kafue Flats and the Busanga and Liuwa Plains, and max. 500 in the Luangwa Valley. Possibly mainly resident, with only short-distance movements, but this should be studied by satellite-tracking.

Conservation The population (estimated at 5000 in 1993 in Zambia as a whole)[2] is not known to have declined, or to be persecuted excessively.

Breeding	Dec	Jan	Feb	Mar	Apr
(n=26)	7	6	7	4	2

Clutch: C/1 (1); C/2 (1); C/3 (2).

Moult: there is no evidence of flightlessness in this crane, in which moult is apparently gradual.

Taxonomy *B. r. regulorum*. No longer considered conspecific with the northern *B. pavonina*[3].

References [1]Alexander (1899-1900); [2]Dowsett (in press a); [3]Dowsett & Dowsett-Lemaire (1993); [4]Paget-Wilkes (1926); [5]White (1945-46); [6]Winterbottom (1939b).

Heliornithidae

African Finfoot *Podica senegalensis*   B150 **RB**

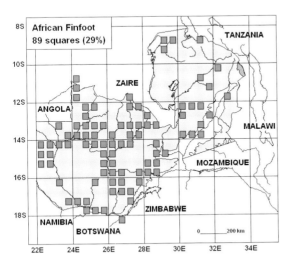

Distribution *Afrotropical* (*Senegal to South Africa*). Perhaps somewhat under-recorded in NE Zambia, where apparently very local from Kundabwika Falls[1] to the Mbala area, then from Mbesuma[1] southwards. Very few records in the Luangwa Valley, from Chifunda south to Luamfwa[2] and the Lukusashi River, and unrecorded on the Eastern Province plateau. Frequent from about Wonder Gorge[3] westwards, along all the major wooded rivers, from as low as Devil's Gorge on the Zambezi (although almost absent from the Middle Zambezi Valley). *Alt.* 500-1660 m (Mbala).

Ecology Perennial rivers and large streams with forested banks, feeding mainly under the cover of over-hanging vegetation.

Status Resident, but with occasional movements to seasonal streams for as long as suitable conditions exist[3].

Breeding	Sep	Dec	Jan	Feb	Mar	Apr
(n=9)	4	1	1	1	1	1

Clutch: C/2 (2); C/4 (1).

Taxonomy *P. s. petersii*.

References [1]Benson (1956f); [2]Benson & White (1957); [3]Dowsett (in press a).

Otididae

Red-crested Korhaan *Eupodotis ruficrista*   B152 **RB**

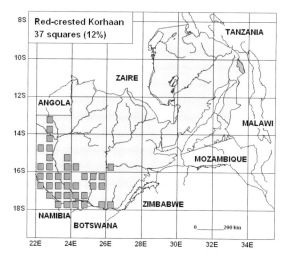

Distribution *Afrotropical (Somalia to South Africa)*. Sparsely in the Kalahari sand woodlands of the south-west, up the Zambezi Valley to near Chavuma, and east of the river to the Loma area[5]. Has occurred once as far east as Namwala[1] on the Kafue (the suggestion that it occurs in flocks in that area[1] is incorrect[2]), and very rarely along the Zambezi as far as Livingstone[2,3]. *Alt.* 950-1150 m.

Ecology Dry grass plains and open woodland on Kalahari sand.

Status Resident, with some wandering.

Breeding   Feb
(n=1)   1   The one breeding record is from near Livingstone[3]. *Clutch*: C/1 (1).

Taxonomy *E. r. ruficrista* (the northern African *savilei* appears to be specifically distinct[4]).

References [1]Benson (1956d); [2]Benson & Irwin (1964b); [3]Benson & Pitman (1963); [4]Chappuis *et al.* (1979); [5]Dowsett (in press a).

White-bellied Bustard *Eupodotis senegalensis*   B153 **RB**

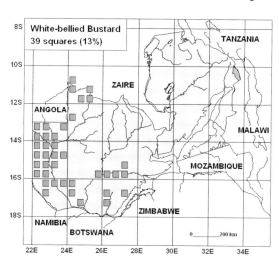

Distribution *Afrotropical (Mauritania to South Africa)*. On the big plains in the west of the country, from the Kakoma area[5], south in the Zambezi drainage to Masese[6] (but common only west of the river). Has bred at Lochinvar[1,3], and wanderers have occurred irregularly on the north side of the Kafue Flats (Blue Lagoon[4]) and the Choma Dist[5]. [A sight record from Bangweulu[3] has never been confirmed.] *Alt.* 950-1460 m.

Ecology Dry grass plains, with carpets of suffrutex (*Parinari capensis*) or very light *Burkea* woodland.

Status Resident in parts of Zambezi Dist. and on Liuwa Plain, usually in pairs but once 10 together; subject to wandering (as above).

Breeding   Dec
(n=1)   1   *Clutch*: C/2 (1).

Taxonomy[2] *E. s. mackenziei* (type locality between L. Mwange and the Lungwebungu River; *type specimen lost*)[7], named for E.K. Mackenzie [1904-?], game warden.

References [1]Benson (1960b); [2]Benson & Irwin (1967b); [3]Benson & White (1957); [4]Dowsett (1966b); [5]Dowsett (in press a); [6]Thompson (1969); [7]White (1945c: 47).

[**Black Korhaan** *Eupodotis afra*

Afrotropical (*N. Namibia to South Africa*). Occurs in Botswana north to the Savuti area, Chobe N.P.[2], but there is no indication that it has ever wandered north of the Zambezi. Northern birds (*afraoides*) may be specifically distinct, but further research needed[1]. **References** [1]Allan in Harrison *et al.* (1997); [2]Penry (1994).]

Black-bellied Bustard *Eupodotis melanogaster*   B154 **RB**

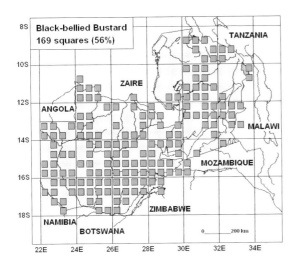

Black-bellied Bustard
169 squares (56%)

Distribution *Afrotropical* (*Senegal to South Africa*). Throughout much of Zambia and locally common, except unrecorded from the whole of the Luapula drainage between Lwela and Tondwa[1]. Also unrecorded from the upper Luangwa Valley, and from the thicket areas to the south of Chilongozi. In the Gwembe Valley, unknown upstream from about Chipepo. *Alt.* 330-2100 m (Manyenjere ridge, Nyika)[2].

Ecology In any light woodland and wooded savanna with rank grass, open grassland of dry floodplains and edges of dambos.

Status Resident.

Breeding	Aug	Sep	Oct	Nov	Dec
(n=34)	1	1	4	5	12
	Jan	Feb	Mar	Apr	
	6	1	1	3	

Clutch: C/1 (4); C/2 (7).

Taxonomy No races recognized (though the southern African form *notophila* may average larger)[3].

References [1]Dowsett (in press a); [2]Dowsett-Lemaire (2006a); [3]Irwin (1981a).

Denham's Bustard *Neotis denhami*   B151 **RB**

Distribution *Afrotropical* (*Mauritania to South Africa*). Breeding populations (black squares) exist on plains in the west of the country, east to the Kafue Flats, on the Nyika Plateau, and possibly in Bangweulu and the Sumbu area[6]. Away from these areas, wanderers can turn up almost anywhere (no records from the Zambian side of the Middle Zambezi Valley, but birds have occurred in Zimbabwe at Mana Pools[10] and Kariba[8]). Wanderers appear regularly on the Copperbelt, less often on the Eastern Province plateau[3,11] and south to Livingstone[1]. Records from the Chikaya Plain and elsewhere in the Luangwa Valley (May-Aug)[11], while presumed to be wanderers from the Nyika or Viphya in Malawi, might possibly be resident (the area is difficult of access for much of the year). *Alt.* although occasionally down to 550 m, most occur from 950 m, to 2000 m in the Mafingas[5] (and above 2200 m on the Malawi side of the Nyika).

Ecology Large, open grasslands, as on dry floodplains and in montane areas; watershed grasslands and ecotone scrub in Mwinilunga.

Status Present year-round in those areas with the largest populations. Groups of up to 7 have been reported during the rains (Nov-Dec) in Kalabo Dist., while as many as 19 have been seen together in Jul at Lochinvar[7]. In addition to the low-altitude Luangwa Valley records, there is a more evident

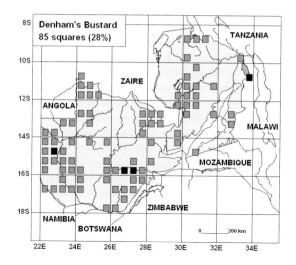

dispersal after breeding to areas such as the Copperbelt, where recorded Nov-May[6].

Conservation Classified as "Near Threatened"[4], but not known to be especially endangered in Zambia.

Breeding   Feb   Jul   Sep
(n=4)   1   2   1

Clutch: no data, but 8 nests on the Malawi side of Nyika[11] were all C/2.

Taxonomy[2,9] The race is apparently *N. d. jacksoni*.

References [1]Aspinwall (1975b); [2]Benson & Irwin (1972b); [3]Benson *et al.* (1970); [4]BirdLife International (2000, 2004a); [5]Clay (1953); [6]Dowsett (in press a); [7]Grimwood & Benson (1960); [8]Hustler (1987); [9]Irwin & Benson (1967a); [10]Riddell (1991); [11]Wilson (1972b).

Kori Bustard *Ardeotis kori*   B - **AV**

Distribution and Status *Afrotropical* (*breeds Ethiopia to Tanzania, and in southern Africa*). A vagrant, which has occurred singly (once two together) on 6 occasions since 1977. Records are from 24 Apr to 2 Nov, in open grassland on the Zambian side of the Zambezi between Simungoma Plain (1724B)[5] and Kazungula (1725C)[3], and the Tongabezi area[4] and Livingstone (1725D)[5]. Reports from the Kafue Flats have never been substantiated[1,2], and were perhaps misidentifications of *N. denhami*. *Alt.* 900-950 m.

Taxonomy No specimen, but presumably the southern African *O. k. kori*.

References [1]Benson & Irwin (1964b); [2]Dowsett & Leonard (in press a); [3]Hustler (1999); [4]Stjernstedt (1998b); [5]Van Daele & Stjernstedt (2001a).

Jacanidae

African Jacana *Actophilornis africanus*   B155 **RB**

Distribution *Afrotropical* (*Mauritania to South Africa*). Probably throughout the country, and usually very common. *Alt.* 330-1800 m (Uningi Pans).

Ecology On any water were there is well-developed surface vegetation, especially water-lilies, occasionally on open sand beaches on the large rivers. Frequently perches on the backs of Hippopotamus[1].

Status Probably mostly resident, but readily moves to seasonal pans. Two birds ringed at Lochinvar (Oct and Jan) have shown movements of 170 and 230 km to the north-east (recovered Sep and Oct) (Appendix 1). The oldest recovery was of a bird 9 years old[3]. Often in concentrations of 50 or more[2].

Breeding[4] Jan Feb Mar Apr May Jun Jul Aug Sep Oct Nov Dec
(n=101)   11   16   27   13   4   8   3   5   2   4   4   4

Clutch: C/2 (3); C/3 (8); C/4 (20).

Moult: probably May-Aug, after the peak of breeding (many showed no moult Jan-Apr, when worn, and Sep-Nov)[2].

Taxonomy No races recognized.

References [1]Benson (1961b); [2]Dowsett (in press a); [3]Dowsett & Leonard (2001); [4]Simpson (1961).

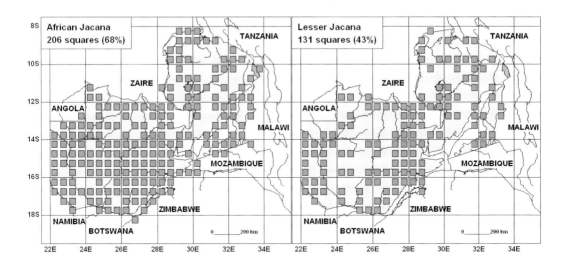

Lesser Jacana *Microparra capensis*   B156 **RB**

Distribution *Afrotropical (mainly Mali to South Africa)*. On most of the Zambian plateau wetlands, although usually scarce. At low altitude known only from a few areas in the upper Luangwa, south to Mfuwe, and from the Siavonga area in the Gwembe Valley. *Alt.* 490-1800 m (Uningi Pans).
Ecology In quiet backwaters of large rivers, (seasonal) floodplains, dambos and pans, and any permanent marsh with emergent vegetation. Eggs are laid directly onto water-lily leaves[1].
Status Resident, in pairs or family groups, rarely in large concentrations (exceptionally 1-2000 at L. Tondwa, Dec 1999)[2].
Breeding   Feb   Mar   Apr   May   Jun   Jul   Aug
(n=14)   3   2   2   1   2   2   2   *Clutch*: C/2 (1); C/3 (8); C/4 (4).
Taxonomy No races recognized.
References [1]Benson & Pitman (1956-57); [2]Dowsett (in press a).

Rostratulidae

Painted Snipe *Rostratula benghalensis*   B157 **RB**

Distribution *Old World Tropics (in Africa, Mauritania to South Africa)*. Through most of the country, but sparse in the north; for example, unrecorded from the Luapula Valley below Chembe, or west of the Mporokoso Dist.[3]. In the Luangwa Valley from Mpanyakunda[2] south to the Mfuwe area only (common at times in Nsefu). From Luangwa town (Feira)[1] westwards in much of the Zambezi and Kafue drainages. *Alt.* 330-1800 m (Uningi Pans).
Ecology Muddy areas in pools and marsh, next to vegetation cover; also in seasonally flooded grass (including floodplains and dambos), edge of dams and even muddy or sandy edges of rivers.
Status Present year-round, but with much local movement in quest of suitable conditions. In most areas the majority of records are from the rains (e.g. Sep-Jan at Lusaka)[3], which is in contrast to the

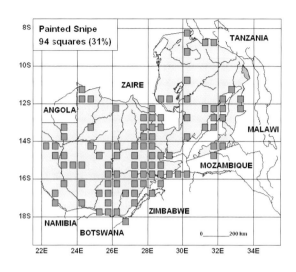

conclusions from an earlier survey[4].

Breeding (n=9)

	Jan	Feb	Mar
	1	1	2
	Apr	Jun	Jul
	3	1	1

Clutch: no data.

Moult: early Feb to Aug, some adults in Jun had suspended moult[3].

Taxonomy No races recognized (in view of the specific status of the Australasian *R. australis*).

References [1]Alexander (1899-1900); [2]Benson (1951); [3]Dowsett (in press a); [4]Tree (1969).

Recurvirostridae

Black-winged Stilt *Himantopus himantopus*   B190 **RB**

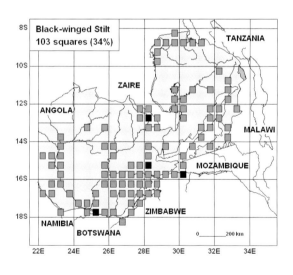

Distribution *Cosmopolitan (in the Afrotropics, Senegal to South Africa).* Throughout the Zambezi and Kafue drainages, southwards from Zambezi Dist.[2], Kasempa[3], Busanga Plain and the Copperbelt. The Luangwa Valley up to the Chiwale area, Bangweulu and the Chambeshi to Mbesuma. Reappears from L. Mweru to Mbala[6]. On Eastern Province plateau, where there is little suitable habitat, known at few places, Lundazi[7] to Chassa[4]. Few nesting sites have been located (colonies of up to a dozen pairs, black squares). *Alt.* 330-1660 m.

Ecology Feeds in shallow water of lagoons, pans, lakes, floodplains, quiet backwaters of large rivers and dams and sewage ponds, less often on the larger sand beaches.

Status There are records all months, and a detailed survey showed no significant pattern, except possibly for a decrease in numbers at artificial wetlands when water levels were high[4]. Often concentrations of up to 400, with as many as 1000 at Kampinda (Mar 1955, when water levels in Mweru Wantipa were low)[1].

Breeding[5]

	Apr	May	Jun	Jul	Aug	Sep
(n=46)	5	2	7	18	4	10

Clutch: C/1 (4); C/2 (5); C/3 (4); C/4 (14).

Taxonomy *H. h. himantopus.* (The possibility that southern African breeding birds are separable as *H. h. meridionalis* remains unproven).

References [1]Benson *et al.* (1955); [2]Britton (1970); [3]Brooke (1966c); [4]Dowsett (in press a); [5]Robinson

(1975b); [6]Shelley & Sclater (1901); [7]Winterbottom (1937).

Avocet *Recurvirostra avosetta*   B191 **AMB**

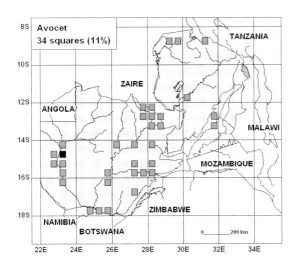

Distribution *Afrotropical (breeds eastern and southern Africa) and Palaearctic.* There are three reports of breeding in Western Province (black square)[2]. Occurs fairly regularly as a non-breeding visitor only in the south-west (north along the Zambezi to Lukulu[1]) and the Kafue basin to the Copperbelt. Otherwise, has occurred in plateau areas as a vagrant to Muckle Neuk and Kabwe and once in Bangweulu[2]. There have been a few recent records in the Luangwa Valley, in the Chinzombo area[2], and a few older ones from Mofwe Dambo to Mbala[1]. *Alt*. 550-1660 m.

Ecology In shallow water of lagoons, lakes, margins of large, slow-flowing rivers, sewage ponds and dams. Nests were scrapes on sand beaches.

Status Recorded all months, but clearly an intra-African migrant, with most records mid-May to Feb. At times especially numerous Sep-Feb (perhaps post-breeding dispersal), with groups of up to 30 in W. Zambia and 19 on artificial waters (Luanshya)[2].

Breeding   Aug

(n=3)   3   In proximity to each other. Also nests probably with eggs were reported on two other occasions from the same area of W. Zambia (Lukulu) in Aug[2-4].

Clutch: C/4 (3).

Taxonomy No races recognized.

References [1]Benson & Irwin (1967b); [2]Dowsett & Leonard (in press a); [3]Sandberg (1908); [4]Van Daele (2001).

Burhinidae

Water Dikkop *Burhinus vermiculatus*   B193 **RB**

Distribution *Afrotropical (mostly Liberia to South Africa).* Through most of the larger river systems, except in the Luapula drainage unrecorded between the southern edge of Bangweulu and L. Mweru[3], or west of Chambeshi Bridge. Likewise rarely reported on the Copperbelt, and on the Eastern Province plateau, whence known only marginally on the Lukusuzi and Rukuzye Rivers. Most numerous in the Luangwa Valley[2]. *Alt*. 330-1800 m (Uningi Pans).

Ecology On sandy or rocky shorelines of lakes and large rivers; normally in territorial pairs, hiding in low riverine vegetation by day. Nests are in slight depressions, on sand or shingle[1]. Often feeds on dirt roads at night a short distance from water.

Status Mostly resident, but in some areas present only during high water levels (e.g. on the Copperbelt Jan-Mar), suggesting at least local movements. Forms flocks when not breeding (Mar to early Jul), up to 100 at times in the Luangwa Valley[2].

Breeding Apr Jul Aug Sep Oct Nov
(n=50)   2   2   11   15   18   2   *Clutch*: C/1 (2); C/2 (17).

Taxonomy *B. v. vermiculatus.*

References [1]Benson & Pitman (1956-57); [2]Dowsett (in press a); [3]Shelley & Sclater (1901).

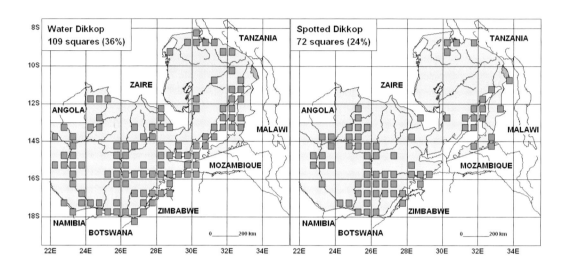

Spotted Dikkop *Burhinus capensis*   B192 **RB**

Distribution *Afrotropical (Mauritania to South Africa).* Much of the drier woodlands in the southern half of the country, but with some notable gaps (in part the result of insufficient exploration for this cryptic species). West of the Zambezi only in the Liuwa Plain area, but ranges through the Zambezi Valley north to near Ntambu[2] and much of the Kafue basin. Absent from most of the Northern Province plateau, and very scarce on the Copperbelt, east to Kasanka[1]. Known from a few places on Eastern Province plateau, from Chassa to Lundazi, in the Luangwa Valley[3], and the Nyika[4]. It reappears between Mpokoso Dist. and Mbala[3]. *Alt.* 370-1700 m, as high as 2150 m (Nyika, where breeds at 2300 m on the Malawi side)[4].

Ecology In short grassland on the edge of woodland or in open wooded grassland. May be found feeding on dirt roads at night.

Status Resident; rarely in groups.

Breeding   Jul Aug Sep Oct Nov
(n=10)   1   1   4   3   1   *Clutch*: C/2 (4).

Moult: two started late Apr[3].

Taxonomy[5] *B. c. capensis.*

References [1]Benson & White (1957); [2]Bowen (1983i); [3]Dowsett (in press a); [4]Dowsett-Lemaire (2006a); [5]Irwin & Benson (1966b).

Glareolidae

[**Double-banded Courser** *Rhinoptilus africanus*
Afrotropical (Ethiopia to South Africa). Mapped as occurring in the Caprivi Strip (1723C, 1724D), adjacent to SW Zambia[2], but this is perhaps based on a misidentification[1], although the species has been reported as far north as 18°S in Botswana[1] and in Hwange N.P., Zimbabwe[3]. **References** [1]Dowsett *et al.* (in prep.); [2]Maclean in Harrison *et al.* (1997); [3]Varden (1999b).]

Three-banded Courser *Rhinoptilus cinctus*   B195 **RB**

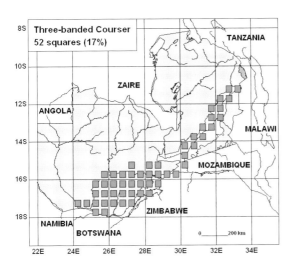

Three-banded Courser
52 squares (17%)

Distribution *Afrotropical (Eritrea to South Africa).* Distribution centred on the drier woodlands of Southern Province, along the Zambezi from the Sinde River confluence[5] to some 15 km upstream from Sesheke, north to the southern edge of the Kafue Flats and the Chirundu area[2]. Has very occasionally been reported to the north, from Blue Lagoon east to Chalimbana[3]. Thence throughout the Middle Zambezi and Luangwa Valleys to Tembwe[4] and Kalinku[2]. *Alt.* 370-1250 m.
Ecology Normally in mopane woodland, much less often in *Acacia* (and exceptionally in light miombo, though it does breed in such habitat in the Choma area)[2]. Nocturnal[1].
Status Resident, occasionally in small groups.

Breeding	Apr	May	Jun	Jul	Aug	Sep	Oct	
(n=46)	5	1	2	11	12	12	3	*Clutch*: C/2 (10); C/3 (2).

Moult: two started late Apr[2].
Taxonomy[3] *R. c. seebohmi.*
References [1]Dowsett (1969d); [2]Dowsett (in press a); [3]Irwin & Benson (1966b); [4]Meyer de Schauensee (1951); [5]Sclater (1905).

Bronze-winged Courser *Rhinoptilus chalcopterus*   B196 **AMB**

Distribution *Afrotropical (Senegal to southern Africa).* Likely to occur in most places, present gaps in distribution being to a great extent artefacts. Recorded south from the Luapula River, Bulaya to Choma (Mweru Wantipa)[5], and the Nyika Plateau (on passage[3]). *Alt.* 330-2200 m (Nyika), unlikely to breed above 1700 m.
Ecology In any woodland (miombo, mopane, mixed *Acacia*), light scrub and ploughed fields, but essentially nocturnal and most often seen when feeding on dirt roads at night. Nests on dry, bare ground, often recently burnt[1].
Status There are records for all months, but most are between Apr and Dec[2,5]. First arrivals are rarely as early as mid-Mar, and at Mwinilunga they were usually during the first week of May each year. Heaviest passage is in May, when it can occur in small groups (up to 12)[2]. A bird ringed in South Africa

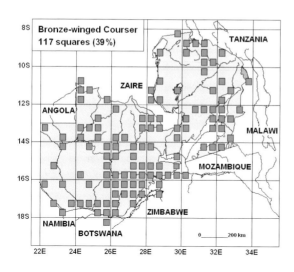

in Apr was recovered in Zambia 26 Oct (Appendix 1), and most southern African records are for the non-breeding season, Jan-May[6].

Breeding[4]

(n=96)	May	Jun	Jul	Aug
	1	2	1	10
	Sep	Oct	Nov	
	48	33	1	

Clutch: C/1 (3); C/2 (20); C/3 (58).

Moult: arrivals in Zambia late Apr are in fresh plumage[2].

Taxonomy No races recognized.

References [1]Benson & Pitman (1956-57); [2]Dowsett & Leonard (in press a); [3]Dowsett-Lemaire (2006a); [4]Pitman (1932b); [5]Tree (1969); [6]Vernon (2004).

Temminck's Courser *Cursorius temminckii*

B194 **AMB/R**

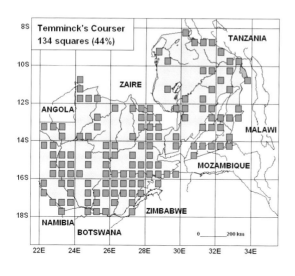

Distribution *Afrotropical (Mauritania to South Africa)*. Occurs almost throughout, the gaps in the map for Northern and Luapula Provinces being probably the result of insufficient exploration. *Alt.* occasionally as low as 370 m, but mostly above 600 m, to 2200 m (Nyika, breeding even higher on the Malawi side)[3].

Ecology Dry margins of floodplains and dambos, airfields and bare ground in fallow cultivation and on roads, frequently burnt open wooded grassland.

Status Mainly a dry season breeding visitor, often in small groups when on passage. A few remain during the rains in relatively dry areas devoid of dense vegetation[2].

Breeding

(n=116)	May	Jun	Jul	Aug	Sep	Oct	Nov
	1	5	12	24	31	30	13

Clutch: C/1 (7); C/2 (67).

Taxonomy[1] The breeding form is said to be *C. t. ruvanensis*. [The suggestion that *C. t. temminckii* occurs as a non-breeding visitor from north of the Equator, also in the southern breeding season (specimens dated Apr-Jun)[1], is not accepted here.]

References [1]Clancey (1984b); [2]Dowsett & Leonard (in press a); [3]Dowsett-Lemaire (2006a).

Common Pratincole *Glareola pratincola*   B197 **RB**

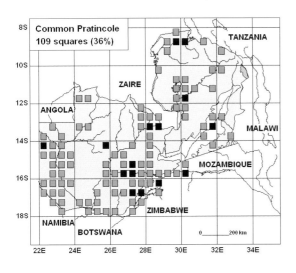

Distribution *Afrotropical* (*the race* fuelleborni, *Senegal to South Africa*) *and Palaearctic.* There are breeding populations (black squares) on floodplains in the Kafue and Upper Zambezi systems, as well as the Middle Zambezi and Luangwa Valleys (rare in the latter), Bangweulu and Mweru Wantipa. It has even bred on occasion at Choma, Luanshya and Ndola. Records elsewhere are of non-breeding visitors, often in some numbers, to the Mwinilunga area, the upper Chambeshi, the Luangwa Valley, and Chipata and Chassa on the Eastern Province plateau[1]. *Alt.* 330-1800 m.

Ecology Breeds on dried mud, sand or recently burnt grass on the edge of floodplains, lakes and sluggish rivers, occurring on ploughed land and pasture at other times. Highly gregarious, both during and outside the breeding season.

Status[1] Recorded throughout the year. Occurs in flocks of thousands in favoured areas when not breeding, e.g. the Kafue Flats. There are some movements (probably just local) outside the breeding season (see above); the only ringed bird recovered so far moved just 135 km from near Choma (Dec) to the Kafue Flats near Mazabuka (Oct)[2].

Breeding   Jun   Jul   Aug   Sep   Oct   Nov
(n=132)   2   4   32   43   43   8   *Clutch*: C/1 (17); C/2 (38).
Moult: mostly Nov-Apr, each bird taking at least 60 days[1].
Taxonomy *G. p. fuelleborni.*
References [1]Dowsett (in press a); [2]Dowsett & Leonard (2001).

Black-winged Pratincole *Glareola nordmanni*   B198 **P**

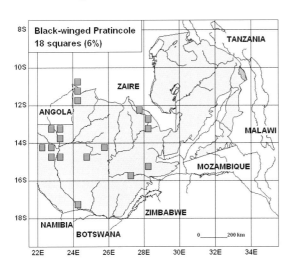

Distribution *Palaearctic, with virtually the whole population wintering in southern Africa* (*mainly Botswana and Free State*). On passage through the floodplains of the Upper Zambezi, with stragglers east to Kaoma Dist., Lochinvar, Lusaka and the Copperbelt. *Alt.* 950-1370 m.

Ecology Open country, especially watershed plains and dry floodplains, but also often near water.

Status A rarely-recorded Palaearctic passage migrant through W. Zambia (a few stay during the rains). Extreme dates are 6 Oct and 19 Apr, most records falling between 22 Oct and 22 Nov or 5 Mar and 19 Apr[4]. Very heavy passage was noted over the Liuwa Plain 15 Nov

1977, hundreds of thousands flying southwards, with far fewer three days later[2]. Outside the period of passage just the odd straggler or small numbers are noted, except that up to 200 were present at Chisamba Jan and Feb 1990[4].

Conservation Classed as "Near Threatened"[3]; there is no evidence of any persecution in Zambia. There are now known to be larger numbers breeding in Asia than hitherto supposed[1].

Taxonomy No races recognized.

References [1]Anon. (2006); [2]Aspinwall (1977g); [3]BirdLife International (2000, 2004a); [4]Dowsett (in press b).

Rock Pratincole *Glareola nuchalis* B199 **AMB**

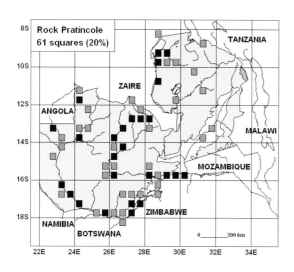

Rock Pratincole
61 squares (20%)

Distribution *Afrotropical (breeds Guinea to Zimbabwe).* Breeds (black squares) commonly on suitable rocky rivers: along the Luapula, the whole of the Kafue and tributaries from the Copperbelt, and the Upper and Middle Zambezi down to Luangwa town (Feira). Outside this area there have been very few records of wanderers or passage birds, at scattered localities in the east, from Bangweulu[4], east to Chusa Falls on the Manshya River[3] (this species, and not *G. pratincola*) and north to L. Chila[1]. There are also a couple of records from the Luangwa Valley[1,2]. *Alt*. 330-1670 m.

Ecology Breeds on emerged rocks in fast-flowing stretches of perennial river; wanderers away from breeding sites noted on sand and gravel beaches.

Status An intra-African migrant, with most records falling between 20 Jul (Victoria Falls) and 30 Mar (Kitwe), and single observations in Apr, May and Jun[6].

Breeding[8]	Aug	Sep	Oct	Nov	Dec	Jan
(n=130)	8	64	24	22	11	1

Clutch: C/1 (10); C/2 (38).

Taxonomy[7] *G. n. nuchalis*. The race *torrens* has been described from Namibia[5], and it is claimed to occur in W. Zambia, but further study is required to confirm its status.

References [1]Benson & Irwin (1965i); [2]Benson *et al.* (1970); [3]Brelsford (1942); [4]Brelsford (1947); [5]Clancey (1981b); [6]Dowsett & Leonard (in press a); [7]Mackworth-Praed & Grant (1957); [8]Penry (1979d).

Charadriidae

Ringed Plover *Charadrius hiaticula* B165 **P(W)**

Distribution *Holarctic (winters Mauritania to South Africa).* Likely to turn up almost anywhere, but at present known in the north-east only between L. Chila[1] and Nchelenge, and in the Bangweulu area. Unrecorded between the Copperbelt (where regular) and Mwinilunga, owing to a lack of suitable habitat. *Alt*. 370-1670 m.

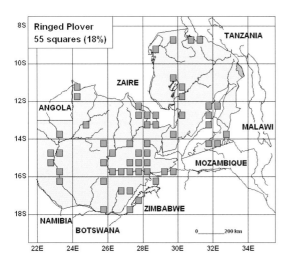

Ecology Mudflats and sand beaches, on the edge of floodplains, lakes, lagoons, dams, sewage ponds.

Status A Palaearctic migrant and winter visitor. Records fall between 3 Sep and 29 May (except for three observations 12 Jun to 26 Jul), with first arrivals often early Sep. The average first date over 28 years was 19 Sep[2]. Mostly on southward passage, with small groups, 5-6 together, occasionally concentrations of 30-100 at Lochinvar, mid-Oct to early Nov. Small numbers (up to 6) stay during the rains when conditions suitable. Exceptionally 36 were still at Lochinvar early Feb 1995 (when conditions were very dry, with lots of mud). Fewer on northward passage[2].

Taxonomy[3] *C. h. tundrae*.

References [1]Benson *et al.* (1955); [2]Dowsett (in press b); [3]Irwin & Benson (1966b).

Little Ringed Plover *Charadrius dubius* B - **PV**

Distribution and Status *Old World* (*in the Afrotropics, winters Mauritania to Tanzania, once Zimbabwe*). A Palaearctic vagrant, recorded (since 1984) at small dams on 5 occasions: from the Copperbelt at Luanshya (twice, 1328A)[2,3], Huntley farm (1528A) and near Kafue town (1528C), and in the east at Chipata (1332D)[1]. It is here at the southern limit of its wintering range in Africa. Usually singly (but once 3 immatures together). Extreme dates are 27 Sep and 20 Feb[1]. *Alt.* 1140-1300 m.

Taxonomy No Zambian specimen, but doubtless *C. d. curonicus*.

References [1]Dowsett (in press b); [2]Taylor (1980b); [3]Taylor (1981).

Kittlitz's Plover *Charadrius pecuarius* B168 **AM/RB**

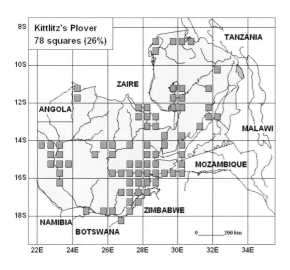

Distribution *Mainly Afrotropical* (*Mauritania to South Africa*). As a breeding bird, occurs abundantly on the floodplains from Mweru Wantipa, Bangweulu, the Kafue basin and Upper Zambezi. In recent years it has also taken to breeding at dams and sewage ponds along "line of rail". Away from these areas it is scarce, in the Luangwa Valley (no sign yet of breeding), the Chambeshi to Mbesuma, and N. Mwinilunga. *Alt.* 330-1500 m.

Ecology Prefers dried mud and short grass on the edge of lakes, floodplains, natural and artificial ponds.

Status Although there are records throughout the year, the great majority fall in the period Apr to Dec[2]. Only very small numbers are present in the rains in suitable habitat in dry years, maximum 74 at Lochinvar in Jan 1997[2].

Breeding (n=165)

	Apr	May	Jun	Jul	Aug	Sep	Oct	Nov	Jan
(n=165)	2	5	13	23	42	53	22	4	1

The Jan record is from the shore of L. Kariba[2]. *Clutch*: C/1 (16); C/2 (60).
Moult: in a small sample of adults, mid-Sep to Nov[2,3].
Taxonomy[1] *C. p. pecuarius.*
References [1]Clancey (1971b); [2]Dowsett & Leonard (in press a); [3]Traylor (1965b).

Three-banded Plover *Charadrius tricollaris* B166 **RB**

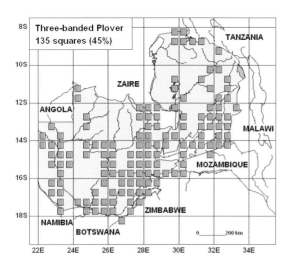

Three-banded Plover
135 squares (45%)

Distribution *Afrotropical* (*known to breed Ethiopia to South Africa*). At any small area of water throughout the country, but curiously absent from the whole of the Luapula Valley, between Nsombo[2] and Kampinda[1], and from much of Northern Province to the east. There are no records between the Copperbelt and Mwinilunga, nor immediately west of Kafue N.P., where suitable habitat is largely lacking. *Alt.* 330-1780 m.

Ecology Shores of lakes and pans, dams and sewage ponds, also streams and rivers. Breeds at a number of artificial dams.

Status Present throughout the year, the greater volume of records available not providing support for the movements suggested by an earlier survey[3,4]. More investigation needed.

Breeding (n=96)

	Feb	Mar	Apr	May	Jun	Jul	Aug	Sep	Oct	Nov
(n=96)	1	1	2	9	5	14	27	22	10	5

Clutch: C/1 (3); C/2 (61).
Taxonomy *C. t. tricollaris.*
References [1]Benson (1956f); [2]Brelsford (1947); [3]Dowsett (in press a); [4]Tree (1969).

Forbes's Plover *Charadrius forbesi* B167 **RB**

Distribution *Afrotropical* (*Senegal to Angola and Zambia*). Confined to rocky outcrops (usually near water) in the northern half of the country, from Kampinda and Kasaba[3], east to Malole[1], thence south-westwards to Ndola[5], Kitwe[4], the upper Kafue basin and the NW Lukanga Swamps[6] (the most souther-ly locality for the species). It reappears in the north-west, south to Mwinilunga, and to west of the Zambezi on the North Kashiji River[2]. Rarely reported, and found regularly only in one area, Zambezi Rapids. *Alt.* 1100-1550 m.

Ecology Where the habitat has been described, birds were associated with rock slabs, either on streams or outcrops in dambos (Zambezi Rapids, Pwira Pan)[6].

Status All records are for the period 20 Apr to 31 Jan, but it is possibly resident, with no more than short-distance movements during the heaviest rains. Does not flock.

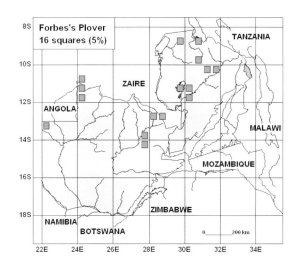

Breeding   Oct   Nov
(n=2)   1   1
Clutch: C/2 (1); C/3 (1).
Both records are from Zambezi Rapids, but birds at Pwira Pan were displaying mid-Aug 1963[6].
Taxonomy No races recognized.
References   [1]Benson   (1956d);   [2]Benson (1960c); [3]Dowsett (in press a); [4]Penry (1975c); [5]Robinson (1973a); [6]Tree (1969).

[**Kentish Plover** *Charadrius alexandrinus*

This *Palaearctic* migrant is reported from Upemba in S. Zaire (under the name of *C. a. alexandrinus*)[1]; however, the original reference clearly refers to *C. a. mechowi*[2], which is now treated separately as a race of *C. marginatus*. Similarly Richard Böhm's record from L. Tanganyika[1] is of the next species, and there is no evidence that *C. a. alexandrinus* occurs so far south in inland Africa. **References** [1]Schouteden (1971); [2]Verheyen (1953).]

White-fronted Sand Plover *Charadrius marginatus* B169 **RB**

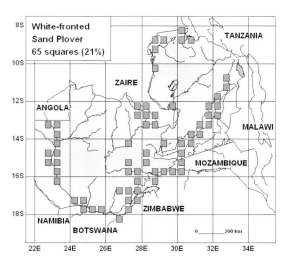

Distribution *Afrotropical* (*Senegal to South Africa*). Breeds on the larger sandy rivers and lake-shores, essentially the Luangwa from about 10°45'S, throughout the Middle and Upper Zambezi to Chavuma. It is also on Lakes Tanganyika and Mweru (south to Kasenga[4]). Elsewhere, it has bred on dams at Luanshya, but the few others on the Copperbelt and upper Kafue[3], south to Lusaka, Kafue Flats and Southern Province plateau are non-breeders. *Alt.* 330-1500 m.
Ecology Breeds on sand beaches on the edge of rivers and lakes; visitors also frequent dams and sewage ponds.
Status Subject to local movements. Records at natural sites (e.g. rivers liable to extreme flooding) fall between Mar and late Jan, whereas birds occur at artificial sites (e.g. dams) in all months, particularly during the rains[2].
Breeding   Jun   Jul   Aug   Sep   Oct
(n=43)   1   6   11   21   4   *Clutch*: C/1 (2); C/2 (5); C/3 (8).
Taxonomy[1] *C. m. tenellus*.
References [1]Benson & Benson (1975); [2]Dowsett (in press a); [3]Tree (1969); [4]White (1944e).

Chestnut-banded Plover *Charadrius pallidus* B - **AV**

Distribution and Status *Afrotropical* (*breeds East Africa and southern Africa*). There are acceptable sight records of single vagrants at Luanshya Dam (1328A; 23 Aug-13 Sep 1980)[3] and (twice) the Livingstone area, on the Zambezi and nearby sewage ponds (1725D; 14 Oct 1979, 23 Sep-27 Oct 1999)[1,2]. [Other claimed records may have been misidentifications of *C. marginatus* with richly-coloured breasts.]
Taxonomy No Zambian specimen. *C. p. pallidus* (from the south-west) is probably more likely than *C. p. venustus* (from eastern Africa).
References [1]Dowsett & Leonard (in press a); [2]Pollard (1980); [3]Taylor (1982a).

Mongolian Sand Plover *Charadrius mongolus* B170 **PV**

Distribution and Status *Palaearctic* (*winters on the coasts from Sudan to South Africa*). There are four acceptable records (including one specimen) of single birds, from floodplains and dams at Malole (1031B; Mar 1954)[1], Ndola (1228D; 28 Feb-1 Mar 1982), Blue Lagoon (1527A; 8-11 Mar 1976)[3] and Lochinvar (1527C; 28 Oct 1979)[2].
Taxonomy *C. m. atrifrons.*
References [1]Benson *et al.* (1955); [2]Dowsett (in press b); [3]Dowsett & Lemaire (1976).

Greater Sand Plover *Charadrius leschenaultii* B - **P**

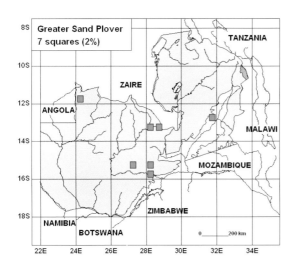

Distribution *Palaearctic* (*winters on the coasts from Sudan to South Africa*). Since 1972 there have been 7 acceptable records (including a specimen) of singles at: Mwinilunga, the Copperbelt at Luanshya and Kafubu, south to Blue Lagoon N.P., Lusaka[2] and near Kafue town[1], east to Kaingo, South Luangwa N.P.[4]. *Alt.* 1000-1370 m.
Ecology Dams and floodplains.
Status A Palaearctic passage migrant, all records falling between 25 Sep and 22 Nov (one bird stayed 13 days)[4].
Taxonomy Probably *C. l. crassirostris*, but the specimen has not been re-examined since the species was shown to be polytypic[3].
References [1]Aspinwall (1973b); [2]Aspinwall (1975c); [3]Clancey (1982); [4]Dowsett (in press b).

Caspian Plover *Charadrius asiaticus* B171 **P**

Distribution *Palaearctic* (*winters Sudan to South Africa*). Regular in very large numbers on Liuwa Plain and at Lochinvar, and generally commonest in the western half of the country (though it is scarce in the well-wooded country between the Copperbelt and Mwinilunga). It is unrecorded in the Luapula

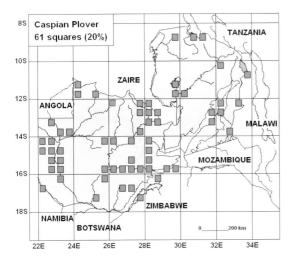

Valley between Mweru Marsh[1] and Bangweulu, and the plateau eastwards to Mbesuma. Very scarce at low altitude, it has been recorded occasionally in the Luangwa Valley, south to Mfuwe[2], and the Middle Zambezi to Nchete Is[3]. *Alt.* 370-1670 m, but mostly above 900 m.

Ecology In very short grassland at edges of dams, dambos or floodplains, also on airfields, ploughed land and playing fields.

Status Extreme dates for this Palaearctic migrant are 8 Aug and 18 Apr. The average first date over 26 years was 27 Aug[3]. In favoured areas occurs in flocks of thousands on southward passage (mid-Sep to early Dec), with 30-35,000 counted at Lochinvar in Nov 1995[5]. In very dry years a few may remain during the rains, exceptionally a few hundred. Return passage northwards is much smaller[3].

Taxonomy No races recognized[4].

References [1]Benson *et al.* (1955); [2]Berry (1981a); [3]Dowsett (in press b); [4]Irwin & Benson (1966b); [5]Leonard (2005).

Pacific Golden Plover *Pluvialis fulva*   B - **P**

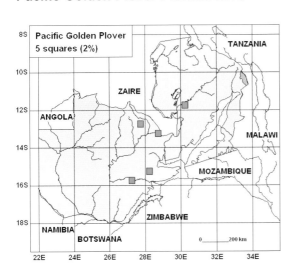

Distribution *Palaearctic and W. Nearctic (wintering mainly on the coasts, Sudan to Tanzania).* Since 1972 there have been ten acceptable records (including a specimen), from Chikuni and the Copperbelt[4,5], south to Lusaka[1] and Lochinvar[2] (with the proviso that most sight records do not eliminate the possibility of American Golden Plover *P. dominica*, in the past treated as conspecific)[3]. *Alt.* 1160-1260 m.

Ecology By any body of water.

Status Rare Palaearctic visitor, records falling between 16 Oct and 26 Nov, with singles 12 Feb and 18 May. Up to 6 birds have been seen on one day[2].

Taxonomy No races (previously treated as a race of *P. dominica*).

References [1]Aspinwall (1975c); [2]Dowsett (in press b); [3]Leonard (2001b); [4]Madge (1972e); [5]Richards (1974).

Grey Plover *Pluvialis squatarola*   B164 **P(W)**

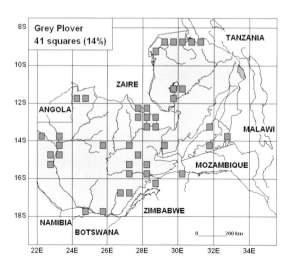

Distribution *Holarctic* (*Mauritania to South Africa, winters mainly on the coasts*). Fairly widespread, not only in well-watched areas along "line of rail" (especially the Copperbelt and Lochinvar), but also in the area between L. Tanganyika and Chiengi[1], and in the Upper Zambezi[5]. There is a single record from the upper Luangwa Valley, and it is also known from Luangwa town (Feira)[2] and Chirundu[4]. Only twice reported from the small dams of Eastern Province plateau. *Alt.* rarely as low as 330 m, usually 950-1670 m.

Ecology On sand beaches and mudflats on the edge of water (lakes, dams), once on an airstrip[2].

Status Extreme dates for this Palaearctic migrant are 29 Jul and 5 Apr; there are records throughout this period, but mostly on southward passage Aug-Nov (when present at times in small groups of up to 25)[2].

Taxonomy *P. s. squatarola* (trinomials used, now that is it shown to be polytypic)[3].

References [1]Benson *et al.* (1955); [2]Dowsett (in press b); [3]Engelmoer & Roselaar (1998); [4]Smith (1950); [5]White (1948c).

Senegal Wattled Plover *Vanellus senegallus*   B163 **RB**

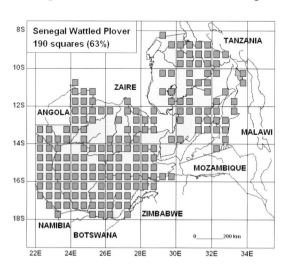

Distribution *Afrotropical* (*Mauritania to South Africa*). The commonest large plover, through much of the country, but unrecorded from the Luapula Valley west of Mweru Wantipa, Mwenda and Monga[3]. There are also no records from the Luangwa Valley below Chilongozi[1] (an area dominated by dense thicket), until Jeki in the Middle Zambezi is reached. On the Eastern Province plateau south-west to the Chadiza area[3]. *Alt.* as low as 370 m at times, but usually 550-1800 m (Uningi Pans), only as a vagrant on the Nyika at 2200 m[4].

Ecology Mainly in short moist grassland on the edge of marsh, dambos and in floodplains, often at rural dams. Nests on dry, bare ground, without any lining[2]. Usually in small flocks.

Status Significantly more frequent Jul-Jan, compared to the rest of the year. Large groups may be found, especially Mar-Apr, all of which suggests there may be an arrival for the start of the breeding season (and possibly some movements out of the country post-breeding)[3].

Breeding[5]   Jul Aug Sep Oct Nov
(n=86)   2   13   30   31   10   *Clutch*: C/1 (1); C/2 (4); C/3 (13); C/4 (22).
Taxonomy *V. s. lateralis.*
References [1]Benson & Irwin (1967b); [2]Benson & Pitman (1956-57); [3]Dowsett (in press a); [4]Dowsett-Lemaire (2006a); [5]Wright (1963).

White-crowned Plover *Vanellus albiceps*   B162 **RB**

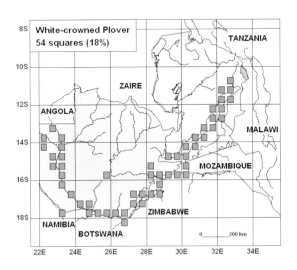

Distribution *Afrotropical (Mauritania to South Africa).* Throughout (and common in) the Luangwa and Zambezi Valleys, and on the major tributaries. Ranges from the Kaunga stream on the upper Luangwa[1], to Wonder Gorge in the Luano Valley, through to Chavuma[2] on the Upper Zambezi, and on the Mashi in the Imusho area[1]. It is still present in the Kariba Valley, despite the flooding of the lake, with the odd vagrant to the nearby Southern Province plateau near Choma. It has only rarely wandered up the Kafue drainage, to Lusaka and the Namwala to Itezhi-Tezhi area[1]. *Alt.* 330-1050 m (Chavuma), once 1260 m (Lusaka).

Ecology Sand beaches of large rivers, normally as territorial pairs. Nests in a scrape on open ground, especially sand.

Status Resident as a whole, some moving to higher ground during floods, and rarely any distance (as above). The generally sedentary nature of this species is well shown by the rarity of records at plateau dams. When not breeding may assemble in groups of up to 50.

Breeding   Jul Aug Sep Oct
(n=56)   3   7   37   9   *Clutch*: C/2 (2); C/3 (8); C/4 (9).
Taxonomy No races recognized.
References [1]Dowsett (in press a); [2]White (1945-46).

Blacksmith Plover *Vanellus armatus*   B158 **RB**

Distribution *Afrotropical (breeds Kenya to South Africa).* Essentially a species of the Zambezi and Kafue drainages, occurring commonly also in the Bangweulu and Mweru Wantipa areas, with a few up the Chambeshi to the Kalungu River[2]. In the past it was scarce and local in the Luangwa Valley, but there are now records from several places, south to Chilongozi. It has occurred rarely at dams on the Eastern Province plateau, at Chipata[4] and Chassa. In the north-west has reached Kakoma (Caenby)[5] as a wanderer, but there are no records from Mwinilunga itself[1], and the species does not occur much further north in the western half of Africa. *Alt.* 330-1400 m.

Ecology On mudflats and short moist grassland mainly on the edge of floodplains, also pools, lakes and dams, sometimes on sand beaches and at salt pans. A few breed at rural dams and sewage ponds.

Status Mainly resident, but there is some wandering at the height of the rains. Breeding pairs are strongly territorial; flocks of up to 100 may occur outside the breeding season[2]. The oldest recovery is of a ringed bird at least 10 years of age[3].

Breeding

	Mar	Apr	May	Jun	Jul	Aug	Sep	Oct
(n=92)	1	10	17	17	15	16	12	4

Clutch: C/1 (5); C/2 (4); C/3 (15); C/4 (9).

Moult: Sep-Feb, lasting *c.* 4 months [2].

Taxonomy No races recognized.

References [1]Bowen (1983j); [2]Dowsett (in press a); [3]Dowsett & Leonard (2001); [4]Tree (1969); [5]White & Winterbottom (1949).

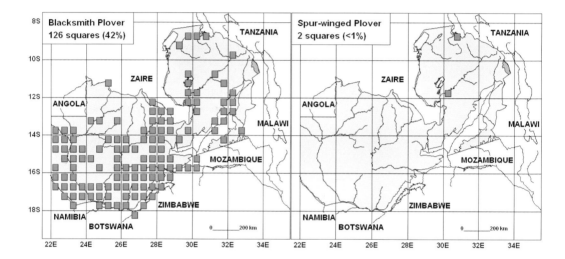

Spur-winged Plover *Vanellus spinosus*   B - R

Distribution *S. Palaearctic and Afrotropical* (*breeds mainly Senegal to Tanzania*). This species turned up at Kasaba Bay in Dec 1999, and has since been seen on several occasions there[6] and in Bangweulu[3]. In recent years it has occurred further south as a vagrant to Botswana (in 1989)[1], and in several places in Malawi (from 1993), breeding in the latter country[4]. *Alt.* 760-1170 m.

Ecology Open sand and hippo-grazed grass along the edge of L. Tanganyika, and short grass floodplain. Occurs alongside the closely-related *V. armatus* (with which it has possibly hybridized in East Africa, and apparently so in Malawi)[4,5].

Status Although records fall between 30 Aug and 8 May[3], it has in fact probably established itself as a resident in N. Zambia in a short space of time; a species that is expanding its range[2].

Breeding No record yet.

Taxonomy No races recognized.

References [1]Aspinwall (1989); [2]Baker (1994); [3]Dowsett (in press a); [4]Dowsett-Lemaire & Dowsett (2006); [5]Pearson (1983); [6]Robinson *et al.* (2001).

Brown-chested Wattled Plover *Vanellus superciliosus*   B - AV

Distribution and Status *Sudanian near-endemic* (*breeds Nigeria and Cameroon, wintering in East Africa*). Vagrants have occurred (the most southerly such records) on playing fields at Mwinilunga (1124C; three 1-2 Oct 1978, and a possible sighting 6 Oct 1976)[1] and by sewage ponds at Kalulushi

(1228C; an immature 3-4 Oct 1998)[2].
Taxonomy No races recognized.
References [1]Bowen (1979f); [2]Van Daele (1999a).

Lesser Black-winged Plover *Vanellus lugubris*   B159 **RB**

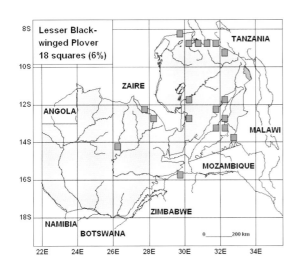

8S Lesser Black-winged Plover 18 squares (6%)

TANZANIA

10S

ZAIRE

12S

ANGOLA

MALAWI

14S

MOZAMBIQUE

16S

ZIMBABWE

18S

NAMIBIA

BOTSWANA   0___200 km

22E   24E   26E   28E   30E   32E   34E

Distribution *Afrotropical (breeds Sierra Leone to South Africa).* Sparse and confined mainly to the extreme north and east of the country, from Sumbu N.P. and Mweru Wantipa[1], down the Luangwa Valley to Chinzombo, and exceptionally to Chipata[2]. But it has also wandered further west, to Mushika in the Middle Zambezi, Chililabombwe[7] and Kitwe on the Copperbelt, and to Treetops in Kafue N.P.[4]. [To the south, it has occurred as a vagrant in Hwange N.P., Zimbabwe[6].] *Alt.* mostly 370-1350 m, to *c.* 1600 m (Mbala area).
Ecology On bare ground and short (often burnt) grassland, airstrips, at dambo margins and clearings in woodland.
Status All but three records are for the period Apr-Dec (most Apr-Oct), but the species is present all year round in neighbouring Malawi[5], so movements are probably not distant. Small groups (up to 6) in the off-season.
Breeding[3]   Aug   Sep   Oct
(n=3)   1   1   1   *Clutch*: C/1 (1).
Taxonomy No races recognized.
References [1]Benson (1956d); [2]Benson (1958c); [3]Coates (1974); [4]Dowsett (in press a); [5]Dowsett-Lemaire & Dowsett (2006); [6]Irwin (1981a); [7]Scott (1983).

Crowned Plover *Vanellus coronatus*   B160 **AMB**

Distribution *Afrotropical (Ethiopia to South Africa).* A common species of the dry plains in the south and west, ranging also to Bangweulu, and reappearing in the far north between Chisenga Is.[1] and the Mbala area. In recent years it has been reported more often in the Luangwa Valley (perhaps as a result of drought conditions), and it has occasionally wandered onto the Eastern Province plateau (e.g. at Manda Hill and the Chipata area)[3]. There are several records from the Middle Zambezi Valley[4]. In the north-west vagrants have occurred to Jivundu and Yowela[3], and even to Mwinilunga[2]. *Alt.* rarely down to 370 m, mostly 650-1660 m.
Ecology Frequents short, often burnt grassland in dry floodplains, at margins of large dambos, also ploughed fields and airstrips. Nests are a scrape on dry ground.
Status Perhaps mainly migratory, with large flocks Apr-Jun suggesting passage. There are few records, of small groups, at the peak of the rains, Jan-Mar[3].
Breeding   Apr   May   Jun   Jul   Aug   Sep   Oct   Nov
(n=132)   3   5   11   20   32   35   25   1

Clutch: C/1 (4); C/2 (37); C/3 (59); C/4 (2).
Taxonomy *V. c. coronatus*.
References [1]Benson & Irwin (1967b); [2]Bowen (1983i); [3]Dowsett & Leonard (in press a); [4]Irwin (1981b).

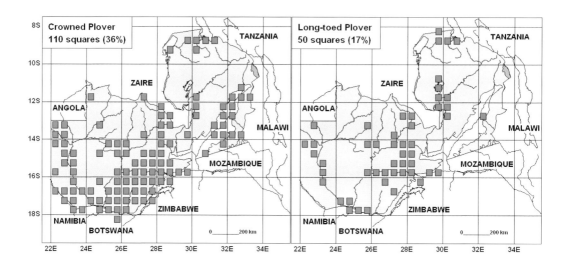

Long-toed Plover *Vanellus crassirostris* B161 **RB**

Distribution *Afrotropical* (*Ethiopia to South Africa*). Usually in swamps, in the north centred on Mweru Wantipa (east to the Lufubu River mouth[1]) and Bangweulu. In the west, throughout the Upper Zambezi from L. Chimwange[3] to Kazungula, exceptionally towards Livingstone[4]. Throughout the Kafue basin, from Kyimbwe salt pan[6] and irregularly on the Copperbelt, down to the Kafue Flats, and even the Middle Zambezi to Mushika (in recent drought years has colonized sites on the Zimbabwe side too)[5]. It has wandered to Muckle Neuk on the Southern Province plateau. Surprisingly, 5 visited Nyakotoko lagoon in the Luangwa Valley, 9 Jun 1993[4]. *Alt.* rarely as low as 370 m, mostly 900-1300 m.
Ecology Always near water, feeding on floating vegetation (such as water hyacinth), on the fringe of *Typha* reedbeds and floodplains.
Status Most are probably resident, but see above, and a bird ringed at Blue Lagoon in Nov was recovered in the Lukanga Swamp, 120 km to the north, in Jul (17 years later) (Appendix 1). Such a movement between these two wetlands has also occurred in *Thalassornis leuconotus*, *Nettapus auritus* and *Actophilornis africanus*. Rarely in flocks (although large, loose concentrations occur).
Breeding   Jul   Aug   Sep
(n=12)   1   8   3   *Clutch*: C/2 (2); C/3 (4); C/4 (1).
Moult: adults finish in Mar-Apr[4].

Taxonomy *V. c. leucopterus*[2], but some individuals show an approach to the northern *V. c. crassirostris* (secondaries and inner primaries black instead of white) at Tondwa and as far south as the Kafue Flats[4].
References [1]Benson & Irwin (1967b); [2]Benson *et al.* (1971a); [3]Britton (1970); [4]Dowsett (in press a); [5]Rockingham-Gill (1988); [6]Tree (1969).

Scolopacidae

Common Snipe *Gallinago gallinago*

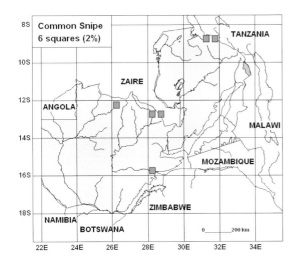

Distribution *Holarctic (in the Afrotropics, winters Senegal to Kenya).* At the southern limit of its distribution in Africa, it has occurred in the Mbala area (seen 1996 and 1999)[2], at Solwezi (shot 1961)[1], Kitwe (ringed 1963 and 1964)[4] and Ndola (specimens 1944, seen 1979)[3,5], with sight records exceptionally from Kafue (Jan 1997)[2]. Recorded very rarely, as easily overlooked unless captured or killed. *Alt.* 980-1670 m.

Ecology Marsh, feeding in mud amongst short grass and sedges in dambos and on the edge of dams.

Status Rare Palaearctic winter visitor. Dates of acceptable records are 11 Nov to 9 Mar[2].

Taxonomy Zambian specimens have not been examined critically, but they are doubtless *G. g. gallinago*.

References [1]Button (1973); [2]Dowsett (in press b); [3]Taylor (1983); [4]Tree (1966b); [5]White (1945e).

Ethiopian Snipe *Gallinago nigripennis*

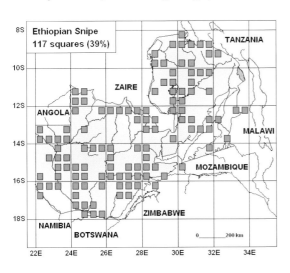

Distribution *Afrotropical (Ethiopia to South Africa).* Widespread in dambos, marshes and by dams through most of the Zambian plateau. At times abundant on the Liuwa Plain, Kafue Flats and Bangweulu floodplain. Scarce in the few marshes of the Eastern Province plateau, and only occasionally recorded from valley areas. Unrecorded from the north-east, between Sumbi and Lundazi[4]. *Alt.* 370-1700 m, not often below 950 m (up to 2300 m on the Malawi side of the Nyika)[5].

Ecology Probes in mud, usually in flooded short grass areas, but at times even on exposed mudflats (especially outside the breeding season).

Status There is a significant increase in frequency of reports Oct-Apr, and a decrease May-Sep (when the species is breeding). Often in groups of up to 10, with local concentrations at times of 50 or more (even during the breeding season)[4]. It seems likely that influxes during the rains represent local breeding birds dispersing (but only ringing can prove this). Most valley records are Sep-Oct, probably post-breeding dispersal.

Breeding May Jun Jul Aug
(n=12) 8 2 1 1 Drumming has been noted (by day and at night) 12 Apr
(exceptionally 12 Mar) to 30 Aug. *Clutch*: C/1 (1); C/2 (7).
Moult: one early Dec in fresh plumage, 3 mid-Apr slightly worn[4].
Taxonomy[2,3] Perhaps all *G. n. angolensis* (with bill length 83-105 mm), although one possible *G. n. nigripennis* or *aequatorialis* (bill 75 mm) collected Chipata (Dec)[6] (and others in Malawi)[1].
References [1]Benson (1952b); [2]Benson (1956f); [3]Clancey (1974a); [4]Dowsett (in press a); [5]Dowsett-Lemaire (2006a); [6]Tree (1969).

Great Snipe *Gallinago media*   B183 **PW**

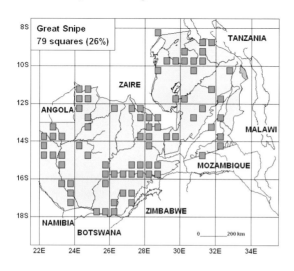

Distribution *Palaearctic* (*the whole population winters Ghana to South Africa*). Occurs throughout the country, in any wetland, locally common. *Alt.* 550-1900 m (higher on the Malawi side of the Nyika).
Ecology Wintering birds occur in any wet habitat, especially marshes, floodplains, dambos and the edge of ponds. When on passage, often in drier areas (cultivation, bush tracks).
Status Palaearctic migrant and winter visitor. First arrivals are late Oct (earliest 6 Oct in Mwinilunga), but most arrive from mid-Nov onwards. Numbers remain high until late Jan, but far fewer thereafter, suggesting many move on. There are possibly signs of return passage to Apr (last 9 May)[4]. [A report of it having been "obtained" on the Copperbelt as early as 3 Aug[2] cannot be verified, and must be rejected[4].]
Conservation Although considered to be globally endangered ("Near Threatened")[3], it seems probable that its numbers breeding in the Palaearctic have been greatly underestimated. The most numerous snipe in the 1940s[5], and this is probably still the case (though numbers vary annually). It is common in Zambia (e.g. Lochinvar), at times even abundant (e.g. Liuwa Plain). Shot by expatriate sportsmen in the past (one person accounted for 208 over a period of years in the 1950s)[1], this snipe is no longer hunted in any numbers.
Taxonomy No races recognized.
References [1]Benson *et al.* (1970); [2]Benson *et al.* (1971a); [3]BirdLife International (2000, 2004a); [4]Dowsett (in press b); [5]White (1945e).

Jack Snipe *Lymnocryptes minimus*   B185 **PV**

Distribution and Status *Palaearctic* (*winters Mauritania to Kenya*). There is a specimen from Mwinilunga (1124C, 26 Oct 1946)[2] and acceptable sight records from flooded short grassland at Ndola (1228D, in both 1979 and 1980, extreme dates 4 Feb and 6 Mar)[1]. The most southerly records, and probably not of annual occurrence. *Alt.* 1330-1370 m.
Taxonomy No races recognized.
References [1]Taylor (1983); [2]White (1948c).

Black-tailed Godwit *Limosa limosa*   B - **PW**

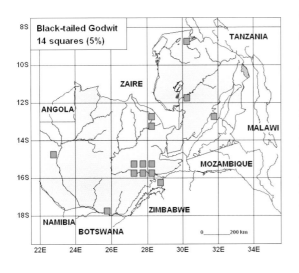

Distribution *Palaearctic (in the past wintered essentially in the Sahel, Senegal to Ethiopia, but since the 1980s this range has been greatly extended to the south).* Since the first records in 1972[1] this species has been reported from L. Tondwa to the Victoria Falls area[5], including Bangweulu, the Copperbelt and especially the Kafue Flats[2], west to Liuwa Plain[3]. Also vagrants at Muchenja in the Luangwa Valley and Chirundu in the Middle Zambezi[3]. *Alt.* 400-1300 m.

Ecology Mostly large floodplains, less often at dams or on sand beaches when on passage.

Status A Palaearctic winter visitor, usually in small groups, but 250-500 on several occasions on the Kafue Flats late Oct to early May, and maxima of over 2000 (including a flock of 1000) at Lochinvar 24 Oct-30 Nov 1997 and 4300 there Oct 2000[4]. There are records for all months, but few present Jun to Sep. There has been a great increase in recent years, possibly displaced from usual winter quarters in the Sahel by extreme drought, and favoured by habitat changes on the Kafue Flats since the creation of dams[3]. Prior to 1984 there were fewer than 10 records, but since then it has become annual, and increasingly abundant.

Taxonomy No Zambian specimen, but doubtless *L. l. limosa*.

References [1]Dowsett (1973a); [2]Dowsett (1979a); [3]Dowsett (in press b); [4]Leonard (2005); [5]Pollard (1989b).

Bar-tailed Godwit *Limosa lapponica*   B174 **P**

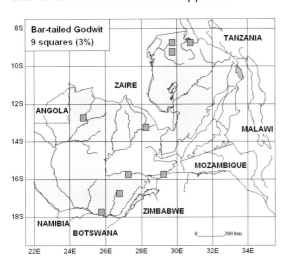

Distribution *Mainly Palaearctic (winters on coasts, Mauritania to South Africa).* Uncommon, recorded from a few localities in the Mweru Wantipa area[1], south to above Victoria Falls[3] and west to West Lunga N.P.[5]. Reported once in the Middle Zambezi Valley (Ruckomechi)[4]. *Alt.* 370-1670 m.

Ecology On muddy shores of lakes, dams and rivers.

Status Palaearctic migrant, which has occurred only on southward passage, between 27 Aug and 6 Dec, once 16 Jan. Mostly singles, but once 3 together. Birds usually stay just 1-2 days[2]. Recorded annually 1975-80, but none since 1994[2].

Taxonomy *L. l. lapponica.*

References [1]Benson *et al.* (1955); [2]Dowsett (in press b); [3]Pollard (1989a); [4]Riddell (1990); [5]Robinson & Casalis de Pury (1978).

Whimbrel *Numenius phaeopus*   B172 **P**

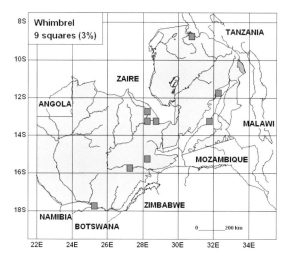

Distribution *Holarctic* (*winters on all African coasts, Mauritania to South Africa*). Irregular visitor at a scattering of localities, from Kasaba Bay[2], southwards along "line of rail" from the Copperbelt to Kazungula. Has occurred twice in the Luangwa Valley[1,3]. *Alt.* 550-1250 m.

Ecology Shores of any wetland.

Status Palaearctic migrant, with records for all months, mostly of singles on southward passage Sep-Nov[3]. Not reported annually.

Taxonomy No Zambian specimen, but probably *N. p. phaeopus*.

References [1]Benson *et al.* (1970); [2]Campbell (1965); [3]Dowsett (in press b).

Curlew *Numenius arquata*   B173 **PW**

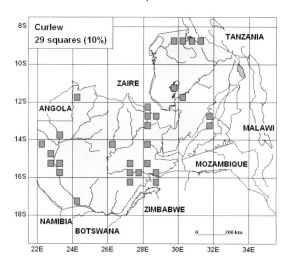

Distribution *Palaearctic* (*winters Mauritania to South Africa*). Recorded annually in small numbers in several parts of Zambia, but it apparently avoids small areas of water, and there is only one record from a dam on the Southern Province plateau (Monze in Feb)[3], and none from dams in Eastern Province. *Alt.* 400-1670 m.

Ecology On muddy shores of various extensive wetlands, especially floodplains and sand beaches.

Status There are records of this Palaearctic migrant for all months of the year. Usually singly, but on southward passage (Aug to Jan) in groups of up to 18 (never more than 3 on return passage)[2].

Taxonomy *N. a. orientalis*[1].

References [1]Benson & Irwin (1967b); [2]Dowsett (in press b); [3]White (1944f).

Spotted Redshank *Tringa erythropus*   B p.106 **PV**

Distribution and Status *Palaearctic* (*winters Mauritania to Tanzania*). There is only one acceptable record, one seen on the Busanga Plain (1425B; 24 Oct 1964) in Kafue N.P.[1]. [There is one possible sound record from Lochinvar, 28 Sep[2].] This species has been confused by observers in southern Africa, and care is needed to eliminate other waders.

Taxonomy No races recognized.

References [1]Brooke (1966c: 86); [2]Dowsett (in press b).

Common Redshank *Tringa totanus* B180 **P**

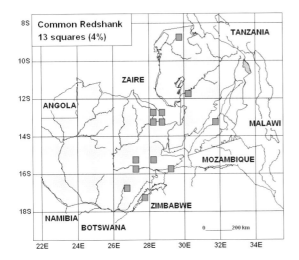

Distribution *Palaearctic (winters mainly on the coasts, Mauritania to South Africa).* Scarce passage migrant. From Kampinda and Bangweulu, especially from the Copperbelt to Choma Dist., but also at lower levels, from Mfuwe to Sinamalima in the Gwembe Valley[1]. *Alt.* 370-1300 m.

Ecology Muddy shores of floodplains, rivers and dams.

Status Palaearctic migrant with all records between 10 Sep and 22 Apr, mostly on southward passage, though the odd one may stay during the rains[1]. Usually singly, once 3 together. Recorded annually 1969-83, but no report since 1993. *Moult:* one mid-Mar was very worn[1].

Taxonomy[2] *T. t. totanus.*

References [1]Dowsett (in press b); [2]Williams (1955a).

Marsh Sandpiper *Tringa stagnatilis* B176 **PW**

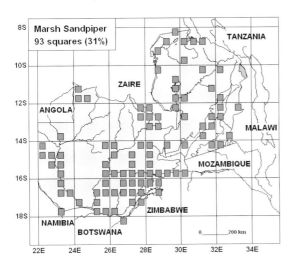

Distribution *Palaearctic (winters Mauritania to South Africa).* Throughout the country, especially common from Mweru Wantipa to L. Tondwa, Bangweulu and the Kafue Flats. *Alt.* 330-1670 m.

Ecology In a variety of wetlands, often wading in shallow water; associates frequently with *T. nebularia* and *T. glareola.*

Status Palaearctic migrant and winter visitor, present throughout the year, with totals of over 100 at several localities Oct-Mar. Reduced numbers in the northern summer, but sometimes 50 on the Kafue Flats throughout Jul[1].

Taxonomy No races recognized.
References [1]Dowsett (in press b).

Lesser Yellowlegs *Tringa flavipes* B - **Nearctic V**

Distribution and Status *Nearctic (very few records in Africa, of vagrants).* There is one record, from a dam at Ndola (1228D), of a bird (photographed) which stayed from 21 Jan to 18 Feb 1979[1].
Taxonomy No races recognized.
References [1]Taylor (1980a).

Greenshank *Tringa nebularia* B175 **PW**

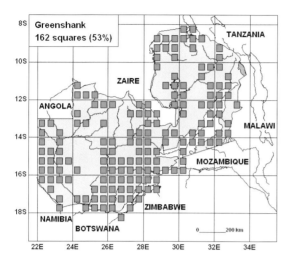

Distribution *Palaearctic* (*winters Mauritania to South Africa*). Common throughout Zambia, especially at lower levels. *Alt.* 330-1800 m (Uningi Pans).

Ecology On mudflats and sand beaches, by any water.

Status Palaearctic migrant, present in all months of the year, and on sand beaches such as along the Luangwa River the population May-Sep is substantial[1]. Often in small groups, frequently 20-30 together (late Jun-early Dec, early Mar to mid-Apr)[2]. A bird ringed in Zimbabwe in Jan was recovered in Zambia in Mar (2 years later) (Appendix 1).

Taxonomy No races recognized.

References [1]Benson *et al.* (1970); [2]Dowsett (in press b).

Green Sandpiper *Tringa ochropus* B178 **PW**

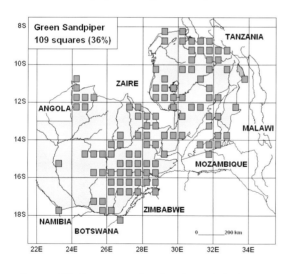

Distribution *Palaearctic* (*winters Mauritania to South Africa*). Regular in moderate numbers in the moister plateau areas, scarce in the Luangwa and Middle Zambezi Valleys. The only records in the south-west are from Mongu[3] and Imusho[1]. *Alt.* 550-2150 m (Nyika).

Ecology Usually at small pools, ditches and on muddy patches on edge of dams and sewage lagoons; also by fast-running streams.

Status Palaearctic migrant and winter visitor, with most records between Oct and Apr (extreme dates 19 Aug and 22 Apr), exceptionally three reports late Jul[1]. The average first date over 27 years was 19 Sep, the average last (in 19 years) 28 Mar[1]. Rarely more than 3 together, exceptionally concentrations of up to 25[1]. One returned to the place of ringing the next year[2]. *Moult*: one in Jan had suspended moult after replacing most feathers[1].

Taxonomy No races recognized.

References [1]Dowsett (in press b); [2]Dowsett & Leonard (2001); [3]Winterbottom (1942a).

Solitary Sandpiper *Tringa solitaria* B - **Nearctic V**

Distribution and Status *Nearctic.* One was seen (photographed and tape-recorded) at a pond at Lilayi,

near Lusaka (1528C), 23 Jan to 27 Feb 1994[1]. A species very rarely reported in the Old World.
Taxonomy No races recognized.
References [1]Aspinwall *et al.* (1995).

Wood Sandpiper *Tringa glareola*   B177 **PW**

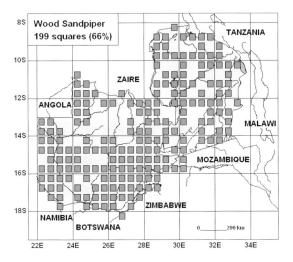

Distribution *Palaearctic* (*winters Mauritania to South Africa*). Throughout the country, often abundant. *Alt*. 330-1800 m.

Ecology On mudflats and any shallow water with low emergent vegetation (especially floodplains, dambos, dams and sewage ponds).

Status Palaearctic migrant and winter visitor, with records for all months of the year, but largest numbers by far (concentrations of over 500) are wintering birds, between Sep and Apr[1]. The origins of 4 birds ringed or recovered in Zambia were Finland (2), Russia and Poland (Appendix 1); 12 birds returned to the place of ringing after 1 year, one after 2 years[2]. *Moult*: finishing late Mar[1].

Taxonomy No races recognized.

References [1]Dowsett (in press b); [2]Dowsett & Leonard (2001).

Terek Sandpiper *Xenus cinereus*   B181 **P**

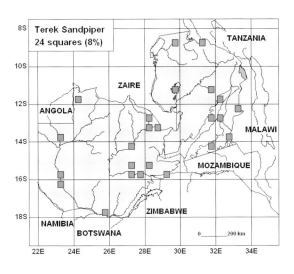

Distribution *Palaearctic* (*winters on coasts, especially on the eastern side, from Sudan to South Africa*). Scarce but annual, throughout, west to the Zambezi, from Zambezi town (Balovale)[1] to Senanga[5]. *Alt*. 370-1670 m.

Ecology On muddy or sandy edges of floodplains, rivers, dams and sewage ponds.

Status Palaearctic migrant, most on southward passage; extreme dates are 18 Aug-26 Dec and 21 Mar-28 Apr (with only three records on northward passage). Usually singly, rarely up to 3 together[3,4].

Taxonomy[2] *X. c. cinereus.*

References [1]Britton (1970); [2]Clancey (1981a); [3]Dowsett (in press b); [4]Penry (1975d); [5]Winterbottom (1942a).

Common Sandpiper *Actitis hypoleucos*   B179 **PW**

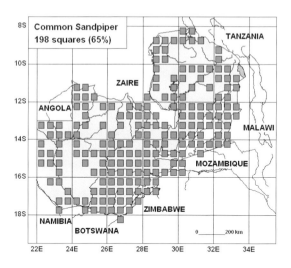

Distribution *Palaearctic (winters Mauritania to South Africa); doubtfully breeds in the Afrotropics, claims that it has done so in East Africa being unconfirmed*[1,2]. Occurs commonly throughout the country, even on small areas of water. *Alt.* 330-1800 m.

Ecology On muddy or rocky shores of any water, flowing or not.

Status Palaearctic migrant with records for all months, mostly late Jul to late Apr, often in large groups (max. 50-60), even throughout the rains[2]. A bird ringed in Zambia 25 Aug was recovered in Russia (near Moscow) on 1 Sep the next year (Appendix 1). Two birds returned to the place of ringing after a year[4].

Taxonomy No races recognized. Previously placed in the genus *Tringa*[3].

References [1]Benson & Irwin (1974); [2]Dowsett (in press b); [3]Dowsett & Dowsett-Lemaire (1993); [4]Dowsett & Leonard (2001).

Turnstone *Arenaria interpres*   B182 **P**

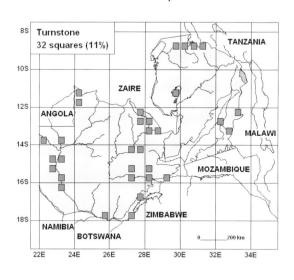

Distribution *Holarctic (winters on coasts from Mauritania to South Africa)*. Known from quite a few localities in the western half of the country (from "line of rail" westwards), Bangweulu, and between Kampinda (Mweru Wantipa)[1] and the south end of L. Tanganyika[2]. Has also occurred twice at small dams on the Eastern Province plateau, at Lundazi[2] and Chipangali[3], and in the Luangwa Valley[4]. *Alt.* 370-1670 m.

Ecology On sandy and muddy edges of any water.

Status Palaearctic migrant of annual occurrence, mainly on southward passage between 24 Aug and 28 Dec. The average first date over 20 years was 21 Sep[4]. Once in Jan, twice in Feb, and once 19 Apr. Usually 1-2, but occasionally large groups in Oct (up to 10)[4].

Taxonomy *A. i. interpres*.

References [1]Benson *et al.* (1955); [2]Benson & Irwin (1967b); [3]Dowsett (1962); [4]Dowsett (in press b).

Sanderling *Calidris alba* B188 **P**

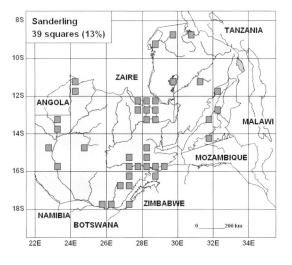

Distribution *Holarctic (winters on coasts Mauritania to South Africa).* Especially on sand beaches, and even at small dams, so likely to occur almost anywhere, although there are some gaps still. Locally common (Kafue Flats). *Alt.* 370-1460 m.

Ecology On sand beaches and mudflats.

Status Palaearctic migrant of annual occurrence, reported mostly on southward passage between 17 Aug and 12 Dec, with first arrivals usually the second half of Sep (being sometimes in groups of up to 16, Oct to early Nov). There is only one acceptable record in Jan, and two or three records of return passage 25 Mar-12 Apr[1].

Taxonomy No races recognized.

References [1]Dowsett (in press b).

Red Knot *Calidris canutus* B - **PV**

Distribution and Status *Holarctic (winters on coasts from Mauritania to South Africa).* Has occurred once, a single bird at a dam at Luanshya (1328A; 7-9 Dec 1985)[2]. Very rare inland in Africa[1].

Taxonomy No Zambian specimen, but probably *C. c. canutus*.

References [1]Dowsett (1980a); [2]Dowsett *et al.* (1999a).

Little Stint *Calidris minuta* B187 **PW**

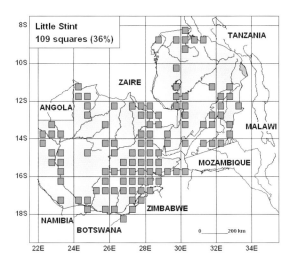

Distribution *Palaearctic (winters Mauritania to South Africa).* Occurs almost throughout the country (but rare in the Luapula drainage, with little suitable habitat for waders), and locally numerous. *Alt.* 330-1670 m.

Ecology Muddy (and sandy) shores of any wetland, especially floodplain.

Status Palaearctic migrant and winter visitor, recorded in all months, but few May-Aug (and then not annual). First arrivals are usually mid-Aug, with peak numbers during Nov (when there are sometimes concentrations of thousands on the Kafue Flats), numbers decreasing in early Dec[1]. One ringed at Blue Lagoon on 1 Dec was recaught on passage in Kenya 25 Mar (Appendix 1). *Moult*: some birds Oct in advanced, suspended moult[1].

Taxonomy No races recognized.

References [1]Dowsett (in press b).

Temminck's Stint *Calidris temminckii*   B - **PW**

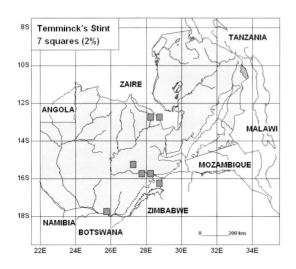

Distribution *Palaearctic (winters mainly Senegal to Kenya).* Since the first records in 1977 (which involved birds at four localities – Nakambala[1], Kitwe, Kanini and Blue Lagoon), there have been four further reports, from the Copperbelt south to Livingstone[2]. These are considerably south of their normal winter range. *Alt.* 420-1300 m.

Ecology Muddy edges to dams and pools in floodplains.

Status A rare Palaearctic winter visitor (extreme dates 29 Oct and 10 Apr). Singly except for once 3 together[2].

Taxonomy No races recognized.

References [1]Brogger-Jensen (1977); [2]Dowsett (in press b).

Pectoral Sandpiper *Calidris melanotos*   B - **P**

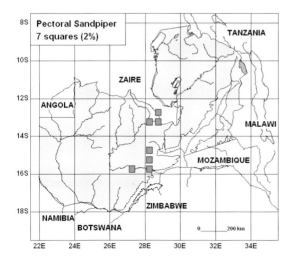

Distribution *Perhaps of Palaearctic (rather than Nearctic) origin.* Since the first in 1978 there have been a few records along "line of rail", from Ndola[2] south to near Kafue town and Lochinvar[1]. *Alt.* 1000-1330 m.

Ecology Dams, sewage ponds, floodplains.

Status An irregular Palaearctic visitor, some seven records in all, four falling between 12 Nov and 24 Dec, once 4 Feb and twice 8-21 Apr[1]. All were singles. In contrast to the three Nearctic vagrants known from Zambia (*Tringa flavipes, T. solitaria* and *Larus pipixcan*), all Jan-Feb, the dates of *C. melanotos* are similar to the passage of other Palaearctic waders.

Taxonomy No races recognized.

References [1]Dowsett (in press b); [2]Taylor (1980a).

Curlew Sandpiper *Calidris ferruginea*   B186 **P**

Distribution *Palaearctic (winters Mauritania to South Africa).* Widespread and locally numerous (as on the Kafue Flats), though rare in the well-wooded regions with few large areas of water, such as Mwinilunga[1] and Eastern Province plateau (where scarce, Chipata[2] and Chassa[3]). *Alt.* 330-1670 m.

Ecology On muddy shores of any wetlands, including sewage works and dams, less often on sand beaches.

Status Palaearctic migrant, recorded in all months of the year. Large numbers occur on southward

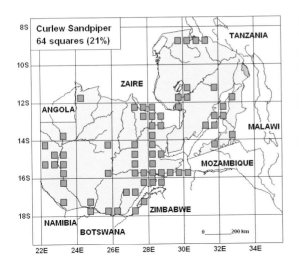

passage between late Jul and Nov (the actual timing varying from year to year). Northward passage is also variable, but it usually begins in Mar, ends in May and invariably peaks in Apr. It involves smaller numbers of birds and at this time suitable habitat is much scarcer. The occasional birds or even groups of up to 100 recorded in Jun and Jul are presumably non-breeding (mostly first-year) birds. At smaller wetlands, flocks of up to 10 are common and flocks of over 50 are rare. At larger wetlands, concentrations of several hundreds are not uncommon. Max. counts all come from Lochinvar N.P. on the Kafue Flats (over 1000 present at times in Oct or Jan)[2,4].

Moult: traces of breeding dress may be seen in any month. Some replace flight feathers while in Zambia, starting Sep, but others arrive with moult suspended[2].

Taxonomy No races recognized.

References [1]Bowen (1983h); [2]Dowsett (in press b); [3]Garcia (1975); [4]Leonard (2006).

Broad-billed Sandpiper *Limicola falcinellus* B - **PV**

Distribution and Status *Palaearctic (winters on coasts from Yemen to Kenya, rarely to South Africa and Namibia).* Singles have occurred on the Copperbelt, at Mufulira (1228C; 1-2 Nov 1975)[2], Ndola (1228D; 21 Oct 1979)[3] and Luanshya (1328A; 9-11 Nov and 4 Dec 1983)[1].

Taxonomy No Zambian specimen, but presumably *L. f. falcinellus*.

References [1]Dowsett (in press b); [2]Robinson (1976); [3]Taylor (1983).

Ruff *Philomachus pugnax* B189 **PW**

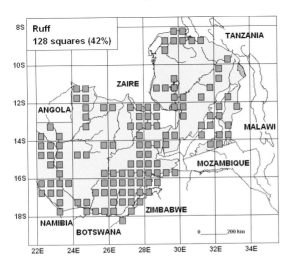

Distribution *Palaearctic (winters Mauritania to South Africa).* Recorded throughout, and locally abundant. *Alt.* 370-1800 m.

Ecology On mudflats, short grassland in shallow water or dry floodplains, less numerous at dams and on airfields.

Status Palaearctic migrant and winter visitor, with records throughout the year, though numbers are small mid-May to mid-Jul. At other times locally abundant, with concentrations of thousands in favoured areas, such as the floodplains of the Kafue Flats, the Bangweulu area and Mweru Wantipa[1,2].

Taxonomy No races recognized.

References [1]Dowsett (in press b); [2]Maclaren (1955).

Red-necked Phalarope *Phalaropus lobatus*

B - **PV**

Distribution and Status *Holarctic* (*wintering mainly at sea*). One vagrant from 29 Sep to 1 Oct 1985 at Itawa Swamp, Ndola (1228D)[1].
Taxonomy No races recognized.
References [1]Dowsett *et al.* (1999a).

Laridae

Lesser Black-backed Gull *Larus fuscus*

B201 **PW**

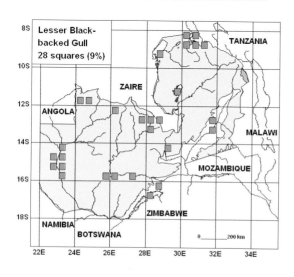

Distribution *Palaearctic* (*winters Mauritania to South Africa*). Regular only in the area between Lakes Tanganyika and Mweru[1]. Occasional on the Zambezi Floodplain, the Kafue Flats, and L. Kariba. Rarely reported elsewhere, especially so in Mwinilunga[2] and the Luangwa Valley[3], and so far unrecorded from much of the Northern Province, Eastern Province plateau, the lower Luangwa-Middle Zambezi and such a well-watched area as the Zambezi near Livingstone[5]. *Alt.* 500-1450 m.
Ecology Lakes and large rivers, less often on dams.
Status[4,5] Palaearctic migrant and winter visitor, with records for all months of the year, but mostly during the rains, when as many as 16 have been seen on L. Tanganyika (the one annual wintering area). A young bird ringed in Finland was recovered in Zambia in early Mar the following year (Appendix 1).
Taxonomy *L. f. fuscus* (as proven by the Finnish-ringed bird).
References [1]Benson (1956d); [2]Benson (1962a); [3]Benson *et al.* (1970); [4]Donnelly (1974); [5]Dowsett (in press b).

Franklin's Gull *Larus pipixcan*

B - **Nearctic V**

Distribution and Status *Nearctic.* A single adult in non-breeding dress on the Kafue Floodplain at Lochinvar (1527C; 25 Jan 1997) [and perhaps again in the same area 17 Nov 1997[1]].
Taxonomy No races recognized.
References [1]Leonard *et al.* (1998).

Grey-headed Gull *Larus cirrocephalus*

B200 **RB**

Distribution *Afrotropical* (*Mauritania to South Africa*) *and Neotropical.* Throughout the country, especially common on L. Tanganyika, in Bangweulu and on the Kafue Flats. Scarce in the Luangwa Valley,

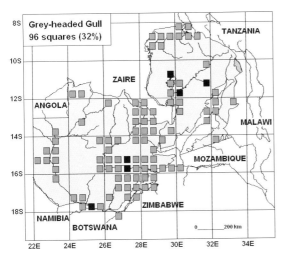

and rare on the Eastern Province plateau (known only from Lundazi and Chadiza)[2] and in Mwinilunga[1]. In addition to the Zambian colonies (black squares), known also to nest on the Zimbabwe side of L. Kariba[3]. *Alt*. 330-1670 m, but not often below 650 m.

Ecology Lakes and large rivers, more rarely artificial dams. Stomach contents examined on the Kafue Flats contained fish of little economic importance: the catfish *Schilbe mystus* (Schilbeidae), the carnivorous *Alestes lateralis* (Characidae) and various small *Barbus* spp. (Cyprinidae)[2].

Status Mostly resident, especially in those fishing areas where commonest. But there is perhaps a dry season influx, with the greatest frequency of occurrence Apr-Nov, least Dec-Mar[2]. Two young birds ringed in South Africa (May and Jun) were recovered in Zambia (Jul and Sep) (Appendix 1).

Breeding   Jan   Apr   May   Jun   Jul   Aug   Nov
(n=19)   1   1   4   2   2   6   3   *Clutch*: C/2 (1); C/3 (4).

Moult: in at least Apr-Jun and Nov-Dec, even when breeding[2].

Taxonomy Most authors recognize no races.

References [1]Bowen (1983i); [2]Dowsett (in press a); [3]Rockingham-Gill & Tayler (1995).

Sternidae

Gull-billed Tern *Sterna nilotica*   B202 **PW**

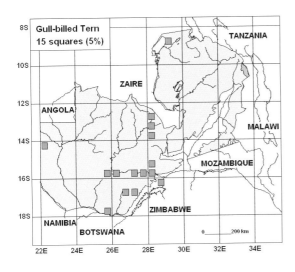

Distribution *Almost Cosmopolitan (Palaearctic birds winter from Mauritania to Zimbabwe; breeds marginally south to Senegal).* Since first noted in 1969[1], this species has been recorded from a number of localities, from Chiengi on L. Mweru and the Copperbelt, south to Choma[3] and Victoria Falls on the Zimbabwe border[5], and as far west as Liuwa Plain[2]. *Alt*. 400-1300 m.

Ecology Large rivers, lakes, pans and occasionally smaller dams.

Status Palaearctic migrant and winter visitor, recorded in all months, but mostly mid-Oct to mid-Feb, when often up to 20 at Lochinvar. It has also increased noticeably in Malawi[4], and generally its inland non-breeding range in Africa has been spreading southwards since the 1970s[2].

Taxonomy *S. n. nilotica*. Molecular studies have suggested that the monotypic genus *Gelochelidon* should be recognized[6].
References [1]Dowsett (1969b); [2]Dowsett (in press b); [3]Dowsett & Osborne (1971); [4]Dowsett-Lemaire & Dowsett (2006); [5]Pollard (1992); [6]Sangster *et al.* (2005).

Caspian Tern *Sterna caspia*   B203 **AM/P?**

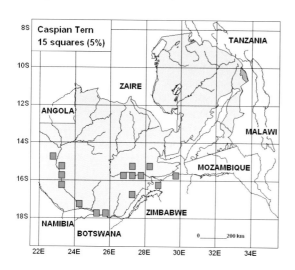

Distribution *Almost Cosmopolitan (in the Afrotropics breeds mainly West Africa and southern Africa; Palaearctic migrants occur north of the Equator).* Most records are from floodplains and large rivers in the south and west, up the Zambezi to Libonda[5], to the northern edge of the Kafue Flats, and less often wandering further east to Lusaka, and Jeki in the Middle Zambezi Valley[3]. The lack of records from well-watched areas such as the Copperbelt argues against these being Palaearctic migrants. *Alt.* 370-1050 m, rarely as high as 1260 m.
Ecology Lakes and large rivers, more rarely sewage ponds.
Status Whereas known only during the dry season until the 1970s, the species is now present throughout the year, though still with most early Mar to late Nov. Numbers have also increased impressively: up to 1971 a party of 20 was exceptional, most being ones and twos, but from the mid-1980s large flocks became common at Lochinvar. Concentrations of 40-100, max. 109, have been noted there during the dry season[3]. These dates suggest these terns are of southern African origin.
Breeding No records (yet).
Taxonomy No races recognized here, but southern African breeding birds are said to differ[2]. There appears to be only one Zambian specimen[1]. Molecular studies have suggested that the monotypic genus *Hydroprogne* should be recognized[4].
References [1]Benson (1959c); [2]Clancey (1971c); [3]Dowsett & Leonard (in press a); [4]Sangster *et al.* (2005); [5]Winterbottom (1942a).

Common Tern *Sterna hirundo*   B - **PV**

Distribution and Status *Holarctic (winters on coasts mainly from Ivory Coast to South Africa).* A single vagrant in non-breeding dress was seen and photographed at a dam at Luanshya (1328A; 5-7 Oct 1979)[1]. The species occurs only very rarely inland south of the Equator.
Taxonomy No Zambian specimen, but most likely *S. h. hirundo*.
References [1]Taylor (1980c).

Whiskered Tern *Chlidonias hybrida*　　　　　　　　B204 **RB**

Distribution *Old World* (*in the Afrotropics, breeds Mali, and Kenya to South Africa; Palaearctic migrants occur locally north of the Equator*). Known to breed only on Liuwa Plain (black square)[2], though probably does so on the Kafue Flats, these being the only two areas where it occurs regularly in numbers. Away from these sites there are records throughout the southern half of the country, to the Copperbelt and Bangweulu, and L. Tondwa to Uningi Pans in the north-east[3]. Vagrants (open squares) have been reported from areas such as L. Kamakawu[1] in the north-west, the upper Luangwa Valley and Luangwa town (Feira)[3]. *Alt.* 330-1800 m.
Ecology Lakes, pans and large rivers, feeding over water and emergent vegetation.
Status There are records for all months of the year, with influxes of 50 or so on Liuwa Plain and the Kafue Flats about Mar, apparently just prior to breeding. Post-breeding groups (usually of up to 70) occur in known or probable breeding areas. On the Kafue Flats numbers increased dramatically in the 1990s, with counts of over 1000 at Lochinvar in Jul 1997 and 1998[3]. This was probably the result of more stable water levels, through the hydrological control associated with the two dams.
Breeding　　　Mar　　Apr
(n=24)　　　　　3　　　21　　Records from a colony of 27 nests[2]. Breeding dress noted in most months.
Clutch: C/1 (4); C/2 (8); C/3 (9).
Taxonomy *C. h. delalandii*. There is no evidence of the Palaearctic nominate race occurring[4].
References [1]Bowen (1983i); [2]Conant (1980); [3]Dowsett (in press a); [4]Mees (1977).

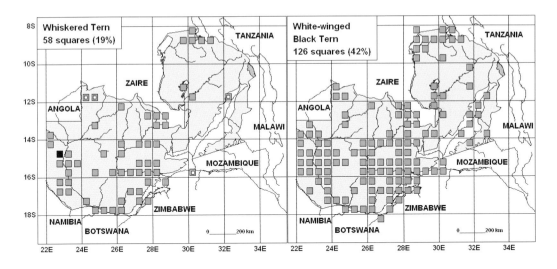

White-winged Black Tern *Chlidonias leucopterus*　　　　B205 **PW**

Distribution *Palaearctic* (*winters Senegal to South Africa*). Throughout Zambia, abundant at L. Tondwa, Bangweulu and on the Kafue Flats[1]. *Alt.* 330-1800 m.
Ecology Over large expanses of water or marsh (less often small dams), feeding aerially and near the surface, largely on insects.
Status Palaearctic visitor, present in all months, with concentrations of thousands Nov to mid-May and several hundreds Jun-Oct[1]. *Moult*: two-thirds of birds in Jan-Mar were in early stages of wing moult[2], with full breeding dress from mid-Apr[1].
Taxonomy No races recognized.
References [1]Dowsett (in press b); [2]Tucker (1975b).

Rynchopidae

African Skimmer *Rynchops flavirostris*   B206 **RB**

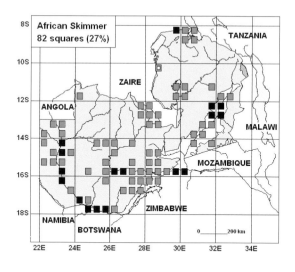

Distribution *Afrotropical (Senegal to South Africa)*. The main nesting populations (black squares) are in the Luangwa Valley, between Luambe and Nsefu[1], and the Upper Zambezi[3,4] to near Livingstone. Has also bred on the Kafue Flats in the Namwala area[5], on the Middle Zambezi between Chikwenya and Luangwa town (Feira)[4,6] and at Chocha, Mweru Wantipa. Away from these sites it can turn up on any body of water, though amongst the gaps in present distribution is most of the Luapula River (only a wanderer, open square)[3] and L. Mweru. *Alt.* 330-1200 m, wandering as high as 1400 m outside the breeding season.

Ecology Breeds in colonies on sand beaches on the larger rivers. Feeds both diurnally and nocturnally.

Status Outside the breeding period flocks of up to 380 wander to a few favoured areas such as the Kafue Flats (where few breed), though elsewhere flocks over floodplains are usually in the region of 50, and on small dams rarely exceed 10. Movements away from nesting beaches at high flood may not be very distant[3].

Conservation Considered "Near Threatened"[2], but there is no evidence of any decline in numbers (nor significant human predation) in most of Zambia. The present status in the Middle Zambezi is not clear: it has been suggested that the Kariba Dam has withheld sediment important for forming sand beaches[7], and we have no breeding report since 1991. The breeding population on the Luangwa and Upper Zambezi Rivers is certainly of the order of several thousand pairs[3].

Breeding   May   Jun   Jul   Aug   Sep   Oct
(n=294)   5   8   67   149   43   22

Clutch: C/1 (16); C/2 (37); C/3 (72); C/4 (19); C/5 (1).

Moult: late Nov to at least late Feb[3].

Taxonomy No races recognized.

References [1]Attwell (1959); [2]BirdLife International (2000, 2004a); [3]Dowsett (in press a); [4]James (1970); [5]Pitman (1932c); [6]Took (1955); [7]Wood & Tree (1992).

Pteroclididae

[Namaqua Sandgrouse *Pterocles namaqua*

Afrotropical (SW Angola to South Africa). Has occurred as a vagrant in Hwange N.P., Zimbabwe (1826D)[3], but reports from the Caprivi Strip (1724A,D) adjacent to SW Zambia[2] lack documentation, and the species is unlikely so far north in this sector[1]. **References** [1]Dowsett *et al.* (in prep.); [2]Little in Harrison *et al.* (1997); [3]Hustler (2000).]

Double-banded Sandgrouse *Pterocles bicinctus*   B208 **RB**

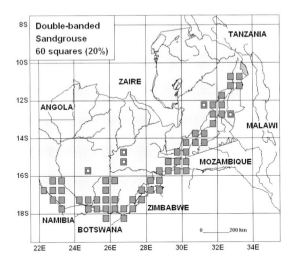

Distribution *Kalahari/Zambezian (Angola to South Africa).* As a breeding resident, confined to the mopane woodlands of S. Zambia and the Luangwa Valley. In the Zambezi Valley, north to the Nangweshi to Shangombo road[1,2], and on the Southern Province plateau to the Nanzhila area. Birds presumably from this population have wandered to south of Afumba[6], Nalusanga and west of Mumbwa[2] (open squares). Throughout the Middle Zambezi Valley, and up the Luano and Luangwa Valleys to Kapisya[7] and near Chikonta[5]. Wanderers were seen on the Northern Province plateau at Mutinondo Wilderness[6], and in Eastern Province north of Diwa Hill[4]. *Alt.* 330-1500 m.

    Ecology In light woodland (essentially mopane, though wandering at times into light miombo), often on dry, stony hills. The nest is a scrape, lined with a little grass[3].

Status Resident in small groups, though numbers coming to drink at dusk in favoured areas in the Luangwa and Upper Zambezi Valleys can total 50-200. Wanders only short distances from the low-lying breeding areas.

Breeding   Dec   Jan   Apr   May   Jun   Jul   Aug   Sep

(n=24)   1   1   2   5   4   8   2   1   *Clutch*: C/3 (4); N/6 (2).

Taxonomy[2] The race in most areas is *P. b. multicolor*, replaced by *P. b. bicinctus* (or perhaps *chobiensis*) in the extreme south-west (lacking dark brown and chestnut markings on the mantle). There is possibly some tendency towards the smaller *P. b. usheri* in the Luangwa and Gwembe Valleys.

References [1]Benson (1956f); [2]Benson & Irwin (1967b); [3]Benson & Pitman (1956-57); [4]Benson & Pitman (1964); [5]Clay (1953); [6]Dowsett (in press a); [7]Meyer de Schauensee (1951).

Yellow-throated Sandgrouse *Pterocles gutturalis*   B207 **AMB**

Distribution *Afrotropical (breeds locally Ethiopia to South Africa).* The species breeds in south-central Zambia (black squares) and presumably also in the west, occurring north to Liuwa Plain[5] and the Busanga Plain[2]. A short distance from the breeding areas there are frequently records of birds on passage. But surprisingly for a migrant which leaves the country for part of the year, there are very few vagrants elsewhere: once at Greystone (near Kitwe), once at Siavonga in the Gwembe Valley (in stunted mopane, more typical of *P. bicinctus*), and at two other places in the Middle Zambezi Valley[3]. A further population occurs in the Chishela Plain area of the north[1], perhaps breeding there in suitable years. *Alt.* 900-1300 m, rarely as low as 370 m on passage.

Ecology Mainly on extensive dry floodplains, but has bred once in a cattle pasture near Choma. Chishela Plain, on the edge of Mweru Wantipa, is frequently flooded (see references under *Phoeniconaias minor*) and so probably not occupied each year. Flies at dusk to drink in rivers and pans.

Status An intra-African migrant, arriving to breed in the dry season. The great majority of records fall between mid-Apr and mid-Dec. Flocks of hundreds (max. 800, but usually up to 200) occur at any time during this period, but especially on passage (Apr and mid-Oct to mid-Dec). There are a handful of

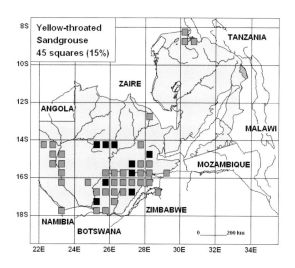

records during the rains (never more than 20 birds together)[3], and it is suggested that such occurrences are becoming more frequent, as a result of local drought providing suitable conditions.

Breeding

	May	Jun	Jul	Aug	Sep
(n=36)	4	10	12	8	2

Clutch: C/2 (1); C/3 (4).

Taxonomy *P. g. gutturalis*, except in extreme NE Zambia where *P. g. saturatior*[4].

References [1]Benson (1956f); [2]Benson & Pitman (1961); [3]Dowsett & Leonard (in press a); [4]Irwin & Benson (1967b); [5]Traylor & Hart (1965).

Burchell's Sandgrouse *Pterocles burchelli*   B - **AM?**

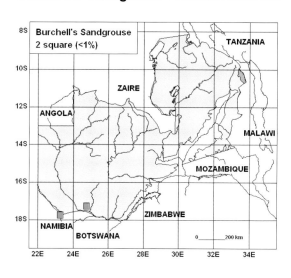

Distribution *Kalahari-Highveld near-endemic (Angola to South Africa)*. Singles and small groups seen in recent years in the extreme south-west, from Imusho east to Simungoma[1,2]. *Alt.* 970 m.

Ecology Dry floodplains, with scattered *Terminalia*, coming to pools to drink.

Status This is another species that has spread in recent drought years, for it was not found in Zambia until 1994, despite previous dry season exploration in the Imusho and (especially) Simungoma areas. In late Aug of 1999 as many as 50 were on the Zambezi Floodplain at Simungoma[2]. Records within Zambia fall between 10 Jul and early Dec[1], and it is not known to what extent the species might be present in other months.

Breeding No record.

Taxonomy No Zambian specimen, but presumably *P. b. makarikari*.

References [1]Dowsett & Leonard (in press a); [2]Leonard *et al.* (2001c).

Columbidae

Afep Pigeon *Columba unicincta*   B209 **AMB**

Distribution *Guineo-Congolian near-endemic (Guinea to NW Tanzania, south to Zambia)*. At several forest localities in N. Mwinilunga, south to the Source of the Zambezi[1] (the most southerly records of

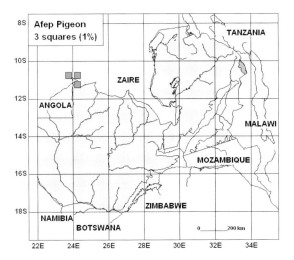

the species), being especially common at Hillwood and (in the past) on the Isombu stream. *Alt.* 1240-1460 m.

Ecology Mainly in the canopy of moist evergreen forest (including gallery) and drier *Marquesia* forest, and occasionally in adjacent miombo. Frugivorous, diet not known in Zambia.

Status[2] Largely or entirely an intra-African migrant. All Zambian records fall between 22 Jul and mid-Jan, and observers have particularly noted an apparent absence Mar to May (presumably due to a lack of suitable fruits). Song heard from first arrival to at least mid-Nov. Groups of 6-8, with up to 15; reported at times with *Streptopelia semitorquata*.

Breeding   Oct
(n=1)   1

Clutch: no data (this record being based on a juvenile).
Taxonomy No races recognized.
References [1]Carter (1973); [2]Dowsett & Leonard (in press a).

Rameron Pigeon *Columba arquatrix*   B210 **AMB**

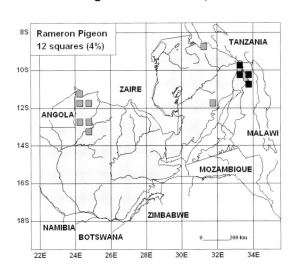

Distribution *Afromontane near-endemic (E. Nigeria/Cameroon to South Africa).* The breeding population (black squares) is apparently confined to the eastern highlands: Mafingas[5], Makutu[3] and Nyika Plateau[7]. Most other records probably represent wanderers, recorded at a number of places on the "montane southern route" in particular: Mbala (22 Jun) and Danger Hill (8 Jan, 29 Mar)[1,4], and from Hillwood in N. Mwinilunga south to Jivundu (for dates see below)[4]. This has doubtless resulted in the dispersal of such trees as the wild olive *Olea capensis*[9] and *Podocarpus latifolius*. *Alt.* 1660-2200 m (higher on the Malawi side of the Nyika[8]) in its breeding areas, but wanderers in NW Zambia are at 1130-1460 m.

Ecology Mainly in the canopy of montane forest. A highly-specialized frugivore, whose local densities vary according to distribution of favourite fruit trees (especially *Cornus (Afrocrania) volkensii, Olea capensis* and *Polyscias fulva*). The highest breeding densities are recorded on SW Nyika with 1-3 pairs/3 ha; small forest patches where *Olea* provides the main fruit source are occupied by territorial pigeons only in "olive years" (i.e. in alternate years); in non-olive years, breeding densities are more closely tied to the distribution of *Cornus volkensii*. Breeding pairs there and elsewhere are still, however, outnumbered by non-breeders[6,7]. The odd pair has been found breeding in small pine plantations.

In NW Zambia reported from riparian forest.

Status Largely migratory. On the Nyika, over 90% of the population leaves in Dec and returns earlier (Jun rather than Aug) in years when *Chionanthus battiscombei* (another favourite Oleaceae) are fruiting. In the breeding season, non-breeding birds roost communally at traditional sites (e.g. Chowo forest) and undertake daily feeding movements of up to 20 km. Altitudinal movements, reported in the Mafingas in Oct[2] (the breeding season), may not have been over any great distance. The species was unrecorded from NW Zambia prior to 1988, but there are now records for the months of Mar-Apr, Jun and Oct-Dec (when song suggests some may even breed)[4].

Breeding   Aug   Sep   Oct   Nov   Dec

(n=12)   1   4   3   2   2   (Including 3 records from the Malawi side of the SW Nyika.)   *Clutch*: N/1 (3); C/2 (1).

Taxonomy *C. a. arquatrix*.

References [1]Benson (1956d); [2]Clay (1953); [3]Dowsett (1971h); [4]Dowsett & Leonard (in press a); [5]Dowsett & Stjernstedt (1973); [6]Dowsett-Lemaire (1988b); [7]Dowsett-Lemaire (1989b); [8]Dowsett-Lemaire (2006a); [9]Dowsett-Lemaire & Dowsett (2006: 50).

Bronze-naped Pigeon *Columba delegorguei*   B211 **RB**

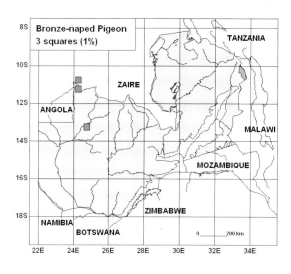

Distribution *Afrotropical* (*Guinea to South Africa*). N. Mwinilunga at a few forest localities, from Chilula and Hillwood, south (in the past) to the Isombu stream[1] and Mpudi River[3]. Two birds seen far to the south at Jivundu[3] may have been wanderers, or an indication of a local population in *Cryptosepalum* forest, hitherto overlooked. Generally uncommon. *Alt.* 1170-1460 m.

Ecology Largely in the canopy of moist evergreen and dense *Marquesia* forest, once in *Cryptosepalum*. Another frugivorous, arboreal pigeon, and so not in competition with *Aplopelia larvata* – the latter mainly a seed-eater, feeding on the ground. The suggestion that these two superficially similar birds might be in competition[1] is unfounded. A big size difference separates this species and the larger *C. unicincta*.

Status It is perhaps resident.

Conservation Like most of the forest birds of N. Mwinilunga, its habitat is greatly threatened by deforestation. However, it is locally common in much of Central and West Africa.

Breeding   Oct

(n=1)   1   *Clutch*: no data.

Taxonomy[2,4] *C. d. iriditorques* (often treated as a distinct species, Guineo-Congolian in distribution).

References [1]Benson (1959a); [2]Benson & Irwin (1965c); [3]Dowsett (in press a); [4]Dowsett & Dowsett-Lemaire (1993).

Speckled (Rock) Pigeon *Columba guinea*   B - **AV?**

Distribution and Status *Afrotropical* (*Mauritania to South Africa*). First seen (two birds) in Livingstone (1725D) Sep 2004 and Mar 2005, and then in and near Choma (a single, May-Jun 2006, 1626D)[3], perched on buildings. *Alt.* 970-1270 m. These are the only recent records of a bird that was said to have existed in the past (with at least one reportedly shot) in the gorges below the Victoria Falls[3]. There are rocky hills in the escarpment areas of Kalomo Dist. (Simwami Hill)[3] and the Middle Zambezi Valley (Chilaunga Hill, Chakwenga area)[1] that are said by local tradition to have held colonies of wild pigeons in the past. *C. guinea* has been reported in N. Botswana in the Kasane area (within sight of Zambia)[5], and in Zimbabwe in recent years wanderers have reached Hwange N.P.[3]. [Reports from the Zimbabwe side of the Zambezi Valley (e.g. the Chewore escarpment[2]) have been rejected as erroneous[4].] It may become established in S. Zambia, at a time of increased aridity.
Taxonomy The breeding form in most of Botswana and Zimbabwe is *C. g. phaeonotus*.
References: [1]Beeston Bancroft (1957); [2]Cooper (1972); [3]Dowsett (in press a); [4]Hustler (1998); [5]Penry (1994).

[Feral Pigeon *Columba livia*   B - **Introduced B**
Birds of domestic stock are present in many towns and villages, but it is not clear where there might be self-sustaining feral populations, though in the 1970s it was thought they might exist "wild" in parts of Lusaka and Choma Dists[1]. **References** [1]Dowsett (1977b).]

Cinnamon Dove *Aplopelia larvata*   B221 **RB**

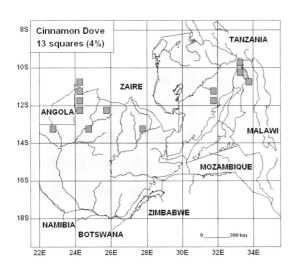

Distribution *Afromontane near-endemic* (*Guinea to South Africa*). Locally common in forest. In the north-west throughout N. Mwinilunga, south to Mbulo (Zambezi Dist.) and Jivundu, east to Mwombezhi, and south of the Copperbelt in Imanda mushitu[2]. It reappears in the north-east at Shiwa Ngandu[2], Danger Hill, the Mafingas[3], Makutu[1] and Nyika. *Alt.* 1770-2200 m in the eastern highlands and Muchingas, 1160-1460 m in NW Zambia.
Ecology Ground stratum of montane and other evergreen forest; territories of 2-4 ha (Nyika), always with a stream. Picks up a variety of seeds from the ground, as well as small invertebrates[4].
Status Resident, although the few records from peripheral areas might suggest some irregular movements: Mwombezhi (seen once early May) and Imanda mushitu (three sight records, Aug and Apr (2), no song)[2].

Breeding	Aug	Sep	Oct	Nov	Dec
(n=12)	1	2	2	2	5

From Zambian Nyika and Mafingas, except for single Aug and Oct records NW Zambia. *Clutch*: C/1 (1); C/2 (5).
Moult: starts about Nov (although the timing in one ringed bird, retrapped 3 years running, varied greatly),

and completed before Jun[2].

Taxonomy *A. l. larvata* in the NE highlands, *A. l. samaliyae* (type locality Kansoko; *NHM*)[5] in the north-west (the latter differing in being blackish rather than brownish on the back, and usually in showing sexual dimorphism).

References [1]Dowsett (1971h); [2]Dowsett (in press a); [3]Dowsett & Stjernstedt (1973); [4]Dowsett-Lemaire (1988b); [5]White (1948a: 20).

[Eurasian Turtle Dove *Streptopelia turtur*

Palaearctic (*wintering mainly in the Sahel, from Mauritania to Ethiopia*). There is an Oct specimen of this Palaearctic migrant from Lulingi in Katanga[3], and it has been recorded further south, in Zimbabwe[1] and Namibia to N. South Africa[2]. It might occur as a vagrant in Zambia. **References** [1]Douglas *et al.* (2000); [2]Cohen in Harrison *et al.* (1997); [3]Louette (1988b).]

Pink-breasted Turtle Dove *Streptopelia lugens* B212 **R(B)**

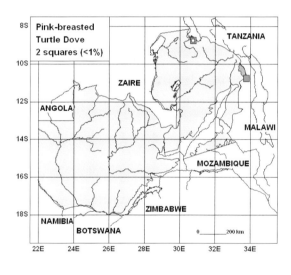

8S Pink-breasted
Turtle Dove
2 squares (<1%)

Distribution *Afromontane endemic* (*Ethiopia to Malawi*). Regular only on the Nyika Plateau, one heard at Kambole[2] (18 May 1954, open square) being presumably a wanderer from the Ufipa Plateau in Tanzania, where it is common. *Alt. c.* 2150 m on the Nyika Plateau (higher Malawi side) and *c.* 1620 m in Mbala Dist. Might be expected from the Mafingas, whence known from the Malawi side[1].

Ecology Feeds mainly in montane grassland, sheltering on edge of forest patches.

Status There are few Zambian records, but it is probably resident, as in neighbouring Malawi[3].

Breeding No records.

Taxonomy *S. l. lugens*[2].

References [1]Benson (1940-41); [2]Benson *et al.* (1970); [3]Dowsett-Lemaire & Dowsett (2006).

Laughing Dove *Streptopelia senegalensis* B216 **RB**

Distribution *Old World* (*in the Afrotropics, Mauritania to South Africa*). Widespread and common in wooded savanna and cultivation in relatively dry country at low and medium elevations, only rarely wandering into higher-rainfall areas, such as Mwinilunga[3]. *Alt.* mainly 330-1400 m, though locally to 1700 m.

Ecology Natural habitats include several types of open dry woodland or wooded savanna (*Acacia*, edges of miombo or mopane) but not dense woodland. Has adapted widely to cultivation and gardens.

Status Present throughout the year, and resident in much of the country[3], although what are mass movements have been observed in Apr at Luangwa town (Feira)[5]. Flocks of 100 or more are common in the dry season almost anywhere, presumably feeding concentrations[3]. As elsewhere in southern Africa[4] numbers have apparently increased with the spread of cultivation and deforestation.

Breeding   Feb   Mar   Apr   May   Jun   Jul   Aug   Sep   Oct
(n=109)   1   3   8   6   12   30   24   19   6
Clutch: C/1 (6); C/2 (37).

Taxonomy[1] *S. s. senegalensis* is the breeding form, but it is possible SW African *S. s. divergens* migrate here on occasion. A partial albino visited Lochinvar in two successive years[2].

References [1]Clancey (1970f); [2]Dowsett (1971d); [3]Dowsett (in press a); [4]Colahan & Harrison in Harrison *et al.* (1997); [5]Tree (1963d).

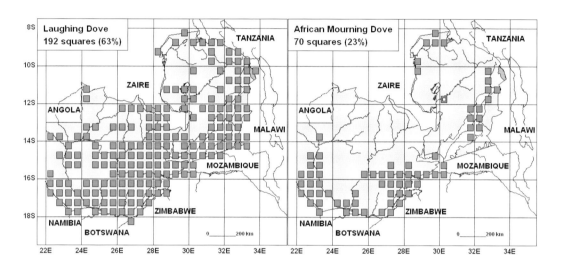

African Mourning Dove *Streptopelia decipiens*   B214 **RB**

Distribution *Afrotropical* (*Mauritania to South Africa*). Common in the *Acacia* woodlands of the south, the Luangwa Valley and between Lakes Mweru and Tanganyika. In the Zambezi basin north to Chitokoloki[5], the Middle Zambezi and parts of the Southern Province plateau (where very localized), north to Blue Lagoon and just east of Lusaka. There is at present a gap between the Luano Valley and Msoro, whence it ranges north to Chama and even Isoka. The most northerly population is between Sumbu[1] and Mwense. A single bird wandered to Shoebill Is. (open square)[2]. *Alt.* 330-1250 m (perhaps marginally to 1500 m), but usually below 1000 m.

Ecology Mostly in thorn savanna and adjacent riparian woodland, especially where there are large *Acacia* trees. Takes seeds on the ground like other members of the genus. Always in smaller numbers than its more catholic congeners *S. capicola* and *S. senegalensis*.

Status Apparently resident.

Breeding   Feb   Mar   Jun   Jul   Aug   Sep
(n=9)   1   2   1   2   2   1   *Clutch*: C/1 (1); C/2 (1).

Taxonomy[3] *S. d. ambigua* (syn. *S. d. kafuensis*, type locality Namwala; *type specimen not traced*)[4].

References [1]Benson & White (1957); [2]Dowsett (in press a); [3]Irwin & Benson (1966b); [4]Reichenow (1921: 264); [5]Winterbottom (1942a).

Cape Turtle Dove *Streptopelia capicola*   B215 **RB**

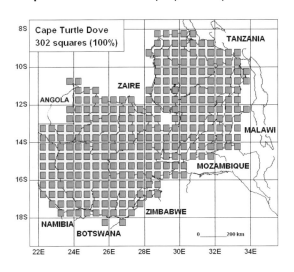

Cape Turtle Dove
302 squares (100%)

Distribution *Afrotropical* (*Ethiopia to South Africa*). Throughout the country, and the commonest dove in any light woodland and cultivation. *Alt.* 330-1900 m (Mafingas), exceptionally at *c.* 2000 m (Nyika)[1].

Ecology In any light woodland, wooded savanna, cultivation and gardens; avoids dense, closed woodland and forest.

Status Resident.

Breeding	Jan	Feb	Mar	Apr	May
(n=142)	2	4	10	14	14
Jun	Jul	Aug	Sep	Oct	Nov	Dec
13	21	32	12	12	6	2

Clutch: C/1 (7); C/2 (47).

Taxonomy[2] *S. c. tropica*, but perhaps replaced by *S. c. damarensis* (paler above and less pink on the breast) in the extreme south.

References [1]Dowsett-Lemaire (2006a); [2]Irwin & Benson (1966b).

Red-eyed Dove *Streptopelia semitorquata*   B213 **RB**

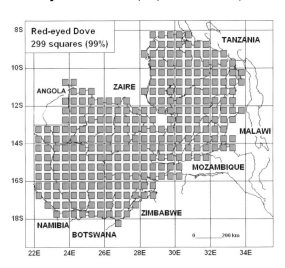

Red-eyed Dove
299 squares (99%)

Distribution *Afrotropical* (*Senegal to South Africa*). Another very widespread and common species, especially at edges of riparian vegetation. *Alt.* 330-1700 m.

Ecology Usually requires some large trees near permanent water; most common in strips of riparian woodland or forest, at the ecotone of dambos and miombo, and at edges of riparian thickets (occasionally in *Cryptosepalum*). Adapts well to exotic plantations and gardens; feeds also in marshland. Like other *Streptopelia* feeds mainly on seeds taken on the ground, but also occasionally on small canopy fruit.

Status Resident; often in quite large flocks[1].

Breeding	Jan	Mar	Apr	May	Jun	Jul	Aug	Sep	Oct	Nov	Dec
(n=64)	3	5	7	9	6	5	11	12	3	2	1

Clutch: C/1 (4); C/2 (12).

Taxonomy Most authorities recognize no races[2].

References [1]Dowsett (in press a); [2]Irwin & Benson (1967b).

Emerald-spotted Wood Dove *Turtur chalcospilos*   B220 **RB**

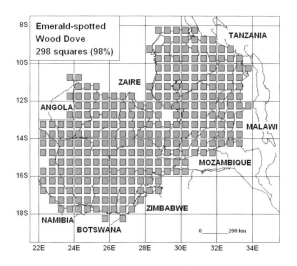

Distribution *Afrotropical (Ethiopia to South Africa).* Throughout the country, very common in woodland and dry thickets, even in higher-rainfall regions. *Alt.* 330-1650 m.

Ecology In any woodland, wooded savanna and dry thickets, thus largely separated ecologically from *T. afer* (see under that species), although they may feed close to each other on the edge of cultivation. Also in *Cryptosepalum* (very common) and locally in *Marquesia* forest; adapts to gardens.

Status Resident.

Breeding
(n=75)

Jan	Feb	Mar	Apr	May
5	3	8	3	1

Jun	Jul	Aug	Sep	Oct	Dec
1	4	6	28	15	1

Clutch: C/2 (24).

Taxonomy[1] *T. c. zambesiensis.*
References [1]Irwin (1981a).

Blue-spotted Wood Dove *Turtur afer*   B219 **RB**

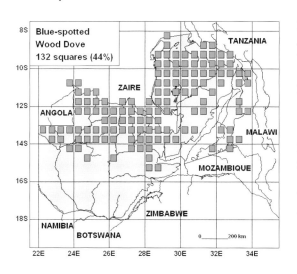

Distribution *Afrotropical (Senegal to South Africa).* The moister woodlands and forests of the northern half of Zambia, in the west to the South Kashiji River, to Kaoma and Lubungu pontoon. Present very locally and irregularly around Lusaka. On Eastern Province plateau south to Chassa[1]. *Alt.* mostly 950-1500 m, locally to 1700 m.

Ecology Inhabits the moister types of miombo, riparian forest or thickets (and thus normally separated from *T. chalcospilos*, in woodland), the edge of evergreen forest (including *Marquesia*). Absent from *Cryptosepalum* forest (where *T. chalcospilos* very common) and surprisingly from transition woodland in forestry plots at Ndola[2].

Status Resident.

Breeding
(n=6)

Jun	Sep
2	4

Clutch: C/2 (4).

Taxonomy No races recognized.
References [1]Dowsett (in press a); [2]Madge (1972b).

Tambourine Dove *Turtur tympanistria* B218 **RB**

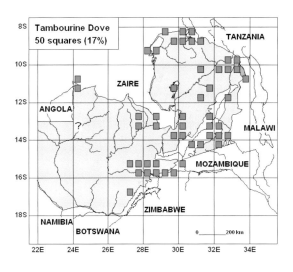

Distribution *Afrotropical* (*Guinea to South Africa*). Occurs in all montane forests of the eastern highlands[3,5]. In riparian forest and thickets from Mbala[1] to Nchelenge, and down the Chambeshi Valley to Bangweulu and the Copperbelt. It ranges down the Luangwa Valley from about the Lufila River confluence to Probert's Point, then the lower Kafue from Gwabi upriver to Nambala Mission[2], south on the plateau even to Batoka. Further west curiously sparsely distributed and rare, from N. Mwinilunga south to Isombu, with a possible sound record from near Kabompo Bridge (1324A[4], "?" on map). *Alt*. 370-2200 m.

Ecology Locally common in ground stratum of evergreen forest (including montane), but mostly in riparian forest and deciduous or (semi-)evergreen thicket. On the Malawi side of the Nyika densities are of 20 pairs/40 ha at 2000 m[6].

Status Resident.

Breeding   Mar   Aug   Sep
(n=4)   1   1   2   *Clutch*: no data.
Moult: Nov-Apr[4].

Taxonomy[7] No races recognized.

References [1]Benson (1956f); [2]Benson (1959c); [3]Dowsett (1971h); [4]Dowsett (in press a); [5]Dowsett & Stjernstedt (1973); [6]Dowsett-Lemaire (1983c); [7]Irwin & Benson (1966b).

Namaqua Dove *Oena capensis* B217 **AMB**

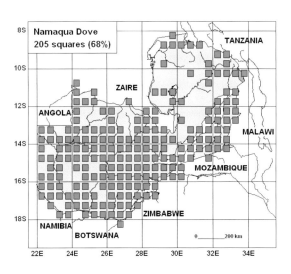

Distribution *Mainly Afrotropical* (*Mauritania to South Africa*). In wooded grassland in dry sandy areas, throughout the west and south of the country, although only an irregular non-breeding visitor in the north-west[2]. North of the Luangwa Valley it is essentially confined to the Chambeshi drainage[5], Bangweulu[3] and the low-lying country between Lakes Tanganyika and Mweru. In this last area it is known west to Chiengi and Kawambwa[1]. *Alt*. 330-1450 m, mostly below 1200 m.

Ecology Typically in open (often sandy) wooded savanna or cultivation, and short grassland, such as dry dambos.

Status Most records are between Mar and Nov or Dec, with few remaining during the rains[5]. Sometimes in small groups. The species is likely on the increase now with the spread of cultivation, and a series of drought years.

Breeding   Mar   Apr   May   Jun   Jul   Aug   Sep   Oct   Nov   Jan
(n=105)   4   14   7   17   8   28   15   9   2   1
Clutch: C/1 (5); C/2 (30). *Moult*: Oct-Apr[5].
Taxonomy[6] *O. c. capensis*.
References [1]Benson & White (1957); [2]Bowen (1983d); [3]Brelsford (1946); [4]Clay (1953); [5]Dowsett & Leonard (in press a); [6]Irwin & Benson (1966b).

African Green Pigeon *Treron calvus*   B222 **RB**

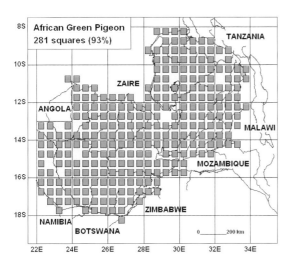

Distribution *Afrotropical* (*Senegal to South Africa*). Widespread and fairly common throughout, in densely wooded country. *Alt.* 330-2200 m, records at highest levels being of wandering birds outside the breeding season.
Ecology In the canopy of miombo and mixed woodland, thickets, riparian forest and (seasonally) feeding also in montane rain forest. Wanders in pairs or flocks in search of fruiting trees: 16 food plants have been reported for Malawi, of which *Ficus* and *Syzygium* spp. are particular favourites[3].
Status Resident, but wanders extensively in search of fruit, e.g. visiting the Nyika forests yearly from late Dec to Feb or Mar (latest date 1 Apr)[4]. Flocks of up to 30 are frequent, exceptionally 150 birds reported feeding in *Ficus* on the Copperbelt mid-Mar[2].

Breeding   Jun   Jul   Aug   Sep   Oct   Nov   Dec
(n=91)   1   5   10   41   20   13   1   *Clutch*: C/1 (57); C/2 (4).
Taxonomy[1,5] *T. c. schalowi*, with *T. c. orientalis* (head and underside tinged grey) in the east (syn. *T. c. clayi*, type locality Isoka; *type specimen lost*; named for Gervas Clay)[6]. The Madagascar population is now generally considered to be a separate species, but if this view is not accepted the name of the species becomes *T. australis*.
References [1]Benson *et al.* (1971a); [2]Dowsett (in press a); [3]Dowsett-Lemaire (1988b); [4]Dowsett-Lemaire (2006a); [5]Irwin & Benson (1966b); [6]White (1943a: 63).

Psittacidae

Brown-necked (Cape) Parrot *Poicephalus robustus*   B223 **RB**

Distribution *Afrotropical* (*The Gambia to South Africa*). Breeds sparsely through much of Zambia, in woodland and forest at low and medium altitude. More widespread when not nesting, but scarce in some areas (as on the Copperbelt and Eastern Province plateau). *Alt.* 330-2200 m, records at highest levels being of wandering birds outside the breeding season[7].
Ecology In richer woodland and evergreen forest, feeding on seeds of medium-sized fruits such as *Parinari curatellifolia, P. excelsa*[6], seeds of *Pterocarpus* and young pods of *Acacia polyacantha* and

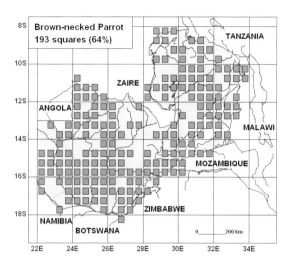

Erythrina abyssinica[5]. In Malawi and East Africa also fond of Baobab *Adansonia digitata* seeds[1] (although captive birds in Zambia did not open these large fruits)[8]. Nests in holes in trees (including 5 m up in a *Brachystegia spiciformis* in cultivation cleared in miombo woodland)[2].

Status Resident, but with local movements. A national survey showed overall frequency to increase Sep-Jan, and to decrease Feb-Aug. In several areas just a visitor after breeding (Sep-Feb) in flocks of up to 25, as in the Lusaka area, and on the Nyika plateau (where annual Nov-Feb)[7], while numbers increase during this period at Livingstone and Mongu. In the Luangwa Valley it is common May-Jul[5].

Conservation Large numbers are reported to be trapped with bird lime, to be sold as cage birds[9]. The effects of this on wild populations needs to be investigated; the nominate population in southern Africa is endangered[10].

Breeding   Apr   May   Jun
(n=4)   1   1   2   Nesting perhaps timed such that young have access to suitable fruit in their first few months (peak fruiting of *Parinari* at Lusaka being Oct-Nov)[3]. *Clutch*: N/2 (3); C/3 (1). *Moult*: an adult had nearly finished early Dec[11].

Taxonomy *P. r. suahelicus*. Some authorities consider the South African population to be specifically distinct, in which case the Zambian species becomes *P. fuscicollis*[4], but see ref. 6.

References [1]Belcher (1930); [2]Benson (1962a); [3]Bingham (2000); [4]Clancey (1997); [5]Dowsett (in press a); [6]Dowsett-Lemaire (2004); [7]Dowsett-Lemaire (2006a); [8]Fosbrooke (1968); [9]Leonard (2005: 101); [10]Symes (1999); [11]Traylor (1965b).

Meyer's Parrot *Poicephalus meyeri*   B224 **RB**

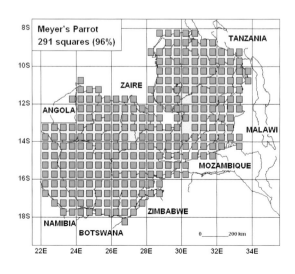

Distribution *Afrotropical* (*Ethiopia to South Africa*). Common and throughout the country in any woodland. *Alt.* 330-1500 m, locally to 1650 m.

Ecology In any woodland, especially the drier riparian, miombo and mopane.

Status Resident, but flocks range widely outside the breeding season. There is not the seasonally significant variation of numbers shown by *P. robustus*[1].

Conservation Fairly often kept in captivity, but this parrot is very numerous and under no threat. Present in nearly every national park.

Breeding   Apr   May   Jun
(n=26)   1   5   5
                      Jul   Aug   Sep
                       4   5   6

Clutch: C/2 (2); C/3 (7); C/4 (2).

Taxonomy[2] *P. m. matschei*, with *P. m. transvaalensis* south of about 16°S (distinguished by its greyer, less sooty brown upperparts, and bluer, less greenish, rump and abdomen), but range overall continuous and variation clinal.

References [1]Dowsett (in press a); [2]Irwin & Benson (1966a).

Lilian's Lovebird *Agapornis lilianae*   B225 (part) **RB**

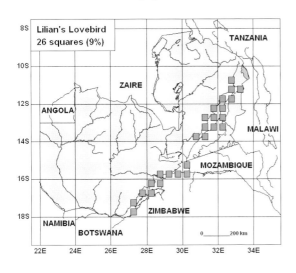

Distribution *Zambezian endemic* (*Tanzania to Zimbabwe*). A bird of the mopane of the Middle Zambezi and Luangwa Valleys. Common in the Luangwa Valley, north at least to the Muzi River and near Chama[5]. Reported to occur in the Luano and Rufunsa Valleys[8] ("?" on map), but later said not found by White[7]: no firm record traced, and there may be a gap between the lower Luangwa and Chisomo. From the Kapoche area (1530A) ranges up the whole Middle Zambezi Valley to Kanchindu (1727C), but not numerous along L. Kariba[5]. *Alt.* 330-1300 m.

Ecology Mainly in mopane woodland and nearby *Acacia* groves. Nests in tree holes; said by villagers to breed in the nests of *Bubalornis niger*, but this requires confirmation[1]. Feeds on (among others) grass seeds, including Millet *Eleusine coracana*, Sorghum *Sorghum bicolor*, cultivated sunflower seeds and flowers (e.g. of *Acacia albida*).

Status Resident, in flocks of hundreds at times in the dry season.

Conservation It is still caught in large numbers for the cage bird trade[4], despite legal protection in both Zambia and Zimbabwe. It occurs within four national parks in the Luangwa Valley and Middle Zambezi (where there is no sign of any diminution of numbers, and where flocks of up to 600 are reported from the Zimbabwe side[6]). But it is scarce in the heavily-populated Gwembe (Kariba) Valley. Recently raised to the status of "Near Threatened"[2].

Breeding Nests colonially, but few observations in the wild. Two nests were occupied mid-Oct. A feral population laid Jan-Feb[3].

Taxonomy No races (if the next bird is treated as a distinct species).

References [1]Benson & White (1957); [2]BirdLife International (2004a); [3]Button (1953); [4]Couto (1996); [5]Dowsett (in press a); [6]Maasdorp (1995); [7]White & Winterbottom (1949); [8]Winterbottom (1939a).

Black-cheeked Lovebird *Agapornis nigrigenis*   B225 (part) **RB**

Distribution *Zambezian endemic* (*mainly Zambia, but perhaps marginally south of the Zambezi*)[7]. Occurs south to the Zambezi from the Kaunga and Nanzhila areas of the Kafue N.P.[1], exceptionally (at least in the past) to the vicinity of Livingstone (open square). Ranges as far west as Sichili, and between Mulobezi and Sesheke. It is still numerous locally in the mid-Machile, Sichifula and Ngwezi River drainages, where there is in places subsistence farming[14]. The other significant pocket of lovebirds is

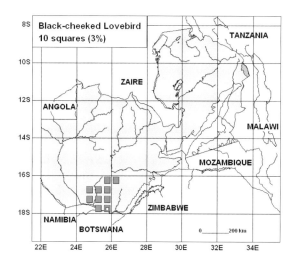

Black-cheeked Lovebird
10 squares (3%)

further north in the thinly-inhabited Nanzhila area. *Alt.* 950-1200 m.

Ecology Mainly in mopane and on the edge of *Baikiaea* (teak) forest, usually not far from rivers or pans. It feeds either on the ground (mainly on seeds) or on flowers (such as *Euphorbia*) and small fruit. Where Millet *Eleusine coracana* and Sorghum *Sorghum bicolor* are grown, they are favoured foods[15], a fact that has been used as a means of capturing huge numbers[9]. When these crops are ripening, *A. nigrigenis* can be a pest for subsistence cultivation locally[15]. However, for much of the year it feeds on weed seeds, especially the alien *Acanthospermum hispidum*[13]. Its essentially granivorous diet means it is highly dependent on the availability of water, and it is absent from mopane areas with no standing water[14]. A large sample of nests showed them to occur in mopane in small, loose colonies, but one nest per tree, in a hole on average 10 m up[12].

Status Resident. Still occurs at times in quite large flocks (up to 175 birds), though most often small groups of up to 10[14].

Conservation[5] Classed as "Endangered"[2]. The core range of the species is less than 2500 sq. km[13]. It seems thousands were caught for the cage bird trade in the past; in 1910, 1000 had been "just brought down from Rhodesia"[8]. 16,000 were said to have been captured in four weeks in 1929[9]. Rainfall in this region has declined notably during the past 50 years (at a rate of some 5 mm p.a.)[14]. It is possible that this lovebird has also been adversely affected by the local reduction of Elephant numbers, in that it needs to drink regularly, and there may now be fewer waterholes accessible. They make use of human-made waterholes and dams in the Machile/Ngwezi area, which (with their feeding on subsistence crops) brings them into close contact with man. The present status is probably stable[13], but the population is now very small (perhaps less than 10,000 birds)[5]. The species breeds readily in captivity.

Breeding   Nov   Dec
(n=80)   1   1   Also 78 occupied nests early Feb to mid-Apr. The two dated nests were from near Katombora and near Sesheke[3]. *Clutch*: C/3 (1); C/4 (1); N/6 (1); N/7 (1).

Taxonomy No races (though it has in the past been treated as a race of *A. lilianae*); the suggestion that the two species may hybridise in the wild[11] is unproven. Type locality Ngwezi River[6], not Muguazi[10] or Muguzzi[4]; *SAM*.

References [1]Benson (1958c); [2]BirdLife International (2000, 2004a); [3]Brooke (1967b); [4]Collar in del Hoyo *et al.* (1997); [5]Dodman (n.d.=1996); [6]Dowsett (1972a); [7]Dowsett (in press a); [8]Haagner (1910); [9]Moreau (1948: 214); [10]Sclater (1906: 61); [11]Them (1984); [12]Warburton (2000); [13]Warburton (2002); [14]Warburton & Perrin (2005); [15]Warburton & Perrin (2006).

Musophagidae

Schalow's Turaco *Tauraco schalowi*   B226 **RB**

Distribution *Zambezian/Afromontane* (*Kenya to Zimbabwe*). Widespread and usually common in densely-wooded and forested country on the plateau; absent from the floor of the Luangwa and Middle

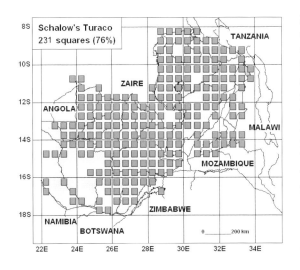

Zambezi Valleys, but otherwise occurs nearly throughout, west to the Zambezi, except for the dry *Baikiaea* forest west of Kafue N.P. Scarce too on the Southern Province plateau, south to the Zambezi at Livingstone (where resident) and upriver to Kalobolelwa[2]. West of the Zambezi known from Kalabo and Liumba Hill[7], and a few localities on the Mashi. The sibling, allopatric species Livingstone's Turaco *T. livingstonii* occurs in SW Tanzania to the area of Mount Rungwe and Isoko, but not N. Malawi. *Alt.* 800-2200 m; mostly above 1100 m, rarely down to 370 m (Chiawa)[2].

Ecology Common in canopy and upper strata of any evergreen forest (including montane), riparian and miombo woodland; scarce in *Cryptosepalum* forest. Nests have been in trees such as *Bauhinia* and mango *Mangifera indica*, 4-5 m above the ground[1]. In Malawi (including the Nyika) has a diet of at least 58 spp. of fleshy fruits[3]. May compete with *T. porphyreolophus* in areas of altitudinal overlap.

Status Resident; usually in pairs, but feeding groups of up to 18 noted. Densities of 40 pairs in 160 ha of forest patches on the SW Nyika (2100-2200 m)[4].

Breeding   Sep   Oct   Nov   Dec   Jan   Feb
(n=33)   1   8   10   6   5   3
The Sep record is from the Malawi/Zambia Nyika (Zovochipolo). *Clutch*: C/1 (8); C/2 (19).

Taxonomy No races recognized. It is no longer considered conspecific with other green turacos (e.g. the Guinea Turaco *T. persa*, or *T. livingstonii*)[5,6].

References [1]Benson & Pitman (1961); [2]Dowsett (in press a); [3]Dowsett-Lemaire (1988b); [4]Dowsett-Lemaire (1989b); [5]Dowsett-Lemaire & Dowsett (1988); [6]Moreau (1958); [7]Traylor & Hart (1965).

Purple-crested Turaco *Tauraco porphyreolophus*   B227 **RB**

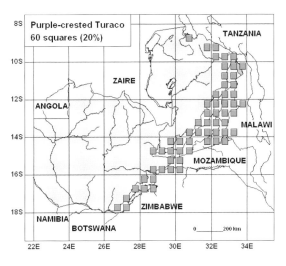

Distribution *Zambezian/Eastern (Kenya to South Africa)*. Common in thicket and riparian vegetation, throughout the Middle Zambezi and Luangwa Valleys, north-eastwards from Sianzovu. Throughout the Eastern Province plateau too, and spilling onto the Northern Province plateau in Isoka Dist., even (perhaps just wandering) to Nkamba Bay[2]. *Alt.* 330-1470 m (Jombo)[1].

Ecology In thicket, dry forest, riparian and miombo woodland (rarely thinner types). This species and *T. schalowi* both occur on the Eastern Province plateau, and in the Lukusashi Valley and on the Mutinondo River at the foot of the Muchinga escarpment[2], but it is not known how they are separated eco-

logically at the same localities (in Malawi they defend inter-specific territories)[3]. *T. schalowi* is unrecorded at places where the lower-altitude *T. porphyreolophus* is common, as at Lundazi (1140 m)[5].
Status Resident.
Breeding   Dec
(n=1)   1   *Clutch*: C/1 (1).
Taxonomy *T. p. chlorochlamys*, tending to intergrade with nominate *porphyreolophus* (with a reddish wash on the green breast) in the Zambezi Valley[4]. Sometimes retained in the monotypic genus *Gallirex*.
References [1]Benson (1951); [2]Dowsett (in press a); [3]Dowsett-Lemaire & Dowsett (2006); [4]White (1965); [5]Winterbottom (1941a).

[**Red-crested Turaco** *Tauraco erythrolophus*
Endemic to W. Angola. One photographed at Victoria Falls, Zimbabwe in 1972 was 1100 km from the nearest population in Angola, and presumably an escape from captivity[1]. **References** [1]Hustler (1989).]

Lady Ross's Turaco *Musophaga rossae*   B228 **RB**

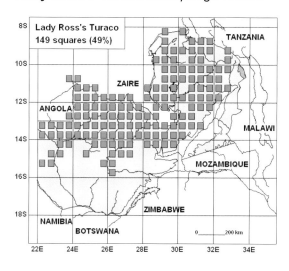

Lady Ross's Turaco
149 squares (49%)

Distribution *Afrotropical* (*Sudan to Zambia, exceptionally to Botswana*[7]). A forest species ranging in the west south to Sikongo[9] and Mapungu[2]; locally common. Does not occur much south of 15°S in the Zambezi basin, but along the Kafue regularly in the Chunga area, and once even to Itezhi-Tezhi. [Vagrants have been reported south of the Zambezi in neighbouring countries, including sightings claimed from the Katombora area[6], but these are considered unconfirmed[8]; the Zambezi above the Victoria Falls has been well explored from the Zambian side, with no trace of this species. Other wanderers have been reported elsewhere in central Zambia, but they are unconfirmed[5].] Does not occur east of a line from Old Fife[4] to Muzyatama[1], being unknown east of the Luangwa Valley (except for a possible sight record of a wanderer to Vwaza Marsh in Malawi)[10]. *Alt.* 1000-1650 m.
Ecology Usually in moist evergreen forest, riparian forest and rich miombo (especially where there are large termite mound thickets). Also common locally in drier *Cryptosepalum* and *Marquesia* forest in North-Western Province, and occasionally wanders into light *Burkea* woodland in Zambezi Dist. Two nests were 3-4 m high in or on the edge of riparian evergreen[3], a third in a similar situation but 15-16 m high, just below the canopy. At this last nest (in West Lunga N.P.) the chick(s) received many *Syzygium* fruits, seeds of which were regurgitated below the nest, and also a snail[5].
Status Resident, but with some wandering.
Breeding   Aug   Sep   Oct   Nov   Feb
(n=10)   1   2   4   2   1   *Clutch*: C/1 (2).
Taxonomy No races recognized.
References [1]Benson (1951); [2]Benson & Irwin (1967b); [3]Benson & Pitman (1961); [4]Benson & White (1957); [5]Dowsett (in press a); [6]Hustler (1996); [7]Irwin (1984); [8]Riddell (2004b); [9]Traylor (1965b); [10]Turner (1978).

[Great Blue Turaco *Corythaeola cristata*
Guineo-Congolian near-endemic (*Guinea to W. Kenya, south to S. Zaire*). This forest species occurs as
near to Mwinilunga Dist. as the Luau River in Moxico, Angola[1] and Kasaji in Katanga, Zaire[2]. Being
a target for hunters it is unlikely now to occur in Zambia, but may have done in the past. **References**
[1]Hall (1960); [2]Schouteden (1971).]

Grey Lourie *Corythaixoides concolor*   B229 **RB**

Distribution *Afrotropical* (*Zaire to South Africa*). Locally common in light dry woodland, replaced in
the extreme north-east by *C. personatus*. Almost throughout the rest of the country, but absent from
higher-rainfall NW Zambia beyond a line from Liuwa Plain to West Lunga N.P.[1]. Occurs sparingly
down the Luapula to Katuta[2] and Chisenga Is.[1]. In Northern Province, north to Munkonje[2] and
Kampumbu, and on Eastern Province plateau to Mahobe[4]. *Alt.* 330-1400 m.
Ecology In various open woodlands, wooded or thicket-clump savanna, including *Acacia*, palms,
mopane and light miombo; avoids mature miombo.
Status Resident; in pairs or small groups.

Breeding   Feb   Mar   Apr   May   Jun   Jul   Aug   Sep   Oct   Nov
(n=71)   3   4   10   2   1   8   14   14   10   5
Clutch: C/1 (1); C/2 (9); C/3 (16).
Taxonomy[5] *C. c. molybdophanes* (type locality five miles east of Lusaka; *DM*)[3], replaced by *C. c.
bechuanae* in the south-west (with a distinct green wash on the chest).
References [1]Benson (1962a); [2]Benson & White (1957); [3]Clancey (1964a: 129); [4]Dowsett (in press a);
[5]Irwin & Benson (1966b).

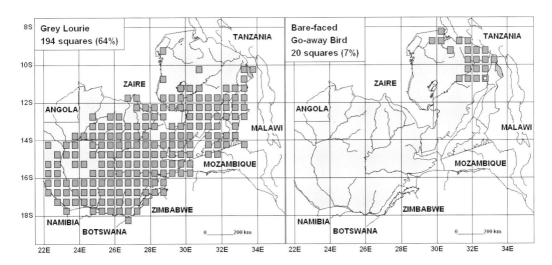

Bare-faced Go-away Bird *Corythaixoides personatus*   B230 **R(B)**

Distribution *Afrotropical* (*Ethiopia to Zambia*). Occupies essentially that part of NE Zambia whence
C. concolor is absent. West sparingly to Mweru Wantipa[1], then to Kabwe Swamp[1] and near Chinsali[2],
even wandering to within the range of *C. concolor* in the upper Luangwa on the Musi River[3] (open
square). These are the most southerly records of the species. Locally common on the Chambeshi
Floodplain. *Alt.* 950-1600 m, exceptionally down to *c.* 700 m (Musi River).

Ecology Floodplain thickets and wooded savanna, open miombo and thin riparian woodland.
Status Resident; in groups of up to 8.
Breeding No records.
Taxonomy *C. p. leopoldi.*
References [1]Benson & White (1957); [2]Brelsford (1941); [3]Dowsett (in press a).

Cuculidae

Great Spotted Cuckoo *Clamator glandarius*   B231 **AMB**

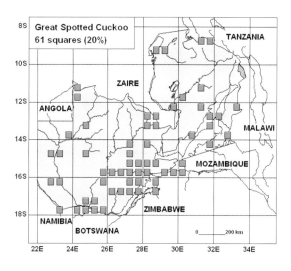

Great Spotted Cuckoo
61 squares (20%)

Distribution *Afrotropical* (*Mauritania to South Africa*) *and S. Palaearctic.* Known mainly from light woodland around the Kafue Flats and in the Luangwa Valley. In the Northern and Luapula Provinces only from the *Acacia* country near Lakes Mweru and Tanganyika. Further west, wanderers at Mwinilunga, Liuwa, the Sitoti-Shangombo road and Nasiongo[1,4]. *Alt.* 330-1400 m.
Ecology Usually in well-developed *Acacia*, less often in other open types of woodland. Feeds mainly on caterpillars, frequently on the ground.
Status An intra-African migrant and breeding visitor (there is no good evidence that Palaearctic birds occur this far south). The great majority of records are from late Sep to mid-May, extreme dates 31 Aug (Kafue Flats) and 29 May (Blue Lagoon)[4]. In a sample of more than 120 dated observations, exceptions are six records of one or two birds in Jun-Jul on the Kafue Flats, at Monze and in the Lower Zambezi N.P. (one adult, two immatures, the rest not aged)[4]. This status accords well with that throughout southern Africa.
Breeding   Sep   Oct   Mar
(n=3)   1   1   1   "*Clutch*": C/1 (1); N/2-3 (1).
Hosts: *Corvus albus* (2), *Lamprotornis mevesii* (1)[5]. Adult cuckoos have been seen to be harried by *Lamprotornis chalybaeus*[4]. The young are raised together with those of the host.
Taxonomy Many authorities recognize no races, although *C. g. choragium* has been described from South Africa, and it is claimed that Palaearctic birds of the nominate race migrate to southern Africa[2,3]. The differences are mainly in the smaller wing and tail lengths of birds breeding in southern Africa. The question warrants more detailed investigation.
References [1]Benson & Irwin (1967b); [2]Clancey (1951); [3]Clancey (1973); [4]Dowsett & Leonard (in press a); [5]Greenberg & Colebrook-Robjent (1976).

Jacobin Cuckoo *Clamator jacobinus*   B232 **AMB**

Distribution *Afrotropical* (*Senegal to South Africa*) *and Oriental.* Throughout, in relatively open country (the paucity of records from west of the Zambezi may merely reflect incomplete exploration). *Alt.*

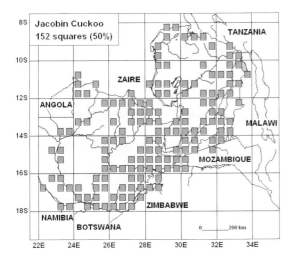

mostly 330-1500 m, even wandering as high as 2200 m on the Nyika.

Ecology In various types of light woodland or wooded savanna (miombo, mopane, *Acacia*, *Combretum*, etc.). Especially at edges or eco-tone of woodland, small thickets and grass-land, even Papyrus swamp.

Status An intra-African migrant and breeding visitor. Records are for the period 25 Sep to 17 May (exceptionally 13 Sep and 15 Jun[5], with one black phase *serratus* in the Middle Zambezi 6 Jul)[3]. The average first date over 19 years was 10 Oct, the average last (in 22 years) 12 Apr[3]. 11 specimen records of *pica* are all from the eastern half of Zambia (west to Kitwe and Kariba), and fall between 27 Oct and 27 Mar[4]. It is possible some are non-breeding visitors from north of the Equator.

Breeding   Oct   Nov   Dec   Jan   Feb   Mar
(n=18)   1   3   4   7   2   1

Calling noted 3 Oct to 17 May, but mainly late Oct to late Dec. "*Clutch*": C/1 (6). Hosts: *Pycnonotus barbatus* (11)[3]. The colour of 7 of 8 eggs south of 15°S was white, and they are thought to have been laid by *C. j. serratus*[2,3]. One egg from Ndola (in a nest of *P. barbatus*) was blue, as was an oviduct egg from Bulaya (which matched the eggs of *Turdoides leucopygia* taken locally)[1] – these are thought to be of *C. j. pica*. In Asia the hosts are babblers *Turdoides*[6], but in southern Africa at least this niche appears to be exclusive to *C. levaillantii*. *Moult*: three birds in Jan and Feb[3].

Taxonomy[4] Both *C. j. pica* and *C. j. serratus* occur commonly (the former creamy white below, the latter distinguished by a grey wash on the underside and better defined dark streaking; *serratus* also occurs quite often in a black phase). The form *pica* breeds in Africa mostly north of the Equator, while *serratus* is the race breeding in southern Africa (including S. Zambia). *C. j. jacobinus* may occur as a migrant from the Oriental region, birds with shorter wings from Malawi and elsewhere being so referred by some authors. Sometimes placed in the genus *Oxylophus*.

References [1]Benson & Pitman (1956-57); [2]Benson & Pitman (1966); [3]Dowsett & Leonard (in press a); [4]Irwin & Benson (1966a); [5]Tucker & Tucker (1975); [6]Vaurie (1965).

Striped Crested Cuckoo *Clamator levaillantii*   B233 **AMB**

Distribution *Afrotropical* (*Mauritania to South Africa*). In woodland and riparian growth throughout Zambia, at all levels, usually markedly more common than *C. jacobinus*. *Alt.* 330-1500 m, rarely wandering to 2150 m on the Nyika.

Ecology In miombo and other woodland, also thickets and riparian vegetation, altogether in more wooded country than *C. jacobinus*. They feed to a great extent on hairy caterpillars.

Status An intra-African migrant and breeding visitor, mostly from mid-Oct (in some years Nov) to early May, first arrivals each year falling between the last week of Sep and the third week of Oct. Extreme dates are 22 Sep and 28 Jun (the several late records in Jun often being of juveniles still accompanying babblers)[2]. The average first date over 26 years was 10 Oct, the average last (in 28 years) 9 May[2]. One unusual record on 22 Aug may have been a case of over-wintering[2].

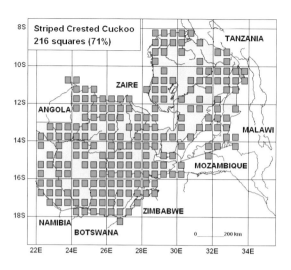

Breeding

	Oct	Nov	Dec	Jan
(n=61)	5	10	3	4
	Feb	Mar	Apr	May
	21	9	8	1

Calling heard from first arrival (and often at night, after rain), 22 Sep to mid-Apr, exceptionally to mid-Jun. "*Clutch*": C/1 (15); C/2 (7); C/3 (1). The C/2 include cases where two female cuckoos were believed to be involved, and also where a single female was suspected. Hosts: *Turdoides jardineii* (53), *T. leucopygia* (7)[1,2].

Taxonomy No races recognized. Sometimes placed in the genus *Oxylophus*.

References [1]Benson & Pitman (1966); [2]Dowsett & Leonard (in press a).

Thick-billed Cuckoo *Pachycoccyx audeberti*   B238 **RB**

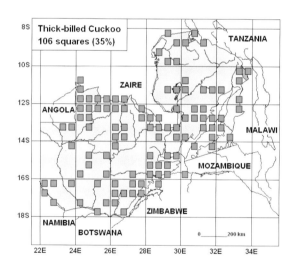

Distribution *Afrotropical (Guinea to South Africa)*. In woodland and thicket sparsely throughout Zambia, except that so far unrecorded from west of the Zambezi north of the Shangombo area (occurring just to Dipalata)[2], and from a large part of the Northern Province plateau in the north-east. *Alt.* 330-1600 m.

Ecology In various woodlands, including miombo, mopane, *Acacia* and *Combretum*, also some forest situations (mainly riparian) and deciduous thickets, but unrecorded from *Cryptosepalum*.

Status Probably largely resident, but subject to some wandering or local movements; there are records for all months[2].

Breeding

	Sep	Oct
(n=5)	3	2

Song flights (especially early morning) noted in most months, but mainly late May to Oct[2]. "*Clutch*": C/1 (1) & N/1 (1); C/2 (3). Host: *Prionops retzii* (5)[2]. (NB: a nestling reported as *P. retzii*[3] was in fact a young *Pachycoccyx*[1]).

Taxonomy *P. a. validus.* (There is no evidence that the nominate, Malagasy, race migrates to Africa)[1].

References [1]Benson & Irwin (1972a); [2]Dowsett (in press a); [3]White (1943c).

Red-chested Cuckoo *Cuculus solitarius*   B234 **AMB**

Distribution *Afrotropical (Senegal to South Africa)*. Throughout the country, and the commonest cuckoo in dense vegetation, the few gaps being probably the result of insufficient exploration. *Alt.* 330-2200 m.

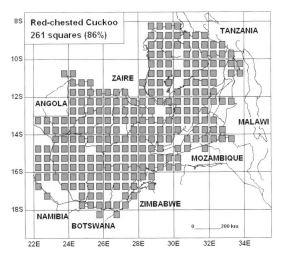

Ecology In dense woodland (miombo especially), thickets, riparian growth, forest edges and well-wooded gardens. In the north-west very common in *Cryptosepalum* and *Marquesia* forest.

Status An intra-African migrant and breeding visitor. Records fall between 1 Aug (N. Mwinilunga) and 1 May. The average first date over 29 years was 26 Aug, the average last (in 24 years) 16 Mar[2]. Few birds are noted after early Mar, and very few in Apr[2] (when silent).

Breeding   Oct   Nov   Dec   Jan
(n=24)   7   4   12   1

Calling occurs from first arrival (1 Aug) and has usually stopped by mid-Mar, being rarely heard after late Feb[2]. "*Clutch*": C/1 (13); C/2 (1). Hosts[2]: *Cossypha heuglini* (5), *Pinarornis plumosus* (1), *Erythropygia barbata* (2), *E. quadrivirgata* (9), *E. leucophrys* (2), *Turdus libonyana* (1), *Melaenornis pammelaina* (1), *Bradornis pallidus* (1).

Taxonomy No races recognized[1].

References [1]Payne in del Hoyo *et al.* (1997); [2]Dowsett & Leonard (in press a).

Black Cuckoo *Cuculus clamosus*   B235 **AMB**

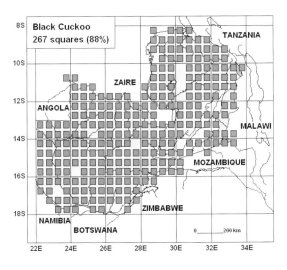

Distribution *Afrotropical (mainly Guinea to South Africa)*. Very widespread and locally common in woodland throughout the country. *Alt.* 330-1650 m.

Ecology In miombo and other woodland, also dry thickets. Present in *Cryptosepalum* forest, but uncommon.

Status An intra-African migrant and breeding visitor. Extreme dates for this cuckoo are 17 Aug and 6 May (exceptionally the "full call" heard as late as 19 May[1]). The average first date over 27 years was 5 Sep, the average last (in 26 years) 1 Apr. First arrivals are in the north, and it seems probable there is still passage and arrival in the south as late as Oct[2].

Breeding   Sep   Oct   Nov   Dec   Jan
(n=13)   4   3   3   2   1

Calling is spasmodic after Feb (mainly the winding call). As with most cuckoos, calling (often at night) starts and finishes earlier in N. Mwinilunga[2]. "*Clutch*": C/1 (4). Hosts[2]: *Oriolus auratus* (6), *Laniarius aethiopicus* (2).

Taxonomy[3] *C. c. clamosus*.

References [1]Benson & White (1957); [2]Dowsett & Leonard (in press a); [3]Irwin & Benson (1966b).

Eurasian Grey Cuckoo *Cuculus canorus*   B236 (part) **PW**

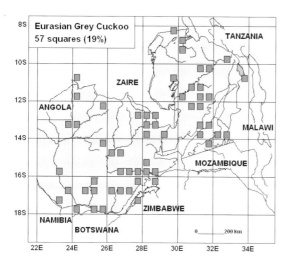

Distribution *Palaearctic (most populations wintering in eastern and southern Africa; west to Sierra Leone).* Scattered localities throughout, though sparse at low altitudes, and recorded west of the Zambezi in the dry south-west only at Semende on the Mashi[1]. *Alt.* 950-1750 m, less often down to 370 m or as high as 2200 m (Nyika).

Ecology In any woodland, wooded grassland, gardens, thickets (especially where there are termitaria), and also in patches of evergreen forest. Like many cuckoos eats hairy caterpillars.

Status A Palaearctic migrant and winter visitor. Extreme dates are 13 Oct and 16 Apr, with first arrivals usually late Oct. Normally in ones and twos; but groups of up to 7 are noted on passage late Mar to early Apr, with exceptionally a loose group of *c.* 50 in low bushes at Lochinvar 3 Mar[2]. Hepatic females are occasionally reported, but the difficulties of separating this species visually from *C. gularis* mean that its true status is not clear.

Taxonomy *C. c. canorus* is the common form, though *C. c. subtelephonus* (and perhaps other eastern forms, if valid) might occur, but they are very difficult to identify in non-breeding quarters[4]. Forms a superspecies with *C. gularis* (formerly considered conspecific)[3,5].

References [1]Benson & Irwin (1967b); [2]Dowsett (in press b); [3]Dowsett & Dowsett-Lemaire (1980); [4]Irwin & Benson (1966a); [5]Payne (1977).

African Grey Cuckoo *Cuculus gularis*   B236 (part) **AMB**

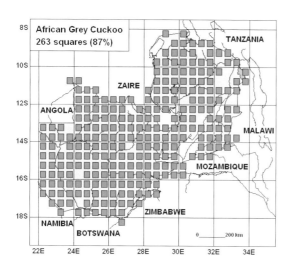

Distribution *Afrotropical (Senegal to South Africa).* Throughout the country in dry woodland; usually common, but scarcer in the valleys. *Alt.* 330-1650 m.

Ecology Common in relatively dry and open woodland, including miombo, mopane and mixed *Acacia-Combretum*.

Status An intra-African migrant and breeding visitor. All records fall between 31 Jul and 6 May, except for a doubtful report from Mapanza, 24 May[2] (visual separation from *C. canorus* can present problems). The average first date over 25 years was 2 Sep, the average last (in 23 years) 11 Apr. First arrivals are consistently earlier in N. Mwinilunga, but birds have reached even S. Zambia by late Aug[1].

Breeding Sep Oct Nov
(n=61)   23   28   10   Calling from first arrival (early Aug), to mid-Dec (occasionally to early Jan). "*Clutch*": C/1 (40); C/2 (1). Host[1]: *Dicrurus adsimilis* (63).
Taxonomy No races recognized. (See last species).
References [1]Dowsett & Leonard (in press a); [2]White & Winterbottom (1949).

Asian Lesser Cuckoo *Cuculus poliocephalus*   B237 (part) **PV**

Distribution and Status E. *Palaearctic (the westerly, nominate, race wintering mainly in the Indian sub-continent and eastern Africa)*. A vagrant this far west, with three specimen records, from Danger Hill (1131D; 20 Mar 1952, 28 Mar 1972) and Jumbe (1332A; 20 Mar 1953, an hepatic female)[2]. [Sight records which might refer to this species or to *C. rochii*, or even to abnormally small *C. canorus* or *C. gularis*, are from: Filolo Dambo (18 Oct 1974), Ndola (17 Apr 1992) and Lusaka (20 Nov 1992)[3]. They cannot be considered acceptable beyond question.] *Alt.* 790-1770 m. The extreme dates of Zambian records (20-28 Mar) suggest they may have been on passage, en route from non-breeding quarters in SE Africa.
Taxonomy *C. p. poliocephalus*. Although it was thought that Malagasy birds are conspecific, they are vocally very different and now generally treated as a separate species *C. rochii*[1].
References [1]Becking (1988); [2]Benson *et al.* (1970); [3]Dowsett (in press b).

Madagascar Lesser Cuckoo *Cuculus rochii*   B237 (part) **AV**

Distribution and Status *Madagascar, some or most migrating to eastern Africa outside breeding season.* There is one specimen, from Kasama (1031A; 16 Nov 1954), considered to be of this species[2-4]. The description of a bird seen and heard in riparian thicket near Luangwa town (Feira, 1530C; 13 Apr 1973)[1] accords well with this species too. *Alt.* 330-1450 m. Presumed to be a non-breeding migrant from Madagascar (the dates suggest birds on passage), although the possibility of an eastern African breeding population should be borne in mind, especially as some do sing on the African continent[5].
Taxonomy No races recognized. Formerly treated as conspecific with *C. poliocephalus*[2].
References [1]Aspinwall (1973f); [2]Becking (1988); [3]Benson (1956d); [4]Benson *et al.* (1970); [5]Dowsett & Leonard (in press a).

Olive Long-tailed Cuckoo *Cercococcyx olivinus*   B239 **R(B)**

Distribution *Guineo-Congolian near-endemic (from Guinea to Uganda and Zambia).* Present at a number of forest localities in N. Mwinilunga Dist., south to the Mayau area[2]. These records are the most southerly for the species (well to the south of those from Gabela in Angola)[3]. *Alt.* 1130-1300 m. Note that specimens of this species were originally misidentified as Dusky Long-tailed Cuckoo *C. mechowi*[1].
Ecology Moist evergreen riparian forest, as well as dry evergreen *Cryptosepalum* (where uncommon) and *Marquesia* forest.
Status The species is probably resident (judging by its status elsewhere in Central Africa), but dated records for Zambia are from 23 Aug to 15 Apr[4]. Very discreet when not calling.
Conservation Like most of the forest birds of NW Zambia, its habitat there is greatly threatened by deforestation. However, it is a common species in much of Central and West Africa.
Breeding No records, but calling 23 Aug to mid-Jan at least (often after sunset), although in some years

stops singing as early as Nov[4].
Taxonomy No races recognized.
References [1]Benson (1964c); [2]Benson & Irwin (1965a); [3]Dean (2000); [4]Dowsett (in press a).

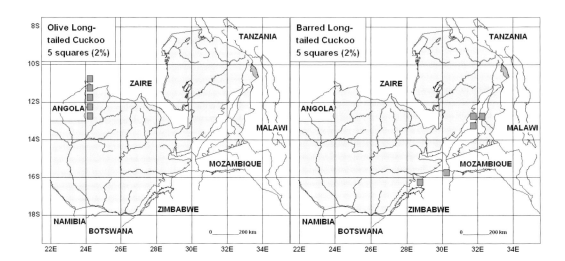

Barred Long-tailed Cuckoo *Cercococcyx montanus*   **B - AM(B)**

Distribution *Afromontane/Eastern* (*Kenya to Zimbabwe*). Known mainly from one area in the Middle Zambezi Valley (Mutulanganga, where first found in 1983)[5] and readily located in some years. Less often noted in the Luangwa Valley (Chibembe to Mfuwe) Oct and Mar, perhaps on passage (though one in song 29 Oct)[1], as there have been several resident observers in the area over the years[2]. Seen once near Luangwa town (Feira) in the 1950s[4]. Known also on the Zimbabwe side of the Middle Zambezi Valley at Mana Pools (1529C)[3]. [Sight records have been claimed from Lusaka and the Copperbelt, but these are thought to have been misidentifications[1].] *Alt.* 330-550 m.
Ecology Deciduous riparian thicket and forest.
Status Probably an intra-African migrant and breeding visitor, but easily overlooked when not calling. Extreme dates are 29 Oct and 17 Mar (records at Mutulanganga being 23 Nov to 26 Feb). May not be annual, as at the regular Middle Zambezi site, found only in about one year in two, despite enthusiastic searches. Two or three birds have been noted calling there, often at night[1]. The local *Cossypha natalensis* does a good imitation of this cuckoo.
Breeding No records (but likely to breed in the Middle Zambezi, potential host not known). Song noted 29 Oct to 26 Feb[1].
Taxonomy No Zambian specimen, but presumably *C. m. patulus*.
References [1]Dowsett & Leonard (in press a); [2]Dowsett *et al.* (1999a); [3]Hustler (1985a); [4]Irwin (1987); [5]Stjernstedt (1984).

Emerald Cuckoo *Chrysococcyx cupreus*   **B242 AMB**

Distribution *Afrotropical* (*mainly Guinea to South Africa*). Almost throughout and locally common in dense vegetation, except for a large part of the Northern Province plateau and west of the Zambezi north of the Kalabo area. Its scarcity in the far west can be explained by the lack of dense woodland. *Alt.*

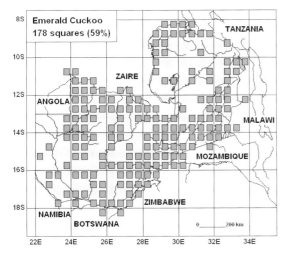

330-1800 m.

Ecology In rich miombo, evergreen and deciduous forest and thicket, including *Cryptosepalum* forest (where uncommon). It is regular in well-wooded gardens, and indeed its best-known host in Zambia is very much a commensal species.

Status Although at least partially resident in neighbouring Malawi (based on specimens and sound records)[3], there is still no evidence in Zambia that the species is other than an intra-African migrant and breeding visitor. Most records are from early or mid-Sep to late Mar, after which there are very few. Extreme dates are 5 Aug and 3 May (exceptionally perhaps to 19 May and even 8 Jun), with one immature seen near Livingstone 11 Jul being

possibly a late-bred bird[2]. Groups of up to 8 have been reported early May[4]. Females and immatures can be difficult to separate from other *Chrysococcyx*.

Breeding Oct Nov Dec Jan

(n=13)   1   6   4   2   Calling is recorded 5 Aug to 26 Apr, but rarely after Jan[2].

"*Clutch*": no data. Hosts[2]: *Pycnonotus barbatus* (13), *Camaroptera brachyura* (1)[2].

Taxonomy No races recognized[1].

References [1]Payne in del Hoyo *et al.* (1997); [2]Dowsett & Leonard (in press a); [3]Dowsett-Lemaire & Dowsett (2006); [4]Leonard (1998f).

Klaas's Cuckoo *Chrysococcyx klaas*   B240 **RB**

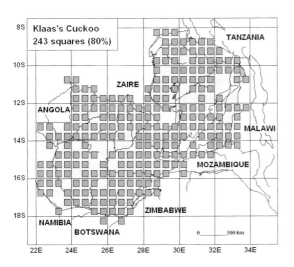

Distribution *Afrotropical* (*Mauritania to South Africa*). Almost throughout the country, and usually common. *Alt.* 330-2200 m.

Ecology In all woodland types except the driest, including edges of evergreen forest and thicket, and any riparian growth.

Status Probably largely resident (although the possibility of some influx during the rains cannot be ruled out). Present, and even calling, in all months of the year, except at high altitude (Nyika), where present and breeding Sep-Mar[2].

Breeding Aug Sep Oct

(n=50)   1   11   21

Nov Dec Feb

9   5   3

"*Clutch*": C/1 (14); N/1+C/1 (1). Hosts[1,5]: *Eremomela icteropygialis* (2), *Sylvietta rufescens* (7), *Cisticola njombe* (1), *Bradornis pallidus* (5), *Batis molitor* (11), *Terpsiphone viridis* (1), *Anthreptes collaris* (1), *Nectarinia amethystina* (1), *N. senegalensis* (1), *N. venusta* (1). Courtship feeding has been described[4], as have observations of adults

feeding juveniles[1]. *Moult*: noted in Sep (males with slight gonad activity)[3].
Taxonomy No races recognized.
References [1]Dowsett (in press a); [2]Dowsett-Lemaire (2006a); [3]Payne (1969); [4]Stjernstedt (1998a); [5]Sweetman (1979).

Didric Cuckoo *Chrysococcyx caprius* B241 **AMB**

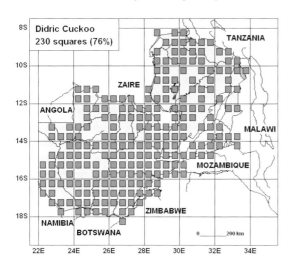

Didric Cuckoo
230 squares (76%)

Distribution *Afrotropical* (*Mauritania to South Africa*). Almost throughout, in more open country than *C. klaas*. *Alt.* 330-1700 m.
Ecology In a variety of open woodland, wooded savanna and cultivation, swamps or grassland (including dambos) with scattered bushes, edges of thicket and gardens.
Status An intra-African migrant and breeding visitor. Records are between 15 Aug and 31 May[6] (there are also half-a-dozen records of birds seen, and even once heard, into Jul (e.g. ref. 1), some of which may have been misidentifications).

Breeding[2-5]	Aug	Sep	Oct	Nov
(n=248)	1	4	12	19
	Dec	Jan	Feb	Mar
	12	63	76	61

Aug-Sep records from Mwinilunga. Calling from 15 Aug (after rain) to end Apr, even to 11 May[6].
"*Clutch*": C/1 (193); C/2 (8); C/3 (1). Multiple clutches are laid by more than one female.
Hosts essentially Ploceidae, *Ploceus*, 8 spp. (mainly 27 *P. velatus* and 25 *P. intermedius*), *Euplectes*, 5 spp. (principally *E. orix*, 123 records) and *Anaplectes* (12). Also *Emberiza flaviventris* (9, Mwinilunga and Copperbelt). Reports of sunbirds as hosts probably in error for *C. klaas*[5,6].
Moult: late Feb (a female)[6].
Taxonomy No races recognized.
References [1]Aspinwall & Atkins (1978); [2]Colebrook-Robjent (1975a); [3]Colebrook-Robjent (1977); [4]Colebrook-Robjent (1980); [5]Colebrook-Robjent (1984); [6]Dowsett & Leonard (in press a).

Green Coucal *Ceuthmochares aereus* B243 **RB**

Distribution *Afrotropical* (*Senegal to South Africa*). Inexplicably local. Present in the low-lying thickets between Lakes Tanganyika and Mweru, south to Nchelenge[1]. Reappears in the north of Mwinilunga Dist., south to Isombu, with an apparently isolated population on the Mwombezhi[3] (the furthest south in the western half of the continent). [There is a single record on the Zimbabwe side of the Middle Zambezi (1630B)[4].] *Alt.* 760-920 m in Northern Province, 1220-1280 m in the north-west.
Ecology In dense understorey of riparian forest and thickets.
Status Resident.

Breeding	Dec
(n=1)	1

Clutch: no data.
Taxonomy[2] *C. a. extensicaudus*.

References [1]Benson (1956d); [2]Benson & Irwin (1964b); [3]Dowsett (in press a); [4]Masterson & Parkes (1998).

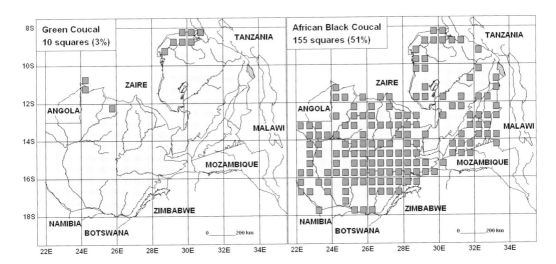

African Black Coucal *Centropus grillii*   B244 **AMB**

Distribution *Afrotropical (Senegal to South Africa).* Throughout the floodplains and dambos of the western half of the country and the Eastern Province plateau, in the low country down the Luapula and across to L. Tanganyika. Absent from most of the Northern Province plateau, except in the chain of dambos along the edge of the Muchingas. Present in some years in small numbers locally in the low-lying Luangwa Valley, but in the Middle Zambezi known only as a vagrant, except at Nyamuomba, where perhaps annual in small numbers[2]. *Alt.* 350-1700 m, but very local below 1000 m.

Ecology Moist rank grassland, especially in seasonally inundated floodplains and dambos, and at the edge of marshes.

Status At least partly a breeding migrant, most records are for the period Oct to May, with arrivals each year in the southern half of the country usually Dec, and most departures by late Mar[2]. Small numbers may remain in the dry season in unburnt areas (long grass and swamp edge), some clearly immatures[2]. Numbers reported vary annually.

Breeding[3,4]   Jan   Feb   Mar   Apr

(n=16)   4   6   5   1   *Clutch*: C/2 (1); C/3 (2); C/5 (1).

Breeding dress (and song) from late Oct-Nov until late Apr (exceptionally in breeding dress Jun-Jul)[2].

Taxonomy No races recognized. No longer considered a race of the Madagascar Coucal *C. toulou*[1].

References [1]Benson *et al.* (1970); [2]Dowsett & Leonard (in press a); [3]Symmes (1960a); [4]Vernon (1971).

[Blue-naped Coucal *Centropus monachus*

Afrotropical (Guinea to Ethiopia, south to S. Zaire). This forest- or marsh-associated coucal was listed from Kasaji in Katanga[2], but this is in error for *C. cupreicaudus*[1], with which it has at times been considered conspecific. Both do occur in Upemba[1], but there is no suggestion that *C. monachus* reaches N. Zambia. **References** [1]Louette (1986); [2]Schouteden (1971).]

Coppery-tailed Coucal *Centropus cupreicaudus*   B245 **RB**

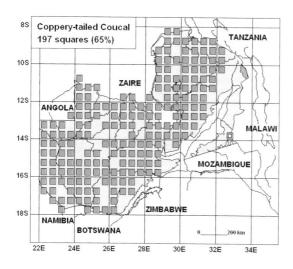

Distribution *Zambezian endemic (Zaire to Zimbabwe)*. A common marshland bird of the western and northern plateaux, completely absent from the low-lying Middle Zambezi and Luangwa Valleys, and the Eastern Province plateau, apart from a single vagrant (open square) in a dambo near Chipata (21 Dec)[2] (presumably from the population in adjacent Malawi, in the Bua drainage)[3]. In Northern Province, it occurs east only to the Sumbi area in the upper Chambeshi system. *Alt.* 880-1670 m.

Ecology Tall permanent marsh with dense reedbeds (*Phragmites, Typha*) and Papyrus, often on small dams. Nests in dense reeds, 1 m above the water[1].

Status Resident, with only local wandering.

Breeding	Sep	Nov	Dec	Jan	Feb	Mar	Apr
(n=14)	2	4	1	2	2	2	1

Clutch: C/1 (2); C/2 (1); C/4 (1).

Moult: one finishing late Oct, but another then in very worn plumage[5].

Taxonomy *C. c. cupreicaudus*. In the past sometimes considered a race of *C. monachus*[4].

References [1]Benson & Pitman (1964); [2]Dowsett (in press a); [3]Dowsett-Lemaire & Dowsett (2006); [4]Louette (1986); [5]Traylor (1965b).

Senegal Coucal *Centropus senegalensis*   B246 **RB**

Distribution *Afrotropical (Mauritania to South Africa)*. Through most of the country in rank grass and thickets, common in the south but becoming rare or absent as one moves north. For example, in the west occurs sparsely north to Chavuma Dist. and Chizera[1], with no more than the occasional vagrant in Mwinilunga Dist.[1]. Although it ranges down the Luapula to the Kawambwa area, it is absent from the immediate vicinity of L. Mweru, reappearing around L. Tanganyika. *Alt.* 330-1700 m (2200 m on the Nyika)[2].

Ecology Rank grass in wooded savanna, edges of woodland or thickets, overall in drier situations than *C. superciliosus* and possibly competing with it.

Status Resident.

Breeding	Nov	Dec	Jan	Feb	Mar	Apr	May
(n=31)	7	3	5	7	6	2	1

Clutch: C/2 (1); C/3 (2); C/4 (2); C/5 (2).

Taxonomy *C. s. flecki*.

References [1]Dowsett (in press a); [2]Dowsett-Lemaire (2006a).

Burchell's (White-browed) Coucal *Centropus superciliosus*   B247 **RB**

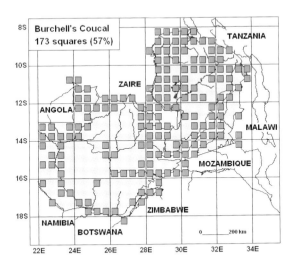

Burchell's Coucal
173 squares (57%)

Distribution *Afrotropical* (*Ethiopia to South Africa*). Locally common in rank growth in the eastern half of the country (although scarce on the Eastern Province plateau), to the Copperbelt (scarce south of Kabwe) and the Middle Zambezi escarpment (almost absent from the Southern Province plateau). Further west it is essentially confined to the larger river systems, up the Kafue to the north of Kafue N.P., on the Mashi, and throughout the Zambezi to N. Mwinilunga[1]. *Alt*. 330-1800 m, fewer to 2150 m on the Nyika Plateau (where slightly higher on the Malawi side)[2].

Ecology In rank grass and thickets, moist herbage along streams or edge of forest, occasionally also in reeds.

Status Resident.

Breeding	Dec	Jan	Feb
(n=5)	2	1	2

Clutch: C/2 (1).

Taxonomy *C. s. loandae*, with a tendency to *C. s. burchellii* (lacking the white eye-stripe) in the Middle Zambezi Valley and Misale, with hybrids in the area of Luangwa town (Feira)[1]. *C. s. burchellii* is sometimes treated as specifically distinct.

References [1]Dowsett (in press a); [2]Dowsett-Lemaire (2006a).

Tytonidae

Barn Owl *Tyto alba*   B248 **RB**

Distribution *Cosmopolitan* (*in the Afrotropics, Mauritania to South Africa*). Commensal and also in any woodland, throughout Zambia at all levels (except montane). *Alt*. 330-1650 m.

Ecology In light woodland, wooded savanna, cultivation, farms and villages as readily breeds on buildings, also in holes in trees and nest of *Scopus umbretta*. Feeds mainly on rodents, and is also recorded preying on swallows *Hirundo* sp.[3] and bats[2]. Has benefited from expansion of agriculture.

Status Resident.

Breeding	Jan	Feb	Mar	Apr	May	Jun	Jul	Aug	Sep	Oct
(n=64)	1	3	13	17	11	8	6	2	2	1

Clutch: C/1 (3); C/2 (2); C/3 (3); C/4 (2); C/5 (1); C/6 (1); C/7 (2); C/8 (2); C/12 (1); C/18 (1).
Largest clutch sizes are presumably at times of rodent abundance.

Taxonomy *T. a. poensis*[1].

References [1]Bruce & Dowsett (2004); [2]Dowsett (in press a); [3]Mitchell (1964).

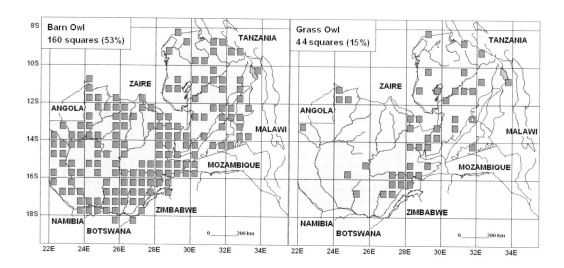

Grass Owl *Tyto capensis*   B249 **RB**

Distribution *Afrotropical (Cameroon to South Africa, in a series of isolated populations).* Essentially in the dambos of N. and south-central Zambia, with some outlying pockets, and in rank grass at high altitude in the east. In the north-west, south to Mundwiji Plain[2] and Minyanya[1]. In the Kafue basin, west to Chunga and Afumba[4], south to the Choma area, and Machile[3]. Not uncommon on the high Nyika, but only once recorded on the Eastern Province plateau, at Chassa[4], and seen once in the Luangwa Valley in Oct[4] (open square). [A report from Fothergill Is., L. Kariba (1628D), Zimbabwe[5], is doubtfully correct.] Easily overlooked. *Alt.* 950-2150 m (Nyika, higher on the Malawi side), rarely down to 550 m.

Ecology Typically in dambos and dense herbaceous growth at edges of marsh, also rank montane grassland and bracken-briar at forest edges. Rarely on larger floodplains. Nests are on the ground in a tunnel in rank grass, in the middle or at the head of a dambo (e.g. ref. 2).

Status Resident, with no more than local wandering. Maximum seen together 4 birds, presumably a family.

Breeding   Dec   Feb   Mar   Apr   May   Jun
(n=31)   2   9   11   5   2   2   *Clutch*: C/2 (1); C/3 (2); C/4 (4); C/5 (1).

Taxonomy *T. c. capensis* (following those authors who treat it as polytypic).

References [1]Aspinwall (1979b); [2]Benson (1965); [3]Benson *et al.* (1970); [4]Dowsett (in press a); [5]Hustler (1987).

Strigidae

African Scops Owl *Otus senegalensis*   B250 **RB**

Distribution *Afrotropical (Mauritania to South Africa).* Throughout, including the low-lying Luangwa Valley (where scarce)[1,3], locally common in plateau and escarpment woodland. *Alt.* 330-1770 m (Danger Hill).

Ecology Mainly in miombo woodland; also in other woodlands (including mopane) and gardens, but avoids the wetter types, as well as thicket and forest. A nest was in a hole (used the previous year by *Poicephalus meyeri*) 5 m up in a *Brachystegia spiciformis* tree[4]. Mainly insectivorous, but the remains

of a rat were found in a nest[4].
Status Resident, with no more than local wandering.
Breeding   Aug   Sep
(n=8)   2   6   *Clutch*: C/1 (1).
Taxonomy *O. s. senegalensis* (forms a superspecies with the Palaearctic *O. scops*, with which considered conspecific in the past)[2].
References [1]Dowsett (in press a); [2]Dowsett & Dowsett-Lemaire (1993); [3]Madge (1972f); [4]Traylor & Hart (1965).

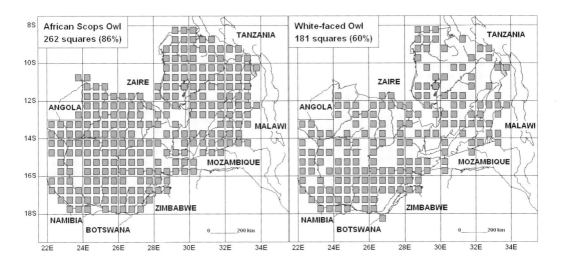

White-faced Owl *Otus leucotis*   B251 **RB**

Distribution *Afrotropical* (*Mauritania to South Africa*). Fairly widely distributed in woodland and thicket, typically in drier areas, especially those dominated by *Acacia* (where locally common). In the far north-west known only from scattered localities, such as the Chifuwe River, Mayau[4] and very rarely at Mwinilunga[3]. *Alt.* 330-1600 m.
Ecology Occurs in a greater variety of habitats than the smaller *O. senegalensis*, including deciduous thickets. It is most regularly recorded in dry woodland, such as *Acacia-Combretum*. In plateau miombo it is normally found in smaller numbers than *O. senegalensis*. Nests have been in holes in the branches of *Brachystegia* trees, one 5 m above the ground, and also on an old raptor's nest[4].
Status Resident, with some local wandering.
Breeding[1,2] Jun   Jul   Aug   Sep   Oct
(n=70)   2   12   30   23   3   *Clutch*: C/1 (1); C/2 (12); C/3 (4); C/4 (1).
Taxonomy *O. l. granti* (treated by some as a distinct species). Sometimes placed in the genus *Ptilopsis*.
References [1]Benson (1956f); [2]Benson & Pitman (1958-59); [3]Bowen (1983i); [4]Dowsett (in press a).

[Cape Eagle Owl *Bubo capensis*   B p.138
Afromontane near-endemic (*Ethiopia to South Africa*). There is a specimen from Dedza in Malawi[1], and it is possible it will be found in the rocky kopjes of Eastern Province, which are similar to its habitat in Zimbabwe[2] and where a favoured prey the Cape Hyrax *Procavia capensis* occurs[3]. **References** [1]Benson & Irwin (1967a); [2]Gargett & Grobler (1976); [3]Osborne (1987).]

Spotted Eagle Owl *Bubo africanus* B252 **RB**

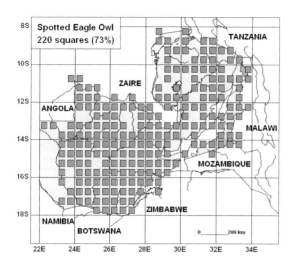

Distribution *Afrotropical* (*Senegal to South Africa*). Almost throughout, but known from the Kalahari sands west of the Zambezi only at Nyatanda, Sinjembela[4] and Cholola[2]. *Alt.* 400 m up to 2200 m (Nyika, higher on the Malawi side).

Ecology Occupies a broad range of habitats including various woodlands, montane grassland, edges of cultivation (often hunts along roads) and gardens. Shows a slight preference for rocky hills or outcrops, and avoids dense forest. Nests on the ground in woodland, often under the shelter of a rock[3], or in a tree cavity. Mainly insectivorous (especially beetles and grasshoppers), but has also taken a shrew and a bushbaby *Galago moholi*[1,6].

Status Resident. Present throughout the year, small peaks in observations Jan-Apr at scattered localities reflecting perhaps no more than local post-breeding dispersal[4] (particularly by naive juveniles which often allow close approach during their first few months of independence), and the presence of more birds hunting along roads when grass is long.

Breeding   May   Jun   Jul   Aug   Sep   Oct
(n=61)   2   2   5   22   29   1   *Clutch*: C/2 (15); C/3 (4).

Taxonomy *B. a. africanus*. It has been claimed that birds north of the Equator (*B. a. cinerascens*) are specifically distinct, based a difference in iris colour[5], but no vocal or other significant differences have been demonstrated.

References [1]Benson (1962b); [2]Benson & Irwin (1967b); [3]Benson & Pitman (1956-57); [4]Dowsett (in press a); [5]König *et al.* (1999); [6]Mitchell (1964).

Giant Eagle Owl *Bubo lacteus* B253 **RB**

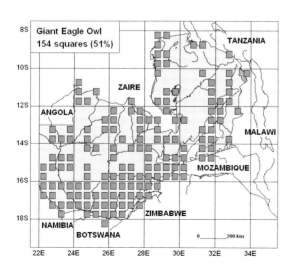

Distribution *Afrotropical* (*Senegal to South Africa*). Thinly but widely distributed in wooded country with large trees (especially *Acacia*), and very sparse in high-rainfall miombo. *Alt.* 330-1650 m.

Ecology Occupies a variety of woodland habitats (but partial to *Acacia*), also riparian woodland or forest. Uses old nests of other species, particularly *Scopus umbretta* and *Aquila rapax*[2]. Feeds on much larger prey than *B. africanus*, even as large as adult *Numida meleagris, Tyto capensis* and chickens[1], and has been known to attack dogs, cats and piglets[3].

Status Resident.

Breeding	Apr	May	Jun	Jul	Aug	Sep	
(n=33)	2	4	12	13	1	1	*Clutch*: C/1 (7); C/2 (3).

Taxonomy No races recognized.
References [1]Benson (1962b); [2]Benson & Pitman (1966); [3]Dowsett (in press a).

Pel's Fishing Owl *Scotopelia peli*   B254 **RB**

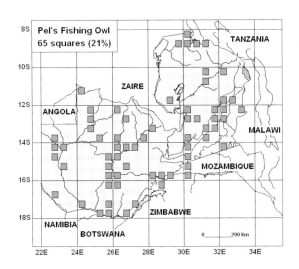

Distribution *Afrotropical (Senegal to South Africa)*. On all major rivers[4], except unrecorded in most of the Luapula drainage (although known from the Zaire side[5]). *Alt.* 330-1500 m.
Ecology Along large rivers with dense riparian vegetation for roosting and nesting. A nest in the hollow trunk of a *Ficus* tree, 10 m above the ground, was apparently used in two successive years[1]. Has also used an old *Scopus umbretta* nest[2]. Feeds mainly on fish, but once on a young *Crocodilus niloticus*[3].
Status Resident.

Breeding	Feb	Mar	Apr	May	Jun
(n=7)	2	1	1	2	1

Clutch: C/1 (1).
Taxonomy No races recognized.
References [1]Benson & Pitman (1956-57); [2]Benson & Pitman (1958-59); [3]Berry & Dowsett (2003); [4]Dowsett (in press a); [5]Mouritz (1914).

Pearl-spotted Owlet *Glaucidium perlatum*   B255 **RB**

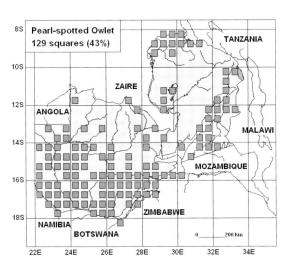

Distribution *Afrotropical (Senegal to South Africa)*. Locally common in open woodland in the drier country of the south and west, north to Chavuma, Zambezi town (Balovale) and Kasempa. It has been noted once at Mwinilunga[1], though there are also specimens from Kasaji in Zaire[5]. In the north-east, confined to the Luangwa Valley, the area between the Luapula and Bangweulu, and the low-lying country between Lakes Mweru and Tanganyika[3]. *Alt.* 330-1300, rarely 1400 m.
Ecology Prefers light woodland or wooded grassland, and can adapt to gardens. Avoids dense woodland such as primary miombo. Largely insectivorous, but has been recorded eating the eggs of *Eurystomus glaucurus*[4].
Status Resident, with some wandering.

Breeding   Aug   Sep   Oct
(n=7)   1   5   1   *Clutch*: C/2 (3); C/3 (1); N/4 (1). *Moult*: one starting early Mar[3].
Taxonomy *G. p. diurnum*[2].
References [1]Bowen (1983i); [2]Clancey (1968c); [3]Dowsett (in press a); [4]Lees (1935); [5]Schouteden (1971).

Barred Owlet *Glaucidium capense*   B256 **RB**

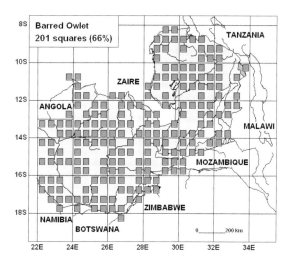

Distribution *Afrotropical* (*Liberia to South Africa*). Thinly distributed in densely-wooded country, irrespective of local rainfall, throughout. *Alt.* 330-1650 m.
Ecology Favours tall, dense miombo, including moist transition woodland, and other types usually with a riparian component; also at edges of forest and thicket.
Status Resident.
Breeding[2]   Sep
(n=1)   1   *Clutch*: C/1 (1).
Taxonomy[1,4,5] *G. c. capense*, with perhaps some tendency towards the greyer *G. c. ngamiense* in the west. This species has been split into several by some authors (Zambian birds would become *G. scheffleri*), but bioacoustic evidence suggests these forms are conspecific[3].
References [1]Clancey (1968c); [2]Dowsett (in press a); [3]Dowsett & Dowsett-Lemaire (1993); [4]Irwin & Benson (1966a); [5]White (1965).

Wood Owl *Strix woodfordii*   B257 **RB**

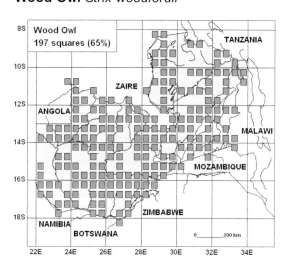

Distribution *Afrotropical* (*Senegal to South Africa*). Widespread and locally common in forested and densely-wooded country, throughout, even in the dry south-west[2]. *Alt.* 350 m to 2200 m (Nyika, higher on the Malawi side).
Ecology Widespread and common in all forest and thicket types, and equally common in dense miombo in higher-rainfall areas, more local in other woodland. Nests in hollow trees, sometimes less than a metre above the ground, or even on the ground, under a fallen tree[1,5,6].
Status Resident. Defended territory of a pair on Nyika (Malawi) at least 10 ha, but home range nearer 50 ha[3].

Breeding   Jul   Aug   Sep   Oct
(n=16)   3   6   6   1   *Clutch*: C/2 (5); C/3 (1).
Taxonomy[4] *S. w. woodfordii.*
References [1]Benson & Pitman (1956-57); [2]Dowsett (in press a); [3]Dowsett-Lemaire (1989b); [4]Irwin & Benson (1966a); [5]White (1945-46); [6]White (1946b).

Marsh Owl *Asio capensis*   B258 **RB**

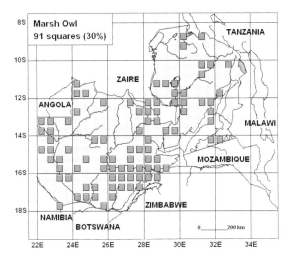

Distribution *Mainly Afrotropical (The Gambia to South Africa)*. Locally common in floodplains and dambos of the west and centre, sparser on the Eastern Province plateau (e.g. at Chassa[4]). In the north-east, north of Bangweulu, known only from pockets of habitat on the Chambeshi[5], east to Isoka, Mbala[4] and the Mporokoso area[3]. There are a few dry season records (Jun-Jul) from the Luangwa Valley (e.g. Chifungwe Plain and Nsefu[2,3]), and also suggestive of dispersal is a record from the grassy foreshore of L. Kariba at Chipepo (late May)[4]. *Alt*. 550-1660 m (Mbala).

Ecology Mainly in moist herbaceous vegetation in floodplain and marshland; also in dambos, rarely in dry grassland at low altitude. The only record of prey taken in Zambia concerns insects[1], but elsewhere it is known also to eat rodents.

Status Resident, with some wandering to low levels. Present all months, with numbers locally high Jun-Dec, probably post-breeding flocking. Up to 50 have been seen together on Liuwa Plain in Oct[4], its abundance probably influenced by rodent numbers.

Breeding   Jan   Feb   Mar   Apr   May   Jul   Aug
(n=30)   1   5   3   14   5   1   1   *Clutch*: C/2 (2); C/3 (4); C/4 (2).
Taxonomy *A. c. capensis.*
References [1]Benson (1960d); [2]Benson (1965); [3]Benson & White (1957); [4]Dowsett (in press a); [5]Neave (1910).

Caprimulgidae

Eurasian Nightjar *Caprimulgus europaeus*   B259 **PW**

Distribution *Palaearctic (the whole population wintering in Africa, The Gambia to South Africa)*. Sparsely recorded (though doubtless overlooked) in the plateau woodlands. West of 26°E known only from Mwinilunga[1], Liuwa Plain[4], Matabele Plain, and Livingstone[2]. *Alt*. 1000-2150 m.

Ecology In any light woodland, also more open country (e.g. edge of floodplain), gardens and roads when on passage.

Status A Palaearctic migrant and winter visitor; extreme dates are 20 Oct and 20 Apr[3] (a sight record as early as 5 Sep[5] is questionably correct). Apart from Livingstone (25 Feb), the western records are

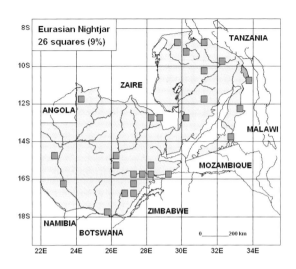

dated Oct to 14 Dec, and may have been on passage, although the area is little-explored during the heavy rains. A bird ringed in Finland was recovered in Zambia 22 Nov (Appendix 1).

Taxonomy Zambian specimens are attributed to *C. e. europaeus* and (two) *C. e. unwini*, the latter being paler, while the males have larger white spots on the primaries. Also likely to occur are *C. e. meridionalis* and *C. e. plumipes*.

References [1]Bowen (1983h); [2]Brooke (1965); [3]Dowsett (in press b); [4]Traylor (1965b); [5]Tree (1967).

Rufous-cheeked Nightjar *Caprimulgus rufigena* B260 **AMB**

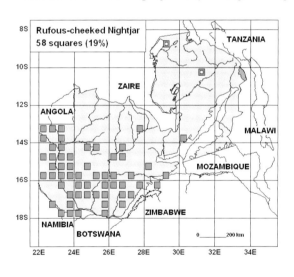

Distribution *Afrotropical* (*breeds Angola to South Africa, and some at least winter north of the Equator*). Inhabits the dry woodlands of the west and south (mainly on Kalahari sand), north-east to Ndubeni[3]. There are few records outside this area, and the only one suggestive of breeding other than in the south and south-west, is of birds singing mid-Nov near Chibale (1330C)[2]. A specimen from Kasama in Nov[1] was perhaps on passage (and as a road casualty may even have been transported inadvertently), and on passage too was one seen at Chiengi 8 May[2] (open squares). *Alt.* 880-1300 m in the breeding range, to 1400 m elsewhere.

Ecology As a breeding bird it inhabits mainly open woodland, including miombo and a mosaic of *Baikiaea* forest and grassland.

Status An intra-African migrant and breeding visitor. Recorded between 24 Aug and 8 May[2] (reports outside this period requiring confirmation).

Breeding   Sep   Oct   Nov   Dec
(n=46)   15   22   8   1   Most records are from the Choma area. Song has been noted from first arrival (24 Aug) to 21 Nov. *Clutch*: C/1 (1); C/2 (36).

Taxonomy No races recognized.

References [1]Benson *et al.* (1970); [2]Dowsett & Leonard (in press a); [3]Tree (1967).

Freckled Rock Nightjar *Caprimulgus tristigma*   B263 **RB**

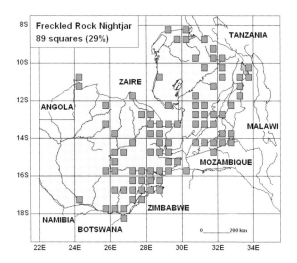

Distribution *Afrotropical (Guinea to South Africa).* Rocky areas, widespread in the northeast, down the Middle Zambezi escarpment to Victoria Falls, and further upriver at Ngambwe Rapids[5]. In the middle Luapula drainage at Johnston Falls[2]. West from the Copperbelt to Mwombezhi[1], with an isolated population in N. Mwinilunga at Zambezi Rapids[1] and Salujinga[3]. Absent from the rock-free Kalahari sands of the extreme west. *Alt.* 370-2200 m (Nyika Plateau).

Ecology Rocky hills and gorges surrounded with some woodland, also dry miombo on stony terrain. The eggs are laid on bare rock, often in a slight depression.

Status Resident.

Breeding   Aug   Sep   Oct   Nov
(n=35)   1   29   4   1   Song reported Aug to April, even a little in May.
Clutch: C/1 (4); C/2 (26).
Taxonomy[4] *C. t. granosus.*
References [1]Benson & Irwin (1965b); [2]Benson & White (1957); [3]Dowsett (in press a); [4]Irwin & Benson (1966b); [5]Winterbottom (1942a).

Fiery-necked Nightjar *Caprimulgus pectoralis*   B261 **RB**

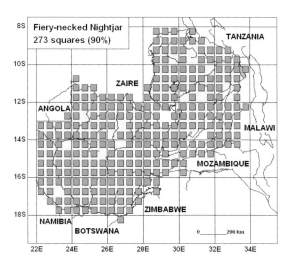

Distribution *Afrotropical (known to breed only from Central African Republic to South Africa, but reported as far west as Guinea-Bissau).* The most widespread and common nightjar, in any woodland and rank vegetation. *Alt.* 330-1770 m (Danger Hill).

Ecology Dense woodland, especially miombo, also at edges of riparian forest and thicket, *Cryptosepalum* forest (uncommon), and edge of marsh with scrub.

Status Probably resident, as recorded all months and no firm evidence of movements. Most noticeable late Mar to mid-Apr, least May and Dec[1], probably a reflection of song seasonality (see below).

Breeding   Jul   Aug   Sep   Oct   Nov
(n=129)   1   14   49   52   13

Song is noted all months, but especially in the dry season (Mar-Apr and again Aug-Nov), with reduced activity in the coldest months.
Clutch: C/1 (15); C/2 (95). (One of the C/1 was a complete clutch).

Moult: noted in Nov[3].

Taxonomy *C. p. fervidus*. We believe the form *nigriscapularis* of the forest and savanna zone of West-Central Africa (treated as a distinct species by some people) to be no more than a race of *C. pectoralis*[2].

References [1]Dowsett (in press a); [2]Dowsett & Dowsett-Lemaire (1993); [3]Traylor (1965b).

Mountain Nightjar *Caprimulgus poliocephalus*   B262 **R(B)**

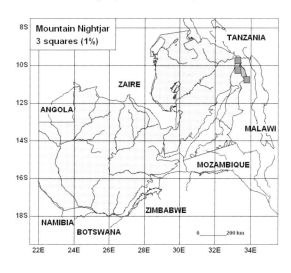

Distribution *Afromontane endemic* (*Ethiopia to Malawi*). Common on the Nyika Plateau. Noted occasionally on the top of the Mafingas[1,5] and one was collected at 2100 m on Makutu[2]. *Alt.* 1900-2200 m (higher on the Malawi side).

Ecology In montane grassland and shrubland (often takes shelter in bracken) and at forest edges.

Status Resident (heard singing Nyika from Feb-early Nov, rarely late Nov or Dec)[4].

Breeding No records, but in Malawi egg-laying is Sep-Oct.

Taxonomy *C. p. guttifer*. Some authorities would make several species out of *C. poliocephalus* (some placing *guttifer* in *C. ruwenzorii*), but the variation is clinal and we believe all are conspecific[3].

References [1]Clay (1953); [2]Dowsett (1971h); [3]Dowsett & Dowsett-Lemaire (1993); [4]Dowsett-Lemaire (2006a); [5]Leonard *et al.* (2001a).

Natal Nightjar *Caprimulgus natalensis*   B265 **RB**

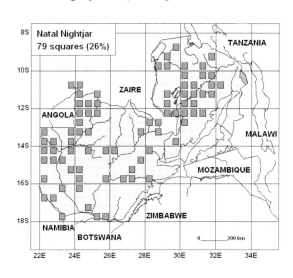

Distribution *Afrotropical* (*breeds from Sierra Leone to South Africa*). Widespread in grassland to the north and west of the Luangwa-Zambezi Rift. In the north, ranges east to near Chinsali[2], further south on the Muchinga escarpment to the Mkushi River (Chalata) area[2]. Throughout the Upper Zambezi above about Katombora[2]. Most numerous in the Upper Zambezi drainage and in the Bangweulu-Chambeshi area, decidedly scarce on the Kafue Flats. *Alt.* 980-1430 m.

Ecology Grassland of the larger floodplains and dambos; drier watershed plains in the far west.

Status Resident.

Breeding	Aug	Sep	Oct	Nov
(n=10)		1	7	1	1

Clutch: C/1 (1); C/2 (1).

Calling noted 12 Mar to 30 Apr and again early Aug to 6 Dec, thus silent just after breeding and in the coldest months.

Taxonomy *C. n. mpasa*[1] (type locality Mpasa; *NMZB*)[3], but *C. n. carpi* (paler and more sandy) may occur in the south-west.

References [1]Benson & Irwin (1967b); [2]Dowsett (in press a); [3]Smithers (1954: 84).

Gaboon (Mozambique) Nightjar *Caprimulgus fossii*   B264 **RB**

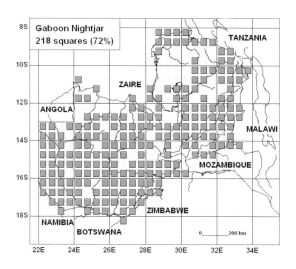

Distribution *Afrotropical* (*Gabon to South Africa*). Fairly widespread in lightly-wooded country, especially on sand; almost throughout, but sparser in the north, and locally absent. For example, there is a gap between records in N. Mwinilunga[4] and the main range. In the north-east there is large gap between Chisenga Is.[1] and the Matanda area on the Luapula, and Chilufya and Ntatumbila further east[2]. *Alt.* 330-1700 m, but common only below 1300 m.

Ecology On the edge of woodland, including degraded forms (e.g. through grazing) and in wooded grassland or savanna, edge of dambos, floodplain grassland; overlaps with *C. pectoralis* in many areas, but overall in more open vegetation.

Status At least partly resident, as reported year-round in some medium-altitude areas. However, at low levels most records are during the dry season, and movements off the plateau are reported in some areas in the coldest months[2]. More investigation needed.

Breeding   Aug   Sep   Oct   Nov

(n=120)   1   52   44   23   Calling noted especially Apr and Aug-Oct.

Clutch: C/1 (6); C/2 (59).

Moult: adults Nov to late Mar-Apr, juveniles late Mar to mid-May[2].

Taxonomy[3] *C. f. welwitschii.*

References [1]Benson & Pitman (1956-57); [2]Dowsett (in press a); [3]Irwin & Benson (1967b); [4]White (1945-46).

[Long-tailed Nightjar *Caprimulgus climacurus*

Afrotropical (*Senegal to central Zaire*). Mentioned from Musosa, on the Zambia/Zaire border, just north of Mweru Wantipa[2], but this is a misidentification, the species being unknown as far south as Katanga[1].

References [1]Louette (1990); [2]Schouteden (1971).]

Pennant-winged Nightjar *Macrodipteryx vexillarius*   B266 **AMB**

Distribution *Afrotropical* (*breeds Zaire to South Africa, winters north of the Equator as far west as Nigeria*). Widespread and locally abundant in plateau woodland; the records from low-lying mopane in

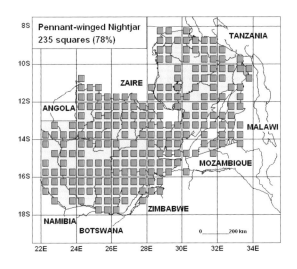

the Luangwa and Middle Zambezi Valleys are of non-breeding birds on passage. *Alt. c.* 800-1800 m when breeding, but passage birds have occurred down to 330 m, and as high as 2100 m in the Mafingas[3] and 2200 m on the Nyika (higher on the Malawi side)[5].

Ecology Mainly in miombo woodland but can be seen anywhere on passage.

Status An intra-African migrant and breeding visitor. All records fall within the period 1 Aug to 31 Mar, except for one late bird at Mfuwe 12 Apr and one near Ndola 4 Jun[4]. The average first date over 28 years was 23 Aug, the average last (in 20 years) 7 Mar[4]. Large concentrations occur on passage in the north-west, late Aug to mid-Oct[1,2].

Breeding   Aug   Sep   Oct   Nov
(n=254)   6   57   147   44   *Clutch*: C/1 (20); C/2 (161); C/3 (1); C/4 (1).
The C/4 eggs all appeared similar, and may have been laid by just one female.
Moult: first arrivals in NW Zambia in Aug have fully-grown pennants and start to display immediately[1]. Pennants of many broken by mid-Oct to mid-Nov, said to be done by the bird intentionally, although a fracture line is visible before pennants broken. "Post-nuptial moult" started late Nov in one bird[4].
Taxonomy No races recognized.
References [1]Bowen (1977c); [2]Britton (1969); [3]Clay (1953); [4]Dowsett & Leonard (in press a); [5]Dowsett-Lemaire (2006a).

Apodidae

Scarce Swift *Schoutedenapus myoptilus*   B p.147 **AM(B)**

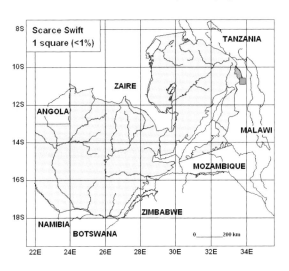

Distribution *Afromontane endemic (Cameroon and Ethiopia to Zimbabwe).* Common on the Nyika Plateau[3]. *Alt.* 2000-2200 m. [Swifts seen on the Mafingas (1950 m) early Aug were thought possibly to be this species[2]; this would be very early and requires confirmation. There is a possible sight record of one on passage at Chipata (5 Nov)[1].]

Ecology Feeds essentially over forest canopy, and probably breeds in tree holes (see below).

Status An intra-African migrant and breeding visitor (as in Zimbabwe[5] and Malawi[4]). First arrivals are 1 Sep, becoming common from mid-Sep; all Sep records are of birds passing over. Settle from late Oct or early Nov and common until Mar, then suddenly disappear in

Apr, latest record 12 Apr[3] (exceptionally, a possible observation 26 Apr)[1]. The few reports from outside this period require confirmation[1].

Breeding Aerial matings seen frequently from late Oct to Dec. A bird picked up on the floor well inside Chowo forest 3 Jan, and later released[6], appears (from a photo) to have been a juvenile, suggesting the species may nest in hollow trees there. There are unsubstantiated reports in other countries that it may nest on rocks, but there has been no suggestion of this in neighbouring Malawi[4].

Taxonomy No Zambian specimen, but presumably *S. m. myoptilus*.

References [1]Dowsett & Leonard (in press a); [2]Dowsett & Stjernstedt (1973); [3]Dowsett-Lemaire (2006a); [4]Dowsett-Lemaire & Dowsett (2006); [5]Brooke in Harrison *et al.* (1997); [6]Scott (1979).

Mottled Spinetail *Telacanthura ussheri*   B267 **RB**

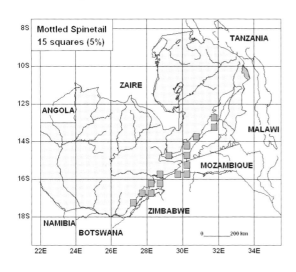

Distribution *Afrotropical (Senegal to South Africa)*. Confined to low-lying woodland. The traditional range of this species was in the Middle Zambezi and lower Luangwa Valleys[1], up the latter to about the Luangwa Bridge. During the 1980s there were records from previously well-explored areas further north, and it is now known up to the Nsefu area[3]. Its known range in the Middle Zambezi is also much wider than hitherto, and it occurs south to the Zongwe River near Sinazongwe. That this normally Baobab-associated bird may be spreading is suggested by the sight of 5 flying around a water tower in the centre of Munyumbwe (in Mar 1985)[3], nesting on buildings being quite normal elsewhere in Africa. *Alt.* 330-640 m.

Ecology In woodland or wooded grassland, including mopane and *Acacia*. Nests so far known from hollow Baobabs.

Status Probably resident, with records year-round.

Breeding   Dec   Jan
(n=3)   2   1   All nests are from the Gwembe Valley. *Clutch*: C/3 (1); C/4 (1); C/5 (1).

Taxonomy[2] *T. u. benguellensis*.

References [1]Benson (1977); [2]Clancey (1968c); [3]Dowsett (in press a).

Bat-like Spinetail *Neafrapus boehmi*   B268 **RB**

Distribution *Zambezian/Eastern (mainly Zaire to South Africa)*. There are two populations, one in the northern miombo areas, the other in the low-lying valleys. The northern birds occur east to Malole[1] and west only to Zambezi town (Balovale)[4], but there is a string of observations continuing south through the mopane woodlands of Kafue N.P. and the Machile, to the Kazungula area. From 1726D in the Gwembe Valley it ranges throughout the Middle Zambezi and the Luangwa Valley to Tembwe[3]. On the Eastern Province plateau perhaps only a vagrant (Chipata)[5]. [There is an unconfirmed report from the Chadiza area[3]]. *Alt.* 330-1670 m.

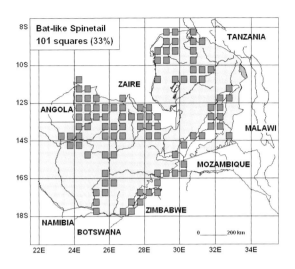

Ecology In woodland, edges of thickets and riparian growth. All nests (on the Copperbelt) were in excavation pits[2].

Status Resident. Present throughout the year, and overall there is no pattern suggestive of any movements. Large groups (up to 50 or more) are most often seen May-Aug[3], and may merely represent flocking outside the breeding season.

Breeding   Sep   Oct   Jan   Mar
(n=14)   3   9   1   1
Clutch: C/2 (2); C/3 (3).
Moult: one completing moult in May[2].
Taxonomy *N. b. boehmi*, replaced in the Middle Zambezi Valley (and perhaps other low-lying areas) by *N. b. sheppardi*.
References [1]Aspinwall (1975b); [2]Brooke (1966a); [3]Dowsett (in press a); [4]White (1946b); [5]Winterbottom (1939b).

African Palm Swift *Cypsiurus parvus* B269 **RB**

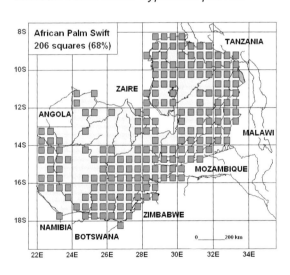

Distribution *Afrotropical* (*Mauritania to South Africa*). The commonest breeding swift, almost throughout, but there are some gaps. It is very sparse between the Copperbelt and Mwinilunga Dist., i.e. in the headwaters of several arteries of the upper Kafue and Zambezi drainages. In the south-west there is only one record along the Mashi River (where there are very few palms), of one near Imusho early Dec[4]. *Alt.* 330-1780 m.
Ecology In various woodlands (except blocks of pure miombo), wooded savanna, towns and gardens; usually near palms (*Borassus, Hyphaene*), on whose leaves it nests. It also breeds on bridges[2] and has nested on Kawambwa rest house[5].

Status Resident and subject to local wandering as occasionally recorded away from suitable habitat. Likely to spread, in view of its adaptation to man-made structures.

Breeding   Jan   Feb   Mar   Apr   May   Jun   Jul   Aug   Sep   Oct   Nov   Dec
(n=105)   6   6   2   1   5   1   12   18   18   9   22   5
Clutch: C/1 (3); C/2 (16).
Taxonomy[3] *C. p. myochrous*, but a tendency towards *C. p. parvus* (paler, with less green gloss) in the south-west. The form *C. p. laemostigma* (with a more strongly streaked throat) might occur in the Middle Zambezi Valley[1].
References [1]Benson *et al.* (1970); [2]Brooke (1963); [3]Brooke (1972b); [4]Dowsett (in press a); [5]Keith & Vernon (1969).

Alpine Swift *Apus melba* B270 **AMW**

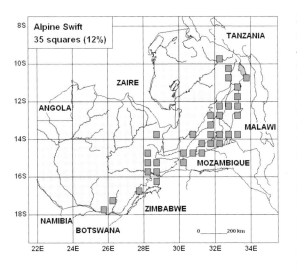

Distribution *Old World* (*in the Afrotropics, breeds mainly Ethiopia to South Africa, in a series of isolates*; *Palaearctic migrants may occur only north of the Equator*). Regular in the Luangwa Valley and on the Eastern Province plateau, but scarce elsewhere. West exceptionally as far as Victoria Falls[1], and on the Southern Province plateau also near Kalomo[1]. Otherwise, from the Zambezi escarpment in Gwembe Dist.[1], north-eastwards to Chinsali Dist. It has exceptionally been noted in the Lusaka area, north to Kapiri Mposhi[3]. *Alt.* 350 m to about 2200 m on the Zambian Nyika[2] (higher on the Malawi side).
Ecology Can occur almost anywhere on passage, but wintering flocks especially over rocky ridges and plateaux.

Status An intra-African migrant and non-breeding visitor, all records for the period 29 Mar to 30 Nov. The average first date over 12 years was 22 Apr (data insufficient to determine mean departure date)[1]. Some are on passage, but large numbers stay throughout this period in Eastern Province, a significant non-breeding area (flocks totalling over 1000 late Aug-early Sep at Chipata)[1].
Taxonomy No Zambian specimen, but doubtless *A. m. africanus*. Sometimes placed in the genus *Tachymarptis*.
References [1]Dowsett & Leonard (in press a); [2]Dowsett-Lemaire (2006a); [3]Irwin & Benson (1966a).

Mottled Swift *Apus aequatorialis* B271 **RB**

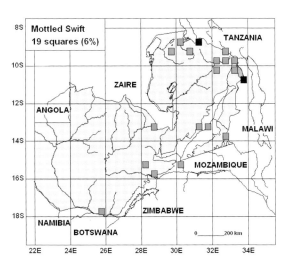

Distribution *Afrotropical* (*Guinea to Zimbabwe*). A large breeding colony has long been known at Kalambo Falls[1], and the species has bred also on the Nyika Plateau (Kungwala Hill near Manyenjere)[6,7] (black squares). This swift probably breeds too in Victoria Falls Gorges[4]. There are acceptable sight records of singles or small, wandering groups from several localities in the north and east, from Chinsali Dist.[5] west to Kafubu Dam[3], Leopardshill[10], Lusaka and the Victoria Falls[2,3]. *Alt.* 880 m (Victoria Falls) to 2150 m (Nyika), exceptionally down to 440 m (Katondwe).
Ecology Breeds in vertical rock cracks, usually in granite hills, but feeds over any nearby vegetation or over water. Ecological competitor of *A. melba*, whose breeding range is allopatric in the southern third of Africa and separated by altitude further north[9].

Status Resident in most areas, but some migrants from southern Africa might occur (indicated by birds seen sometimes in association with *A. melba*)[4].
Breeding   Oct   Dec
(n=3)   2   1   *Clutch*: N/1 (2).
Taxonomy *A. a. aequatorialis* (syn. *A. a. alfredi* type locality Mbala (i.e. Kalambo Falls)[8], *NHM*; named for Alfred Sharpe). Sometimes placed in the genus *Tachymarptis*.
References [1]Benson (1956d); [2]Brooke (1973); [3]Dowsett (1976b); [4]Dowsett (in press a); [5]Dowsett & Dowsett-Lemaire (1978a); [6]Dowsett *et al.* (1974); [7]Osborne (1975a); [8]Shelley (1900: 345); [9]Brooke in Snow (1978); [10]Tree (1962b).

Pallid Swift *Apus pallidus*   B273 **PV**

Distribution and Status *Essentially S. Palaearctic (appears to winter mainly from Senegambia to Sudan)*. There is a single specimen of a vagrant, from Chilanga (1528C, 1270 m), 10 Dec 1957[4]. (*A. pallidus* is known further south by just one specimen from South Africa[1]). ["Possible" sight records have been claimed of 1-2 birds at three different places along "line of rail", in Feb and Nov., but there may have been confusion with the pale race of *Apus apus* (*pekinensis*)[2].]
Taxonomy[3] *A. p. pallidus*.
References [1]Clancey (1969a); [2]Clancey (1981c); [3]Irwin & Benson (1967a); [4]Lack (1958).

Eurasian Swift *Apus apus*   B274 **PW**

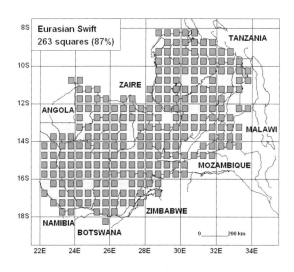

Eurasian Swift
263 squares (87%)

Distribution *Palaearctic (all wintering in the Afrotropics, mainly south of the Equator)*. Throughout the country and locally abundant. *Alt*. 330-2200 m.
Ecology Over any vegetation, often very high and largest concentrations observed around storm clouds or on passage; often feeds with other species of swifts and swallows at termite emergences. There is no evidence that large numbers are killed by man in Zambia, but other sources of mortality include heavy storms, as reported from Mwinilunga[1].
Status A Palaearctic passage migrant and winter visitor. Extreme dates are 15 Sep and 25 Apr[3]. The average first date over 28 years was 1 Oct, the average last (in 26 years) 25 Mar[3]. First arrival dates are variable from year to year, linked to storms associated with the Inter-tropical Convergence Zone. A British-ringed bird was recovered in Zambia 25 Nov (7 years later) (Appendix 1). By contrast, there have been 18 recoveries of European-ringed birds in nearby Malawi[4].
Taxonomy[2,5] *A. a. apus*, although the paler eastern *A. a. pekinensis* (very easily confused with *A. pallidus*) must occur too on passage. In addition, a specimen with the characters of *A. a. marwitzi* (blacker than *A. a. apus*, with a whiter throat patch) has been claimed from Mporokoso[2].
References [1]Bowen (1977a); [2]Clancey (1981c); [3]Dowsett (in press b); [4]Dowsett-Lemaire & Dowsett (2006); [5]Irwin & Benson (1966b).

African Black Swift *Apus barbatus* B272 **RB/AM**

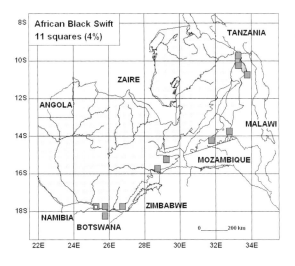

Distribution *Afrotropical* (*a series of isolates from Sierra Leone to South Africa*). Very local, in the vicinity of rocky hills. Known to breed with certainty only at Victoria Falls (880 m), but reports from possible breeding sites come from Leopardshill[8], Mwapula Gorge[4], Nyanje and the Mafingas[3]. *Alt.* 880 m up to *c.* 2200 m on the Nyika Plateau[4], where it could breed[5].

Ecology Breeds on cliff overhangs and feeds over open country.

Status Resident, although hundreds in the Victoria Falls area mid-Aug to late Oct in some years (max. 2000)[2] probably include South African migrants; indeed, 2000 calling over the Bovu River, Kazungula (open square) 5 Mar[2] were almost certainly migrants. Significant influxes noted in S. Malawi in Apr-Sep[6].

Breeding No detailed records, but nests were occupied in the Victoria Falls Gorges in May[2].

Taxonomy[7] The only specimens (from Victoria Falls) are *A. b. hollidayi* (type locality Fifth Gorge; *NMZB*)[1]; named for C.S. Holliday. However, it is likely that *A. b. roehli* (blacker, rather than brown, on the mantle) occurs in the east, and that the larger nominate *barbatus* is a migrant from South Africa. A partial albino has been reported from Victoria Falls[2].

References [1]Benson & Irwin (1960: 98); [2]Dowsett (in press a); [3]Dowsett & Stjernstedt (1973); [4]Dowsett *et al.* (1974); [5]Dowsett-Lemaire (2006a); [6]Dowsett-Lemaire & Dowsett (2006); [7]Irwin & Benson (1967a); [8]Tree (1962b).

Little Swift *Apus affinis* B275 **RB**

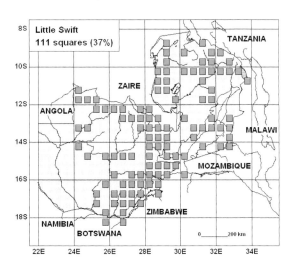

Distribution *Old World* (*in the Afrotropics, Mauritania to South Africa*). Throughout the eastern half of the country and central areas, usually where there are rocky hills, west to localities in Mwinilunga Dist.[1] and between Kaoma and Lukulu[6]. Further south unknown so far west of the Victoria Falls[2] and Mulobezi areas. *Alt.* from 330 m up to 2200 m on the Nyika Plateau[7] (as wanderers).

Ecology Feeds over any vegetation type. Nests both on rock faces (the original site) and on bridges and buildings[2], either making its own nest or taking over an old one (e.g. of *Hirundo fuligula*[3]).

Status Resident, with some wandering. Prior to the 1960s not known with certainty west of

Kitwe, Chililabombwe[8] and Victoria Falls (an old report from Zambezi Dist.[9] being unconfirmed[6]). Appears to have spread in recent years[5,6].

Breeding[3]   Sep   Oct   Dec   Jan   Feb   Mar   Apr
(n=25)   2   2   1   6   8   5   1   *Clutch*: C/2 (2).

Taxonomy[4] *A. a. aerobates* in the north and north-east, replaced in the south and south-west by *A. a. theresae* (with more white on throat and rump).

References [1]Bowen (1983j); [2]Brooke (1963); [3]Brooke & Vernon (1961b); [4]Clancey (1980b); [5]Dowsett (1977e); [6]Dowsett (in press a); [7]Dowsett-Lemaire (2006a); [8]Tree (1966a); [9]White (1945-46).

Horus Swift *Apus horus*   B276 **RB**

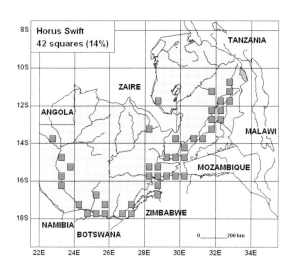

Distribution *Afrotropical* (*Ghana to South Africa*). Essentially a bird of the low-lying Luangwa and Middle Zambezi Valleys, but ranging sparsely along the Upper Zambezi to the South Kashiji[2]. Is also present at Chembe ferry on the Luapula[1], whence perhaps came a record of a wanderer at Luanshya[3]. Other acceptable sightings of wanderers have come from the Lusaka area[3]. *Alt.* breeding 330-1050 m, wandering higher (to *c.* 1260 m).

Ecology Normally in the vicinity of rivers with sand cliffs, where it nests in holes, usually several pairs usurping those excavated by *Merops bullockoides* or *M. nubicoides*[3].

Status Resident, with local wandering and perhaps some migrants; most observations from low-lying areas are in the dry season, with small numbers wandering outside the breeding season[3].

Breeding   Jun   Aug   Sep
(n=5)   3   1   1   *Clutch*: C/3 (1).

Taxonomy *A. h. horus*.

References [1]Aspinwall (1975b); [2]Britton (1970); [3]Dowsett (in press a).

African White-rumped Swift *Apus caffer*   B277 **AMB**

Distribution *Afrotropical* (*Senegal to South Africa*), *and SW Palaearctic*. Throughout the eastern and central parts of Zambia, west to the Mwinilunga area[1] (from 1971), and further south to the upper Mutondo and Sesheke (where first found in the early 1990s). *Alt.* 330-2200 m (Nyika Plateau).

Ecology Can be found feeding anywhere; frequently associated with other swifts and swallows near rocks and man-made structures (bridges and houses). For breeding, takes over retort-shaped nests, such as those of *Hirundo abyssinica*[3] and *H. rufigula*[4].

Status Mainly an intra-African migrant and breeding visitor. There are significant differences in the monthly frequency, although there are records throughout the year: it is most common Aug-Apr and least May-Jul[2]. For a species not recorded in Zambia before 1949, this swift has spread remarkably since.

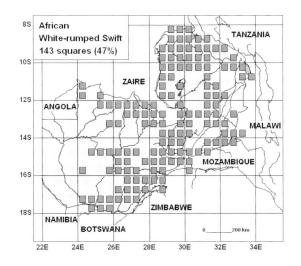

Breeding Aug Sep Oct Nov
(n=62)   2   22 11   8
           Dec Jan Feb Mar
            5   4   4   6
Clutch: C/1 (3); C/2 (6); C/3 (2).
Taxonomy No races recognized.
References [1]Bowen (1983j); [2]Dowsett &
Leonard (in press a); [3]Haydock (1949a); [4]Tree
(1964).

Coliidae

Speckled Mousebird *Colius striatus*   B278 **RB**

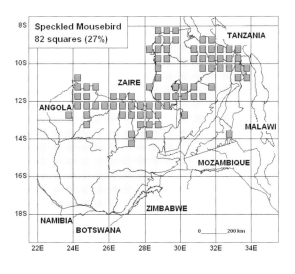

Distribution *Afrotropical (mainly Nigeria to
South Africa)*. In any rank vegetation, almost
throughout the northern part of the Zambian
plateau (except, as with some other species,
for a gap in the well-wooded Northern
Province). In the west occurs south to Jivundu
(West Lunga N.P.)[2] and in the Kafue basin to
Chilenga[6]. In the north-east ranges south to
the Musola River and Kasanka N.P.[1,5], but on
the Eastern Province plateau south of the
Nyika only at Chipata (although more widespread on the Malawi side of the border)[4]. *Alt.*
from 950 m to 2200 m (Nyika)[3].
Ecology A gregarious species found in rank
growth at edges of evergreen forest, thickets
and riparian scrub; overall in moister habitat
than *U. indicus*. Eats a variety of fruit, seeds,
leaves and flowers, also some insects.
Status Resident.
Breeding Aug Sep Oct Nov Dec Jan
(n=17)   3   4   5   1   3   1   *Clutch*: C/1 (1); C/2 (1); C/3 (2); C/4 (1).
Taxonomy *C. s. congicus* (syn. *lungae*, type locality Mwinilunga[7], *NHM*). Replaced in Eastern
Province by *C. s. berlepschi* (barring on chest more evident) and marginally at Mbala by *C. s. cineras-
cens* (more olive above).
References [1]Benson (1956d); [2]Dowsett (in press a); [3]Dowsett-Lemaire (2006a); [4]Dowsett-Lemaire &
Dowsett (2006); [5]Farmer (1992); [6]Tree (1966a); [7]White (1947c: 36).

Red-faced Mousebird *Urocolius indicus* B279 **RB**

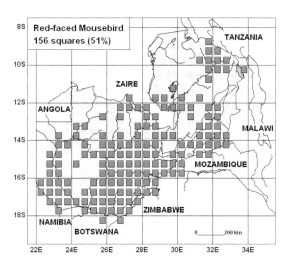

Distribution *Afrotropical* (*Zaire to South Africa*). Widespread and common in the south. In the west, north to Zambezi town (Balovale) (where rare)[2], West Lunga N.P. and Matebo. In the north-east, occurs in the belt of flood-plain country to the Tanzania border, but west-wards only to Chishinga Swamp[3]. [There have been a couple of reports from the Luapula in the Kawambwa area, but they require confir-mation. It is unrecorded from Katanga in this region[6].] Unreported from the north of the Luangwa Valley, and on the Eastern Province plateau absent between Chipata and Buluma[3]. *Alt*. 330-1600 m.

Ecology In drier situations than *C. striatus,* including dry thickets, *Acacia* scrub, palm savanna, gardens. The two species occur close to each other on the Copperbelt[3]; there is no record of them together, although they do mix marginally in habitat such as gardens in S. Malawi[4]. A nest was near the top of a 5 m *Acacia* tree on the edge of a dambo[1]. Gregarious and with a varied mixed diet.

Status Resident. Although present in every month, the abundance of this species appears greatest Mar-Jun[3]; this is likely to be related to post-breeding flocking and local fruit availability.

Breeding   Aug   Sep   Oct   Nov   Dec   Jan
(n=83)   9   18   18   17   10   11   *Clutch*: C/2 (15); C/3 (11); C/4 (1).

Taxonomy[5,7] *U. i. pallidus.*

References [1]Benson & Pitman (1956-57); [2]Britton (1970); [3]Dowsett (in press a); [4]Dowsett-Lemaire & Dowsett (2006); [5]Irwin & Benson (1966b); [6]Schouteden (1971); [7]White (1954b).

Trogonidae

Narina's Trogon *Apaloderma narina* B280 **RB/AM?**

Distribution *Afrotropical* (*Guinea to South Africa*). In forest and thicket, probably throughout the country at low and medium altitudes. *Alt*. 330-1670 m.

Ecology In understorey of evergreen forest – including *Cryptosepalum* (very common) and *Marquesia* – transition woodland, evergreen and deciduous thickets and (as a wanderer) occasionally in gardens and drier woodland. A nest was in a tree hole in evergreen forest, 10 m up[1].

Status Present throughout the year in many areas. Subject to local movements, wandering to gardens, dry woodland and edge of floodplain[2], and perhaps to some extent an intra-African migrant.

Breeding   Sep   Dec
(n=4)   3   1   Song noted 3 Aug to late Apr, though in the south usually from early Nov.
Clutch: C/2 (1); C/3 (1). *Moult*: a female was moulting mid-Mar[2].

Taxonomy *A. n. narina.*

References [1]Benson & Pitman (1958-59); [2]Dowsett (in press a).

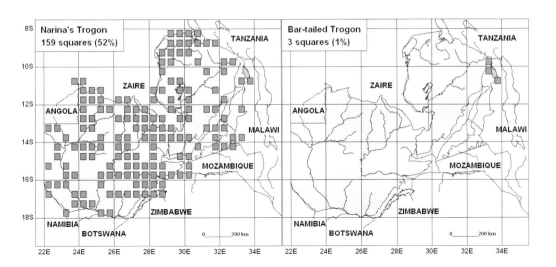

Bar-tailed Trogon *Apaloderma vittatum*   B281 **RB**

Distribution *Afromontane endemic* (*E. Nigeria/Cameroon to Malawi*). Common in the Mafingas (1950 m)[4], Makutu (2100 m[2], down to 1800 m at Jombo in Aug[1]) and the Nyika (up to 2200 m)[6].
Ecology Mid-stratum of montane rain forest (mostly 4-20 m) under fairly closed canopy. Prey (often caterpillars, moths) is snatched off bark of trunk or branches and foliage. Highest densities of 5 pairs/10 ha known from Chowo on Zambian Nyika (2100-2200 m) under closed canopy[5].
Status Largely resident, but a few individuals are prone to local movements and there are inter-montane movements of up to 100 km in Malawi[5,7].
Breeding   Oct   Nov
(n=8)   6   2
All from SW Nyika (Zambia and adjacent Zovochipolo in Malawi). *Clutch*: no data.
Moult: all birds Dec-Jan were moulting, none was Jun-Nov[3].
Taxonomy No races recognized.
References [1]Benson (1949a); [2]Dowsett (1971h); [3]Dowsett (in press a); [4]Dowsett & Stjernstedt (1973); [5]Dowsett-Lemaire (1989b); [6]Dowsett-Lemaire (2006a); [7]Dowsett-Lemaire & Dowsett (2006).

Alcedinidae

Half-collared Kingfisher *Alcedo semitorquata*   B284 **RB**

Distribution *Afrotropical* (*Ethiopia to South Africa*). Widespread in the north on wooded rivers, even small streams, further south usually only on the larger rivers. Throughout the Upper Zambezi, south to the Mongu area, and then again from Sioma Falls down to Batoka Gorge. In the Kafue drainage down to Leopardshill[4]. In the Gwembe Valley now very local (after the flooding of L. Kariba), in the Chipepo area[2]. Only a visitor to the Middle Zambezi Valley (e.g. Chiawa, Oct[5]), and no record from the lower Luangwa below the Lunsemfwa River confluence[2]. On the Eastern Province plateau north to Lundazi[6], reappearing in the Mafingas[3]. Absent from much of the Northern Province plateau, and so far unknown from the lower Luapula. *Alt.* 500-1950 m (Mafingas)[3], but most below 900 m are wanderers.
Ecology On perennial rivers and streams with well-timbered banks, and on some of the larger rivers

such as the Zambezi, possibly only where there are rapids. On the Southern Province plateau occasionally on small, seasonal rivers. Feeds predominantly on fish such as species of *Alestes* and cichlids, but also on fresh-water crabs[6].

Status Resident, with local movements (e.g. altitudinal).

Breeding   Feb   Mar   Apr   Jun   Aug   Sep   Oct
(n=9)   1   1   1   1   1   1   3   *Clutch*: C/3 (1); C/4 (1).

Taxonomy[1] *A. s. tephria*.

References [1]Clancey (1978a); [2]Dowsett (in press a); [3]Dowsett & Stjernstedt (1973); [4]Tree (1962b); [5]Tree (1992); [6]Trollope (1966).

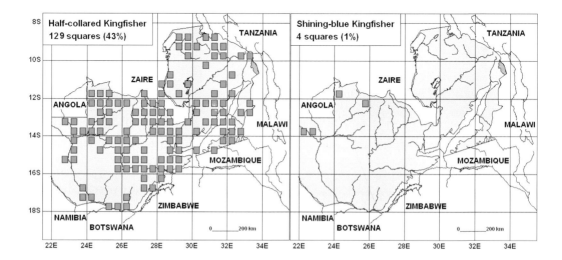

Shining-blue Kingfisher *Alcedo quadribrachys*   B285 **R(B)**

Distribution *Afrotropical* (*Senegal to Zambia; mainly Guineo-Congolian*). Known from scattered localities along the forested rivers of the north-west[5]. From the West Lunga near Mwinilunga[4], further east on the Mwombezhi[3], and west of the Zambezi at L. Mwange and on the South Kashiji River[1,2]. The population west of the Zambezi is the most southerly known. *Alt.* 1050-1370 m.

Ecology Along rivers where there is dense evergreen forest, apparently confined more to the well-wooded sections than is the larger *A. semitorquata*; the two coexist in places (e.g. Mwinilunga town[4] and Mwombezhi River[3]).

Status Resident.

Breeding No records.

Taxonomy *A. q. guentheri*.

References [1]Aspinwall (1979b); [2]Benson (1960c); [3]Benson (1964d); [4]Bowen (1983i); [5]Dowsett (in press a).

Malachite Kingfisher *Alcedo cristata*   B286 **RB**

Distribution *Afrotropical* (*Mauritania to South Africa*). By any shallow water with fringing vegetation, thus common throughout. *Alt.* 330-1900 m.

Ecology By any pools, streams, dams, riversides. Hunts from perches in reeds or rank vegetation, feeding largely on very small fish.

Status Resident, with local movements to seasonal ponds and streams[1].

Breeding   Jan   Feb   Mar   Apr   May   Jun   Aug   Sep   Oct   Dec

(n=43)   2   9   6   2   1   4   7   8   3   1

Clutch: C/1 (1); C/2 (1); C/3 (1); C/4 (4); C/5 (2); C/6 (2).

Moult: noted Dec-Mar[1].

Taxonomy *A. c. cristata* (trinomial, if various island forms are treated as conspecific). Sometimes placed in the genus *Corythornis.*

References [1]Dowsett (in press a).

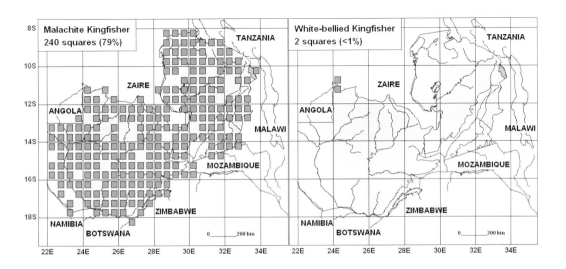

White-bellied Kingfisher *Alcedo leucogaster*   B287 **R(B)**

Distribution *Guineo-Congolian near-endemic* (*Guinea-Bissau to SW Uganda, south to Zambia*). A forest species of the extreme north of Mwinilunga Dist., from Salujinga[1], Mudileji River, south to Isombu[2]. Unrecorded from Kasaji in Zaire[3], but ought to occur there. These are the most southerly records of the species. *Alt.* 1250-1460 m.

Ecology Moist evergreen forest, apparently absent from the drier types (such as *Marquesia*). Usually in the interior, often along small streams (but not confined to them).

Status Resident.

Conservation Like most of the forest birds of N. Mwinilunga, its habitat there is greatly threatened by deforestation. However, it is a common species in most of Central and West Africa.

Breeding No records. *Moult*: one in moult early Aug[2].

Taxonomy[1] *A. l. leopoldi.*

References [1]Benson & Irwin (1964b); [2]Dowsett (in press a); [3]Schouteden (1971).

Pygmy Kingfisher *Ceyx pictus*   B288 **AMB/R?**

Distribution *Afrotropical* (*Senegal to South Africa*). Breeds in densely-wooded country throughout the

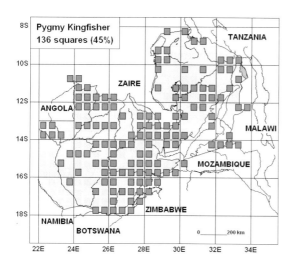

Zambian plateau, except on Kalahari sands not occurring west of the Zambezi south of the South Kashiji River[2]. Further down the Zambezi ranges to Sefula, Kakenge and the Kazungula area. Does breed at lower levels, as in the Gwembe Valley in the Mutulanganga and Mbendele area, and present too in the Luangwa Valley during the breeding season[3]. *Alt.* 450-1750 m (irregularly 2000-2100 m on the Malawi side of Nyika).

Ecology In any woodland with small thickets (as on termite hills), especially miombo, and often near water, although it feeds mostly on dry land. Also at edges of forest and larger thickets, and even inside forest patches (e.g. N. Mwinilunga). Likely almost anywhere while on migration. May be absent from woodland on Kalahari sand, as in much of Western Province, where there are few banks suitable for nesting.

Status Mainly an intra-African migrant and breeding visitor during the rains, throughout most of the country, arriving late Aug in the north-west, from mid-Sep elsewhere. The average first date over 27 years was 4 Oct, the average last (in 22 years) 20 Apr[3]. There are instances of them flying into windows or walls when on passage. There are very few dry season records (Jun to late Aug): several from Mwinilunga (including a bird ringed late Jun retrapped late Aug the same year), and once each Kashiji and L. Kashiba, may be residents. A few in the Luangwa Valley may be wintering birds from southern Africa[3].

Breeding   Oct   Nov   Dec
(n=24)   6   13   5   *Clutch*: C/3 (3); C/4 (4).

Moult: many examined Oct-Mar showed no sign of moult (which presumably takes place in winter quarters), but a juvenile in Zambezi Dist. was moulting 24 Jun[3].

Taxonomy[1] *I. p. natalensis* is a widespread intra-African migrant, while *I. p. picta* (lacking the blue patch on the ear coverts) is present (perhaps resident) in extreme NW Zambia.

References [1]Benson & Irwin (1964b); [2]Britton (1970); [3]Dowsett & Leonard (in press a).

Brown-hooded Kingfisher *Halcyon albiventris*   B292 **RB**

Distribution *Afrotropical* (*Somalia to South Africa*). Locally common throughout the country (especially in riparian woodland), except for the dry Kalahari sands of the south-west and the Barotse Floodplain. Ranges up the Zambezi drainage to Kalobolelwa and Sioma[2], then a gap until it reappears in the Luena Flats area[2]. Further investigation of the better wooded rivers in this area might expand its distribution. *Alt.* 330-1700 m.

Ecology Usually in riparian forest, or thickets, but in the North-Western Province on the edges of moist evergreen forest, and even at times in the interior of *Cryptosepalum*. Nests in a hole in a bank. Seen killing and eating a snake[3].

Status Resident.

Breeding   Aug   Sep   Oct   Jan
(n=23)   1   5   16   1   *Clutch*: C/4 (3).

Moult: Jan-Apr[2].

Taxonomy[1] *H. a. orientalis.*
References [1]Benson & Irwin (1967b); [2]Dowsett (in press a); [3]Tree (1963b).

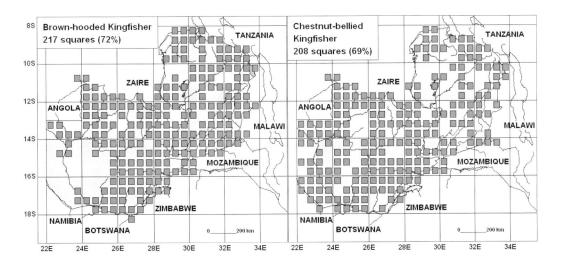

Chestnut-bellied Kingfisher *Halcyon leucocephala* B293 **AMB**

Distribution *Afrotropical (Mauritania to South Africa).* Locally common throughout the dry wood-lands of the country, except unknown from parts of the Luapula drainage. *Alt.* 330-1900 m.
Ecology In any woodland, and not directly associated with water. Nests in a hole in a bank or termite mound.
Status An intra-African migrant[1] and breeding visitor, although there are reports throughout the year. Most records overall are Apr-May and Aug-Nov, fewest Jun-Jul (and then especially at low altitude)[4]. Local breeding birds are quiet and inconspicuous when in moult, but abundance is probably influenced too by the through passage of other populations. It is probable that the off-season is spent to the north of Zambia, and a bird ringed in Malawi has been recovered in S. Zaire late May[5]. One ringed bird, present Jan-Feb, was retrapped where ringed the following Dec-Jan[3].

Breeding	Sep	Oct	Nov	Dec	Jan	Feb	
(n=111)	21	56	28	4	1	1	*Clutch*: C/1 (2); C/2 (3); C/3 (9); C/4 (12).

Moult: both adults and juveniles moult mid-Dec to late Apr[2].
Taxonomy *H. l. pallidiventris.*
References [1]Dowsett (1988a); [2]Dowsett (in press a); [3]Dowsett & Leonard (2001); [4]Dowsett & Leonard (in press a); [5]Dowsett-Lemaire & Dowsett (2006).

Blue-breasted Kingfisher *Halcyon malimbica* B290 **RB**

Distribution *Afrotropical (Senegal to Zambia; mainly Guineo-Congolian).* A forest species of the north-west, in Mwinilunga at several places south to Mwinilunga town. Reappears further south at Manyinga[2], and west of the Zambezi south and east to Lukolwe[3] and Kashiji[1]. The localities west of the Zambezi are the most southerly for the species. *Alt.* 1060-1460 m.
Ecology Moist evergreen and riparian forest. Absent from the drier types like *Cryptosepalum.*

Status Recorded every month, and apparently resident[2].

Breeding   Oct

(n=1)   1   Also a female with enlarged ovaries 23 Aug[1]. Song has been heard from late Jul, especially Sep to mid-Nov, and again late Apr[2]. *Clutch*: no data.

Taxonomy *H. m. malimbica.*

References [1]Aspinwall (1979b); [2]Dowsett (in press a); [3]Leonard (1998b).

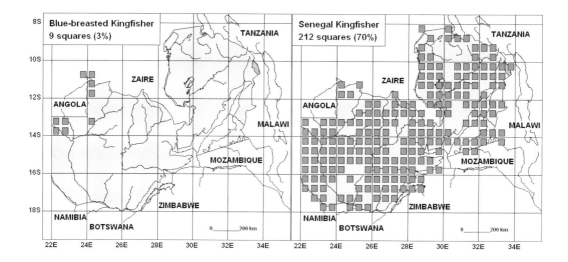

Senegal (Woodland) Kingfisher *Halcyon senegalensis*   B289 **AMB**

Distribution *Afrotropical* (*Mauritania to South Africa*). Probably throughout the dry woodlands of Zambia, locally very common. *Alt.* 500-1700 m.

Ecology In any dry woodland or wooded savanna, being especially numerous in *Acacia* and mopane in the Luangwa Valley, and, though feeding on land, may breed in the vicinity of water. Avoids dense miombo. Nests in tree holes, at times competing with species such as *Lybius torquatus*, and there are several instances of nest holes being taken over by *Halcyon chelicuti* once *H. senegalensis* has bred.

Status An intra-African migrant and breeding visitor. Most records fall between 24 Aug and 6 May, with first arrivals usually in the second half of Sep, and largest numbers present Oct to mid-Apr. The average first date over 23 years was 4 Oct, the average last (in 22 years) 27 Apr[3]. There are a dozen records outside this period, mostly from the low-lying Luangwa Valley[3] (possibly wintering birds from another breeding area). Site fidelity was shown by one bird returning to the place of ringing after 4 years[2].

Breeding   Nov   Dec   Jan

(n=22)   7   13   2   *Clutch*: C/3 (1).

Moult: none Feb-Apr showed signs of moult (which presumably takes place in winter quarters nearer the Equator)[3].

Taxonomy *H. s. cyanoleuca*[1].

References [1]Benson *et al.* (1970); [2]Dowsett & Leonard (2001); [3]Dowsett & Leonard (in press a).

Mangrove Kingfisher *Halcyon senegaloides*   B - **AV**

Distribution and Status *Eastern endemic (Somalia to South Africa).* A vagrant (photographed) was present at Kasikezi lagoon in the Luangwa Valley (1231D, alt. 500 m) two years running, in Oct-Nov 2004 and 2005. It held a territory in riparian vegetation on the edge of the Luangwa River. In song and territorial, it was apparently unmated[1]. The possibility of breeding (even as a mixed pair with *H. senegalensis*) should not be ruled out. The species's association with mangroves on the coast of eastern Africa is mostly in the non-breeding season; it is thought that breeding normally takes place inland. The varying extent of red on the bill of the closely-related *H. senegalensis* in S. Malawi has raised the suggestion that hybridisation may occur. The nearest certain record hitherto was from Inhamintanga near the Lower Zambezi, in Mozambique, some 650 km distant[1].
Taxonomy Probably monotypic, although some authorities recognize *H. s. ranivorus.*
References [1]Tittle & Dowsett (2006).

Striped Kingfisher *Halcyon chelicuti*   B291 **RB**

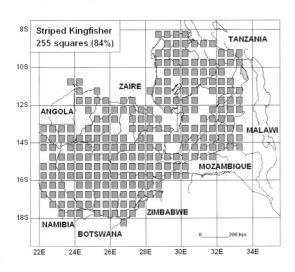

8S Striped Kingfisher
255 squares (84%)

Distribution *Afrotropical (Mauritania to South Africa).* The most widespread dryland kingfisher, and locally very common. *Alt.* 330-1800 m (Uningi Pans).
Ecology Any woodland, especially more open types in drier areas, wooded grassland, small thickets and gardens. Never directly associated with water. Nests in tree holes, sometimes one used previously by *H. senegalensis*[2].
Status Resident; strongly territorial.

Breeding	Sep	Oct	Nov
(n=21)	6	12	3

Clutch: C/3 (1); C/4 (1).
Moult: one bird started mid-Nov[2].
Taxonomy[1] *H. c. chelicuti.*
References [1]Benson & Irwin (1967b); [2]Dowsett (in press a).

Giant Kingfisher *Megaceryle maxima*   B282 **RB**

Distribution *Afrotropical (Senegal to South Africa).* Almost throughout, especially on all large rivers, but localized and rarely common. *Alt.* 330-1600 m.
Ecology By perennial rivers, lakes and dams with well-wooded banks. Nests in holes in high banks. Feeds on fish[1] and fresh-water crabs[2].
Status Resident.

Breeding[1]	Feb	Mar	Apr	Jun	Jul	Aug	
(n=12)	1	1	1	2	2	5	*Clutch*: C/4 (1).

Taxonomy No races recognized.
References [1]Dowsett (1971g); [2]Haydock (1951).

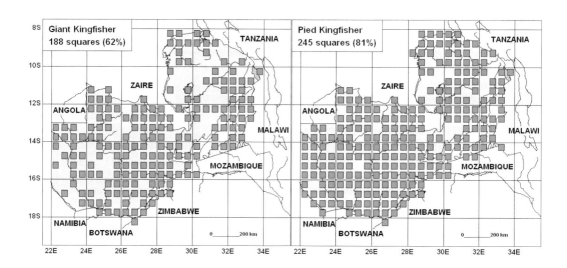

Pied Kingfisher *Ceryle rudis* B283 **RB**

Distribution *Mainly Afrotropical (Mauritania to South Africa) and Oriental.* By any open water, widespread and locally numerous. *Alt.* 330-1800 m (Uningi Pans).

Ecology By water, either in pairs or small parties of up to about 8[1]. Avoids the most densely-wooded watercourses. It frequently nests semi-colonially (up to 20 pairs). Hunts mainly by hovering and diving; predominantly piscivorous (especially *Alestes* spp., *Barbus* spp. and Cichlidae), it also feeds on insect larvae (especially dragonflies Odonata)[1,2].

Status Resident.

Breeding	Jan	Feb	Mar	Apr	May	Jun	Jul	Aug	Sep	Oct	Nov	Dec
(n=54)	1	4	4	2	4	14	8	10	2	3	1	1

Clutch: C/4 (4); C/5 (5); C/6 (2); C/7 (1).

Moult: birds in moult noted at various times Oct-Jun[1].

Taxonomy *C. r. rudis.*

References [1]Dowsett (in press a); [2]Tjomlid (1973).

Meropidae

Little Bee-eater *Merops pusillus* B298 **RB**

Distribution *Afrotropical (Mauritania to South Africa).* Common in open country throughout. *Alt.* 330 m to 2100 m on the Mafingas[2] and 2150 m on the Nyika[4].

Ecology In grassland with light cover (including floodplains and dambos), and in any open woodland. Often in association with water or seasonal watercourses. Nests solitarily[3].

Status Resident.

Breeding	Jul	Aug	Sep	Oct	Nov	Dec
(n=192)	1	5	33	123	28	2

Clutch: C/1 (6); C/2 (21); C/3 (17); C/4 (38); C/5 (20).

Moult: noted Dec-Mar[3].

Taxonomy[1] *M. p. meridionalis*, with *M. p. argutus* (paler below, and with a smaller throat spot) in the

south-west.
References [1]Clancey (1968c); [2]Clay (1953); [3]Dowsett (in press a); [4]Dowsett-Lemaire (2006a).

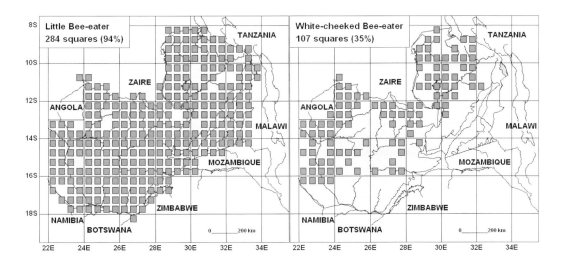

White-cheeked Bee-eater *Merops variegatus* B299 **RB**

Distribution *Afrotropical* (*Nigeria to Zambia*). The dambos and floodplains of N. Zambia. In the west, south to the plains between the Mashi (Shangombo) and Zambezi (Matabele Plain)[1], where the species reaches its southern limit. Locally on the Kafue Flats, east to Mazabuka. Occurs in the dambos north-west of the Muchingas, from the Kabwe area to about Chibesakunda (the most easterly record in the country)[4]. Locally common (e.g. Mweru Wantipa and Lusenga Plain N.Ps, Bangweulu, Mongu Dist.). *Alt.* 950-1650 m.
Ecology Associated with dambos and damp plains with rank grass. Where it occurs next to the smaller *M. pusillus*, the present species is usually in wetter situations[2]. Nests solitarily.
Status Resident.
Breeding Sep Oct
(n=8) 7 1 *Clutch*: C/1 (1); C/2 (2).
Moult: one began early Dec[6].
Taxonomy *M. v. bangweoloensis* (type locality near Nsombo; *NHM*)[3,5].
References [1]Benson (1964f); [2]Britton (1968); [3]Dowsett (1980b); [4]Dowsett (in press a); [5]Grant (1915a: 55); [6]Traylor (1965b).

Swallow-tailed Bee-eater *Merops hirundineus* B301 **AMB**

Distribution *Afrotropical* (*Senegal to South Africa*). Throughout and locally common in the open woodlands of the country. *Alt.* 330-1700 m.
Ecology Any woodland or wooded savanna, especially where the conditions are fairly open or in clearings.
Status An intra-African migrant and breeding visitor. The frequency of occurrence is greatest May-Nov, least Dec-Apr[1]. Most records during the rains are from central and eastern areas, although it is not clear

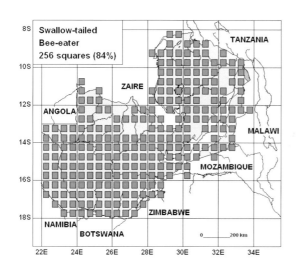

if this merely represents insufficient exploration of the west at that season.

Breeding   Sep   Oct   Dec
(n=20)   9   9   2
Clutch: C/1 (2); C/3 (3); C/4 (4).
Moult: adults start late Nov[3].

Taxonomy[2] Two subspecies are recorded, both essentially dry season visitors: *M. h. hirundineus* (mainly to W. Zambia) and *M. h. furcatus* (with a broader and deeper blue throat band, mostly in the east).

References [1]Dowsett & Leonard (in press a); [2]Irwin & Benson (1966b); [3]Traylor (1965b).

White-fronted Bee-eater *Merops bullockoides*   B300 **RB**

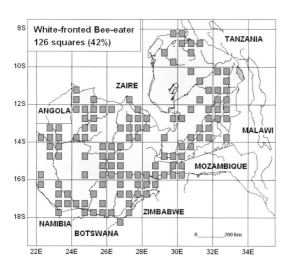

Distribution *Afrotropical* (*Gabon to South Africa*). Common on all the major river systems, except for the Luapula (overall too rocky), which it approaches no nearer than the Kalungwishi area[1]. Uncommon on the Eastern Province plateau, and a vagrant to Chipata[1]. *Alt.* 330-1700 m.

Ecology Usually in any woodland along rivers (perennial or not), nesting colonially in banks.

Status Resident. Present in some breeding areas throughout the year, but flocks do occur outside the breeding season, and there is some local wandering (e.g. to Chipata, Lochinvar).

Breeding   Jul   Aug   Sep   Oct
(n=74)   1   22   47   4
Clutch: C/2 (4); C/3 (11); C/4 (3).
Moult: starting late Nov[3].

Taxonomy[2] No races recognized.
References [1]Dowsett (in press a); [2]Irwin & Benson (1966b); [3]Traylor (1965b).

White-throated Bee-eater *Merops albicollis*   B - **AV**

Distribution and Status *Afrotropical* (*breeds in the Sahel, Mauritania to Kenya; winters south to the Equator, mainly in the Guineo-Congolian forest zone, records further south are of birds that have overshot*). Up to 6 birds were on the edge of a small patch of evergreen thicket at Uningi Pans (0831C), 11 Dec 1999 to 13 Jan 2000[2]. [Claimed specimens in the past were mislabelled[1]. A reported sighting of two in the Luangwa Valley on and about 18 Nov 1994 has never been substantiated[2].]
Taxonomy No races recognized.

References [1]Dowsett (2002); [2]Leonard *et al.* (2001b).

Böhm's Bee-eater *Merops boehmi*   B297 **RB**

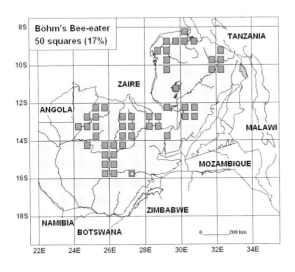

Distribution *Zambezian endemic (Zaire to Malawi).* Locally common along the major rivers of N. Zambia (but very patchy). In the Chambeshi drainage down to Mbesuma, and from between Lakes Tanganyika and Mweru south to the upper Luena. Reappears on the Lukulu River, thence through much of the Copperbelt. Occurs west to Manyinga and north-west to Chisasa[3], and down the Kafue to Itezhi-Tezhi[1,2]. Exceptionally a vagrant was photographed to the east at Lochinvar, 27 Apr[3] (open square). [A sight record from further south (the well-known Victoria Falls), mapped in ref. 6, has never been repeated, and cannot be accepted[4].] *Alt.* 950-1600 m.

Ecology On the edges of thickets and riparian forest by perennial rivers. Nest holes are solitary or in small colonies (up to 5), in flat open ground, in woodland or on forest edge.

Status Resident, with local wandering.

Breeding   Aug   Sep
(n=8)   1   7   *Clutch*: C/4 (1).

Taxonomy[5] No races recognized.

References [1]Benson (1959d); [2]Brooke (1966c); [3]Dowsett (in press a); [4]Dowsett & Dowsett-Lemaire (1979a); [5]Irwin & Benson (1967a); [6]Snow (1978).

Madagascar (Olive) Bee-eater *Merops superciliosus*   B295 (part) **AMB**

Distribution *Afrotropical (breeding in Madagascar and parts of eastern and southern Africa).* Occurs mostly in E. Zambia, west to the Luapula at Nchelenge and the Copperbelt at Kitwe. Regular in the low-lying Luangwa Valley (mainly on passage), but few records from the Middle Zambezi Valley. Reappears in the Victoria Falls area, where non-breeding birds occur during the rains, west to Imusho on the Mashi, where present in early Dec[6]. Has bred at Bimbi Hot Springs (black square)[6], and there is a single record of a colony of 100 pairs in Mana Pools (1529C), Zimbabwe[3]. *Alt.* 450-2200 m.

Ecology The two sibling species (this and *M. persicus*) show marked habitat differences. *M. superciliosus* occurs in any woodland, but usually the more open types, and not necessarily near water. Hawks from tall trees, or even telephone wires. The one nest known was solitary, in a sand cliff.

Status[1,2] An intra-African migrant and (occasional) breeding visitor. Extreme dates are 16 Aug to 27 May, with three reports Jun and Jul. Passage southerly is very heavy Sep into Oct, smaller numbers returning Apr-May[6]. Many of these birds are probably from eastern African breeding colonies, rather than Madagascar. The few records during the rains may relate to local breeding birds (it is reported at the same season in Hwange N.P., Zimbabwe[7]). Much remains unknown about movements and breeding distribution.

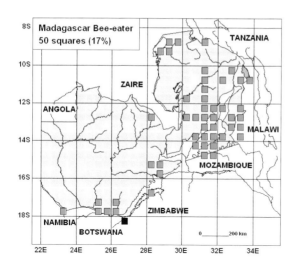

Breeding   Sep
(n=1)   1   A single nest, containing
young on 3 Oct 1993. A report by David
Livingstone claimed this bee-eater nested on
the Upper Zambezi[5], but there is no evidence
to support this. *Clutch*: no data.

Taxonomy[4] *M. s. superciliosus* apparently
occurs mainly as a non-breeding migrant, and
it is probable that *M. s. alternans* is the form
found to breed locally. *M. (s.) persicus* is here
treated as a separate species (see below).

References [1]Aspinwall & Hustler (1997);
[2]Benson (1966); [3]Brooke & Hougaard (1971);
[4]Clancey (1971a); [5]Dean & Brooke (1991);
[6]Dowsett & Leonard (in press a); [7]Riddell
(1999).

Blue-cheeked Bee-eater *Merops persicus*   B295 (part) **PW**

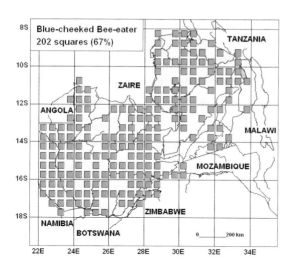

Distribution *S. Palaearctic, Oriental and
Afrotropical* (*breeds throughout the Sahel;
Palaearctic birds winter mainly Ethiopia to
South Africa*). Can occur anywhere on passage
(although scarcer in the low-lying valleys than
M. superciliosus). Most abundant in larger
swamps and floodplains. *Alt.* 330-2200 m.

Ecology Winters typically on the edges of
marsh, dambos, floodplains or along rivers,
roosting in reedbeds.

Status A Palaearctic migrant and winter visitor. All acceptable records fall between 7 Oct
and 1 May[1] (some earlier records may relate to
M. superciliosus). The average first date over
26 years was 4 Nov, the average last (in 28
years) 18 Apr[1].

Moult: undertaken in Zambia, between early
Nov and late Mar, lasting *c.* 3 months[1].

Taxonomy *M. p. persicus.* Sometimes treated as a race of *M. superciliosus*, but differences in voice
(slight) and head pattern suggest they may best be treated as specifically distinct[2].

References [1]Dowsett (in press b); [2]Dowsett & Dowsett-Lemaire (1993).

Eurasian Bee-eater *Merops apiaster*   B294 **PW/AM?**

Distribution *Palaearctic* (*the whole population wintering Senegal to South Africa*)*, with a small
population also breeding in Namibia and South Africa*. A common visitor throughout the country, the
gap in distribution shown west of the Zambezi, in the Liuwa and other plains, being perhaps the result

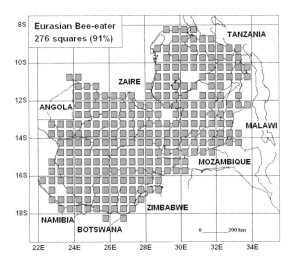

of insufficient exploration. *Alt.* 330-2200 m, wintering below 1700 m.

Ecology Passes over any vegetation, winters mainly in woodland, principally the drier, more open types.

Status A Palaearctic migrant and winter visitor. The great majority recorded between 22 Aug and 8 May, with flocks of hundreds (max. 400+) Sep-Oct and Apr. The average first date over 29 years was 4 Sep, the average last (in 29 years) 21 Apr[2]. There are at least three records well outside this period (between mid-Jun and 6 Aug) which might indicate the presence of birds from the South African breeding population. Birds in fresh plumage in N. Mwinilunga 22 Aug might be of the same origin (Palaearctic birds being worn at this time)[1,2]. Immatures fed by adults on the Copperbelt (24 Sep)[3] may also have been South African-bred.

Breeding No records.

Taxonomy No races recognized.

References [1]Brooke & Herroelen (1988); [2]Dowsett (in press b); [3]Robinson & Robinson (1975).

Northern Carmine Bee-eater *Merops nubicus*   B - **AV**

Distribution and Status *Afrotropical* (*breeds Mauritania to Kenya*). A single bird was filmed 5 Oct 1999 in a colony of *M. nubicoides* in the Nsefu sector of the Luangwa Valley (Bakabaka lagoon, 1231D, at 530 m)[1]. Doubtless an exceptional overshoot from the northern Tropics.

Taxonomy No races, now that *M.* (*nubicus*) *nubicoides* is treated as a separate species (see below).

References [1]Gurney *et al.* (2001).

Southern Carmine Bee-eater *Merops nubicoides*   B296 **AM/RB**

Distribution *Afrotropical* (*breeds Zambia-Malawi to South Africa, some wintering north to Kenya*). Occurs throughout the country on passage, but breeding (black squares) mostly in the low-lying valleys, being especially numerous in the Luangwa. There are many colonies of up to 300 pairs in the Luangwa Valley, and the largest known are of 2000 pairs, on the Luangwa River near the Kapamba confluence (in 2006)[4] and near Yakobe (in 1975)[1]. Elsewhere largest colonies reported have been 200 pairs near Luangwa town (Feira) and 75 holes on the Lungwebungu (Zambezi Dist.) in the 1950s[2], hundreds on the Zambezi above Mongu in 1981[6]. No survey has been undertaken such as that in Zimbabwe, which estimated 25,000 birds breeding in the 1980s, mostly in the Middle Zambezi[7]. *Alt.* 330-1770 m (Danger Hill).

Ecology Any light woodland or open savanna, but during the breeding season virtually restricted to the vicinity of rivers with sand cliffs, where it may breed in large colonies. Has also nested on flat sand beaches in W. Zambia, and attempted to do so in piles of sand during the construction of Itezhi-Tezhi Dam, Jul 1976[6].

Status Partially an intra-African migrant and breeding visitor. There are records throughout the year, but very few remain in the vicinity of the colonies during the rains, and flocks in plateau areas (Mar-

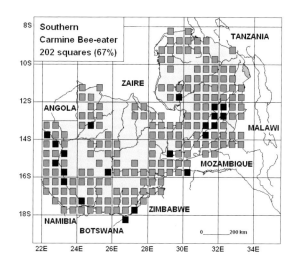

Apr and Aug-Sep in particular) are indicative of at least local migration[6]. A bird killed near Kasisi 9 Apr 1991 had a colour ring and wing tag, but its origin could not be determined[5].

Conservation Zambia holds a large proportion of the breeding population of this species. Nesting colonies outside strictly protected areas are likely to be raided by humans for food, as in Zimbabwe[7], but this has not been investigated in Zambia.

Breeding   Sep   Oct   Nov
(n=28)   16   7   5
Clutch: C/2 (3).

Taxonomy No races recognized. Treated by some authors as a race of *M. nubicus*[3], but we believe the differences in head pattern and voice are significant, and point to specific distinctness[4].

References [1]Baillie (1983); [2]Benson & White (1957); [3]Fry in del Hoyo *et al.* (2001); [4]Dowsett & Dowsett-Lemaire (1993); [5]Dowsett & Leonard (2001); [6]Dowsett & Leonard (in press a); [7]Feather (1997).

Coraciidae

Eurasian Roller *Coracias garrulus*   B302 **PW**

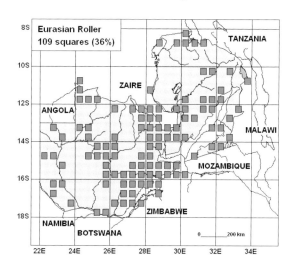

Distribution *Palaearctic (all winter in the Afrotropics, mainly Nigeria to South Africa).* Widespread in open country, but unrecorded from large parts of the dense miombo woodland of the north, and the *Baikiaea* forest mosaic of the south-west. *Alt.* 330-1800 m.

Ecology In any open woodland or wooded grassland, and in floodplains with scattered trees.

Status A Palaearctic migrant and winter visitor. All records fall between 12 Oct (Kaoma) and 9 May (Mwinilunga), with most on passage Nov and mid-Feb to late Mar. The average first date over 28 years was 9 Nov, the average last (in 21 years) 7 Apr[2]. Numerous in the past, in groups of up to 30 or exceptionally 50 in the 1970s, in recent years no more than 10 together[2]; this may reflect a real reduction in numbers, as in neighbouring Malawi[3], but there have also been fewer observers active in the field during the past 10 years.

Taxonomy[1] *C. g. garrulus* and *C. g. semenowi* are likely, as both occur in southern Africa (the latter with head and neck paler green, less saturated).

References [1]Clancey (1974a); [2]Dowsett (in press b); [3]Dowsett-Lemaire & Dowsett (2006).

Lilac-breasted Roller *Coracias caudatus*   B303 **RB**

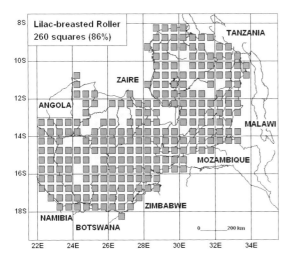

Distribution *Afrotropical* (*Ethiopia to South Africa*). Common almost throughout, but absent from some densely-wooded areas. *Alt.* 330-1700 m, wandering rarely to 1950 m (Nyika, Jan)[2].

Ecology In any light woodland, especially on edges, or in wooded or open grassland.

Status Resident, with local movements. Present in all months, but in many areas it is most frequently observed from Nov or Dec to Apr (after breeding). The pattern in the north-west, in Mwinilunga, is different, however, with the species abundant May-Sep and very rarely recorded in other months[1].

Breeding	Aug	Sep	Oct	Nov
(n=31)	2	16	8	5

Clutch: C/2 (2); C/3 (10).

Taxonomy[3] *C. c. caudatus.*

References [1]Dowsett (in press a); [2]Dowsett-Lemaire (2006a); [3]Irwin & Benson (1967b).

Racket-tailed Roller *Coracias spatulatus*   B304 **RB**

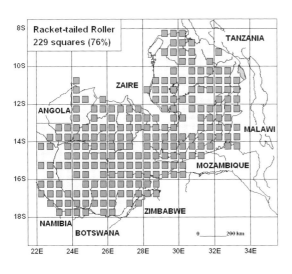

Distribution *Zambezian near-endemic* (*Tanzania to South Africa*). A widespread woodland bird, but locally distributed in the plains west of the Zambezi and in higher-rainfall areas such as parts of the north-west and Northern Province plateau; unrecorded from the lower Luapula[3]. *Alt.* 330-1800 m.

Ecology Not uncommon in mopane woodland and the drier types of miombo, usually where there are tall trees and little ground cover; also occurs in *Baikiaea* forest mosaic and mixed woodland, as in the south of Western Province.

Status Probably resident, with local wandering. Observations of this roller are significantly more numerous Jul-Nov, but they are more vocal then, when breeding, and there are records throughout the year.

Breeding	Sep	Oct	Nov	Dec		
(n=19)	4	11	3	1	*Clutch*: C/3 (2).	*Moult*: recorded Nov and Dec[4].

Taxonomy No races recognized. The pink-breasted form "*weigalli*"[2] is an immature plumage[1].

References [1]Benson & Benson (1975); [2]Clancey (1969b); [3]Dowsett (in press a); [4]Traylor (1965b).

Purple Roller *Coracias naevius* B305 **AM(B)**

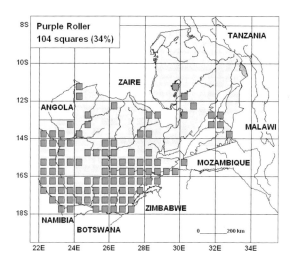

Distribution *Afrotropical (Mauritania to South Africa)*. Widespread in the open woodlands of the south and west, birds outside this area being on passage. Rarely in Mwinilunga and on the Copperbelt, to Chilubi Is.[5] and the Lukulu River (1230B)[1]. Occasional in the upper Luangwa Valley, and once on passage at Chipata (5 Jun)[3]. *Alt.* 350-1350 m, even wandering to 1450 m, rare below 880 m.

Ecology In any fairly open woodland or wooded savanna.

Status An intra-African migrant (and, perhaps, local breeding resident). The great majority of records fall between 6 Apr and 23 Nov; there is a handful of observations during the early rains, all from the south and west (where the species may be resident) except for a report of one near Kitwe 28 Nov. There is no definite record between 2 Jan and 5 Apr inclusive[3]. There have been big invasions in some drought years (e.g. 1992 and 1994), with far fewer in 1993 (after good rains)[3].

Breeding No definite records, but birds appeared to be strongly territorial and vocal in the Mulobezi area in Oct[3] (when the species nests in Zimbabwe)[2].

Taxonomy[4] *C. n. mosambicus*.

References [1]Benson & White (1957); [2]Benson *et al.* (1964); [3]Dowsett & Leonard (in press a); [4]Irwin & Benson (1966b); [5]Neave (1910).

Broad-billed Roller *Eurystomus glaucurus* B306 **AMB**

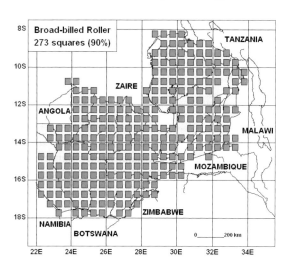

Distribution *Afrotropical (Senegal to South Africa and Madagascar)*. The race *suahelicus* is recorded throughout the country, being especially common in riparian situations. Specimens of the Malagasy nominate race are known from the east: L. Chishi, Kampinda, Kawambwa, Mpika[1] and Chitungulu[2]. However, dry season sight records suggest they might occur as far west as Kafue N.P. and Livingstone[4]. *Alt.* 330-1900 m, with a vagrant as high as 2100 m on the Mafingas 20 Oct[3] (and higher on the Malawi side of the Nyika)[5].

Ecology Any woodland, but principally miombo and on the edges of drier riparian forest.

Status *E. g. suahelicus* is an intra-African migrant and breeding visitor. Extreme dates for the species as a whole are 15 Aug (Hillwood) and 19 May (Kafue N.P.). Specimens of the Malagasy nominate race are dated 15 Oct to 24 Nov, and 26 Feb. First arrivals (including large numbers 22 Aug) are in the north-west and on the Copperbelt[4]. Flocks and concentrations of 30 up to 100 are frequent after breeding, mid-Jan to early Mar[4].

Breeding   Sep   Oct   Nov
(n=28)   1   13   14   *Clutch*: C/1 (1); C/2 (1); C/3 (2).

Taxonomy *E. g. suahelicus* is the breeding form, the larger *E. g. glaucurus* a non-breeding migrant from the Malagasy region.

References [1]Benson (1956d); [2]Benson (1960d); [3]Clay (1953); [4]Dowsett & Leonard (in press a); [5]Dowsett-Lemaire (2006a).

Phoeniculidae

Red-billed Wood Hoopoe *Phoeniculus purpureus*   B308 **RB**

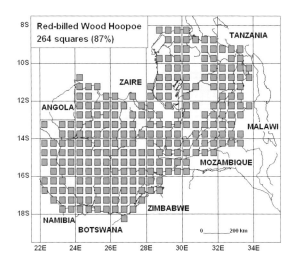

Red-billed Wood Hoopoe
264 squares (87%)

Distribution *Afrotropical* (*Mauritania to South Africa*). Throughout most of the country and usually common (although it seems to be genuinely absent from parts of N. Zambia)[1]. *Alt.* 330-1700 m.

Ecology Any woodland, dry forest and thickets, gleaning largely on tree trunks, and nesting in tree holes. Most often in large monospecific groups.

Status Resident.

Breeding   Mar   Apr   May   Jun   Jul
(n=85)   4   5   5   2   2
                  Aug   Sep   Oct   Nov
                  10   34   21   2

Clutch: C/1 (1); C/2 (6); C/3 (12); C/4 (17); C/5 (3); C/6 (2). *Moult*: noted Nov[3].

Taxonomy[2] In the west birds approach *P. p. angolensis*, and in the centre and east *P. p. marwitzi* (on average shorter-winged).

References [1]Dowsett (in press a); [2]Irwin & Benson (1966a); [3]Traylor (1965b).

Scimitarbill *Phoeniculus cyanomelas*   B309 **RB**

Distribution *Afrotropical* (*Somalia to South Africa*). Throughout the woodlands of Zambia, even more widespread than *P. purpureus*. *Alt.* 330-1700 m, exceptionally wandering to 2150 m (Nyika)[7].

Ecology Any woodland, dry forest and thickets, probing on the smaller branches and outermost twigs. Not in large monospecific groups (unlike *P. purpureus*), but often joining mixed bird parties.

Status Resident.

Breeding   Aug   Sep   Oct
(n=33)   3   17   13
Clutch: C/2 (11); C/3 (6); C/4 (2).

Taxonomy *P. c. schalowi*, replaced in the north-west by the short-tailed *P. c. anomalus* (type locality South Lueti River; *FMNH*)[10] and with a tendency towards *P. c. cyanomelas* (even shorter-tailed) in the

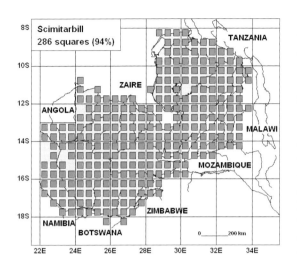

south-west[1,2]. The suggestion that there are two species in W. Zambia (*P. aterrimus anomalus* in *Acacia*, and *P. c. schalowi* in miombo) is for the moment rejected[1,5], although the matter should be investigated further. *P. a. anomalus* (or *anchietae*) is described as having the bill slender and arched, with black tomia (cutting edges), as opposed to the long, decurved bill (with pale tomia) of *P. c. schalowi*[10]. But intergrades occur in W. Zambia[1], and even within Angola *anchietae* shows considerable variation[10]. It has been suggested in addition that there are vocal differences between *P. aterrimus* and *P. cyanomelas*[4,8], but in our experience this is not so[3]. We had earlier placed this species in the genus *Rhinopomastus*[6], following the DNA studies of Sibley & Monroe[9] (putting it in a separate family, Rhinopomastidae, or sub-family)[4]; but we did so with reservations, in part because the Forest Wood Hoopoe *P. castaneiceps* is a linking species, with both the rattles or laughter of other *Phoeniculus* and the isolated whistles of the *Rhinopomastus*[6]. We now revert to the genus *Phoeniculus*, pending further study of all the species.

References [1]Benson & Irwin (1965d); [2]Benson & Irwin (1967b); [3]Chappuis (2000); [4]Ligon in del Hoyo *et al.* (2001); [5]Dowsett (in press a); [6]Dowsett & Dowsett-Lemaire (1993); [7]Dowsett-Lemaire (2006a); [8]Ligon & Davidson in Fry *et al.* (1988); [9]Sibley & Monroe (1990); [10]Traylor (1964: 81).

Upupidae

Hoopoe *Upupa epops*   B307 **RB/AM**

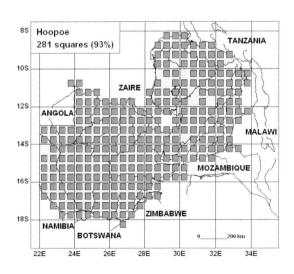

Distribution *Old World* (*in the Afrotropics, Mauritania to South Africa; Palaearctic birds winter mainly south to Kenya*). Throughout, in lightly-wooded country. *Alt.* 330-1700 m.

Ecology Any open woodland and wooded savanna. Nests usually in holes in termite mounds or banks[3]. Frequently seen on dirt roads. Usually singly or in pairs; does not accompany bird parties.

Status Resident, but with a dry season influx. Present in all months, but frequency is significantly greater May-Dec than Jan-Apr[1].

Breeding   Aug   Sep   Oct   Nov
(n=45)   2   23   18   2
Clutch: C/3 (1); C/4 (2); C/5 (1); C/6 (2).

Taxonomy[2] *U. e. africana* (sometimes treated as a distinct species). The Palaearctic *U. e. epops* (paler, with more white in the wing) may occur as a vagrant.

References [1]Dowsett (in press a); [2]Irwin & Benson (1966b); [3]Tucker (1975a).

Bucerotidae

Red-billed Hornbill *Tockus erythrorhynchus*   B311 **RB**

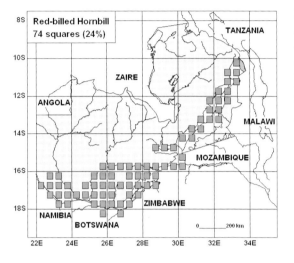

Distribution *Afrotropical* (*Mauritania to South Africa*). Common in the mopane (and to a lesser extent *Acacia*) woodlands of the south and the Luangwa Valley. In the south-west up the Zambezi to Nangweshi[1] and the Mashi to Lupuka. In the Kafue drainage from the Nanzhila area and along the southern edge of the Kafue Flats. Through much of the Southern Province plateau and the Middle Zambezi, throughout the Luano Valley, and the Luangwa north to Kampumbu and Nganjo[4]. *Alt.* 330-1300 m.

Ecology Mopane and *Acacia* woodland, feeding usually on the ground.

Status Resident.

Breeding	Jan	Feb	Mar
(n=11)	1	6	4

Clutch: C/4 (1).

Taxonomy[2,3] *T. e. ngamiensis* in Western Province, tending towards the smaller *T. e. degens* further east.

References [1]Benson & Irwin (1967b); [2]Benson *et al.* (1971a); [3]Clancey (1972a); [4]Dowsett (in press a).

Southern Yellow-billed Hornbill *Tockus leucomelas*   B312 **RB**

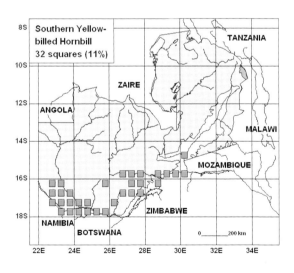

Distribution *Afrotropical* (*Angola to South Africa*). Unlike the smaller, mopane-associated *T. erythrorhynchus*, this hornbill is principally in *Acacia*, and is surprisingly absent from the upper Luangwa and most of the Gwembe Valley. It occurs in the south-west up the Zambezi from near Livingstone to Nangweshi[3]. Locally on the Southern Province plateau and along the southern edge of the Kafue Flats[5], thence in the Middle Zambezi from Chipepo[2] down to Luangwa town (Feira)[1]. Further north known only as a wanderer to Mkunkunya, just west of the Luangwa Bridge[6]. *Alt.* 330-1250 m.

Ecology *Acacia* woodland, wooded grassland or thicket-clump savanna, less often mopane; usually feeding on the ground. Crop and stomach contents have included beetles, termites, grasshoppers and seeds[6].

Status Resident.

Breeding	Oct
(n=1)	1

Clutch: no data.

Taxonomy[4,8] Perhaps *T. l. parvior*, with a local tendency towards the longer-winged *T. l. leucomelas* in the west. Previously considered conspecific with the Northern Yellow-billed Hornbill *T. flavirostris*[7]. **References** [1]Benson (1960d); [2]Benson (1962a); [3]Benson (1964f); [4]Benson & Irwin (1967b); [5]Dowsett (1966b); [6]Dowsett (in press a); [7]Dowsett & Dowsett-Lemaire (1993); [8]Irwin & Benson (1966a).

Crowned Hornbill *Tockus alboterminatus*   B314 **RB**

Distribution *Afrotropical (Ethiopia to South Africa)*. Common in the denser woodlands of the country, almost throughout except for the extreme south-west. West of the Zambezi, absent south of Kalabo[7] until Imusho[3]. Occurs in all eastern highlands: Mafingas[4], Makutu[2] and Nyika[6]. *Alt.* 330-2200 m.
Ecology Any tall woodland, particularly well-developed miombo. Also in deciduous and evergreen forest (including *Cryptosepalum*), riparian and montane rain forest. Mainly an arboreal feeder, but also feeding on termites on the wing. It appears more insectivorous than frugivorous[5], and frequently takes dwarf chameleons[3,6].
Status Resident. No real sign of movements, apart from local flocking (often up to 50-60) outside the breeding season[3].
Breeding   Aug   Sep   Oct   Nov   Feb
(n=10)   1   6   1   1   1   *Clutch*: no data.
Taxonomy[1] *T. a. geloensis*; replaced in the east and south-east by *T. a. suahelicus* (paler, more greyish-brown).
References [1]Benson (1956f); [2]Dowsett (1971h); [3]Dowsett (in press a); [4]Dowsett & Stjernstedt (1973); [5]Dowsett-Lemaire (1988b); [6]Dowsett-Lemaire (2006a); [7]Traylor & Hart (1965).

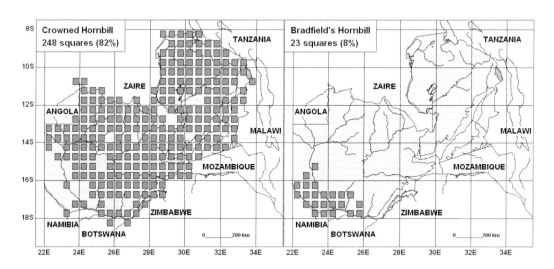

Bradfield's Hornbill *Tockus bradfieldi*   B315 **R(B)**

Distribution *Zambezian endemic (Angola to Zimbabwe)*. Locally common in the dry Kalahari sands woodland of the south-west, especially east of the Zambezi (from Masese to Simonga). It ranges north to Lushushwa and Namushakende[1], and further east may be seasonally common near Livingstone[2,5]. [Reports of wanderers to Ngoma and Muckle Neuk are unconfirmed[2], but possibly correct, as extensive movements are known in NW Zimbabwe[4].] The species reaches its northern limit in SW Zambia.

Alt. 950-1200 m.

Ecology Virtually confined to *Baikiaea* forest, less often in mixed, undifferentiated *Burkea-Combretum* woodland. Crop contents have included Dipterous larvae and termites[1,2]; also feeds on fruit (e.g. arillate seeds of *Sterculia quinqualoba*). Pairs occasionally join bird parties.

Status Resident, but groups of up to 8 wander locally May-Sep.

Breeding No records. In Zimbabwe, egg-laying recorded Sep and Nov[3].

Taxonomy No races recognized.

References [1]Benson & Irwin (1967b); [2]Dowsett (in press a); [3]Irwin (1981a); [4]Irwin (1982a); [5]Winterbottom (1952).

Pale-billed Hornbill *Tockus pallidirostris* B313 **RB**

Distribution *Zambezian endemic* (*Tanzania to Zambia-Malawi*). Fairly common in the plateau woodlands of north-central Zambia, west of the Zambezi only in the Sikongo area. Occurs south to Nawinda, and east on the Southern Province plateau to Simamba. Absent below the escarpments of the Luangwa and Middle Zambezi Valleys, but occurs along the edge of the latter, south to the Chirundu area and Chikankata[1]. *Alt.* 650-1700 m.

Ecology Endemic to miombo woodland, both the denser formations in the northern half of the country and drier areas. A frequent member of bird parties.

Status Resident.

Breeding Sep Nov
(n=3) 2 1 *Clutch*: no data.

Taxonomy *T. p. pallidirostris*, with *T. p. neumanni* (bill with a red tip) east of the Luangwa Valley (with intermediates at Kasama)[2].

References [1]Dowsett (in press a); [2]Irwin & Benson (1966a).

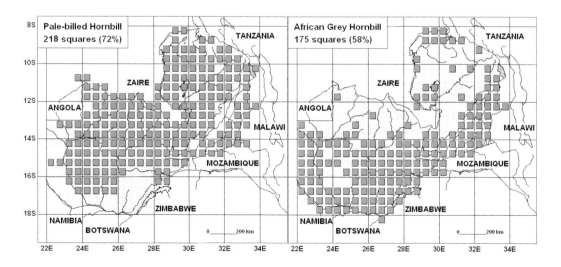

African Grey Hornbill *Tockus nasutus* B310 **RB**

Distribution *Afrotropical* (*Mauritania to South Africa*). Throughout the dry woodlands of the south and east, and usually very common. Its normal distribution in the west is north to Chizera[4], to Chunga (upper Kafue), and in the east throughout the Luangwa Valley and Eastern Province plateau. Scarce or rare in the Lusaka and Kabwe areas. It is present in the Luapula Valley, the low country between Lakes Mweru and Tanganyika, and locally in the Chambeshi drainage. Birds have very occasionally turned up outside this area, rarely in cultivation at Mwinilunga[1] for example, between Kasempa and Solwezi and at Luanshya[2]. *Alt.* 330-1600 m.

Ecology Any woodland, but most typically in the drier types of miombo, *Baikiaea* forest mosaic, mopane and *Acacia*. In dense miombo it is replaced by *T. pallidirostris*, the two occurring together in degraded miombo, as in parts of the upper Luangwa Valley. Mainly arboreal; like other hornbills feeds frequently on emerging termites, and has also been reported eating the arillate seeds of *Trichilia*[2].

Status Recorded throughout the year in most places, and probably resident in the south, although the few records of stragglers to the north are (not surprisingly) in the non-breeding season, May-Jul. Often in large groups of up to 30 in the dry season, with 100 roosting in *Typha* reedbeds near Choma in May and 70 near Kafue late Aug[2].

Breeding   Aug   Sep   Oct   Dec
(n=31)   2   15   12   2   *Clutch*: C/1 (1); C/2 (2); C/3 (1).
Moult: three adults were half-way through in mid-Nov[3].

Taxonomy *T. n. epirhinus*.

References [1]Bowen (1983j); [2]Dowsett (in press a); [3]Traylor (1965b); [4]White (1945-46).

Trumpeter Hornbill *Bycanistes bucinator*   B316 **RB**

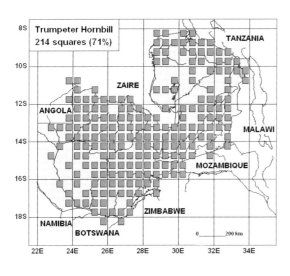

Distribution *Afrotropical (Kenya to South Africa)*. Widespread in densely-wooded country, thus throughout most of Zambia, except the far west, where it occurs beyond the Zambezi only in the Kalabo area[1], otherwise reaching that river at various places between Chavuma and Kalobolelwa[2]. However, it is absent from large parts of the Luapula and Chambeshi Rivers, and unrecorded from Lundazi or north from there, until the Nyika is reached. *Alt.* 330-1900 m, seasonally up to 2150 m on the Nyika Plateau[3].

Ecology Evergreen and deciduous forest, riparian forest, thickets, and rich woodland (principally miombo), especially where there are fig trees, occasionally in suburban gardens. Scarce in *Cryptosepalum* forest. Readily feeds on emerging termites, otherwise mainly frugivorous, e.g. taking the arils of *Sterculia africana*, the fruits of *Diospyros* and very partial to figs[2].

Status Resident, with some local movements seasonally. A few pairs move to the Nyika forests in late Aug-Mar and likely breed there. Often in parties of 20 or more Mar-Oct, maxima 70 roosting in mushitu near Chingola, and over 40 in the Luangwa Valley, both in Jun[2].

Breeding   Oct   Nov
(n=5)   4   1   *Clutch*: no data.

Taxonomy No races recognized.

References [1]Benson & White (1957); [2]Dowsett (in press a); [3]Dowsett-Lemaire (2006a).

Silvery-cheeked Hornbill *Bycanistes brevis*   B - **AMB**

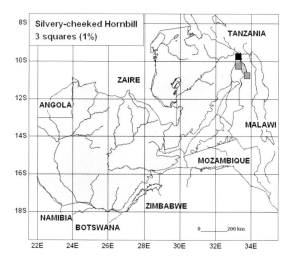

Distribution *Afromontane/Eastern* (*Ethiopia to South Africa*). An occasional visitor to the montane forests of the eastern highlands (first reported 1975), from the Mafingas[1] (where it has nested, black square)[2], Nyikamwaka[7] and Nyika Plateau[5]. *Alt.* 1500 (Mafingas) to 2200 m (Nyika, wandering higher on Malawi side).
Ecology In the canopy of montane forest. The one Zambian nest was high up in a dead broken-off *Newtonia* trunk, some 20-30 m off the ground[2]. Mainly frugivorous[3], and clearly competes with *B. bucinator*[4].
Status Only a rare vagrant to Nyika (few records from Sep-Dec, once in Apr)[5] and elsewhere in NE Zambia (mid-May and Dec). Extreme dates overall in Zambia are 5 Sep-19 Dec and 9 Apr-19 May[2]. Most likely these originate from the large breeding population in the nearby Misuku Hills, Malawi[6].
Breeding Noisy nest occupant fed by male, Dec 2005, suggestive of egg-laying 2-3 months earlier[2].
Taxonomy No races recognized.
References [1]Aspinwall (1977c); [2]Dowsett & Leonard (in press a); [3]Dowsett-Lemaire (1988b); [4]Dowsett-Lemaire (1989b); [5]Dowsett-Lemaire (2006a); [6]Dowsett-Lemaire & Dowsett (2006); [7]Osborne (1975d).

Southern Ground Hornbill *Bucorvus leadbeateri*   B317 **RB**

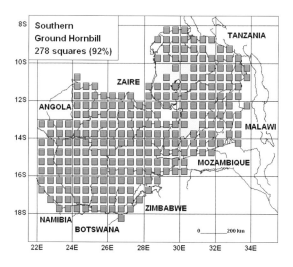

Distribution *Afrotropical* (*Kenya to South Africa*). Throughout the country, except so far unrecorded from part of the heavily-populated Luapula Valley[4]. *Alt.* 330-2200 m.
Ecology Any open or dense woodland (including thick miombo), wooded grassland with thicket clumps, also in floodplains, dambos and montane grassland. Feeds on the ground, taking in particular snakes (and even a sub-adult hare *Lepus* sp. has been recorded)[1]. Occurs in family groups.
Status Resident.

Breeding	Jul	Aug	Sep
(n=22)	3	1	5
	Oct	Nov	Dec
	8	4	1

Clutch: C/2 (5).
Taxonomy No races recognized. Now called *B. leadbeateri*[2,3], rather than *B. cafer* as in many references.
References [1]Benson (1962a); [2]Brooke & Kemp (1973); [3]Browning (1992); [4]Dowsett (in press a).

Lybiidae (ex-Capitonidae)

Anchieta's Barbet *Stactolaema anchietae*   B323 **RB**

Distribution *Zambezian endemic* (*S. Zaire to W. Zambia*). Inhabits the miombo woodlands and riparian forests of central Zambia, generally to the west and south of the closely-related *S. whytii*. In the west occurs to the southern part of Mongu Dist.[8] (the most southerly records of the species), in the Kafue drainage to the NW Lukanga Swamps and Chilenga[7]. It thence ranges north to the Kanchibya River (Mpika Dist.)[2]. It reappears to the north-east of L. Mweru at Kasangu[5], alongside *S. whytii*. Their main zone of overlap extends north and east to the Chilonga and Mbati areas[3], a total of some 70,000 sq. km. *Alt.* 1000-1770 m (Danger Hill).

Ecology In miombo woodland (and *Burkea* variants), usually in the canopy of the better developed types, and also recorded in fringing *Syzygium* forest and mushitu. Groups of up to 6, including helpers, nest in holes in dead stumps or branches in miombo woodland and clearings, 2-10 m high[4]. Essentially frugivorous. Occurs in the same woodland as *S. whytii* at several places on the Copperbelt (e.g. Misaka and Mufulira), and the more common of the two there. On one occasion singles of each species were seen, on the same branch (50 cm apart), over the Kafubu stream, apparently not interacting[3]. But when nesting, they are aggressive towards *S. whytii*, as well as towards other barbets[6].

Status Resident.

Breeding[4,6] Sep   Oct
(n=5)   4   1   *Clutch*: C/5 (1).

Taxonomy[1] *S. a. katangae*, with some tendency in the north-west towards *S. a. anchietae* (yellow on the breast less extensive, and crown less greenish yellow).

References [1]Benson (1962a); [2]Benson *et al.* (1961); [3]Dowsett (in press a); [4]Short & Horne in Fry *et al.* (1988); [5]Leonard (1998d); [6]Payne (1967); [7]Tree (1966a); [8]Winterbottom (1942a).

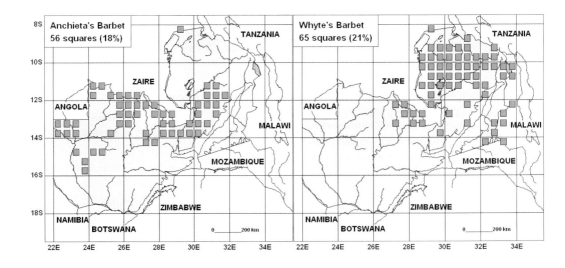

Whyte's Barbet *Stactolaema whytii*   B324 **RB**

Distribution *Zambezian endemic* (*SW Tanzania to Zimbabwe*). The eastern half of the country, on the Eastern Province plateau from east of Lundazi to near Katete. North of the Luangwa Valley, ranges south along the escarpment to Masase[2], and from Kasangu near L. Mweru to the Copperbelt, west to Kalilele and Funda Dambo[2]. Common in the area Luwingu to Mansa and around Kasama. *Alt.* 950-1800 m (Nyikamwaka). For overlap with *S. anchietae*, see above.

Ecology Inhabits the edges of evergreen forest (perhaps more often in riparian than is the sibling *S. anchietae*), and also miombo woodland. Nests were 2-10 m up in dead stumps of live *Ficus* sp. or *"Brachystegia"* trees[3]. When nesting, groups of up to 6 birds, including helpers. Territories estimated at 5 ha (nests as close to each other as 100 m)[3]. Frugivorous, except that young nestlings are fed insects[3]. Occasionally in bird parties.

Status Resident.

Breeding Nests "with incubating adults and nestling" Oct-Nov[3].

Taxonomy There are reputedly at least three races in Zambia: *S. w. stresemanni*, replaced by *S. w. angoniensis* (with cheek stripe white, not pale yellow: type locality 20 miles SSE of Chipata, *NMZB*)[1] in Eastern Province and by *S. w. buttoni* (centre of crown bluish-black, not pale yellow: type locality Ndola, *OUM*)[4], named for E.L. Button, from Kawambwa to the Copperbelt.

References [1]Benson (1964a: 3); [2]Dowsett (in press a); [3]Short & Horne in Fry *et al.* (1988); [4]White (1945a: 18).

Moustached Green Tinkerbird *Pogoniulus leucomystax*   B325 **RB**

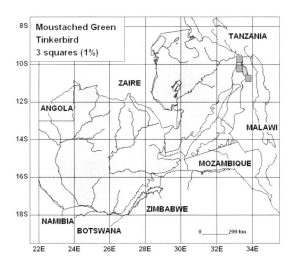

Distribution *Afromontane endemic* (*Kenya to Malawi*). Common in the montane forests of the Mafingas[2] and the Nyika Plateau[4]. *Alt.* 1950 m (Mafingas) to 2200 m (Nyika).

Ecology At all levels in montane forest, including edges. Highly dependent on fruit of mistletoe species, especially *Englerina inaequilatera*: pairs move to breed in small patches when this common mistletoe is fruiting. The surrounds of nest holes are decorated with the sticky seeds of mistletoe berries[3]. It also feeds to a great extent on insects, caught by flycatching in gaps in the mid-stratum. Highly territorial, with 1-2 pairs/ha on the SW Nyika[4].

Status Resident on the Zambian Nyika, although in some parts of Malawi there are limited altitudinal or inter-montane movements.

Breeding   Sep Oct Nov Dec
(n=81)   5   54   19   3   (Including 59 from Malawi side of SW Nyika.)

Clutch: no data, but many N/2.

Moult: after breeding, as 30 birds Aug-Feb showed no signs of moult[1].

Taxonomy *P. l. meridionalis*.

References [1]Dowsett (in press a); [2]Dowsett & Stjernstedt (1973); [3]Dowsett-Lemaire (1988b); [4]Dowsett-Lemaire (1989b).

Yellow-fronted Tinkerbird *Pogoniulus chrysoconus*   B326 **RB**

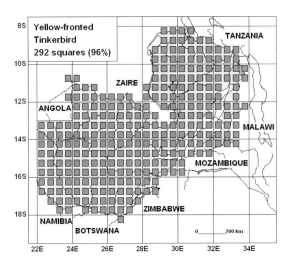

Distribution *Afrotropical* (*Senegal to South Africa*). Common throughout, in any woodland. *Alt.* 330-2000 m (Mafingas)[3].

Ecology In all woodland types and wooded grassland, riparian woodland and dry thickets. Rarely at edges of evergreen forest, but common in the canopy of dry *Cryptosepalum* forest (mixed with *Brachystegia*), next to *P. bilineatus*[2]. Occasionally in bird parties.

Status Resident.

Breeding	Aug	Sep	Oct
(n=48)	3	17	18
	Nov	Dec	May
	8	1	1

Clutch: C/1 (1); C/2 (14); C/3 (17).

Moult: adults noted Aug-Nov[2].

Taxonomy[5] *P. c. extoni* (syn. *P. c. rhodesiae*, type locality Chambeshi Valley[4], *NHM*; though some would recognise it)[1].

References [1]Clancey (1968c); [2]Dowsett (in press a); [3]Dowsett & Stjernstedt (1973); [4]Grant (1915b: 100); [5]Irwin & Benson (1967a).

Golden-rumped Tinkerbird *Pogoniulus bilineatus*   B327 **RB**

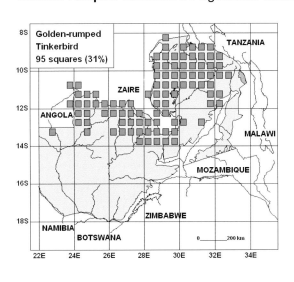

Distribution *Afrotropical* (*The Gambia to South Africa*). In forest and thicket in the northern half of the country, west of the Muchinga escarpment, and locally very common. In the west, south to just over the Zambezi at Muyeke and Mbulo[4], and to Mayau[2]. Throughout the Copperbelt south to Luansobe, thence east to the Muchingas near Mupamadzi[3], and throughout the north, east to Isoka town[1]. *Alt.* 950-1770 m (Danger Hill).

Ecology Moist evergreen forest, also dry *Cryptosepalum* (abundant at Mayau) and *Marquesia* forest, transition woodland at Ndola (common)[5], and richer riparian forest.

Status Resident.

Breeding	Sep	
(n=1)	1	*Clutch*: no data.

Moult: several adults were moulting in Aug[3].

Taxonomy *P. b. mfumbiri*.

References [1]Aspinwall (1977f); [2]Benson & Irwin (1965a); [3]Dowsett (in press a); [4]Leonard (1998b); [5]Madge (1972b).

[White-chested Tinkerbird *Pogoniulus makawai*   **B328 R?**
Known only from the unique type specimen (*NHM*; named for Jali Makawa) collected in *Cryptosepalum* forest near Mayau, 6 Sep 1964[1] and treated by some authorities as a good species[3], but may well be an aberrant *P. bilineatus*[4]. In the absence of DNA analysis of the type, and rediscovery of this taxon in the field, its status must remain uncertain. Attempts have been made to locate similar birds at the type locality, but so far without success. *"P. makawai"* is classed as "Vulnerable"[2]. **References** [1]Benson & Irwin (1965g: 6); [2]BirdLife International (2000, 2004a); [3]Collar & Fishpool (2006); [4]Dowsett & Dowsett-Lemaire (1993).]

Spot-flanked Barbet *Tricholaema lacrymosa*   B - R(B)

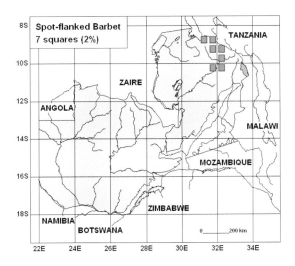

Distribution *Afrotropical* (*Sudan to Zambia*). Occurs locally in lightly-wooded areas in the upper Chambeshi, south to Mbesuma[1,2] and Malole, and along the Tanzanian border, west to Kawimbe, near Mbala[3]. First found in 1972, these are the most southerly records of the species. *Alt.* 1230 (Mbesuma) to 1750 m (Kawimbe).
Ecology *Acacia* scrub on ant-hills (as on floodplains) and often located in fig trees.
Status Resident.
Breeding No records.
Taxonomy *T. l. ruahae.*
References [1]Aspinwall (1973c); [2]Dowsett *et al.* (1999a); [3]Dowsett (in press a).

Acacia Pied Barbet *Tricholaema leucomelas*   B321 RB

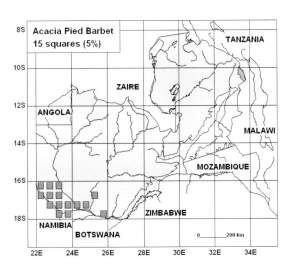

Distribution *Afrotropical* (*NW Angola to South Africa*). Enters Zambia in the south-west corner, north to Shangombo and the southern edge of the Matabele Plain[1], east to 6 km south-west of Machile[4] and sparsely to Livingstone[2]. *Alt.* 950-1050 m.
Ecology *Acacia* woodland, penetrating into the interior of *Baikiaea* forest (as at Livingstone), where it meets *T. frontata*, and whence hybrids are known. Mixed pairs have also been observed further west, in the Simungoma area[5] (see also under next species). Occupies a discrete dry *Acacia* niche, perhaps coming into contact with such species as *Lybius torquatus* only where there are fruiting trees.

Status Resident.

Breeding   Nov   Dec   Mar

(n=3)   1   1   1   *Clutch*: no data.

Taxonomy[3] *T. l. affinis*. Has hybridized with *T. frontata* (see below). Formerly placed in the genus *Lybius*[6].

References [1]Benson (1964f); [2]Benson & White (1960); [3]Benson *et al.* (1971a); [4]Bruce-Miller & Dowsett (1977); [5]Dowsett (in press a); [6]Dowsett & Dowsett-Lemaire (1993).

Miombo Pied Barbet *Tricholaema frontata* B322 **RB**

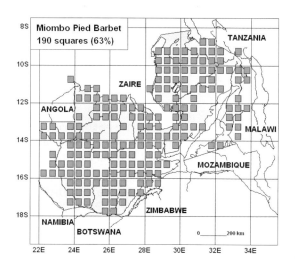

Miombo Pied Barbet
190 squares (63%)

Distribution *Zambezian near-endemic (S. Congo-Brazzaville and Angola to Zambia, where it reaches the southern limit of its range)*. Throughout most of the plateau miombo woodlands of Zambia. Unrecorded between Lakes Mweru and Tanganyika and in the extreme south-west; in the far west, south to the South Lueti River[6], otherwise to the Zambezi itself at Kalobolelwa and Livingstone[2]. On the Eastern Province plateau no further west than the Nyanje area[3]. Absent from the Luangwa and Gwembe Valleys, in the latter area only in the escarpment woodlands. *Alt.* 950-1700 m, rarely down to 650 m.

Ecology Miombo woodland (including *Burkea* variants), and in mixed miombo/ *Baikiaea* at places from Livingstone to Sesheke, feeding mainly in the canopy. Also in *Cryptosepalum* forest (where rare in the canopy, and mainly where it is mixed with *Brachystegia*). Replaced in *Acacia* by the closely-related *T. leucomelas*. Hybrids between these two have occurred at Livingstone (1725D)[1], where *T. leucomelas* penetrates the understorey of *Baikiaea*[4]. Several mixed pairs have been observed in the area of Simungoma to Sesheke (1724A,B), in degraded *Baikiaea*[3]. The voices of the two are very similar, and they react strongly to each other's vocalisations on tape-playback[3]. Often present in bird parties.

Status Resident.

Breeding   Sep   Oct   Nov   Dec

(n=16)   6   8   1   1   *Clutch*: C/2 (1); C/2 (3); C/3 (2) & N/3 (1).

Taxonomy[4] No races recognized; *T. f. alexandri* (type locality Namwewe; *NHM*)[5] is a synonym, named for Boyd Alexander. *T. frontata* has in the past been considered a race of *T. leucomelas*, and the two hybridize in part of S. Zambia.

References [1]Benson & Irwin (1967b); [2]Benson & White (1960); [3]Dowsett (in press a); [4]Irwin & Benson (1967a); [5]Shelley (1903: 61); [6]Traylor (1965b).

Black-collared Barbet *Lybius torquatus* B320 **RB**

Distribution *Afrotropical (Kenya to South Africa)*. Throughout the country, locally very common. *Alt.* 330-1800 m.

Ecology Any woodland, but perhaps absent from virgin miombo and some mopane. Also occurs

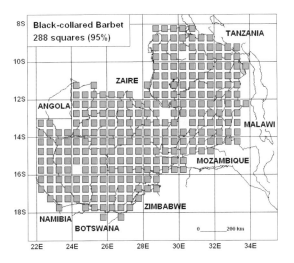

frequently on the edges of riparian forest. It appears rather unspecialized, though as with so many of the larger barbets is often associated with the presence of fig trees *Ficus* spp.

Status Resident.

Breeding	Sep	Oct	Nov	Dec
(n=171)	54	62	31	9
	Jan	Feb	Mar	
	7	5	3	

Clutch: C/2 (1); C/3 (3); C/4 (2).

Moult: late Oct-Apr (starting date probably depending on whether the bird bred early or not: one ringed individual moulted at much the same time in two successive years)[3].

Taxonomy[2,4] *L. t. lucidiventris*, but with an approach to *L. t. bocagei* (darker red on the head, darker mantle) especially in W. Zambia, and apparently to *L. t. zombae* (birds with the throat paler brick-red) in the extreme east[1].

References [1]Benson (1946); [2]Clancey (1968c); [3]Dowsett (in press a); [4]Irwin & Benson (1966b).

Chaplin's (Zambian) Barbet *Lybius chaplini*   B319 **RB**

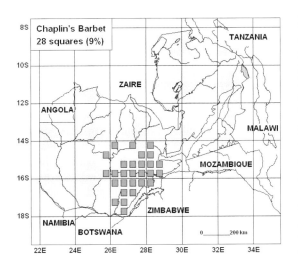

Distribution *Zambezian endemic (the only species endemic to Zambia)*. The centre of this species's distribution is an area of some 20,000 sq. km based on the southern Kafue basin, south to Choma (where locally not uncommon in the past, elsewhere being rare). There are irregular records from further afield, from Ntemwa camp[3] and Chilenga[12] in the upper Kafue down to Itezhi-Tezhi[3], east to Chalimbana[14], and as far south in Kalomo Dist. as Kabanga[14]. At these peripheral localities the species may be absent over long periods of time, and this is even the case at Blue Lagoon, near the centre of distribution, and where the species has nevertheless bred at times[7]. This relict distribution is difficult to explain. *Alt.* 980-1350 m.

Ecology Usually found in fig trees, *Ficus* spp. (especially *F. sycomorus*), in more open or lightly-wooded country, and it does not normally appear to be associated with either riparian forest or miombo woodland. While it is absent from the higher-rainfall areas of Zambia (where the same *Ficus* spp. occur), this is true too of the drier areas of the west (whereas White-headed Barbet *L. leucocephalus* is in part a bird of arid and semi-arid regions). Nests in holes in trees (especially figs), 5-18 m up. The extent to which it might feed on fruit other than figs has not been studied. As a rule in pairs or family groups of 5-6, but more at fruiting trees on occasion. There is inter-specific competition for nest sites with the similar-sized *L. torquatus* (they never nest in the same tree, and *L. chaplini* seems to be dominant)[7]. Some aspects of its vocal and other behaviour have been described[9].

Status Resident.

Conservation Classed as "Near Threatened"[2]. Clearly dependent on large fig trees with medium-sized fruit, and in the 1940s numbers of the barbet at Mazabuka declined noticeably when fig trees died[13]. This may be the explanation for its irregular occurrence in some areas (especially peripheral ones). The distribution, health and vulnerability to human activities of *Ficus sycomorus* in this area has obvious relevance for the conservation of this barbet, but its general diet needs to be studied. In some areas dead trees, still suitable for nesting, have been cut down for firewood. Present only irregularly in previously favoured areas (e.g. Muckle Neuk and Blue Lagoon N.P.) and for practical purposes no longer in any nationally protected area. Still present in small numbers on private property in Choma, Monze and Chisamba Dists[7].

Breeding[5,10]

	Aug	Sep	Oct	Nov	Feb
(n=27)	2	15	8	1	1

Details of the Feb record[1] have not been traced, and may result from a misreading of data in an earlier checklist.

Clutch: C/2 (4); C/3 (2); C/4 (2). 8 of 17 nests were parasitized by *Indicator minor*[11].

Moult: an adult in Mar was half-way through[7].

Taxonomy[8] No races recognized. The type locality of this, the only Zambian endemic species, is Maala, near Namwala[4,6] (*NHM*, named for Sir Drummond Chaplin). Forms a superspecies with *L. leucocephalus*; far removed from populations of that barbet (the nearest being in W. Angola and SW Tanzania). Although at times considered conspecific with *L. leucocephalus*, *L. chaplini*'s colour pattern is unlike that of all populations of that species.

References [1]Benson *et al.* (1971a); [2]BirdLife International (2000, 2004a); [3]Brooke (1966c); [4]Clarke (1920: 50); [5]Colebrook-Robjent & Stjernstedt (1976); [6]Dowsett (1980b); [7]Dowsett (in press a); [8]Goodwin (1964); [9]Short & Horne (1985); [10]Short & Horne (1988); [11]Spottiswoode *et al.* (2005); [12]Tree (1966a); [13]Winterbottom (1944); [14]Winterbottom (1951-52).

Black-backed Barbet *Lybius minor* B318 **RB**

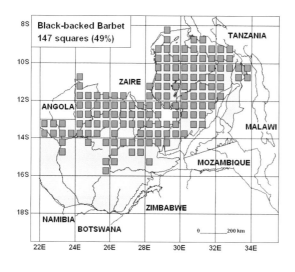

Black-backed Barbet
147 squares (49%)

Distribution *Zambezian near-endemic (SE Gabon to central Zambia, where it reaches the southern limit of its range)*. A discreet forest-edge species, throughout N. Zambia, west of the Muchingas. In the Upper Zambezi occurs south to Tiger camp (Lukulu Dist.)[7], and in the Kafue basin to a few km north of Itezhi-Tezhi[1]. In central Zambia, normally south to Malambanyama and Mita Hills, exceptionally to Huntley farm near Chisamba and Trotover near Lusaka[7]. Absent from the Luangwa Valley proper, but occurs in several riparian strips at the foot of the Muchingas, as at Julius[4,5]. Absent from Eastern Province south of the Nyika. *Alt.* mainly 900-1700 m, as low as 680 m (Julius, perhaps as wanderers).

Ecology On the edge of rich riparian or evergreen forest, including fringing *Syzygium*, also in *Cryptosepalum* forest (where rare) and thickets, or cover on termite mounds.

Status Resident, apparently with some seasonal wandering to lower levels[4].

Breeding[3]   Sep   Oct   Nov   Dec
(n=23)   3   17   1   2   *Clutch*: C/3 (2); C/4 (1).
Taxonomy[2] *L. m. macclounii* (type locality Luchinde Stream, *NHM*; named for John McClounie)[6,8].
There is no justification for considering this form a distinct species[9], as some writers have done.
References [1]Benson (1959d); [2]Benson *et al.* (1970); [3]Dawson (1967); [4]Dowsett (1969e); [5]Dowsett
(1978c); [6]Dowsett (1980b); [7]Dowsett (in press a); [8]Shelley (1899a: 35); [9]Short (1982).

Crested Barbet *Trachyphonus vaillantii*   B329 **RB**

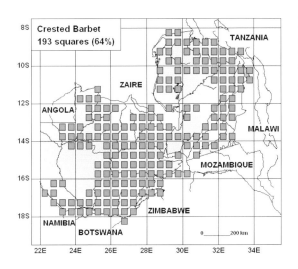

Distribution *Afrotropical (Zaire to South
Africa; mainly Zambezian)*. Through much of
the drier woodland at low and medium elevations (common in the Luangwa and Middle
Zambezi Valleys), but with some well-marked
gaps in distribution. Sparse or absent from
much of the more heavily-wooded and higher-
rainfall areas, and the open woodlands of
Western Province (which generally lack termite
mound thickets). For example, absent from
most of the dry *Baikiaea* forest west of the
Kafue drainage, and west of the Zambezi
north only to Natukoma and near Senanga,
reappearing to the east of the river in
Kabompo Dist. In the north-west reported
only very rarely from Mwinilunga. Also
unrecorded from much of the lower
Chambeshi basin, and sparse on the Eastern Province plateau[1]. *Alt.* 330-1700 m.
Ecology Any woodland, more particularly *Acacia*, mopane, thicket-clump savanna or the more open
types of drier miombo with termite mounds. It obtains much of its food on or near the ground.
Status Resident.
Breeding   Sep   Oct   Nov   Dec   Feb
(n=70)   16   32   17   1   4   *Clutch*: C/1 (1); C/3 (12); C/4 (2).
Moult: one bird was starting in mid-Oct[1].
Taxonomy[2] *T. v. vaillantii*, tending perhaps in the north to *T. v. suahelicus*.
References [1]Dowsett (in press a); [2]Short & Horne in Fry *et al.* (1988).

Indicatoridae

Green-backed Honeyguide *Prodotiscus zambesiae*   B335 **RB**

Distribution *Afrotropical (Kenya to Zimbabwe)*. Widespread and not uncommon in the miombo woodlands of the plateau (but easily overlooked unless call known). Ranges west to the Zambezi town
(Balovale) area[4], the Kakenge River[5] and Livingstone[2], exceptionally on the Angolan border on the
South Lueti River[7]. In N. Zambia, southwards from Mbala[1], also at Kaputa, and in the central Luapula
at Musonda Falls[5]. Absent from the Luangwa Valley, and in the Middle Zambezi only reaching the
escarpment around Chirundu and near Munyumbwe[5]. *Alt.* 1000-1900 m (Mafingas), rarely down to

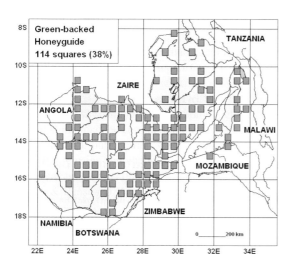

650 m.

Ecology Typically in tall, mature miombo woodland, where usually in the canopy (thus feeding higher than its sibling *P. regulus*), and at edges of riparian forest. But it also occurs locally in degraded *Cryptosepalum*, drier miombo and *Baikiaea* forest. Frequently in bird parties.

Status Resident.

Breeding   Sep   Oct   Nov
(n=8)   2   4   2

Host: *Zosterops senegalensis* (7)[5].

The species has a distinctive display flight[6], but observers have usually not distinguished between single-bird displays (which may be in any month) and two-bird displays (usually related to breeding activity)[8]. *Moult*: one moulting, another in fresh plumage, Dec[7].

Taxonomy *P. z. zambesiae* (formerly considered conspecific with the Guineo-Congolian Cassin's Honeyguide *P. insignis*)[3].

References [1]Benson (1956d); [2]Benson (1959c); [3]Benson *et al.* (1970); [4]Britton (1970); [5]Dowsett (in press a); [6]Leonard (1999b); [7]Traylor (1965b); [8]Vernon (1987).

Brown-backed Honeyguide *Prodotiscus regulus*   B336 **RB**

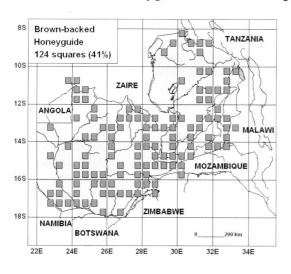

Distribution *Afrotropical* (*Liberia to South Africa*). Generally widespread in dry woodland, including the valleys; locally scarce, or even apparently absent. In the Luapula drainage only at Mununga and in the Luena area (Chilubi Dist.)[4]. Occurs westwards to Lukolwe[1], the Kalabo area and Kaungo. Unrecorded on the Eastern Province plateau between the vicinity of Lundazi and the Makutu Plateau[4]. *Alt.* 330-1700 m, exceptionally to about 2100 m in the Makutus[3].

Ecology Any woodland (especially the drier types, where certainly commoner than *P. zambesiae*), but like its congener most typically in miombo, also *Baikiaea* and perhaps to some extent on the edges of riparian forest. Feeds at all levels, often in mid-stratum or lower, thus with an ecological difference from the finer-billed *P. zambesiae*, and overall in drier vegetation types. *Prodotiscus* spp. are not known to eat bees' wax (unlike *Indicator* spp.), although *P. regulus* has been seen to feed on the wax produced by scale insects *Ceroplastes* spp[4]. Occasionally in bird parties.

Status Resident.

Breeding   Nov   Dec   Jan   Mar
(n=9)   2   4   1   2
Hosts[4]: *Cisticola fulvicapilla* (5), *Prinia subflava* (1). Also juvenile soliciting *Camaroptera brachyura*. Display flights noted Sep-Feb[5].
Taxonomy[2] *P. r. regulus.*
References [1]Britton (1970); [2]Clancey (1975); [3]Dowsett (1971h); [4]Dowsett (in press a); [5]Leonard (1999b).

Scaly-throated Honeyguide *Indicator variegatus*   B330 **RB**

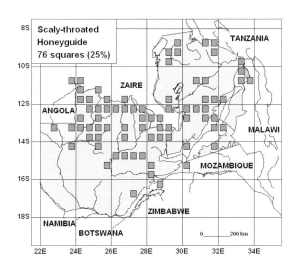

Distribution *Afrotropical* (*Ethiopia to South Africa*). Sparse but fairly widespread in densely-wooded country on the northern plateau, except (like quite a few other species) unrecorded from much of the deforested Luapula basin, south and west of the Mporokoso area and Nsama. Ranges west to Kapweletete[1] and between Lukolwe and Luzu[7], and south on the Kafue to the Mwengwa confluence, exceptionally once to near Choma. Known from scattered localities in the Luangwa Valley, on the Eastern Province plateau, and along the Zambezi to near Mutulanganga[4]. *Alt.* 1050-2200 m, uncommonly down to 400 m.

Ecology In all forest types (evergreen and deciduous, also montane) and tall miombo woodland, also termitaria and large thickets. Feeds in canopy and understorey, often at bees' nests, and hawks for insects.

Status Resident, but a bird netted on the Nkanga River (Choma) on 12 Apr (considered juvenile) was far from any known population[4].

Breeding   Aug   Sep   Oct
(n=3)   1   1   1   Host: *Dendropicos fuscescens* (1)[4]. On the Malawi side of the Nyika parasitizes *Mesopicos griseocephalus* (laying Aug-Sep)[5].
Moult: recorded Jan to late Jul, possibly very slow[4].
Taxonomy No races recognized[6], although several have been described[2] (syn. *I. v. satyrus,* type locality Solwezi[3]; *NMZB*).
References [1]Beel (1992b); [2]Clancey (1977b); [3]Clancey (1979:14); [4]Dowsett (in press a); [5]Dowsett-Lemaire (1983a); [6]Irwin & Benson (1967a); [7]Leonard (1998b).

Greater Honeyguide *Indicator indicator*   B331 **RB**

Distribution *Afrotropical* (*Senegal to South Africa*). The commonest honeyguide, throughout the woodlands of Zambia. *Alt.* 330-1700 m, wandering occasionally to 1950 m (Mafingas)[3] and 2200 m (Nyika)[4].
Ecology Very widespread in any woodland but most typically in miombo or mopane, feeding in the

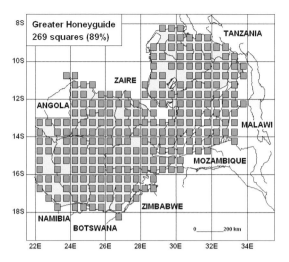

canopy or the vicinity of bees' nests in any situation.

Status Resident, with local wandering (e.g. to higher altitudes).

Breeding (n=99)

	Jul	Aug	Sep	Oct	Nov
(n=99)	1	4	25	59	10

Two females collected in Mar were said to be laying[5]. Hosts[2,7]: *Ceyx pictus* (1), *Halcyon albiventris* (1), *H. chelicuti* (5), *Merops pusillus* (64), *M. bullockoides* (1), *M. hirundineus* (1), *Upupa epops* (15), *Phoeniculus purpureus* (11), *P. cyanomelas* (6), *Myrmecocichla nigra* (1), *Parus niger* (1), *Lamprotornis chloropterus* (1). *Moult*: two were finishing in Mar[2].

Taxonomy[1,6] Most authorities recognize no subspecies, but *I. i. inquisitor* has been reported west to the Luangwa Valley.

References [1]Clancey (1970d); [2]Dowsett (in press a); [3]Dowsett & Stjernstedt (1973); [4]Dowsett-Lemaire (2006a); [5]Friedmann (1955); [6]Irwin & Benson (1966b); [7]Spottiswoode & Colebrook-Robjent (2007).

Lesser Honeyguide *Indicator minor* B332 **RB**

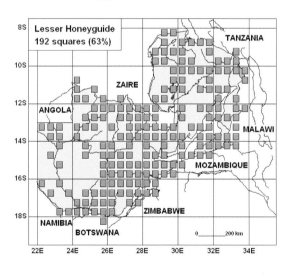

Distribution *Afrotropical* (*Senegal to South Africa*). Widespread, in woodland, forest or thicket. Through most of the country, except that in the south-west it seems to be confined to riparian along the major rivers, and it is also less often in woodland on the Southern Province plateau. It is so far unrecorded from much of the Luapula basin. *Alt.* 450-1700 m, occasionally wandering to 2200 m (Nyika)[5].

Ecology In different woodland types (except the driest), evergreen and deciduous forest and thicket.

Status Resident, with local wandering.

Breeding (n=68)

	Sep	Oct	Nov
(n=68)	17	25	16
	Dec	Jan	Feb
	4	4	2

Hosts[3,4]: *Lybius chaplini* (8), *L. torquatus* (47), *Trachyphonus vaillantii* (11).
Moult: recorded Nov-Apr[4].
Taxonomy[1] *I. m. minor* (syn. *I. m. valens*, type locality Salujinga[2], *NMZB*).
References [1]Benson (1956f); [2]Clancey (1977a: 182); [3]Colebrook-Robjent & Spottiswoode (in prep.); [4]Dowsett (in press a); [5]Dowsett-Lemaire (2006a).

Western Least Honeyguide *Indicator exilis*   B333 **RB**

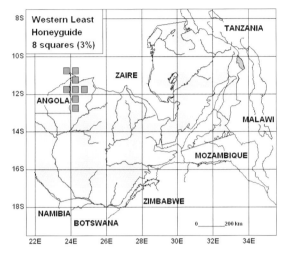

Distribution *Guineo-Congolian near-endemic* (*Guinea-Bissau to W. Kenya, south to NW Zambia*). Present in most forests in the extreme north-west, south to Mayau[3] and east to Mundwiji Plain[1]. The species reaches its southern limit of range in Zambia. *Alt.* 1130-1460 m.

Ecology Evergreen forest and thicket, including *Cryptosepalum* (where common)[4].

Status Resident.

Breeding   Jul   Aug   Sep   Oct
(n=5)   1   2   1   1

Hosts: Unknown (but possibly *Pogoniulus bilineatus*, as both are common in *Cryptosepalum*). All records are based on collected females, soon to lay.

Taxonomy *I. e. cerophagus* (type locality: the Zambezi Rapids, *NMZB*)[2].

References [1]Benson & Irwin (1965b); [2]Clancey (1977c: 216); [3]Dowsett (1973b); [4]Dowsett (in press a).

Eastern Least (Pallid) Honeyguide *Indicator meliphilus*   B334 **R(B)**

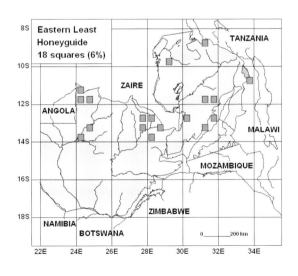

Distribution *Afrotropical* (*Kenya to Zimbabwe; mainly Zambezian*). A scattering of localities in forest in the northern half of the country, from Mbala[1] and the Nyika Plateau, south to the Muchinga escarpment at Masase. Known from several places on the Copperbelt, south to Luansobe[3]. Also in the north-west on Mundwiji Plain[3], south to Kabompo[2]. [Previously reported from Chipata, on the basis of a specimen collected by E.L. Button[6], but there is no mention of this species in the later report on Button's collection[5], and so it must be considered unsubstantiated.] *Alt.* 1130-1770 m, rarely to 2150 m (Nyika Plateau).

Ecology Riparian forest, occasionally in *Cryptosepalum* and *Marquesia* forest and on the edge of montane forest, rarely straying into miombo woodland.

Status Resident.

Breeding No records.

Taxonomy[4] No races recognized.

References [1]Benson (1956d); [2]Benson (1959c); [3]Dowsett (in press a); [4]Irwin & Benson (1967a); [5]Meyer de Schauensee (1951); [6]White & Winterbottom (1949).

Picidae

Red-throated Wryneck *Jynx ruficollis*   B337 **RB**

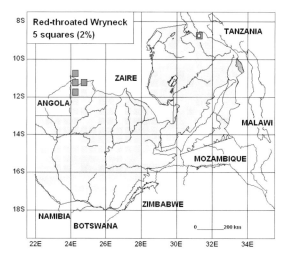

Distribution *Afrotropical* (*E. Nigeria to South Africa*). The few records of this species in Zambia are all but one from Mwinilunga Dist., including Salujinga, Isombu[1] and (especially) the Chitunta Plain, south to the West Lunga River (north of Mwinilunga town), and east to Munyakeshii Plain[3]. There was also an isolated sighting from Mbala (open square) in Feb 1952[2], presumably a wanderer, as the species is unrecorded from adjacent areas in Tanzania. *Alt.* 1170-1460 m, once to 1660 m at Mbala.

Ecology The few records have been associated either with wooded grassland with termitaria (on which the species feeds) or the edge of riparian forest, except for a vagrant at Mbala, in miombo.

Status Perhaps resident, although the possibility of local movements cannot be ruled out, and records are between 18 Jul and 18 Nov[4] (except for the Mbala vagrant, in Feb). Unfortunately the few observers who have lived in Mwinilunga Dist. seem not to have known the voice of this species, and it could have been overlooked at times.

Breeding   Aug
(n=1)   1   *Clutch*: no data (based on a juvenile collected 6 Oct, still dependent).
Taxonomy[5] *J. r. ruficollis.*
References [1]Benson & Irwin (1964b); [2]Benson & White (1957); [3]Bowen (1983f); [4]Dowsett (in press a); [5]White (1965).

Bennett's Woodpecker *Campethera bennettii*   B338 **RB**

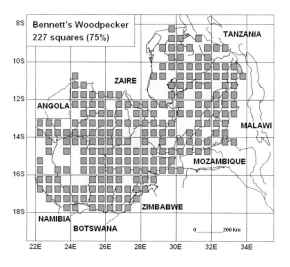

Distribution *Zambezian/Kalahari* (*Zaire to South Africa*). Widespread (but rarely common) in light woodland, although there are some gaps, particularly in the Luapula Valley (known only from near Musonda Falls), and it is scarce on the Copperbelt[1]. *Alt.* 330-1700 m.

Ecology Most often found in light miombo woodland, but also in other types (not uncommon in mopane and mixed *Acacia* woodland or wooded grassland). Avoids the moister woodlands (as on the Copperbelt). Forages both on the ground and on trees, taking mainly ants. Sometimes in bird parties.

Status Resident.

Breeding	Aug	Sep	Oct	Nov	Dec
(n=22)	1	4	11	5	1

Clutch: C/3 (2).

Taxonomy[2] *C. b. bennettii*, replaced by *C. b. capricorni* (finely, not heavily, spotted below) in the west.

References [1]Dowsett (in press a); [2]Irwin & Benson (1966b).

Golden-tailed Woodpecker *Campethera abingoni*   B339 **RB**

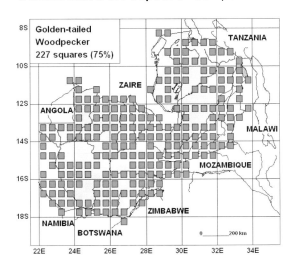

Golden-tailed Woodpecker
227 squares (75%)

Distribution *Afrotropical (Senegambia to South Africa)*. Widespread in any woodland, forest and thickets, but scarce in the Luangwa and Middle Zambezi Valleys[1]. *Alt.* 330-2200 m (Nyika)[2].

Ecology Usually common in miombo, also in other woodland types, thickets, riparian and other forest (less common in evergreen). Rarely breeds in montane forest on the Nyika[2]. Unlike *C. bennettii* it is completely arboreal; like other members of the genus, feeds mainly by gleaning, tapping and probing, taking mainly ants. Occasionally in bird parties.

Status Resident.

Breeding	Aug	Sep	Oct
(n=20)	3	14	3

Clutch: C/2 (5); C/3 (7); C/4 (2).

Taxonomy[3] *C. a. smithii*, replaced in the east by *C. a. suahelica* (throat streaked black, rather than mottled).

References [1]Dowsett (in press a); [2]Dowsett-Lemaire (2006a); [3]Irwin & Benson (1967b).

Little Spotted Woodpecker *Campethera cailliautii*   B340 **RB**

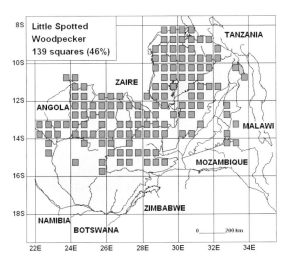

Little Spotted Woodpecker
139 squares (46%)

Distribution *Afrotropical (Ghana to Zimbabwe)*. The moist plateau woodlands and forests of the northern half of the country, south on the Eastern Province plateau just to Vubwe. It ranges down the Muchingas to Chinyunyu and in the Kafue basin to Ngoma. Further west it reaches Luampa[2], and west of the Zambezi to the Luambimba River[3]. *Alt.* 950-1800 m.

Ecology In dense miombo woodland (including transition woodland), or a mixture of riparian forest and woodland, also *Cryptosepalum* forest (uncommon) and thickets. Feeds by gleaning and tapping, eating small arboreal ants and termites.

Status Resident.

Breeding	Sep	Oct	Nov
(n=4)	2	1	1

Clutch: C/2 (1).
Taxonomy[1] *C. c. nyansae.*
References [1]Clancey (1971d); [2]Dowsett (in press a); [3]Winterbottom (1942a).

Brown-eared Woodpecker *Campethera caroli*   B p.181 **R(B)**

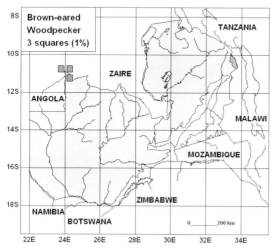

Distribution *Guineo-Congolian near-endemic* (*Guinea to W. Kenya, south to NW Zambia*). Occurs sparsely in a few of the forests of N. Mwinilunga, from Kadata River, Chilula and the Jimbe stream, south to Hillwood (where rare) and the Isombu stream (where perhaps extinct)[1,2]. These localities are the most southerly for the species. *Alt.* 1170-1350 m.
Ecology In Zambia, records have been from thin riparian evergreen forest, where it feeds in the mid-stratum and understorey.
Status Resident.
Conservation With the rapid destruction of much forest habitat in Mwinilunga Dist. this species is vulnerable in Zambia (though it is common in most other parts of its wide range).
Breeding No records.

Taxonomy *C. c. caroli.*
References [1]Dowsett (1973c); [2]Dowsett (in press a).

Cardinal Woodpecker *Dendropicos fuscescens*   B341 **RB**

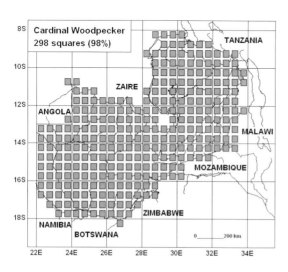

Distribution *Afrotropical* (*Senegal to South Africa*). The commonest woodpecker in Zambia, occurring in woodland throughout. *Alt.* 330-2000 m in the Mafingas[1], rarely as high as 2100 m on the Nyika[3].
Ecology In all woodland types (especially the more open), also in deciduous forest and thickets, and in dry evergreen forest, including *Cryptosepalum* (quite common). Feeds at all levels from base of trunk to canopy, mainly probing and tapping. A frequent member of mixed bird parties.
Status Resident.

Breeding
(n=52)	Jul	Aug	Sep	Oct
		5	8	29	10

Clutch: C/1 (3); C/2 (30); C/3 (1).
Moult: two adults started about late Nov[2].

Taxonomy[4] *D. f. stresemanni* in the south and *D. f. centralis* (darker, more olive, above and more boldly patterned on the mantle) in the north – variation is clinal.

References [1]Aspinwall (1976b); [2]Dowsett (in press a); [3]Dowsett-Lemaire (2006a); [4]Irwin & Benson (1966b).

Bearded Woodpecker *Thripias namaquus*   B343 **RB**

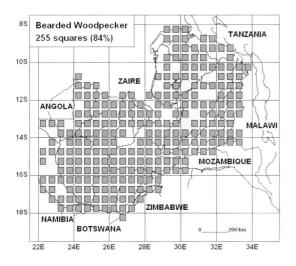

Distribution *Afrotropical (Ethiopia to South Africa)*. Almost throughout the country, though there are a few small gaps, and it is rather local on the Northern Province plateau. *Alt.* 330-1900 m.

Ecology Regularly encountered in tall miombo woodland (may avoid the wetter types) and other dry woodland (mopane, mixed *Acacia-Baikiaea*) or wooded savanna with large trees. Occasionally in riparian forest. Feeds at all levels, often on larger trees than *D. fuscescens*.

Status Resident.

Breeding	May	Jun	Jul
(n=16)	1	5	3
	Aug	Sep	Oct
	4	1	2

Clutch: C/1 (1); C/2 (2); C/3 (1).

Moult: adult moult was well-advanced mid-Nov[1].
Taxonomy *T. n. namaquus*.
References [1]Traylor (1965b).

Olive Woodpecker *Mesopicos griseocephalus*   B342 **RB**

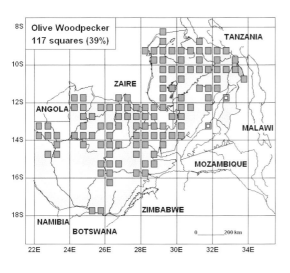

Distribution *Afrotropical (Zaire to South Africa); montane in many parts of its range.* The forests of the northern half of the country, west of the Muchingas, south along the escarpment to Chongwe, and near Mazabuka[4] and Kafue Bridge[4]. Elsewhere down the Kafue to Nanzhila Mission[9], and in the Upper Zambezi to Kalabo[1] and Tiger camp. In recent years there have been records from the Victoria Falls[4,8] to Kazungula, where it may be a sparse resident rather than wanderer (it was already known from the south bank). The records in the upper Luangwa, even as low as near Mfuwe[4] (open squares), are clearly non-breeding vagrants from the Northern Province plateau. *Alt.* 950-2200 m, rarely down to 500 m, and higher on the Malawi side of Nyika.

Ecology Mainly in moist evergreen and riparian forest, and montane forest (especially smaller patches). Taps, probes and excavates from bark, mostly in the upper levels of trunks and on small branches.

Prefers soft bark of fast-growing trees (near edges and in gaps). Very common on SW Nyika where pairs occupy home ranges of 4-5 ha of fragmented forest[6].

Status Generally resident, but some wander when not breeding. One ringed bird on the Nyika was retrapped after 5 years[3].

Breeding   May   Jun   Jul   Aug   Sep   Oct

(n=44)   2   2   12   18   8   2   (Includes 26 from Zovochipolo, Malawi side of SW Nyika.) Single-brooded[7].

Clutch: no data, but always 1 or 2 juveniles on Nyika Plateau. On the Malawi Nyika several were parasitized by *Indicator variegatus*[5].

Moult: starting Dec and completed by Mar[4].

Taxonomy *M. g. persimilis*[2].

References [1]Benson (1964f); [2]Benson *et al.* (1970); [3]Dowsett (1985a); [4]Dowsett (in press a); [5]Dowsett-Lemaire (1983a); [6]Dowsett-Lemaire (1983b); [7]Dowsett-Lemaire (1985a); [8]Varden (1991); [9]Winterbottom (1951-52).

Eurylaimidae

African Broadbill *Smithornis capensis*   B344 **RB**

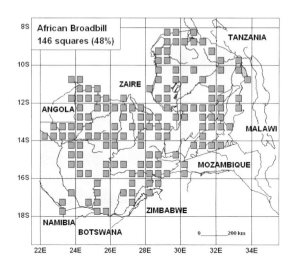

Distribution *Afrotropical* (*Sierra Leone to South Africa*). Locally common in thicket and forest throughout much of the country, but unrecorded west of the Zambezi between the Chinyama Litapi area and Mize[1] and the Semende area on the Mashi River[3]. Sparse on the Eastern Province plateau. *Alt.* 330-1950 m (quite common in the Mafingas[8]), rare above this on the Nyika Plateau, up to 2150 m[9].

Ecology In understorey of moist evergreen (riparian) forest, montane forest, dry *Cryptosepalum* and *Marquesia* forest; also deciduous thickets generally, including in *Baikiaea* forest and cover in exotic pine plantations[7]. A nest was 2 m up in riparian forest[3]. Flycatches and gleans; stomach contents have included caterpillars and other insects. Does not join bird parties.

Status Resident.

Breeding[2]   Sep   Oct   Nov   Dec   Jan

(n=27)   4   2   6   11   4   We reject the suggestion of egg-laying in Mar, based on a juvenile of uncertain age; advertising flights have been noted most months (few in the dry season).

Clutch: C/1 (1); C/2 (7); C/3 (16).

Moult: recorded Mar-May[7].

Taxonomy[4,6,10] *S. c. suahelicus*, replaced in the north-west and extreme north-east by *S. c. albigularis* (which differs mainly in the female having the crown feathers dull black, narrowly edged with rusty, rather than paler and broadly edged with grey). The form in the south-west is *S. c. conjunctus* (type locality west of Victoria Falls, Zimbabwe[5]; paler above, whiter below).

References [1]Aspinwall (1979b); [2]Benson (1969); [3]Benson & Irwin (1967b); [4]Benson *et al.* (1970); [5]Clancey (1963a); [6]Clancey (1974a); [7]Dowsett (in press a); [8]Dowsett & Stjernstedt (1973); [9]Dowsett-Lemaire (2006a); [10]Irwin (1981a).

Pittidae

African Pitta *Pitta angolensis* B345 **AMB**

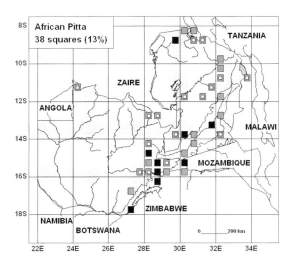

Distribution *Afrotropical* (*Sierra Leone to South Africa*). Locally common in thicket. Map shows confirmed or suspected breeding (black squares), other breeding season records (solid blue) and passage (open squares). All but one record are from the eastern half of the country, including the Luangwa Valley[6] and Middle Zambezi (where Alexander was the first to find it)[1], west to the Pemba area of the Southern Province plateau and the Chimene stream in the Zambezi Valley[3]. The exception was one seen in riparian at Hillwood farm, Mwinilunga Dist. 16 Nov[7]. During the breeding season can be common in low-lying thicket at Mutulanganga (Gwembe Valley) and Katondwe (lower Luangwa). *Alt.* 330-1230 m, usually in low-lying areas, but probably breeding also at the higher levels: e.g. displaying on the Serenje Dist. plateau at Mukopa (29 Nov)[7]. On passage has exceptionally been found as high as 1830 m on Mwanda Mtn[4].

Ecology Dense deciduous tickets (birds sometimes arriving before they are fully in leaf). The nest is a large untidy dome, placed in a fork inside thicket. Feeds on the ground; stomach contents included carabid beetles.

Status[5] An intra-African migrant and breeding visitor, extreme dates in Zambia 23 Oct (Mazabuka, passage)[5] and 16 Apr (Mbendele)[2]. Passage birds have flown into buildings on several occasions in Nov and Dec, including one fall of more than a dozen at Lake View Hotel, Mbala, 24 Nov, an evening of heavy mist[5].

Breeding   Dec   Jan
(n=15)   12   3   Displaying period 18 Nov to 16 Feb (very rarely in the last month).
Clutch: C/1 (2); C/2 (4); C/3 (5); C/4 (3).

Taxonomy *P. a. longipennis.*

References [1]Alexander (1899-1900); [2]Aspinwall (1972a); [3]Benson (1960d); [4]Benson *et al.* (1970); [5]Benson & Irwin (1964a); [6]Berry & Ansell (1978); [7]Dowsett & Leonard (in press a).

Alaudidae

Monotonous Lark *Mirafra passerina* B346 **AMB**

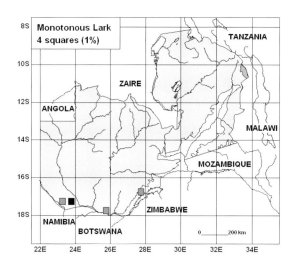

Distribution *Kalahari/Zambezian (S. Zambia to South Africa)*. Recorded some years in rocky woodland in the Victoria Falls Gorges near Livingstone (between the Falls and the Songwe/Zambezi River confluence), where it was first discovered in Jul 1964[2]. Elsewhere it was found to be common at Mfubakazi in the south-west 5 Apr 1964 (two were collected), one was seen in the Gwembe Valley at Chaboboma in Sep 1975[1], and west of the Zambezi (nest-building, black square) in Oct 1993[3]. *Alt.* 520 (Chaboboma) to 1000 m.

Ecology Dry country, often rocky, at the edge of woodland, lightly-wooded areas with long grass, thin mopane woodland. Sings perched on bushes.

Status Extreme dates overall are 5 Apr and 26 Dec. In the Victoria Falls area there are records for Jun to Dec, with a sighting from the Zimbabwe side in mid-Mar. The species is known to be irruptive in parts of Zimbabwe[4,5].

Breeding Nest-building west of the Zambezi, on the Imusho road, 27 Oct 1993 (after rain)[3]. Song mid-Mar (Zimbabwe).

Taxonomy No races recognized (in the past treated as conspecific with Horsfield's Bush Lark *M. javanica* or Singing Bush Lark *M. cantillans*).

References [1]Aspinwall (1976a); [2]Benson & Irwin (1967b); [3]Dowsett & Leonard (in press a); [4]Thomson (1983); [5]Vernon (1983).

Rufous-naped Lark *Mirafra africana* B347 **RB**

Distribution *Afrotropical (Guinea to South Africa)*. Locally numerous on plains, mostly in the south and west of the country, north occasionally to Maplehurst (Kabwe) and east to Sakala (near Lusaka)[6]. In Mwinilunga it occurs east to the Kabompo River headwaters[11]. There is an isolated population in the Bangweulu area, from south-east of Mukuku[2] to Mayuka[4] and Chalabesa[6], and another on the Nyika Plateau (where common). *Alt.* 900-2200 m (Nyika, higher on the Malawi side).

Ecology Open grassland with scattered bushes or small termite mounds on watershed plains, montane grassland and edges of dambos. Sings on low perches or small protuberances, and often produces a "flappet" with the wings during short vertical jumps[7].

Status Resident.

Breeding[8]

	Aug	Sep	Oct	Nov	Dec	Jan	Feb	Mar
(n=87)		4	6	18	23	12	11	8	5

Clutch: C/1 (3); C/2 (62); C/3 (18).

Moult: birds in body moult Nov-Dec, probably starting moult of flight feathers after that[9].

Taxonomy *M. a. transvaalensis* is the widespread form, in the southern half of the country. The following are isolates: *M. a. chapini* locally in the Mwinilunga and Bangweulu areas; *M. a. kabalii* (type

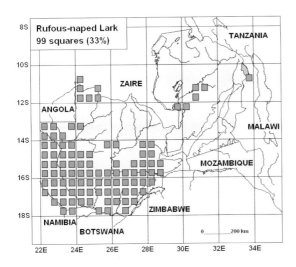

locality Minyanya Plain; *AMNH*; named for White's collector, Kabali Muzeya[10]) in the west; *M. a. gomesi* in the south-west; *M. a. griscescens* in the extreme south-west; *M. a. nyikae* (type locality Nyika Plateau, Malawi)[1,5]. For discussion, see ref. 3.

References [1]Benson (1939); [2]Benson *et al.* (1961); [3]Benson & Irwin (1967b); [4]Benson & White (1957); [5]Dowsett (1972d); [6]Dowsett (in press a); [7]Dowsett-Lemaire & Dowsett (2005); [8]Symmes (1960b); [9]Traylor (1965b); [10]White (1943b: 20); [11]White (1948b).

Angola Lark *Mirafra angolensis*   B348 **RB**

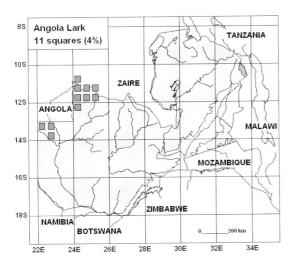

Distribution *Zambezian endemic (SW Tanzania to south-central Angola)*. Occurs on watershed plains in the north-west. Ranges east to Kakoma[2] and Mufundwa Bridge[4], south to Mitashi Plain[1,3]. Although unknown in NE Zambia, it does reappear in the Marungu highlands of SE Zaire[5]. *Alt.* 1050-1550 m.

Ecology Watershed plains with open grassland, and edge of large dambos; in moister situations than *M. africana*. Has an aerial song flight[1].

Status Resident.

Breeding	Sep	Oct
(n=4)	2	2

Song Jul to late Apr.
Clutch: C/2 (1); C/3 (1).

Taxonomy *M. a. antonii* (syn. *M. a. minyanyae* type locality Minyanya Plain[6]; *NMZL*).

References [1]Aspinwall (1979b); [2]Benson & White (1957); [3]Benson *et al.* (1971a); [4]Dowsett (in press a); [5]Dowsett & Prigogine (1974); [6]White (1958: 163).

Flappet Lark *Mirafra rufocinnamomea*   B350 **RB**

Distribution *Afrotropical (Mauritania to South Africa)*. Common in light woodland throughout the country. *Alt.* 330-1700 m.

Ecology Any wooded grassland, open woodland (including cut lines for power cables) or ecotone of woodland and grassland. Also regenerating miombo and mopane with a short, sparse grass layer. Absent from treeless areas.

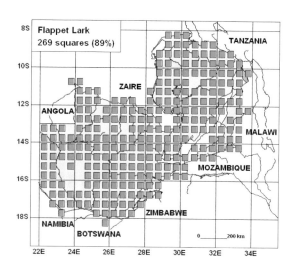

Status Resident.

Breeding	Sep	Oct	Nov	Dec
(n=72)	3	5	11	12
	Jan	Feb	Mar	
	16	18	7	

Flappetting most months (especially Sep-Apr, starting with or just before first rains)[3].
Clutch: C/1 (1); C/2 (50); C/3 (7).
Taxonomy *M. r. smithersi*, replaced by or intergrading with *M. r. lwenarum* (type locality between the South Kashiji and Litapi Rivers; *NMZL*)[2,4] throughout the north and north-west, and *M. r. mababiensis* in the extreme south-west[1].
References [1]Benson & Irwin (1967b); [2]Dowsett (1980b); [3]Dowsett (in press a); [4]White (1945d: 15).

[Sabota Lark *Mirafra sabota*

Afrotropical (*Angola to South Africa*). Recorded from the Caprivi Strip (1725C,D)[1], and it might thus be expected north of the Zambezi. In Zimbabwe occurs north to Matetsi[2] and near Victoria Falls[4], and reported seen near Kariba, Jun 1997[3]. **References** [1]Dean in Harrison *et al.* (1997); [2]Irwin (1981a); [3]Jones (1997); [4]Pollard (1991a).]

Clapper Lark *Mirafra apiata*   B349 **RB**

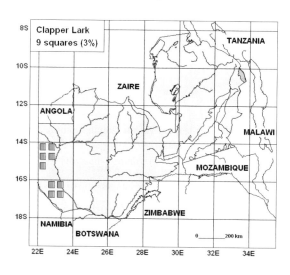

Distribution *Afrotropical* (*W. Zambia to South Africa*). There are two populations on the plains west of the Zambezi: together they range from the Liuwa Plain[8] (where it is common[6]) south to Lupuka and south of Nasiongo, east to Nangweshi[1]. (Unrecorded from E. Angola[2], but must surely occur). [Extralimitally, it is mapped as occurring in the Caprivi Strip as far east as near Sesheke[4]; this is likely in error, as the Kalahari sand plains frequented by this sedentary lark are absent[5].] *Alt.* 950-1050 m.
Ecology Sparsely grassed, dry Kalahari sand plains (sometimes seasonally inundated).
Status Resident.

Breeding	Oct	
(n=1)	1	Flight display late Sep to

mid-Apr[3]. *Clutch*: no data. *Moult*: started mid-Nov[8].
Taxonomy *M. a. jappi* (type locality Liuwa Plain; *FMNH*; named for Richard Japp, labour agent)[7] is the form in the north-west, and *M. a. reynoldsi* (type locality Nasiongo; *NMZL*; named for Barrie

Reynolds, Director of the National Museums of Zambia)[1] further south.

References [1]Benson & Irwin (1965f: 1); [2]Dean (2000); [3]Dowsett (in press a); [4]Dean in Harrison *et al.* (1997); [5]Hunter (1990); [6]Osborne (1978); [7]Traylor (1962a: 113); [8]Traylor (1965b).

Fawn-coloured Lark *Mirafra africanoides*   B351 **R(B)**

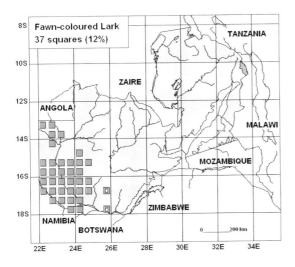

Distribution *Afrotropical (Ethiopia to N. Tanzania, and SW Zambia to South Africa).* Quite common in light woodland on Kalahari sands in the south and west, north to the Litapi headwaters[1] and Lukolwe (and has wandered to just east of Zambezi town (Balovale)). In Kaoma Dist. occurs east to the Ngunda stream[3]. Further south, single wanderers have been recorded in cold, dry years east to Dimba Dambo near Ndumdumwense (7 Nov 1983)[4], and Livingstone (12 Sep 1964)[2] (open squares). *Alt.* 900-1050 m.
Ecology Open woodland or scattered bushes in long grass, on Kalahari sand adjacent to dry plains. Sings perched in trees.
Status Resident, with some wandering.
Breeding No records (but male gonad activity Aug, Oct and Nov; song Sep and May).
Moult: starting early Dec[6].
Taxonomy[5] *M. a. trapnelli* (type locality between the Kashiji and Litapi Rivers; *OUM*; named for the botanist C.G. Trapnell)[7] in the north and *M. a. makarikari* in the south, the two intergrading in the Loma area.
References [1]Aspinwall (1979b); [2]Benson & Irwin (1967b); [3]Bruce-Miller & Dowsett (1977); [4]Dowsett (in press a); [5]Irwin & Benson (1966a); [6]Traylor (1965b); [7]White (1943b: 21).

Dusky Lark *Pinarocorys nigricans*   B352 **AMB**

Distribution *Afrotropical (breeds S. Zaire to south-central Zambia, wintering south to South Africa).* Locally common in light woodland. Breeding activity (nests and birds in display flight) noted at several localities, from Mporokoso and Mwinilunga Dists south to Itezhi-Tezhi[2] and (exceptionally) Choma, east to Shiwa Ngandu (black squares). Birds have also been noted at this time of year south to Liuwa Plain in the west, and the Luangwa Valley (rarely, but several in 1999, throughout the dry season). Can turn up almost anywhere on passage, except it is scarce at low altitude, and there is only one record from the Eastern Province plateau (Lundazi)[3]. *Alt.* 400-1500 m.
Ecology Territorial birds settle on dry (lightly-wooded) plains, the edges of dambos, in light woodland or cultivation, almost invariably recently burnt and often still smouldering. On passage in miombo and mopane woodland, fields and gardens.
Status An intra-African migrant and breeding visitor. Post-breeding (southward) passage starts as early as late Sep and lasts to mid-Dec, mostly from mid-Oct. Northward passage is the more pronounced, with flocks of up to 25-30 (especially in the Livingstone area) early Mar to early Jun, mainly mid-Apr to mid-May. The average first date over 24 years for northward passage was 28 Apr (data insufficient

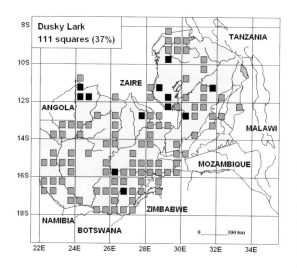

to determine mean last date on southward passage[2]. Outside this period there have exceptionally been single birds reported in Jan at Livingstone and in Feb at Luanshya and Mfuwe[2].

Breeding   Oct
(n=2)   2   From   Choma   (burnt, open woodland). Display song flights mid-Jul to Oct. *Clutch*: C/2 (1); C/3 (1).
Moult: started early Nov[4].

Taxonomy *P. n. nigricans*, but one specimen from Livingstone has been attributed to *P. n. occidentis*[1], which may pass through the west of the country.

References [1]Clancey (1968b); [2]Dowsett & Leonard (in press a); [3]Meyer de Schauensee (1951); [4]Traylor (1965b).

[Spike-heeled Lark *Chersomanes albofasciata*
Afrotropical (*open plains, Tanzania to South Africa*). A sight record from the Victoria Falls N.P. in Zimbabwe[2] has not been accepted[3]. A specimen listed from Kundelungu in Katanga (Zaire), is astonishing, undocumented and perhaps mislabelled[1]. **References** [1]Dowsett (in press a); [2]Jensen (1965); [3]Riddell (2003).]

Red-capped Lark *Calandrella cinerea*   B353 **AMB**

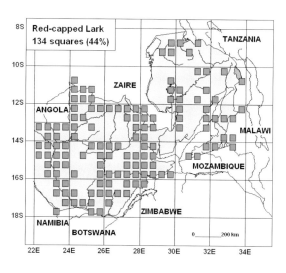

Distribution *Afrotropical* (*Nigeria to South Africa*). Locally common on open ground through most of the Zambian plateau, but unrecorded from densely-wooded areas and some plains in the extreme south-west, and generally scarce in the valleys. *Alt.* 370-2200 m (Nyika, where it has bred on Malawi side), few below 900 m and above 1800 m.

Ecology In short grass (sometimes freshly burnt) on dry plains and floodplains, edges of dambos, airfields, fallow cultivation or ploughed land.

Status An intra-African migrant and breeding visitor. Significantly less frequent Nov-Mar than Apr-Oct, with first arrivals second half of Apr in the south. Pre-breeding flocks up to 200+ late Apr to early Jun at favoured localities such as Lochinvar and other places on the middle Kafue, and in Kasempa and Lukulu Dists, are likely to be newly arrived. Departures from breeding areas start mid-Sep, mostly from late Oct to late Nov/early Dec. The species moves north in the non-breeding season[5]. Few during the rains, but in a few favoured areas (e.g. Lochinvar) parties of up to 25 present in some years.

Breeding[3] May   Jun   Jul   Aug   Sep   Oct
(n=43)   4   3   10   8   11   7   *Clutch*: C/1 (4); C/2 (24); C/3 (1).
Moult: a few started late Oct[4].
Taxonomy[1] *C. c. saturatior*, but individuals approaching *C. c. cinerea* (crown darker, upperparts more sepia) are known from parts of the south and west.
References [1]Clancey (1977e); [2]Dowsett & Leonard (in press a); [3]Symmes (1960b); [4]Traylor (1965b); [5]White (1961c).

Pink-billed Lark *Spizocorys conirostris*   B354 **RB**

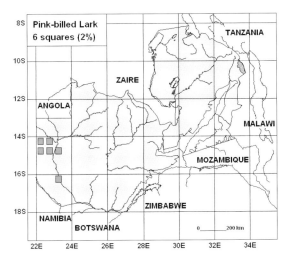

Distribution *Kalahari/Zambezian (SE Angola*[3] *and W. Zambia to South Africa*). From Liuwa Plain[4] (where it is sparse) it ranges south and east to Ndanda Plain, and there is another population further south on the Matabele Plain[1], where it is common at times[2]. *Alt.* 950-1050 m.
Ecology Sparsely grassed, relatively dry Kalahari sand plains.
Status Probably resident, but not enough records to be certain.
Breeding   Apr
(n=1)   1
(based on a juvenile on Mutala Plain, recently out of the nest). *Clutch*: no data.
Moult: adults in late Oct were finishing or had already completed moult[5].

Taxonomy *S. c. makawai* (type locality Liuwa Plain; *FMNH*; named for Jali Makawa)[4] is the form in the northern part of its Zambian range, *S. c. harti* (type locality Matabele Plain; *NMZL*; named for Robert Hart Jr, ornithologist)[1] is the southern population.
References [1]Benson (1964e: 106); [2]Dowsett (in press a); [3]Mills (2006); [4]Traylor (1962a: 114); [5]Traylor (1965b).

Chestnut-backed Sparrow-Lark (Finch Lark) *Eremopterix leucotis*   B356 **RB**

Distribution *Afrotropical (Mauritania to South Africa)*. Locally common on open ground in S. and central Zambia; absent from most of the extreme west (occupied by *Eremopterix verticalis*). It also occurs regularly in small numbers in the Luangwa Valley (apparently breeding) below the Mangalala River confluence, and on the adjacent Eastern Province plateau (where not occupied by *E. leucopareia*). It occurs west to Sianda Mission[2], and west of the Zambezi on the Matabele Plain[1] and at Shangombo. In central Zambia not known north of Maplehurst (where small numbers occur mid-May to Aug). Apparently resident in the Kariba basin[6]. *Alt.* 330-1400 m.
Ecology Dry plains and floodplains, edges of dambos, airfields and old cultivation, especially recently burnt. May, however, be absent from sandy plains. Usually in monospecific groups, occasionally with *Calandrella cinerea* and (in years of irruption) *E. verticalis*.
Status Some appear to be resident, including those at low altitude at Kariba and in the Luangwa

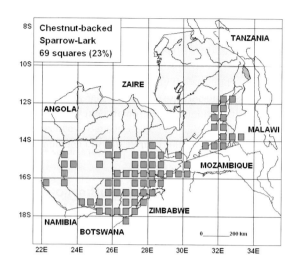

Valley[4,6]. But it often flocks in Dec and mid-Apr to Jun, usually groups of up to 30, but not infrequently up to 200 in Southern Province. A 2-year survey showed it to be least common only during the three months Nov-Jan[4].

Breeding (n=13)	Mar	Apr	May	Jun
	2	4	1	1
	Jul	Aug	Sep	
	1	3	1	

Clutch: C/2 (9).

Taxonomy[3,5] *E. l. smithii*, but *E. l. hoeschi* may occur in the south-west (female is colder and greyer above).

References [1]Benson & Irwin (1965e); [2]Bruce-Miller & Dowsett (1977); [3]Clancey (1980d); [4]Dowsett (in press a); [5]Irwin (1981a); [6]Irwin (1982b).

Grey-backed Sparrow-Lark *Eremopterix verticalis* B355 **RB/AM**

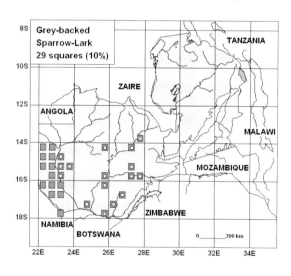

Distribution *Afrotropical (breeding W. Zambia to South Africa)*. Local, but at times numerous, in short open grassland of the south-west. The breeding area (where common) is confined to the extreme west, from Liuwa Plain[5], south to Siloana Plains, Lupuka[2] and Imusho[4]. It is not clear whether or not the few found east of the Zambezi in Mongu Dist. breed. In irruptive years populations from SW Africa arrive in S. and central Zambia, north and east to the Ipumbu Plain[3] (open squares). *Alt.* breeding populations are all 950-1050 m, wanderers 880-1270 m.

Ecology Breeds on sparsely grassed, dry Kalahari sand plains. In years of irruption may be found on any open area, plains, dambos, old cultivation, recently burnt. In such years sometimes in mixed groups with *E. leucotis*[3].

Status Observations from the breeding area suggest that population may be sedentary, although outside the breeding season flocks of hundreds have been noted on the Liuwa. All records of irruptions are between 16 Apr and 8 Nov, except for one sighting of two birds in Choma Dist. in Feb. The largest influx noted was in 1964 (a cold year), when parties of up to 70 occurred in Lochinvar. There was a fairly large influx in 1970, and a few birds in some other years (1982, and the cold drought year of 1992)[4].

Breeding (n=1)	Feb
	1

Clutch: no data.

Moult: in the Liuwa area late Oct/early Nov birds were completing moult[5].

Taxonomy The Zambian breeding form is *E. v. harti* (type locality Nasiongo; *NMZL*; named for the ornithologist Robert Hart Jr)[2], while the following races have irrupted into the country from the south-

west in some years: *E. v. verticalis*, *damarensis* and *khama*[1,3].
References [1]Benson *et al.* (1971a); [2]Benson & Irwin (1965e: 3); [3]Benson & Irwin (1967b); [4]Dowsett (in press a); [5]Traylor (1965b).

Fischer's Sparrow-Lark *Eremopterix leucopareia*   B - R(B)/AM?

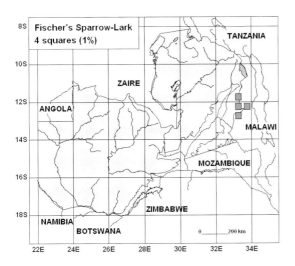

Distribution *Afrotropical* (*Kenya to Malawi*). Present only in small numbers on open ground in the Lundazi-Lumezi area, where apparently arrived in the 1970s, the first being found at Lundazi on 22 Dec 1976[1,2]. *Alt.* 1100-1300 m.
Ecology In cultivated land, in particular maize fields when fallow or when plants are still small, even rather small clearings in woodland. In Malawi, similar to that of *E. leucotis*, including short grass of dry dambos and airfields; there, it probably competes with *E. leucotis*, but in Zambia the two species are allopatric. The clearing of woodland for cultivation is favourable to this species.
Status Uncertain, mainly from 28 Apr to 23 Dec (with only two records outside that period), but in Malawi recorded also in the rains. Present, at times numerous, from Jun to late Dec (up to 30 "pairs" Aug-Sep, perhaps even as many as 100 birds 22-23 Dec 1976). Exceptionally a few birds early Feb to 22 Mar (a time of year when fields are over-run by weeds, and this lark difficult to find, or perhaps largely absent). In Malawi this species is expanding its range slowly southwards[4]. Large numbers noted in Zambia in 1976, 1977, 1980, 1991, 1993 and 1995[3], but unfortunately the presence of observers has been irregular in the Lundazi area.
Breeding Apparent nest-building early Sep (Lumezi), carrying food (perhaps to a nest) mid-Aug near Lundazi, and 20-30 "pairs" reported in Sep[3]. In Malawi breeds Apr-May[4], months when there are few Zambian observations.
Taxonomy No races recognized.
References [1]Aspinwall (1977b); [2]Dowsett (1979a); [3]Dowsett (in press a); [4]Dowsett-Lemaire & Dowsett (2006).

Hirundinidae

Black Saw-wing *Psalidoprocne pristoptera*   B376 **RB**

Distribution *Afrotropical* (*Nigeria to South Africa*). *P. s. reichenowi* is locally quite common on the edge of woodland or forest. Breeds in central Zambia, south to about 14°30'S, and west to the Zambezi and the Kabompo River[8]. A different race (*orientalis*, open squares) occurs in parts of the Eastern Province plateau. In NE Zambia the distribution of the species is perhaps restricted by the presence of *P. albiceps*: they coexist from L. Mweru to L. Tanganyika, thence towards the Tanzanian border and from the Nyika (where perhaps only a non-breeding visitor), south to the Danger Hill area of the Muchinga escarpment (although it is not clear if it too nests in this area). Both populations wander

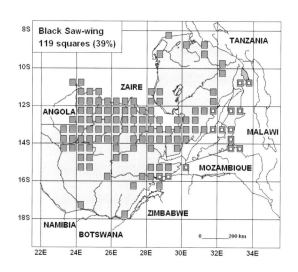

considerably when not breeding, even to Seseke[2,3] and to Kafwambila in the Gwembe Valley. *Alt.* 950-2200 m, wandering down to 500 m at times.

Ecology In clearings or on the edges of riparian and evergreen forest (including *Cryptosepalum*), or the richer miombo woodland. Nests in earth banks.

Status Resident, but with some local movements outside the breeding season. Recorded in all months, but significantly more frequent Oct-May than Jun-Sep, except on the Nyika, where mainly a dry-season passage migrant[4].

Breeding	Dec	Jan	Feb	Mar
(n=8)		1	3	3	1

Clutch: C/2 (3).

Moult: starting Jun or Jul[3].

Taxonomy The main breeding form is *P. p. reichenowi*, but *P. p. orientalis* (with underwing coverts white rather than grey) is on the Eastern Province plateau, and has occurred as a vagrant at low altitude on the Munyamadzi[1], elsewhere in the Luangwa Valley down to Katondwe, and along the Middle Zambezi Valley west to Mazabuka[7]. The southern African breeding form *P. p. holomelas* has wandered as far north as Lilongwe in Malawi, but the suggestion that it has been reported from the Chirundu area in Zambia[5] is erroneous. Some authors would treat the *orientalis* group as a separate species, but molecular analysis shows this group to be monophyletic[6] (note that the sample of *"orientalis"* examined by those authors was in fact *reichenowi* from Angola).

References [1]Benson (1956d); [2]Benson (1959b); [3]Dowsett (in press a); [4]Dowsett-Lemaire & Dowsett (2006); [5]Mundy & Maasdorp (1993); [6]Sheldon *et al.* (2005); [7]Winterbottom (1938a); [8]Winterbottom (1942a).

White-headed Saw-wing *Psalidoprocne albiceps*   B377 **AMB**

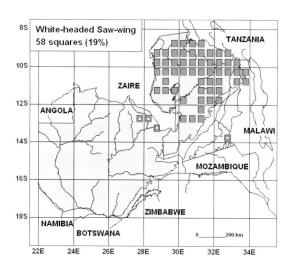

Distribution *Afromontane near-endemic (Sudan to Zambia-Malawi).* A breeding visitor to NE Zambia, locally sparse on the edge of woodland and forest, common in the highlands south to the Nyika Plateau, and (west of the Rift) to the Musa Hills. Wanderers (open squares) have occurred on the Copperbelt, west to Chingola[4], and even to Chipata on the Eastern Province plateau[1]. Absent from NW Zambia: a specimen from Kasaji in Zaire[6] must have been a vagrant. *Alt.* 930 (Nchelenge) to 2200 m (Nyika).

Ecology In clearings or on the edges of riparian and evergreen forest, and especially the richer miombo woodland; common on the edge of montane forest. The nest is lined with *Usnea* lichen and grass, at the end of a 45-60 cm tunnel in a bank[1,2]. On the Nyika and elsewhere in their zone of overlap (see *P. pristoptera*), the two *Psalidoprocne* are often seen feeding alongside each other.

Status An intra-African migrant and breeding visitor. Most records are between late Sep and late Apr, with departures from mid-Mar (groups of up to 25 on passage over the Nyika late Apr, and 30-40 in Nchelenge Dist. 5-15 May). Apart from two on the Makutu Plateau 4 and 7 Aug 1970, extreme dates are 21 Aug (north of Nsama) and 18 May (Isoka Dist.)[3]. It is possible the Nsama and Nchelenge areas fall within the non-breeding quarters. Vagrants were recorded at Chipata (16 Apr) and on the Copperbelt west to Chingola (4 Nov, 20 Dec and 28 Mar)[3].

Breeding   Nov   Dec   Jan
(n=4)   1   2   1   *Clutch*: C/1 (1); C/2 (2) & N/2 (1). From Nyika and Kasama.
Taxonomy *P. a. albiceps* (syn. *P. a. pallidigula* named from the Zaire side of L. Mweru)[5].
References [1]Benson & Pitman (1956-57); [2]Benson & Pitman (1961); [3]Dowsett & Leonard (in press a); [4]Penry (1979b); [5]Salvadori (1907); [6]Schouteden (1971).

Eurasian Sand Martin *Riparia riparia*   B358 **PW**

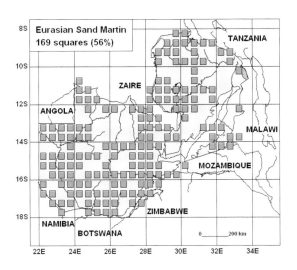

Distribution *Holarctic* (*winters Mauritania to South Africa*). May be locally numerous, near water. Occurs almost throughout, although there are few records in the east, whence large floodplains are lacking. *Alt.* 370-1800 m.

Ecology   Open areas near water. Roosts in *Typha* reedbeds, often along with *Hirundo rustica*.

Status A Palaearctic migrant and winter visitor. Usually rather scarce, but at times in concentrations of thousands (e.g. L. Wasa, Itawa Swamp, Zambezi near Victoria Falls). The great majority of records fall between early Sep and early May, with mean first date (over 27 years) 28 Sep, main arrivals from mid-Oct and mean last date (in 26 years) 5 May[1]. There are half a dozen records of single birds over-summering. A bird ringed in Zambia 15 Dec was recovered in Russia in Jun (Appendix 1). One bird returned to the place of ringing after 2 years[2].

Moult: between Nov and Mar; most passage birds mid-Nov to mid-Dec were in moult, a few nearly half-completed[1].
Taxonomy *R. r. riparia*.
References [1]Dowsett (in press b); [2]Dowsett & Leonard (2001).

African Sand Martin *Riparia paludicola*   B359 **RB**

Distribution *Old World* (*in the Afrotropics, mainly Mali to South Africa*). Confined mainly to the larger sandy rivers, throughout the Zambezi and Luangwa Valleys, and parts of the Kafue basin, north to Bangweulu. Local and often scarce, usually near sand cliffs. *Alt.* 330-1500 m.
Ecology Nests in sand cliffs, in small to large colonies (12-50 holes, exceptionally 200)[3]. Feeds near

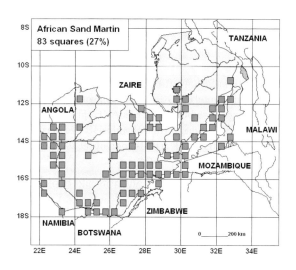

larger rivers or lakes, wandering occasionally to dams.

Status Most are resident at low levels, but some wander when not breeding to dams on the plateau around Lusaka, the Copperbelt and one even at Mwinilunga (May 1976)[2].

Breeding

	Jun	Jul	Aug	Sep
(n=16)	1	3	9	3

Clutch: N/2 (1); N/3 (3). Also a colony of some 200 nests "occupied...in April" on the Chambeshi near the Bangweulu Swamps[1].

Moult: one had just finished moult late Nov[3].

Taxonomy *R. p. paludicola*.

References [1]Benson (1956f); [2]Bowen (1983i); [3]Dowsett (in press a).

Banded Martin *Riparia cincta*   B357 **AMB**

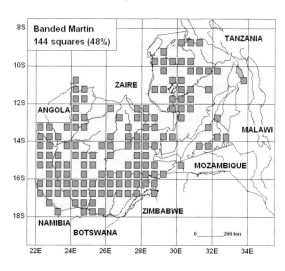

Distribution *Afrotropical (main breeding range Gabon to South Africa)*. Almost throughout, but overall sparse and rare in the Luangwa and Middle Zambezi Valleys, and the Eastern Province plateau. *Alt.* 370-1700 m, regularly in small numbers to 2200 m on the Nyika Plateau[2] (higher on the Malawi side, where breeding).

Ecology Open grassy plains and dambos, some populations on watershed plains or drier Kalahari sand. Nests in small banks or large termite mounds.

Status An intra-African migrant and breeding visitor. Recorded throughout the year, but fewest May-Oct (which is the main breeding season in Zambia), most Nov-Apr (perhaps just local post-breeding dispersal, as this is the main breeding season in much of southern Africa)[1].

Breeding

	Jan	Mar	May	Jul	Aug	Oct	Dec
(n=17)	1	1	1	1	10	2	1

All from west of 29°S (on the Nyika, in Malawi, breeding is in the rains)[2].

Clutch: N/1 (2); N/2 (2); C/3 (2) & N/3 (1).

Taxonomy *R. c. suahelica* is the widespread breeding form, replaced by *R. c. xerica* (slightly paler brown) in the west and the smaller *parvula* (wing <124 mm) in the north-west. Individuals apparently of *R. c. cincta* (paler, wing 125-134 mm) have been handled near Choma in Nov and Dec[1], as migrants from South Africa.

References [1]Dowsett & Leonard (in press a); [2]Dowsett-Lemaire (2006a).

Grey-rumped Swallow *Pseudhirundo griseopyga*

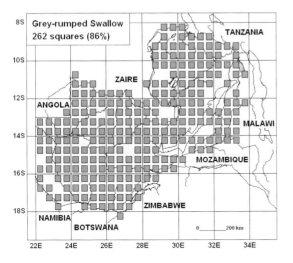

Distribution *Afrotropical (Guinea to South Africa).* Occurs locally in open country throughout Zambia, though less common in the low-lying valleys (and known breeding records are all above *c.* 950 m). Particularly numerous on dry floodplains such as the Kafue Flats. *Alt.* 450-2200 m (higher on the Malawi side of the Nyika).

Ecology Dry plains, the edges of dambos and other bare or burnt ground. Nests in disused rodent holes or cracks in flat ground.

Status Resident, but perhaps in part an intra-African migrant and breeding visitor. Present throughout the year, and although numbers are greatest in the dry season Apr-Oct the majority of birds may not move far during the other months (e.g. flocks of 100-200 on occasion in Jan around Lusaka). Small numbers occur in roosts of migratory *Hirundo rustica* Oct-Dec[2].

Breeding   Jun   Jul   Aug   Sep
(n=26)   2   7   13   4   *Clutch*: C/1 (1); C/2 (2); C/3 (2); C/4 (3); C/5 (2).
Moult: starting late Nov or early Dec[2].
Taxonomy[1] *P. g. griseopyga.*
References [1]Dowsett (1972b); [2]Dowsett (in press a).

Red-breasted Swallow *Hirundo semirufa*

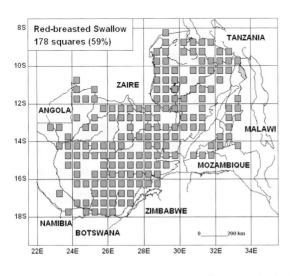

Distribution *Afrotropical (breeds Guinea to South Africa).* A bird of the plateau grasslands, absent from the Luangwa and Middle Zambezi Valleys, and at present barely west of the Zambezi (e.g. on Siloana Plains)[1]. But it is spreading, with the extension of a road system with associated culverts suitable for nesting, and is locally not uncommon (e.g. along the road from Lusaka to Livingstone). Before 1957 it was not known in Zambia west of the Copperbelt, Lalafuta River or Choma, but in that year it was found in N. Mwinilunga. Further south, by the 1970s it was well established in Kaoma Dist., and ranged west to the Simungoma area. It was first reported in the Mongu area on Loma Plain in 1985, and on Siloana Plains in 1999[1]. *Alt.* 950-1700 m, exceptionally 1900 m on passage (Mafingas, early Oct)[2].

Ecology Dambos, grassy plains and lightly-wooded country. Nests in road culverts, but also under bridges and on power pylons (none known from natural sites).

Status An intra-African migrant and breeding visitor. There are records for all months, but there is a significantly higher frequency Jul-Mar compared to Apr-Jun. There are in fact only two May records[1].

Breeding
	Oct	Nov	Dec	Jan	Feb	
(n=43)	7	11	12	8	5	*Clutch*: C/1 (1); C/2 (6); C/3 (13); C/4 (6).

Taxonomy *H. s. semirufa.*
References [1]Dowsett & Leonard (in press a); [2]Leonard *et al.* (2001a).

Mosque Swallow *Hirundo senegalensis* B368 **RB**

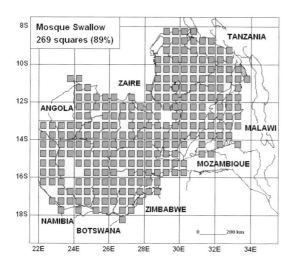

Distribution *Afrotropical* (*Mauritania to South Africa*). Locally quite common in open woodland in all parts of the country. *Alt.* 330-2200 m.
Ecology Woodland (avoiding denser types) or wooded grassland, even montane, and often at the ecotone of woodland and grassland. Nests in holes in trees, on brick buildings, and even on metal telegraph poles. Overall in more wooded situations than *H. semirufa.*
Status Largely resident (recorded year-round), but there are seasonal absences which vary from one part of the country to another. The species may be absent from some plateau areas May-Nov (e.g. Mazabuka), and present during those months at low altitude (e.g. the Luangwa Valley)[1]. Often in flocks of 30-60 (once 85), mid-May to early Nov, when not breeding.

Breeding
	Aug	Oct	Nov	Dec	Jan	Feb	Mar	Apr	May
(n=26)	2	4	3	6	1	2	3	3	2

Clutch: C/1 (1); C/2 (2); C/3 (2).
Taxonomy *H. s. monteiri.*
References [1]Dowsett (in press a).

Lesser Striped Swallow *Hirundo abyssinica* B371 **RB**

Distribution *Afrotropical* (*Mauritania to South Africa*). Common, in savanna areas almost throughout, although in the west it occurs mainly along the larger river systems. *Alt.* 330-2200 m.
Ecology Lightly-wooded country or (where more heavily-wooded) in association with rivers, and often near rocky hills. Nested originally on rocks, but now on brick buildings, as well as under culverts and bridges, while some pairs of the race *ampliformis* breed on tree branches (Mwinilunga and the Senanga-Sesheke area)[1].
Status Resident. Present in all months, but significantly less numerous Jan-Apr, abundant May-Dec[3] (perhaps involving an influx of migrants from southern Africa, as noted Apr-Aug in the Shire Valley of Malawi)[4].

Breeding
	Mar	Apr	May	Jun	Jul	Aug	Sep	Oct	Nov	Dec	Jan
(n=68)	1	1	1	2	4	5	22	11	12	6	3

Clutch: C/1 (1); C/2 (10); C/3 (17); C/4 (2).

Taxonomy *H. a. unitatis*, replaced by *H. a. ampliformis* in the west (larger, with coarser black streaking below)[2].
References [1]Aspinwall (1980); [2]Benson *et al.* (1970); [3]Dowsett (in press a); [4]Dowsett-Lemaire & Dowsett (2006).

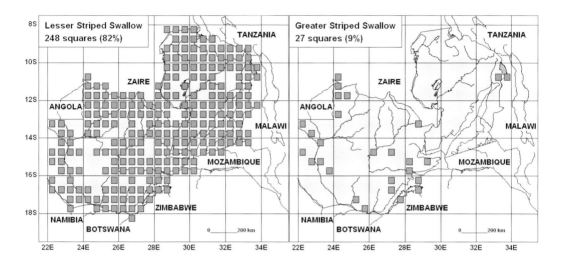

Greater Striped Swallow *Hirundo cucullata*   B370 **AM**

Distribution *Afrotropical* (*breeds Angola to South Africa, wintering north to Zaire*). Migrates mainly through the western half of Zambia, en route between its southern breeding range and Congo basin non-breeding areas. It has been identified east to the "80-mile" Dambo[1], and again in the Nyika area. *Alt.* 1000-1500 m, occasionally down to 550 m, and as high as 2100 m on the Nyika Plateau.
Ecology Open country, in particular watershed plains, on passage.
Status An intra-African passage migrant, mostly 4 Apr-6 Jun and 28 Aug-22 Nov (the Nyika records, 27 and 30 Dec[3], being late). There are 5 records in S. Zambia mid-Dec to early Mar, at which time the main population is breeding in southern Africa. There are also two acceptable records in Jul, one of them (19 Jul) in Mwinilunga Dist.[2], perhaps at the southern limit of the non-breeding range.
Taxonomy No races recognized.
References [1]Aspinwall (1973f); [2]Dowsett & Leonard (in press a); [3]Dowsett-Lemaire (2006a).

Red-rumped Swallow *Hirundo daurica*   B369 **RB**

Distribution *Old World* (*in the Afrotropics, Mauritania to Malawi; Palaearctic birds winter mainly in the Sahel*). Locally common around rocky hills associated with the eastern highlands, from Kasangu[8] and Kambole[1], south to the Mafingas (1950-2000 m)[3] and Nyika Plateau (to 2200 m)[4]. Known also from Diwa Hill[9] (and adjacent Kasungu N.P. in Malawi)[5], and has exceptionally wandered as far south as the Lusitu stream on the Zambezi escarpment in Mar (open square)[2]; vagrants have occurred in Zimbabwe near Harare and even as far west as Hwange N.P. (1826C), at the same time of year[6,7]. *Alt.* 1130-2200 m, exceptionally down to 410 m (Lusitu).
Ecology Usually not far from rocky hills, but breeds occasionally on buildings (Nyika).

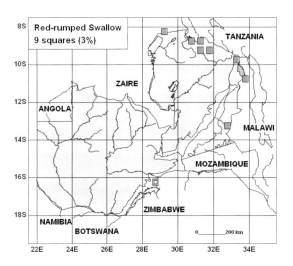

Status Resident on the whole, with some wandering.

Breeding   Nov   Jan   Mar

(n=3)   1   1   1

Nest-building also 26 Feb 1981 on the Nyika, where cooperative breeding observed[4].

Clutch: no data.

Taxonomy *H. d. emini.*

References [1]Benson (1956d); [2]Benson *et al.* (1970); [3]Dowsett & Stjernstedt (1973); [4]Dowsett-Lemaire (2006a); [5]Dowsett-Lemaire & Dowsett (2006); [6]Hustler & Irwin (1995); [7]Irwin (1981a); [8]Leonard (1998d); [9]Winterbottom (1939a).

South African Cliff Swallow *Hirundo spilodera*   B - **AM**

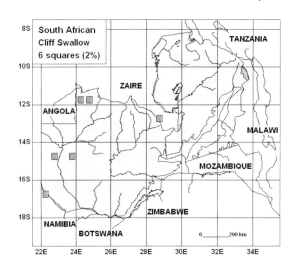

Distribution *Afrotropical* (*breeds Botswana to South Africa, most wintering in Zaire*). First identified in Nov 1978 in Mwinilunga[1]. As with *H. cucullata*, this species breeds in southern Africa, and passes through W. Zambia, perhaps regularly (exceptionally east to Ndola)[2], en route to Zaire. *Alt.* 1050-1460 m.

Ecology Any open areas on passage, especially grassy plains.

Status An intra-African passage migrant: of the seven acceptable sight records (single birds, except once a party of 8), six fall between 7 Aug and 13 Nov, and one was on return passage north 25 Apr[3].

Taxonomy No races recognized.

References [1]Dowsett (1979b); [2]Dowsett & Leonard (in press a); [3]Dowsett *et al.* (1999a).

Red-throated Cliff Swallow *Hirundo rufigula*   B373 **AMB**

Distribution *Zambezian near-endemic* (*Gabon to S. Angola*). Locally common at bridges in NW Zambia, from Mwinilunga[2] east to the Copperbelt[5] (Ndola and Miengwe), south to the Chikata Rapids (the site of its original discovery in the country, and the only natural site reported)[7]. There has probably been a slow spread in this area, utilising bridges. Recent records in NE Zambia to the Lukulu Bridge on the Kasama-Luwingu road (where found nesting in 1993) and Chishimba Falls (present in 2005)[3], are by far the most easterly of the species. *Alt.* 1100-1480 m.

Ecology Originally associated with rocky areas near water (Chikata Rapids, not visited in recent years),

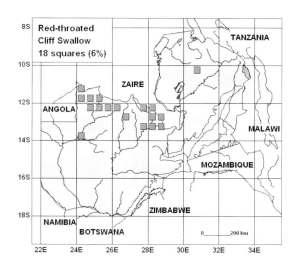

but now known to nest only on bridges, and under the overhang on dam walls[4].

Status An intra-African migrant and breeding visitor. Records fall within the period 8 Mar to 3 Dec[3], but first arrivals are usually in Apr-May or even Jun. A species which has adapted very well to man-made structures, although there may have been some decrease in numbers more recently[6]. Colonies of up to *c.* 150 nests have been observed at Kafubu Dam[4].

Breeding Jul Aug Sep Oct
(n=25)   1   4   7   13
Occupied nests also noted at Mutanda Bridge mid-Apr, but outcome not known; there may be two clutches per year[6].

Clutch: C/1 (2); C/2 (15); C/3 (3).

Taxonomy[1] No races recognized. Formerly considered conspecific with *H. spilodera*.

References [1]Benson & Irwin (1964b); [2]Bowen (1978); [3]Dowsett & Leonard (in press a); [4]Taylor (1982b); [5]Tree (1964); [6]Van Daele (1999d); [7]White (1949b).

African Rock Martin *Hirundo fuligula*   B374 **RB**

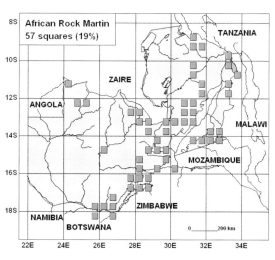

Distribution *Afrotropical* (*Mauritania to South Africa*) *and S. Palaearctic.* Common on rocky hills, essentially down the Muchingas and the Zambezi escarpment, and the kopjes of the Eastern Province plateau. It ranges from the Kalambo Falls[1] down to the Victoria Falls[2]. West of Chingola it reappears in the Kabompo Gorge and on Mujimbeji Hill[7], and at Kalene Hill[4] and the Zambezi Rapids in Mwinilunga[3]. Two seen at a granite hill by the Lufupa River (1426C) in Aug may have been wanderers[6]. *Alt.* 330-2200 m.

Ecology Rocky gorges, cliffs and caves; associated with buildings in some urban areas (has bred at Kasama since the 1950s[5], and prospected buildings in Lusaka in the 1970s[6]). No substantial spread observed yet. Breeds in small colonies.

Status Resident.

Breeding Feb Mar Apr Jul Aug Sep Oct Nov
(n=24)   2   4   2   2   1   7   3   3   *Clutch*: C/2 (5); C/3 (6).

Taxonomy *H. f. fusciventris*[8].

References [1]Aspinwall (1973a); [2]Benson & Irwin (1967b); [3]Benson *et al.* (1970); [4]Bowen (1979c); [5]Brooke & Vernon (1961a); [6]Dowsett (in press a); [7]White (1945-46); [8]White (1957).

Blue Swallow *Hirundo atrocaerulea*   B362 **AMB**

Distribution *Afromontane endemic (breeding S. Tanzania to South Africa, wintering north to Uganda).* As a breeding bird known only from grasslands on the Nyika Plateau (mainly the Malawi side), where common, but wanderers (open squares) were seen at Kitwe (one, 7 Jan 1995)[7] and Mutinondo Wilderness (six, including one male, 5 Sep 2003). [A possible sighting was reported over the Kafue River near Chunga ("?" on map), on 21 Jan 2006, but details were incomplete[3]. A sighting from Lusaka 12 Sep 1971[8] is considered misidentified.] Just extralimitally to the north there is a breeding population in the Marungu highlands of SE Zaire[4]. *Alt.* 1900-2200 m (higher on the Malawi side of the Nyika), with vagrants 1220 to *c.* 1600 m.

Ecology Montane grassland, breeding mainly under overhangs of banks or in holes in the ground, more rarely on buildings (Malawi side of Nyika).

Status An intra-African migrant and breeding visitor. Extreme dates are 17 Aug and 30 Apr (exceptionally once 13 May); most arrive by mid-Sep, and depart during the first half of Apr[5].

Conservation Classed as "Vulnerable"[1] and considered endangered in marginal parts of its breeding range (South Africa). In the Nyika N.P. the population is under no threat, with some 300 pairs (mostly on the Malawian side)[5,6].

Breeding   Nov   Dec   Jan
(n=4)   1   2   1   *Clutch*: N/1 (1); C/3 (1) & N/3 (1); C/4 (1).

Taxonomy[2] No races recognized.

References [1]BirdLife International (2000, 2004a); [2]Chapin (1953); [3]Dowsett & Leonard (in press a); [4]Dowsett & Prigogine (1974); [5]Dowsett-Lemaire (2006a); [6]Dowsett-Lemaire & Dowsett (2006); [7]Leonard (1995); [8]Tucker (1971).

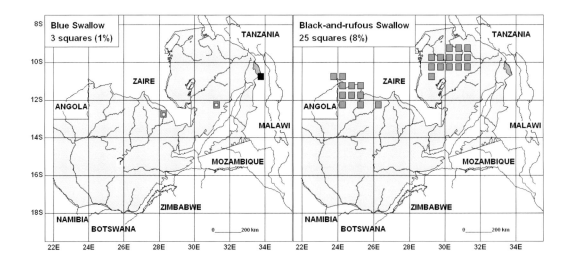

Black-and-rufous Swallow *Hirundo nigrorufa*   B363 **RB**

Distribution *Zambezian endemic (NE Zambia to south-central Angola).* Locally common in some of the dambos of N. Zambia, in the west south to Kamapanda Plain[3,4] and east to Solwezi[2], and in the north-east eastwards to Mwilozi Dambo[4] and Kasama[1]. [Sight records from the Copperbelt and Shiwa Ngandu are considered unreliable, some at least being misidentifications of *H. semirufa*[6].] *Alt.* 1200-

1600 m.

Ecology Mainly dambos and some watershed plains. Breeds in holes in the ground, or more especially in streamside banks.

Status Reported in all months, but there are few records Jan to Mar inclusive, so some may be seasonal breeding visitors (late Mar to early Nov)[6].

Breeding[5]   Jul   Aug   Sep   Oct
(n=26)   1   4   19   2   *Clutch*: C/1 (2); C/2 (4); C/3 (19).

Taxonomy No races recognized. From its behaviour, seems closely related to *H. atrocaerulea*.

References [1]Benson (1956d); [2]Benson & Irwin (1965b); [3]Bowen (1979b); [4]Bowen (1983e); [5]Bowen & Colebrook-Robjent (1984); [6]Dowsett (in press a).

[**White-throated Blue Swallow** *Hirundo nigrita*
Guineo-Congolian near-endemic (*Guinea-Bissau to S. Zaire*). A species of well-wooded rivers, this swallow has been collected at Kasaji in Katanga[1] and might occur on some of the less accessible larger rivers in Mwinilunga. **References** [1]Schouteden (1971).]

Wire-tailed Swallow *Hirundo smithii*   B364 **RB**

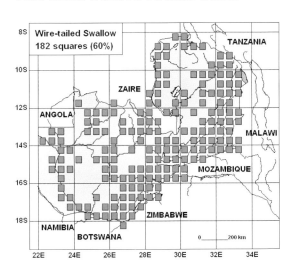

Wire-tailed Swallow
182 squares (60%)

Distribution *Old World Tropics* (*in Africa, Mauritania to South Africa*). Common through most of the country, although in the west does not occur far from the Upper Zambezi and Kafue River basins. *Alt.* 330-1700 m.

Ecology Usually near water, where it nests on bridges, rocks, even on operational ferries, and often now on buildings.

Status Resident. Present in all months, but most observations Jul-Oct and fewest Nov-Jan[2]. It is unlikely there is any regular movement.

Breeding   Jan   Feb   Mar   Apr   May
(n=130)   1   9   22   7   2
               Jun   Jul   Aug   Sep   Oct
                4   6   43   19   17

Clutch: C/1 (2); C/2 (10); C/3 (37); C/4 (2); C/5 (1).
Moult: noted Nov and Dec[2].
Taxonomy[1] *H. s. smithii*.
References [1]Chapin (1953); [2]Dowsett (in press a).

Pearl-breasted Swallow *Hirundo dimidiata*   B366 **RB**

Distribution *Afrotropical* (*Angola to South Africa, east to Malawi*). Sparse in lightly-wooded country and grassland, throughout much of the Zambian plateau. Rare in the lower Luapula, absent from the Luangwa Valley, and in the Middle Zambezi known only from one vagrant to near Sinazongwe (open

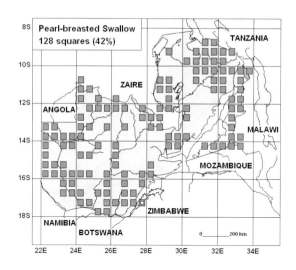

square)[2]. *Alt.* 950-1800 m.

Ecology Dambos and clearings (natural or man-made) in miombo woodland, or edges of pans and swampy ground. Nests have been in pits, an outhouse and chicken hut[5].

Status Perhaps mainly resident, but with some seasonal movements. Reported in all months, but the frequency of occurrence is significantly greater May-Nov than Dec-Apr. Records Dec-Feb are only from the south and east of the country, and there is possibly some movement southwards in the rains[2]. Occurs in groups of up to 20.

Breeding Aug Sep
(n=4)   3   1
Clutch: C/3 (1).
Moult: well advanced late Nov[4].

Taxonomy[1,3] *H. d. marwitzi.*

References [1]Benson (1949b); [2]Dowsett (in press a); [3]Irwin & Benson (1967a); [4]Traylor (1965b); [5]White (1947d).

White-throated Swallow *Hirundo albigularis*   B365 **AMW**

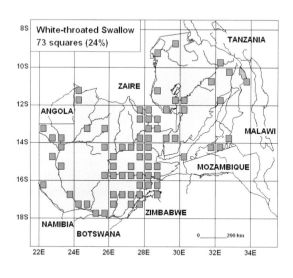

Distribution *Afrotropical (breeds mostly southern Africa, wintering north to Zaire).* Locally common in open areas on passage throughout the Zambian plateau, but especially in the west; largest numbers on the Kafue Flats and in the Bangweulu basin. Very scarce in the Middle Zambezi Valley, rare in the Luangwa Valley[2]. *Alt.* 950-1600 m, rarely down to 500 m, and wandering to 2200 m (Nyika)[3].

Ecology Floodplains and open grasslands.

Status An intra-African migrant and non-breeding visitor. All acceptable records are for the period 5 Mar to 18 Dec (a few sightings outside this period may be misidentifications). Peak numbers are Apr-Jun and Sep-Oct, during this latter period flocks being especially in evidence locally[2].

Breeding There is a single breeding record claimed from Mansa, of C/3 on 20 Oct 1961, in the eaves of a deserted barn[1]; it is not possible to accept this purely visual record without question.

Moult: Aug-Nov in a sample of 19 presumed *H. a. albigularis* (wing-lengths 127-137 mm) in Southern Province[2].

Taxonomy Most Zambian records are of migrant *H. a. albigularis* from southern Africa (shorter-winged *H. a. ambigua* are reported from the western half of the country, east to Mweru Wantipa)[4]. Zambian wing-lengths as a whole (119-137 mm) cover almost the entire range reported for the two

populations, *H. a. albigularis* (South Africa: 125-135) and *H. a. ambigua* (Angola: 117-124 mm)[4], but in all cases sample sizes are small.
References [1]Benson & Pitman (1964); [2]Dowsett & Leonard (in press a); [3]Dowsett-Lemaire (2006a); [4]Irwin & Benson (1967a).

Eurasian (Barn) Swallow *Hirundo rustica*   B360 **PW**

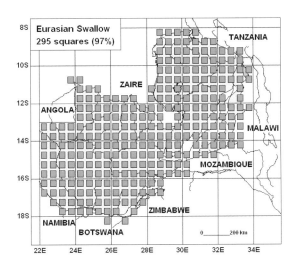

Distribution *Holarctic* (*winters mainly Sierra Leone to South Africa*). Throughout the country, and by far the most numerous hirundine seasonally. *Alt.* 330-2200 m.
Ecology Roosts usually in reedbeds, otherwise in any open habitat (avoiding densely-wooded areas).
Status A Palaearctic migrant and winter visitor. Large roosts occur in a few places on southward passage (Oct-Dec), those containing 500,000 birds or more at Itawa (maximum estimated 2-3 million)[6], Kitwe[8] and Muckle Neuk (near Choma)[3]. Fewer birds (though still many millions in all) stay throughout Zambia during the rains. The only significant roost reported on northward passage was of "thousands" at Kalabo, Feb-Mar[7]. There are a dozen reports of birds staying during the Palaearctic breeding season (singly, apart from a report of "several"). There have been recoveries in the Palaearctic of 45 birds ringed in Zambia, and a further 20 ringed in Europe have been recovered here. The origins of these birds extend from England (only one) to as far east as 86°E in Russia (14 recoveries: Appendix 1). The oldest recovery was aged more than 7 years (from Ukraine); 14 birds returned to the place of ringing in Zambia after 1 year, and two after 3 years[4]. *Moult*: Nov-Apr[1,5].
Taxonomy *H. r. rustica* and *H. r. gutturalis* both occur, the latter distinguished by having the blue-black chest band mixed with pale red brown. Occasionally rufous-breasted birds are seen, with the characters of the race *transitiva* (not known to occur so far south). A hybrid between this species and *Delichon urbicum* was caught near Choma[2].
References [1]Dowsett (1966a); [2]Dowsett (1978a); [3]Dowsett (in press b); [4]Dowsett & Leonard (2001); [5]Francis (1980); [6]Taylor (1982b); [7]Traylor (1965b); [8]Tree (1966c).

Angola Swallow *Hirundo angolensis*   B361 **AMB/R**

Distribution *Afrotropical* (*SE Gabon to N. Zambia*). Apart from a population on the Nyika Plateau[6], it ranges (locally quite common) through much of the higher plateau of N. Zambia, from Mbala south to Chishimba Falls[3], across to Johnston Falls on the Luapula[2], down to L. Wasa (Kasanka N.P.) and the Copperbelt. [There is an unconfirmed sight record from further south, from the Mkushi River above Old Mkushi III, "?" on map[9].] Reappears in N. Mwinilunga, in the Chitunta Plain-Luakela Bridge area[1,4]. *Alt.* 1000-2200 m.
Ecology Montane or mid-altitude grassland, or by perennial rivers or swamps. Breeding on buildings,

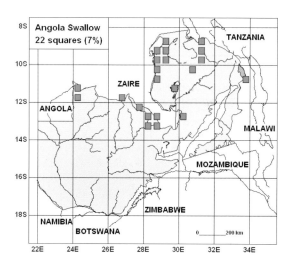

dam walls or under the overhang of a stream-bank.

Status An intra-African migrant and breeding visitor. On the Copperbelt, reported in all months, but most numerous in the dry season (Mar-Sep)[7]. Similarly in the north-west it is apparently absent from the latter part of the rains (records being May-Nov only), and on the Nyika all records but one are May-Jan[8].

Breeding

	May	Jun	Oct	Nov	Dec
(n=8)	1	1	2	3	1

On the Nyika egg-laying is Oct-Dec, on the Copperbelt May-Oct. Nest-building and occupied nests have also been noted in the latter area Jul and Aug. *Clutch*: N/1 (1); N/2 (2); C/3 (1) & N/3 (2).

Taxonomy[5] No races recognized. One of the African representatives of the *H. rustica* species-group.

References [1]Aspinwall (1971b); [2]Benson & Pitman (1964); [3]Benson & White (1957); [4]Bowen (1983i); [5]Chapin (1953); [6]Dowsett (1970a); [7]Dowsett & Leonard (in press a); [8]Dowsett-Lemaire (2006a); [9]Winterbottom (1939a).

Eurasian House Martin *Delichon urbicum*   B375 **PW**

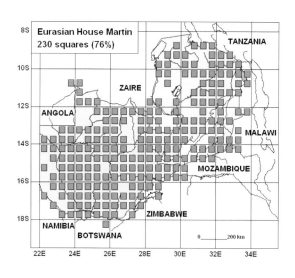

Distribution *Palaearctic (winters mainly Sudan to South Africa)*. Can occur anywhere, sometimes in numbers, but more especially at higher altitude in hilly areas. *Alt.* 330-2200 m.

Ecology Usually flying high, often over open country; at lower levels sometimes near water. Rarely in roosts of *Hirundo rustica* (it has been suggested they may roost on the wing). Has been seen to associate in Oct with nesting *H. rufigula*[4], and to roost in Oct in the nests of *H. abyssinica*[3].

Status A Palaearctic migrant and winter visitor. Extreme dates are 10 Sep to 27 May, except for single sightings in Jul and Aug[2], most Oct to mid-Apr. The average first date over 29 years was 27 Sep, the average last (in 28 years) 29 Apr[2]. As with *Apus apus*, movements appear to be related to the arrival of the Intertropical Convergence Zone. There have been recoveries in Zambia of two ringed birds from Germany and one from Sweden (Appendix 1).

Breeding In the Palaearctic. No records in Zambia (but has nested very rarely in southern Africa).

Taxonomy *D. u. urbicum*. A hybrid between this species and *Hirundo rustica* was caught near Choma[1].

References [1]Dowsett (1978a); [2]Dowsett (in press b); [3]Fellowes (1971); [4]Taylor (1982b).

Motacillidae

Yellow Wagtail *Motacilla flava*   B550 **PW**

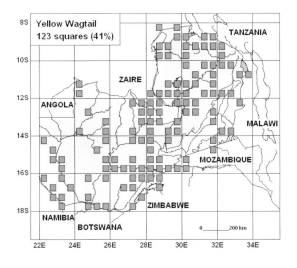

Distribution *Palaearctic and marginally W. Nearctic (winters Mauritania to South Africa).* Can be expected on open ground anywhere, but usually in small numbers, most commonly on the larger floodplains, and very scarce in the Luangwa and Middle Zambezi Valleys. *Alt.* 330-2200 m.

Ecology On bare ground and short grass usually near water, including pastures, dambos, floodplains, edge of marshes and dams.

Status A Palaearctic migrant and winter visitor. All records are within the period 23 Sep to 9 Jun, with main arrivals mid-Oct and few after mid-Apr. The average first date over 29 years was 7 Oct, the average last (in 22 years) 29 Apr[2]. Numbers are usually small, though loose concentrations of up to 2000 occur at Lochinvar[2].

Moult: body moult only, Nov-Mar (flight feathers being replaced in the Palaearctic).

Taxonomy[3] The subspecies commonly recognized in Zambia (confirmed by specimens) are, in descending order of abundance: *M. f. flava, lutea* and *thunbergi*. A single specimen of *M. f. leucocephala* has been claimed, but this might be an aberrant *M. f. flava*. [Birds with the apparent characters of W. European *flavissima* have been reported, but are probably variant *lutea*[1].]

References [1]Dowsett (1965b); [2]Dowsett (in press b); [3]Irwin & Benson (1967a).

Cape Wagtail *Motacilla capensis*   B551 **RB**

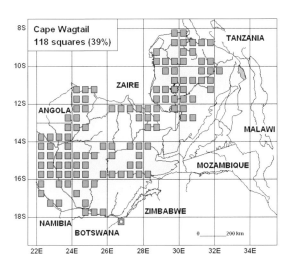

Distribution *Afrotropical (Kenya to South Africa).* Small numbers in wetlands throughout much of the country west of the Rift, being absent from the Eastern Province plateau, Luangwa Valley, Southern Province plateau, and Middle Zambezi Valley (except for a vagrant to Bimbi, open square)[3]. [Records have been claimed from the Luangwa Valley[1], but there was probably confusion with *M. flava*[6]. This species was listed as one that had disappeared from the Kariba area since the flooding of the Lake[2], but we are aware of no acceptable record from the Valley up to then[4].] In Northern Province, not east of Mbesuma on the Chambeshi[3]. *Alt.* 900-1700 m (once 630 m).

Ecology Floodplain and edges of marsh and swamp vegetation; unlike the nominate race of southern Africa it is not commensal.

Status Resident, with no more than local movements[6]. Occasionally in small, temporary groups.

Breeding   Jul   Aug   Sep   Oct
(n=11)   3   2   5   1   *Clutch*: C/3 (5).
Moult: finishes mid-Nov to early Dec[3].

Taxonomy[5] *M. c. simplicissima*. Some sight records are thought to represent vagrant *M. c. capensis*; that at Bimbi may be correct (although as a vagrant from the Zimbabwe plateau, the nearest population is far distant), but aberrant *simplicissima* are known from Zambia[3] and the occurrence of nominate *capensis* remains hypothetical.

References [1]Berry (1981b); [2]Donnelly & Donnelly (1983); [3]Dowsett (in press a); [4]Irwin (1981a); [5]Irwin & Benson (1967a); [6]Leonard (2001c).

Grey Wagtail *Motacilla cinerea*   B - **PW**

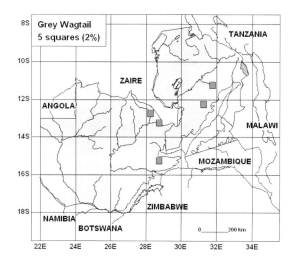

Distribution *Palaearctic* (*winters mostly Ethiopia to Tanzania*). Here, almost at the southern limit of its non-breeding range, this wagtail is in some years present on a few northern streams: known from Shiwa Ngandu and Mutinondo Wilderness[3], west to Mwekera[2] and Kafubu, and once as far south as near Lusaka[1,4]. *Alt.* 1200-1450 m.

Ecology Alongside *M. clara* on small fast-flowing streams and rivers.

Status An irregular Palaearctic winter visitor or passage migrant. There are six acceptable records of single birds, five of them 25 Oct-9 Dec[3], and one 1 May (this last, in 1979, the first Zambian record)[1]. Reported increasingly in southern Africa since the 1980s[5], but most winter in the highlands of eastern Africa.

Taxonomy No Zambian specimen, but doubtless *M. c. cinerea*.

References [1]Aspinwall (1981); [2]Casalis de Pury (1979); [3]Dowsett (in press b); [4]Dowsett *et al.* (1999a); [5]Piper in Hockey *et al.* (2005).

Long-tailed (Mountain) Wagtail *Motacilla clara*   B552 **RB**

Distribution *Afrotropical* (*Guinea to South Africa*). Small numbers present on streams in the Kawambwa area and around L. Tanganyika; reappears in the eastern highlands, down the Muchingas[3] (and a few on Eastern Province plateau), locally on the Copperbelt at Mwekera[7], then south along the Zambezi escarpment to the Nankoli stream[6] and Sinazongwe[4]. It is not found again on the Zambezi until the immediate vicinity of the Victoria Falls[2]. Widespread in N. Mwinilunga, but unknown between there and the Copperbelt, except for a sighting from the Kifubwa River Gorge, 1226A[4]. *Alt.* 530-1850 m, to 1950 m on the Mafingas[5].

Ecology Favours perennial, fast-flowing streams with rocks and waterfalls, sometimes inside forest;

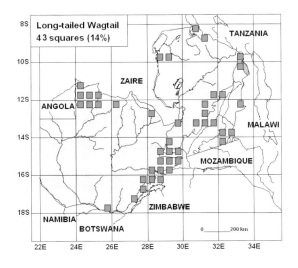

Long-tailed Wagtail
43 squares (14%)

also recorded at nearby dams. Breeds on rocks near water and may compete locally with *M. aguimp*.

Status Essentially resident; some wander to dams and seasonal streams, and one near Mfuwe was perhaps displaced when a dam burst in the nearby Luangwa escarpment, on the Lutembwe River[4]. The few Copperbelt observations may represent a very small local population.

Breeding   Mar   Sep   Oct

(n=10)   1   5   4

Clutch: C/2 (4); C/3 (2).

Taxonomy[1] *M. c. torrentium*.

References [1]Benson (1962a); [2]Benson & Irwin (1967b); [3]Berry (1981b); [4]Dowsett (in press a); [5]Dowsett & Stjernstedt (1973);

[6]Duval (1969); [7]Penry (1980).

African Pied Wagtail *Motacilla aguimp*   B553 **RB**

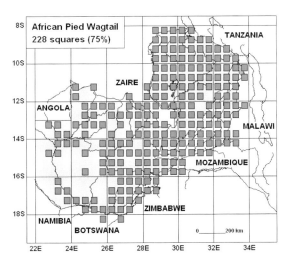

African Pied Wagtail
228 squares (75%)

Distribution *Afrotropical (Senegal to South Africa).* Common through most of the country; often commensal in the east, in the western quarter restricted to the larger waterways, and barely occurs west of the Zambezi. *Alt.* 330-2150 m (Nyika, higher on the Malawi side)[3].

Ecology In open country on the edge of any water; also commonly in urban areas and breeds on buildings (houses and bridges) as well as rocky banks of streams, where likely to compete locally with *M. clara*. In much of the west its place may be taken by *M. capensis*.

Status Resident and numerous locally (100 or more congregating at times at Chipata in the rains). Present in all months, a 2-year survey showing no evidence of movements, other than purely local[2].

Breeding   Feb   Mar   Apr   May   Jun   Jul   Aug   Sep   Oct   Nov   Dec

(n=113)   2   7   7   3   2   11   16   29   18   12   6

Clutch: C/1 (3); C/2 (10); C/3 (11); C/4 (4).

Taxonomy[1] *M. a. vidua*. A melanistic example has been reported[4].

References [1]Chapin (1953); [2]Dowsett (in press a); [3]Dowsett-Lemaire (2006a); [4]Taylor (1978b).

Richard's Pipit *Anthus richardi*   B554 **RB**

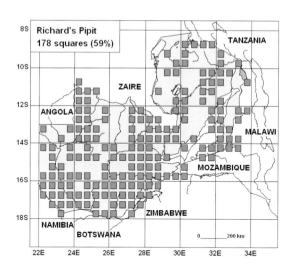

Distribution *Old World (in the Afrotropics, breeds Guinea to South Africa; Palaearctic birds rarely winter in the Sahel).* Locally common in open country throughout Zambia. *Alt.* 330-*c.* 2250 m on the Mafingas[3] (higher on the Malawi side of Nyika).

Ecology In grassland, preferably short or recently burnt, of dambo margins, dry floodplain, light open savanna, airfields, edges of pans, and commonly on agricultural land left fallow; also very common in short montane grassland.

Status Resident. Present in all months, although with a preponderance of records May-Nov[4]. In 3 years 85% of Copperbelt records were Apr-Oct. Dates for *A. r. lwenarum* are 3 and 5 Jun (Mwinilunga)[7], 23 Oct (Balovale, now Zambezi town, type); a detailed survey in Aug 1974 did not find it[1].

Breeding	May	Jun	Jul	Aug	Sep	Oct	Nov	Dec
(n=35)	1	1	3	5	9	5	8	3

Clutch: C/1 (1); C/2 (1); C/3 (9); C/4 (1); N/5 (1).

Moult: Feb-Apr, birds examined mid-Apr to mid-Jan showing no moult[4].

Taxonomy[6,7] Most Zambian breeding birds are closest to *A. r. katangae*, with darker birds in montane grassland on the Nyika and in the Mafingas perhaps *A. r. lichenya*. *A. r. lwenarum* (type locality Balovale; *NHM*)[8] occurs (apparently as a non-breeding visitor) in the north-west. The latter has been considered conspecific with the Mountain Pipit *A. hoeschi* of South Africa[2] (Afromontane), but this remains unproven. The pallid *A. r. bocagei* occurs as a dry season visitor in the south and west, and so may the even greyer *A. r. grotei*. African birds are sometimes considered specifically distinct from Palaearctic *A. richardi* (under the name of Grassveld Pipit *A. cinnamomeus*), but we believe them to be very closely related[5].

References [1]Aspinwall (1979b); [2]Clancey (1984a); [3]Clay (1953); [4]Dowsett (in press a); [5]Dowsett & Dowsett-Lemaire (1993); [6]Irwin (1981a); [7]Irwin & Benson (1967b); [8]White (1946a: 9).

Long-billed Pipit *Anthus similis* (including Wood Pipit *A. s. nyassae*)   B557 **RB**

Distribution *Old World (in the Afrotropics, mainly Sierra Leone to South Africa).* Quite common in all the plateau woodlands, being absent only from the Luangwa and Middle Zambezi Valleys below the escarpments (except present on Nchete Is.)[4]. *Alt.* 510-2200 m (Nyika)[6].

Ecology Most common in miombo woodland, but also in *Burkea* and open *Baikiaea*. In the eastern highlands in montane grassland with large rocks. Populations from miombo and montane grassland may approach each other closely, as on the Nyika Plateau, where birds occur almost in a continuum from the upper limit of miombo woodland on the western escarpment (2050 m) to adjacent grassland with boulders and low bush[6].

Status Resident. Unlike other pipits, rarely congregating.

Breeding	Jul	Aug	Sep	Oct	Nov	Dec	
(n=56)	1	4	20	19	10	2	(Includes 2 Oct records of *winterbottomi*.)

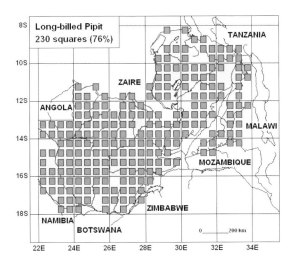

Clutch: C/2 (13); C/3 (33).

Moult: from about Nov[9].

Taxonomy *A. s. nyassae* is the widespread miombo woodland form, and we prefer not to give *nyassae* (the "Wood Pipit") specific status[5], on present evidence. Possibly replaced in the eastern highlands by *A. s. winterbottomi* (type locality the Mafinga Mts; *NHM*; named for J.M. Winterbottom)[3], although some authorities treat all as *nyassae*[1]. The taxon *winterbottomi* has erroneously been allied with the extralimital Jackson's Pipit *A. latistriatus* (itself probably a form of *A. richardi*[8]). The existence of parapatric woodland and rocky hillside populations has also been observed in Zimbabwe[2,7].

References [1]Benson & Irwin (1967b); [2]Clancey (1968c); [3]Clancey (1985: 165); [4]Dowsett (in press a); [5]Dowsett & Dowsett-Lemaire (1987); [6]Dowsett-Lemaire (2006a); [7]Irwin (1981a); [8]Pearson in Keith *et al.* (1992); [9]Traylor (1965b).

Plain-backed Pipit *Anthus leucophrys* 　　　　　　　B555 **RB**

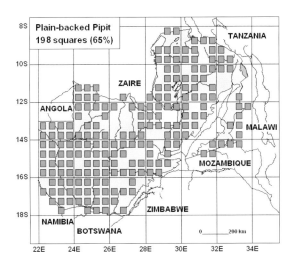

Distribution *Afrotropical* (*Mauritania to South Africa*). Ranges in small numbers in moist grasslands throughout the plateau, being absent only from the eastern highlands, the Luangwa and Middle Zambezi Valleys[2]. *Alt.* 550-1400 m.

Ecology Short moist grassland of floodplain (less common on the largest) and dambo margins, often alongside *A. richardi*; in burnt areas in the dry season, when it may also be found occasionally next to *A. vaalensis*.

Status Resident, but concentrating in dozens at times on burnt ground[2].

Breeding	Aug	Sep	Oct	Nov
(n=20)	2	8	7	3

Clutch: C/1 (1); C/2 (2); C/3 (8); C/4 (1).

Moult: started end Oct[3].

Taxonomy *A. l. bohndorffi* in the north, *A. l. tephridorsus* (paler, greyer above) in the south-west (with birds from the north-west and west intermediate, "*A. l. prunus*")[1].

References [1]Benson *et al.* (1970); [2]Dowsett (in press a); [3]Traylor (1965b).

Buffy Pipit *Anthus vaalensis* B556 **AMB**

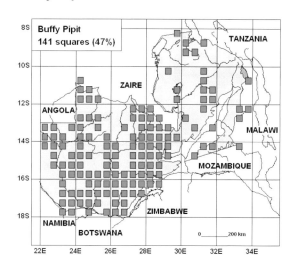

Distribution *Afrotropical (S. Tanzania to South Africa)*. Quite common in grassland throughout the western half of the country (although so far unrecorded from parts of the extreme south-west, and occurring in the Middle Zambezi Valley only on passage). Locally on the Eastern Province plateau, and regularly visiting the high Nyika[3], but only a few vagrant records (Apr, May and Sep) from the Luangwa Valley. There are a few pockets in Northern Province, especially around Bangweulu, but it occurs no further east than Shiwa Ngandu, and not west of Mwense Dist. and Choma (Mweru Wantipa)[1]. *Alt.* mostly 950-2150 m (higher on the Malawi side of the Nyika)[3], rarely down to 520 m.

Ecology In short, frequently burnt, grassland of dambo margins, cattle ranch, airfields, edge of floodplain, and also on dirt roads and bare agricultural land. Overall in drier situations than *A. leucophrys*, but found alongside its congener (and *A. richardi*) at dambo margins in several places.

Status Mainly an intra-African migrant and breeding visitor. Although there are records for all months, there is a highly significant increase Apr-Oct, compared to Nov-Mar[2]. On the Nyika recorded only 1 May to end of Sep[3].

Breeding
	Jun	Jul	Aug	Sep	Oct	Nov	
(n=82)	1	3	20	27	24	7	*Clutch*: C/1 (1); C/2 (33); C/3 (32).

Moult: started late Oct[4].

Taxonomy *A. v. chobiensis.*

References [1]Benson (1956f); [2]Dowsett & Leonard (in press a); [3]Dowsett-Lemaire (2006a); [4]Traylor (1965b).

[Long-tailed Pipit *Anthus longicaudatus*

South African endemic. This recently described pipit has been reported to occur in N. Mwinilunga[2], including an individual video-filmed; we have examined photos of this bird, and believe it to be perhaps *A. vaalensis*[1]. The taxonomy of pipits, and the identity of some in Mwinilunga (see also *A. richardi* above, concerning *A. hoeschi*), requires much further investigation, and it is not even certain that *A. longicaudatus* is a valid species. **References** [1]Dowsett (in press a); [2]Sinclair & Ryan (2003).]

Short-tailed Pipit *Anthus brachyurus* B558 **AMB**

Distribution *Afrotropical (SE Gabon to South Africa, in a series of isolates, mainly Zambezian)*. Small numbers, mainly confined to the grasslands of N. Mwinilunga, from the Kakoma area[3], south to Kalabo[6] and Kambe Plain[3]. A small population reappears in the Kawambwa area[1] in the north, and Mkushi River (Chalata)[5], to the Copperbelt (whence only three observations). A few records from the Choma area, one of a specimen[5], may be of wanderers. The species has been reported further south as a vagrant to Zimbabwe, but the South Africa population has supposedly only altitudinal movements[4]. It remains to be determined, therefore, if Zambian birds migrate towards the Equator or to the south between May and Aug. *Alt.* 1050-1450 m.

Ecology A species of watershed plains, preferring dry short grass, with scattered bushes or trees.

Status An intra-African migrant and breeding visitor, with all Zambian records between 25 Aug and 24 Apr. In Oct and Nov noted in small groups, up to 6 together[3].

Breeding[2]   Nov
(n=1)   1   Display noted in Mwinilunga Dist. to late Dec. *Clutch*: C/3 (1).

Taxonomy No races recognized.

References [1]Aspinwall (1974); [2]Benson (1976); [3]Dowsett & Leonard (in press a); [4]Clancey in Harrison *et al.* (1997); [5]Keith & Vernon (1969); [6]Traylor & Hart (1965).

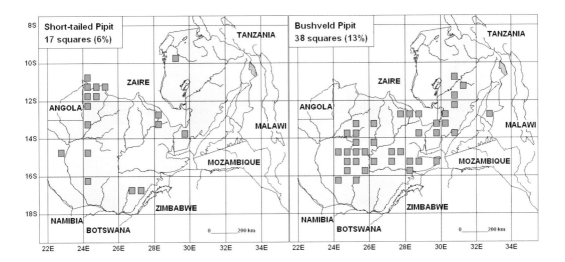

Bushveld (Little Tawny) Pipit *Anthus caffer*   B559 **R(B)**

Distribution *Afrotropical* (*Ethiopia to South Africa*). Small numbers, confined almost entirely to the plateau woodlands west of the Luangwa Valley. From Munwa F.R. and Mpika Dist., south to Chisomo and Manenekera[1], then westwards through the Copperbelt and most of Central Province to Mufumbwe, south and west to Namayonga. East of the Rift known only from Chidonga in Lundazi Dist.[2], but present just over the border in Malawi, in Kasungu N.P.[6] [Possible sightings from Lochinvar and Muckle Neuk would be no more than vagrants.] *Alt.* 660-1600 m.

Ecology In short grass, usually (though not exclusively) under tall miombo woodland. It thus occupies a niche not dissimilar to that of *A. similis* and the Palaearctic migrant *A. trivialis*. Frequently in mixed bird parties, up to 4 together (family groups?).

Status Probably resident. Present in every month, but observed significantly more frequently May-Sep, suggesting that at least part of the population may have movements. Most observations Oct-Apr are from the western half of the country, where the species may be resident[3,5].

Breeding No records, but noted in song Aug and Nov (in Zimbabwe has bred Nov and Jan).

Taxonomy *A. c. caffer*, though *A. c. mzimbaensis* (if a valid taxon) would be the form in the east. The suggestion has been made that southern African birds are referable to *mzimbaensis*, and that they migrate as non-breeding birds to much of Zambia[4], though this remains unproven.

References [1]Aspinwall (1973e); [2]Aspinwall (1975b); [3]Aspinwall (1990); [4]Clancey (1989); [5]Dowsett (in press a); [6]Dowsett-Lemaire & Dowsett (2006).

Tree Pipit *Anthus trivialis*   B560 **PW**

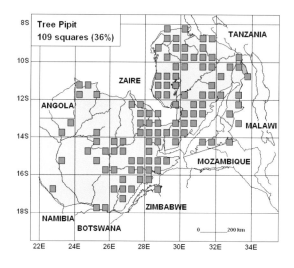

Distribution *Palaearctic* (*winters Mali to South Africa*). Quite common in plateau woodland through most of Zambia, south to Livingstone and west to Sefula. But only once west of the Zambezi, at Kaungo, and generally scarce in the Kalahari sand *Baikiaea* woodlands. *Alt.* 900-2200 m (absent from the low-lying valleys, except once at Kariba).

Ecology Miombo woodland on the Zambian plateau, but also exotic pine plantations.

Status A Palaearctic migrant and winter visitor. The average first date over 25 years was 1 Nov (most from mid-Nov, once 100 on 19 Oct and rarely from 1 Oct in Mwinilunga Dist). Large numbers (concentrations of 100-200) are not infrequent Dec-Feb, and there may still be some passage to mid-Dec. Numbers decline after mid-Mar, and the last date is 30 Apr (the average last in 22 years, 24 Mar)[2]. *Moult*: birds examined Nov-Jan showed no sign of moult (there is a complete one in the Palaearctic)[2].

Taxonomy *A. t. trivialis* (although *A. t. differens* has been claimed from E. Zambia)[1].

References [1]Clancey (1987); [2]Dowsett (in press b).

Red-throated Pipit *Anthus cervinus*   B - **PV**

Distribution and Status *Palaearctic* (*wintering Mauritania to Tanzania, very rarely South Africa*[2]). Exceptional vagrant this far south, reported only from the Copperbelt at Ndola (1228D) and Kitwe (1228C), whence recorded in short damp grassland in four seasons, between 1979 and 1986[1,3,4], 19 Nov to 18 Mar. Singly or at most two together.

Taxonomy No races recognized.

References [1]Dowsett *et al.* (1999a); [2]Cohen in Harrison *et al.* (1997); [3]Taylor (1979b); [4]Taylor (1980d).

Striped Pipit *Anthus lineiventris*   B561 **RB**

Distribution *Afrotropical* (*Kenya to South Africa*). Small numbers in rocky escarpments and wooded hills throughout the eastern half of the country; west to the Chingola area, to Lubungu in the upper Kafue basin and along the Zambezi escarpment to the Victoria Falls[4]. It reappears in N. Mwinilunga, south to Kalene Hill [A possible sight record from Chavuma Hill[1] ("?" on map) has not been repeated[3].] *Alt.* 550-1800 m.

Ecology In miombo woodland underlain with boulders and on rocky escarpments; may be found locally next to *A. similis* and the two may be competing somewhat.

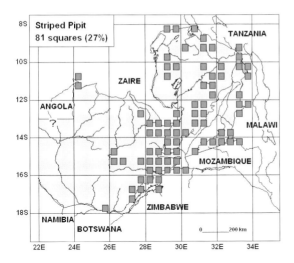

Status Resident.
Breeding   Oct   Nov   Dec
(n=14)   1   3   10
Clutch: C/1 (1); C/3 (10).
Taxonomy[2] *A. l. angolensis.*
References [1]Britton (1970); [2]Clancey (1980d); [3]Dowsett (in press a); [4]White & Winterbottom (1949).

Yellow-throated Longclaw *Macronyx croceus*   B562 **RB**

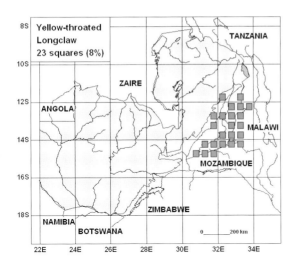

Distribution *Afrotropical (Senegal to South Africa).* Moderate numbers occur in the rather dry, small dambos of the Eastern Province plateau, from the Chasefu area south to the Nyimba area[3]. (On the Malawi side of the border it occurs as far north as Vwaza Marsh and Misuku Hills)[4]. Records in the Luangwa Valley, from the Mwaleshi River south to the Manze River[1,2], are possibly dry season non-breeding visitors. *Alt.* 1000-1400 m (wandering down to 550 m).

Ecology Favours short moist grassland with scattered bushes, dambos, edges of marsh, more occasionally fallow cultivation.

Status Resident, with some local movements. It has been reported in several years at low altitude in the Luangwa Valley, records falling between 16 May and 29 Oct, including pairs and birds singing Jul[3]. The first record was in 1979[1,2], and observations from areas that were well explored throughout the 1960s and 1970s suggest this is a recent phenomenon[3]. Originally reported as *M. fuelleborni*, but all those examined carefully have proved to be *M. croceus*[1,2].

Breeding   Jun   Dec
(n=9)   1   8   *Clutch*: C/2 (1); C/3 (6).
Taxonomy *M. c. tertius.*
References [1]Beel (1994); [2]Berry (1994); [3]Dowsett (in press a); [4]Dowsett-Lemaire & Dowsett (2006).

Fülleborn's Longclaw *Macronyx fuellebornii*   B563 **RB**

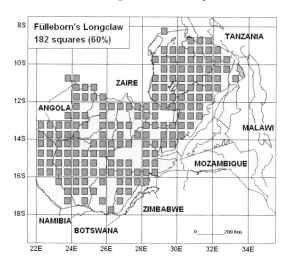

Distribution *Zambezian near-endemic (N. Tanzania to S. Zambia).* Common throughout the plateau dambos (except for the Eastern Province, where replaced by the ecologically similar *M. croceus*). Ranges throughout much of the country west of the Muchingas, south to Kalomo and Livingstone Dists (the most southerly records of the species)[2]. Present west of the Zambezi throughout the area south to the South Lueti River[5] and Nguma, but in the extreme south-west not beyond Kalobolelwa[2]. Occurs east of the upper Luangwa only at Muyombe[3]. *Alt.* 930-1800 m (Uningi Pans).

Ecology Dambos and wet grassland by dams and marshes. Rare on the edge of some major wetlands (e.g. Kafue Flats). Where other species of longclaw occur in the same area, this one inhabits the drier sections.

Status Mostly resident. There are some (probably purely local) movements, reported from Mwinilunga and Kabwe, for example.

Breeding	Sep	Oct	Nov	Dec	Jan	Feb	Mar	Apr	Jun	Jul
(n=61)	2	11	4	8	15	10	8	1	1	1

Clutch: C/1 (2); C/2 (6); C/3 (34); C/4 (3). *Moult*: one started late Nov[5].

Taxonomy[1] *M. f. ascensi* (type locality Zaire side of L. Mweru)[4]. A partial albino (with a white head) reported from Ndola.

References [1]Chapin (1953); [2]Dowsett (in press a); [3]Dowsett & Dowsett-Lemaire (1978c); [4]Salvadori (1907); [5]Traylor (1965b).

Rosy-breasted Longclaw *Macronyx ameliae*   B564 **RB**

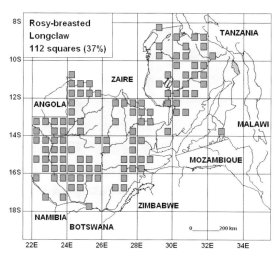

Distribution *Zambezian/Eastern (Kenya to South Africa).* Small numbers in dambos of the plateau west of the Rift, and at Sanjika Dambo near Chipata[4,7] (it is common just over the border in Malawi)[5]. Ranges south to the Choma Dist.[1] (Muckle Neuk) on the Southern Province plateau, and Kazungula on the Zambezi[4]. *Alt.* 950-1800 m (Uningi Pans).

Ecology Occurs in damp grassland, in the moist centres of dambos and marshy places in plains, usually in wetter situations than its larger congeners *M. croceus* and *M. fuelleborni*.

Status Resident. Present in all months, and any movements are probably only local and opportunistic, as different areas become flooded or dry out.

Breeding   Sep Nov Dec   Jan   Feb   Mar   Apr   Jun
(n=10)   2   1   1   2   1   1   1   1   *Clutch*: C/3 (1); C/4 (1).
Moult: a partial pre-nuptial moult reported mid-Nov[6].
Taxonomy[2] *M. a. altanus* (type locality Mayau; *NMZB*)[3].
References [1]Benson (1962a); [2]Benson *et al.* (1970); [3]Clancey (1966: 528); [4]Dowsett (in press a);
[5]Dowsett-Lemaire & Dowsett (2006); [6]Traylor (1965b); [7]Winterbottom (1938a).

Grimwood's Longclaw *Macronyx grimwoodi*   B565 **RB**

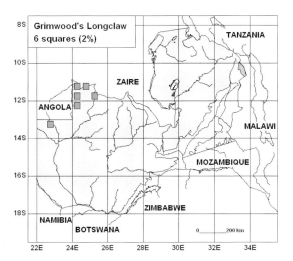

Distribution *Zambezian endemic* (*SW Zaire to south-central Angola*). Locally common in dambos on the edge of watershed plains in N. Mwinilunga, east to West Lumwana[3] and south to Kamunoka Plain[4]. *Alt.* 1100-1460 m.
Ecology Dambos, in wet sedges and long grass, less often in short dense grass.
Status Resident.
Conservation Classed as "Near Threatened"[2]. Not in any protected area, but its habitat does not seem to be under any threat, and the species is locally common (e.g. Chitunta, where a pair every 300 m)[3].
Breeding   Sep   Oct
(n=4)   3   1
Also adult carrying food Jan.
Clutch: C/2 (1) & N/2 (2).

Taxonomy No races recognized (type locality Chitunta Plain; *NMZB*; named for I.R. Grimwood)[1].
References [1]Benson (1955a: 102); [2]BirdLife International (2000, 2004a); [3]Dowsett (in press a); [4]Leonard & Peters (1998).

Campephagidae

Black Cuckoo-shrike *Campephaga flava*   B398 **AMB**

Distribution *Afrotropical* (*Sudan to South Africa*). Common in woodland throughout the country. *Alt.* 330-2200 m (mainly a non-breeding winter visitor above 2000 m, although it has bred once at 2150 m on the Nyika)[4].
Ecology In the canopy of miombo woodland and *Cryptosepalum* forest, also thickets and on the edge of riparian forest; rarely in mopane or montane forest.
Status An intra-African migrant and breeding visitor. There are records for all months of the year, but they are significantly more frequent Oct-Apr than May-Sep[3], except on the Nyika[4]. One bird was controlled at the place of ringing the following year[2].
Breeding   Oct Nov   Dec   Jan   Feb
(n=56)   10   16   17   10   3   *Clutch*: C/1 (3); C/2 (41).
Moult: adults start Jan-Feb[3].

Taxonomy No races recognized. Considered specifically distinct from (though closely related to) Red-shouldered Cuckoo-shrike *C. phoenicea*[1]. Yellow-shouldered males are rarely reported, from a few scattered localities[3].

References [1]Britton (1973); [2]Dowsett & Leonard (2001); [3]Dowsett & Leonard (in press a); [4]Dowsett-Lemaire (2006a).

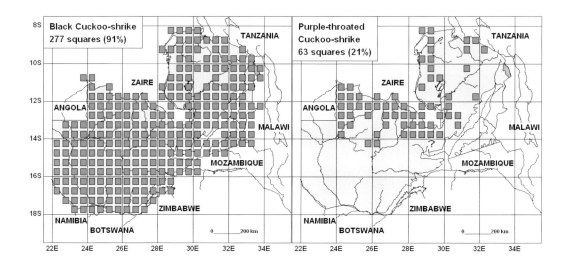

Purple-throated Cuckoo-shrike *Campephaga quiscalina*   B397 **RB**

Distribution *Afrotropical* (*Guinea to Angola and N. Zambia*). Common in the evergreen forests of N. Zambia, though in Mwinilunga not north of Sakeji[1] (and no record from Kasaji to the north in Zaire)[6]. It ranges south to Kabompo (possibly a wanderer), and just north of the Kafue N.P. boundary near Moshi[3] (the most southerly record of the species). One was perhaps seen below Mita Hills Dam[3] ("?" on map). It occurs east to Danger Hill and Chozi (in Nakonde Dist.). *Alt.* 950-1770 m (Danger Hill).

Ecology The canopy of moist evergreen forest (mushitu, where locally common), also *Cryptosepalum* forest (uncommon). Exceptionally joins bird parties in adjacent miombo woodland.

Status Resident. There has been no recent report from N. Mwinilunga[4] (since the 1980s)[3], for unknown reasons.

Breeding   Nov   Jan
(n=2)   1   1   *Clutch*: C/2 (1), from the Zaire/Zambia border[5].

Taxonomy[2] *C. q. martini.*

References [1]Benson (1959c); [2]Chapin (1953); [3]Dowsett (in press a); [4]Leonard & Van Daele (1999a); [5]Madge (1972d); [6]Schouteden (1971).

White-breasted Cuckoo-shrike *Coracina pectoralis*   B396 **RB**

Distribution *Afrotropical* (*Senegal to South Africa*). Common in woodland throughout the country. *Alt.* 550-1700 m (Nyika)[2].

Ecology Mainly the canopy of miombo woodland, also at times *Baikiaea*, *Cryptosepalum* forest, even *Acacia*, mopane and riparian forest. Perhaps largely an off-season wanderer into the drier woodlands.

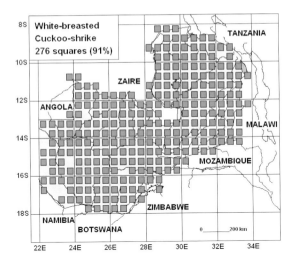

Status Essentially resident, but there are perhaps some seasonal altitudinal movements (to lower levels in the colder months). Present in all months, but the frequency of occurrence is significantly greater Apr-Nov[1].

Breeding (n=76)	Jul	Aug	Sep	Oct
	1	1	41	20
	Nov	Dec	Feb	
	10	2	1	

Clutch: C/1 (8); C/2 (56). *Moult*: adults start Dec-Jan[3].

Taxonomy No races recognized.

References [1]Dowsett (in press a); [2]Dowsett-Lemaire (2006a); [3]Traylor (1965b).

Pycnonotidae

Eastern Mountain Greenbul *Andropadus nigriceps*   B403 **RB**

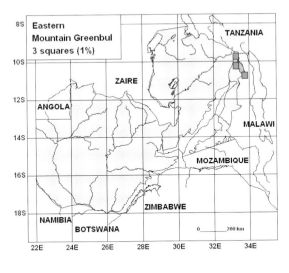

Distribution *Afromontane endemic* (*Uganda to S. Malawi*). Throughout the eastern highlands (Mafingas[3], Makutu and Nyika), where very common. *Alt.* 1950-2200 m (Nyika Plateau, higher on the Malawi side)[6].

Ecology In tall or low-canopy montane forest, and montane shrubland 2-4 m high, feeding at all levels and at edges. Eats a wide variety of fruit (over 60 species recorded, mostly in adjacent Malawi)[5] and takes insects in various ways (gleaning, flycatching, snatching); follows ant swarms frequently[9]. This generalist is numerous, reaching highest densities in fragmented forest (2-3 pairs/ha), with 1 pair/ha in larger forest blocks[4].

Status Resident. One retrapped bird was at least 8 years old[1].

Breeding (n=61)	Aug	Sep	Oct	Nov
	8	25	22	6

All from SW Nyika (including Malawi side). *Clutch*: C/2 (1).

Moult: highly synchronized late Oct-early Mar, lasting *c.* 4 months[2].

Taxonomy *A. n. fusciceps*. This taxon (ex-*A. tephrolaemus*) may be specifically distinct from *A. nigriceps* of East Africa[8], and best placed in the genus *Arizelocichla*[7].

References [1]Dowsett (1985a); [2]Dowsett & Dowsett-Lemaire (1984); [3]Dowsett & Stjernstedt (1973); [4]Dowsett-Lemaire (1983c); [5]Dowsett-Lemaire (1988b); [6]Dowsett-Lemaire (2006a); [7]Johansson *et al.* (2007); [8]Roy *et al.* (1998); [9]Willis (1983).

[Stripe-cheeked Greenbul *Andropadus milanjensis*

Afromontane endemic (Kenya to Zimbabwe). Occurs in several montane forests in Malawi, including the Jembya Plateau[1], in forest patches within 100-200 m of the Zambian highlands of Nyikamwaka (where it should be sought). **References** [1]Dowsett-Lemaire & Dowsett (2006).]

[Slender-billed Greenbul *Andropadus gracilirostris*

Afrotropical, mainly Guineo-Congolian (Senegal to S. Zaire). This forest species has been collected at Kasaji in Katanga[1], and should be sought in Mwinilunga. **References** [1]Schouteden (1971).]

Little Greenbul *Andropadus virens*   **B402 RB**

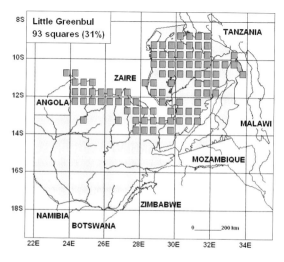

Distribution *Afrotropical (Senegal to S. Malawi).* Usually the most common bulbul in the evergreen forests of the northern plateau, in the east south to the Nyika, down the Muchingas to 14°S (e.g. to north of Kapiri Mposhi, in Katanino F.R.)[2]. Further west it ranges throughout N. Mwinilunga, south to the Kamapanda area and rarely West Lunga N.P.[2] (in riparian forest). Absent west of the Zambezi[7]. *Alt.* 950-2050 m (Manyenjere, Nyika)[5], common in the Mafingas to 1950 m[4].
Ecology In the understorey of evergreen riparian and other forest (even where thinned-out), and drier evergreen thicket in higher-rainfall areas; takes fruit occasionally in the canopy. Not found in *Cryptosepalum* forest.
Status Resident. The oldest bird so far is over 5 years of age[3].

Breeding   May   Jul   Aug   Sep   Oct   Nov
(n=24)   1   2   3   12   5   1   *Clutch:* C/2 (11).
Moult: late Jul or early Aug to Jan[2].

Taxonomy[1] *A. v. zombensis*, with perhaps some approach to the browner *A. v. virens* in Mwinilunga. DNA studies suggest it may be best placed in the genus *Eurillas*[6].
References [1]Chapin (1953); [2]Dowsett (in press a); [3]Dowsett & Leonard (2001); [4]Dowsett & Stjernstedt (1973); [5]Dowsett-Lemaire (1983c); [6]Johansson *et al.* (2007); [7]Leonard (1998b).

Sombre Bulbul *Andropadus importunus*   **B401 RB**

Distribution *Eastern near-endemic (Somalia to South Africa).* Locally common in thickets in a small area: the Middle Zambezi Valley from Namatelo Gorge, northwards to Luembe on the Luangwa River[3]. It ranges up the Kafue to Kafue Bridge and Nanga Hill, and has been reported further along the Kafue Flats at the Mwembeshi River[4] [and possibly Chitongo[2] (where there is little suitable habitat[3]; "?" on map)]. *Alt.* 330-1300 m (mostly below 600 m).
Ecology In the canopy and on the edge of dense thickets (e.g. *Acacia* spp. in Kariba Gorge) in dry

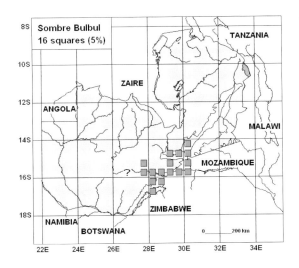

country, where predominantly frugivorous. Often alongside the larger *Chlorocichla flaviventris.*

Status Resident.

Breeding   Sep   Nov   Dec   Mar
(n=4)   1   1   1   1

Song all months, but mostly Nov-May[5].

Clutch: C/2 (1).

Taxonomy[1] *A. i. hypoxanthus.*

References [1]Benson (1956f); [2]Bruce-Miller & Bruce-Miller (1975); [3]Dowsett (in press a); [4]Leonard (1998e); [5]Leonard (1999b).

Honeyguide Greenbul *Baeopogon indicator*   B404 **R(B)**

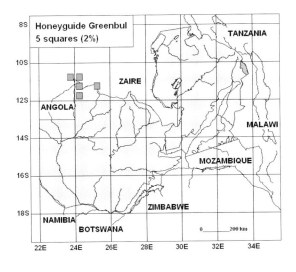

Distribution *Guineo-Congolian near-endemic (Guinea to W. Kenya and N. Zambia).* Widespread in small numbers, many places throughout N. Mwinilunga Dist., south to the Isombu and Sakeji streams[1] and Luakela River (the most southerly records of the species), east to the Kakoma area[3]. *Alt.* 1170-1460 m.

Ecology In the canopy and on the edge of moist evergreen forest, even riparian strips, exceptionally in dry *Cryptosepalum* south of Salujinga[4].

Status Resident.

Conservation The habitat in Mwinilunga is threatened by deforestation, for subsistence farming. The species is, however, common elsewhere within its wide range.

Breeding No records; male gonad activity Aug-Nov, and a male was seen to feed a female with berries Sep[3]. The eggs are unknown.

Moult: in slightly worn plumage Jul-Aug[3].

Taxonomy[2] *B. i. indicator.*

References [1]Benson (1958b); [2]Chapin (1953); [3]Dowsett (in press a); [4]Van Daele (1999e).

Joyful Greenbul *Chlorocichla laetissima*   B406 **R(B)/Extinct?**

Distribution *Afromontane near-endemic (Sudan to N. Zambia, where it reaches the southern limit of its range).* Rare, known only from a limited area of evergreen forest in the Kasangu (Chitunda) area, on the border with Zaire[1], in which country it is known from the nearby Marungu highlands[3]. *Alt.* not

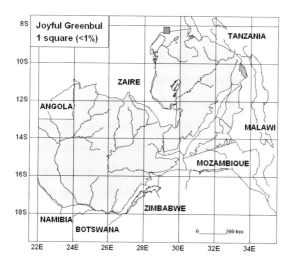

known for certain, but the plateau rises as high as 1500 m.

Ecology In the interior and on the edge of moist evergreen (riparian) forest.

Status Resident.

Conservation Not in any protected area, and its habitat (though still reasonably intact in 1997) has subsequently been destroyed for cultivation. There have been no certain records since 1983[2], and the species probably no longer occurs[4]. It is not endangered in the rest of its range, north of Zambia.

Breeding No records.

Taxonomy *C. l. schoutedeni.*

References [1]Benson (1956g); [2]Dowsett (in press a); [3]Dowsett & Prigogine (1974); [4]Leonard (2005).

Yellow-bellied Bulbul (Greenbul) *Chlorocichla flaviventris*   B405 **RB**

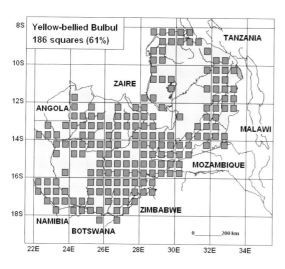

Distribution *Afrotropical (Somalia to South Africa).* Locally common in thicket and dry riparian forest in much of the country, except unrecorded from large blocks of N. and W. Zambia (where no suitable habitat). In the north-west known as far north as Mwinilunga only as a single vagrant[1] (and unrecorded at Kasaji in nearby Zaire)[3]. *Alt.* 330-1700 m.

Ecology Avoids moist evergreen forest; in the canopy and mid-stratum of the drier types of evergreen forest (including *Cryptosepalum*, where very common), and generally thickets, termite mounds in miombo and dry riparian forest. Has a mixed diet of insects and fruits (much like *Andropadus* bulbuls)[2].

Status Resident.

Breeding	Sep	Oct	Nov	Dec	Jan	Feb
(n=96)	1	15	23	27	22	8

Clutch: C/1 (12); C/2 (72); C/3 (5).

Moult: Jan-Apr, lasting *c.* 4 months; no individual moulted while breeding[2].

Taxonomy *C. f. occidentalis*, replaced by *C. f. zambesiae* (if valid, slightly paler yellow below) in the Zambezi Valley. The form *dilutior* (type locality Balovale, now Zambezi town; *NHM*)[4] is a synonym.

References [1]Bowen (1983j); [2]Dowsett (in press a); [3]Schouteden (1971); [4]White (1945-46: 80).

Yellow-throated Leaflove *Chlorocichla flavicollis*   B407 **RB**

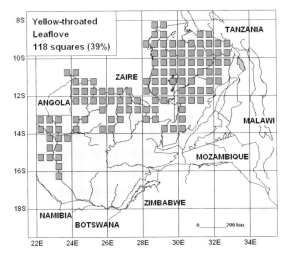

Distribution *Afrotropical* (*Senegal to Angola and N. Zambia*). Locally common in the evergreen riparian and swamp forests of N. Zambia, east to Isoka[2]. It ranges down the Muchingas to Mkushi Dist.[3], across to the Upper Zambezi drainage and downriver to 25 km south of Senanga[6] (the most southerly record of the species). *Alt.* 950-1700 m.

Ecology In the mid-stratum and canopy or on the edge of evergreen forest, with a preference for riparian situations (unrecorded from *Cryptosepalum*) and mushitu (swamp forest), even somewhat secondary or degraded. Occasionally in mango trees in cultivation. In no way in competition with the smaller *Chlorocichla flaviventris,* which inhabits a drier niche, overall at lower elevations.

Status Resident.

Breeding   Sep   Oct   Nov
(n=11)   6   4   1   *Clutch*: C/2 (7).
Moult: noted Sep and mid-Nov[5].

Taxonomy[1] *C. f. flavigula*. DNA analysis would place it in the monotypic genus *Atimastillas*[4].

References [1]Chapin (1953); [2]Clay (1953); [3]Dowsett (in press a); [4]Johansson *et al.* (2007); [5]Traylor (1965b); [6]Winterbottom (1942a).

Terrestrial Bulbul *Phyllastrephus terrestris*   B408 **RB**

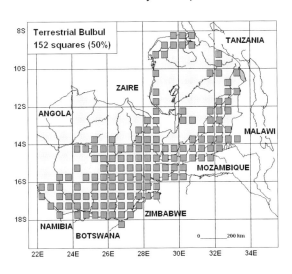

Distribution *Afrotropical* (*Somalia to South Africa*). Commonly throughout the dry thickets and riparian forest of S. and central Zambia, including the Middle Zambezi and Luangwa Valleys. It also occurs the length of the Luapula Valley, in the low-lying area between Lakes Mweru and Tanganyika (where common), and in the upper Chambeshi. Otherwise unknown on the northern plateau north of the Mlembo River[1] and Chitambo[3]. West to the Luena River[3], and to 40 km north of Senanga[6]. Absent from NW Zambia, but isolated records in the Katanga, from Kapolowe and Kasaji[5]. *Alt.* 330-1600 m.

Ecology Dense scrub, thicket and dry riparian, *Cryptosepalum* forest in the Luena area (scarce); feeding mainly on the ground (occasionally in dense vegetation 1-2 m high). Sometimes occurs in the same places in central Zambia as *P. cerviniventris*, but the latter is usually restricted to riparian habitats and is less terrestrial.

Status Resident.

Breeding	Sep	Oct	Nov	Dec	Jan	Feb	Mar	Apr
(n=121)	1	5	11	61	35	5	2	1

Clutch: C/1 (15); C/2 (81); C/3 (15).

Moult: between Nov and May (mostly in the second part of this period)[3].

Taxonomy[2] *P. t. rhodesiae* (type locality probably the Machile River; *TMP*)[4], but the limits between this and *P. t. intermedius* (darker, more earth brown) are not clear.

References [1]Benson *et al.* (1971a); [2]Clancey (1980d); [3]Dowsett (in press a); [4]Roberts (1917: 258); [5]Schouteden (1971); [6]Winterbottom (1942a).

Grey-olive Bulbul *Phyllastrephus cerviniventris*   B409 **RB**

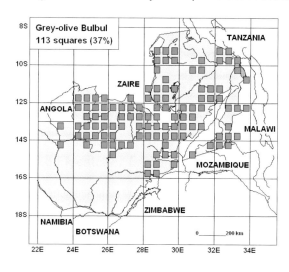

Distribution *Eastern near-endemic (Kenya to S. Malawi)*. Local and uncommon in riparian forest and mushitu of the northern plateau, but not found in N. Mwinilunga. In the north-east reaches the lower Kalungwishi[6], Kasama Dist.[1], Ntatumbila[4] and the Mafingas[5]. South to the Kabompo/Zambezi River confluence[7], to Lubungu in the upper Kafue[4], and in central Zambia to Marble Hill[2]. *Alt.* 950-1800 m, up to 1900 m on the Mafingas[5].

Ecology Moist evergreen forest, mostly riparian, gleaning at low levels (up to 4 m) on bark and foliage in liane and shrubby tangles, often near streams with steep banks. Possibly competes with *P. cabanisi*.

Status Resident.

Breeding	Sep	Oct	Nov	Apr
(n=9)	3	4	1	1

Clutch: C/1 (2); C/2 (2); C/3 (1).

Moult: one half-way through moult mid-Jul[4].

Taxonomy[3] No races recognized.

References [1]Benson (1956f); [2]Benson (1962a); [3]Chapin (1953); [4]Dowsett (in press a); [5]Dowsett & Stjernstedt (1973); [6]Neave (1910); [7]White & Winterbottom (1949).

Cabanis's Bulbul (Greenbul) *Phyllastrephus cabanisi*   B410 **RB**

Distribution *Afromontane near-endemic (Sudan to S. Malawi)*. Locally quite common in evergreen formations in the northern half of the country, but in the east only to the Mafingas. Down the Muchinga escarpment to Masase[5], and in the west south to Kashiji[1,9] and the vicinity of Zambezi town (Balovale)[3]. *Alt.* 1050-1700 m, with the race *placidus* present in small numbers at 1950-2050 m on the Mafingas[7].

Ecology Ground stratum of evergreen plateau forest (*cabanisi*) including *Cryptosepalum* forest (very common), and montane rain forest (*placidus*). Feeds on the ground, or in low shrubs and thickets, usually below 1-2 m. Attends ant swarms.

Status Resident.

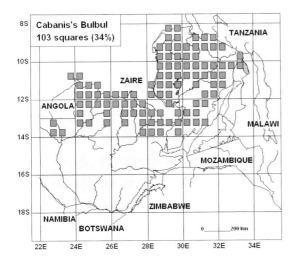

Breeding   Jul   Aug   Sep   Oct   Mar
(n=13)   1   3   6   2   1
Clutch: C/1 (1); C/2 (5).
All records relate to *P. c. cabanisi.*
Moult (*P. c. cabanisi*): in adults well advanced by late Oct to mid-Nov; immatures starting moult late Jul or early Aug[5].
Taxonomy[2,8] *P. c. cabanisi* in the plateau forests, and *P. c. placidus* (smaller, and browner, less yellow), sometimes treated as a separate species[4], in the NE mountains. Has at times been considered conspecific with coastal *P. fischeri*, but the voice is different[6].
References [1]Aspinwall (1979b); [2]Benson *et al.* (1970); [3]Britton (1970); [4]Dowsett (1972c); [5]Dowsett (in press a); [6]Dowsett & Dowsett-Lemaire (1993); [7]Dowsett & Stjernstedt (1973); [8]Irwin & Benson (1966a); [9]Leonard (1998b).

Yellow-streaked Bulbul *Phyllastrephus flavostriatus*   B411 **RB**

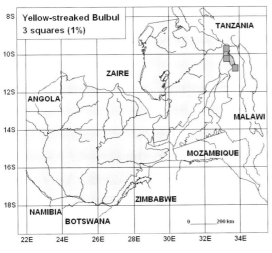

Distribution *Afromontane/Eastern* (*Uganda to South Africa*); *the race* alfredi *is an Afromontane endemic.* Common in montane rain forest on all three massifs in the eastern highlands: Mafingas[5], Makutu and Nyika Plateau. *Alt.* 1950-2200 m.
Ecology In the mid-stratum of montane rain forest. Gleans from trunks of trees and lianes and along branches, mostly above 4 m. Much attracted to bark covered in mossy epiphytes and various vegetation debris and is often quite common, with 3-4 pairs/10 ha (larger forests of SW Nyika)[6].
Status Resident. Eleven of 22 territorial birds on the Nyika were controlled in following seasons, including one for up to 9 years[1] and another (male) after 14 years[4] (ringed as an adult thus at least 15 years of age).
Breeding   Aug   Sep   Oct   Nov   Dec   Jan
(n=11)   1   1   2   4   2   1
Clutch: C/2 (2).
Moult: Nov-Mar, lasting *c.* 145 days per individual[2].
Taxonomy *P. f. alfredi* (type locality Mwenembwe, Nyika Plateau, Malawi)[7]. This form is sometimes treated as a distinct species, but without full justification[3].
References [1]Dowsett (1985a); [2]Dowsett & Dowsett-Lemaire (1984); [3]Dowsett & Dowsett-Lemaire (1993); [4]Dowsett & Leonard (2001); [5]Dowsett & Stjernstedt (1973); [6]Dowsett-Lemaire (1989b); [7]Shelley (1903).

African Bristlebill *Bleda syndactylus*   B413 **RB**

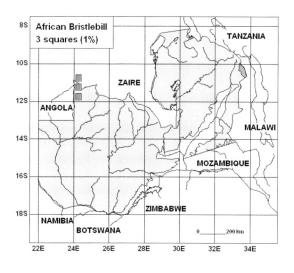

Distribution *Guineo-Congolian near-endemic (Guinea to W. Kenya and N. Zambia)*. Widespread in small numbers in the evergreen forests of N. Mwinilunga, south to the West Lunga River near Mwinilunga town[2] (the most southerly record of the species). Reported as common only in the extreme north, in the Chilula area[2]. *Alt.* 1170-1460 m.

Ecology Mostly in untouched moist evergreen forest, rarer in disturbed forest[4] and remnants of *Cryptosepalum-Marquesia* forest[5]. In the ground- and mid-strata.

Status Resident. A retrapped bird was at least 6 years old[3].

Conservation The habitat in Mwinilunga is threatened by deforestation, but the species is common elsewhere within its wide range.

Breeding   Aug
(n=1)   1   *Clutch*: no data.
Moult: two adults in Nov[2].
Taxonomy[1] *B. s. woosnami.*
References [1]Benson & Irwin (1964b); [2]Dowsett (in press a); [3]Dowsett & Leonard (2001); [4]Leonard & Van Daele (1999a); [5]Van Daele (1999e).

Black-eyed (Common) Bulbul *Pycnonotus barbatus*   B399 **RB**

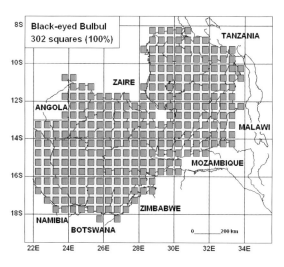

Distribution *Afrotropical (Mauritania to South Africa) and S. Palaearctic*. One of the most numerous birds in Zambia, throughout. *Alt.* 330-2200 m.

Ecology Any open woodland, thicket clumps, wooded grassland and gardens, scrub on the edge of cultivation; avoids the denser types of miombo or mopane woodland, and similarly absent from the interior of forest.

Status Resident. The oldest bird so far was one ringed more than 7 years earlier[2].

Breeding	Jul	Aug	Sep	Oct	Nov
(n=473)	1	12	88	127	109
	Dec	Jan	Feb	Mar	Apr
	62	49	21	2	2

Clutch: C/1 (33); C/2 (195); C/3 (78).

Moult: mainly Dec-Apr, lasting *c.* 3 months[1].

Taxonomy[3] *P. b. naumanni* (crown black) is the form in the south and east, *P. b. tricolor* (crown brown, like back) that in the west and north-west, *P. b. micrus* (crown darker brown than back) perhaps that in the north. [The race *vaughanjonesi*, type locality Mwinilunga[6]; *type specimen lost*; named for T.C.G.

Vaughan-Jones, is a synonym of *tricolor*. The form *annectans* (type locality the Machile area[5], i.e. the Chobe/Zambezi River confluence; *TMP*) is a synonym of *naumanni*. *P. b. limes* has been declared an invalid name: ICZN Opinion 480[4].]
References [1]Dowsett (in press a); [2]Dowsett & Leonard (2001); [3]Irwin & Benson (1967a); [4]Melville & Smith (1987); [5]Roberts (1932: 29); [6]White (1944e: 146).

Red-eyed Bulbul *Pycnonotus nigricans*   B400 **AM**

Distribution *Afrotropical* (*Angola to South Africa*). First noted in Zambia in 1962, when two were collected at Dambwa, near Livingstone, on 5 and 7 Jul[1]. Later that year two more were collected at Livingstone, 16 Sep[4]. Records have since come from a narrow belt, just north of the Zambezi, from Imusho to Livingstone, with one vagrant as far north as Mapanza[3]. *Alt*. 880-1250 m.
Ecology Gardens, edge of riparian forest and in light *Baikiaea* forest. Largely frugivorous (e.g. fond of *Lantana* berries).
Status Possibly just an irregular dry season visitor at present; at Livingstone, not noted annually, but common in 1979, and there were more observations than usual in 1999. Although claimed to have been seen at Livingstone all months of the year[4], there are definite Zambian records only 1 Jun to 26 Oct[3].
Breeding No records, although allopreening between adults watched at Livingstone in late Aug 1979[3] (in southern Africa, egg-laying is Nov to Mar).
Taxonomy[2] *P. n. grisescentior*.
References [1]Benson & Irwin (1964b); [2]Clancey (1980d); [3]Dowsett & Leonard (in press a); [4]Holliday (1965a).

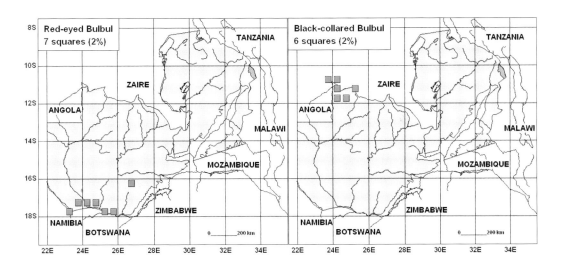

Black-collared Bulbul *Neolestes torquatus*   B412 **RB**

Distribution *Guineo-Congolian/Zambezian* (*SE Gabon to N. Zambia*). Occurs in small numbers in secondary habitats in N. Mwinilunga Dist., where discovered in 1957 at Sakeji and the Nyambela Plain[1]. It ranges south to Mwinilunga town and Mundwiji Plain[2], and east to just south of Kakoma[4]; locally common (e.g. Hillwood). Although unknown from NE Zambia, it occurs as near as the Marungu highlands in SE Katanga[5]. *Alt*. 1170-1460 m.

Ecology[6] Lightly-wooded grassland and secondary growth on the edge of evergreen forest. Insectivorous, but also takes fruit[3].
Status Resident.
Breeding[3]   Oct   Jan
(n=4)   2   2   *Clutch*: C/2 (1) & N/2 (1). *Moult*: Jul (two birds)[4].
Taxonomy No races recognized. Thought by some authorities to be a "shrike" (Malaconotidae), but now shown by DNA and other studies to be a bulbul, of uncertain position in the Pycnonotidae[6].
References [1]Benson (1958b); [2]Benson & Irwin (1965b); [3]Bowen (1983b); [4]Dowsett (in press a); [5]Dowsett & Prigogine (1974); [6]Dowsett *et al.* (1999a).

[Western Nicator *Nicator chloris*

Guineo-Congolian near-endemic (*Senegal to S. Zaire, east to NW Tanzania*). A bird shot by Jali Makawa, but not recovered, in *Marquesia* forest at Salujinga in Sep 1962[1] ("?" on map of *N. gularis*), may have been this species (known from as near as Kasaji in Katanga (some 120 km distant), as well as the Upemba area[2]). **References** [1]Benson & Irwin (1965c); [2]Schouteden (1971).]

White-throated Nicator *Nicator gularis*   B414 **RB**

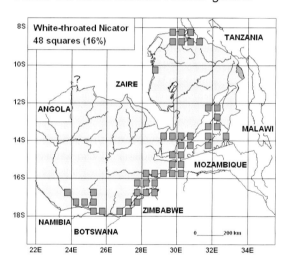

Distribution *Eastern near-endemic* (*Somalia to South Africa*). Small numbers, in thickets; there are two well-separated populations in Zambia. In the north, between L. Tanganyika (Kalambo Falls) and Mweru Wantipa[2], with an isolated record near Mwense on the Luapula River[1]. In the Luangwa Valley, it ranges from the Mutinondo River[2,5] southwards, to the Chipata area on the plateau, then throughout the Middle Zambezi Valley, west to Katombora[3] and the Buwe Pool-Mulanga area[9], to Silolo and Sioma[6]. A *Nicator* from N. Mwinilunga ("?" on map) was more likely *N. chloris* (*q.v.*). *Alt.* 330-1550 m.
Ecology Understorey of dry forest and especially (semi-) evergreen or deciduous thicket, often in riparian situations.

Status Resident.
Breeding   Dec   Jan
(n=13)   7   6   Song Oct to early Apr. *Clutch*: C/1 (3); C/2 (9).
Taxonomy[10] *N. g. gularis*, replaced by *N. c. phyllophilus* (brighter above, but browner on crown; type locality the Mutinondo River at Kazembe, *NMZB*)[5] in the Luangwa and Middle Zambezi Valleys, although the status of the latter form requires confirmation. It may turn out that *N. gularis* is best treated as a subspecies of *N. chloris* (they are allopatric)[7]. The taxonomic status of the genus *Nicator* is not yet confirmed, but for practical purposes we treat them here as closer to the Pycnonotidae than to the Malaconotidae[8]. The 3 species may comprise a distinct family, as independent molecular studies suggest they are neither bulbuls nor bush shrikes[4,11].
References [1]Aspinwall (1974); [2]Benson (1956d); [3]Benson & Irwin (1967b); [4]Beresford *et al.* (2005); [5]Clancey (1980a: 132); [6]Dowsett (in press a); [7]Dowsett & Dowsett-Lemaire (1993); [8]Dowsett *et al.* (1999a); [9]Dowsett-Lemaire & Dowsett (1978b); [10]Irwin (1981a); [11]Moyle & Marks (2006).

Turdidae

Rufous Ant Thrush *Stizorhina fraseri*   B439 **RB**

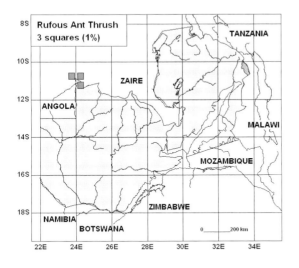

Distribution *Guineo-Congolian near-endemic* (*Guinea to W. Uganda and Zambia*). Small numbers in some of the forests in the extreme north of Mwinilunga Dist., from several localities including Salujinga[2], Isombu[1], Jimbe Bridge and Hillwood (where common), to the Source of the Zambezi[4,5] (the most southerly record of the species). *Alt.* 1240-1460 m.

Ecology Undisturbed moist evergreen forest, feeding in the mid-stratum, by snatching. May follow ant swarms. The nest site in Gabon is a semi-cavity, usually 10-20 m in a forest tree[3].

Status Resident.

Conservation The habitat in Mwinilunga is threatened by deforestation. The species is, however, common elsewhere within its wide range.

Breeding   Oct

(n=1)   1   *Clutch*: no data (a female contained a shelled egg in mid-Oct)[1].

Taxonomy *S. f. rubicunda.*

References [1]Benson (1958b); [2]Benson & Irwin (1964b); [3]Brosset & Erard (1986); [4]Dowsett (in press a); [5]White & Grimwood (1954).

Eurasian Rock Thrush *Monticola saxatilis*   B424 **PV**

Distribution and Status *Palaearctic* (*winters from Senegambia to Tanzania*). There are three records of vagrants south of their normal wintering range, all from the north-east of the country. The first from Ngitwa (0930D, 14 Dec 1964, not 1 Dec as in ref. 2)[4], a second from Mbala (0831C, 8 Dec 1976)[1], and a third from the Nyika rest house (1033D, 25 Dec 2001)[3]. In rocky miombo woodland, including a quarry (Mbala). *Alt.* 1560-2150 m.

Taxonomy No races recognized.

References [1]Aspinwall (1977d); [2]Benson *et al.* (1971a); [3]Dowsett (in press b); [4]Keith & Vernon (1969).

Miombo Rock Thrush *Monticola angolensis*   B425 **RB**

Distribution *Zambezian near-endemic* (*Rwanda and Tanzania to Zimbabwe*). Common in the plateau miombo woodlands, occurring at lower altitudes only where there is rocky miombo, as on the eastern escarpment of the Luangwa Valley, at Chiromwe Hill[1], and on the Middle Zambezi escarpment[5]. Ranges throughout most of the Southern Province plateau, west to Livingstone[8], and as far as Zambezi town (Balovale)[3], though absent from the country further west. It is also unrecorded from the low-lying country between Lakes Mweru and Tanganyika. *Alt.* 650-1900 m, to nearly 2100 m on the Mafingas[6] and 2050 m on the Nyika[7] (at the upper limit of miombo).

Ecology In miombo woodland, from drier, thinner types on stony ground to mossy transition woodland

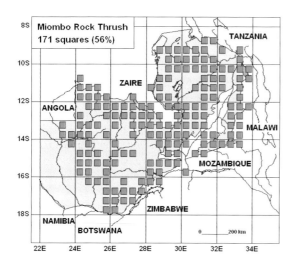

(without rocks) on the northern plateau. Nests are situated in tree holes.

Status Resident; occasionally wanders from miombo, e.g. to Mwinilunga sewage ponds[2].

Breeding	Aug	Sep	Oct	Nov	Dec
(n=33)	3	16	5	7	2

Clutch: C/2 (7); C/3 (11); C/4 (3).

Taxonomy[4] *M. a. niassae*, perhaps replaced in the south and south-east by *M. a. hylophilus* (belly white, not buff, and breast paler orange).

References [1]Benson *et al.* (1971a); [2]Bowen (1983j); [3]Britton (1970); [4]Clancey (1974a); [5]Dowsett (in press a); [6]Dowsett & Stjernstedt (1973); [7]Dowsett-Lemaire (2006a); [8]Irwin & Benson (1966a).

Olive Thrush *Turdus olivaceus* B442 **RB**

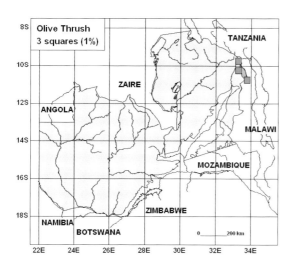

Distribution *Afromontane near-endemic (Ethiopia to South Africa).* In montane forest on the Mafingas (scarce)[5], Makutu and Nyika. *Alt.* 2050-2200 m (higher on the Malawi side of Nyika).

Ecology Montane forest, feeding mainly in leaf litter, but occasionally picking insects on large branches; takes fruit in the canopy, less often on the ground. At dusk comes to forest edges; may occasionally venture into nearby pine plantations; attends ant swarms rather infrequently[6,8]. Common on the Nyika where the forest is very fragmented (Zambia, Zovochipolo and central plateau, Malawi): breeds in patches as small as 0.5 ha, but no more than two pairs in larger patches of 6-12 ha[6].

Status Resident. Seven of 15 birds ringed on the Nyika were controlled locally, up to 5 years after first capture[2].

Breeding	Sep	Oct	Nov	Dec
(n=23)	3	11	8	1

All SW Nyika (including Malawi side). *Clutch*: N/2 (2).

Moult: Dec to Feb or Mar[4].

Taxonomy *T. o. nyikae* (type locality Nyika Plateau, Malawi)[7]. *Turdus abyssinicus* is not treated as specifically distinct here[3], although molecular studies suggest some populations should be split off[1] (more research needed).

References [1]Bowie *et al.* (2005); [2]Dowsett (1985a); [3]Dowsett & Dowsett-Lemaire (1980); [4]Dowsett & Dowsett-Lemaire (1984); [5]Dowsett & Stjernstedt (1973); [6]Dowsett-Lemaire (1989b); [7]Reichenow (1904); [8]Willis (1985).

West African Thrush *Turdus pelios*   B441 **RB**

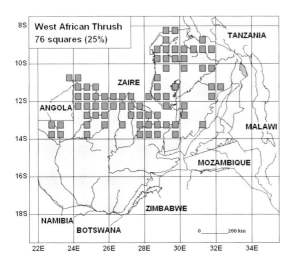

Distribution *Afrotropical* (*Senegal to Angola and Zambia*). A common bird of the northern evergreen forests, not known south of 14°S, and absent from the whole of the Eastern Province. Occurs east to Chibesakunda[5], thence very locally down the Muchinga escarpment to Musense[4], then throughout the Copperbelt to Chavuma[5], and west of the Zambezi at Mize (Ndungu)[1,6]. *Alt.* 950-1750 m.
Ecology Moist evergreen forest (where usually common), including mushitu (swamp forest), less common in drier types, e.g. *Crypto-sepalum*. Tolerates disturbed conditions. A nest was in a fork some 5 m high in dense riparian forest[3].
Status Resident.

Breeding   Sep   Oct   Nov   Dec
(n=9)   3   3   2   1   *Clutch*: C/1 (1); C/2 (3); C/3 (1).
Taxonomy[2] *T. p. stormsi* (syn. *T. p. williami* type locality Kansoko; *AMNH*; named for a local villager, W. Chikundulo)[7].
References [1]Aspinwall (1979b); [2]Benson (1956f); [3]Benson & Pitman (1961); [4]Benson *et al.* (1970); [5]Dowsett (in press a); [6]White (1945-46); [7]White (1949a: 57).

Kurrichane Thrush *Turdus libonyana*   B443 **RB**

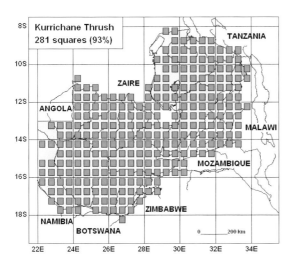

Distribution *Zambezian near-endemic* (*Burundi and Tanzania to South Africa*). Common throughout the country, in any woodland. *Alt.* 330-1800 m, even to *c.* 2000 m on the Mafingas[3] (and 2050 m on the Malawi side of the Nyika)[4].
Ecology Particularly common in miombo woodland, but also in other woodland, edge of thickets, riparian forest, exotic plantations, palm savanna and gardens. Nests are placed in trees, in forks or cavities, often very visible. Feeds almost entirely on the ground.
Status Resident.

Breeding	Aug	Sep	Oct	Nov
(n=186)	2	67	59	43
	Dec	Jan	Mar	Apr
	10	1	2	2

Clutch: C/1 (1); C/2 (37); C/3 (96); C/4 (1).
Moult: starts in Dec[2].
Taxonomy[1,5] *T. l. tropicalis*, replaced in the west by *T. l. verreauxi* and perhaps by *T. l. chobiensis*.

References [1]Benson (1956f); [2]Dowsett (in press a); [3]Dowsett & Stjernstedt (1973); [4]Dowsett-Lemaire (2006a); [5]Irwin (1981a).

Groundscraper Thrush *Psophocichla litsitsirupa*   B444 **RB**

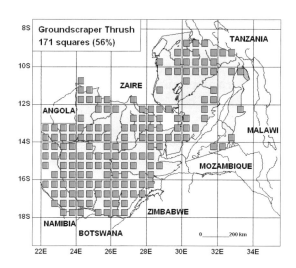

Distribution *Afrotropical* (*Ethiopia to South Africa*). Present locally in small numbers in light woodland through most of the plateau areas, except very sparse in parts of the north and in Lundazi Dist. east of the Luangwa. On the whole uncommon, but locally quite numerous (e.g. Kasanka, and in *Burkea* west of the Zambezi[1]). [Records from the Luangwa and Middle Zambezi Valleys are rejected[2,4].] *Alt.* 950-1700 m.

Ecology In tall miombo woodland or *Burkea* with open understorey or patches of bare ground (especially if recently burnt), and in adjacent cultivation; also on secluded garden lawns. Often alongside *T. libonyana* but usually much less common. Nests are untidy affairs, often very visible, in tree forks at moderate height.

Status Present all months, and although in most areas there are fewest records Dec-Feb this possibly reflects its post-breeding moult period, when it is likely to be more discreet[2].

Breeding   Aug   Sep   Oct   Nov
(n=68)   8   32   23   5   *Clutch*: C/1 (1); C/2 (17); C/3 (35).
Moult: starts late Oct to early Nov[6].

Taxonomy *P. l. litsitsirupa*. Note that this is the correct original spelling, not *litsipsirupa*. Previously placed in the genus *Turdus*[3,5].

References [1]Britton (1970); [2]Dowsett (in press a); [3]Dowsett & Dowsett-Lemaire (1993); [4]Irwin (1983a); [5]Irwin & Benson (1966a); [6]Traylor (1965b).

Orange Thrush *Zoothera gurneyi*   B445 **RB**

Distribution *Afromontane endemic* (*Kenya to South Africa*). Small numbers present in montane forest on the Makutu[1] and Nyika Plateaux[5]. [Known from the Malawi side of the Mafingas[5], but not from the Zambian[4].] It is unlikely to occur elsewhere, although present on the Ufipa Plateau in SW Tanzania, not far north of Mbala[2]. *Alt.* 2050-2150 m (higher on the eastern side of the Nyika in Malawi).

Ecology In montane rain forest, feeding in leaf litter and on mossy logs, and takes fruit in the understorey. On SW Nyika present only in the largest forests (Chowo, Manyenjere and Kasoma) and drops out above 2150 m where the forest becomes drier and more fragmented[5].

Status Mainly resident (some altitudinal movements known in Malawi).

Breeding   Nov   Dec
(n=2)   1   1   *Clutch*: no data.
Moult: Feb-Jun[3].

Taxonomy *Z. g. otomitra*.

References [1]Dowsett (1971h); [2]Dowsett (in press a); [3]Dowsett & Dowsett-Lemaire (1984); [4]Dowsett & Stjernstedt (1973); [5]Dowsett-Lemaire (1989b).

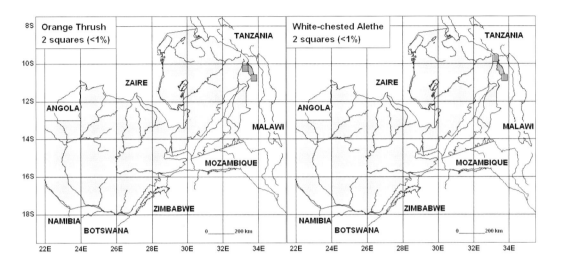

White-chested Alethe *Alethe fuelleborni*   B431 **RB**

Distribution *Afromontane endemic* (*Tanzania to Mozambique*). Locally common in montane forest in the Mafingas[6] and on the Nyika Plateau. *Alt.* 1950-2200 m.
Ecology Ground stratum of montane rain forest, feeding almost exclusively at ant swarms. Catches small arthropods flushed by ants, from ground, logs, low trunks, etc., by pouncing from low perches or hopping and pecking[3,4,7]. Sometimes takes small ants. Seen feeding away from ants only in the dry season when these may remain inactive for some weeks. All breeding territories studied on the Nyika contained an active nest of ants (or, rarely, were in a small forest patch next to one with ants, then visited daily) and varied from 0.5-4 ha in fragmented forest. Overall densities in continuous forest of 2 pairs/10 ha (SW Nyika).
Status Probably mainly sedentary, but from ringing data on the Nyika some females are thought to move out of the area from Apr to Sep. Highly elusive in the dry winter months, the species could easily be overlooked at lower altitudes. Twenty-two of 25 territorial ringed birds on the Nyika were retrapped locally in subsequent seasons, up to 7 years after first capture[1].
Breeding   Oct   Nov   Dec   Jan
(n=39)   2   20   13   4   All from SW Nyika (including Malawi side). Single-brooded[2].
Clutch: N/2 (1). *Moult*: mostly Dec-Mar, lasting *c.* 4 months[5].
Taxonomy *A. f. fuelleborni*.
References [1]Dowsett (1985a); [2]Dowsett-Lemaire (1985a); [3]Dowsett-Lemaire (1987); [4]Dowsett-Lemaire (1989b); [5]Dowsett & Dowsett-Lemaire (1984); [6]Dowsett & Stjernstedt (1973); [7]Willis (1985).

Starred Robin *Pogonocichla stellata*   B433 **RB**

Distribution *Afromontane endemic* (*Sudan to South Africa*). Common in montane forest on the Nyika Plateau (up to 2200 m, higher on the Malawi side), Makutu and north to the Mafingas[6], with non-breeding

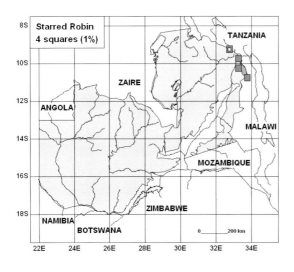

season wanderers to lower levels nearby, and to Ikawa[1] at 1680 m (open square).

Ecology Usually the ground- and mid-stratum of montane forest. Nests are on or near the ground. Has many different feeding techniques including gleaning and flycatching at all levels and on sunny edges, also drops to the ground and snatches off bark and branches like an akalat[8,9]. In its winter quarters at low altitudes in Malawi, seen feeding mainly below 2 m; birds that remain at high altitudes, however, feed more in the upper strata and often pass unnoticed from Mar to Aug. Always attends ant swarms when they pass in or near the territory. The most numerous forest robin in montane forest, with usually 5-10 pairs/10 ha in continuous forest, but territories of 0.2-0.5 ha in small patches[8].

Status A partial altitudinal migrant: a ringing study on the Nyika[2,3] showed that females (adults and immatures) depart after breeding whereas the territorial males and some of the immature males are resident. Distances involved in this migration are of the order of 20-100 km or more in Malawi. The majority of females return to the same territory each year (Nyika)[2,3]. On the Nyika 137 of 166 territorial birds were controlled in subsequent seasons, up to 8 years later[3] with one male 11 years later (having been ringed as a full adult it had reached the age of at least 13 years)[5].

Breeding   Sep   Oct   Nov   Dec   Jan
(n=204)   4   39   89   70   2   (Including Malawi side of SW Nyika.)
Single-brooded[7]. *Clutch*: C/2 (8); C/3 (4).

Moult: in adults mostly Jan-Mar, lasting *c.* 3 months. Juveniles moult only body plumage the first year, into an olive dress quite unlike that of the brightly-coloured, monomorphic adults[4].

Taxonomy[2] *P. s. orientalis.*

References [1]Benson (1956d); [2]Dowsett (1982); [3]Dowsett (1985a); [4]Dowsett & Dowsett-Lemaire (1984); [5]Dowsett & Leonard (2001); [6]Dowsett & Stjernstedt (1973); [7]Dowsett-Lemaire (1985a); [8]Dowsett-Lemaire (1989b); [9]Willis (1985).

Bocage's Robin (Akalat) *Sheppardia bocagei*   B434 **RB**

Distribution *Sub-Afromontane endemic* (*E. Nigeria to Angola and Zambia*). A common species of the northern evergreen plateau forests (and one specimen from the Mafingas), absent from Eastern Province (no suitable habitat). Ranges down the Muchinga escarpment to Musense[4], thence through the Copperbelt westwards to Swanandumba on the Kabompo River[5]. On the Copperbelt occurs south to near Kantolo[1]. [There is a sight record from Kasempa Dist. on the Lusokosoko stream[3] ("?" on map) which requires confirmation[6].] Absent from the extreme north of Mwinilunga Dist. (north of Sachibonda and the Sakeji source), where it is perhaps replaced by the similar-sized *Cossypha polioptera. Alt.* 1100-1770 m (Danger Hill), exceptionally to 1950 m (Mafingas)[7].

Ecology Mainly moist evergreen forest, including mushitu and montane forest (Muchinga escarpment and Mafingas)[7], also moist transitional woodland at Ndola[8]. Feeds on the ground or low trunks (dropping from low perches) on various invertebrates (stomachs contained ants[9]). The nest is on or

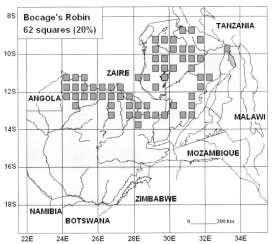

near the ground, and may be in the cavity of a stump.

Status Resident.

Breeding   Sep   Oct   Nov
(n=6)   1   3   2
Clutch: C/2 (3).

Taxonomy *S. b. chapini* (type locality Mporokoso; *NHM*)[2]; named for James P. Chapin [1889-1964], pioneering ornithologist in Zaire.

References [1]Aspinwall (1975b); [2]Benson (1955a: 104); [3]Benson & Irwin (1965b); [4]Benson *et al.* (1961); [5]Dowsett (1973b); [6]Dowsett (in press a); [7]Dowsett & Stjernstedt (1973); [8]Madge (1972b); [9]Oatley (1969).

Sharpe's Akalat *Sheppardia sharpei*   B - **RB**

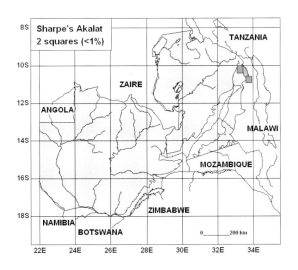

Distribution *Afromontane endemic* (*Tanzania to N. Malawi*). First found in 1972, in the Mafingas (Zinza stream)[1], and occurs locally on the SW Nyika (25-30 pairs in Manyenjere forest[3,4], but rarely in Chowo and exceptional visitor to Kasoma). *Alt.* 1750 m (Mafingas) to 2100 m (Nyika).

Ecology In montane rain forest, in dense understorey of shrubs and tangles of creepers, usually below 2 m. Attends ant swarms frequently, but also feeds away from ants in impenetrable shrubberies. Pecks small prey on ground, logs and low branches, by hopping or dropping from low perches[3,5]. Its near-absence from Chowo forest is probably a result of the microclimate, Manyenjere appearing wetter than Chowo, with ranker understorey.

Status Resident.
Breeding   Oct   Nov   Dec
(n=9)   5   3   1   *Clutch*: no data.
Moult: an adult started end Dec[2].
Taxonomy *S. s. sharpei*.
References [1]Aspinwall (1973d); [2]Dowsett (in press a); [3]Dowsett-Lemaire (1989b); [4]Osborne (1975c); [5]Willis (1985).

Thrush Nightingale *Luscinia luscinia* B440 **PW**

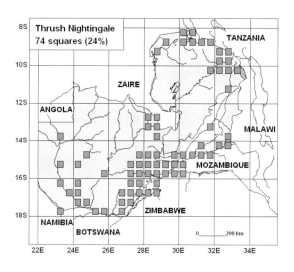

Thrush Nightingale
74 squares (24%)

Distribution *Palaearctic (the whole popula-tion wintering Kenya to South Africa).* Although locally common in thickets in much of the Central and Southern Province plateau and the Middle Zambezi Valley, sparsely reported elsewhere, and unrecorded from some higher-rainfall areas of the Northern, Luapula and North-Western Provinces. Thus, west of the Copperbelt and north of 14°S known only from Zambezi town (Balovale), and west of the Zambezi only from Imusho in the extreme south-west[1]. These gaps cannot be entirely the result of poor observer coverage (although it is likely to be more widespread in the Luangwa Valley than shown on the map). The lack of records from Mwinilunga is mir-rored by a similar lack from the Kasaji area of Katanga[5]. *Alt.* 330-1660 m (Mbala)[2].

Ecology In any thickets, but most common in deciduous types, coming into leaf when the birds arrive, also riparian forest.

Status All acceptable records are for the period 12 Nov to 10 Apr[3] (reports as early as 2 Nov and as late as 21 Apr are not entirely convincing). The average first date over 24 years was 15 Dec, the average last (in 28 years) 13 Mar[3]. Song is heard from first arrival. One bird was retrapped where ringed the following year[4].

Moult: in the Palaearctic (birds examined Dec-Mar showed no sign of moult)[3].

Taxonomy No races recognized.

References [1]Benson & Irwin (1967b); [2]Benson & White (1957); [3]Dowsett (in press b); [4]Dowsett & Leonard (2001); [5]Schouteden (1971).

Olive-flanked Robin *Cossypha anomala* B432 **RB**

Distribution *Afromontane endemic (Tanzania to Malawi and Mozambique).* Common in forest on the Nyika Plateau. *Alt.* 2050-2200 m (higher on the Malawi side).

Ecology In understorey of montane rain forest; feeds on the ground, logs and in low shrubs, mostly while hopping, occasionally sallies to snatch from bark. Is a regular attendant at ant swarms[4,6]. Territories can be as small as 0.25 ha, as in dense shrubs near streams, but are larger in more open understorey. Overall densities of 10 pairs/10 ha on SW Nyika[4]. Nests are usually less than 2 m up, against a streambank, on a stump or other similar situation.

Status Resident; 26 out of 43 territorial birds ringed on the Nyika were controlled locally for up to 9 years after first capture[1].

Breeding

	Oct	Nov	Dec	Jan
(n=46)	1	23	18	4

(Including Malawi side of SW Nyika.) Single-brooded[3]. *Clutch*: C/2 (2). *Moult*: adults and young start early Jan and finish by Apr[2].

Taxonomy *C. a. macclounii* (type locality Mwenembwe, Nyika Plateau, Malawi)[5].

References [1]Dowsett (1985a); [2]Dowsett & Dowsett-Lemaire (1984); [3]Dowsett-Lemaire (1985a); [4]Dowsett-Lemaire (1989b); [5]Shelley (1903); [6]Willis (1985).

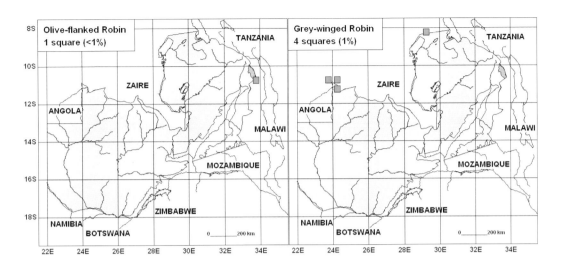

Grey-winged Robin *Cossypha polioptera*   B435 **RB**

Distribution *Afrotropical (circum-Congo, Guinea to NW Zambia).* Very local, in small numbers, in forest in the extreme north of Mwinilunga Dist., south to Hillwood (where common)[4] and the Source of the Zambezi[1] (the most southerly record of the species), reappearing on the border with Zaire between Lakes Mweru and Tanganyika at Kasangu[6]. Is not found in the same localities as *Sheppardia bocagei* (*C. polioptera* occurring further north), and they may be in competition. *Alt.* 1200-1460 m.
Ecology Moist evergreen forest, feeding usually on or near the ground on invertebrates (stomachs contained ants)[7]. It seems to occupy a niche similar to that of *S. bocagei*. The one nest site known (from the Source of the Zambezi) was in an earth bank, some 0.5-1 m above the ground[2].
Status Resident.
Conservation With the destruction of much forest habitat in Mwinilunga and Nchelenge Dists this species is vulnerable in Zambia (though it is common in most other parts of its wide range).
Breeding   Aug   Sep   Oct   Nov
(n=6)   2   2   1   1   *Clutch*: C/3 (1).   *Moult*: an adult started in Nov[4].
Taxonomy *C. p. grimwoodi* (type locality the Source of the Zambezi; *NHM*; named for Ian Grimwood)[8]. Fresh specimens in series confirm the validity of this race, *contra* ref. 5. Treated here as a species of *Cossypha,* agreeing in behaviour, vocal mimicry and egg coloration, although bio-molecular and some other aspects have been considered to warrant the use of *Sheppardia*[3].
References [1]Benson & Irwin (1965b); [2]Charge (1998); [3]Collar in del Hoyo *et al.* (2005); [4]Dowsett (in press a); [5]Oatley in Keith *et al.* (1992); [6]Leonard (1998d); [7]Oatley (1969); [8]White (1954c: 88).

Cape Robin *Cossypha caffra*   B437 **RB**

Distribution *Afromontane near-endemic (Sudan to South Africa).* Present at forest edges and in scrub in the three eastern highland areas: the Mafingas[6], Makutu[1] and Nyika (common only in the last)[5]. It has not been found in the Mbala area (although common in neighbouring Zaire and Tanzania, in the Marungu highlands[4] and on the Ufipa Plateau[3]), no doubt through the lack of habitat. *Alt.* 1950 m (Mafingas) to 2200 m on the Nyika Plateau (higher on the Malawi side).
Ecology Mainly in montane shrubland and at forest edges. An untidy nest, built low down as a rule, and

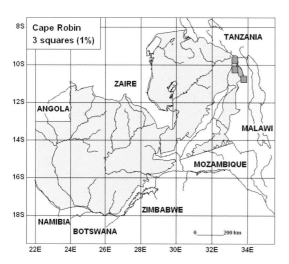

often in thick bush.

Status Resident. Several birds retrapped locally on the Nyika, up to 6 years after first capture[2].

Breeding

	Oct	Nov	Dec	Jan
(n=46)	4	16	24	2

Clutch: C/1 (4); C/2 (10); C/3 (2).

Moult: most adults start Jan and finish by about Apr[3].

Taxonomy *C. c. iolaema.*

References [1]Dowsett (1971h); [2]Dowsett (1985a); [3]Dowsett (in press a); [4]Dowsett & Prigogine (1974); [5]Dowsett-Lemaire (1989b); [6]Leonard *et al.* (2001a).

Heuglin's Robin *Cossypha heuglini*   B438 **RB**

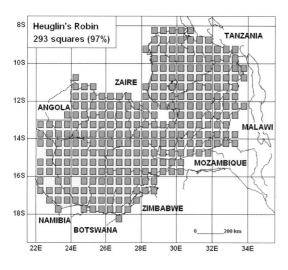

Distribution *Afrotropical (Sudan to South Africa).* Common in dense vegetation throughout the country. *Alt.* 330-1900 m, rarely to 2000 m on the Mafingas[4] and 2050 m on the Nyika[3].

Ecology In any thickets, riparian vegetation and gardens, also at edges of evergreen forest, more locally in the interior, usually near a stream. Nests are usually less than 2 m up, against a streambank, on a stump or other similar situation in thick vegetation. At several localities *C. natalensis* also occurs seasonally (e.g. Nangweshi, Lochinvar, Mayau)[1] but potential competition between these two similar-sized robins has not been studied.

Status Resident; a ringed bird was recovered where first caught when at least 9 years old[2].

Breeding

	Sep	Oct	Nov	Dec	Jan	Feb	May	
(n=123)	9	22	12	32	27	20	1	*Clutch*: C/1 (8); C/2 (80); C/3 (5).

Moult: late Dec (rarely late Nov) to late May[1,6].

Taxonomy *C. h. euronota.* [*C. h. mwinilunga* has been declared an invalid name: ICZN Opinion 480[5].]

References [1]Dowsett (in press a); [2]Dowsett & Leonard (2001); [3]Dowsett-Lemaire (2006a); [4]Leonard *et al.* (2001a); [5]Melville & Smith (1987); [6]Traylor (1965b).

Red-capped Robin *Cossypha natalensis*   B436 **AMB/R**

Distribution *Afrotropical (Nigeria to South Africa).* Locally common in forest and thickets in W. and

S. Zambia and between Lakes Mweru and Tanganyika. In central Zambia known only north to Kasanka. Present locally in the Luangwa Valley, and on the Eastern Province plateau in the Kazimuli-Chadiza area, exceptionally in the Mafingas (Mulangale forest)[7]. *Alt.* 450-1500 m, to 1950 m in the Mafingas.

Ecology Ground-stratum of evergreen forest, including *Cryptosepalum* forest (very common), moist transition woodland (with evergreen undergrowth, at Ndola), deciduous and evergreen (riparian) thickets. In Ndola forestry plots there were 12 singing males in 15 ha, noted between 20 Aug and 20 Mar[8]. It occurs next to *C. heuglini* in several places. In Malawi known to attend ant swarms regularly[5,10]. The nest is placed on or near the ground, in thick cover, often against a tree buttress.

Status In most areas an intra-African migrant and breeding visitor, though resident in Mwinilunga (including retrap of a bird ringed 28 Jun on 5 Oct)[4] and perhaps a few other places in the north (e.g. Imanda)[3,4]. There are a very few Jun-Jul records from elsewhere, even a specimen 25 Jun as far south as Itezhi-Tezhi[1]. One presumed migrant at Muyeke, ringed 27 Sep, was retrapped where ringed the same day the following year[6].

Breeding   Sep   Nov   Dec   Jan   Feb
(n=19)   1   2   10   5   1   *Clutch*: C/1 (2); C/2 (9); C/3 (6).

Moult: adults in moult Apr-May[3], while a juvenile was completing partial moult late Oct[9].

Taxonomy[2] *C. n. hylophona* appears to be the subspecies arriving to breed throughout most of the country, replaced by *C. n. egregior* in the Middle Zambezi Valley. Resident birds in the extreme north-west may be a third race.

References [1]Benson (1958c); [2]Benson *et al.* (1971a); [3]Dowsett in Britton (1971); [4]Dowsett & Leonard (in press a); [5]Dowsett-Lemaire (1989b); [6]Leonard (1998b); [7]Leonard *et al.* (2001a); [8]Madge (1972b); [9]Traylor (1965b); [10]Willis (1985).

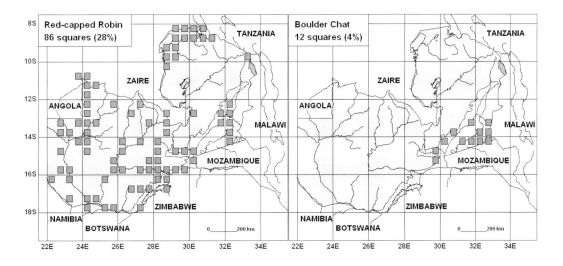

Boulder Chat *Pinarornis plumosus*   B426 **RB**

Distribution *Zambezian endemic (Zambia and Malawi to Mozambique and Zimbabwe).* Sparse and local, essentially tied to the rocky kopjes of the Eastern Province plateau and neighbouring escarpments. It ranges from the Machechete Hills to Nakasalwa Hill[2] (between the Lukusashi and the Luangwa), and north-east to Kalikali[1]. Has once wandered to the Valley floor at Nyamaluma[4]. *Alt.* 1050-1350 m (exceptionally down to 530 m). Easily overlooked, and likely under-recorded.

Ecology Large boulders surrounded with thin miombo woodland. A nest was placed on the ground,

under an overhanging rock[3].
Status Resident.
Breeding   Nov   Dec
(n=3)   2   1   *Clutch*: C/1 (1), with an egg of the parasitic cuckoo *Cuculus solitarius*.
Taxonomy No races recognized.
References [1]Benson & Irwin (1964b); [2]Benson & Irwin (1967b); [3]Benson & Pitman (1956-57); [4]Dowsett (in press a).

Collared Palm Thrush *Cichladusa arquata*   B430 **RB**

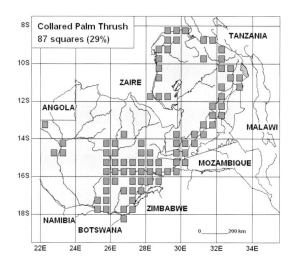

Distribution *Zambezian near-endemic* (*SE Uganda and Kenya to Zimbabwe*). Common in thickets with some palms (*Borassus, Hyphaene, Raphia*), from Chembe on the Luapula, along that river, across to L. Tanganyika, then in a large loop round to the upper Luangwa. It occurs throughout the Luangwa and Middle Zambezi Valleys[4,5]. Widespread on the Southern Province plateau, north in the Kafue drainage to the Kaungashi River at 13°54'S, 26°38'E, and up the Zambezi to Kazungula[1]. It reappears at Kalabo[2] and Silonga[8], thence north to near the Angola border on the Kashinji/Minyanya Plain[6]. This last appears to be an isolated population, and the species is unrecorded from Angola[3]. *Alt.* 400-1660 m (L. Chila, Mbala).

Ecology In small thickets dotted about with *Borassus* or *Hyphaene*, but also at edges of riparian woodland or forest with *Raphia*, thicket clumps with Baobabs. Nests on palm fronds and also in the eaves of brick buildings. Food of one specimen was a wide variety of insects[7].
Status Resident.
Breeding   Sep   Oct   Nov   Feb   Mar
(n=9)   1   2   3   1   2   *Clutch*: C/2 (2) & N/2 (1).
Moult: an adult in moult mid-Jan[4].
Taxonomy No races recognized.
References [1]Aspinwall (1975b); [2]Benson & Irwin (1967b); [3]Dean (2000); [4]Dowsett (in press a); [5]Hustler (1985b); [6]Van Daele (1999f); [7]Wilson (1964); [8]Winterbottom (1942a).

Central Bearded Scrub Robin *Erythropygia barbata*   B428 **RB**

Distribution *Zambezian endemic* (*SW Tanzania to Angola and Zambia, where it reaches the southern limit of its range*). Widespread, and locally common (including Nkumbula Is., L. Tanganyika)[4], in the plateau miombo woodlands. In the Luangwa present only on the escarpments, absent from the valley floor. It occurs south to near Kafue town and to the Sonso River, ranging west to Nyatanda[4] and Chavuma[2]. *Alt.* 950-1700 m.

Ecology Normally in the understorey of mature miombo woodland with scattered small thickets, also

Itigi thicket in the north, and locally common in *Cryptosepalum* forest in the west. Nests in a hollow stump, a metre or so above the ground[5] (see cover photo).

Status Resident.

Breeding   Aug   Sep   Oct   Nov
(n=36)   3   16   15   2   *Clutch*: C/1 (1); C/2 (5); C/3 (17).

Taxonomy[3] *E. b. barbata* in the west, intergrading with *E. b. thamnodytes* (warmer brown, less greyish, above) in the eastern half of Zambia. May possibly be conspecific with *E. quadrivirgata*, although no hybridisation is known[1] and there are (slight) vocal differences. The situation in areas of close proximity requires investigation. Some authors would place all *Erythropygia* in *Cercotrichas*[6], but we retain that genus just for *C. podobe*.

References [1]Benson & White (1962); [2]Britton (1970); [3]Clancey (1974c); [4]Dowsett (in press a); [5]Lees (1938); [6]Collar in del Hoyo *et al.* (2005).

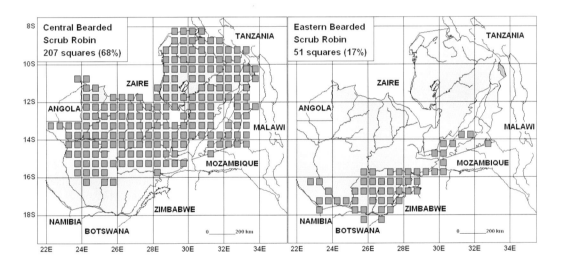

Eastern Bearded Scrub Robin *Erythropygia quadrivirgata*   B429 **RB**

Distribution *Eastern near-endemic (Somalia to South Africa)*. Quite common in thickets, centred on the Middle Zambezi and lower Luangwa Valleys, in the latter up to just below the Mwendengombe River confluence[2]. West in the Luano Valley to about Shikabeta, the whole of the Southern Province plateau and southern edge of the Kafue Flats, west to Natukoma. The species has also been recorded from Mwangazi (on the Eastern Province plateau in the Chadiza area[3]), in the lower country at the head-waters of rivers flowing into Mozambique. *Alt.* 330-1350 m.

Ecology Ground stratum in dense understorey of dry riparian forest and (semi-) evergreen or decid-uous thickets. Usually this species and *E. barbata* are allopatric and ecologically separated. But they come into close contact in some areas (e.g. in the Kafue Gorge area), and in some situations it is not clear which species is present; they readily react to tape playback of each other's song[3]. Nests in a hollow stump, a metre or so above the ground[1], a situation identical to that used by *E. barbata*.

Status Resident.

Breeding   Sep   Oct   Nov   Dec   Jan
(n=66)   5   9   14   36   2
Clutch: C/1 (6); C/2 (18); C/3 (27); C/6 (1). The C/6 was perhaps laid by two females.

Taxonomy[4] *E. q. interna*. Closely related to *E. barbata* (*q.v.*).
References [1]Benson & White (1962); [2]Berry (1981a); [3]Dowsett (in press a); [4]Irwin & Benson (1966a).

[Kalahari Scrub Robin *Erythropygia paena*
Kalahari-Highveld near-endemic (*W. Angola to South Africa*). Mapped as occurring in the Caprivi Strip
(1724D), adjacent to SW Zambia[2], but it is based on a misidentification, and this sedentary species is
improbable so far north[1]. **References** [1]Dowsett *et al.* (in prep.); [2]Oatley in Harrison *et al.* (1997).]

White-browed Scrub Robin *Erythropygia leucophrys*   B427 **RB**

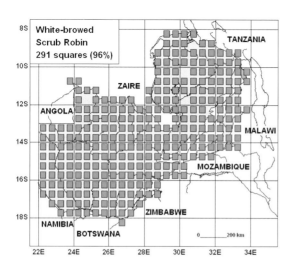

Distribution *Afrotropical* (*Ethiopia to South
Africa*). Occurs commonly in woodland
throughout the country. *Alt.* 330-1770 m
(Danger Hill), and to 2050 m on the Nyika[2].
Ecology In the understorey of almost any
open woodland and wooded savanna with fairly rank ground cover (tall grass, shrubs, ant-
hill thickets) and has adapted well to secondary habitats. Also in *Cryptosepalum* forest
(but scarce). Is often found near *E. barbata*
although normally segregated ecologically by
the latter's preference for more mature
miombo; but it is possible there is competition
locally. The nest is bulky, placed on or near the
ground, in bushes or even grass clumps.
Status Resident.

Breeding   Sep   Oct   Nov   Dec   Jan
(n=111)   7   40   35   28   1   *Clutch*: C/1 (3); C/2 (46); C/3 (40).
Moult: in adults recorded from Jan[1].
Taxonomy[3] *E. l. munda* (syn. *E. l. kabali*, type locality Chikonkwelo stream[4]; *NHM*; named for K.
Muzeya, White's collector), replaced by *E. l. ovamboensis* in the south and west, and by *E. l. zambe-
siana* (red on the tail more extensive) in the Middle Zambezi Valley. Variation is clinal.
References [1]Dowsett (in press a); [2]Dowsett-Lemaire (2006a); [3]Irwin & Benson (1967a); [4]White
(1944b: 49).

Stonechat *Saxicola torquatus*   B416 **RB**

Distribution *Afrotropical* (*breeds Senegal to South Africa*) *and Palaearctic* (*winters rarely in the
Sahel*). Locally common in grassland or the edge of swamps throughout the whole of the Zambian
plateau, but known from the low-lying valleys only by a single vagrant to Nsefu in the Luangwa Valley
(31 Jul), and once in the Middle Zambezi Valley[2] (open squares). *Alt.* 950-2200 m (higher on the
Malawi side of the Nyika), exceptionally down to 370 m.
Ecology In moist situations such as dambos and edge of marsh, reedbeds or tall grass bordering
streams. In montane areas also in dry grassland with some bushes and bracken-briar. The nest is placed
on or very near the ground, usually in a clump of grass.

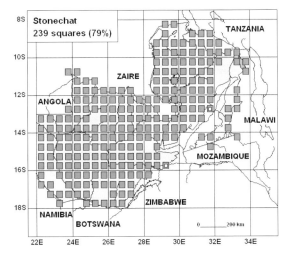

Status Present all months; most frequently recorded Aug-Dec[2], perhaps because it is more conspicuous in the breeding season. In Malawi there is partial altitudinal movement to low levels in the cold months[3], but regular movements are unlikely in Zambia, as there are so few records at low altitude.

Breeding

(n=67)	Jul	Aug	Sep
	1	14	27
	Oct	Nov	Dec
	17	6	2

Clutch: C/1 (4); C/2 (1); C/3 (18); C/4 (7).
Moult: adults moult Oct-Mar[2]; juveniles have a partial first moult[5].
Taxonomy[1] *S. t. stonei*. An albino has been reported[4].
References [1]Chapin (1953); [2]Dowsett (in press a); [3]Dowsett-Lemaire & Dowsett (2006); [4]Madge (1971e); [5]Traylor (1965b).

Whinchat *Saxicola rubetra* B415 **PW**

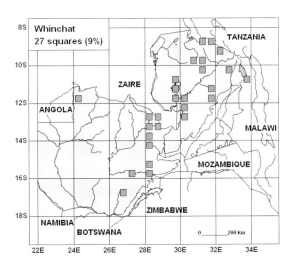

Distribution *Palaearctic* (*winters Mauritania to Zambia-Malawi*). A scarce bird of open country on the central and northern plateau, so far unrecorded from the Luangwa Valley or even the Eastern Province plateau. It ranges from Mbala and Nsombo on L. Bangweulu[1], to the Copperbelt[3,4] and "line of rail", south to Choma[3]. The most westerly was a vagrant at Mwinilunga[2]. *Alt.* 1000-2200 m (Nyika).

Ecology In grassland with scattered bushes or low trees, including dambos, fallow cultivation and montane grassland.

Status A Palaearctic migrant and winter visitor, probably annual south to the Copperbelt. Records are from 25 Oct to 6 Apr, but few after Feb (when the habitat becomes overgrown). The average first date over 17 years was 16 Nov, the average last (in 14 years) 27 Feb[3]. Usually singly, but up to 10 on occasion[3].

Taxonomy No races recognized.

References [1]Benson (1956d); [2]Bowen (1983h); [3]Dowsett (in press b); [4]Serle (1955).

Northern (Eurasian) Wheatear *Oenanthe oenanthe* B417 **PW**

Distribution *Holarctic* (*the whole population winters Mauritania to Zambia-Malawi*). A scarce bird of open areas on the northern and central plateau, from Mweru Wantipa[2], south on the Eastern Province plateau to Lundazi, and to "line of rail". There is one satisfactory record from the low-lying Luangwa

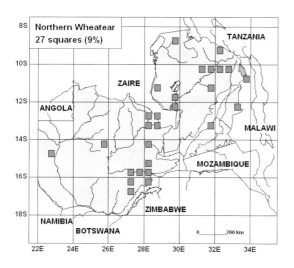

Valley[4]. The most southerly is a specimen from Choma, and there is only one record further west than Busanga Plain, from Liuwa Plain[4]. A few unsatisfactory records have been rejected: most relate to misidentifications of immature *O. pileata*. *Alt.* 530-2200 m (Nyika, higher on the Malawi side)[5].

Ecology Forages on bare ground and short grass in freshly turned fields, airstrips, dambo margins, and montane grassland; fond of perching on rocks, ant-hills or low bushes.

Status A Palaearctic migrant and winter visitor, annual in small numbers (e.g. Nyika). Extreme dates are 7 Oct to 20 Mar[4], except for a male in breeding dress, in winter (2-21 Jul) at Lusaka[1].

Taxonomy[3] *O. o. oenanthe.*

References [1]Aspinwall (1975a); [2]Benson (1956d); [3]Benson *et al.* (1970); [4]Dowsett (in press b); [5]Dowsett-Lemaire (2006a).

Capped Wheatear *Oenanthe pileata*   B419 **AMB**

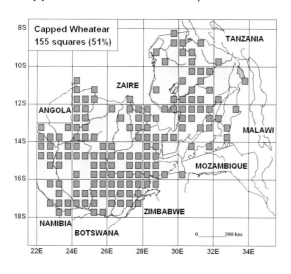

Distribution *Afrotropical (Somalia to South Africa)*. Locally common (or even numerous) in open country throughout most of Zambia; although usually scarce at low altitude, it has since 1982 invaded part of the shoreline of L. Kariba[1]. *Alt.* 330-2200 m (Nyika, higher on the Malawi side).

Ecology On short or recently burnt grassland of dry floodplains, dambo margins, airfields or montane areas; at times alongside *O. oenanthe*. Breeds in disused rodent holes.

Status An Intra-African migrant, although there are records throughout the year. Most are for the period mid-May to late Dec, and numbers usually decline from mid-Oct. The average first date over 29 years was 16 May, the average last (in 28 years) 29 Nov[1]. A few stay during the rains (all but 3 or 4 were juveniles), but this may not be annual. In places numerous as a breeding bird (e.g. on the Kafue Flats), and as a migrant (concentrations of 30, even 100, May-Jun)[1].

Breeding	Jun	Jul	Aug	Sep	Oct	
(n=26)	1	3	10	11	1	*Clutch*: C/2 (1); C/3 (4); C/4 (2).

Moult: had started late Oct[2].

Taxonomy[3] No races recognized.

References [1]Dowsett & Leonard (in press a); [2]Traylor (1965b); [3]White (1961b).

Isabelline Wheatear *Oenanthe isabellina*   B418 **PV**

Distribution and Status *Palaearctic (winters from Mauritania to Tanzania).* There are four records of single vagrants of a species essentially at the limit of its wintering range: Mbala (0831C, 25 Nov 1954), Kalonda and north of Isoka (both 0932D, respectively 9 Dec 1976 and 25 Feb 1980)[2] and Lundazi (1233A, 22-23 Dec 1976)[1]. *Alt.* 1220-1660 m, in degraded woodland and gardens.
Taxonomy No races recognized.
References [1]Aspinwall (1977e); [2]Dowsett (in press b).

Familiar Chat *Cercomela familiaris*   B420 **RB**

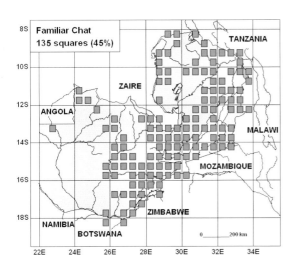

8S Familiar Chat
135 squares (45%)

Distribution *Afrotropical (Mauritania to South Africa).* Quite common throughout the rocky hills and escarpments of the eastern half of the country (though very local at low altitude), north-west to the upper Kafue, and further west to north of Mwinilunga[5] and to Chavuma Hill on the Zambezi[1]. It occurs along the Middle Zambezi escarpment to Victoria Falls[2]. *Alt.* from 550 m up to 2000 m on the Mafingas[3] and Nyika[4].
Ecology Most frequently encountered in open miombo woodland on stony hillsides, escarpments and near rocky outcrops; but also in any wooded savanna with some rocks, including waste rock dumps at Copperbelt mines. Sometimes near human habitations (mostly outside the breeding season). Nests in rock crevices and dry ravines, rarely in brick buildings.
Status Resident, with some local wandering in the off-season.

Breeding   Sep   Oct   Nov   Dec
(n=34)   17   14   2   1   *Clutch*: C/1 (1); C/2 (2); C/3 (6); C/4 (4).
Taxonomy *C. f. falkensteini.*
References [1]Britton (1970); [2]Dowsett (in press a); [3]Dowsett & Stjernstedt (1973); [4]Dowsett-Lemaire (2006a); [5]White (1945-46).

Sooty Chat *Myrmecocichla nigra*   B421 **RB**

Distribution *Afrotropical (Senegal to S. Zambia).* Locally very common on dry dambos and plains on the central Zambian plateau, from Bangweulu to Mupamadzi village on the Muchinga escarpment, and from Chinyunyu, thence down the Zambezi escarpment to Kalomo Dist., wandering to Senkobo[2] (the most southerly record of the species). It is only a vagrant on the Copperbelt (at Itawa, open square). From Kalilele Dambo[5] ranges to west of the Zambezi, south to Liuwa Plain and Sililo (Kalabo Dist.)[4], but further downriver reaching only the area of Sioma[2] and the Njoko River. Although unknown in NE Zambia north of Bangweulu, it reappears in Zaire in the Marungu highlands[3]. *Alt.* 950-1500 m.
Ecology Open watershed plains, dry dambos, wooded grassland with termitaria; has adapted to fallow

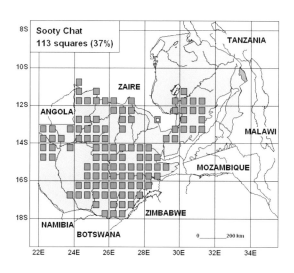

cultivation in Mkushi Dist. Spreading in parts of N. Zambia, where "chitemene" (slash-and-burn) farming is opening up woodland[2].

Status Resident.

Breeding	Sep	Oct	Nov	Feb	Mar
(n=27)	1	12	12	1	1

Clutch: C/1 (2); C/2 (3); C/3 (16); C/4 (2).

Taxonomy[1] No races recognized (syn. *M. n. stoehri* type locality Lavusi; *SAM*; named for F.O. Stoehr)[6].

References [1]Benson (1956f); [2]Dowsett (in press a); [3]Dowsett & Prigogine (1974); [4]Osborne (1978); [5]Penry (1976b); [6]Roberts (1941: 116).

Arnot's Chat *Myrmecocichla arnotti* B422 **RB**

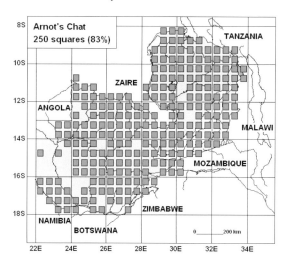

Distribution *Zambezian endemic (Burundi to South Africa)*. Common in most woodlands, throughout the country, except for the far west; although in the extreme south-west north to Nangweshi[7] and near the Mashi[6], further north known well west of the river only in the Nasilele area[4], otherwise crossing it barely near Chinyingi[1]. *Alt.* 330-1700 m.

Ecology In fairly dry miombo (avoids dense formations) and mopane woodland with open understorey, foraging on ground and trunks. Nests in hollow trunks and branches.

Status Resident.

Breeding	Aug	Sep	Oct
(n=60)	7	24	19
	Nov	Dec	Jan
	8	1	1

Clutch: C/2 (11); C/3 (22); C/4 (3).

Taxonomy[2] *M. a. arnotti* (syn. *M. a. shelleyi*, named for the ornithologist G.E. Shelley [1840-1910]; type locality Victoria Falls, Zimbabwe/Zambia; *NHM*)[5]. It has been placed in the genus *Pentholaea*[3], but the justification for this is unclear.

References [1]Aspinwall (1979b); [2]Benson (1956f); [3]Collar in del Hoyo *et al.* (2005); [4]Dowsett (in press a); [5]Sharpe (1877: 246); [6]Traylor & Hart (1965); [7]Winterbottom (1942a).

Mocking Chat *Myrmecocichla cinnamomeiventris* B423 **RB**

Distribution *Afrotropical (Mauritania to South Africa)*. A locally common rock-associated species, occurring from near Sumbu and on the Kalaye escarpment[1], southwards down the Muchingas and

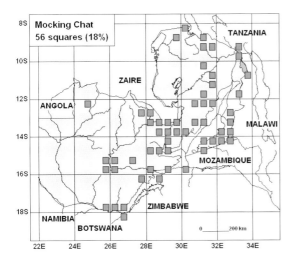

throughout the Eastern Province plateau, west to Munkonko and Chiwemupala on the Copperbelt[3]. In the Kafue basin it extends to Kaindabaila Hill[4] and Itezhi-Tezhi, and in the Middle Zambezi to Paradise Rocks, reappearing in the gorges above L. Kariba[6], west to Victoria Falls[4]. There is a very isolated population in the far north-west at Sailunga[3]. *Alt.* 600-2200 m (Nyika)[8].

Ecology Favours cliff faces, rocky outcrops and wooded hills with large boulders but has adapted locally to brick houses (e.g. Kasama)[6].

Status Resident.

Breeding   Sep   Nov   Dec
(n=5)   1   2   2
Clutch: N/2 (2); C/3 (1).

Taxonomy[2] *T. c. subrufipennis*, replaced by *T. c. odica* (deeper, tawny chestnut below) in the extreme south. Some authors would recognize the genus *Thamnolaea*[5,7].

References [1]Benson (1956f); [2]Benson & Irwin (1967b); [3]Benson *et al.* (1970); [4]Brooke (1965); [5]Collar in del Hoyo *et al.* (2005); [6]Dowsett (in press a); [7]Dowsett & Dowsett-Lemaire (1993); [8]Dowsett-Lemaire (2006a).

Sylviidae

Broad-tailed Warbler *Schoenicola platyurus*   B450 **RB**

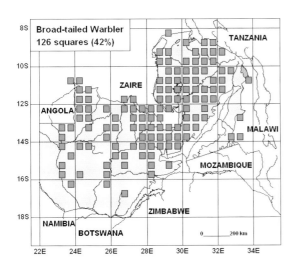

Distribution *Afrotropical (Guinea to South Africa) and Oriental (India)*. Quite common in the dambos of N. Zambia, from Lambwe Chikwama[6], Sumbu and Lusenga Plain, southwards west of the Muchinga escarpment to Mount Makulu[2] and near Kafue town, east in Central Province to "80-mile" Dambo[1]. It has occurred rarely even to Choma on the Southern Province plateau, westwards to the Zambezi River, from Mize (on the west bank)[6] south to the Siandi area and Kakenge River. On the Eastern Province plateau south of the Nyika it occurs at only a few places from Lumezi to Chipata[6]. *Alt.* 950-2150 m (Nyika, a bit higher on the Malawi side).

Ecology Below 1700 m mainly in dambos (common 1100-1400 m); above that (Nyika) in rank montane grassland. Discreet species that feeds hidden in rank grass, but sings perched on stalks 1-2 m high or in flight.

Status[4,5] Present throughout the year; there are fewer observations during the dry season (May-Sep), but this is probably because this species is easily overlooked when not singing. Records of vagrants at the limit of its range (e.g. Kafue, Choma) are in the rains.

Breeding   Dec   Jan   Feb   Mar
(n=8)   1   3   3   1   Song flight early Oct to mid-Apr. *Clutch*: C/2 (3).

Taxonomy[3] *S. p. alexinae*, with some tendency towards *S. p. brevirostris* in the south. Sometimes considered specifically distinct from Indian birds (as *S. brevirostris*) but vocally and behaviourally they appear inseparable[6].

References [1]Aspinwall (1975b); [2]Benson & Holliday (1964); [3]Benson & Irwin (1967b); [4]Brooke (1966b); [5]Dowsett (1979c); [6]Dowsett (in press a).

Little Rush Warbler *Bradypterus baboecala*   B446 **RB**

Distribution *Afrotropical (Ghana to South Africa).* Common in swamps throughout the Zambian plateau, but the scarcity of suitable habitat at low altitudes means that the only valley records are: near Jumbe (upper Luangwa); Chingombe (Luano); Katondwe (lower Luangwa); Ibwe Munyama, near Sinamalima, Nchete Is. and Bimbi Hot Springs (Middle Zambezi)[2]. *Alt.* 500-1800 m.

Ecology In permanent swamp including centres of dambos; keeps low down in *Typha* reedbeds, Papyrus and sedges, feeding close to water.

Status Resident.

Breeding   Mar   Sep
(n=2)   1   1   *Clutch*: no data.

Moult: reported Feb, Apr and Aug[2].

Taxonomy[1] *B. b. msiri*, replaced by *B. b. tongensis* in Eastern Province.

References [1]Benson *et al.* (1971a); [2]Dowsett (in press a).

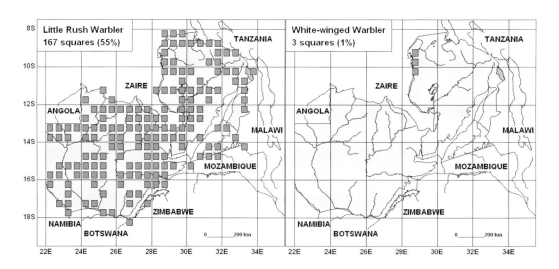

White-winged Warbler *Bradypterus carpalis*   B - **R(B)**

Distribution *L. Victoria basin near-endemic (Uganda to N. Zambia).* Common on L. Mweru (where discovered in 1996), from around the mouth of the Luapula[1] to Chabilikila[2] and near Mwense[1]. This (the most southerly) population is far-removed from the main centre of distribution in the Great Lakes

area. *Alt.* 930-960 m.
Ecology Rather dense Papyrus swamp, where it feeds low down.
Status Resident; estimated to be three times as numerous as *B. baboecala*, with perhaps 2 pairs/ha[2].
Breeding No records. The nest and eggs are unknown.
Taxonomy No races recognized.
References [1]Dowsett (in press a); [2]Leonard & Beel (1999).

Cinnamon Bracken Warbler *Bradypterus cinnamomeus*   B449 **RB**

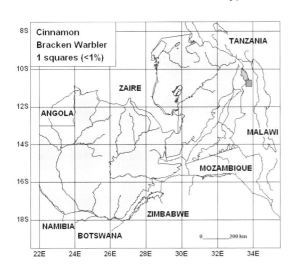

Distribution *Afromontane endemic (Ethiopia to S. Malawi).* Known only from the Nyika Plateau, where common (in shrubland). Might be expected on the Mafingas: no definite record yet from the Zambian side (two reports being indeterminate as to species)[1,7], but known from the Malawi side at 1950 m[2]. It is also present extralimitally in SE Katanga, in the Marungu highlands[4]. *Alt.* 1900-2200 m (Nyika, higher on the Malawi side).
Ecology Montane shrubland and at forest edges, penetrating the herbaceous understorey of some small forest patches above 2150 m (Malawi), not occupied by *B. lopezi*. Some breeding territories are as small as 0.1 ha[6].
Status Resident.

Breeding	Nov	Dec	Jan	Feb
(n=16)	4	9	2	1

(Including Malawi side of SW Nyika.) *Clutch*: C/2 (5).
Moult: from Mar or Apr[3].
Taxonomy *B. c. nyassae.* In the past its status was confused with that of its sibling *B. lopezi mariae* in places[5].
References [1]Aspinwall (1973a); [2]Benson (1940-41a); [3]Dowsett (in press a); [4]Dowsett & Prigogine (1974); [5]Dowsett & Stjernstedt (1979); [6]Dowsett-Lemaire (1983c); [7]Leonard *et al.* (2001a).

Evergreen Forest Warbler *Bradypterus lopezi*   B448 **RB**

Distribution *Afromontane near-endemic (Cameroon to S. Malawi).* Common in the upland evergreen forests of the Northern Province, widespread from Ikawa[1], down the Muchinga escarpment to Masase and Mkushi River (Chalata). It then occurs throughout the Copperbelt, west to the Mwombezhi River[2], Mundwiji Plain[9], and much of N. Mwinilunga (but not north of Hillwood)[4]. In the eastern highlands known with certainty only from the Nyika, where common[7] (a *Bradypterus* sp. has been recorded in the Mafingas, but as only *B. cinnamomeus* is known from that part of Malawi, it is likely that species)[4]. *Alt.* 1150-2200 m (higher on the Malawi side of the Nyika).
Ecology Inhabits dense shrubby understorey in deep shade, mainly below 2 m, of moist evergreen forest; avoids grass. Densities on Nyika (3-6 pairs/10 ha[7]) vary in part according to type of undergrowth.
Status Resident. On the Nyika some ringed birds were retrapped in following seasons, one up to 6 years

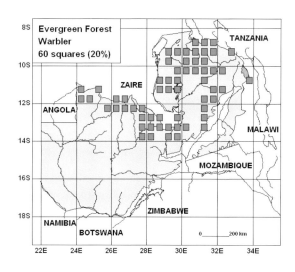

after first capture[3].

Breeding Nov Dec Jan
(n=13)   2   8   3
Clutch: C/2 (1). From SW Nyika (including Malawi side) and Danger Hill. *Moult*: on the Nyika starting Feb[4].

Taxonomy *B. l. ufipae*, with Nyika Plateau birds *B. l. usambarae*. The population of *B. l. ufipae* in N. Zambia was in the past considered to be a race of *B. cinnamomeus*, but its correct identity is now clear, based on study of morphology and voice[5,6], as its conspecificity with what was known as *B. mariae*[8].

References [1]Benson (1956d); [2]Benson & Irwin (1965b); [3]Dowsett (1985a); [4]Dowsett (in press a); [5]Dowsett & Prigogine (1974); [6]Dowsett & Stjernstedt (1979); [7]Dowsett-Lemaire (1989b); [8]Dowsett-Lemaire & Dowsett (1989); [9]Oatley (1969).

Bamboo Warbler *Bradypterus alfredi*   B447 **R(B)**

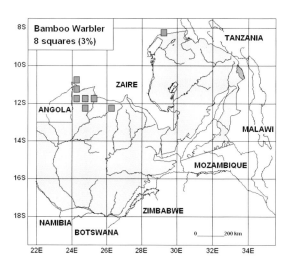

Distribution *Sub-Afromontane near-endemic* (*Ethiopia to NW Zambia*). Scarce in evergreen forest at a few localities in N. Mwinilunga, such as Salujinga, Hillwood and Isombu, south to Mwinilunga town[1], Mundwiji Plain[2], Kabompo Bridge (1125C) and Ntambu, east to Mutanda Bridge[4] (the most southerly records of the species). It reappears to the north of L. Mweru at Kasangu[5]. Discreet and easily overlooked unless vocal. *Alt.* 1200-1460 m.

Ecology Dense undergrowth in moist evergreen forest, including forest regrowth and thin riparian strips. Overlaps locally with *B. lopezi*.

Status Resident.

Breeding No records. Song Oct-Dec. The nest and eggs are unknown.

Taxonomy[3] *B. a. kungwensis*.

References [1]Benson & Irwin (1964b); [2]Benson & Irwin (1965b); [3]Chapin (1953); [4]Dowsett (in press a); [5]Leonard (1998d).

African Moustached Warbler *Melocichla mentalis*   B462 **RB**

Distribution *Afrotropical* (*Senegal to Zimbabwe*). Locally common in rank growth throughout the eastern half of Zambia (but absent from the Nyika), then right across the country north of a line joining

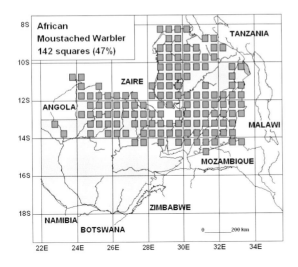

Manyani[5] and the Luamala River[1], to Zambezi town (Balovale)[3] and Chavuma[2]. *Alt.* 550-1700 m.

Ecology In lush grassland, long-grass dambos and floodplain, neglected cultivation, edges of woodland with grass and scattered bushes, and rank riparian and secondary growth.

Status Resident.

Breeding	Oct	Nov	Dec	Jan	Mar
(n=7)	1	1	1	2	2

Clutch: C/2 (4).

Taxonomy *M. m. mentalis*, with the Eastern Province form *M. m. luangwae* (type locality Mupamadzi River; *NMZB*)[1,4].

References [1]Benson (1958a: 91); [2]Benson (1960c); [3]Britton (1970); [4]Dowsett (1980b); [5]Dowsett (in press a).

River Warbler *Locustella fluviatilis*   B451 **PW**

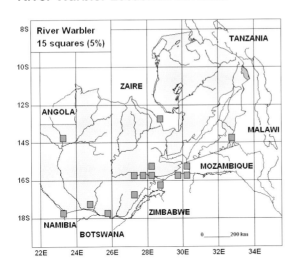

Distribution *Palaearctic (winters mainly Zambia and S. Malawi to South Africa).* Probably regular in small numbers in thicket. Passage migrants at Chipata and Ndola, but there are several records in the area between Chiriwe (in the lower Luangwa) and Livingstone, west to Imusho[1] and Zambezi town (Balovale)[3]. [Also a tentative sight record from Mwinilunga[2], felt by the observer to be uncertain.] *Alt.* 330-1330 m.

Ecology In rank grass with low bush or patches of thickets.

Status A Palaearctic migrant and winter visitor. All records are for the period 5 Dec to 26 Mar (with one possible sighting 6 Apr), small numbers evidently wintering in the south of the country[5], but it is easily overlooked, even when vocal.

Moult: two started moult late Jan, and another was advanced in Feb[4,6]. Some sing Jan-Mar.

Taxonomy No races recognized.

References [1]Benson & Irwin (1965h); [2]Bowen (1983h); [3]Britton (1970); [4]Dowsett (1973g); [5]Dowsett (in press b); [6]Tucker (1978).

Sedge Warbler *Acrocephalus schoenobaenus*   B452 **PW**

Distribution *Palaearctic (winters Mauritania to South Africa).* Numerous in aquatic vegetation throughout, but there are few records from the Luangwa Valley. *Alt.* 330-1800 m.

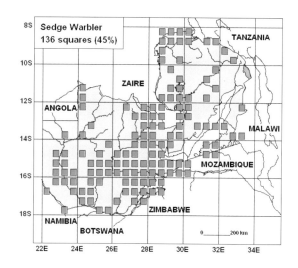

Ecology In reeds and sedges in standing water, rank grass by streams, at edges of dams, marshes and sewage ponds; occasionally in drier situations such as thickets and long grass.

Status A Palaearctic migrant and winter visitor, with extreme dates 10 Oct and 18 May. The average first date over 25 years was 7 Nov, the average last (in 24 years) 26 Apr[1]. The passage of this species is well shown by a bird ringed in Lusaka 23 Mar which was recaught 210 km to the south-west, near Choma, on 13 Dec, and was again at Lusaka 24 Mar the following year[1]. A Finnish-ringed bird was recovered 16 Mar (Appendix 1). Altogether 36 birds have been controlled after one year, 6 after two, and 3 after three years[2].

Moult: between late Nov and Apr, lasting 65 days[3].

Taxonomy No races recognized.

References [1]Dowsett (in press b); [2]Dowsett & Leonard (2001); [3]Francis in Ginn & Melville (1983).

Eurasian Reed Warbler *Acrocephalus s. scirpaceus & fuscus*   B454 **PW**

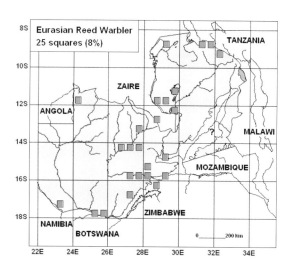

Distribution *Palaearctic* (*winters Mauritania to N. Botswana*). It is convenient to treat the two populations of this species in different accounts, although a number of the records cannot be ascribed with certainty to either as they have identical songs. Palaearctic birds are known definitely in small numbers from thickets at Chiengi and Mbala, south through the Copperbelt to Kazungula, with records further west from Mwinilunga[2] and Sinjembela[1]. Although reports from the Luangwa Valley ("?" on map) require confirmation, it is known from the Middle Zambezi Valley at Chiawa and Mutulanganga. *Alt.* 370-1660 m.

Ecology Palaearctic *A. s. scirpaceus* frequents much the same habitat as its congener *A. palustris*, i.e. patches of thickets with some rank grass, near water or not, sometimes in small clumps of mixed grass and reeds, but it does not usually penetrate the extensive reedbeds where the African *Acrocephalus* (*A. gracilirostris*, *A. s. baeticatus*) breed[6].

Status A scarce Palaearctic migrant and winter visitor (here near the southern limit of the non-breeding range). Extreme dates recorded are 15 Oct and 23 Apr, but most likely from Nov; the early records were identified by song, and thus confusion with *A. s. baeticatus* is possible[4]. Four ringed birds were recaptured the following year[5]. *Moult*: Jan-Mar[4].

Taxonomy Both *A. s. scirpaceus* and *A. s. fuscus* occur[1], though the eastern *fuscus* is likely to be

much the commoner. For the differences between these taxa, see ref. 3.
References [1]Benson & Irwin (1967b); [2]Bowen (1983h); [3]Clancey (1963b); [4]Dowsett (in press b);
[5]Dowsett & Leonard (2001); [6]Dowsett-Lemaire & Dowsett (1987b).

African Reed Warbler *Acrocephalus scirpaceus baeticatus*-group   B456 **AMB/R**

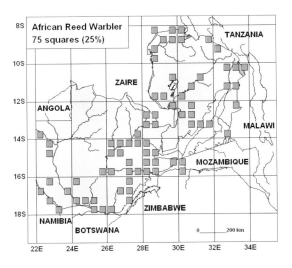

Distribution *Afrotropical (Senegal to South Africa)*. Definite African birds are more widespread than Palaearctic, locally common in wetlands throughout the eastern and southern parts of the country (even locally in the Luangwa Valley), west to the Copperbelt and upper Kafue, becoming abundant in the southwest along the Zambezi and Mashi Rivers to 55 km west of Nangweshi[4], and as far north as Chinyama Litapi. *Alt.* 330-1300 m.

Ecology The local birds normally breed in aquatic vegetation, especially mixed reedbeds and sedges, and seasonally flooded grassland; many spend the off-season in drier situations such as thickets and rank grass on the edge of streams, a habitat also occupied by *A. palustris* and *A. s. scirpaceus* but largely at different seasons.

Status Present in all months, but at least two populations are involved: one breeding (resident?), another a winter visitor from southern Africa[2]. Careful examination of birds in the hand will be necessary to elucidate the seasonal distribution of these populations.

Breeding   Feb
(n=2)   2   *Clutch*: C/2 (1).

Moult: local breeding *A. s. cinnamomeus* start mid-Mar and finish by Jul. Nominate *A. b. baeticatus* that spend the non-breeding season in S. Zambia are in fresh plumage Aug-Sep[2].

Taxonomy The local breeding forms (sometimes treated as a separate species, *A. baeticatus*[1], but see refs 3,5,6) are *A. s. cinnamomeus* and *A. s. hallae* (the latter in the extreme south-west), while *A. s. baeticatus* appears as a non-breeding visitor from southern Africa[2]. For the differences between these taxa, see ref. 1.

References [1]Clancey (1963b); [2]Dowsett & Leonard (in press a); [3]Dowsett-Lemaire & Dowsett (1987a); [4]Irwin & Benson (1966a); [5]Knox *et al.* (2002); [6]Parkin *et al.* (2004).

(European) Marsh Warbler *Acrocephalus palustris*   B453 **PW**

Distribution *Palaearctic (winters mainly Tanzania to South Africa)*[5]. Occurs (usually commonly) in dense vegetation through much of the country, west to Imusho[1] and the Lweti area, although there is no certain record from north of Kabompo[2]. *Alt.* 330-1670 m.

Ecology Mainly in rank grass with thicket clumps, also inside patches of deciduous thicket (coming into leaf when the birds arrive), occasionally at edges of evergreen forest[6].

Status A Palaearctic migrant and winter visitor. Birds are present between 15 Nov and 29 Apr, and hold territories locally[8]. The average first date over 21 years was 14 Dec, the average last (in 22 years)

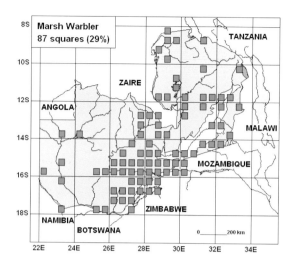

8 Apr[3]. Very numerous on passage (second week Dec to early Jan; mid-Feb to early Apr) and as a wintering species[3]. Sing throughout their stay, with vocal output increasing in Feb. Two birds ringed on southward passage in Kenya (11 and 15 Dec) were recovered in Zambia in the following Jan and Feb (Appendix 1). Three birds were retrapped where ringed one year later[4].

Moult: late Dec-late Mar[3].

Taxonomy[7] Both *A. p. palustris* and the eastern *A. p. laricus* occur, the latter darker and greener above.

References [1]Benson & Irwin (1967b); [2]Bowen (1983h); [3]Dowsett (in press b); [4]Dowsett & Leonard (2001); [5]Dowsett-Lemaire (1979); [6]Dowsett-Lemaire & Dowsett (1987b); [7]Irwin (1981a); [8]Kelsey (1989).

Great Reed Warbler *Acrocephalus arundinaceus*   B455 **PW**

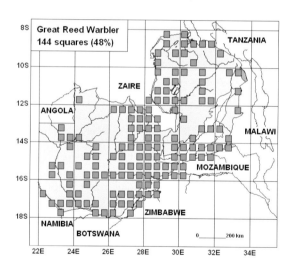

Distribution *Palaearctic* (*winters mainly Ivory Coast to South Africa*). Locally common in moist rank vegetation throughout Zambia. *Alt.* 330-1670 m.

Ecology Usually in mixed reeds, *Typha*, tall grass and thickets near water, but also in similar rank growth away from water, including gardens.

Status A Palaearctic migrant and winter visitor. All certain records are for the period 10 Nov to 16 Apr, most arriving Dec[1]. The average first date over 24 years was 20 Nov, the average last (in 25 years) 4 Apr[1]. This species is very faithful to its winter quarters, with 19 ringed birds returning after one year, 4 after two and 3 after three years[2].

Moult: a few moult late Nov to Mar[1].

Taxonomy[3] Both *A. a. arundinaceus* and *A. a. zarudnyi* occur (the latter paler above, less rufous below).

References [1]Dowsett (in press b); [2]Dowsett & Leonard (2001); [3]Irwin & Benson (1967a).

Lesser Swamp Warbler *Acrocephalus gracilirostris*   B458 **RB**

Distribution *Afrotropical* (*Nigeria to South Africa*). Common in aquatic vegetation almost throughout the country; scarce in the Luangwa Valley above Mwape, and unknown on the Eastern Province plateau north of Khulamayembe[3]. *Alt.* 330-1700 m.

Ecology In any tall aquatic vegetation, including *Phragmites, Typha* reedbeds and Papyrus; also seasonally in thickets and scrub not far from water, irrigated gardens and sugar-cane[3]. Its niche partly overlaps that of local breeding *A. scirpaceus* ssp., but the two are clearly separated by size. More clearly competes with *A. rufescens*, but this subject has not been studied in detail.

Status Resident.

Breeding Aug Sep Oct Nov Dec Jan Feb Mar Apr May
(n=34)   1   5   1   3   4   5   6   5   1   3

Clutch: C/1 (6); C/2 (13); C/3 (3).

Moult: most adults moult Nov-Apr, timing probably depending on whether or not a second clutch has been laid[3].

Taxonomy Most of Zambia is divided roughly between three races: *A. g. winterbottomi* in the north, *A. g. leptorhynchus* in the east and south, *A. g. cunenensis* in the west and south-west[1,2].

References [1]Benson (1956f); [2]Benson *et al.* (1971a); [3]Dowsett (in press a).

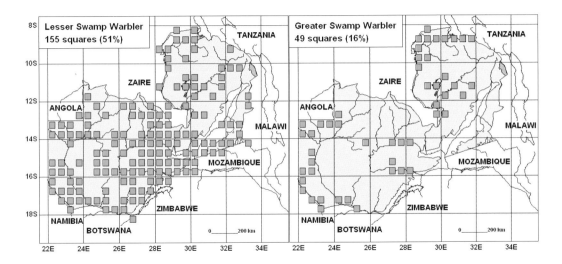

Greater Swamp Warbler *Acrocephalus rufescens*   B457 **RB**

Distribution *Afrotropical (Mauritania to N. Botswana)*. Locally quite common in permanent swamps (particularly Papyrus) from the area between Lakes Tanganyika and Mweru, through the lower Luapula to Bangweulu and Shiwa Ngandu[4]. It reappears in the Lukanga Swamp[2], with further isolated populations in the Busanga Swamps and the Kafue Flats, eastwards towards Kafue Bridge[4]. In the Upper Zambezi it is widespread from Katombora[6] north to Mayau[3]. *Alt.* 950-1580 m (near Pumpa, Mbala Dist.)[4].

Ecology Usually associated closely with Papyrus swamps, where they feed at or near water level, but in a few places in *Phragmites* (e.g. parts of the Mashi, Mayau and South Kashiji)[2]. This and its smaller sibling *A. gracilirostris* are both in Papyrus and *Phragmites*, and occur near each other in several places throughout the range of *A. rufescens* (e.g. the Luapula drainage[1], Kafue Flats[5] and Upper Zambezi[4]). Whether they defend interspecific territories has not been studied.

Status Resident.

Breeding Oct Dec Feb
(n=3)   1   1   1   *Clutch*: C/2 (1).

Taxonomy[7] *A. r. ansorgei.*
References [1]Aspinwall (1974); [2]Benson (1959c); [3]Benson (1960c); [4]Dowsett (in press a); [5]Dowsett & Osborne (1973); [6]Pollard (1991b); [7]Traylor (1966).

Olive-tree Warbler *Hippolais olivetorum*   B - **PW**

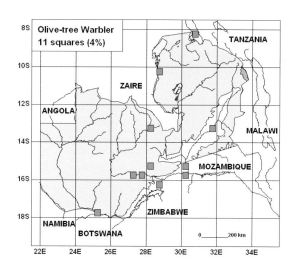

Distribution *Palaearctic* (*winters Tanzania to South Africa*). Sparse, with records from scattered localities (particularly in *Acacia*), from Inangu peninsula (Kasaba Bay) and Kashiba on the Luapula, once in the Luangwa Valley, south to the Kafue Flats[1] and Mambova on the Zambezi[2]. *Alt.* 330-1330 m (mostly below 1100 m).
Ecology In dry, open woodland (particularly *Acacia mellifera* and *Dichrostachys cinerea*) and wooded savanna, also patches of thicket with rank grass.
Status A Palaearctic migrant and winter visitor, probably annual (but not located before 1972)[1]. All records are for the period 15 Nov to 17 Apr, and it winters in small numbers in the south (with one Jan record from Kasaba Bay), often in song[3]. *Moult*: an adult 27 Nov was in very worn plumage[3].
Taxonomy No races recognized.
References [1]Dowsett (1973d); [2]Dowsett (1975a); [3]Dowsett (in press b).

Icterine Warbler *Hippolais icterina*   B463 **PW**

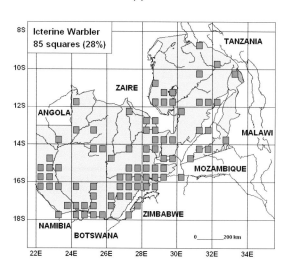

Distribution *Palaearctic* (*winters mainly Zaire to South Africa*). Occurs quite commonly at times in woodland almost throughout the country (especially in *Acacia*); the lack of records between Mbala and Musonda Falls is perhaps an artefact. *Alt.* 330-1660 m (Mbala).
Ecology Wintering birds favour the canopy of tall *Acacia* and *Albizia* trees (including *Acacia tortilis*), but on passage also occasionally in other open woodland (miombo and, rarely, mopane).
Status A Palaearctic migrant and winter visitor, with extreme dates 13 Oct and 16 Apr[1]. One ringed bird was retrapped the following season, and one after 2 years[2].
Moult: from mid-Dec, lasting *c.* 2 months[1,3].
Taxonomy No races recognized.
References [1]Dowsett (in press b); [2]Dowsett & Leonard (2001); [3]Traylor (1965b).

Papyrus Yellow Warbler *Chloropeta gracilirostris* B461 **R(B)**

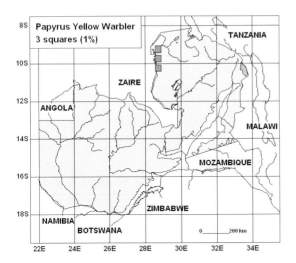

Distribution *L. Victoria basin near-endemic* (*Uganda to N. Zambia*). Small numbers confined to Papyrus swamp on the Luapula, from the mouth of the river on L. Mweru[4] south to the Mwense area[3] (the most southerly record of the species). *Alt.* 930-960 m.

Ecology Dense Papyrus swamps, feeding by flycatching and gleaning, at or near water level. Its sibling *C. natalensis* does not occur in the same habitat[5].

Status Resident.

Conservation Classed as "Vulnerable"[2], but at present the Papyrus habitat in Zambia is not under excessive pressure.

Breeding No records. Nest and eggs unknown.

Taxonomy *C. g. bensoni* (type locality Luapula River mouth, L. Mweru; *AMNH*)[1]; named for C.W. Benson.

References [1]Amadon (1954: 141); [2]BirdLife International (2000, 2004a); [3]Dowsett (in press a); [4]Keith & Vernon (1969); [5]Leonard & Beel (1999).

African Yellow Warbler *Chloropeta natalensis* B459 **RB**

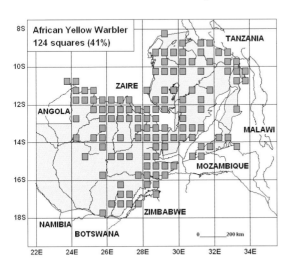

Distribution *Afrotropical* (*Nigeria to South Africa*). Locally not uncommon in rank growth over much of the Zambian plateau, westwards to Mayau and Kabompo[2]. On the Southern Province plateau absent from the Kafue Flats between Nakambala and Ngoma, but ranges sparsely south to Kalomo[7], and very locally north-east of Livingstone[4]. Although the only record from the Luangwa Valley is from a small marsh at Kazikizi, it is present at several places in the Middle Zambezi Valley, from the Kafue confluence[4] and Chirundu[6] to the Sinamalima area. *Alt.* 470-2200 m (both Mafingas[1] and Nyika), usually above 950 m.

Ecology Varies with altitude: mainly in rank growth (thickets and long grass) near streams or on the edge of marsh. On the Northern Province plateau it is common at forest edges, in the eastern highlands also in bracken-briar, overlapping with *C. similis* on the Nyika.

Status Present all months, and probably largely resident. However, known to be a partial altitudinal migrant in Malawi[5], and a non-breeding, dry season visitor to the Kafue Flats[4].

Breeding	Oct	Nov	Dec	Jan	Feb	
(n=14)	1	1	4	6	2	*Clutch*: C/1 (2); C/2 (8).

Taxonomy[6] *C. n. natalensis* is reported from the east and south (although this has been questioned[3]), and *C. n. major* (crown less brown and contrasting less with mantle) from the north and west. An approach to *C. n. massaica* (darker green above than last) is shown by eastern highland birds.
References [1]Aspinwall (1976b); [2]Benson (1960c); [3]Clancey (1974a); [4]Dowsett (in press a); [5]Dowsett-Lemaire & Dowsett (2006); [6]Irwin & Benson (1967a); [7]Keith & Vernon (1969).

Mountain Yellow Warbler *Chloropeta similis* B460 **RB**

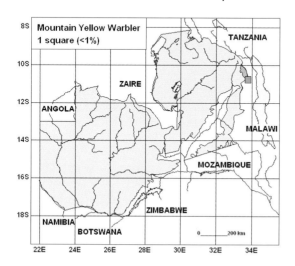

Distribution *Afromontane endemic (Sudan to N. Malawi)*. Common at forest edges and in scrub on the Nyika Plateau[3]. *Alt.* 1950-2200 m (higher on the Malawi side).
Ecology On the edge of montane forest (in Malawi also inside small patches) and in shrubland 1-4 m high, where overlaps (locally) with *C. natalensis*[2,3] but is probably dominant over its congener. Vernon found the two species nesting within 50 m of each other[4].
Status Resident.

Breeding	Dec	Jan	Feb	Mar
(n=13)		2	6	4	1

(Including Malawi side of SW Nyika.)
Clutch: C/2 (2).
Moult: noted Feb and Apr[1].
Taxonomy No races recognized.

References [1]Dowsett (in press a); [2]Dowsett-Lemaire (1983c); [3]Dowsett-Lemaire (1989b); [4]Vernon in Keith & Vernon (1966).

Green-capped Eremomela *Eremomela scotops* B484 **RB**

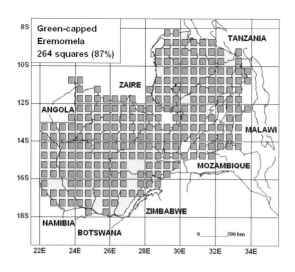

Distribution *Afrotropical (SE Gabon to South Africa; mainly Zambezian)*. Very common in woodland throughout the country, absent from the central Kafue Flats (where no suitable habitat), and in the lower Luangwa Valley and Middle Zambezi known below Luangwa Bridge only from Munyumbwe, Chirundu and Chiawa[3]. In the upper Luangwa it occurs sparsely in miombo to within a few km of the river, as north of Mfuwe at Kapiri Kamfumu[2,3]. *Alt.* 700-2000 m (Mafingas and Malawi side of Nyika), rarely down to 550 m.
Ecology In the canopy of tall miombo woodland and one of the most characteristic species of this habitat on the Zambian plateau. Also in *Baikiaea* forest, at edges of *Cryptosepalum* and sparsely (at lower altitudes) in undifferen-

tiated woodland and (rarely) mopane. A frequent member of mixed bird parties.
Status Resident.
Breeding　　Sep　Oct　Nov
(n=15)　　　　　6　　7　　2
Clutch: C/1 (1); C/2 (9); C/5 (1). The C/5 may have been laid by more than one female.
Moult: adults in moult early Dec[4].
Taxonomy[1] *E. s. pulchra* (syn. *E. s. extrema* type locality Lungwebungu River; *NMZB*)[5].
References [1]Benson & Irwin (1967b); [2]Berry (1981a); [3]Dowsett (in press a); [4]Traylor (1965b); [5]White (1960b: 151).

Black-collared Eremomela *Eremomela atricollis*　　　　　　　B485 **RB**

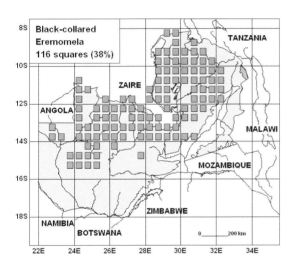

Distribution *Zambezian endemic* (*NE Angola to Zambia*). Quite common in the miombo woodlands of the northern plateau, east to 8 km west of Isoka town. It ranges southwards down the Muchingas to near Chisomo, exceptionally to Chikana near Kabwe[3]. It occurs further west to near Zambezi town (Balovale)[1,4], and south to Loma Plain and Namando (the most southerly records of the species). *Alt.* 950-1800 m.
Ecology The richer miombo woodlands, and the edge of riparian evergreen forest, feeding in the mid-stratum and canopy by snatching and gleaning. Often in mixed bird parties.
Status Resident.
Breeding　　Sep　Oct　Nov　Dec
(n=8)　　　　　2　　3　　2　　1

Clutch: C/2 (1).
Taxonomy[2] *E. a. venustula* (type locality the Mlembo River; *NMZB*)[2], hybridizing with *E. a. atricollis* at some more northern localities.
References [1]Britton (1970); [2]Clancey (1974d: 100); [3]Dowsett (in press a); [4]Winterbottom (1942a).

Burnt-necked Eremomela *Eremomela usticollis*　　　　　　　B486 **RB**

Distribution *Zambezian/Kalahari* (*Zambia, where it reaches the northern limit of its range, to South Africa*). Small numbers locally in large *Acacia* trees in the Zambezi, Kafue and Luangwa River systems[2]. Down the Zambezi from Shangombo[1] and Nasiongo[4], throughout the Middle Zambezi and much of the Southern Province plateau, north to Chilenga on the upper Kafue. It occurs to the Luano Valley at Chembe, then reappears from near Mfuwe to the upper Luangwa in the Chiwale area[2] (the intermediate area from which it is unrecorded being mostly dense thicket). *Alt.* 330-1350 m.
Ecology In the crowns of large Acacias (such as *Acacia albida* and *A. tortilis*). Feeds by gleaning and snatching. Not a member of mixed bird parties.
Status Resident.
Breeding　　Mar
(n=2)　　　　　2　　*Clutch*: no data.

Taxonomy[1,3] *E. u. rensi*, perhaps replaced by *E. u. baumgarti* in the south-west (paler grey above).
References [1]Benson (1956f); [2]Dowsett (in press a); [3]Irwin (1981a); [4]Irwin & Benson (1967a).

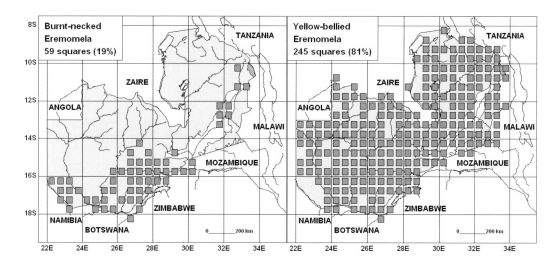

Yellow-bellied Eremomela *Eremomela icteropygialis*   B483 **RB**

Distribution *Afrotropical* (*Mauritania to South Africa*). Common in open woodland throughout Zambia, although there are no records yet in the extreme south-west, along the Mashi, south of the South Lueti River[8]. *Alt.* 500-1800 m.
Ecology In fairly open miombo woodland, more often at edges and in regenerating stages, also in riparian and *Acacia/Combretum* savanna, low bush or edges of thickets, rarely in mopane. Often in mixed bird parties; may occur alongside other *Eremomela* species but less specialized ecologically.
Status Resident: a 2-year survey showed no evidence of any regular movements[2].
Breeding   Jun   Aug   Sep   Oct   Nov   Feb
(n=95)   1   3   57   32   1   1   *Clutch*: C/1 (8); C/2 (75); C/3 (3).
Moult: noted Nov[8].
Taxonomy *E. i. polioxantha*, replaced by *E. i. lundae* in the west and by *E. i. viriditincta* (type locality 25 km west of Victoria Falls = Kasusu[9]; *NMZB*) in the south-west[1]. *E. i. salvadorii* is perhaps extra-limital (although claimed for NW Zambia), and does not warrant treatment as a distinct species, as has been suggested[6]. We published reasons for rejecting specific status[3,4], including their very similar vocalisations[5], but have been wrongly credited with the opposite point of view[7].
References [1]Benson & Irwin (1967b); [2]Dowsett (in press a); [3]Dowsett & Dowsett-Lemaire (1980); [4]Dowsett & Dowsett-Lemaire (1993); [5]Dowsett-Lemaire (1997); [6]Hall & Moreau (1970); [7]Berutti in Harrison *et al.* (1997); [8]Traylor (1965b); [9]White (1961a: 91).

Red-capped Crombec *Sylvietta ruficapilla*   B487 **RB**

Distribution *Zambezian near-endemic* (*SE Gabon and Congo-Brazzaville to Zambia-Malawi, marginally NW Zimbabwe*). Quite common in the plateau miombo woodlands, throughout the north of the country, south to the Middle Zambezi escarpment, and in the south-west to Sekute and Mushukula[3]. It occurs west of the Zambezi only south to the Luachi River[6]. Absent from the valley floors, it does occur

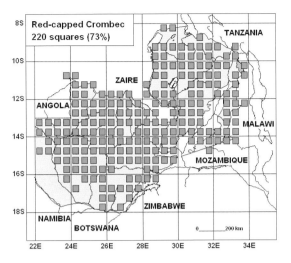

at low altitude in places, as in the lower Luangwa in the Mwape area (where there is thin miombo on small hills)[4]. *Alt.* 600-1800 m, up to 1980 m in the Mafingas[1] and 2050 m on the Nyika.

Ecology In the canopy of miombo woodland, also in *Cryptosepalum* forest (quite common). An active member of mixed bird parties.

Status Resident.

Breeding   Sep   Oct   Nov
(n=21)   14   6   1

Clutch: C/1 (3); C/2 (11); C/3 (1).

Moult: an adult in moult as early as 10 Nov[6].

Taxonomy[2] *S. r. chubbi* (type locality Kabwe; *NHM*)[5], named for the zoologist E.C. Chubb [1884-1972], replaced by *S. r. gephyra* (type locality Mwinilunga; *NHM*)[7] in the north-west (with red on the crown). Intermediates occur.

References [1]Aspinwall (1976b); [2]Benson & Irwin (1967b); [3]Bruce-Miller & Dowsett (1977); [4]Dowsett (in press a); [5]Ogilvie-Grant (1910: 10); [6]Traylor (1965b); [7]White (1953a: 68).

[**Red-faced Crombec** *Sylvietta whytii*

Afrotropical (*Ethiopia to Zimbabwe*). The implication that this species might occur in E. Zambia[3] is without foundation[1], the nearest records being from the South Viphya Plateau in Malawi[2].

References [1]Dowsett (in press a); [2]Dowsett-Lemaire & Dowsett (2006); [3]Pollard in Harrison *et al.* (1997: 690).]

Long-billed Crombec *Sylvietta rufescens*   B488 **RB**

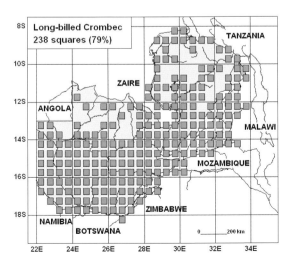

Distribution *Afrotropical* (*Burundi to South Africa*). Quite common throughout most of the country in open woodland and thickets, but more local in the higher-rainfall areas, in the north-east being essentially in the drier *Acacia* country along the Chambeshi and between Lakes Tanganyika and Mweru. In the north-west there are very few records, e.g. from Ntambu[1] and Mwinilunga[2] (also very rare at Kasaji in nearby Zaire)[5]. *Alt.* 330-1600 m.

Ecology Low down in various open and secondary woodlands, thickets, riparian growth and gardens. Not inside mature miombo but is rather partial to thorn scrub, including the canopy of *Acacia*. Rarely in bird parties.

Status Resident.

Breeding	Aug	Sep	Oct	Nov	Dec	Jan	Feb	Mar	Apr
(n=236)	1	81	68	58	15	3	5	4	1

Clutch: C/1 (24); C/2 (176); C/3 (1). *Moult*: in adults mid-Nov to Mar[2,4].
Taxonomy[3] *S. r. flecki*, with *S. r. pallida* in the Middle Zambezi Valley.
References [1]Bowen (1983i); [2]Dowsett (in press a); [3]Irwin & Benson (1966b); [4]Traylor (1965b); [5]Schouteden (1971).

Willow Warbler *Phylloscopus trochilus* B469 **PW**

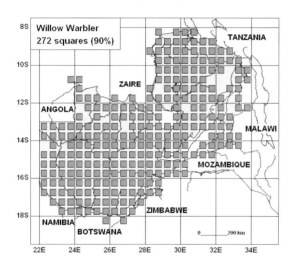

8S
Willow Warbler
272 squares (90%)
TANZANIA
10S
ZAIRE
12S
ANGOLA
MALAWI
14S
MOZAMBIQUE
16S
18S
ZIMBABWE
NAMIBIA
BOTSWANA
0   200 km
22E   24E   26E   28E   30E   32E   34E

Distribution *Palaearctic* (*the whole population winters Mauritania to South Africa*). One of the most abundant Palaearctic migrants, throughout the country in any open woodland. *Alt.* 330-2200 m.
Ecology In the canopy of woodland or wooded savanna, edges of evergreen forest, thicket or plantations, gardens, even isolated trees in cultivation.
Status A Palaearctic migrant and winter visitor, at times abundant on passage and still numerous during winter. Extreme dates are 11 Sep and 5 Jun; the average first date over 24 years was 24 Sep, the average last (in 22 years) 27 Apr[1]. Large concentrations (>100) occur on passage mid-Oct and mid-Mar[1]. Five birds ringed in Scandinavia and the Baltic States were recovered in Zambia (3 of them in Apr) (Appendix 1). There is one example of a bird returning to the place of ringing after one year[2].
Moult: early Dec to mid-Mar[1].
Taxonomy Both *P. t. trochilus* and *P. t. acredula* (brighter olive above, no yellow on flanks and abdomen) are common, while a few *P. t. yakutensis* (brownish above, greyish tinge to breast) have been identified among specimens[3].
References [1]Dowsett (in press b); [2]Dowsett & Leonard (2001); [3]Irwin & Benson (1966a).

Yellow-throated Warbler *Phylloscopus ruficapilla* B - **R(B)**

Distribution *Afromontane endemic* (*Kenya to South Africa*). Known only from forest on the Mafingas (first found in 1971), where quite common[1,2]. Its absence from SW Nyika is difficult to understand. *Alt.* 1950-2000 m (note that 2150 m[1] is probably too high).
Ecology In montane rain forest, feeding mainly in middle and upper storeys.
Status Resident.
Breeding No records.
Taxonomy *P. r. johnstoni*.
References [1]Dowsett (1971b); [2]Dowsett & Stjernstedt (1973).

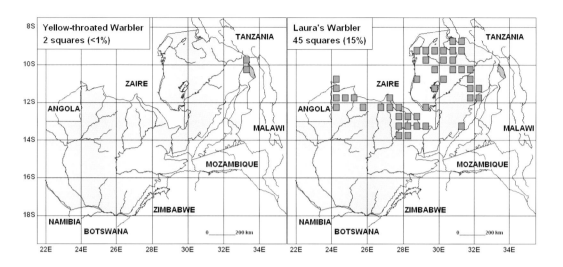

Laura's Warbler *Phylloscopus laurae*   B470 **RB**

Distribution *Zambezian endemic, with Afromontane affinities (SW Tanzania to W. Angola).* Locally common in the northern evergreen plateau forests, from Mbala[1] and near Nchelenge to east of Shiwa Ngandu and Musense[3] on the Muchingas, to south of the Copperbelt at Imanda and the Mpongwe area in general. It then ranges sparingly across to N. Mwinilunga, but does not occur as far south as the Mayau area[5]. Its distribution in Zambia is very similar to that of *Sheppardia bocagei* (another species with Afromontane affinities), except that the latter reaches the Mafingas (where *P. laurae* is replaced by *P. ruficapilla*). In Angola it is so far known only from montane forest on Mt Moco[4]. *Alt.* 1000 m (Nchelenge Dist.) to 1770 m (Danger Hill).
Ecology Undisturbed moist evergreen forest, including mushitu (swamp forest) and montane forest (Muchinga escarpment). It feeds mainly in the mid-stratum, by flycatching and snatching.
Status Resident; occasionally joins mixed bird parties.
Breeding   Jul   Sep   Oct
(n=4)   1   1   2   *Clutch*: no data. The eggs have not been described.
Taxonomy[2] *P. l. eustacei* (type locality Danger Hill; *NMZB*)[1]. Named for Eustace Poles, game warden.
References [1]Benson (1954: 77); [2]Benson & Irwin (1964b); [3]Benson *et al.* (1961); [4]Dean (2000); [5]Dowsett (in press a).

Yellow-bellied Hyliota *Hyliota flavigaster*   B489 **RB**

Distribution *Afrotropical (Senegal to Mozambique).* Common in miombo woodland, thus over most of the plateau. It is essentially absent south of 17°S, occurring to Choma (rare) and marginally in the *Baikiaea* forest further west to Sichili; exceptionally it has been reported from the Chijalile Hills on the Zambezi escarpment (together with *H. australis*)[3]. Further west it crosses the Zambezi to Sihole[8], to Nyatanda[3] and to the north of Zambezi town (Balovale)[1]. Absent from the valley floors, except where there is miombo on isolated hills, as in the lower Luangwa; in the Middle Zambezi it no more than reaches the escarpment near Chirundu and near Gwembe[3]. A sight record from Victoria Falls in Zimbabwe[7] was probably an off-season wanderer. *Alt.* 600-1950 m (Mafingas)[6].
Ecology In the canopy of miombo woodland, apparently absent from *Cryptosepalum*[4]. A frequent member of mixed bird parties, and observed alongside *H. australis* in many localities.

Status Resident.

Breeding   Sep   Oct   Nov   Dec

(n=18)   7   7   3   1   *Clutch*: C/2 (1); C/3 (4). *Moult*: started early Dec[8].

Taxonomy[2] *H. f. barbozae*. DNA evidence suggests that *Hyliota* is not a member of the Sylviidae, but its relationship is unclear[5].

References [1]Aspinwall (1979b); [2]Chapin (1953); [3]Dowsett (in press a); [4]Irwin & Benson (1967b); [5]Fuchs *et al.* (2006); [6]Leonard *et al.* (2001a); [7]Pollard (2003); [8]Traylor (1965b).

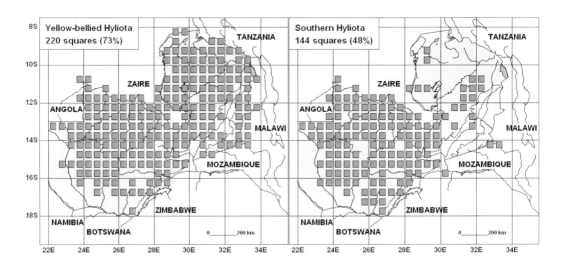

Southern Hyliota *Hyliota australis*   B490 **RB**

Distribution *Afrotropical* (*Uganda to South Africa; mainly Zambezian*). Absent from the extreme north-east, but otherwise common in the miombo woodlands of the plateau from Nyatanda in the west and the Chijalile Hills area on the Zambezi escarpment, northwards through the Copperbelt to Kawambwa[1] and Mununga, east to Mulanga (Chinsali Dist.)[2]. There are isolated records elsewhere: Chiromwe Hill near Luangwa town (Feira)[4], the Eastern Province plateau around Vubwi and Misale, and what were perhaps vagrants to Chinzombo and Frank's Lakes in the Luangwa Valley[2]. East of the Luangwa Rift it ranges somewhat further north, on the Malawi side of the border to Kasungu N.P.[3]. *Alt.* 950-1770 m (Danger Hill), exceptionally down to 530 m.

Ecology In the canopy of miombo woodland, *Cryptosepalum* forest (quite common); a frequent member of mixed bird parties and found alongside its congener in several localities. Recorded from *Acacia* and other woodland in the off-season (e.g. in the Luangwa Valley, Aug-Oct)[2].

Status Resident, with some local wandering.

Breeding   Jul   Aug   Sep   Oct   Dec   Jan

(n=22)   1   2   11   6   1   1   *Clutch*: C/2 (5); C/3 (10).

Taxonomy[4] *H. a. pallidipectus* (type locality Solwezi; *NMZB*)[5].

References [1]Irwin & Benson (1967b); [2]Dowsett (in press a); [3]Dowsett-Lemaire & Dowsett (2006); [4]Irwin & Benson (1967b); [5]Lawson (1964a: 149).

Garden Warbler *Sylvia borin*   B464 **PW**

Distribution *Palaearctic (winters mainly Sierra Leone to South Africa)*. Common in thick vegetation in much of Zambia. *Alt.* 330-2200 m.

Ecology In deciduous or evergreen forest and thicket, mostly at edges or in small patches, also in tall bracken-briar, riparian growth and locally in gardens, where fond of *Lantana, mulberries (Morus)* and similar small fruits.

Status A Palaearctic migrant and winter visitor, with all records between 20 Sep and 23 Apr (early Aug[1] being a typing error)[4]. The average first date over 26 years was 7 Oct, the average last (in 24 years) 3 Apr[4]. Common at times on southward passage (e.g. 100 estimated in 3 ha at Mwinilunga in Oct, with large arrivals after heavy rain[2]), but much scarcer on northward passage. Also common in winter (especially in the higher-rainfall areas). A bird ringed in Finland was recovered in Zambia in Feb (Appendix 1). Nine birds were controlled where ringed after 1 year, one after 2 years and two after 3 years[5].

Moult: rapid, early Jan to mid-Mar[4], exceptionally from mid-Nov[6].

Taxonomy Both *S. b. borin* and the larger, more greyish-olive *S. b. woodwardi* occur[3].

References [1]Benson *et al.* (1971a); [2]Bowen (1983h); [3]Clancey (1974a); [4]Dowsett (in press b); [5]Dowsett & Leonard (2001); [6]Traylor (1965b).

Blackcap *Sylvia atricapilla*   B465 **PW**

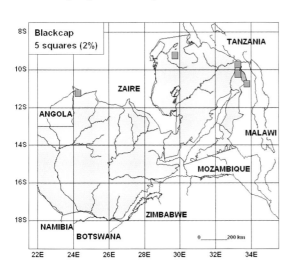

Distribution *Palaearctic (winters Senegambia to Malawi, rare further south)*. Small numbers occur annually on the Nyika Plateau, and there are also records from the Mafinga Mts. Less expectedly, the species was found on the edge of mushitu at Njalamimba, in Mporokoso Dist., and at Hillwood, Mwinilunga[1]. *Alt.* about 1400 m, up to 2200 m on the Nyika (higher on the Malawi side).

Ecology In patches of moist evergreen and montane forest, also thick montane scrub. On the Nyika regularly observed feeding on fruit in the forest canopy (especially in *Polyscias*) as well as at edges[2].

Status A Palaearctic migrant and winter visitor. Winters on the Nyika Plateau, and possibly in the Mafingas and elsewhere in the north of the country. Extreme dates are 5 Nov and 21 Feb[1] (once on the Malawi side of the Nyika to 15 Mar)[2]. Sometimes several birds together. It is possible that these (doubtless from E. Palaearctic populations, those from W. Europe staying in Europe and NW Africa) are extending their range south of the Equator. Prior to 1993 there was no record in this country away from the high Nyika, but on 15 Dec there were at least 3 in Mporokoso Dist., while one was at Mwinilunga 5 Nov 2000[1]. Several have occurred in southern Africa in recent years[3].

Moult: in the Palaearctic (23 birds examined between 18 Nov and 6 Jan showed only body moult)[1].

Taxonomy *S. a. atricapilla.*

References [1]Dowsett (in press b); [2]Dowsett-Lemaire (2006a); [3]Earlé in Hockey *et al.* (2005).

Common Whitethroat *Sylvia communis*   B466 **PW**

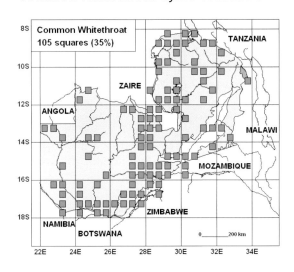

Common Whitethroat
105 squares (35%)

Distribution *Palaearctic (winters Mauritania to South Africa)*. Moderate numbers occur seasonally in open country. *Alt.* 330-2150 m (Nyika).

Ecology On passage in any open woodland or wooded savanna and even cultivated fields; wintering birds in *Acacia* scrub and thicket.

Status A Palaearctic migrant and winter visitor, sometimes common on passage; small numbers winter, most often in the south and south-west. Extreme dates for this warbler are 19 Oct and 29 Apr; the average first date over 19 years was 14 Nov, the average last (in 24 years) 8 Apr[4]. Main passage south is usually mid-Nov to mid-Dec (occasionally large numbers in the north-east[5] and the western half of Zambia, especially the Kafue Flats[4]). On return passage Mar to early Apr it is at times locally numerous (e.g. Lusaka and Simungoma)[4].

Moult: Jan-Mar (suggesting that these birds are of the eastern breeding populations, as W. European birds have a complete moult before migration)[6]. A few arrive in late Nov having interrupted primary moult[4].

Taxonomy *S. c. icterops*[3], with perhaps some *S. c. rubicola* ("*volgensis*")[1,2].

References [1]Benson & Benson (1977); [2]Benson & Irwin (1967b); [3]Benson *et al.* (1970); [4]Dowsett (in press b); [5]Leonard & Van Daele (2001a); [6]Williamson (1968).

Chestnut-vented Tit-babbler *Sylvia subcaerulea*   B467 **AM**

Distribution *Afrotropical (W. Angola to South Africa)*. Irregular in very small numbers in thornbush in a limited area in the south-west, in the Mashi-Zambezi drainage north to Shangombo[5] and near Nasiongo, rarely east to Livingstone and north-east to Mubi Pools[2] and near Choma[4]. *Alt.* 950-1100 m.

Ecology Open or thick *Acacia* scrub, where it feeds low or near the ground, but occasionally joins bird parties in *Acacia* woodland.

Status Usually singly (sometimes two together). Although it was suggested it might be "largely sedentary"[1], all records in Zambia fall between 28 Apr (Simungoma) and 10 Oct (Sekute)[4]. It could not be found in favoured areas in Dec 1991 (whereas another species of the south-west *Acacia* bush, *Laniarius atrococcineus*, is clearly resident). Three years in particular produced a large proportion of the records, 1952, 1964 and 1994, and the last two were certainly very cold dry seasons, following poor rains.

Conversely, 1951-52 was very wet in S. Zambia. The species is probably an irregular cold weather visitor from breeding areas further south (although the possibility of occasional breeding in SW Zambia should be borne in mind).
Breeding No records (breeds mainly Sep-Nov in neighbouring Zimbabwe). Alarm and contact calls often noted, but apparently not song[4].
Taxonomy *S. s. subcaerulea*. It has in the past been placed in the genus *Parisoma*, which is now considered to be a subgenus of *Sylvia*[3].
References [1]Benson *et al.* (1971a); [2]Brooke (1965); [3]Dowsett & Dowsett-Lemaire (1993); [4]Dowsett & Leonard (in press a); [5]Smithers (1956).

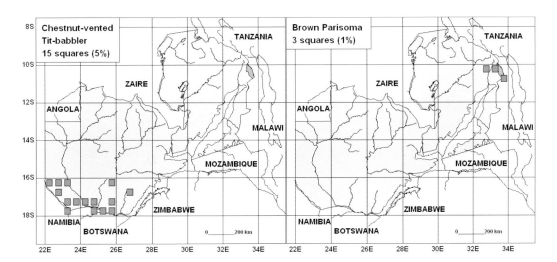

Brown Parisoma *Sylvia lugens* B468 **R(B)**

Distribution *Afromontane endemic* (*Ethiopia to S. Malawi*). Small numbers occur in *Acacia* trees in the eastern highlands (the Nyika Plateau and the Zinza stream in the Mafingas). It is also present on the Muchinga escarpment near Mumbwe, east of Isoka[3]. Extralimitally, it occurs north-west of Mbala in the Marungu highlands, SE Zaire[4]. *Alt.* 1750-1980 m in the Mafingas[1] and on the Nyika Plateau[2,5], and *c.* 1400 m on the Muchinga escarpment. [NB: it occurs on the Malawi side of SW Nyika, very close to Zambia; a patch of *Acacia* long thought to be in Zambia is the other side of the border[5].] Discreet and easily overlooked.
Ecology Very specialized, as usually found only in the canopy of *Acacia abyssinica*, a tree of forest edges which forms small groves locally, often along streams.
Status Resident.
Breeding No records.
Taxonomy *S. l. jacksoni*. Formerly in the genus *Parisoma* (see previous species).
References [1]Aspinwall (1976b); [2]Aspinwall *et al.* (1973); [3]Dowsett (in press a); [4]Dowsett & Prigogine (1974); [5]Dowsett-Lemaire (2006a).

Cisticolidae

Cloud Cisticola *Cisticola textrix* B511 **RB**

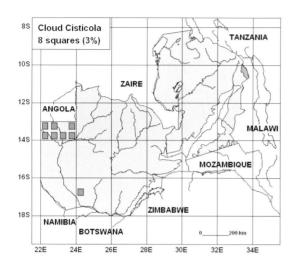

Cloud Cisticola
8 squares (3%)

Distribution *Afrotropical (NE Angola to South Africa).* On several dry plains in the far west, either side of the Zambezi, from Minyanya[2] and Kansalya[3], south and east to the Mpandapanda pan area[1]. Even noted on the dry floodplain at Zambezi town (Balovale)[1], perhaps exceptionally. Also present some 320 km further south, near the Lwampungu/Njoko stream confluence[10]. These populations are more than 950 km from that in the N. Transvaal[11] and SE Botswana[6]. Locally common on Minyanya[2], scarcer elsewhere. *Alt.* 1000-1160 m.

Ecology Watershed plains, in short dry grassland, even on grassy "shelves" in quite small areas. It was suggested that this species does not occur alongside *C. aridulus* in Zambia[4], and that it might even be excluded by it[5], but both species were already known from Minyanya Plain[3], and have since been shown to occur on the same ground there[2] and at Lwampungu[10]. In South Africa, the two species also overlap in parts of their range[8]. On other plains east of the Zambezi *C. textrix* occurs alongside *C. juncidis*[1].

Status Resident.

Breeding Mar
(n=1) 1 Song also noted Dec. *Clutch*: no data.

Taxonomy *C. t. anselli* (type locality Minyanya Plain; *NMZB*)[12]; named for W.F.H. Ansell. Although distinct morphologically, Zambian birds appear to have a similar voice to birds in Natal[9,10].

References [1]Aspinwall (1973f); [2]Aspinwall (1979b); [3]Benson (1959c: 285); [4]Benson *et al.* (1971a); [5]Benson & White (1960); [6]Brewster (2007); [7]Dowsett (in press a); [8]Berutti in Hockey *et al.* (1997); [9]Leonard *et al.* (2001c); [10]Stjernstedt (2003); [11]Tarboton *et al.* (1987); [12]White (1960a: 146).

Pale-crowned Cisticola *Cisticola cinnamomeus* B513 **RB**

Distribution *Afrotropical (SE Gabon to South Africa), mainly Zambezian.* Locally common in dambos through most of the plateau west of the Rift. Ranges east to Isoka, and in central Zambia to "80-mile" Dambo. There is a small pocket on the Southern Province plateau near Choma, south to Dimbwe. Otherwise it ranges south to Kalobolelwa[2], and west of the Zambezi to the South Lueti River[1]. *Alt.* 950-1700 m (Mbala area).

Ecology Damp, short grassland, usually in dambos, sometimes larger floodplains. May occur alongside other *Cisticola* spp., especially the generalist *C. juncidis*.

Status Resident.

Breeding[3]	Oct	Nov	Dec	Jan	Feb	Mar	Apr	May
(n=63)	1	6	4	14	18	14	5	1

Clutch: C/2 (8); C/3 (25); C/4 (17); N/5 (1).

Taxonomy *C. c. cinnamomeus*. Previously considered conspecific with the northern *C. brunnescens*[4].

References [1]Benson & Irwin (1967b); [2]Dowsett (in press a); [3]Penry (1985); [4]Tye in Urban *et al.* (1997).

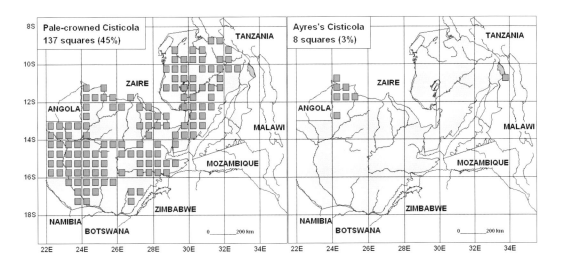

Ayres's (Wing-snapping) Cisticola *Cisticola ayresii*   B514 **RB**

Distribution *Afromontane near-endemic* (*Sudan to South Africa*). Locally common in short (sub-)montane grassland. There are two different populations: in the eastern highlands it is known only from the Nyika Plateau, but could well be found at Nyikamwaka (as it is recorded from Jembya on the Malawi side)[3]; in N. Mwinilunga it occurs on the plateau south and east to Mundwiji[4] and the West Lumwana River, reappearing on Mayau Plain[1]. In SE Zaire it is common in the Marungu highlands[2]. *Alt.* 1150-1460 m (NW Zambia), 2000-2200 m (Nyika Plateau, higher on the Malawi side).
Ecology In short montane grassland (dominated by *Loudetia simplex*) and in the north-west in short watershed plain grassland; it avoids grassland that is too tall and rank.
Status Resident.
Breeding   Nov   Dec   Jan
(n=6)   3   2   1   *Clutch*: C/3 (2).
The Nov records are from NW Zambia, the others from Nyika.
Taxonomy[2] *C. a. ayresii.*
References [1]Dowsett (in press a); [2]Dowsett & Prigogine (1974); [3]Dowsett-Lemaire & Dowsett (2006); [4]Irwin & Benson (1966a).

Black-tailed Cisticola *Cisticola dambo*   B512 **RB**

Distribution *Zambezian near-endemic* (*SE Gabon to NW Zambia*). A generally scarce and localized species of watershed plains and large dambos. There are definite records from a few localities in N. Mwinilunga: Salujinga[4], Hillwood (common) and Nyambela south to Chitunta[3,8], and east to the Lunga-Muzela area[5]. It reappears on Minyanya and Kambuyu Plains west of the Zambezi[1] (the most southerly records of the species). Its presence considerably further east at Kalilele is accepted[7], but its occurrence elsewhere remains unproven[2,5]. In SE Zaire it is known from the Marungu highlands[6]. *Alt.* 1100-1460 m.
Ecology Watershed plains in medium-long grass, often at the ecotone between wet, marshy bottoms and

dry ridges. Occurs alongside *C. juncidis* west of the Zambezi, and with *C. cinnamomeus* at Kalilele, but normally in longer grass[1,7].
Status Resident.
Breeding   Apr
(n=1)   1   *Clutch*: C/3 (1).
Taxonomy *C. d. dambo*.
References [1]Aspinwall (1979b); [2]Beel (1992c); [3]Benson (1958b); [4]Benson & Irwin (1964b); [5]Dowsett (in press a); [6]Dowsett & Prigogine (1974); [7]Penry (1976a); [8]White (1951a).

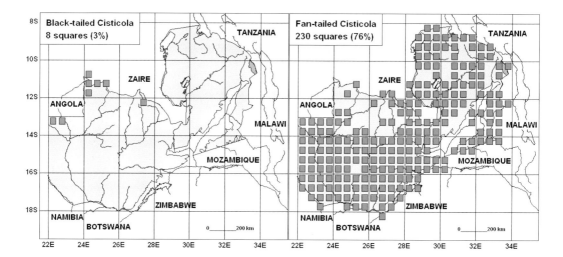

Fan-tailed Cisticola *Cisticola juncidis*   B509 **RB**

Distribution *Old World (in the Afrotropics, Mauritania to South Africa)*. Common in grassland almost throughout the country, and although it is recorded from only a limited area in the Luangwa Valley, it is common there[1,4], and it is widespread in the Kariba basin. In the north-west it is common to the West Lunga N.P., but recorded to the north only rarely in the Kakoma-Mundwiji Plain area, otherwise no nearer than Solwezi and Kalilele to the east[1]. Largely replaced in Mwinilunga by *C. ayresii* (it is unknown from Kasaji, to the north in Zaire)[3]. *Alt.* 330-1700 m (Mbala area).
Ecology In a variety of grassland habitats (excluding high montane) including dambos, seasonal flood-plains, edge of marsh, abandoned cultivation (provided the grass is fairly short) and airfields. Not known to overlap anywhere with (sub-)montane *C. ayresii*. Possibly polygamous, as in the Palaearctic, but not studied in detail here.
Status Resident.
Breeding[2] Nov   Dec   Jan   Feb   Mar   Apr   May   Jun
(n=194)   7   21   38   42   46   34   5   1
Clutch: C/1 (5); C/2 (15); C/3 (46); C/4 (61); C/5 (18).
Moult: as with most cisticolas, adults have distinctive breeding and non-breeding plumages. In W. Zambia birds were completing primary moult in Oct-Nov[5].
Taxonomy *C. j. terrestris*.
References [1]Dowsett (in press a); [2]Penry (1985); [3]Schouteden (1971); [4]Scott (1991); [5]Traylor (1965b).

Desert Cisticola *Cisticola aridulus*   B510 **RB**

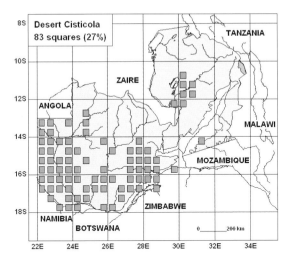

Distribution *Afrotropical* (*Mauritania to South Africa*). Locally common and widespread in the dry grasslands of W. and S. Zambia, in the west north to West Lunga N.P.[3], and in the Kafue basin to the Lukanga Swamp[6]. It even occurs on parts of the shore of L. Kariba[3], and on sand beaches in the Middle Zambezi Valley further east at Mushika[4]. There are two isolated populations, one certainly very small, at Minga on Eastern Province plateau[1,8]; the other is in the Bangweulu Floodplain[1] (it is uncertain if this extends as far as the Copperbelt at Itawa, as has been claimed)[3]. *Alt.* 550-1350 m.

Ecology Rather short grassland in various dry plains (watershed on the Kalahari sands, alluvial around Bangweulu); on the Kafue Flats (seasonally flooded) prefers drier sections. This cisticola inhabits drier areas always than other species, though often parapatric with *C. juncidis* in particular.

Status Resident, with some local movements (retreating to non-flooded grassland in the rains).

Breeding   Oct Nov Dec Jan Feb Mar Apr
(n=62)   1   6   4   12   4   27   8

Clutch: C/2 (5); C/3 (17); C/4 (23); C/5 (7). *Moult*: noted Oct-Nov[5].

Taxonomy[2] *C. a. kalahari*, replaced by *C. a. traylori* in the far west and by *C. a. perplexus* (type locality L. Chaya; *NHM*)[7] in the Bangweulu area.

References [1]Benson (1956f); [2]Benson & Irwin (1967b); [3]Dowsett (in press a); [4]Irwin (1982c); [5]Traylor (1965b); [6]Tree (1966a); [7]White (1947e: 174); [8]Winterbottom (1936).

Croaking Cisticola *Cisticola natalensis*   B505 **RB**

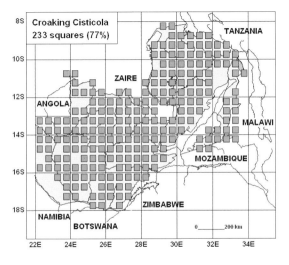

Distribution *Afrotropical* (*Senegal to South Africa*). Common in rank grasslands and dambos throughout practically the whole of the Zambian plateau; in the extreme southwest so far unknown between Lweti and Kalobolelwa. Absent from the Luangwa and Middle Zambezi Valleys. *Alt.* 930 to 2100 m (on the Nyika)[3].

Ecology Mainly in dambos and floodplain grassland, where there are scattered bushes. Also locally in lush submontane grassland (e.g. *Themeda*, Nyika)[3] and occasional in marsh.

Status Resident.

Breeding Nov Dec Jan Feb Mar Apr
(n=117)   1   18   35   40   19   4
Clutch: C/1 (1); C/2 (14); C/3 (64); C/4 (21); C/5 (1).
Moult: noted Jul to end Oct[2,4].
Taxonomy[1] *C. n. katanga* (syn. *C. n. willi*, type locality Kashima; *TMP*; named for Dr. J.W.O. Will, Colonial Medical Service)[5], replaced by *C. n. natalensis* in the east and by *C. n. holubi* in the south.
References [1]Benson & Irwin (1967b); [2]Dowsett (in press a); [3]Dowsett-Lemaire (2006a); [4]Traylor (1965b); [5]White (1945f: 138).

Stout Cisticola *Cisticola robustus*   B504 **RB**

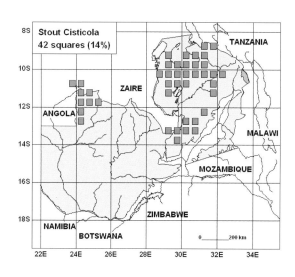

Distribution *Afrotropical (E. Nigeria to south-central Angola, east to Kenya).* Quite common in the dambos of N. Zambia west of the Rift, in the north-east from Mwense and the Mbala area[3], east to Mbesuma and south to Mkushi River (Chalata). It is also widespread in N. Mwinilunga, south to Mayau and east to the area of the West Lumwana River[1]. *Alt.* 1150-1700 m.
Ecology In (usually) medium to long grass in extensive and moist dambos.
Status Resident.

Breeding Oct Nov Dec
(n=21)   2   4   5
            Jan Feb Mar
            5   4   1
Clutch: C/1 (2); C/2 (6); C/3 (2).

Taxonomy *C. r. awemba* (type locality Luwingu; *NHM*)[2], with *C. r. angolensis* in the extreme north-west.
References [1]Dowsett (in press a); [2]Lynes (1933: 169); [3]Lynes & Sclater (1933-34).

Wailing Cisticola *Cisticola lais*   B499 **RB**

Distribution *Afromontane endemic (Kenya to South Africa).* Common in grassland in the major eastern highlands, the Mafingas[1] and the Nyika Plateau. *Alt.* 1740-2200 m (Nyika, higher on the Malawi side).
Ecology In montane grassland, usually with some bracken or scattered shrubs and with a preference for rocky areas. On the SW Nyika partly overlaps with *C. njombe* but is more often found in shorter grassland and near rocks[2].
Status Resident.
Breeding Nov Dec Jan
(n=14)   3   10   1   *Clutch*: C/2 (1); C/3 (6).
(Including two from Malawi side of SW Nyika.)
Taxonomy *C. l. semifasciatus.*
References [1]Dowsett & Stjernstedt (1973); [2]Dowsett-Lemaire (2006a).

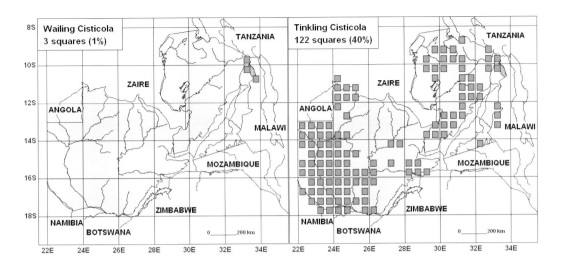

Tinkling Cisticola *Cisticola rufilatus*   B498 **RB**

Distribution *Zambezian near-endemic (SE Gabon to South Africa)*. Its distribution, in light woodland, is partly discontinuous. In the western half of the country it ranges to N. Mwinilunga, east to the West Lumwana, and (in the extreme south) east to Kabuyu (Livingstone Dist.). It is present in the Kafue basin from the Luamala River confluence along the northern edge of the Kafue Flats to Mulilansoro in the Middle Zambezi Valley[3]. Not present on the Copperbelt, but from the Mkushi farming block ranges northwards (except not in the Luapula Valley and the low-lying country between Lakes Mweru and Tanganyika), east to the Malawi border[3]. Further south it occurs from the Lundazi area south just to Chadiza[1]. Common locally (especially in the west). *Alt.* 950-1750 m.

Ecology In short miombo woodland (*Brachystegia, Parinari, Uapaca*) in regenerating stages or dwarf woodland on thin, stony soils (often on the edge of plains or dambos). Also in *Burkea* and other undifferentiated short, open woodland or wooded grassland. Feeds in both grass and low trees and overlaps marginally with *C. chiniana* in places.

Status Resident.

Breeding   Jan
(n=1)   1   *Clutch*: C/3 (1). *Moult*: finishing Oct-Nov[4].

Taxonomy[2] *C. r. rufilatus* is the form in the south and west, *C. r. ansorgei* (colder above, more heavily streaked) that in the north and east (with an area of intergradation in the Upper Zambezi).

References [1]Benson (1958c); [2]Benson & Irwin (1967b); [3]Dowsett (in press a); [4]Traylor (1965b).

Rattling Cisticola *Cisticola chiniana*   B497 **RB**

Distribution *Afrotropical (Ethiopia to South Africa)*. Numerous in bushy places throughout the country, the gap in W. Zambia having no obvious explanation at present[1]. *Alt.* 330-1600 m (Mbala area).

Ecology In any wooded grassland, but only on the edges of woodland (including miombo) and dry thicket, and also generally in secondary growth in abandoned cultivation.

Status Resident.

Breeding   Nov   Dec   Jan   Feb   Mar   Apr
(n=173)   14   34   54   45   21   5   *Clutch*: C/2 (16); C/3 (112); C/4 (28); C/5 (1).

Moult: finishing Oct-Nov[1].
Taxonomy *C. c. fortis*, replaced by *C. c. procerus* in the east, *C. c. chiniana* in the south, *smithersii* south-west and *bensoni* (type locality Liuwa Plain; *FMNH*; named for C.W. Benson)[2] in the west.
References [1]Dowsett (in press a); [2]Traylor (1964: 83).

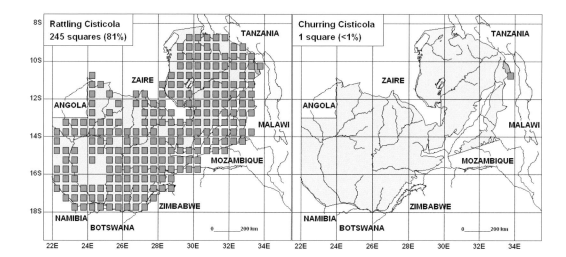

Churring Cisticola *Cisticola njombe*   B500 **RB**

Distribution *Afromontane endemic* (*SW Tanzania to N. Malawi*). Known only from rank grass on the Nyika Plateau (where common). *Alt*. 1950-2200 m (higher on the Malawi side).
Ecology In rank grass, as near forest edges or roadsides, with some bracken, and in valleys. Overlaps locally with *C. lais*, but largely separated as the latter prefers shorter grassland, often near rocks.
Status Resident.
Conservation Declassified from "Near Threatened" to "Least Concern"[3]; the habitat of this restricted-range bird is remote and extensive and the species is considered to be completely unthreatened at present.
Breeding   Nov   Dec   Jan   Feb
(n=20)   4   10   4   2   *Clutch*: C/2 (3); C/3 (7); C/4 (2).
(Including Malawi side of SW Nyika.)
Taxonomy[4] No races recognized. (*C. n. mariae*, syn. *C. n. nyikae*, was described from the Nyika Plateau, Malawi)[1,2].
References [1]Benson (1941b); [2]Benson (1945); [3]BirdLife International (2004a); [4]Irwin & Benson (1966a).

Short-winged Cisticola *Cisticola brachypterus*   B508 **RB**

Distribution *Afrotropical* (*Senegal to Zimbabwe*). Common in the ecotone between woodland and grassland over most of the Zambian plateau, but absent from the drier south-west. It reaches Livingstone on the Southern Province plateau, but is generally local in that area, and further west reaches only the Sichili area, Mongu[4] and west of the Zambezi south to Sililo (Kalabo Dist.)[1]. It occurs not uncommonly in the Luangwa Valley in the Chifungwe-Mfuwe area[2], but is unrecorded from the Middle Zambezi

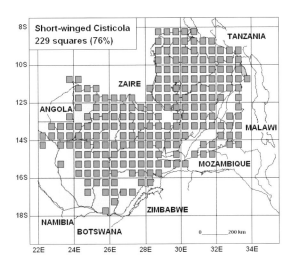

Valley. *Alt.* 550-2050 m (Nyika)[3].

Ecology In grassland with scattered bushes or low trees, particularly frequent at the ecotone of woodland and grassland as on the edge of dambos, absent from drier areas.

Status Resident.

Breeding	Oct	Nov	Dec
(n=27)	1	1	7
	Jan	Feb	Mar
	11	5	2

Clutch: C/2 (4); C/3 (13); C/4 (1).

Taxonomy *C. b. loanda* in the north and west, *C. b. isabellinus* (paler, less brown above) in the south and east.

References [1]Benson & Irwin (1967b); [2]Dowsett (in press a); [3]Dowsett-Lemaire (2006a); [4]White & Winterbottom (1949).

Neddicky *Cisticola fulvicapilla*   B506-7 **RB**

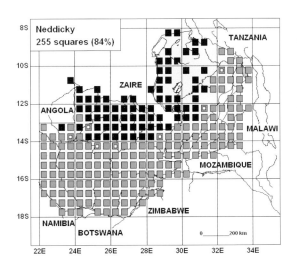

Distribution *Afrotropical* (*SE Gabon to South Africa*). The species as a whole is common in woodland through most of the country, although it is more local in parts of the north-east[1]. *Alt.* 330-1700 m (Mbala area).

Ecology In understorey (short grass and low bush) of any woodland, including miombo (richer types locally in the north), mopane, *Burkea* and mixed *Acacia-Combretum*.

Status Resident.

Breeding	Oct	Nov	Dec	Jan
(n=161)	3	27	48	41
	Feb	Mar	Apr	
	31	10	1	

Clutch: C/1 (2); C/2 (21); C/3 (94); C/4 (11); C/5 (1).

Moult: finishing early Nov[6].

Taxonomy[4] *C. f. muelleri* (syn. *C. f. stoehri*, type locality Mterize, Luangwa Valley; *NHM*; named for F.O. Stoehr)[5], replaced by *C. f. hallae* in the south and west, *C. f. dispar* in the north-west and *C. f. angusticaudus* throughout much of the north. *C. f. hallae* is very pale above, white below; *dispar* is darker above than *muelleri* (crown less contrasting, tail blacker); *angusticaudus* is very grey above, with a contrasting red cap and very black, long tail. Sometimes considered to consist of two species[3]: Short-tailed *C. fulvicapilla* (blue squares) and Long-tailed Neddicky *C. augusticaudus* (black squares). However, hybrids (open squares) occur between the forms *angusticaudus* and both *muelleri* and *dispar*, and there appear to be no significant behavioural or ecological differences[2].

References [1]Dowsett (in press a); [2]Dowsett & Dowsett-Lemaire (1980); [3]Irwin (1993); [4]Irwin & Benson (1967a); [5]Neave (1907: 65); [6]Traylor (1965b).

Rock (Rock-loving) Cisticola *Cisticola aberrans* B496 **RB**

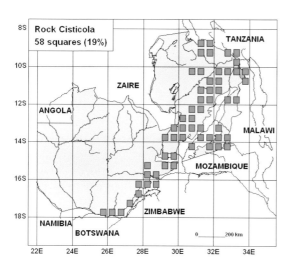

Distribution *Afrotropical* (*Guinea to South Africa*). Dependent upon rocks along the Rift escarpments and on the Eastern Province plateau, although unlike some other rock-loving species it does not reach the isolated hills of the upper Kafue or North-Western Province. Locally quite common. It ranges southwards from Mbala and Sunzu Mtn[7], west to Chishimba Falls[1], to as near the Copperbelt as the Mkushi area[3], then along the Zambezi escarpment to Songwe Gorge, below the Victoria Falls[2]. *Alt.* 650-2000 m (at these higher levels small numbers in the Mafingas[4] and Nyika[5]).
Ecology In grass and scrub among rocks, under miombo (locally thin mopane), or in more open situations.

Status Resident.
Breeding Nov Dec
(n=12) 6 6 *Clutch*: C/3 (4) & N/3 (5).
Taxonomy[1] *C. a. nyika* (type locality Nyika Plateau, Malawi)[6].
References [1]Benson (1956f); [2]Benson & Irwin (1967b); [3]Dowsett (in press a); [4]Dowsett & Stjernstedt (1973); [5]Dowsett-Lemaire (2006a); [6]Lynes (1930); [7]Lynes & Sclater (1933-34).

Whistling Cisticola *Cisticola lateralis* B494 **RB**

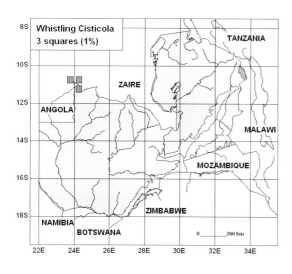

Distribution *Afrotropical* (*Senegal to NW Zambia*). Locally common in secondary growth on the edge of forest in N. Mwinilunga, at several localities including the Jimbe stream[4], Salujinga[3], the Luinga River[1], Hillwood and Sakeji[2] south to the Source of the Zambezi[5]. In S. Zaire it occurs further east, reportedly even to Mopala (1229D)[6]. *Alt.* 1170-1460 m.
Ecology Rank grass and secondary growth, abandoned cultivation, on the edge of evergreen forest.
Status Resident.
Breeding Oct Feb
(n=3) 2 1 *Clutch*: no data.
Moult: one bird in Jul[5].
Taxonomy *C. l. vincenti*.
References [1]Aspinwall (1971b); [2]Benson (1958b); [3]Benson & Irwin (1965b); [4]Dowsett (1973b); [5]Dowsett (in press a); [6]Schouteden (1971).

Trilling Cisticola *Cisticola woosnami*   B493 **RB**

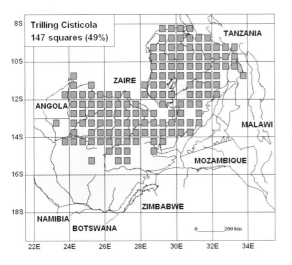

Distribution *Afrotropical (Uganda to Zambia, where it reaches the southern limit of its range; unrecorded from Angola, but must occur in the east).* Locally common in the miombo woodlands of the northern plateau, east just to the slopes of the Nyika (although it occurs further south in Malawi, to 12°30'S, at high altitude[3]). It ranges south along the Muchingas to the Lunsemfwa River (Alala Plateau)[4], in the Kafue basin to Nambala Hill and south of Tatayoyo[2], west almost to the Zambezi, near Dipalata[2]. *Alt.* 900 m (escarpment of Luangwa and Luano Valleys) to 2100 m (Mafingas) and 2050 m (Nyika).

Ecology In grass and low bush in understorey of miombo woodland. Alongside the much smaller *C. fulvicapilla* at lower elevations.

Status Resident.

Breeding   Dec   Jan   Feb   Apr
(n=12)   2   7   2   1   *Clutch*: C/3 (4); C/4 (1).

Taxonomy[1] *C. w. lufira.*

References [1]Benson (1956f); [2]Dowsett (in press a); [3]Dowsett-Lemaire & Dowsett (2006); [4]Lynes (1930).

Red-faced Cisticola *Cisticola erythrops*   B491 **RB**

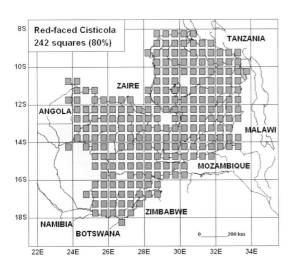

Distribution *Afrotropical (Senegal to South Africa).* Numerous in moist rank growth throughout E. and central Zambia, west to near Kamilende[2] and the Sichili area[5]. Absent from the dry plains of the west, but inexplicably so from the vicinity of the Zambezi River. *Alt.* 330-1650 m.

Ecology In long grass and other herbaceous growth (including reeds) along streams and on the edge of marsh, sometimes away from water but then usually in moist depressions. In Eastern Province found close to *C. cantans*, but always in moister situations with its congener in drier bush away from water.

Status Resident.

Breeding   Dec   Jan   Feb   Mar   Apr
(n=176)   15   66   68   23   4   *Clutch*: C/1 (3); C/2 (25); C/3 (98); C/4 (6); C/5 (1).

Moult: three birds half-way through moult mid-Aug[5].

Taxonomy *C. e. nyasa*[1], *C. e. arcanus* (type locality Kabompo town; *NMZB*)[4] being probably a synonym. However, it has been suggested there may be some tendency to *C. e. lepe* in the west and *C. e. sylvia* in the Zambezi Valley[3]. A partial albino bird has been reported[6].
References [1]Benson & Irwin (1967b); [2]Benson *et al.* (1970); [3]Clancey (1968c); [4]Clancey (1978b: 315); [5]Dowsett (in press a); [6]Taylor (1978a).

Singing Cisticola *Cisticola cantans* B492 **R(B)**

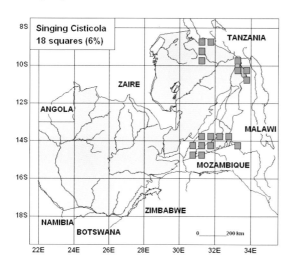

Distribution *Afrotropical (Senegal to Zimbabwe)*. Locally not uncommon in rank growth in the east of the country, from near Mbala[2] south to Nondo, and down the Malawi border to the Nyika. It reappears at Chipata, and is widespread on the Eastern Province plateau, west to Mchimadzi[1]. [There is no evidence to support the sight records claimed as far west as Marble Hill, to the east of Lusaka[4].] *Alt.* 900-2200 m (Nyika, slightly higher on the Malawi side).
Ecology In rank grass with shrubs, especially common in bracken-briar in the highlands, where it also occupies the niche of *C. erythrops* (rank growth along streams). At lower altitudes, where both occur, it stays away from water, in dry grass and bush on the edge of miombo and other woodland.
Status Resident.
Breeding No records. A rains breeder[3] but, unlike most *Cisticola* warblers, sings practically year-round.
Taxonomy *C. c. muenzneri*.
References [1]Dowsett (in press a); [2]Dowsett-Lemaire & Dowsett (1978a); [3]Dowsett-Lemaire & Dowsett (2006); [4]Tree (1962b).

Black-lored Cisticola *Cisticola nigriloris* B495 **RB**

Distribution *Afromontane endemic (SW Tanzania to N. Malawi)*. Known from bracken-briar only on the Nyika Plateau (where common) and (one record) on the Zinza stream in the Mafingas[1] (it is scarce on the Malawi side)[6]. Present north of Mbala, on the Ufipa Plateau in SW Tanzania[3], but in the Marungu highlands the other side of L. Tanganyika in Zaire it is replaced by Chubb's Cisticola *C. chubbi*[5]. *Alt.* 1740-2200 m (Nyika, higher on the Malawi side).
Ecology In rank grass with bracken and scattered shrubs, along forest edges and in moist depressions and valleys. Overlaps mainly with *C. cantans*, also with *C. njombe* and *lais* but these are at least partly segregated, being in somewhat shorter vegetation. A cooperative breeder, in parties of up to 9 individuals[7].
Status Resident.
Breeding   Nov   Dec   Jan
(n=11)   6   3   2   *Clutch*: C/2 (2); C/3 (3) & N/3 (1); C/4 (2).
(Including Malawi side of SW Nyika.) A record claimed for "Apr"[2] could not be dated with certainty[3].

Taxonomy No races recognized. Originally considered conspecific with *C. chubbi* or even *C. hunteri*[4].
References [1]Aspinwall (1976b); [2]Benson & White (1957); [3]Dowsett (in press a); [4]Dowsett & Dowsett-Lemaire (1980); [5]Dowsett & Prigogine (1974); [6]Dowsett-Lemaire & Dowsett (2006); [7]Vernon (1964).

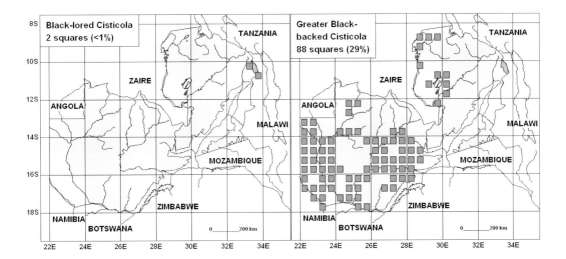

Greater Black-backed Cisticola *Cisticola galactotes*   B501 **RB**

Distribution *Afrotropical* (*Mauritania to South Africa*). Common to abundant in most swampy areas in the west and south, eastwards to the Luswishi/Kafue confluence, east of Lusaka, the Choma area and Livingstone. There is a population in the Ntambu area[1,2]. Absent from the Copperbelt, and the cooler northern plateau but reappears near Mukuku and ranges throughout Bangweulu and the lower Luapula, to Mweru Wantipa[5]. Unknown too from the dry Luangwa Valley and the Eastern Province plateau, though reappearing in Malawi in the upper Bua[3]. *Alt.* 950-1300 m.
Ecology In reeds and long grass in standing water, including seasonally flooded grass plains, and the edge of pans, rivers and lakes. There has been a recent spread to farm dams in the Choma area.
Status Resident, with local seasonal movements as habitat dries out.
Breeding[7]   Nov   Dec   Jan   Feb   Mar   Apr
(n=23)   3   4   11   2   2   1
Clutch: C/1 (1); C/2 (3); C/3 (11); C/4 (1); C/5 (1).
Moult: late Oct birds were completing moult[8].
Taxonomy[5] Birds closest to *C. g. luapula* (type locality L. Bangweulu; *NHM*)[6] occur throughout much of the species's range in Zambia, with *C. g. suahelicus* in the Mweru area and *C. g. schoutedeni* (type locality South Kashiji River; *type specimen lost*)[9], named for Belgian zoologist Henri Schouteden [1881-1972], in the west. An attempt has been made to split the species into two[4], but this was based on incomplete study of vocal dialects, and the name given to the second "species" (*C. luapula*) is in any case pre-dated (e.g. by *C. g. suahelicus*).
References [1]Benson *et al.* (1970); [2]Dowsett (in press a); [3]Dowsett-Lemaire & Dowsett (2006); [4]Hustler (2001); [5]Irwin & Benson (1967b); [6]Lynes (1933: 169); [7]Pitman & Took (1973); [8]Traylor (1965b); [9]White (1954a: 106).

Chirping Cisticola *Cisticola pipiens* B502 **RB**

Distribution *Zambezian endemic (Burundi to N. Botswana)*. Common in wetlands in N. and W. Zambia, from Mweru Wantipa east to Isoka[1], down the Muchinga escarpment to the upper Mupamadzi and Mulungushi areas, and on the upper Kafue to the Luamala River[4]. In the Zambezi drainage it ranges down to Old Mabenga, Luamuloba[2] and Mambova[6], and to near Katombora on the Zimbabwe side[5]. *Alt.* 950-1650 m (Mbala area).

Ecology Dambos and marshes, occupying the taller, denser vegetation (especially Papyrus) in the moist centres[2], thus ecologically apart from *C. galactotes* and *C. tinniens* where they occur together.

Status Resident.

Breeding	Sep	Oct	Nov	Dec	Jan	Feb	Mar	Apr
(n=18)	1	1	1	3	4	5	2	1

Clutch: C/2 (1); C/3 (6); C/4 (2).

Moult: in Nov an adult was in fresh dress[8]; pre-nuptial moult (mainly Oct-Nov) may be suspended during a rapid nesting, followed by its completion afterwards (Nov onwards)[7].

Taxonomy[3] *C. p. congo*.

References [1]Aspinwall (1977f); [2]Aspinwall (1984a); [3]Benson (1956f); [4]Benson (1958a); [5]Butler (1989); [6]Dowsett (in press a); [7]Lynes & Sclater (1933-34); [8]Traylor (1965b).

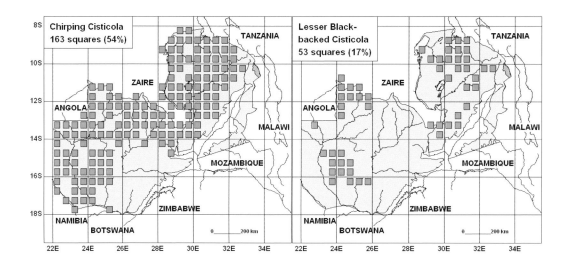

Lesser Black-backed Cisticola *Cisticola tinniens* B503 **RB**

Distribution *Afrotropical (Kenya to South Africa)*. Locally quite common in marshes throughout N. Mwinilunga, east to the Chalamba River[2], south to Mayau[4], and from Lukolwe[5] on the Upper Zambezi south and east to Kalenje[5]. It reappears at Mkushi River (Chalata), ranging up the Chambeshi to Filolo[1], and across to L. Mweru. *Alt.* 950-1750 m.

Ecology Rather short vegetation on permanently wet ground in bogs and the centre of dambos. Occurs locally alongside *C. pipiens* (which prefers taller vegetation)[3], but rarely with *C. galactotes*.

Status Resident.

Breeding	Aug	Sep	Oct	Dec	Jan	Mar	
(n=7)		1	1	1	1	2	1	*Clutch*: C/2 (1).

Taxonomy[6] *C. t. shiwae* (type locality L. Young, Shiwa Ngandu; *NHM*)[7], replaced by *C. t. perpullus* (less reddish on the head, black streaking on the back heavier) in the west.
References [1]Aspinwall (1977f); [2]Aspinwall (1978b); [3]Aspinwall (1984a); [4]Benson (1960d); [5]Dowsett (in press a); [6]Irwin & Benson (1967b); [7]White (1947e: 174).

Tawny-flanked Prinia *Prinia subflava*   B472 **RB**

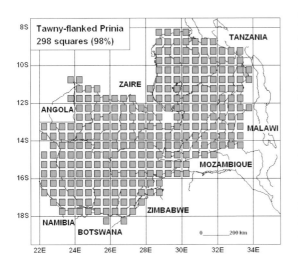

Distribution *Afrotropical* (*Mauritania to South Africa*). Very common to numerous, occurring in long grass throughout the country. *Alt.* 330-2100 m (Nyika, rarely to 2150 m)[5].
Ecology In long grass with shrubs on the edge of woodland or thicket, in dambos, swamp margins (including reeds), riparian growth, bracken-briar, understorey of neglected plantations, gardens, abandoned cultivation. Forages more often in bushes in the dry season when grass is not always available.
Status Resident. One ringed bird was retrapped when at least 11 years of age[4].

Breeding	Sep	Nov	Dec	Jan
(n=961)	2	7	92	348
	Feb	Mar	Apr	May
	351	135	21	5

Clutch: C/1 (26); C/2 (161); C/3 (381); C/4 (145). A major host to *Anomalospiza imberbis*[3].
Moult: most adults moult Oct-Dec, other birds (perhaps mostly juveniles) from late Feb or Apr. One ringed bird starting moult in Apr one year, and in Oct the next[3].
Taxonomy[1,2] *P. s. affinis*, replaced in the west by *P. s. kasokae* (type locality L. Mwange; *NHM*)[6], in the south-west by *P. s. bechuanae*, and perhaps in the east by *P. s. mutatrix*.
References [1]Benson (1956f); [2]Benson *et al.* (1971a); [3]Dowsett (in press a); [4]Dowsett & Leonard (2001); [5]Dowsett-Lemaire (2006a); [6]White (1945-46: 96).

Black-chested Prinia *Prinia flavicans*   B471 **RB**

Distribution *Afrotropical* (*W. Angola to South Africa*). Quite common in light woodland in W. Zambia, mainly west of the Zambezi[4]: from Sesheke[2] west to Imusho[3], north to Minyanya Plain[1]. *Alt.* 950-1050 m.
Ecology In the north of its range (*bihe*) mainly in *Burkea* woodland and scattered shrubs on dry plains, rarely wandering to the edge of riparian[1]. Nominate *flavicans* is typically in *Acacia* or clearings in *Baikiaea* forest. Always in drier situations than its sibling *P. subflava*.
Status Resident.

Breeding	Jul	Oct
(n=3)	1	2

Clutch: N/2 (1). *Moult*: adults completing moult by late Oct[5].
Taxonomy[2] *P. f. flavicans* in the south-west, and *P. f. bihe* (greenish-brown rather than greyish-brown above, yellower below) from the Liuwa Plain northwards.
References [1]Aspinwall (1979b); [2]Benson & Irwin (1964b); [3]Benson & Irwin (1967b); [4]Dowsett (in press a); [5]Traylor (1965b).

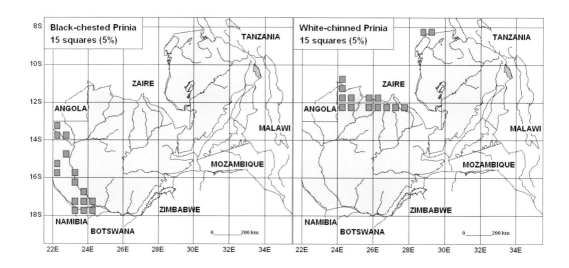

White-chinned Prinia *Prinia leucopogon* B473 **RB**

Distribution *Guineo-Congolian near-endemic (Nigeria to N. Zambia)*. Locally common at forest edges throughout N. Mwinilunga, south to the Lwamakunyi stream (some 30 km SSW of Mwinilunga Boma)[3], though not as far south as Mayau, and it ranges locally east to near Chililabombwe[5] (the most southerly record of the species). It reappears to the north of L. Mweru, at Kasangu[2] and the Lunkinda River near Chipungu[1]. *Alt.* 1150-1460 m (at 950 m near L. Mweru).

Ecology Secondary growth and rank cover, usually on the edge of evergreen (riparian) forest, mushitu or near water. Wanders at times into adjacent miombo woodland. Feeds usually low in thick cover, but at times gleans in the canopy[3]. In family groups (usually of up to 5, but occasionally 10 together)[3].

Status Resident.

Breeding Nov Dec Jan Mar
(n=4)   1   1   1   1   *Clutch*: no data.

Taxonomy[4] *P. l. leucopogon*. Sometimes placed in a separate genus, *Schistolais*.

References [1]Aspinwall (1974); [2]Benson (1956g); [3]Bowen (1983c); [4]Chapin (1953); [5]Dowsett (in press a).

Red-winged Warbler *Heliolais erythropterus* B474 **RB**

Distribution *Afrotropical (Senegal to Zimbabwe)*. Rather uncommon, in rank growth from the slopes of the Mafingas and of the Nyika Plateau (the Mwavumwe River headwaters)[5], west of the Rift to Mpika[1] and south-west to the road to Chingombe[4]. East of the Rift it ranges from Lundazi[7] south-west to Nyimba[4], and is even present on the floor of the Luangwa Valley up to Chinzombo[3]. *Alt.* 950-1800 m (Mafingas)[6], exceptionally down to 550 m in the Luangwa Valley.

Ecology Mainly in patches of long grass in miombo woodland (under fairly open canopy), often where there are rocks. Is partial to slopes and escarpments. In drier country prefers rank grass and bushes along streams. At Chinzombo found in rank growth under *Acacia* (perhaps not resident there). Often alongside *Prinia subflava*.

Status Resident.

Breeding   Sep   Jan   Mar
(n=3)   1   1   1   *Clutch*: C/2 (1).
Taxonomy[2] *H. e. rhodopterus.*
References [1]Benson (1956g); [2]Chapin (1953); [3]Dowsett (1975b); [4]Dowsett (in press a); [5]Dowsett-Lemaire (2006a); [6]Leonard *et al.* (2001a); [7]White (1947b).

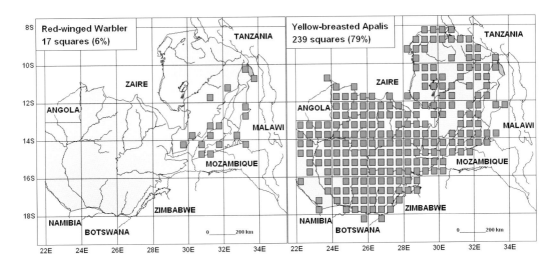

Yellow-breasted Apalis *Apalis flavida*   B476 **RB**

Distribution *Afrotropical (The Gambia to South Africa).* Common in dense vegetation practically throughout the country; local in Northern Province, where suitable thickets are scarce[1]. A few other gaps are not easy to explain (some may be through insufficient exploration). *Alt.* 330-1700 m.
Ecology At all levels of riparian forest and riparian woodland, deciduous to evergreen thicket, dry, broken-canopy evergreen forest (mainly in tangles), as in *Cryptosepalum* forest (where very common). It is reported in the same general area as *A. thoracica* in parts of Mkushi Dist.[1], but it is not known if they occur on the same ground, and if so how they interact. A nest was 3 m up in a small *Acacia.*
Status Resident.
Breeding   Aug   Sep   Oct   Nov   Dec   Jan   Feb   Mar
(n=19)   1   2   6   3   2   2   2   1   *Clutch*: C/2 (6); C/3 (3).
Taxonomy[2] *A. f. tenerrima* (throat white, crown grey) in the north of the country (syn. *A. f. canora,* type locality Sumbu; *NMZB*)[3] and *A. f. neglecta* (like last, but grey on forehead only) in the south, with *A. f. flavida* (throat yellow, crown grey) identified in the extreme south-west.
References [1]Dowsett (in press a); [2]Irwin & Benson (1966a); [3]Lawson (1962: 134).

Bar-throated Apalis *Apalis thoracica*   B475 **RB**

Distribution *Afromontane near-endemic (Kenya to South Africa).* Present in forest patches in the Mafingas[10], Makutu[2] and on the Nyika Plateau (where common), then from Shiwa Ngandu[9] south-west along the chain of the Muchinga escarpment to the Mkushi area and Mita Hills Dam[4]. Extralimitally, it is quite common on the Ufipa Plateau, to the north of Mbala, in SW Tanzania. *Alt.* mostly 1450-2200 m (higher on the Malawi side of the Nyika), down to nearly 1200 m in places.

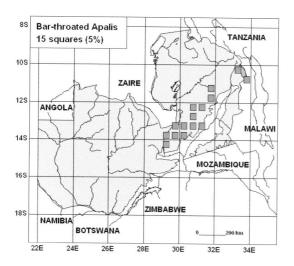

Ecology At edges and in understorey of evergreen forest, mainly montane or high-altitude riparian, also in montane shrubland 3-4 m high. On the Nyika birds countersing frequently with the canopy/edge species *A. chapini* in all areas of overlap. Competes even more clearly with *A. cinerea* (which descends to the lower storeys), as studied in N. Malawi[7]; the situation in the Muchinga escarpment deserves investigation. *A. t. youngi* is numerous in the north-east, with densities of 10 pairs/5 ha in fragmented forest (Nyika 2150-2450 m)[7], the northern plateau birds seem to be less common.

Status Resident; some unmated males wander a few km locally on the Nyika. Thirty of 58 territorial birds ringed on the Nyika were controlled over successive seasons, three for up to 7 years after ringing[3,6].

Breeding   Sep   Oct   Nov   Dec   Jan
(n=49)   2   16   19   6   6

Most records from SW Nyika (including Malawi side). *Clutch*: C/2 (11); C/3 (3).
Moult: in adults late Jan-Apr, estimated to last *c.* 83 days[5].

Taxonomy[1,8] Birds similar to *A. t. whitei* occupy the Muchingas, and *A. t. youngi* (abdomen whitish rather than yellowish) the eastern highlands. Sight records from the Zambian Mafingas probably refer to *murina*, known as a vagrant on the Malawi side, and present also in the Misuku Hills (it is very like *whitei*).

References [1]Benson *et al.* (1971a); [2]Dowsett (1971h); [3]Dowsett (1985a); [4]Dowsett (in press a); [5]Dowsett & Dowsett-Lemaire (1984); [6]Dowsett & Leonard (2001); [7]Dowsett-Lemaire (1989b); [8]Irwin & Benson (1966a); [9]Keith & Vernon (1969); [10]Leonard *et al.* (2001a).

Grey Apalis *Apalis cinerea*   B478 **RB**

Distribution *Afromontane near-endemic (E. Nigeria/Cameroon to SW Angola, east to N. Malawi).* Small numbers in the evergreen forests of N. Zambia, from the Nyika Plateau and Kasangu, southwards, west of the Rift, to Mkushi River (Chalata), on the Copperbelt to Mpongwe, across to the West Lunga N.P.[3] and (just west of the Zambezi) to Mbulo[6]. *Alt.* 1050 m (Mbulo) to 2150 m (Nyika).

Ecology In canopy and upper levels of tall montane rain forest and mushitu (swamp forest); comes down to edges and can feed low down in short, thick riparian forest. On SW Nyika clearly competes with *A. chapini* (countersinging frequent and may defend interspecific territories)[5], and is outnumbered by *A. chapini* there and in the Mafingas[7]. Densities of *c.* 3 pairs/10 ha at 2000 m (SW Nyika)[5]. In the Muchingas and the Mkushi River area likely to compete with *A. thoracica*[3], as in N. Malawi.

Status Resident.

Breeding   Sep   Oct   Nov   Dec   Feb
(n=8)   2   2   1   2   1   *Clutch*: no data.

Taxonomy[1] *A. c. alticola* (type locality Old Fife; *NHM*)[2,8]: often considered a separate species, but voice almost identical and the race *dowsetti* from the Marungu highlands is intermediate[4].

References [1]Benson (1956a); [2]Dowsett (1980b); [3]Dowsett (in press a); [4]Dowsett & Prigogine (1974); [5]Dowsett-Lemaire (1989b); [6]Leonard (1998b); [7]Leonard *et al.* (2001a); [8]Shelley (1899a: 35).

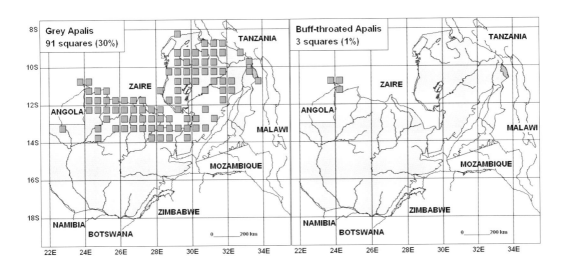

Buff-throated Apalis *Apalis rufogularis* B479 **RB**

Distribution *Guineo-Congolian near-endemic (Benin to NW Zambia)*. Locally common at several forest localities from the Salujinga area[4] and Isombu stream[1] south to the Source of the Zambezi[2] (the most southerly record of the species). It occurs rather further to the east in neighbouring Zaire, to Kipopo (1027C)[5]. *Alt.* 1170-1460 m.

Ecology In the canopy of moist evergreen forest, even where disturbed. Alongside the larger and more widespread *A. cinerea* in places (e.g. at the Source of the Zambezi)[3].

Status Resident.

Conservation The habitat in Mwinilunga is threatened with deforestation (the forest at Isombu has been destroyed), but the species is common elsewhere in Central Africa.

Breeding   Sep   Oct
(n=2)   1   1   *Clutch*: no data. The nest and eggs are unknown.

Taxonomy *A. r. nigrescens.*

References [1]Benson (1958b); [2]Bowen (1983j); [3]Dowsett (in press a); [4]Oatley (1969); [5]Schouteden (1971).

Chestnut-headed Apalis *Apalis chapini* B477 **RB**

Distribution *Afromontane endemic (Tanzania to south-central Malawi)*. Common in the forests of the eastern highlands: Mafingas[3], Makutu[1] and the Nyika Plateau[4]. *Alt.* 1900-2200 m (slightly higher on the Malawi side of the Nyika).

Ecology The canopy and edges of montane forest. On edges competes with the larger *A. thoracica*, and in the canopy with *A. cinerea* (keeping separate territories). Pairs occupy small patches of 0.5-1 ha on SW Nyika but overall densities of 3 pairs/10 ha in more continuous forest at 2000-2200 m[4].

Status Resident.

Breeding   Oct   Nov   Jan
(n=5)   1   2   2   (including the Malawi side of SW Nyika.)
Clutch: no data. The eggs have not been described.

Taxonomy *A. c. strausae.* Previously treated as a race of *A. porphyrolaema*[2].

References [1]Dowsett (1971h); [2]Dowsett & Dowsett-Lemaire (1980); [3]Dowsett & Stjernstedt (1973); [4]Dowsett-Lemaire (1989b).

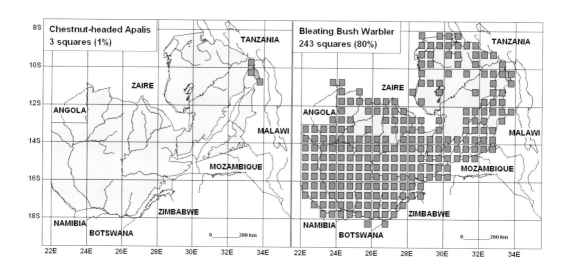

Bleating Bush Warbler *Camaroptera brachyura*   B480 **RB**

Distribution *Afrotropical* (*Mauritania to South Africa*). Very common in thick cover throughout most of the country. Its absence from large parts of the north-east (in much of the Chambeshi drainage and the plateau to the south it is recorded only from Shiwa Ngandu[3]) is a reflection of the lack of suitable thicket. The gap in the north-west is more puzzling on present knowledge. *Alt.* 330-1950 m (Mafingas)[5].

Ecology In any type of thicket, woodland with some rank grass, gardens, riparian and other forest types (abundant in *Cryptosepalum*), feeding normally below 2 m. Occasionally on the edge of dry montane forest, even inside (Mafingas). Marginally penetrates into understorey of neglected plantations.

Status Resident.

Breeding   Oct   Nov   Dec   Jan   Feb   Mar   May
(n=95)   1   6   43   26   15   3   1

Clutch: C/1 (9); C/2 (44); C/3 (32).

Moult: recorded at two seasons, Sep-Nov and Feb-Apr; in one adult it lasted *c.* 10 weeks[3].

Taxonomy[1,2] *C. b. intercalata* (type locality "62 miles" south of Mwinilunga; *NMZB*)[6] in the north and west, replaced by *C. b. beirensis* east of the Luangwa, by *C. b. tincta* in the extreme north-west, and perhaps by *C. b. fugglescouchmani* in the north-east. Differences are evident only in breeding dress: *intercalata* (light grey-brown above, very white below), *beirensis* (colder, greyer above, wings greener), *tincta* (darker grey above and below), *fugglescouchmani* (greener on back). The two main races are grey-backed, with no seasonal change of dress. We do not believe green-backed and grey-backed populations represent separate species[4].

References [1]Benson *et al.* (1970); [2]Clancey (1974a); [3]Dowsett (in press a); [4]Dowsett & Dowsett-Lemaire (1993); [5]Dowsett & Stjernstedt (1973); [6]White (1960b: 149).

[Southern Barred Warbler *Camaroptera fasciolata*

Kalahari-Highveld near-endemic (*W. Angola to South Africa*). Reported to occur in *Acacia* in the Caprivi Strip (1724C), adjacent to SW Zambia[2], but it can be confused with *C. undosa* (present in broad-leaved woodland in that area), and it remains to be confirmed that the species ranges so far north[1]. **References** [1]Dowsett *et al.* (in prep.); [2]Herremans in Harrison *et al.* (1997).]

Miombo Barred Warbler *Camaroptera undosa*   B481-2 **RB**

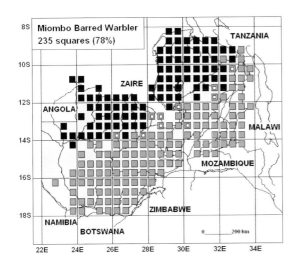

Distribution *Zambezian near-endemic* (*Burundi to South Africa*). Locally common in the miombo and *Baikiaea* woodlands through most of the country, ranging westwards to the Zambezi town (Balovale)-Dipalata area[1], and in the south-west to the Natukoma area[2]. Although it does occur at low altitude on hills in the central Luangwa Valley, it is unrecorded from the Middle Zambezi. *Alt.* 650-1800 m, locally down to 550 m.

Ecology Essentially in miombo woodland and *Baikiaea* forest[5], especially in grassy under-storey and low thickets (as on ant-hills); rarely in mopane. Only occasionally joins mixed bird parties.

Status Resident.

Breeding   Oct Nov Dec Jan Feb
(n=53)   12   22   8   6   5   *Clutch*: C/1 (3); C/2 (35); C/3 (7).

Taxonomy[6] Four races are claimed from Zambia, and they have in the past (wrongly, according to our understanding[3,4]) been divided between two species (*C. stierlingi*, blue squares and *C. simplex*, black squares). N. and NE Zambia is occupied by *C. u. katangae* (barring below well developed), with *C. u. cinerea* (little barring, except on chin) in the north-west: both have been treated as forms of *C. simplex*. The southern half of the country is occupied by the following (often considered races of *C. stierlingi*): *C. u. irwini* south and east, *C. u. buttoni* (type locality Ndola; *type specimen lost*; named for E.L. Button)[7] more central. There is a hybrid zone extending into NW Malawi (open squares represent hybrid specimens), and the two groups are inseparable ecologically. Hybrids are easily recognized because of their intermediate, disyllabic song types[3]. Some authorities place this species in the genus *Calamonastes*.

References [1]Britton (1970); [2]Dowsett (in press a); [3]Dowsett & Dowsett-Lemaire (1980); [4]Dowsett & Dowsett-Lemaire (1993); [5]Irwin (1960); [6]Irwin & Benson (1966b); [7]White (1947a: 55).

Muscicapidae

Marico Flycatcher *Bradornis mariquensis*   B526 **RB**

Distribution *Kalahari/Zambezian* (*S. Angola to South Africa*). Small numbers in thornbush in the extreme south-west, ranging north to Shangombo, 55 km west of Nangweshi[4] and Nangweshi[3]. The

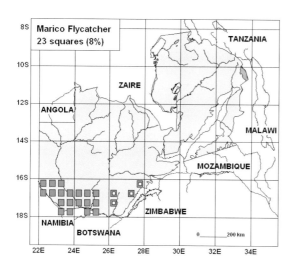

normal eastern limit is the Mulanga area[1] and Kapanda Bridge. But in some years wanderers (open squares) have been reported to the north-east, on the plateau, to the Kalomo area and as far as Gwembe[2]. *Alt.* 950-1250 m.

Ecology *Acacia* scrub and thorn thickets in degraded *Baikiaea*, and on the edge of mixed *Acacia tortilis/Terminalia* woodland. Feeds mainly by dropping to the ground, like its sibling *B. pallidus*. These two species are parapatric, separated by their different habitats.

Status Resident in the south-west, with records in all months east to the Katombora area. In some cold years a few wander further north-east in winter[2].

Breeding   Oct   Jan   Feb
(n=3)   1   1   1

Clutch: C/2 (1) & N/2 (1).

Taxonomy[3] *B. m. mariquensis*.

References [1]Benson (1958c); [2]Dowsett (in press a); [3]Irwin & Benson (1967a); [4]Smithers (1956).

Pallid Flycatcher *Bradornis pallidus*   B527 **RB**

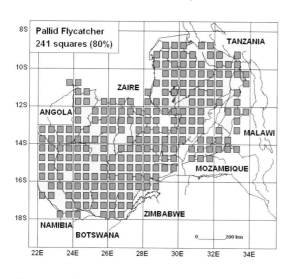

Distribution *Afrotropical* (*Mauritania to South Africa*). Common in most light woodlands throughout the country, but absent from the Middle Zambezi Valley and very scarce in the Luangwa and Luano Valleys[1]. *Alt.* 550-1770 m (Danger Hill).

Ecology In open stands of miombo or other woodland (rarely mopane or *Acacia*), especially near edges, in secondary stages, or in wooded grassland. Perches in low trees and shrubs, taking prey mainly from the ground, occasionally by flycatching.

Status Resident.

Breeding   Aug   Sep   Oct   Nov   Dec
(n=157)   2   65   59   21   10

Clutch: C/1 (3); C/2 (66); C/3 (49).

Moult: a juvenile started moult late Nov[2].

Taxonomy *B. p. griseus* in the north and east, *B. p. murinus* in the south and west.

References [1]Dowsett (in press a); [2]Traylor (1965b).

[Chat Flycatcher *Bradornis infuscatus*
Afrotropical (*W. Angola to South Africa*). Mapped as occurring in the Caprivi Strip (1723D), adjacent to SW Zambia[2], but it is surely based on a misidentification, and this sedentary species is unlikely so far north[1]. **References** [1]Dowsett *et al.* (in prep.); [2]Herremans in Harrison *et al.* (1997).]

Slaty Flycatcher *Melaenornis chocolatinus* B524 **RB**

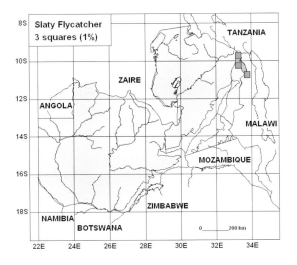

Distribution *Afromontane endemic (Ethiopia to central Malawi)*. Common on the edge of forest in most of the eastern highlands: Mafingas[3], Nyikamwaka, Nyika (not yet recorded from Makutu). It occurs not far north of Mbala in the Marungu highlands (Zaire) and on the Ufipa Plateau (Tanzania)[2]. *Alt.* 1750-2200 m (Nyika, higher on the Malawi side).

Ecology On the edge of montane forest (even of pine plantations), and isolated trees in grassland or dense bracken-briar. Penetrates inside forest mainly to attend ant swarms, and not farther than *c.* 50 m from the edge; feeds by flycatching and hopping on ground and big branches[4].

Status Resident.

Breeding	Aug	Sep	Oct	Nov	Dec	
(n=27)	1	2	9	7	8	(Including Malawi side of SW Nyika.)

Clutch: N/2 (1). *Moult*: noted Nov and Dec[1].

Taxonomy *M. c. nyikensis* (type locality Nyika Plateau, Malawi)[5].

References [1]Dowsett (in press a); [2]Dowsett & Prigogine (1974); [3]Dowsett & Stjernstedt (1973); [4]Dowsett-Lemaire (1983c); [5]Shelley (1899a).

Southern Black Flycatcher *Melaenornis pammelaina* B525 **RB**

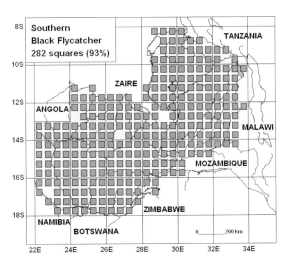

Distribution *Afrotropical (Somalia to South Africa)*. Common in light woodland throughout the country. *Alt.* 330-1700 m, rarely to 2100 m (Mafingas)[4].

Ecology In any light woodland with open understorey; feeds mainly by dropping to the ground from low perches. Nests have been recorded in trees in mopane woodland and village gardens, 3-5 m high. In Malawi known to re-use old nests of various species[1].

Status Resident.

Breeding	Aug	Sep	Oct
(n=179)	1	83	50
	Nov	Dec	Jan
	40	4	1

Clutch: C/1 (1); C/2 (31); C/3 (77); C/4 (2).

Moult: adult males were moulting in Oct and Nov, while females were still nesting and worn[6].

Taxonomy[2,7] *M. p. pammelaina* (syn. *M. p. poliogyna*, type locality Chipata; *NMZB*)[5]. Partial albinos have been noted Lusaka and Muckle Neuk[3].

References [1]Belcher (1930); [2]Benson & White (1957); [3]Dowsett (in press a); [4]Dowsett & Stjernstedt (1973); [5]Lawson (1964a: 145); [6]Traylor (1965b); [7]White (1957).

Collared Flycatcher *Ficedula albicollis*   B516 **PW**

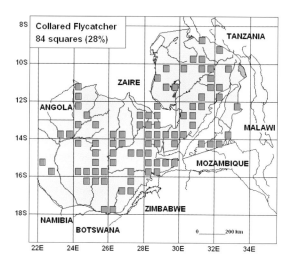

Distribution *Palaearctic* (*winters Zaire to South Africa*). Occurs quite commonly in much of the Zambian plateau woodland south to Livingstone[1] (absent from the Luangwa and Middle Zambezi Valley floors), west of the Zambezi known only from Liande Plain (West) and the Nguma area[2]. *Alt.* 800-1750 m.

Ecology Most records are from miombo woodland, rarely in *Acacia* on passage.

Status A Palaearctic migrant and winter visitor. All records fall within the period 3 Oct to 29 Mar, with arrivals each year usually in the third week of Oct and most departures before Mar[2]. Under-recorded, as few observers know its distinctive call.

Moult: body moult starts before Nov, with some males in full breeding dress from early Dec[2].

Taxonomy No races now recognized, but very closely related to the Half-collared Flycatcher *F. semitorquata* previously considered conspecific.

References [1]Brooke (1965); [2]Dowsett (in press b).

Spotted Flycatcher *Muscicapa striata*   B515 **PW**

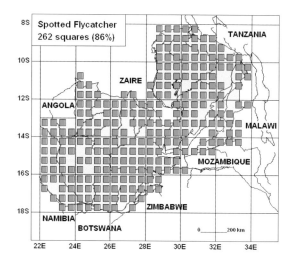

Distribution *Palaearctic* (*winters mainly Zaire to South Africa*). Common in open woodland throughout Zambia. *Alt.* 330-1900 m, rarely to 2150 m (Mafingas)[3], higher on the Malawi side of Nyika.

Ecology In any woodland or wooded grassland, edges of thickets, gardens, feeding at all levels.

Status A Palaearctic migrant and winter visitor. The occasional bird stays during the dry season (more than a dozen acceptable records)[2], but the great majority of reports are between 16 Sep and 6 May, usually mid-Oct to mid-Apr[2]. The average first date over 24 years was 5 Oct, the average last (in 23 years) 18 Apr[2].

Moult: starts mid-Dec, and in some cases is finished by Feb[2].

Taxonomy *M. s. neumanni* (with distinctive white margins to feathers of forehead) and (less commonly) *M. s. striata* are the forms recorded[1].
References [1]Benson & Irwin (1967b); [2]Dowsett (in press b); [3]Leonard *et al.* (2001a).

Dusky Flycatcher *Muscicapa adusta*   B517 **RB**

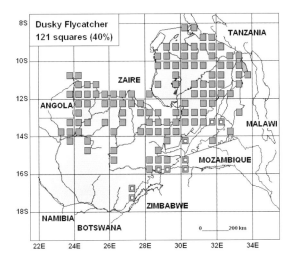

Distribution *Afrotropical* (*Nigeria to South Africa, montane in many parts of range*). Rather uncommon in woodland and on the edge of forest throughout N. Zambia. On the Central Province plateau occurs south to Munali Hills, further west to Kafue Hook[2] and near Zambezi town (Balovale). In the non-breeding season some wanderers (open squares) occur at low altitude, as at Mkwisi, on Chiromwe Hill[1], the Luangwa Valley and to the Zambezi escarpment near Sinazongwe. Has bred once at Choma[4]. *Alt.* normally above 1000 m, to 2200 m (Nyika), down to 370 m in the colder months.
Ecology The edge of riparian and montane forest, and in miombo woodland; also at edges of plantations and of *Cryptosepalum* forest (scarce). On SW Nyika territories may be as small as 1-2 ha, but are more scattered in forest (around clearings) than in miombo[5]. In winter also in thicket and mopane woodland.
Status Present throughout the year in most parts of N. Zambia; records from the Luangwa and Middle Zambezi Valleys and Southern Province are of non-breeding visitors (mostly Dec-Jul)[4], and part of the breeding population on the Nyika Plateau appears to leave in the cold weather (May-Aug)[6].

Breeding   Sep   Oct   Nov   Dec
(n=25)   6   6   9   4   *Clutch*: C/2 (6); C/3 (1).
Moult: recorded in Feb[4].

Taxonomy[3] *M. a. subadusta* (type locality Nyika Plateau, Malawi)[7] is the form in the eastern highlands, replaced by *M. a. angolensis* (darker above, throat whiter) in the rest of N. Zambia, and allegedly by *M. a. mesica* (paler, browner above) in central parts, along the Muchingas (although the sample examined was very small).
References [1]Benson *et al.* (1971a); [2]Brooke (1966c); [3]Clancey (1974a); [4]Dowsett (in press a); [5]Dowsett-Lemaire (1989b); [6]Dowsett-Lemaire (2006a); [7]Shelley & Sclater (1897).

Swamp Flycatcher *Muscicapa aquatica*   B518 **RB**

Distribution *Afrotropical* (*Senegal to Zambia*). Scarce, but easily overlooked, in the northern swamps, from Bulaya and Mweru Wantipa southwards along the Luapula to Kasenga[6]. In the Bangweulu Swamps from Chilubi Is.[5] south and east to Mukuku and near the Livingstone Memorial at Chitambo[4]. Reappears in the Lukanga Swamp[1], and the Kafue Flats between Chulwe Lagoon[3] and immediately upstream of the Kafue rail bridge[4]. These are the southernmost localities for the species. *Alt.* 950-1300 m.
Ecology Papyrus swamp above all, but also 2 m tall patches of ambatch *Aeschynomene elaphroxylon*

(e.g. Kafue Flats), and occasionally thicket by water (its more usual habitat in the northern Tropics).
Status Resident.

Breeding   May   Aug   Sep   Oct   Nov

(n=8)   1   1   2   2   2   *Clutch*: no data.

Taxonomy[1] *M. a. infulata* is the northern form, the southern being *M. a. grimwoodi* (type locality L. Suye; *AMNH*; named for I.R. Grimwood)[2].

References [1]Benson (1956f); [2]Chapin (1952: 22); [3]Douthwaite (1972); [4]Dowsett (in press a); [5]Neave (1910); [6]White (1944e).

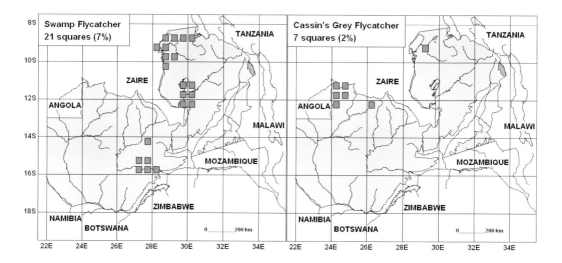

Cassin's Grey Flycatcher *Muscicapa cassini*   B519 **RB**

Distribution *Guineo-Congolian near-endemic* (*Guinea to NW Tanzania and N. Zambia*). Scarce, on some large forested rivers in North-Western Province, southwards from the north at Zambezi Rapids[3], Kalene Hill[1] and Kanyama, south to the Lwamakunyi stream[3] and to the east at Mutanda Bridge[5] (the most southerly record of the species). In Luapula Province there is an old specimen (15 Sep 1908, collected by Neave) from the lower Kalungwishi River area near the Old Kalungwishi boma[7], and it has recently been found on that river in the nearby Lusenga Plain N.P.[6]. *Alt.* 1190-1460 m (the Kalungwishi record would be at *c.* 935 m).

Ecology Along large, wooded rivers, where associated with rocks and fringing evergreen forest, feeding low down (usually over water).

Status Resident.

Breeding[2]   Aug   Sep   Oct   Nov

(n=7)   2   1   3   1   *Clutch*: C/2 (1).

Taxonomy[4] No races recognized.

References [1]Benson (1961c); [2]Benson & Irwin (1983); [3]Bowen (1980b); [4]Chapin (1953); [5]Dowsett (in press a); [6]Leonard (2007); [7]Neave (1910).

Ashy Flycatcher *Muscicapa caerulescens*   B520 **RB**

Distribution *Afrotropical* (*Guinea to South Africa*). Fairly common in densely-wooded country, almost

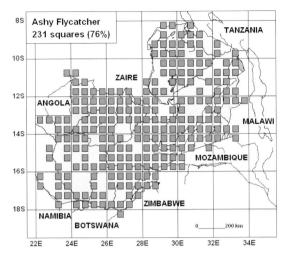

throughout (but absent from open plains)[2]. *Alt.* 330-1700 m, exceptionally to 1950 m on the Mafingas[3].

Ecology In riparian woodland and forest (usually in the canopy), rich miombo and edges of deciduous to evergreen thickets, including *Cryptosepalum* forest (rare).

Status Resident.

Breeding	Sep	Oct	Nov
(n=25)	8	4	4
	Dec	Jan	Feb
	7	1	1

Clutch: C/1 (1); C/2 (6); C/3 (9).

Moult: adults start moult in Nov or Dec, immediately after breeding (one male started before its nestlings flew)[2].

Taxonomy *M. c. impavida*[1].

References [1]Clancey (1968c); [2]Dowsett (in press a); [3]Dowsett & Stjernstedt (1973).

Sooty Flycatcher *Muscicapa infuscata*   B521 **RB**

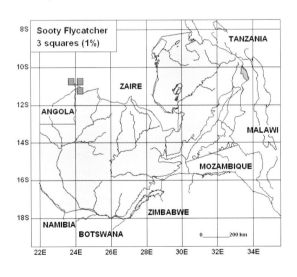

Distribution *Guineo-Congolian near-endemic (E. Nigeria to Uganda and NW Zambia).* Rather local and unobtrusive at several places in the extreme north of Mwinilunga Dist.[4], from the Kadata River and the Jimbe stream[6], south via Salujinga[2], Zambezi Rapids[3], and Kalene Hill[1], to the Source of the Zambezi[6] (the most southerly locality for this species). *Alt.* 1280-1460 m.

Ecology In the canopy of tall trees on the forest edge, even in fields and adjacent woodland.

Status Resident.

Conservation Less dependent on untouched forest than many of the Guineo-Congolian species in NW Zambia, and so may resist rather longer the habitat destruction there.

Breeding	Feb
(n=1)	1

Clutch: no data. The eggs have not been described.

Taxonomy No races recognized. Formerly known as *Artomyias fuliginosa*[5].

References [1]Benson (1961c); [2]Benson & Irwin (1965b); [3]Benson *et al.* (1970); [4]Dowsett (in press a); [5]Dowsett & Dowsett-Lemaire (1993); [6]Leonard & Peters (1999).

Böhm's Flycatcher *Muscicapa boehmi*   B522 **RB**

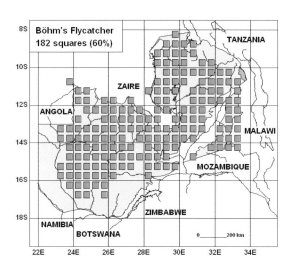

Distribution *Zambezian endemic* (*Tanzania to central Malawi and Zambia, where it reaches the southern limit of its range*). Rather sparse, in the miombo woodlands of the Zambian plateau (absent from the Luangwa Valley). From near Chitimbwa, near Chitimukulu[3] and Chire Bridge ranges throughout Eastern Province, in Central Province south to Lazy J ranch (south-east of Lusaka) and the Manenekera escarpment[1]. It occurs south and west to Mukuni Pool and the Mushukula area[2], and to just east of the Zambezi River near Namushakende and Siandi[3]. *Alt.* 800-1600 m.

Ecology In well-developed miombo woodland, also in tall mixed miombo and mopane in the border area of Vwaza Marsh (Malawi). A rather secretive bird, most frequently noted in mixed bird parties. Nests in cavities in tree branches, but also uses old nests of other species (*Plocepasser rufoscapulatus, Anaplectes melanotis*)[3].

Status Resident.

Breeding   Aug   Sep   Oct   Nov
(n=37)   1   21   12   3   *Clutch*: C/1 (2); C/2 (3); C/3 (3); C/4 (10).

Taxonomy[4] No races recognized. Formerly placed in the genus *Myopornis*[5].

References [1]Aspinwall (1973f); [2]Bruce-Miller & Dowsett (1977); [3]Dowsett (in press a); [4]Irwin & Benson (1967b); [5]Traylor in Mayr & Cottrell (1986).

Lead-coloured Flycatcher *Myioparus plumbeus*   B523 **RB**

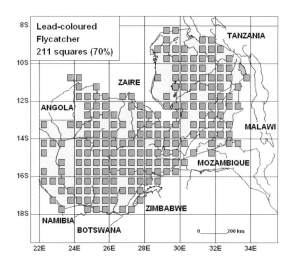

Distribution *Afrotropical* (*Senegal to South Africa*). Widespread in small numbers in thickets and woodland throughout; uncommon in the low-lying Luangwa and Middle Zambezi Valleys[2]. *Alt.* 330-1700 m.

Ecology On the edge of deciduous and semi-evergreen thickets; also on the edge of riparian forest and in adjacent miombo woodland. Feeds in foliage, frequently raising and fanning the tail.

Status Resident.

Breeding   Sep   Oct   Nov
(n=8)   3   4   1
Clutch: C/1 (1). *Moult*: an adult in late Nov had almost completed moult, whereas a juvenile started early Nov[4].

Taxonomy[3] *M. p. grandior* (type locality Nasiongo; *NMZB*)[1].

References [1]Clancey (1962: 62); [2]Dowsett (in press a); [3]Irwin & Benson (1967a); [4]Traylor (1965b).

Platysteiridae

Shrike Flycatcher *Megabyas flammulatus*   B - **AV**

Distribution and Status *Guineo-Congolian near-endemic* (*mainly Guinea to W. Kenya and NW Zambia*). A single bird in female dress (probably an immature male) was tape-recorded in forest in the Jimbe River area, near its confluence with the Kanyengele stream (1024C), 10 Oct to 1 Nov 1998[1]. The species is known to wander in the main parts of its range, and it is perhaps merely a vagrant to N. Mwinilunga, at the southern limit of its range. At Kasaji, some 100 km to the north-west in Katanga, dated specimens suggest it is resident[2]. *Alt.* 1220 m. This habitat is under threat in Zambia, as riparian forest is cleared for gardens.

Taxonomy No specimen, but presumably *M. f. aequatorialis*, as were specimens from Kasaji[2].

References [1]Leonard & Van Daele (1999b); [2]Schouteden (1971).

[Black-and-white Flycatcher *Bias musicus*
Afrotropical (*Guinea to Mozambique*). This species of forest edges is known from Kasaji in S. Zaire, but is apparently not common there[1]. It might possibly occur as far south as N. Mwinilunga. **References** [1]Schouteden (1971).]

Cape Batis *Batis capensis*   B528 **RB**

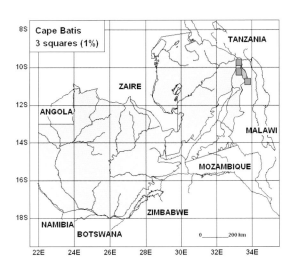

Distribution *Afromontane near-endemic* (*N. Malawi to South Africa*). Common in forests of the eastern highlands: Mafingas[3], Makutu and Nyika. *Alt.* 1850-2200 m (Nyika, higher on the Malawi side).

Ecology Montane forest, foraging at all levels of the understorey, occasionally up to the canopy, and on edges; snatches prey off branches and under the leaves in a short hop or flight, sometimes flycatching 1-2 m from perch, also pecks on bark. Densities of 10 pairs/10 ha in most areas of tall forest on the Nyika (e.g. Chowo), and some territories in fragmented forest are as small as 0.3 ha[5].

Status Resident, with very limited post-breeding wandering (on the Nyika, up to 2.6 km in ringed birds[1]). On the Nyika 45 of 63 territorial ringed birds were checked locally in following seasons, up to 10 years after first capture[1] (this last was ringed as an adult male, so was more than 11 years old when controlled).

Breeding   Sep   Oct   Nov   Dec   Jan   Feb

(n=174)   33   51   41   40   6   3   (Including Malawi side of SW Nyika.)

Single-brooded[4]. *Clutch*: C/2 (2).

Moult: on the Nyika, synchronized and rapid, Dec (or mid-Nov) to Mar, individual duration estimated to be *c.* 105 days. Juveniles do not moult their flight feathers, and usually some body plumage is retained until their second year[2].

Taxonomy[6] *B. c. sola* (type locality Nyika Plateau; *NMZB*)[7].

References [1]Dowsett (1985a); [2]Dowsett & Dowsett-Lemaire (1984); [3]Dowsett & Stjernstedt (1973); [4]Dowsett-Lemaire (1985a); [5]Dowsett-Lemaire (1989b); [6]Irwin & Benson (1966a); [7]Lawson (1964b: 196).

Margaret's Batis *Batis margaritae*   B529 **R(B)**

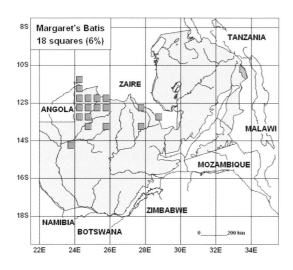

Distribution *Zambezian endemic, with Afromontane affinities* (*W. Angola to N. Zambia*). This species is most common in the *Cryptosepalum* forests of the North-Western Province, rarer in other evergreen forest types on the Jimbe stream and at Hillwood[8,9] (and unrecorded from Kasaji, to the north in Zaire)[12]. It ranges mainly from the Mudyanyama River (at Mwinilunga town)[4] south to Mayau[11] and Swanandumba[6], east to the area of Jivundu River[3,14], the Mwombezhi drainage[6] and 16 km north of Kasempa[3,14]. There are also populations as far south as Kapweletete (the most southerly record of the species)[2], and on the Copperbelt in the Imanda area[1], Chililabombwe[7] and at Ndola[10] (this unobtrusive bird may have been missed at places in between). *Alt.* 1100-1500 m.

Ecology In various types of evergreen forest, especially *Cryptosepalum* (very common), other dry evergreen (as the Forestry Experimental Plots at Ndola)[10], and also wetter riparian situations (e.g. Imanda and Swanandumba).

Status Likely to be wholly or mostly resident; observations suggest that there is a post-breeding movement by all or most birds out of *Cryptosepalum* Nov to Apr[5], but this needs further investigation, being to some extent biased by most ornithologists visiting this habitat during the dry season. It is also possible that birds are more discreet during the period of moult, which is likely to be in the rains.

Breeding No records, but male gonad activity mid-Aug and Sep. The nest and eggs are unknown.

Taxonomy *B. m. kathleenae* (type locality Mwinilunga; *NHM*)[13]; named by C.M.N. White for his sister. The species is a member of the *Batis capensis* superspecies. Birds tested at Ndola with a tape of *B. capensis* (from Nyika) reacted strongly to it[7].

References [1]Aspinwall (1975b); [2]Beel (1992b); [3]Benson & Irwin (1965a); [4]Bowen (1979d); [5]Bowen (1979e); [6]Dowsett (1973b); [7]Dowsett (in press a); [8]Leonard & Peters (1998); [9]Leonard & Peters (1999); [10]Madge (1972b); [11]Oatley (1969); [12]Schouteden (1971); [13]White (1941: 48); [14]White (1945-46).

Chinspot Batis *Batis molitor*   B530 **RB**

Distribution *Afrotropical* (*Sudan to South Africa*). Very common throughout, in all woodland types, and including the eastern highlands[1,3]. *Alt.* 330-2150 m (Nyika)[4].

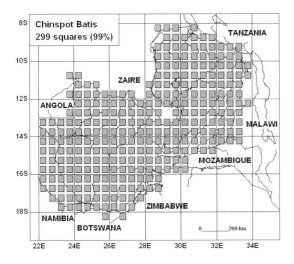

Ecology In any woodland and wooded grassland; also in gardens, edges of plantations, rarely at forest margins, except in dry *Cryptosepalum* forest (surprisingly quite common in the open canopy at Mayau).

Status Resident.

Breeding	Aug	Sep	Oct
(n=168)	6	94	57
	Nov	Dec	Jan
	8	2	1

Clutch: C/1 (10); C/2 (110); N/3 (1).

Moult: an adult female was two-thirds through moult mid-Mar[2]. Juveniles have only a partial moult (starting mid-Nov), young males thus almost resembling adult females[6].

Taxonomy[5] *B. m. palliditergum*, replaced by *B. m. pintoi* in the west (female breast band and throat spot orange chestnut, not dark chestnut). There are local variations in vocalisations[2], but it is not clear if they have any taxonomic importance.

References [1]Dowsett (1971h); [2]Dowsett (in press a); [3]Dowsett & Stjernstedt (1973); [4]Dowsett-Lemaire (2006a); [5]Irwin & Benson (1967a); [6]Traylor (1965b).

Chestnut Wattle-eye *Dyaphorophyia castanea*   B - **RB**

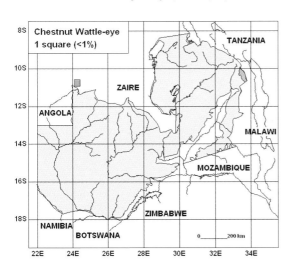

Distribution *Guineo-Congolian near-endemic (Guinea to W. Kenya and NW Zambia).* Known only from a small area of extreme N. Mwinilunga, where first found in three places 14 Oct 1976[1]. There are subsequent records on the Kansombo and Kansoku streams, and others in the Chilula area, south to the upper Jimbe stream[3] (*c.* 11°S, the most southerly locality for the species, where regular in small numbers). The species is certainly absent from apparently suitable, well-known, areas elsewhere in N. Mwinilunga. *Alt.* 1250 m.

Ecology In the mid-stratum and canopy of riparian evergreen forest.

Status Presumably resident.

Conservation By 1995 all the forest in the Chilula area (where first found) had been cleared for subsistence cultivation[2], but the species still exists elsewhere[5]. The long-term future for habitat and bird conservation in NW Zambia seems very doubtful. However, this species is a common bird throughout the Guineo-Congolian forests.

Breeding Very young juveniles in Oct[4].

Taxonomy No Zambian specimen, but presumably *D. c. castanea*, known from Kasaji[6].

References [1]Aspinwall (1976c); [2]Beel (1995); [3]Dowsett (in press a); [4]Leonard & Peters (1999); [5]Leonard & Van Daele (1999a); [6]Schouteden (1971).

Black-throated Wattle-eye *Platysteira peltata*   B531 **RB**

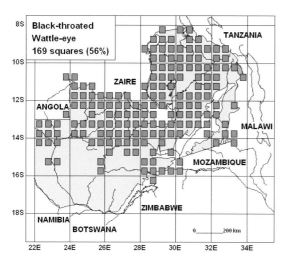

Distribution *Afrotropical* (*Somalia to South Africa*). Locally common throughout the northern half of the country, although very local in the middle Luangwa Valley[6], south to Chinzewe[1]. South to below Chirundu[3], in the Kafue basin to Kalala[5] and "below Namwala"[3] and in the Upper Zambezi to Mapungu[8]. [There are unconfirmed reports from further south in the Upper Zambezi in the Sinjembela area, and the Southern Province plateau near Choma[6].] *Alt*. 330-1770 m (Danger Hill), but on the lower slopes of the Nyika only to 1520 m[7].

Ecology In (semi-) evergreen and deciduous thicket (e.g. Luangwa Valley), riparian and moist evergreen forest, including mushitu. Feeds like a *Batis* and found alongside *B. margaritae* in several places[4], but absent from the main block of *Cryptosepalum* (Mayau), where *B. margaritae* is very common.

Status Resident.

Breeding   Jul   Aug   Sep   Oct   Nov   Apr
(n=22)   1   1   10   4   3   3   *Clutch*: C/1 (2); C/2 (7).
Moult: Nov to Jun[6].

Taxonomy[2] *P. p. mentalis* occurs in most parts, with *P. p. peltata* (greyer on the mantle) in the Luangwa Valley and on the Eastern Province plateau.

References [1]Aspinwall (1971c); [2]Benson (1956f); [3]Benson *et al.* (1971a); [4]Bowen (1979e); [5]Brooke (1966c); [6]Dowsett (in press a); [7]Dowsett *et al.* (1974); [8]Traylor & Hart (1965).

Monarchidae

Livingstone's Flycatcher *Erythrocercus livingstonei*   B532 **RB**

Distribution *Eastern near-endemic* (*Tanzania to Zimbabwe*). Thickets in low-lying situations, known in the Luangwa Valley from the Lupande River confluence (a vagrant in Jul)[4], then southwards from above the Mwendengombe/Luangwa River confluence[3] to East Four in the Luano Valley, and up the Kafue to Mchito Gorge and Munali Hills[4]. Throughout the Middle Zambezi to Chimene stream[2] and Sianzovu. Locally not uncommon (its absence in the upper Luangwa Valley is a result of the lack of extensive thickets). *Alt*. 330-1040 m.

Ecology In the canopy and mid-stratum of various thickets (deciduous, semi-evergreen) and edge of riparian forest. Feeds like a small *Elminia*, fanning tail and darting about, flycatching a short distance from foliage or snatching from leaves.

Status Resident.

Breeding   Dec   Jan
(n=3)   2   1   *Clutch*: no data.

Taxonomy[1] *E. l. livingstonei*. The genus is now thought not to be a member of the Monarchidae[5], but position unclear and left here pending further research.

References [1]Benson (1956f); [2]Benson (1959c); [3]Berry (1981a); [4]Dowsett (in press a); [5]Pasquet *et al.* (2002).

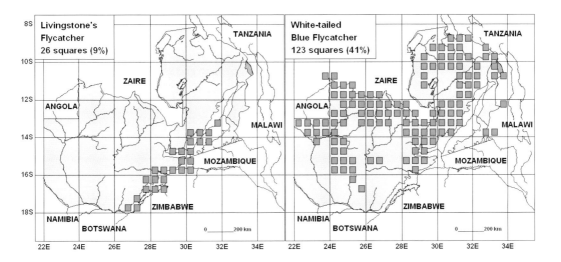

White-tailed Blue Flycatcher *Elminia albicauda* B533 **RB**

Distribution *Zambezian near-endemic (Rwanda to Malawi and Zambia, where it reaches its southern limit of distribution)*. Quite common in rich woodland and on forest edge, throughout the northern half of the plateau. Absent from the low-lying country along the Luapula and between Lakes Mweru and Tanganyika, and from the Luangwa Valley. Occurs sparsely on the plateau in Eastern Province, south to east of Lundazi[4] and between Chipata and the Malawi border near Mchinji[1]. In Central Province south to Leopardshill road, but not south of the Kafue Flats. The whole of the upper Kafue, south to the Kataba area (Kazungula Dist.) and near Kabuzu Pool[4]. In the Upper Zambezi not south of the Kabompo/Zambezi River confluence[2]. *Alt.* 1000-2050 m (rarely 2150 m on the Nyika[5]).
Ecology On the edge of riparian forest (including *Acacia abyssinica* in the highlands) and in adjacent dense miombo woodland; locally in stunted miombo on the edge of dambos.
Status Resident.
Breeding   Sep   Oct   Nov
(n=8)   4   3   1   *Clutch*: C/1 (1); C/2 (5) & N/2 (1).
Taxonomy[3] No races recognized. Forms a superspecies with *E. longicauda*, which replaces it from NE Africa, throughout West Africa. *Elminia* is probably not a member of the Monarchidae[6], but exact position not yet clear.
References [1]Benson *et al.* (1970); [2]Britton (1970); [3]Chapin (1953); [4]Dowsett (in press a); [5]Dowsett-Lemaire (2006a); [6]Pasquet *et al.* (2002).

White-tailed Crested Flycatcher *Elminia albonotata* B535 **RB**

Distribution *Afromontane endemic (Ethiopia to E. Zimbabwe)*. Common in forest in the eastern highlands (Nyika north to Mafingas)[5], then throughout NE Zambia from Nchanga farm near Mbala[2], south along the Muchingas to Danger Hill[11] and Mutinondo Wilderness, north to the road to Shebene and Njalamimba, west of Mporokoso[2]. *Alt.* 1350-2200 m (Nyika, higher on the Malawi side).
Ecology In montane and moist evergreen forest on the high plateau (not in swamp forest). At all levels

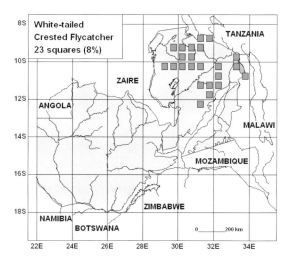

of the understorey, occasionally up to the canopy; hops along branches in a zigzag fashion, fanning tail and drooping wings, catching displaced insects in jerky flights close to foliage and bark. Densities of 5-10 pairs/10 ha on SW Nyika[7], less numerous in some of the moist evergreen forests of the north-east. A type of forest dominated locally by the montane *Podocarpus latifolius* has been described from Kawambwa Dist.[9], where this flycatcher occurs. This denotes the montane micro-climate of the area.

Status Resident, with limited post-breeding wandering (on the Nyika up to 2.5 km in ringed birds). On the Nyika 20 of 38 ringed territorial adults were checked locally in following seasons, two up to 6 and 7 years after first capture[1].

Breeding   Sep   Oct   Nov   Dec   Jan
(n=53)   4   12   21   14   2   (Including Malawi side of SW Nyika.)
Single-brooded[6]. *Clutch*: N/2 (2).
Moult: Dec-Apr (exceptionally starting mid-Nov)[4].

Taxonomy[8] *E. a. albonotata*. Behavioural, morphological and molecular studies show that the genus *Elminia* is very distinct from *Trochocercus* (in which this species was once placed)[3,10].

References [1]Dowsett (1985a); [2]Dowsett (in press a); [3]Dowsett & Dowsett-Lemaire (1980); [4]Dowsett & Dowsett-Lemaire (1984); [5]Dowsett & Stjernstedt (1973); [6]Dowsett-Lemaire (1985a); [7]Dowsett-Lemaire (1989b); [8]Irwin & Benson (1966a); [9]Lawton (1964); [10]Pasquet *et al.* (2002); [11]Smithers (1952).

Blue-mantled Flycatcher *Trochocercus cyanomelas*   B534 **RB**

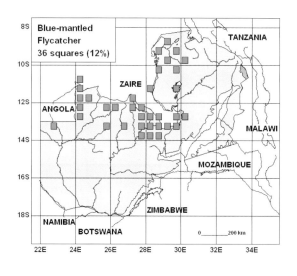

Distribution *Eastern near-endemic (Somalia to South Africa)*. Small numbers in thicket and dense forest in Northern and Luapula Provinces, ranging east only to the headwaters of the Lukulu and Kalungwishi Rivers[4] and Kasanka N.P.[4] On the Copperbelt south to the Mpongwe area[1], further west to the Dengwe River[9]. Throughout Mwinilunga Dist., south to Mayau[2], but west of the Zambezi only at Mbulo and Muyeke[8] (where fairly common). [A sight record from the Zimbabwe side of Victoria Falls[3], although considered reliable[7], seems unlikely, as does a sighting by the same observer from Kariba town[3]. A later claim from Victoria Falls was rejected[6]. There is no acceptable record within several hundred km[5].] *Alt.* 1000-1600 m.

Ecology In thick understorey and liane tangles (usually below 8 m) of evergreen forest and moist transition woodland (Ndola). Very local in *Cryptosepalum* forest. Feeds like an *Elminia* but less demonstrative and rapid, fanning tail less widely, sometimes not at all. Densities are rather low, as it is confined to the thicker sections of the understorey, under broken canopy.

Status Resident.

Breeding   Sep   Dec
(n=3)   2   1   *Clutch*: C/2 (2).

Taxonomy *T. c. vivax*.

References [1]Aspinwall (1975b); [2]Benson & Irwin (1965a); [3]Donnelly & Donnelly (1983: 42); [4]Dowsett (in press a); [5]Oatley in Harrison *et al.* (1997); [6]Hustler (1989); [7]Irwin (1981a); [8]Leonard (1998b); [9]White (1945-46).

African Paradise Flycatcher *Terpsiphone viridis*   B537 **AMB/R**

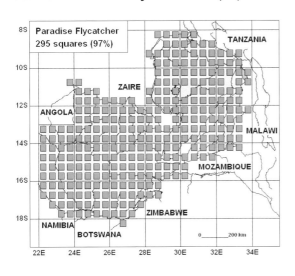

Distribution *Afrotropical (Mauritania to South Africa)*. Very common in any wooded habitat throughout the country. *Alt.* 330-2150 m (Chowo on the Nyika, where it breeds).

Ecology Common in any woodland, thicket, evergreen forest and gardens; adapts to plantations with some natural undergrowth. Very common in *Cryptosepalum* and *Marquesia* forest. Flycatches, or snatches prey off foliage while hovering; occasionally fans tail along branches like an *Elminia*.

Status Largely an intra-African migrant and breeding visitor. The race *plumbeiceps* is resident in parts of the north and north-west. The principal breeding race (*violacea*) is mainly an intra-African migrant, present during the rains, while non-breeding *granti* from southern Africa are present in the winter (in the Luangwa Valley, and at scattered localities on the plateau, east of 25°E)[3]. One ringed bird in N. Mwinilunga was recovered 40 km distant[2]. The oldest ringed bird was at least 8 years old. Ringed migrants returned after one year (4) and after two (2)[2,3].

Breeding   Aug   Sep   Oct   Nov   Dec   Jan   Feb   Mar
(n=189)   1   5   58   68   43   11   2   1

Clutch: C/1 (5); C/2 (41); C/3 (48).

Moult: the post-breeding moult of *T. v. violacea* evidently takes place outside Zambia, in the non-breeding quarters, probably May onwards[3,4].

Taxonomy[1] The common breeding form is the migrant *T. v. violacea*, replaced in parts of the north and north-west by *T. v. plumbeiceps*. The dry season sees an influx of non-breeding *T. v. granti* from southern Africa to the north and east.

References [1]Benson *et al.* (1971a); [2]Dowsett & Leonard (2001); [3]Dowsett & Leonard (in press a); [4]Traylor (1965b).

Red-bellied Paradise Flycatcher *Terpsiphone rufiventer*   B536 **RB**

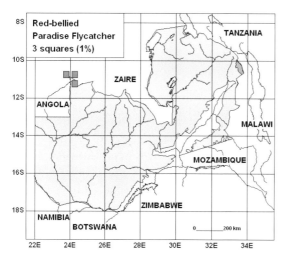

Distribution *Guineo-Congolian near-endemic (Senegal to W. Kenya and NW Zambia)*. A forest bird, present in most patches in the extreme north of Mwinilunga Dist., from the Kadata River and Chilula[3], south to Isombu[1], Hillwood and the Source of the Zambezi[4]. These are the most southerly localities for the species. *Alt.* 1250-1460 m.

Ecology Undisturbed, moist evergreen forest, where feeding in the mid-stratum.

Status Resident.

Conservation Its habitat is under threat in Zambia through deforestation, but this bird has a wide range and is common elsewhere.

Breeding   Aug
(n=1)   1   *Clutch*: no data.

Taxonomy[2] *T. r. ignea*.

References [1]Benson (1958b); [2]Chapin (1953); [3]Dowsett (in press a); [4]White & Grimwood (1954).

Timaliidae

African Hill Babbler *Pseudoalcippe abyssinica*   B392 **RB**

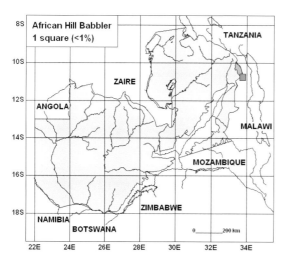

Distribution *Afromontane endemic (E. Nigeria/Cameroon and Ethiopia to S. Malawi)*. Nyika Plateau only (Manyenjere, Kasoma, Chowo). It reappears in the Marungu highlands (Zaire) and on the Ufipa Plateau (Tanzania)[6]. *Alt.* 1970-2200 m (locally up to 2400 m on the Malawi side).

Ecology Montane rain forest, especially in mid-stratum tangles; feeds like a large Sylviid, mainly by gleaning, sometimes hovers; takes some fruit. Densities in Chowo forest of 5-6 pairs in 25 ha[7]. Not gregarious.

Status Resident. Five of 8 birds ringed in Chowo were retrapped in subsequent seasons, up to 7 years after first capture[3].

Breeding   Oct   Nov
(n=7)   4   3   *Clutch*: no data.

Moult: starting in Dec[4].

Taxonomy *P. a. stictigula* (type locality Mwenembwe, Nyika Plateau, Malawi)[8]. Placed by some authors in the genus *Illadopsis*, but this distinctive bird may be more closely related to the Himalayan genus *Alcippe*, although for the moment we use the monotypic Afrotropical *Pseudoalcippe*[5]. It is retained here in the family "Timaliidae" for convenience, pending further research; it seems likely it is

a member of the Sylviidae *s.l.*, and it is even suggested it is a *Sylvia*[1,2].
References [1]Böhning-Gaese *et al.* (2003); [2]Cibois (2003); [3]Dowsett (1985a); [4]Dowsett & Dowsett-Lemaire (1984); [5]Dowsett & Dowsett-Lemaire (1993); [6]Dowsett & Prigogine (1974); [7]Dowsett-Lemaire (1983c); [8]Shelley (1903).

Spotted Thrush-Babbler *Ptyrticus turdinus*　　　　　　　　B393 **R(B)**

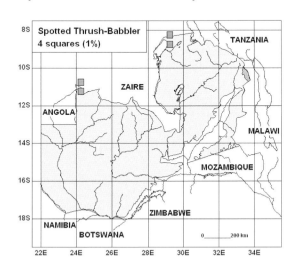

Distribution *Afrotropical, circum-Congo* (*Sudan to NW Zambia*). There are relict populations in both NW and N. Zambia, of a species which is here at the southern limit of its range. Uncommon, in forest at a few localities in N. Mwinilunga Dist.: Chilula, Salujinga, Nyakaseya and south to Isombu and the Jimbe stream[2,3]. This population was first discovered in 1957, but that on the Luao River in the north-east of Zambia not until 1977[1]. [The suggestion that this species is known from Minyanya Plain[4] is in error[3].] *Alt. c.* 930 m (Northern Province) and 1250-1280 m (Mwinilunga Dist.).

Ecology Feeds on the ground in thick undergrowth in moist evergreen, riparian forest, often narrow strips less than 100 m wide. In pairs or small (family) parties of about half a dozen.

Status Resident.

Conservation Not present in any protected area in Zambia, and all populations are in places where habitat destruction is especially worrying. The species has overall a wide range, but is nowhere common.

Breeding No records. The nest and eggs are unknown.

Moult: a bird was a third of the way through primary moult in Nov[3].

Taxonomy *P. t. upembae*.

References [1]Aspinwall (1978a); [2]Benson (1958a); [3]Dowsett (in press a); [4]Fry in Fry *et al.* (2000).

Arrow-marked Babbler *Turdoides jardineii*　　　　　　　　B394 **RB**

Distribution *Afrotropical* (*SE Gabon to South Africa*). Locally very common in rank growth throughout the country, from 330 up to about 2050 m on the Nyika[5].

Ecology Anywhere in thickets or dense cover and rank grass; more local in woodland and sometimes in dry riparian forest. Occurs in gardens where there is sufficient cover in which to retreat. A cooperative breeder, in noisy groups.

Status Resident.

Breeding	Jul	Aug	Sep	Oct	Nov	Dec	Jan	Feb	Mar	Apr	May	Jun
(n=125)	1	1	26	22	16	5	6	18	18	7	4	1

Clutch: C/1 (5); C/2 (23); C/3 (41); C/4 (3); C/5 (2); C/6 (1); C/7 (1).

It is possible the C/6 from Chipata Dist.[3] contained a cuckoo's egg[4]. This species and *T. leucopygia* are

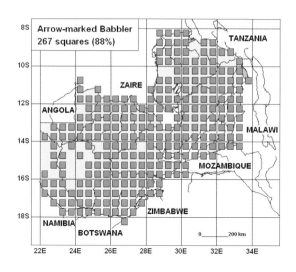

often hosts to *Clamator levaillantii*.
Moult: adults were moulting Nov[6].
Taxonomy *T. j. jardineii* in the south and west, *tamalakanei* the south-west[2], *kirkii* parts of the north and east, *tanganjicae* parts of the north and north-west[1]. The best-marked race is *tanganjicae* (with strongly contrasting black crown and ear coverts), the others being generally greyer. But clearly with four subspecies claimed in a species of continuous distribution variation is clinal, and many individuals difficult to allocate.
References [1]Benson *et al.* (1971a); [2]Benson & Irwin (1967b); [3]Benson & Pitman (1963); [4]Dowsett (in press a); [5]Dowsett-Lemaire (2006a); [6]Traylor (1965b).

[Black-lored Babbler *Turdoides melanops*

Kalahari-Highveld near-endemic (*S. Angola to South Africa*). Mapped as occurring in the Caprivi Strip (1724C), adjacent to SW Zambia[2], but the species is absent from NE Botswana and this report is probably wrong[1]. **References** [1]Dowsett *et al.* (in prep.); [2]Simmons & Herremans in Harrison *et al.* (1997).]

White-rumped Babbler *Turdoides leucopygia*   B395 **RB**

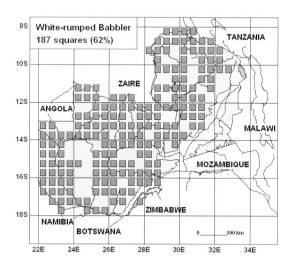

Distribution *Afrotropical* (*Ethiopia to Zimbabwe*). Throughout Zambia west of the Luangwa Rift, but eastwards only to Isoka town[1]; fairly common overall. Generally absent from the Middle Zambezi Valley, the only definite records being from Nyamuomba and Nchete Is[3]. *Alt. c.* 420 m (Nyamuomba) to 1650 m (Mbala area).
Ecology Typically on the edge of dambos and floodplains where there are ant-hill thickets (i.e. thicket-clump savanna). Usually in more open situations than *T. jardineii*, but they do occasionally occur within close proximity of each other. A cooperative breeder.
Status Resident.

Breeding	Jul	Sep	Oct	Nov	Dec
(n=33)	1	1	6	3	4
	Jan	Feb	Mar	Apr	May
	6	6	3	1	2

Clutch: C/2 (6); C/3 (12).
A host to *Clamator levaillantii*.
Moult: adults were in body moult mid-Oct; a juvenile started early Mar[3].
Taxonomy *T. l. hartlaubii*[2]. Treated as a separate species by some authors, but current evidence suggests they are conspecific[4].

References [1]Aspinwall (1973a); [2]Benson *et al.* (1970); [3]Dowsett (in press a); [4]Dowsett & Dowsett-Lemaire (1993).

Paridae

Southern Black Tit *Parus niger*   B387 **RB**

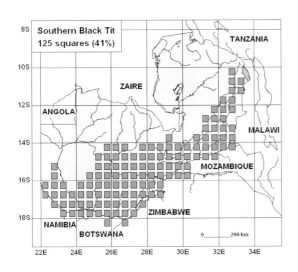

8S Southern Black Tit
125 squares (41%)

Distribution *Afrotropical (NE Zambia to South Africa, mainly Zambezian).* Confined to the drier woodlands of the south and east of the country (with annual mean rainfall not more than 900 or 1000 mm), where quite common. In the Luangwa Valley it occurs northwards at least to the Chiwale road (perhaps to Chifwembe but identity not certain), and ranges to the Malawi border in the Vwaza Marsh area[2]. It does not completely ascend the Muchinga escarpment, but above the Luano Valley does reach the Old Mkushi mine. Throughout the Eastern Province (though absent from higher areas along the Malawi border). Further west it is not north of 14°S, and indeed in the extreme south-west it is no further north than Sihole[2] and Nangweshi on the Zambezi[1] and Shangombo on the Mashi River[2] (a record from Liuwa[5] being in need of confirmation). *Alt.* 330-1300 m.

Ecology Essentially in mopane or *Acacia*-dominated woodland, regular in *Terminalia* or open *Baikiaea* forest, but never in the richer miombo. These are often rather open woodlands with some undergrowth. Also at edges of thickets and dry riparian forest. It feeds at all levels, but especially in the mid-stratum and canopy of small trees, where it gleans insects. It is the only tit in this habitat, and occupies as wide a niche as the two miombo species (*P. griseiventris* and *P. rufiventris*) together[6]. Often associated with other species in mixed bird parties (including, rarely, *P. leucomelas*)[2].

Status Resident.

Breeding   Sep   Oct   Nov   Feb
(n=38)   19   15   3   1

The Feb record is exceptional, and was probably a replacement clutch, as the brooding female was in primary moult[2].

Clutch: C/1 (1); C/2 (1); C/3 (6); C/4 (11); C/5 (3). *Moult*: from Dec[2].

Taxonomy[3,4] *P. n. xanthostomus.*

References [1]Benson (1956f); [2]Dowsett (in press a); [3]Irwin (1981a); [4]Irwin & Benson (1967a); [5]Osborne (1978); [6]Ulfstrand & Alerstam (1977).

White-winged Black Tit *Parus leucomelas* B388 **RB**

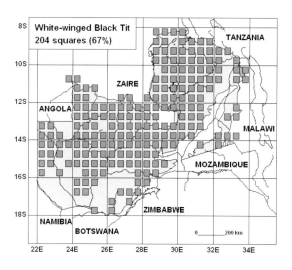

White-winged Black Tit
204 squares (67%)

ZAIRE

ANGOLA

TANZANIA

MALAWI

MOZAMBIQUE

ZIMBABWE

NAMIBIA
BOTSWANA

0 200 km

Distribution *Afrotropical (Mauritania to Malawi and Zambia, where it reaches the southern limit of its distribution).* It occurs throughout the plateau in the higher-rainfall parts of the north, southwards through most of the Eastern Province plateau (to Petauke and Minga), though rather sparse there[4]. It avoids the low-lying Luangwa and Middle Zambezi Valleys, though present in the neighbouring escarpments. It continues south along the Zambezi escarpment (and in adjacent parts of the Southern Province plateau) to Combrinck's farm near Senkobo[2], but west of the Zambezi appears to be allopatric with *P. niger*, thus present in Senanga Dist., but not south of the South Lueti River[3]. *Alt.* from 920 m to the highest limit of the Zambian Nyika (2200 m).

Ecology Typically an ecotone species, in light woodland and bushes on the edge of dambos and plains; also in riparian growth and (Nyika) bracken-briar with scattered trees. Rarely, therefore, in contact with the two miombo tits (*P. griseiventris* and *P. rufiventris*), although occasionally alongside them in light woodland (such as "chipya"). Likewise, not in the *Acacia* or mopane favoured by the superficially similar *P. niger*. Rarely in bird parties.

Status Resident, although the odd bird does wander locally to areas where it does not breed.

Breeding   Sep   Oct   Nov   Dec
(n=18)   10   3   4   1   *Clutch*: C/2 (2); C/3 (3); C/4 (1).
Moult: from Nov[3].

Taxonomy[1] *P. l. insignis.*

References [1]Benson (1956f); [2]Dowsett (in press a); [3]Traylor (1965b); [4]Winterbottom (1936).

[Ashy Tit *Parus cinerascens*
Afrotropical (W. Angola to South Africa). Mapped as occurring in the Caprivi Strip (1724A), adjacent to SW Zambia[2], but this may be wrong, as unknown at Kasane, Botswana[1]. In NW Zimbabwe present on Nampini Ranch[3] and in adjacent Botswana[2]. **References** [1]Dowsett *et al.* (in prep.); [2]Harrison in Harrison *et al.* (1997); [3]Irwin (1981a).]

Miombo Grey Tit *Parus griseiventris* B386 **RB**

Distribution *Zambezian endemic (N. Tanzania to Zambia-Malawi).* Fairly common throughout the plateau miombo woodlands; in the south-west, west of the Zambezi, only south to the South Lueti River[6] and Suu[2], and exceptionally Cholola[1]. It is absent from the low-lying Zambezi and Luangwa Valleys, in the former occurring only in woodland upstream of Victoria Falls. It is also absent from *Acacia*-dominated areas, such as most of the area between Lakes Mweru and Tanganyika and the Kafue Flats, and the Kalahari sand woodland in the extreme south-west of Western Province. *Alt.* 900-2000 m

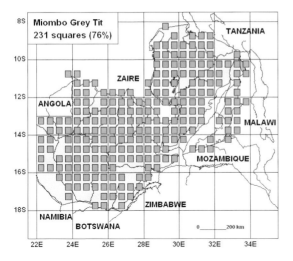

(in the Mafingas and Nyika)[3,4].

Ecology Miombo woodland, feeding by searching for arthropods on the bark and leaves at all levels. It is also in *Baikiaea* forest and the canopy of *Cryptosepalum* forest (where common). Feeds more on larger branches than the (larger) sympatric *P. rufiventris*, and thus the two coexist widely[7]. A frequent member of mixed species flocks (in small parties).

Status Resident.

Breeding   Aug   Sep   Oct
(n=20)   3   16   1
Clutch: C/3 (2); C/4 (4); C/5 (5).
Moult: starts Nov[6].

Taxonomy No races recognized (*P. g. parvirostris* of Zimbabwe being no better than poorly differentiated[5]). *P. g. lundarum* is a synonym (type locality Kahutu[8]; *OUM*).

References [1]Benson (1960d); [2]Dowsett (in press a); [3]Dowsett & Stjernstedt (1973); [4]Dowsett-Lemaire (2006a); [5]Irwin (1981a); [6]Traylor (1965b); [7]Ulfstrand & Alerstam (1977); [8]White (1945-46: 100).

Rufous-bellied Tit *Parus rufiventris*   B389 **RB**

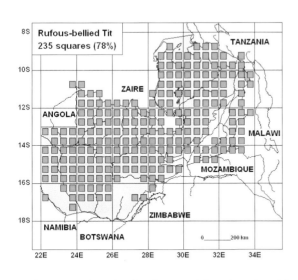

Distribution *Zambezian near-endemic* (*Congo-Brazzaville to Zimbabwe*). Fairly common throughout the plateau woodlands, even occurring at low altitude in the escarpment woodlands of the lower Luangwa Valley[3]. Ranges down the Zambezi escarpment to the Pemba area[3] (but otherwise absent from the Southern Province plateau)[1,6]. Then south and west of the Zambezi to Cholola[1]. *Alt.* 950-2000 m (Mafingas and Nyika)[4,5].

Ecology Commonest in miombo woodland and other broad-leaved woodland on the plateau (*Burkea*, "chipya"); also in *Baikiaea* forest and *Cryptosepalum* (common in the latter). Feeds in the canopy, gleaning on leaves and twigs, and thus can coexist with the sympatric (and smaller) *P. griseiventris*[8]. Wanders at times even into riparian forest and the edge of conifer plantations[3]. A frequent member of bird parties.

Status Resident.

Breeding   Sep   Oct   Nov
(n=22)   17   3   2   *Clutch*: C/3 (1); C/4 (3); C/5 (1).
Moult: starts Nov[7].

Taxonomy *P. r. rufiventris* is the form in the west, replaced by *P. r. masukuensis* over most of the country (paler grey back, paler chestnut abdomen), but with perhaps a slight approach to the even paler *P. r. pallidiventris* (with eye brown, rather than yellowish) in parts of the east[1,2]. The distribution of these forms is continuous, and there is no reason to suppose that two species are concerned (*P. pallidiventris* being claimed a good species by some, on the basis of different iris colour).

References [1]Benson & Irwin (1967b); [2]Benson *et al.* (1971a); [3]Dowsett (in press a); [4]Dowsett & Stjernstedt (1973); [5]Dowsett-Lemaire (2006a); [6]Pitman (1934); [7]Traylor (1965b); [8]Ulfstrand & Alerstam (1977).

Remizidae

Grey Penduline Tit *Anthoscopus caroli*   B390 **RB**

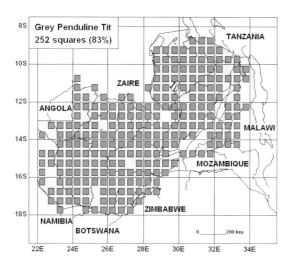

Distribution *Afrotropical (SE Gabon and Uganda to South Africa).* Small numbers throughout the country, including much of the Middle Zambezi Valley[3], except generally absent from the low-lying Luangwa Valley, and from the area between Lakes Mweru and Tanganyika. *Alt.* 370-1800 m, but scarce below 500 m.

Ecology Mainly in miombo woodland and *Baikiaea*, and dry escarpment associations (*Terminalia*). Wholly or almost absent from mopane and *Acacia*. In family parties of up to 6, feeding in foliage in the canopy or mid-stratum. Often in mixed bird parties.

Status Resident.

Breeding

	Aug	Sep	Oct	Nov
(n=46)	1	33	8	4

Clutch: C/1 (2); C/2 (6); C/3 (6); C/4 (16); C/5 (5); C/6 (1).

Moult: mostly Jan-May[1].

Taxonomy[5] No fewer than five forms are recognized tentatively, although this may be questioned in view of the continuous distribution: *A. c. caroli* in the south and west, *winterbottomi* (type locality Mwinilunga; *type specimen lost*; named for J.M. Winterbottom)[7] in the north-west and parts of the north, *rhodesiae* (type locality Sunzu Mtn; *NHM*)[6] in the north-east, *robertsi* in the east, and *rankinei* in the Middle Zambezi Valley. In high-rainfall areas birds have very green backs, those from drier areas being much greyer. Variation is clinal. Sometimes placed in the genus *Remiz*[4].

References [1]Austin (1978); [2]Clancey (1968c); [3]Dowsett (in press a); [4]Dowsett & Dowsett-Lemaire (1993); [5]Irwin & Benson (1967a); [6]Sclater (1932: 143); [7]White (1945-46: 101).

[**Cape Penduline Tit** *Anthoscopus minutus*

Afrotropical (S. Angola to South Africa). Mapped as occurring in the Caprivi Strip (1724D, 1725C), adjacent to SW Zambia[2], but this is based on a misidentification of *A. caroli* (which is fairly common in N. Botswana). *A. minutus* is unrecorded from the Kasane area and is improbable so far north[1].

References [1]Dowsett *et al.* (in prep.); [2]Barnes & Herremans in Harrison *et al.* (1997).]

Certhiidae (ex-Salpornithidae)

Spotted Creeper *Salpornis spilonotus*   B391 **RB**

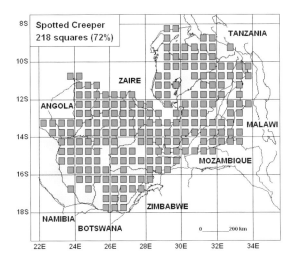

Distribution *Afrotropical (Senegal to Zimbabwe) and Oriental (India).* Small numbers throughout the plateaux of N. and E. Zambia, more sparsely through the Southern Province plateau to Kalomo Dist., south to Chijalile (Malabo) Hills[1]. In the west it reaches the Zambezi at Sioma Falls, but west of the Zambezi only in the Nyatanda area[1] and near Zambezi town (Balovale)[3]. Scarce in the Middle Zambezi Valley; a few records in the Luangwa Valley may indicate a downward movement. *Alt.* 370-1900 m (Nyika).

Ecology Mainly in miombo woodland. Occasionally in other habitats, including edges of riparian or dry forest (e.g. *Cryptosepalum*, where scarce). Wanderers in the Luangwa Valley and elsewhere have been seen in mopane. Feeds by probing the bark (a niche occupied also by small woodpeckers, some tits and weavers). Associates with mixed bird parties.

Status Resident, with local wandering.

Breeding   Aug   Sep   Oct   Nov
(n=40)   1   32   6   1   *Clutch*: C/2 (10); C/3 (13).

Moult: one moulting Dec[2] and another finishing in Jan[3].

Taxonomy *S. s. salvadori.*

References [1]Dowsett (in press a); [2]Lynes & Sclater (1933-34); [3]White (1945-46).

Nectariniidae

Red-and-blue Sunbird *Anthreptes anchietae*   B588 **RB**

Distribution *Zambezian endemic (Angola and Tanzania to Zambia-Malawi).* Throughout the plateau miombo woodlands of the north-east (where locally common), including Eastern Province, where it occurs south to Katete and Misale. In central Zambia, down the Muchinga escarpment to near Chingombe, exceptionally to near Keembe in Kabwe Rural Dist. Westwards to N. Mwinilunga Dist.[4], and south to near Kaoma[1,5], but sparse and very localized west of about 28°E. Has occurred on the Mutinondo River below the escarpment (in Aug)[4], perhaps a seasonal wanderer to the Luangwa Valley foothills. *Alt.* 900-2050 m (Nyika), although has wandered as low as *c.* 650 m.

Ecology Miombo woodland, often short types on thin or rocky soil[3], and more open areas such as the dambo-miombo ecotone, with *Protea* and other flowering plants. Also at *Canthium, Syzygium* and other flowers on the edge of riparian forest.

Status Resident, although its occurrence at lower levels may be the result of some seasonal wanderings.

Breeding   Apr   May   Sep   Oct
(n=17)   1   1   14   1   *Clutch*: C/1 (1); C/2 (5) & N/2 (6).

Moult: this species appears not to have an eclipse plumage.
Taxonomy[2] No races recognized.
References [1]Benson & Irwin (1967b); [2]Chapin (1954); [3]Dowsett (1977c); [4]Dowsett (in press a); [5]Winterbottom (1942a).

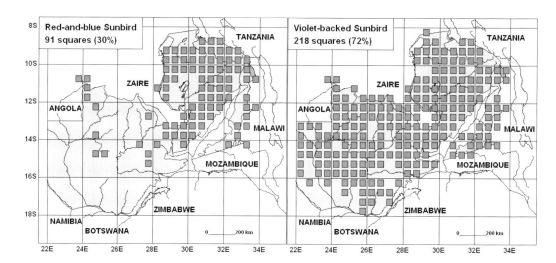

(Western) Violet-backed Sunbird *Anthreptes longuemarei*   B589 **RB**

Distribution *Afrotropical (Senegal to Zimbabwe)*. Throughout the plateau miombo woodlands and locally not uncommon, south in Southern Province to Livingstone, and in the west to Natukoma, Senanga-Shangombo. Absent from the Luangwa and Middle Zambezi Valleys, except at the foot of the Muchinga escarpment in the former[2]. *Alt*. mainly 900-1800 m, down to 680 m or lower at Julius[1] and elsewhere.
Ecology Miombo woodland (feeding on insects or at flowers in the canopy, or lower down in *Protea*) and riparian forest (on the edge). Locally in the canopy of *Cryptosepalum* forest (scarce).
Status Resident, with some records at lower levels being perhaps of wanderers.

Breeding	Feb	Mar	Apr	Jun	Jul	Aug	Sep	Oct	Dec
(n=29)	1	1	1	1	1	1	18	4	1

Clutch: C/1 (1); C/2 (9) & N/2 (4); N/3 (1).
Moult: males do not have a female-like eclipse plumage. *Moult*: well-advanced in Nov[2,3].
Taxonomy *A. l. angolensis*.
References [1]Dowsett (1978c); [2]Dowsett (in press a); [3]Traylor (1965b).

[Yellow-chinned Sunbird *Anthreptes rectirostris*
Guineo-Congolian near-endemic (Sierra Leone to W. Kenya). Known from Kasaji in Zaire (one specimen, as *A. tephrolaemus*)[1]. **References** [1]Schouteden (1971).]

Collared Sunbird *Anthreptes collaris*   B590 **RB**

Distribution *Afrotropical (Senegal to South Africa)*. Common through most of Zambia, but so far

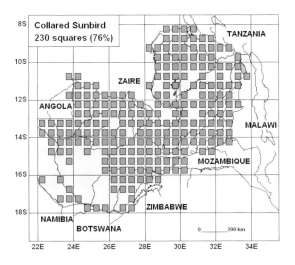

unrecorded from much of the dry *Baikiaea* forest west and south-west of Ngoma. West of the Zambezi there is a gap between the Kalabo area, and Shangombo and Senanga to the south[1]. Nevertheless it might in time be found anywhere along the riparian corridors of the Zambezi and Mashi Rivers. *Alt.* 330-2000 m, rarely wandering to 2150 m (Nyika).

Ecology Often in the canopy and at edges of riparian and other moist evergreen forest, including montane forest, less often inside in the mid-stratum. Also common in dry ever-green forest such as *Cryptosepalum* and *Marquesia*, transition woodland at Ndola, and occasionally in moist miombo. Mainly insect-ivorous, but also takes nectar and fruit.

Status Resident (except for some wandering to flowering plants or with miombo bird parties).

Breeding   Aug   Sep   Oct   Nov   Dec   Jan   Mar   Apr
(n=19)   3   7   1   1   1   3   2   1   *Clutch*: C/2 (4).

Moult: males appear not to have a female-like eclipse plumage. An adult was half-way through moult mid-Feb[1].

Taxonomy[2,3] *A. c. garguensis* (syn. *A. c. phillipsi*, type locality Lofu River; *NHM*; named for J.G. Phillips, a friend of White)[4], replaced in the south by *A. c. chobiensis* (more sulphur yellow below, less olive, in both sexes) and in the east by *A. c. zambesianus* (paler below, more olive on flanks). Sometimes placed in the genus *Hedydipna*.

References [1]Dowsett (in press a); [2]Irwin (1981a); [3]Irwin & Benson (1967b); [4]White (1950: 41).

Bates's Sunbird *Nectarinia batesi*   B591 **RB**

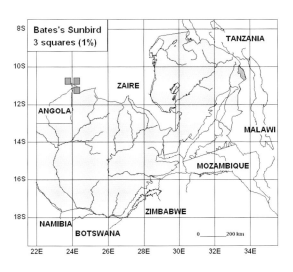

Distribution *Guineo-Congolian near-endemic (Liberia to NW Zambia)*. Only in North-Western Province, at a few forest localities[3]: Kadata River[3], Salujinga, Zambezi Rapids[4], Hillwood, Isombu (formerly)[2], south to the Sakeji Stream and Source of the Zambezi[5] (the most southerly record of the species). Present in small numbers, but easily overlooked or confused with other sunbirds. [A record from Mwombezhi[1] was a misidentification of *N. bouvieri*[2].] *Alt.* 1200-1400 m.

Ecology Canopy of largely undisturbed ever-green riparian forest. (Unrecorded from drier *Marquesia* forest). Stomach contents have included flower anthers and a small seed.

Status Resident.

Conservation With the rapid destruction of much forest habitat in Mwinilunga Dist. this species is vulnerable in Zambia, and the forest at Isombu has been destroyed in recent years; however it has a wide range outside Zambia.

Breeding   Mar   Aug

(n=2)   1   1   Also dependent juveniles Oct. *Clutch*: no data.

Moult: one bird started Jul[3].

Taxonomy No races[6]. Sometimes placed in the genus *Cinnyris*.

References [1]Benson & Irwin (1965b); [2]Benson & Irwin (1966b); [3]Dowsett (in press a); [4]Oatley (1969); [5]Williams (1958); [6]Williams (1959).

Olive Sunbird *Nectarinia olivacea*   B592 **RB**

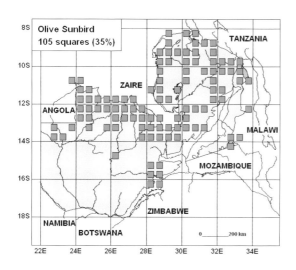

Distribution *Afrotropical* (*SW Senegal to South Africa*). The main population of this forest species is in the northern half of the country (where usually very common), in the east south to Nyika, down the Muchinga escarpment to Masase[6], and in the centre to 14°S. Thence it ranges west to Lukolwe and the South Kashiji River[9], and down the Kafue River to Lubungu. There are isolated populations further south in the Lusaka Dist., from east of Lusaka and Marble Hill[1], to Changa and Ibwe Munyama[6] – this last locality on the Zambezi escarpment, where there is suitable riparian vegetation, and not on the valley floor. On the Eastern Province plateau, it is in the Lundazi and Chipata areas, west exceptionally to the Katete River[6]. *Alt.* 950 m (rarely lower) to 2150 m (on the Mafingas)[7] and breeding irregularly at 2050 m on the Nyika (wandering to 2150 m)[8].

Ecology Moist forest or thicket, especially evergreen, and including *Cryptosepalum* (very common in places), feeding at all levels (mainly on invertebrates). The only forest sunbird occupying the lower sections of the understorey, but competes with several species in the upper strata. Rather aggressive and may defend patches of flowers (e.g. mistletoes) against conspecifics as well as congeners.

Status Resident.

Breeding   Oct   Nov   Mar

(n=5)   3   1   1   (A record for Jul[2] is unconfirmed). *Clutch*:   C/2 (2).

Moult: mostly Jun-Jul[6].

Taxonomy *N. o. ragazzii* (syn. *N. o. lowei*, type locality Kafulafuta River; *NHM*)[10], named for the ornithologist P.R. Lowe [1870-1948], (most females lack pectoral tufts); with *N. o. alfredi* (female with tufts, paler greenish below) in the east and at Marble Hill (syn. *N. o. intercalans*, type locality Chipata; *NMZB*)[4]. Some recent authors have split this species into two, on the basis of females having pectoral tufts (*N. olivacea*) or lacking them ("*N. obscura*")[5]. This feature is variable in some areas; for example, at Marble Hill a female had a trace of tufts, whereas another lacked them[1]. DNA studies do not provide evidence for their being two species[3]. Sometimes placed in the genus *Cyanomitra*.

References [1]Benson (1962a); [2]Benson *et al.* (1964); [3]Bowie *et al.* (2004); [4]Clancey (1978c: 324); [5]Clancey (1994); [6]Dowsett (in press a); [7]Dowsett & Stjernstedt (1973); [8]Dowsett-Lemaire (2006a); [9]Leonard (1998b); [10]Vincent (1934: 91).

Green-headed Sunbird *Nectarinia verticalis*   B594 **RB**

Distribution *Afrotropical* (*Senegal to Zambia-Malawi, where it reaches the southern limit of its range*). In evergreen forest, and allopatric with the next species, widespread in NE Zambia, south to the Nyika[4], and along the Muchinga escarpment to the Kafwa River[3] and Mkushi River (Chalata) area[1]. *Alt.* 1150-2100 m, breeding in some years as high as 2200 m (Nyika).

Ecology Feeds on the edge and in upper levels of dry and moist evergreen forest (including mushitu and riparian). On the Nyika recorded feeding at 15 species of flowers, but insect abundance is probably more important in determining breeding[5]. Often in the same forests as *N. olivacea*, but usually less common (except on the higher levels of the Nyika, where *N. olivacea* is almost absent).

Status Resident.

Breeding   Dec   Jan   Feb   Mar   Apr   May
(n=8)   1   1   1   2   1   2   (including 2 records from Malawi side of SW Nyika.) *Clutch*: N/1 (1).

Moult: this species does not have an eclipse plumage. Moult starts from Jun onwards[3].

Taxonomy[2,6] *N. v. viridisplendens*. Has been considered conspecific with the next species (*q. v.*). Sometimes placed in the genus *Cyanomitra*.

References [1]Benson (1959c); [2]Benson & Irwin (1964b); [3]Dowsett (in press a); [4]Dowsett-Lemaire (1989b); [5]Dowsett-Lemaire (1989c); [6]Louette (1987).

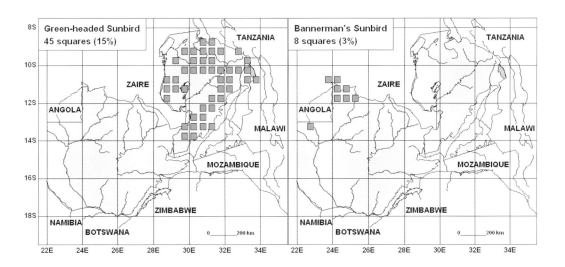

Bannerman's Sunbird *Nectarinia bannermani*   B593 **RB**

Distribution *Zambezian endemic* (*NE Angola to W. Zambia*). Small numbers present only in the forests of the extreme north-west. In Mwinilunga Dist., south to Mwinilunga[7] and Mundwiji Plain[2], and east to the West Lumwana River[3]. It reappears further south in Zambezi Dist. at Mbulo[4] (the most southerly record of the species). *Alt.* 1050-1480 m.

Ecology As for *N. verticalis*, feeding at the edges and in the upper strata of largely undisturbed moist evergreen forest (canopy and tangles in mid-stratum), usually in riparian situations. Insectivorous and nectarivorous, but diet not studied in detail. A nest was 4 m high inside forest. Always outnumbered by *N. olivacea*.

Status Resident.
Conservation The forests of NW Zambia are being destroyed, and this species has a very restricted distribution overall.
Breeding   Sep
(n=1)   1   And nest-building Oct. *Clutch*: C/2 (1).
Moult: centred on Jun-Aug. Does not have an eclipse plumage[3].
Taxonomy[1] No races recognized. Formerly considered a race of *N. verticalis*, and although the two were said to overlap in range in W. Angola[6] they seem to be allopatric[5]. They are certainly very closely related, but their voices differ. Sometimes placed in the genus *Cyanomitra*.
References [1]Benson & Irwin (1964b); [2]Benson & Irwin (1965b); [3]Dowsett (in press a); [4]Leonard (1998b); [5]Louette (1987); [6]Traylor (1962b); [7]White (1945-46).

[Blue-throated Brown Sunbird *Nectarinia cyanolaema*
Guineo-Congolian near-endemic (*Sierra Leone to W. Kenya*). A forest species, known as far south as Kasaji in Zaire[1] and thus to be sought in N. Mwinilunga. **References** [1]Schouteden (1971).]

Green-throated Sunbird *Nectarinia rubescens*   B595 **R(B)**

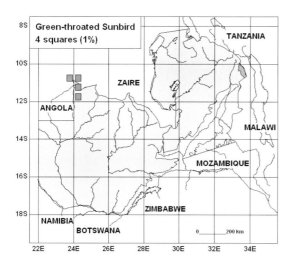

Distribution *Guineo-Congolian near-endemic* (*E. Nigeria to W. Kenya and NW Zambia*). N. Mwinilunga Dist. at several forest localities such as the Mbulungu/Zambezi River confluence[2], Hillwood and Isombu[1], south to Mwinilunga town[5] (the most southerly record of the species). *Alt*. 1170-1460 m.
Ecology Feeds at flowers and on insects on the edge of moist riparian evergreen forest.
Status Probably resident (records for Feb-Apr and Aug-Nov)[4].
Breeding No records. Males in breeding dress 4 Aug to late Oct[4].
Taxonomy[3] *N. r. rubescens*. Sometimes placed in the genus *Chalcomitra*.
References [1]Benson (1959c); [2]Benson & White (1957); [3]Chapin (1954); [4]Dowsett (in press a); [5]White (1953b).

Black (Amethyst) Sunbird *Nectarinia amethystina*   B596 **RB**

Distribution *Afrotropical* (*Ethiopia to South Africa*). Throughout at all elevations, usually common (especially in miombo), though scarce in the low-lying Luangwa Valley. *Alt*. 330 to 2000 m (Mafingas[3]) and to 2050 m on the Nyika (occasionally wandering to 2200 m[4]).
Ecology In the richer woodlands (miombo, *Baikiaea* forest, the canopy of *Cryptosepalum* forest), edge of riparian forest and gardens. Wherever there are flowers (also insectivorous).
Status Largely resident. Present in all months, but most numerous May-Aug, least noticeable Sep-Apr[2] (which is when they are breeding). Huge numbers at times suggest movements, which may only be

local, although one ringed bird moved 115 km between Feb and May[6].

Breeding   Aug   Sep   Oct   Nov   Dec   Jan   Feb   Mar   Apr
(n=123)   2   40   39   14   11   3   8   5   1

Clutch: C/1 (16); C/2 (72) & N/2 (5); C/3 (1).

Moult: males seem not to have a female-like eclipse plumage[2], although they do in South Africa[5].

Taxonomy[1] *N. a. kirkii*, replaced by *N. a. deminuta* in the north and north-west (male with upper tail coverts metallic purple, not sooty black). A broad zone of intergradation is reported, but to what extent this is influenced by any migration is not known. Sometimes placed in the genus *Chalcomitra*.

References [1]Benson *et al.* (1971a); [2]Dowsett (in press a); [3]Dowsett & Stjernstedt (1973); [4]Dowsett-Lemaire (2006a); [5]Skead (1967); [6]Tree (1962a).

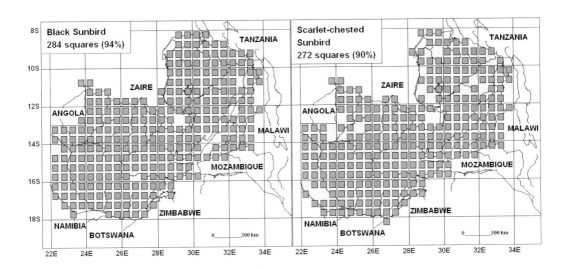

Scarlet-chested Sunbird *Nectarinia senegalensis*   B597 **RB**

Distribution *Afrotropical* (*Mauritania to South Africa*). Almost throughout and usually very common, though less so in the north of the country. *Alt.* 330-1770 m (Danger Hill).

Ecology On the edge of riparian forest, in open woodland, patches of thicket, neglected cultivation and commonly in gardens. Rarely in the canopy of more mature miombo, but common in dry forest and abundant in *Baikiaea* forest when the trees are in flower. The commonest sunbird in mopane woodland[4] and *Acacia* thickets[5].

Status Probably resident, but large concentrations outside the breeding season (e.g. Chembe on the Copperbelt in Jun) may be indicative of some movement[1].

Breeding   Jul   Aug   Sep   Oct   Nov   Dec   Jan   Feb   Mar   Apr   May
(n=138)   1   12   53   45   12   4   4   2   2   2   1

Clutch: C/1 (12); C/2 (54) & N/2 (7); C/3 (1).

Moult: noted Mar-Apr, Oct-Jan. Males seem not to have an eclipse plumage, but there is a parti-coloured first-year male plumage[1,3].

Taxonomy *N. s. gutturalis*, with *N. s. saturatior* in the south-west, west of Victoria Falls[2] (male darker red, with broader blue tips to chest feathers). Sometimes placed in the genus *Chalcomitra*.

References [1]Dowsett (in press a); [2]Irwin (1981a); [3]Traylor (1965b); [4]Winterbottom (1938b); [5]Winterbottom (1941b).

Yellow-bellied Sunbird *Nectarinia venusta*   B600 **RB**

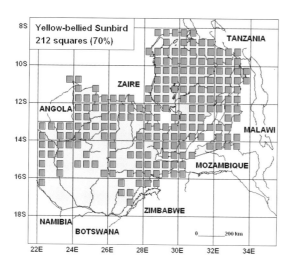

Distribution *Afrotropical (Senegal to South Africa)*. In rank growth throughout N. and E. Zambia, only locally in the low-lying Luangwa Valley. Very common in the northern half of the country and in the north-west. Common in the Middle Zambezi Valley to Makoche near Chirundu. In central Zambia, south locally to the Monze and Choma areas[2], and in the west south to Shangombo[1]. [A specimen labelled "Livingstone" may well have been from Kabwe instead[1].] *Alt.* 330-1900 m, to 2000 m on the Mafingas[3], and a few regularly on the high Nyika to 2200 m[4].

Ecology Rank growth along streams, the edge of riparian forest, any moist thickets and secondary habitats. Occasionally in gardens and clearings in *Cryptosepalum* forest.

Status Essentially resident, including in S. Zambia, where very scarce but breeding (as near Monze).

Breeding

	Feb	Mar	Apr	May	Jul	Aug	Sep	Oct
(n=23)	2	5	3	1	2	3	4	3

Clutch: C/1 (2); C/2 (6) & N/2 (3).

Moult: finishing in Nov. Males have an eclipse plumage in W. Zambia, though not in South Africa[2,6].

Taxonomy[5] Zambian birds appear closest to *N. v. falkensteini*. Sometimes placed in the genus *Cinnyris*.

References [1]Benson (1962a); [2]Dowsett (in press a); [3]Dowsett & Stjernstedt (1973); [4]Dowsett-Lemaire (2006a); [5]Irwin & Benson (1966a); [6]Skead (1967).

(Southern) White-bellied Sunbird *Nectarinia talatala*   B 598 **RB**

Distribution *Zambezian near-endemic (Angola and S. Tanzania to South Africa)*. Throughout and very common in the dry woodlands of S. Zambia, becoming irregular in the north of its range (e.g. on the Copperbelt). Ranges north in the east to North Luangwa N.P. and, west of the Muchinga escarpment, north to Mpika (whence there is a specimen[2]) and a few km further north. There is no definite record further north than this; sightings from the Shiwa Ngandu area (open squares) might be of the next species[3]. Elsewhere it reaches the south of Luapula Province, the Copperbelt and Ntambu (a specimen[1]). Sight records north to Ikelenge (N. Mwinilunga) are thought to be referable to this species[3]. *N. talatala* and *N. oustaleti* are allopatric. *Alt.* 330-1610 m (Kanona).

Ecology Chiefly mopane, *Baikiaea* forest mosaic or *Acacia* woodland, and any low bushy growth and thickets in dry areas. A frequent garden bird. Absent from the richer miombo of higher-rainfall areas, but may occur in thin, degraded types.

Status Resident. Possibly has some movements, reporting rates for adult males were statistically more frequent Mar-Sep, least during the breeding season (when perhaps more discreet)[3].

Breeding

	May	Jul	Aug	Sep	Oct	Nov
(n=89)	1	1	4	39	40	4

Clutch: C/1 (4); C/2 (70); C/3 (5).

Moult: males have been seen in breeding dress all year round, and there is no eclipse plumage. However, first-year males do have a distinctive, rather female-like dress[3,5].

Taxonomy *N. t. talatala* (the species now considered polytypic)[4]. Sometimes placed in the genus

Cinnyris.
References [1]Benson & Irwin (1965b); [2]Benson & White (1957); [3]Dowsett (in press a); [4]Irwin (1981a); [5]Traylor (1965b).

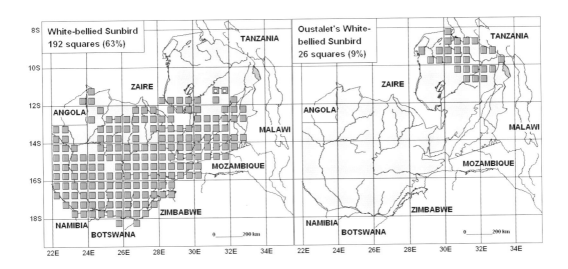

Oustalet's White-bellied Sunbird *Nectarinia oustaleti*   B599 **RB**

Distribution *Zambezian endemic (SW Angola to W. Tanzania).* Occupies only those parts of NE Zambia whence *N. talatala* absent, and rather scarce. In the east, south to the Malawi border west of Chitipa, to Ilondola[7], and further west to the Kawambwa area and Kashikishi on L. Mweru. Although these extreme records are visual they are considered correct (and there are specimens from west to Mporokoso and south to Kasama[7]). This species and the last are very difficult to separate in the field, and their respective ranges in N. Zambia remain to be clarified further. [The suggestion that *N. oustaleti* might have been seen even further south, within the range of *N. talatala*, at Mununga (1231C, Mpika Dist.)[1], remains unconfirmed.] *Alt.* 1000 to *c.* 1800 m (Uningi Pans).
Ecology Thin, often secondary, miombo, at times in rocky situations and regenerating thicket (thus structurally not unlike some of the habitats in which *N. talatala* occurs), often very low down. Has been seen feeding on *Leonotis* flowers in harvested maize fields[2]. Stomach contents included various invertebrates; takes nectar at various flowers (*Parinari curatellifolia*, *Monotes*, and even cultivated *Canna* in a garden)[7].
Status Resident.
Conservation Although a species of very limited distribution (also occurs marginally in SW Tanzania, as well as an isolated area of Angola), the secondary habitats it seems to favour are not under threat.
Breeding   Mar   May
(n=3)   1   2   *Clutch:* no data. The nest and eggs are unknown.
Moult: males have a mostly female-like eclipse plumage, recorded in Jul[8]. A juvenile male was moulting into adult dress mid-Jun[7].
Taxonomy *N. o. rhodesiae* (type locality Kasama; *NHM*)[3]. Despite its great similarity to *N. talatala*, and the fact that (on present evidence) they seem to replace each other, it is usually agreed they are distinct species[4]. [A claimed hybrid from Mazabuka[6], far from any population of *oustaleti*, has been refuted[5].] Sometimes placed in the genus *Cinnyris*.

References [1]Aspinwall (1993a); [2]Beel (1993); [3]Benson (1955a: 106); [4]Benson (1956f); [5]Benson *et al.* (1970); [6]Clancey (1967); [7]Dowsett (in press a); [8]Williams (1955b).

Greater Double-collared Sunbird *Nectarinia afra*   B601 **RB**

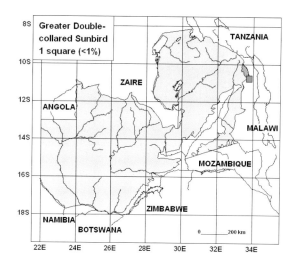

Distribution *Afromontane near-endemic* (*Uganda to South Africa*). Nyika Plateau only, where very common (but see *N. manoensis* concerning some Muchinga escarpment birds). There is another isolated population just north of the Zambia/Zaire border, in the Marungu highlands[6] (sometimes treated as a separate species, *N. (a.) prigoginei*). *Alt.* 1900-2200 m (up to 2500 m on the Malawi side).

Ecology Common at forest edges, in montane shrubland and grassland (where attracted to certain flowers); competes with *N. mediocris* at forest edges and other species elsewhere, and is chased by all except *N. venusta* over which it is dominant; size of breeding territories (in shrubland) varies from 0.1 to 0.5 ha[7]. A typical nectar thief, except for some short-tubed mistletoe flowers (*Englerina*) which it does pollinate; 29 species of food plant identified[7].

Status Resident, subject to local wandering depending on availability of flowers. One colour-ringed bird was resighted when at least 8 years old[5].

Breeding   Feb   Apr   May   Jun   Jul   Aug
(n=19)   5   7   1   3   1   2   (Including Malawi side of SW Nyika.)
Double- or triple-brooded[7]. *Clutch*: C/1 (3).
Moult: half-completed in birds examined Aug. A few males in eclipse plumage Jan-Mar[3].

Taxonomy *N. a. whytei* (type locality Nyika Plateau, Malawi)[1]. This population has been treated as a race of *N. "ludovicensis"*[2], but without clear justification, and this seems to be an unnatural arrangement. We remain unconvinced of the specific distinctness of various members of the *N. afra* group[4]. Sometimes placed in the genus *Cinnyris*.

References [1]Benson (1948b); [2]Clancey & Irwin (1978); [3]Dowsett (in press a); [4]Dowsett & Dowsett-Lemaire (1993); [5]Dowsett & Leonard (2001); [6]Dowsett & Prigogine (1974); [7]Dowsett-Lemaire (1989c).

Miombo Double-collared Sunbird *Nectarinia manoensis*   B602 **RB**

Distribution *Zambezian endemic (W. Tanzania to Zimbabwe)*. The plateaux woodlands of N., central and E. Zambia, and locally common. In the Luapula drainage at scattered localities between Mansa[2] and Kalabwe[5], and absent from the Luangwa and Middle Zambezi Valley floors (but in the former down the escarpment to Natwange on the Mwaleshi River)[5]. Down the Zambezi escarpment to the Mabwingombe Hills[1] and Chilola/Zongwe River confluence[10], and on the plateau south to Simwami[2]. Westwards almost to the Zambezi at Kambizana[3] and south-west to Kakenge and Sichili. *Alt.* 600-1800 m,

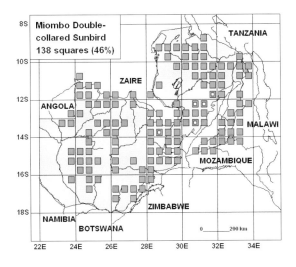

to 2050 m (Nyika)[7] and 2100 m (Mafingas)[8].

Ecology Generally in miombo woodland, including thinner types on rocky hills, but also in the canopy of *Cryptosepalum* forest (scarce) and *Marquesia* thickets, and visiting flowers in gardens. Often alongside other sunbirds such as *Anthreptes anchietae, A. longuemarei* and *Nectarinia shelleyi* by which it is often dominated.

Status Probably resident (although possibly some local seasonal movements).

Breeding   Aug   Sep   Oct   Nov
(n=35)   2   22   9   2

These data include 4 Sep records from the Muchinga range which may relate to an undescribed taxon[5]. *Clutch:* C/1 (11); C/2 (12); N/3 (3); including one C/1 and two C/2 which may relate to a new sunbird.

Moult: one bird started Jul[5]. Males are believed not to have an eclipse plumage[9].

Taxonomy *N. m. pintoi*, to as far east as Lundazi, but otherwise replaced in Eastern Province by *N. m. manoensis* (upper tail coverts blue, not grey). The two are reported to intergrade irregularly in the east[4]. Previously treated as conspecific with the southern African *N. chalybea*, but there are good reasons for considering them different species[6]. Sometimes placed in the genus *Cinnyris*. There may be an unrecognized taxon of this or of *N. afra* in the submontane area mainly along the Muchinga escarpment (Mutinondo to Lukanda Hills, Kapiri Mposhi; open squares)[5], but evidence has not yet been published.

References [1]Benson (1962a); [2]Benson & White (1957); [3]Britton (1970); [4]Clancey & Irwin (1978); [5]Dowsett (in press a); [6]Dowsett & Dowsett-Lemaire (1993); [7]Dowsett-Lemaire (2006a); [8]Leonard *et al.* (2001a); [9]Mackworth-Praed & Grant (1945); [10]Winterbottom (1956a).

Eastern Double-collared Sunbird *Nectarinia mediocris*   B603 **RB**

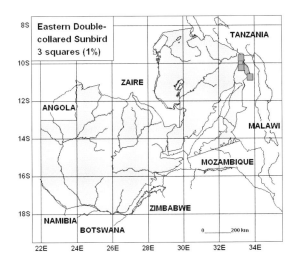

Distribution *Afromontane endemic (Kenya to S. Malawi).* Numerous in montane forest of the Mafinga Mts[6], Makutu[2] and Nyika Plateau[7]. The species reappears as an isolated population in the Marungu highlands, SE Zaire[5]. *Alt.* 1850-2200 m (to 2450 m on the Malawi side of Nyika).

Ecology Montane (rain) forest, where very common (territories of 0.2-0.5 ha on the Nyika), occupying all levels of the forest, but more often in canopy and at edges. Competes with *N. afra* only at forest edges (Nyika), but is dominant over its congener[7,8]. Like *N. afra*, mainly a nectar thief (25 food plants identified), but does pollinate *Englerina* flowers[8].

Status Resident. The oldest ringed bird was at least 6 years old[3].

Breeding   Apr   May   Jun   Jul   Aug   Sep   Oct
(n=32)   1   1   7   7   10   5   1   These records are all from the SW
Nyika (including Malawi side). Insects seem more important than flowers in determining breeding[8].
Clutch: N/1 (1). *Moult*: Aug-Jan, estimated to last 96 days[4]. Males do not have an eclipse dress.
Taxonomy[6,9] *N. m. fuelleborni*, with Nyika birds intermediate with *N. m. bensoni*[1]. Sometimes placed
in the genus *Cinnyris*.
References [1]Benson & Benson (1977); [2]Dowsett (1971h); [3]Dowsett (1985a); [4]Dowsett & Dowsett-
Lemaire (1984); [5]Dowsett & Prigogine (1974); [6]Dowsett & Stjernstedt (1973); [7]Dowsett-Lemaire
(1989b); [8]Dowsett-Lemaire (1989c); [9]Williams (1953).

Shelley's Sunbird *Nectarinia shelleyi*   B604 **RB**

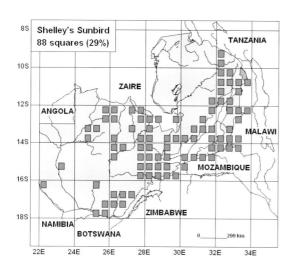

Distribution *Zambezian endemic (Tanzania to central Mozambique and Zambia, where it reaches its southern limit of distribution).* An unusual distribution, though most often associated with escarpment woodland, centred on the central and eastern plateaux. Very common on parts of the Eastern Province plateau, scarcer elsewhere, and decidedly uncommon on the Copperbelt. From the Kapwila River[3] in the north, westwards along the Muchinga escarpment to the Copperbelt and to the Mufumbwe River, and in Southern Province to Katombora Rapids[8]. There are acceptable sight records from two isolated localities in the west, near Kande[4] and Lilondo[5]. Otherwise absent from the west and south-west, as well as much of Northern Province and all of Luapula. At lower levels only a rare, seasonal wanderer to the Luangwa and Middle Zambezi Valleys (e.g. to Mushika, less than 30 km from escarpment woodland)[2]. [A record of this species being common at Uningi Pans in May 1976[10] (a well-known locality whence there are no other observations) requires confirmation[8].] *Alt.* 500-1600 m (Mpika Dist.), exceptionally to 370 m in the Middle Zambezi.
Ecology Usually in dry miombo woodland (even in thin woodland in rocky areas), and also *Baikiaea* forest. However, it is often at flowers on the edge of riparian, especially outside the breeding season, when it also turns up in gardens and in *Acacia*, and even mixed mopane-miombo.
Status Largely resident, but on the Copperbelt and at lower levels there are indications of seasonal movements, birds being noted there from Dec-Apr as a rule.
Breeding   Aug   Sep   Oct
(n=32)   1   20   11   Occasionally double-brooded: one nest at Kachalola from which
N/2 flew soon after 9 Oct contained C/2 by 23 Oct (the female having pulled out the old nest lining)[6].
Clutch: C/1 (3); C/2 (25).
Moult: males have a parti-coloured eclipse plumage[9], noted late Apr to Jun[8].
Taxonomy *N. s. shelleyi* (type locality Mushika; *NHM*)[1,7], named for the ornithologist G.E. Shelley
[1840-1910]. Sometimes placed in the genus *Cinnyris*.
References [1]Alexander (1899: 54); [2]Aspinwall (1972a); [3]Aspinwall (1973a); [4]Aspinwall (1973f); [5]Beel
(1992a); [6]Brooke (1964); [7]Dowsett (1980b); [8]Dowsett (in press a); [9]Mackworth-Praed & Grant (1945);
[10]Taylor (1978c).

Marico Sunbird *Nectarinia mariquensis*   B605 **RB**

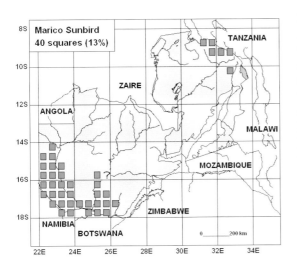

Distribution *Afrotropical (Ethiopia to South Africa)*. There are two populations in areas where dry bush predominates. In the north-east between Uningi Pans[7] and Mwenzo[1], with a sight record exceptionally further south in the Isoka square (1032B)[6]. In the south-west (where locally common), from the Liuwa Plain[8], down the Zambezi Valley to Katombora and rarely Livingstone[2], and on the Southern Province plateau to Litoma Plain[3] and Kalomo[5]. There is a possible sighting from Ngoma thicket ("?" on map)[3]. Occurs extralimitally on the Zimbabwe side of L. Kariba (1727C), but only seasonally[4]. [A specimen labelled "Fort Rosebery" (Mansa), while certainly this species, was probably mislabelled, notwithstanding the collector's suggestion that the species was regular there in miombo.] *Alt.* 950-1250 m in the south-west, 1450-1850 m in the north-east.

Ecology In the north of the country associated with *Acacia* mixed with thin miombo, on the edge of dambos and pans. In the south most abundant in *Baikiaea* formations with *Acacia* understorey; regular too in larger *Acacia* trees, and even at garden flowers.

Status Resident, but subject to seasonal movements on the periphery of its range.

Breeding   Sep   Oct   Feb
(n=3)   1   1   1   *Clutch*: no data.

Moult: post-nuptial moult begins late Oct. Juveniles have a complete post-juvenile moult into a distinctive female-like first-year dress[3,8].

Taxonomy *N. m. mariquensis* in the south-west, *N. m. suahelica* the north-east (male with belly sooty grey, rather than black). Sometimes placed in the genus *Cinnyris*.

References [1]Benson (1956f); [2]Dowsett (1977a); [3]Dowsett (in press a); [4]Irwin (1981a); [5]Irwin & Benson (1966a); [6]Leonard (2001d); [7]Taylor (1978c); [8]Traylor (1965b).

Orange-tufted Sunbird *Nectarinia bouvieri*   B606 **RB**

Distribution *Afrotropical (Nigeria to NW Zambia)*. Known only from a few localities in N. Mwinilunga, south to Zambezi Rapids and Hillwood[2], and reappearing to the south-east on the Mwombezhi River[1] (the southernmost locality for the species). *Alt.* 1190-1460 m.

Ecology The edge of riparian forest and woodland, wherever there are flowers.

Status Presumably resident, but very rarely reported in Zambia; this is perhaps because it is at the limit of its range, as elsewhere in central Africa it is a locally common resident.

Breeding   Mar
(n=1)   1   *Clutch*: no data.

The eggs have not been described.

Taxonomy[3] No races recognized. Sometimes placed in the genus *Cinnyris*.

References [1]Benson & Irwin (1966b); [2]Dowsett (in press a); [3]Irwin & Benson (1966a).

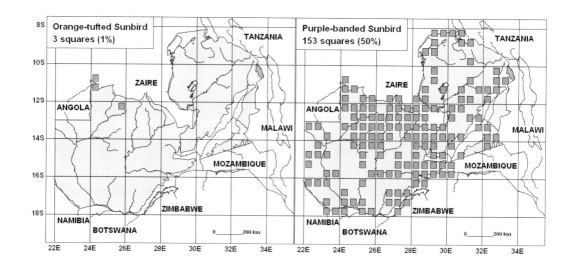

Purple-banded Sunbird *Nectarinia bifasciata* B607 **RB**

Distribution *Afrotropical (Ethiopia to South Africa)*. Patchily distributed throughout, but locally quite common in parts of N. and NW Zambia. Perhaps seasonal at lower levels and absent from the highlands of the north-east. *Alt.* 330-1600 m, but irregular below 500 m and above 1400 m.

Ecology On the edge of riparian and other evergreen forest (including *Cryptosepalum*, and transition woodland at Ndola), also in dense thickets and at times in gardens in the north. Less often wanders into drier *Terminalia* and similar woodland.

Status Resident, but there may be some local movements, possibly altitudinal[1]. Reports are significantly more frequent Apr-Nov than Dec-Mar. The fact that males in breeding dress are more conspicuous means that these results are subject to caution. A ringed bird was found dead after 5 years[2].

Breeding Aug Sep Oct Nov Jan
(n=29)   3   7   11   7   1   *Clutch*: C/1 (5); C/2 (7) & N/2 (3).

Moult: breeding dress noted Mar-Oct. Males have a female-like eclipse plumage, assumed from Dec, or earlier[1,4].

Taxonomy[3] *N. b. microrhyncha*. Sometimes placed in the genus *Cinnyris*.

References [1]Dowsett (in press a); [2]Dowsett & Leonard (2001); [3]Irwin & Benson (1967a); [4]Mackworth-Praed & Grant (1945).

Coppery Sunbird *Nectarinia cuprea* B608 **RB**

Distribution *Afrotropical (Mauritania to Zimbabwe)*. Widespread and locally common in wooded grassland and ecotone of dambos on the plateau. Wandering to the low-lying Luangwa Valley, e.g. North Luangwa N.P. and Mpomwa Hills. *Alt.* 550-1600 m, but breeding probably only above 750 m.

Ecology Typically at flowering plants on the edge of dambos, of riparian forest or at the woodland-floodplain ecotone, also in open *Cryptosepalum*-miombo mosaic (but avoiding closed *Brachystegia* associations).

Status Resident, with probably local movements. A 2-year survey showed frequency of males in breeding dress to be significantly greater Oct-Apr than May-Sep. There are fewest records when birds are in

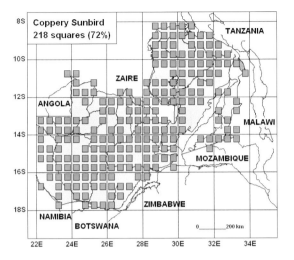

moult; it remains to be shown if there is any significant movement, although there are a few records from low levels, mainly late Apr to mid-Sep[2].

Breeding   Jan   Feb   Mar
(n=20)   6   8   6
Clutch: C/2 (3) & N/2 (4); C/3 (1).
Moult: breeding dress from end Sep to end Mar. Males have an eclipse plumage (Apr-Sep), followed by a complete moult, finishing Nov[2,3].

Taxonomy *N. c. chalcea*[1] (syn. *N. c. vaughan-jonesi*, type locality Kasempa; *OUM*; named for T.G.C. Vaughan-Jones)[4]. Sometimes placed in the genus *Cinnyris*.

References [1]Benson & Irwin (1967b); [2]Dowsett (in press a); [3]Traylor (1965b); [4]White (1944g: 137).

[Bocage's Sunbird *Nectarinia bocagii*

Zambezian endemic (a very limited area, central and E. Angola and W. Zaire). This species has been collected in cultivation in *Baikiaea* forest at Ninda in E. Angola[1,2], just 60 km west of the Zambian border, and should be sought in Kalabo Dist.
References [1]Benson & Irwin (1967b); [2]Dean (2000).]

Yellow-tufted Malachite Sunbird *Nectarinia famosa*   B609 **RB**

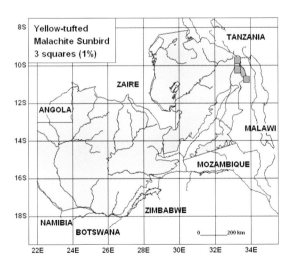

Distribution *Afromontane near-endemic (Ethiopia to South Africa).* Confined to the Mafinga Mts[1] and Nyika Plateau. It occurs too in the Marungu highlands in SE Zaire[3]. *Alt.* 1900-2200 m (up to 2500 m on the Malawi side of Nyika).

Ecology Montane grassland, often with scattered shrubs or trees (especially *Protea* spp.); in some rocky areas of SW Nyika excluded by the dominant *N. johnstoni*, when the latter is breeding[4]. May defend temporal feeding territories (e.g. *Aloe* on Chowo Rocks); 16 food plants identified on the Nyika, all probed frontally[4].

Status Resident, with much local wandering to visit favoured food plants (*Protea, Aloe, Leonotis*)[4].

Breeding   Jun   Aug
(n=2)   1   1   Also Jan-Feb on the Malawi side of Nyika. *Clutch*: C/2 (1).
Moult: recorded Aug. Males have a female-like eclipse plumage[2].
Taxonomy *N. f. cupreonitens.*

References [1]Benson (1959c); [2]Dowsett (in press a); [3]Dowsett & Prigogine (1974); [4]Dowsett-Lemaire (1989c).

Scarlet-tufted Malachite Sunbird *Nectarinia johnstoni*   B610 **R(B)**

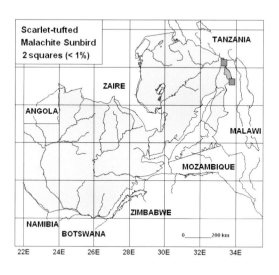

Distribution *Afromontane endemic* (*E. Zaire and Kenya to N. Malawi*). Confined to the Nyika Plateau (except for one record from the Mafingas, on the Malawi border)[4]. *Alt.* 2000-2200 m (up to 2450 m on the Malawi side of the Nyika).

Ecology In *Protea* wooded grassland (e.g. Manyenjere and near Zambian rest house) and in montane shrubland (*Protea-Erica*, using former as main food plants, and latter for nest sites) on rocky outcrops. Disperses locally to feed (on *Protea, Leonotis, Tecomaria*). Common on Chowo Rocks[2,3], with breeding territories of 0.5-1 ha.

Status Probably resident, with local dispersal (e.g. two males in the Mafingas, on the Malawi border Jul 1978)[4]. The possibility of a small population on the high Mafingas cannot be excluded.

Breeding No data from the Zambian Nyika, but lays in Dec-Jan on Malawi side of Chowo Rocks, during peak flowering of *Protea welwitschii*[2].

Taxonomy *N. j. nyikensis* (type locality Nyika Plateau, Malawi)[1] (syn. *N. j. salvadorii*)[5].

References [1]Delacour (1944); [2]Dowsett-Lemaire (1988c); [3]Dowsett-Lemaire (1989c); [4]Dowsett-Lemaire (2006b); [5]Shelley (1903).

Bronze Sunbird *Nectarinia kilimensis*   B611 **RB**

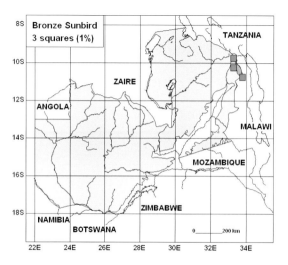

Distribution *Afromontane endemic* (*Ethiopia to E. Zimbabwe*). Limited to the highlands of the north-east (where common): Nyika, Mafingas[4] and Makutu Plateau[1]. [Present to the north of Mbala in the Marungu highlands and on the Ufipa Plateau[3].] *Alt.* 1800-2200 m (to 2350 m on the Malawi side of Nyika).

Ecology Montane grassland, shrubland and forest edges. Visits a variety of flowers but *Protea* only rarely (unlike sympatric *N. famosa* and *johnstoni*); on Nyika depends on abundant flowering of *Tecomaria* and especially *Leonotis* spp. for breeding. Breeding territories of 0.3 to 1 ha (on Malawi side)[5,6].

Status Resident, with local wandering.

Breeding   Dec   Feb   Mar   Jun   Jul
(n=10)   1   1   5   1   2   *Clutch*: N/1 (2).
(Including records from the Malawi side of SW Nyika.)
Moult: active primary moult in Aug. Males do not have an eclipse plumage[2].
Taxonomy[4,7] *N. k. arturi*, but with some approach (especially in the Mafingas) to *N. k. kilimensis* (metallic green, rather than coppery).
References [1]Dowsett (1971h); [2]Dowsett (in press a); [3]Dowsett & Prigogine (1974); [4]Dowsett & Stjernstedt (1973); [5]Dowsett-Lemaire (1988c); [6]Dowsett-Lemaire (1989c); [7]Irwin & Benson (1966b).

Zosteropidae

Yellow White-eye *Zosterops senegalensis*   B612 **RB**

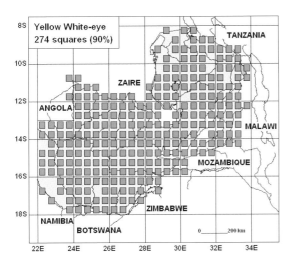

Distribution *Afrotropical* (*Mauritania to South Africa*). Throughout and usually common, though scarce in drier low-lying areas, as in parts of the Luangwa Valley and SW Zambia, and between Lakes Mweru and Tanganyika. *Alt.* 330-2200 m (up to 2450 m on the Malawi side of the Nyika)[7].

Ecology In rich miombo woodland, evergreen forest and thicket (including *Cryptosepalum,* where very common), any riparian vegetation or regrowth, feeding at all levels. Feeds on insects, nectar and some small fruits[7]. Visits flowers in dambos and gardens at times. Very common at higher altitudes (the most numerous forest bird on the SW Nyika, with 26 breeding adults ringed in 3 ha of forest patches)[7]. There may be helpers at the nest[3].

Status Resident. There is no evidence of any movements[4]. Occurs commonly in small groups (up to 50 when not breeding)[3]. The oldest ringed bird was retrapped when at least 8 years of age[2]. One young bird first bred at 12 months old[3].
Breeding   Aug   Sep   Oct   Nov   Dec   Jan   Feb   Apr
(n=171)   11   34   75   32   12   5   1   1
Clutch: C/1 (5); C/2 (40); C/3 (27) & N/3 (4).
Moult: on the Nyika, mid-Nov to mid-Mar, estimated individual duration 85 days[5]. In W. Zambia juveniles in post-juvenile moult Nov[8].
Taxonomy *Z. s. anderssoni*, birds from the Mafingas slightly darker on the mantle[6], and possibly replaced on the Nyika by the much more saturated *Z. s. stierlingi*[1].
References [1]Benson & Irwin (1967b); [2]Dowsett (1985a); [3]Dowsett (1985b); [4]Dowsett (in press a); [5]Dowsett & Dowsett-Lemaire (1984); [6]Dowsett & Stjernstedt (1973); [7]Dowsett-Lemaire (1989b); [8]Traylor (1965b).

Oriolidae

Eurasian Golden Oriole *Oriolus oriolus*

B380 **PW**

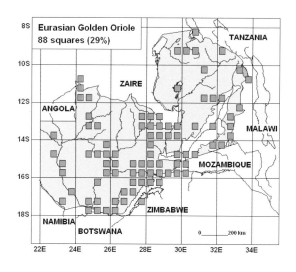

Eurasian Golden Oriole
88 squares (29%)

Distribution *Palaearctic (winters mainly Cameroon to South Africa)*. Sparsely in woodland throughout, but few records from low altitudes. *Alt.* 330 to 2150 m (Nyika).
Ecology Woodland, mainly miombo (rarely in low-lying mopane, and in *Acacia* probably only when on passage). Also in patches of forest and thicket. Has been seen to eat a lizard[4], and fond of fleshy fruit, especially *Ficus* spp.; also *Polyscias* in montane forest[2].
Status A Palaearctic migrant, present mainly on passage, with a small wintering population, mostly in the south. Earliest acceptable date is 20 Sep (there are few records for that month), with first arrivals usually from second week Oct (average first date over 28 years was 22 Oct), and widespread on passage to mid-Nov.
Thereafter few during rains, but a smaller passage northwards noticeable in Feb and Mar (most birds migrate outside Zambia, in a loop migration through eastern Africa). The average last date (in 16 years) was 24 Mar. Few records in Apr (last date, from the Luano Valley, 26 Apr). [Some dates outside these have been rejected, through possible confusion with *O. auratus*.] Usually in ones and twos, occasionally up to 10 together, especially at fruiting trees. Concentrations in the Luangwa Valley of *c.* 20 from late Feb to late Mar point to the more easterly route followed on northward passage[1].
Moult: birds examined late Nov and mid-Mar were not moulting[1], but in Malawi moult recorded mid-Nov and Jan-Mar[3].
Taxonomy *O. o. oriolus*.
References [1]Dowsett (in press b); [2]Dowsett-Lemaire (2006a); [3]Dowsett-Lemaire & Dowsett (2006); [4]Naylor (1975).

African Golden Oriole *Oriolus auratus*

B381 **AMB/R**

Distribution *Afrotropical (Mauritania to South Africa)*. Throughout, and usually quite common. *Alt.* 330-1800 m, even wandering up to 2100 m on the Nyika Plateau[2] (higher on the Malawi side) outside the breeding season.
Ecology Woodland, especially miombo; also various types of dry forest, including *Cryptosepalum* (scarce). Visits montane forest outside the breeding season. Less often in the drier, more open woodland types such as mopane and *Acacia*. As with the other *Oriolus* species feeds on small fruits (occasionally in small groups), as well as invertebrates, mostly in the canopy.
Status Present in all months in the south of the country, but in the north there are signs of post-breeding departures in Mar, with reappearance and increasing numbers Jul-Sep. It is possible that a similar exodus occurs from S. Zambia, but that it is hidden by arrivals of a second (non-breeding) population Jan-Mar[1].

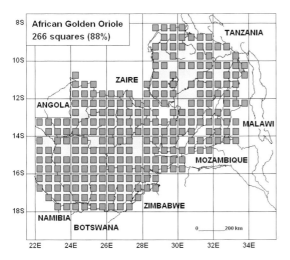

Breeding　　Sep　Oct　Nov
(n=220)　　　　96　114　10
Clutch: C/1 (13); C/2 (103); C/3 (68).
Some C/1 are complete. Occasionally para-sitized by *Cuculus clamosus*.
Moult: adults starting Nov[3].
Taxonomy *O. a. notatus*.
References [1]Dowsett & Leonard (in press a); [2]Dowsett-Lemaire (2006a); [3]Traylor (1965b).

Eastern Black-headed Oriole *Oriolus larvatus*　　　　　B382 **RB**

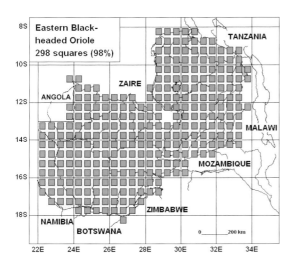

Distribution *Afrotropical* (*Ethiopia to South Africa*). Throughout and very common in woodland, at all elevations. *Alt.* 330-1800 or 1900 m, visiting montane forest in the off-season, to 2200 m (higher on the Malawi side of Nyika)[3].

Ecology More catholic than the similar-sized *O. auratus*, and occurs in any type of wood-land, *Cryptosepalum* forest (very common), and even regularly on the edge of or in neglect-ed exotic plantations (in particular eucalyptus). Defends territories in montane forest in the non-breeding season.

Status Present in all months, but numbers are higher Apr-Nov (when also present on the high Nyika)[3]. Numbers are much reduced Jan-Mar after breeding, and from many areas it appears to be absent at that time[2] (though may be more discreet when moulting).

Breeding　　Aug　Sep　Oct　Nov　Dec　Jan　Apr
(n=99)　　　　2　50　32　12　1　1　1
Clutch: C/1 (3); C/2 (75); C/3 (9).
Moult: juveniles were completing moult into first-year plumage late Nov-early Dec[5].
Taxonomy[1,4] *O. l. rolleti*.
References [1]Benson (1956f); [2]Dowsett (in press a); [3]Dowsett-Lemaire (2006a); [4]Irwin & Benson (1967b); [5]Traylor (1965b).

Laniidae

Sousa's Shrike *Lanius souzae*   B570 **RB**

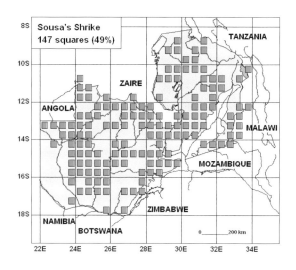

Distribution *Zambezian near-endemic* (*SE Gabon to Zambia-Malawi*). Patchily distributed throughout the plateau miombo woodlands, south to Petauke Dist. on the Eastern Province plateau, sparsely south to Choma Dist. (where very scarce), to Chijalile Hills on the Zambezi escarpment and north of Sinde Mission[6]. (It is not known to extend beyond into Zimbabwe). Common and widespread in the *Baikiaea* forest on Kalahari sand east of the Zambezi, south to Mushukula[4]. Recorded west of the Zambezi at Nyatanda[6], Kamekunga[1], the Liuwa Plain[7] and Cholola in the extreme south[3]. *Alt.* mostly between 1000 and 1800 m. Although normally absent from the Luangwa and Middle Zambezi Valleys, it occurs in sparse miombo in the former at Nabwalya (580 m)[6].

Ecology In light woodland, mainly miombo, more rarely *Burkea* and *Baikiaea*, with a fairly open canopy. Usually seen sitting quietly in the mid-stratum. Feeds like a typical *Lanius* by dropping down to the ground. Eats mostly large insects. It thus acts like some flycatchers (e.g. *Bradornis*), but is effectively separated from all those species by its larger size. Singly or in groups of up to four, presumably families.

Status Probably largely or entirely resident, but data not conclusive. One or two observers who have visited miombo regularly throughout the year have suggested there may be movements, with fewest present early in the year. But this may simply be a reflection of post-breeding discretion during moult. Observations of abnormal numbers in Zambia come from the Mkushi Dist., where they were said to be abundant in early Mar and common mid-Jul, and Lusaka, where "exceptionally abundant" in May[6].

Breeding[8]   Aug   Sep   Oct   Nov   Dec
(n=101)   1   48   28   20   4   *Clutch*: C/2 (30); C/3 (48).

Taxonomy[2] *L. s. souzae*, replaced by *L. s. burigi* (paler and greyer above, less chestnut) in Eastern Province – of which *L. s. tacitus* (type locality Rukuzye Dam; *NMZB*)[5] is perhaps a synonym.

References [1]Aspinwall (1979b); [2]Benson (1959c); [3]Benson *et al.* (1971a); [4]Bruce-Miller & Dowsett (1977); [5]Clancey (1970a: 341); [6]Dowsett (in press a); [7]Osborne (1978); [8]Took (1966).

Red-backed Shrike *Lanius collurio*   B566 **PW**

Distribution *Palaearctic* (*winters mostly Tanzania to South Africa*). Throughout and locally numerous, but scarce in more heavily-wooded parts of the north. *Alt.* 330-2200 m.

Ecology Secondary growth and wooded grassland, especially *Acacia*, thicket-clump savanna, even gardens, not usually in denser miombo or mopane woodland. Is known to impale prey (grasshoppers) on thorns while in its non-breeding territory[2].

Status A Palaearctic migrant, wintering in small numbers but very numerous on passage. The average

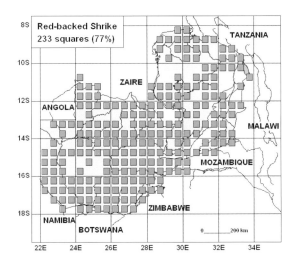

first date over 29 years was 24 Oct, the average last (in 26 years) 22 Apr[3]. First arrivals in the south are usually late Oct (although seen exceptionally as early as 25 Sep in Mwinilunga), with enormous influxes locally early to mid-Nov, especially in the western half of the country. At this time there are sometimes thousands of birds grounded in an area by rain. In favoured places (such as the Kafue Flats) may still be fairly numerous to mid-Dec, but generally numbers decline by the end of that month. Occurs at scattered localities throughout Zambia in Jan-Feb, but in much smaller numbers (except in some years not uncommon in Southern Province). Northward passage is smaller (max. 100 at Ndola 31 Mar), and very brief, Mar to third week Apr with just the odd bird to 15 May (exceptionally one on the Nyika 3 Jun)[1]. It is probable that, as with *Lanius minor*, most northward passage takes place in a loop migration further east, and it is indeed more common in Malawi then[5]. There are 7 ringing recoveries involving Zambia (dates in this country being 13 Nov to 8 Apr), most of Scandinavian or German origin (Appendix 1). One of the birds recovered was at least 8 years old. Ortstreue is shown by 6 birds returning to the place of ringing after one year and two after 2 years[3,4]. *Moult*: there is a complete and rapid moult late Dec to mid-Mar[7].

Taxonomy[1] *L. c. collurio* and *L. c. kobylini* (male with chestnut on the back duller and darker). *L. c. pallidifrons* is known from Zimbabwe[6], and probably occurs too.

References [1]Benson & White (1957); [2]Bowen (1980d); [3]Dowsett (in press b); [4]Dowsett & Leonard (2001); [5]Dowsett-Lemaire & Dowsett (2006); [6]Irwin (1981a); [7]Dowsett in Snow (1965).

[Red-tailed Shrike *Lanius isabellinus*

Palaearctic (*winters mainly Nigeria to Tanzania*). A shrike (apparently male) with the characteristics of the race *phoenicuroides* was seen near Kitwe on 12 Nov 1974, and one or two others have been reported on four occasions elsewhere near the Copperbelt (at Musofu), W. Zambia (near Siandi)[1] and twice on the Zambian Nyika Plateau (whence there is a specimen from the Malawi side)[3]. These are all unsupported single-observer sight records, and in view of the difficulty in separating this species (which winters further north in East Africa and the Sahel) from *L. collurio* they cannot be accepted with certainty. Extreme dates are 12 Nov-2 Dec and 29 Mar-17 Apr[1,2]. **References** [1]Dowsett (in press b); [2]Dowsett *et al.* (1999a); [3]Dowsett-Lemaire (2006a).]

Lesser Grey Shrike *Lanius minor*   B567 **P**

Distribution *Palaearctic* (*winters almost exclusively in Namibia and Botswana*). Throughout and seasonally numerous, but rarely in heavy woodland; in Mwinilunga Dist. much more common than *L. collurio*. *Alt.* 500-1800 m.

Ecology Especially in *Acacia* scrub, but also quite common in mopane, and can be encountered in any wooded grassland. In the miombo zone occurs only in secondary areas and cultivation.

Status A Palaearctic passage migrant which winters in semi-arid SW Africa. First recorded 7 Oct (average first date over 28 years was 20 Oct), there is then an influx from last week Oct, with large numbers

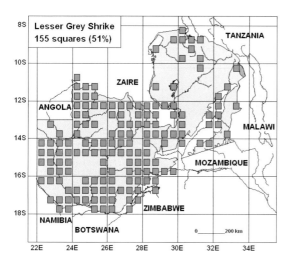

during the first 3 weeks of Nov. There is only a handful of records claimed in Jan or Feb, and none is entirely satisfactory; the species does not winter in Zambia, or at most only exceptionally. From early Mar a few birds reappear on northward passage, especially last week of Mar to mid-Apr, mostly in the eastern half of the country, where they may be quite numerous in the Luangwa Valley (agreeing with suggestions from elsewhere that there is a loop migration, with passage northwards being more to the east)[3]. Average last date (over 26 years) was 16 Apr, the last certain record being 26 Apr[3,4] (a sighting for 4 Jun[1] now being considered doubtfully correct). *Moult*: there is a rather fast moult by adults and first-year birds between late Dec and late Mar[4].

Taxonomy *L. minor* – polytypic if *L. m. turanicus* is accepted (the latter in fresh adult plumage more bluish, silvery grey above)[2], but this has been contested.
References [1]Benson & White (1957); [2]Clancey (1980c); [3]Dowsett (1971f); [4]Dowsett (in press b).

Fiscal Shrike *Lanius collaris*   B569 **RB**

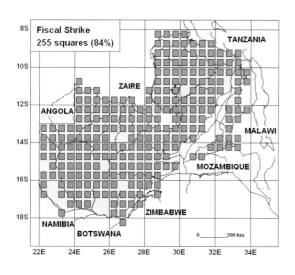

Distribution *Afrotropical* (*Guinea to South Africa*). Throughout plateau areas and locally common in open country, but absent from the Luangwa Valley, although present locally in Kariba, from the Chirundu area to Bimbi. Absent from parts of the west and south, and similarly south of the Zambezi in NW Zimbabwe, where only in the Kazungula area[5] (1725C). Scarce on the Kafue Flats, though this cannot be the result of exclusion by *Urolestes melanoleucus*, which is very much larger. Common on the Nyika (and known on the Malawi side of the Mafingas)[1]. *Alt.* mostly 700-2200 m (rarely down to 500 m), higher on the Malawi side of Nyika.
Ecology Open country such as plains, dambos or montane grassland, with scattered bushes and secondary growth. Feeds by pouncing on invertebrates from a perch.
Status Resident. A 2-year survey produced no evidence of any seasonal movements[3].

Breeding

	Aug	Sep	Oct	Nov	Dec	Jan	Mar	Apr	Jun
(n=123)	11	40	37	20	8	2	2	2	1

Clutch: C/1 (2); C/2 (20); C/3 (37); C/4 (3).
Taxonomy *L. c. capelli* (syn. *L. c. dominator*, type locality Muchinga escarpment[2], near Mumbi stream; *NMZB*). There is a tendency towards *L. c. marwitzi* (with a white supercilium) on the Nyika Plateau[4]; thus the suggestion that *marwitzi* (normally in the highlands of SW Tanzania) might be genetically and

specifically isolated from neighbouring populations is unlikely to be true[4].
References [1]Benson (1953); [2]Clancey & Smithers in Clancey (1954: 81); [3]Dowsett (in press a); [4]Dowsett & Dowsett-Lemaire (1993); [5]Hustler (1998).

Magpie Shrike *Urolestes melanoleucus*   B568 **RB**

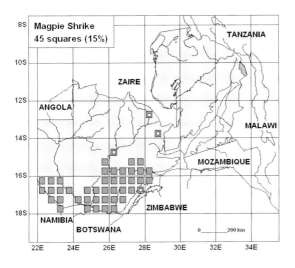

Magpie Shrike
45 squares (15%)

Distribution *Afrotropical (Kenya to South Africa)*. Essentially a species of the Southern Province plateau. Occurs as a breeding species only south of 15°S, from the north side of the Kafue Flats (e.g. Blue Lagoon N.P.), as far west as the Musa River. In the south-west of the country it is not reported north of 16°S (Matabele Plain[1], Sioma and Nangweshi). Extralimitally it reappears in SW Tanzania in the Rukwa Valley[4]. *Alt.* 950-1100 m, rarely up to 1300 m in Choma Dist.

Ecology *Acacia*-dominated parkland or thicket-clump savanna, where it perches in the tops of small trees and bushes. Occasionally in mopane woodland. It feeds on insects, lizards and even small rodents by dropping to the ground. It is only rarely sympatric with the much smaller, but ecologically similar, Fiscal Shrike *Lanius collaris* – as near Ngoma in Kafue N.P. Occurs in groups of up to 6, doubtless family parties.

Status Resident, with irregular vagrancy outside the breeding season (open squares). One was shot in Mar as far north as Kitwe and two were seen north of Kapiri Mposhi on 25 Mar[2]. One seen near Kafwala on 4 Oct[5] was presumably a wanderer, as also the record from Lunga in the Middle Zambezi Valley of several seen in *Acacia* in Jul[3,7]. Numbers have been reported to decline, with local absences even in areas where it is normally common, in Mazabuka and Monze Dists, during Feb-Jul. But it is still present in W. Zambia in early Jul[5].

Breeding   Oct Nov Dec   Jan   Feb   Mar
(n=22)   9   7   1   1   3   1

Extralimitally it has been shown to be a cooperative breeder, with several adults at the same nest[6].
Clutch: C/2 (2); C/3 (2); C/4 (8); C/5 (1).
Moult: one was half-way through moult early Mar[5].
Taxonomy *U. m. melanoleucus*. Sometimes placed in the genus *Lanius.*
References [1]Aspinwall (1973f); [2]Benson (1962a); [3]Benson *et al.* (1970); [4]Britton (1980); [5]Dowsett (in press a); [6]Grimes (2002); [7]Winterbottom (1951-52).

[Southern White-crowned Shrike *Eurocephalus anguitimens*

Afrotropical (central Angola to South Africa). Occurs in the Caprivi Strip adjacent to SW Zambia[2], as well as neighbouring Botswana at Kasane (within sight of Zambia)[1], and places in NW Zimbabwe/Botswana to as far north as Kazuma Pan[3]. The species will very likely be found to wander north of the Zambezi. **References** [1]Dowsett *et al.* (in prep.); [2]Parker in Harrison *et al.* (1997); [3]Irwin (1981a).]

Malaconotidae

Brubru *Nilaus afer* B538 **RB**

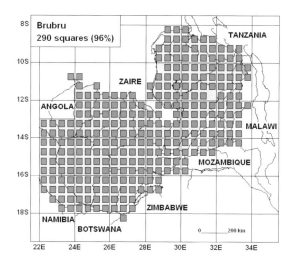

Distribution *Afrotropical (Mauritania to South Africa)*. Common in woodland throughout the country. *Alt.* 330 to 2050 m (Nyika).
Ecology In the canopy of any woodland (most common in miombo, but also in mopane, *Acacia* and undifferentiated woodland) and dry *Cryptosepalum* forest (common); a frequent member of mixed bird parties.
Status Resident.

Breeding	Aug	Sep	Oct
(n=56)	2	36	11
	Nov	Dec	Apr
	5	1	1

Clutch: C/1 (1); C/2 (41); C/3 (1).
Moult: starting early Dec. First-year males appear to have a female-like plumage[4].
Taxonomy[1,3] *N. a. nigritemporalis* (syn. *N. a. occidentalis*, type locality Zambezi town (Balovale); *OUM*[5], replaced by *N. a. brubru* (eye-stripe extending well behind the eye) in the south and south-west, and perhaps with some approach to *N. a. solivagus* (like *brubru*, but with the flanks much less marked with hazel) from the Middle Zambezi Valley to Katombora[2].
References [1]Benson (1956f); [2]Clancey (1968c); [3]Irwin (1981a); [4]Traylor (1965b); [5]White (1945-46: 206).

Southern Puffback *Dryoscopus cubla* B539 **RB**

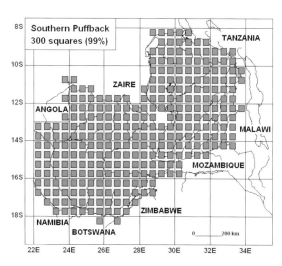

Distribution *Afrotropical (Somalia to South Africa)*. Very common in woodland and forest throughout Zambia. *Alt.* 330-2200 m (Nyika)[3].
Ecology The canopy and mid-stratum of any forest, woodland and thicket. An important member of mixed bird parties in woodland.
Status Resident. A ringed bird was retrapped when at least 11 years old[2].

Breeding	Jun	Jul	Aug	Sep
(n=88)	2	2	3	41
	Oct	Nov	Dec	Mar
	22	13	3	2

Clutch: C/1 (2); C/2 (23); C/3 (31).
Moult: in adults, Jan to Mar or mid-Apr[1].
Taxonomy *D. c. hamatus* in the north and west, *D. c. okavangensis* (greyer, less white, below) in the south and west[4].

References [1]Dowsett (in press a); Dowsett & Leonard (2001); [3]Dowsett-Lemaire (1989b); [4]Irwin & Benson (1967a).

Marsh Tchagra *Tchagra minutus*   B540 **RB**

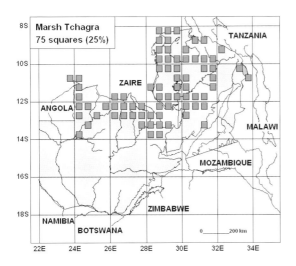

Marsh Tchagra
75 squares (25%)

Distribution *Afrotropical* (*Guinea to E. Zimbabwe*). Small numbers in swamps or rank grass in N. Zambia, west of the Luangwa Valley, in the north-east coming south only to the Nyika[2]. (Over the border in Malawi, it occurs locally through much of the country)[5]. It ranges on the Northern Province plateau south to the upper Lusiwashi, and on the Copperbelt south to Shitwe stream and Imanda[3]. It occurs west to Mayau[1], and south exceptionally to Kabompo[1]. *Alt.* 950-2150 m.
Ecology In tall mixed grass and reeds on the edge of streams and rivers (even Papyrus in the lower Luapula), also typically in rank grass in dambos; on the Nyika in lush grassland with bracken and scattered shrubs. Like all tchagras feeds hidden, close to or on the ground, and sings perched or in flight.
Status Easily overlooked outside the breeding season, but clearly resident.

Breeding   Nov   Dec   Jan   Mar
(n=6)   2   2   1   1   *Clutch*: C/2 (1).

Taxonomy *T. m. anchietae*; sometimes treated as a distinct species, in the genus *Bocagia* (an earlier name than *Antichromus*). However, molecular evidence tends to refute any real distinction between *Bocagia* and *Tchagra*[6], nor do we yet know of any firm reason to recognize *anchietae* as specifically distinct from *minutus*[4].

References [1]Benson (1960c); [2]Benson *et al.* (1970); [3]Dowsett (in press a); [4]Dowsett & Dowsett-Lemaire (1993); [5]Dowsett-Lemaire & Dowsett (2006); [6]Fuchs *et al.* (2004).

Brown-headed Tchagra *Tchagra australis*   B541 **RB**

Distribution *Afrotropical* (*Guinea to South Africa*). Probably throughout the country (locally common in rank growth), although practically unrecorded between Lakes Mweru and Tanganyika. *Alt.* 330 to 2000 m (Mafingas, Nyika)[3,4].
Ecology In rank grass with scattered bushes or patches of thicket, partial to *Acacia* savanna at lower elevations; avoids closed woodland. Also in gardens and neglected cultivation. Overall in denser undergrowth than its large congener *T. senegalus* although both coexist in many localities.
Status Resident.

Breeding   Aug   Sep   Oct   Nov   Dec   Jan   Feb   Mar   Apr   Jun
(n=159)   8   39   31   28   19   17   8   4   4   1
Clutch: C/1 (6); C/2 (83); C/3 (5).
Moult: from mid-Nov[7].

Taxonomy[1,6] No fewer than four races have been reported in Zambia, although the range of the species is now known to be less disjunct than previously supposed (*contra* ref. 2), and there is hybridization in areas of contact. *T. a. tongensis* occurs in the south, *rhodesiensis* in the west, *souzae* in parts of the north-west and north, and *minor* locally in the east. It is also possible that *T. a. damarensis* occurs west of Victoria Falls[5].

References [1]Benson & Irwin (1967b); [2]Benson *et al.* (1971a); [3]Dowsett & Stjernstedt (1973); [4]Dowsett-Lemaire (2006a); [5]Irwin (1981a); [6]Irwin & Benson (1967a); [7]Traylor (1965b).

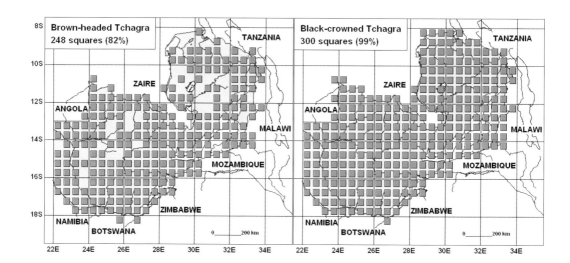

Black-crowned Tchagra *Tchagra senegalus*   B542 **RB**

Distribution *Afrotropical* (*Mauritania to South Africa*) *and SW Palaearctic*. Common, throughout the country. *Alt.* 330 to 2000 m (Mafingas) and 2200 m (Nyika)[1].

Ecology In grass and shrubs in understorey of any light woodland (where *T. australis* is normally absent). Also in more open situations: wooded grassland, patches of thicket and grass (where frequently coexists with *T. australis*), mixed scrub and grass around rocks; overall in lighter and drier cover than its congener.

Status Resident.

Breeding
	Jul	Aug	Sep	Oct	Nov	Dec	Jan	Feb	Mar	Apr	May	Jun
(n=214)	1	2	35	84	48	13	11	11	5	1	1	2

Clutch: C/1 (6); C/2 (120); C/3 (6); C/4 (1).
Moult: in some birds from Nov onwards[2].

Taxonomy *T. s. senegalus*, replaced in the west by *T. s. kalahari*.

References [1]Dowsett-Lemaire (2006a); [2]Traylor (1965b).

Tropical Boubou *Laniarius aethiopicus*   B543 **RB**

Distribution *Afrotropical* (*mainly Sierra Leone to Zimbabwe*). Common almost throughout, but scarce in the south-west, likely because of competition with *L. bicolor* (which is in a somewhat different habitat). *Alt.* 330-2200 m.

Ecology In all types of thicket, riparian vegetation, neglected cultivation and gardens; at higher levels

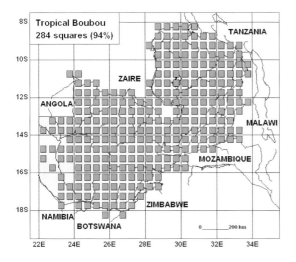

Tropical Boubou
284 squares (94%)

present in small numbers in bracken-briar.

Status Resident. A ringed bird was at least 9 years old when recovered[2].

Breeding	Aug	Sep	Oct	Nov	Dec
(n=151)	1	17	17	24	44
	Jan	Feb	Mar	Jun	
	26	17	4	1	

Clutch: C/1 (9); C/2 (106); C/3 (10).
Parasitized by *Cuculus clamosus*.
Moult: from Jan or Feb onwards[1].

Taxonomy[3] *L. a. mossambicus* is the more widespread form, with *L. a. major* (larger, whiter below) in the north and north-west.

References [1]Dowsett (in press a); [2]Dowsett & Leonard (2001); [3]Irwin & Benson (1967a).

Swamp Boubou *Laniarius bicolor*   B543A **R(B)**

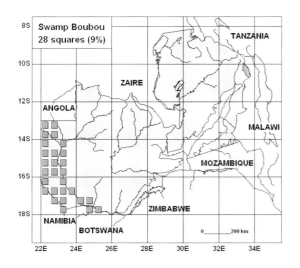

Swamp Boubou
28 squares (9%)

Distribution *Afrotropical (Cameroon to N. Botswana)*. Sparse throughout the Upper Zambezi (though not as far north as Mwinilunga Dist.) and Mashi Valleys, along the former east to Mambova[1] and Kazungula[3]. *Alt.* 950-1150 m.

Ecology Reedbeds and thickets near water (very rarely more than a few metres distant), at times parapatric with *L. aethiopicus* (e.g. at Mambova and Sesheke)[2]. Less common than its congener, and the situation in the 18 squares in which both species occur needs investigation[2].

Status Resident.

Breeding No records, but there is a moult from Nov onwards[4].

Taxonomy *L. b. sticturus*.

References [1]Benson & Irwin (1967b); [2]Dowsett (in press a); [3]Pollard (1991a); [4]Traylor (1965b).

Crimson-breasted Bush Shrike *Laniarius atrococcineus*   B544 **R(B)**

Distribution *Kalahari/Zambezian (S. Angola and Zambia to South Africa)*. Confined to thornbush in SW Zambia, north in the Mashi Valley to Shangombo[7], and in the Zambezi Valley to Kalongola F.R.[5]. Ranges east to Simungoma and Mwandi[2], and in the Machile Valley to Buwe Pool[1] and Ngwezi station[2]. The related species Black-headed Gonolek *L. erythrogaster* is known from Upemba in S. Zaire[6], and might therefore be expected in N. Zambia. *Alt.* 950-1050 m.

Ecology Dense *Acacia* scrub as a rule, also thick *Acacia* undergrowth of logged *Baikiaea*, where it

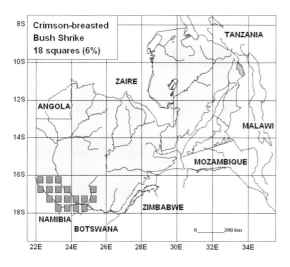

feeds on or near the ground. Often alongside *L. aethiopicus*, with no sign of competition.

Status Resident: records are scattered throughout the year, including the early rains (Nov and Dec)[2].

Breeding No records, but male gonad activity in Oct and Nov[2] accords with the peak of the breeding season in Zimbabwe (which is overall Sep-Jan).

Taxonomy *L. a. atrococcineus*. Sometimes considered conspecific with the northern *L. erythrogaster*[3,4], but we now accept that it is on present evidence best considered a distinct species. Several *Laniarius* have similar vocalisations, and voice may be less important as a species-isolating factor than (in this case) the possession of a long white wing-bar.

References [1]Benson & Irwin (1967b); [2]Dowsett (in press a); [3]Dowsett & Dowsett-Lemaire (1980); [4]Dowsett & Dowsett-Lemaire (1993); [5]Madge & Sitters (1973); [6]Schouteden (1971); [7]Smithers (1956).

Fülleborn's Black Boubou *Laniarius fuelleborni* B545 **RB**

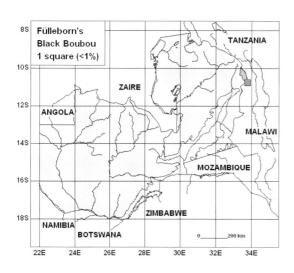

Distribution *Afromontane endemic (E. Nigeria/Cameroon to N. Malawi)*. Nyika Plateau only, where common. *Alt.* 1900-2200 m (to 2500 m on the Malawi side).

Ecology Foliage and bark gleaner in dense understorey (up to 16-18 m), and at edges, of montane (rain) forest; also in thick montane shrubland (3-4 m high). Territories of 0.6-1 ha in forest patches with much edge habitat, with densities of 2-3 pairs/10 ha in continuous forest[4].

Status Resident. A colour-ringed bird lived to be at least 8 years of age[1].

Breeding

	Oct	Nov	Dec	Jan
(n=7)	1	1	3	2

(Including the Malawi side of the SW Nyika.)
Clutch: C/1 (1).

Moult: recorded in Mar and Apr[2].

Taxonomy *L. f. fuelleborni* (thus tentatively treating *poensis* as a race)[3].

References [1]Dowsett (1985a); [2]Dowsett (in press a); [3]Dowsett & Dowsett-Lemaire (1993); [4]Dowsett-Lemaire (1989b).

Orange-breasted Bush Shrike *Malaconotus sulfureopectus*   B546 **RB**

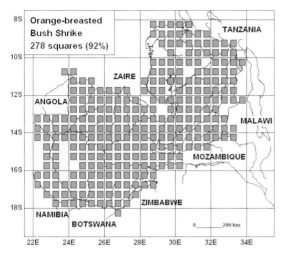

Distribution *Afrotropical (Senegal to South Africa)*. Locally common throughout, some of the gaps in the west perhaps artefacts. *Alt.* 330-1900 m.

Ecology Typically in the canopy of *Acacia* and riparian growth. At low altitudes especially common in patches of deciduous thorn thickets, and generally present in small numbers in riparian woodland and forest, and also in *Cryptosepalum* forest. Rarely coming into contact with *M. multicolor*, except in *Cryptosepalum*, where the two are often in the same mixed bird party (although *M. sulfureopectus* is usually in more open situations)[3].

Status Resident.

Breeding

(n=24)	Aug	Sep	Oct	Nov
	1	2	9	6
	Dec	Jan	Feb	
	2	2	2	

Clutch: C/2 (12).

Moult: finishing in one bird early Mar[2]. There is a distinctive first-year dress[4].

Taxonomy *M. s. similis*, although perhaps with a tendency towards *M. s. modestus* (in which adults are said to lack the orange breast band) in the west[1]. Sometimes placed in the genus *Chlorophoneus* or *Telophorus*. The original spelling was *sulfureopectus*, not *sulphureopectus*.

References [1]Clancey (1968c); [2]Dowsett (in press a); [3]Oatley (1969); [4]Traylor (1965b).

Many-coloured Bush Shrike *Malaconotus multicolor*   B547 **RB**

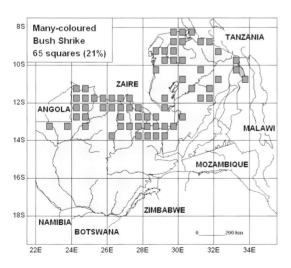

Distribution *Afrotropical (Guinea to South Africa)*. Sparse in the forests of the northern half, including the eastern highlands in the Mafingas and on the Nyika Plateau[6]. It ranges southwards to Changwena Falls, and on the Copperbelt to Imanda, St Anthony's Mission and Mpongwe. Further west to the East Lunga River[5] and west of the Zambezi at Mbulo[8], north to the Mudileji River and Isombu[3]. [Sight and sound records outside this range, which require confirmation: *c.* 90 km east of Mongu in *Cryptosepalum*[2]; Kabwe "breeds"[9]; Lusaka[2]; and Chilanga[1]. While it is possible that some of these records refer to wandering birds, the species may be confused visually with *M. sulfureopectus*.] *Alt.* 950-2200 m.

Ecology Moist evergreen forest, mushitu and *Cryptosepalum* forest (very common) in the plateau areas. Tall (25-30 m) montane rain forest on the SW Nyika, with territories of 6-10 ha[6]. A foliage gleaner in the canopy and mid-stratum tangles.

Status Resident, probably with no more than local movements (although known to have inter-montane movements in Malawi)[6].

Breeding   Oct   Dec   Feb   Mar

(n=4)   1   1   1   1   *Clutch*: C/2 (1). *Moult*: Mar (Nyika)[5].

Taxonomy[1] *M. m. manningi* (type locality Luchinde stream; *NHM*; named for Lt-Col. William Manning)[4,10] is the widespread form, with *M. m. nigrifrons* on the Nyika Plateau (and perhaps Mafingas). In both races there are three colour morphs in Zambia, a red-breasted, a bright yellow and a buff (or fawn) one. Of a pair in Chowo forest (Nyika), one was yellow, the other pink-fawn[7]. Sometimes treated as specifically distinct from *M. multicolor* (as *M. nigrifrons*); by some authorities placed in the genus *Chlorophoneus* or *Telophorus*.

References [1]Benson & Irwin (1967b); [2]Bruce-Miller & Dowsett (1977); [3]Dowsett (1973b); [4]Dowsett (1980b); [5]Dowsett (in press a); [6]Dowsett-Lemaire (1989b); [7]Dowsett-Lemaire (2006a); [8]Leonard (1998b); [9]Pitman (1934); [10]Shelley (1899a: 35).

Gorgeous Bush Shrike *Malaconotus viridis*   B549 **R(B)**

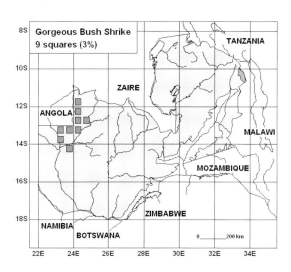

Distribution *Afrotropical* (*Somalia to South Africa, west to Congo-Brazzaville and Gabon*). Confined to *Cryptosepalum* forest in the north-west (where very common), from south of Mwinilunga town, east to the West Lunga N.P., west to Dipalata and south to Kapweletete[1]. There is a record from the Zimbabwean side of the Middle Zambezi Valley, in Chewore Safari Area (1529D)[4] [and unsubstantiated reports from squares 1529C and 1628D[3]]. Unrecorded on the Zambian bank, but this could be indication of a "stepping stone" between populations in the lower Zambezi and Shire Valleys and those in W. Zambia. *Alt.* 1100-1350 m.

Ecology In thick understorey of dry *Cryptosepalum* forest[5].

Status Resident.

Breeding No records, but male gonad activity Sep, and very vocal Aug-Sep[1].

Taxonomy *M. v. viridis*. The Middle Zambezi Valley birds would be of the subspecies *quartus*, treated as a race of a separate species (*M. quadricolor*) by some authors, but we believe they are conspecific[2]. Sometimes placed in the genus *Chlorophoneus* or *Telophorus*.

References [1]Dowsett (in press a); [2]Dowsett & Dowsett-Lemaire (1993); [3]Parker in Harrison *et al.* (1997); [4]Hustler (1989); [5]Oatley (1969).

Grey-headed Bush Shrike *Malaconotus blanchoti*   B548 **RB**

Distribution *Afrotropical* (*Senegal to South Africa*). Throughout the country in any woodland, but sparse in west. *Alt.* 330-1770 m (Danger Hill), wandering exceptionally to 2100 m (Nyika)[3].

Ecology In any dry woodland, feeding from the ground to the canopy; also in well-wooded suburban

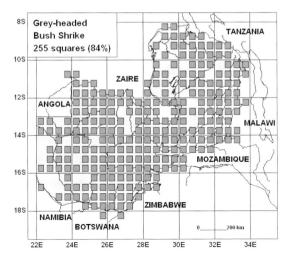

gardens, *Acacia* thickets and riparian forest, and occasionally in patches of light-canopy forest, as in *Cryptosepalum* forest (scarce). Pairs occupy widely-spaced territories. To a great extent carnivorous, killing prey as large as adult *Zosterops senegalensis*[2].

Status Resident.

Breeding
(n=65)

	Jul	Aug	Sep	Oct	Nov
	1	3	26	25	6
	Dec	Jan	Feb	Mar	
	1	1	1	1	

Clutch: C/1 (1); C/2 (11); C/3 (31); C/4 (5).

Taxonomy *M. b. hypopyrrhus* in much of the country, with *M. b. interpositus* in the north and north-west (and intermediates on the Copperbelt)[1].

References [1]Benson & Irwin (1967b); [2]Dowsett (in press a); [3]Dowsett-Lemaire (2006a).

Prionopidae

White Helmet Shrike *Prionops plumatus*   B571 **RB**

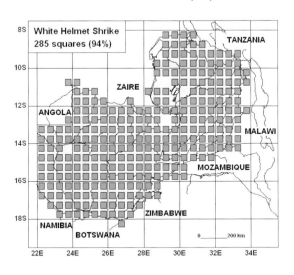

Distribution *Afrotropical* (*Mauritania to South Africa*). Locally common in woodland throughout the country. *Alt.* 330-1700 m, rarely wandering to 1950 m (Mafingas)[2].

Ecology In almost any woodland, especially miombo and mopane, also in town gardens in the non-breeding season. In monospecific groups, often of 5-12 birds, sometimes mixing with *P. retzii* and other species; feeds lower down than its congener, including on the ground.

Status Resident, with much local wandering in the dry season (May-Aug).

Breeding
(n=118)

	Aug	Sep	Oct	Nov
	4	50	40	14
	Dec	Mar	Apr	Jun
	3	2	4	1

Clutch: C/1 (1); C/2 (7); C/3 (21); C/4 (35); C/5 (2); C/6 (2); C/7 (1).

This species is a cooperative breeder, and more than one female may lay in a nest[1]. There is no evidence of it being parasitized by *Pachycoccyx audeberti* in Zambia (cf. *P. retzii*).

Moult: well advanced by early Nov[5].

Taxonomy[4] *P. p. poliocephalus*. DNA studies suggest that the Prionopidae are members of a broad family Malaconotidae[3].

References [1]Dowsett (in press a); [2]Dowsett & Stjernstedt (1973); [3]Fuchs *et al.* (2004); [4]Irwin & Benson

(1966a); [5]Traylor (1965b).

Retz's Red-billed Helmet Shrike *Prionops retzii*   B572 **RB**

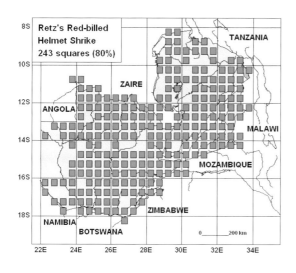

Distribution *Afrotropical* (*Somalia to South Africa; mainly Zambezian*). Locally common throughout most of the country, overall in smaller numbers than *P. plumatus*. In the far west recorded west of the Zambezi only near Lukolwe (where fairly common)[1], Matakala on the Lungwebungu River[3] and south of 16°S. *Alt.* 330-1700 m, rarely wandering to 1950 m (Mafingas)[2].

Ecology In all types of mature woodland, also deciduous and riparian forest; rare in *Cryptosepalum* forest. In monospecific groups, often of 3-12 birds (exceptionally 22)[1], sometimes mixing with *P. plumatus* and other species; feeds usually in the canopy, thus higher than its congener.

Status Resident, except for some wandering outside the breeding season.

Breeding	Aug	Sep	Oct	Nov	Dec	Jan	Apr	May
(n=76)		1	29	32	8	3	1	1	1

Clutch: C/2 (8); C/3 (33); C/4 (12); C/5 (1).

The species is a cooperative breeder, like *P. plumatus,* and is the host of *Pachycoccyx audeberti*[1].

Taxonomy[3] *P. r. tricolor*, replaced by *P. r. nigricans* (mantle blackish slate, not pale brown) in the west and by *P. r. retzii* (mantle darker brown) in the south-west.

References [1]Dowsett (in press a); [2]Dowsett & Stjernstedt (1973); [3]Irwin & Benson (1966a).

Dicruridae

Square-tailed Drongo *Dicrurus ludwigii*   B378 **RB**

Distribution *Afrotropical* (*Senegal to South Africa*). Common in the forests of the northern half of the country, west of the Luangwa Rift. Not known east of 32°E, and indeed absent from the northern half of Malawi[5]. Down the Muchinga escarpment to the Copperbelt, north of 14°S (south to Katanino F.R.)[4], then west to Lukolwe and the South Kashiji River[1,3] (west of the Zambezi). Common at Mwinilunga, but not north of the Kanyama road bridge[4]. *Alt.* 950-1770 m (Danger Hill).

Ecology In mushitu (swamp forest) and other types of moist or dry evergreen forest; very common in *Cryptosepalum* forest. Flycatches and snatches insects from foliage in canopy and below. Often a leader of mixed parties.

Status Resident.

Breeding	Aug	Sep	Oct		
(n=15)		1	7	7	*Clutch*: C/1 (1); C/2 (5); C/3 (3).

Taxonomy *D. l. ludwigii*.

References [1]Aspinwall (1979b); [2]Benson (1956d); [3]Benson (1960c); [4]Dowsett (in press a); [5]Dowsett-Lemaire & Dowsett (2006).

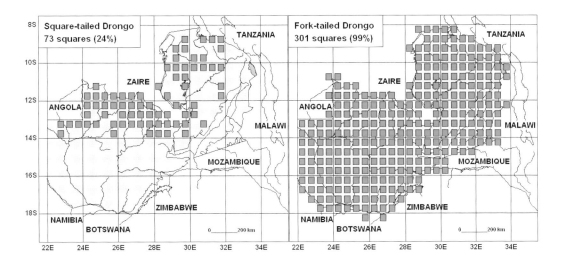

Fork-tailed Drongo *Dicrurus adsimilis*   B379 **RB**

Distribution *Afrotropical* (*Mauritania to South Africa*). Very common in any woodland throughout. *Alt.* 330-1700 m (with winter records at much higher altitude on the Malawi side of the Nyika)[4].
Ecology In any woodland or wooded savanna, gardens, the edge of plantations and (occasionally) of evergreen forest. Drops to the ground or flycatches; an active member (and often a leader) of mixed bird parties. Attracted to bush fires, forming large concentrations (up to 300 at times)[2].
Status Resident, possibly with some local movements (including to higher altitude) Apr-Aug, as in Malawi[4]. A ringed bird was recovered when at least 7 years old[3].

Breeding   Aug   Sep   Oct   Nov   Dec   Jan   May
(n=675)   4   340   234   93   2   1   1

Clutch: C/1 (20); C/2 (189); C/3 (286); C/4 (9).   The favoured host of *Cuculus gularis*.
Moult: there is a distinctive first-year dress[6].
Taxonomy[1,5] Possibly *D. a. fugax*, although it differs only in averaging smaller than *D. a. adsimilis* of southern Africa.
References [1]Benson (1962a); [2]Dowsett (in press a); [3]Dowsett & Leonard (2001); [4]Dowsett-Lemaire (2006a); [5]Irwin (1981a); [6]Traylor (1965b).

Corvidae

Pied Crow *Corvus albus*   B383 **RB**

Distribution *Afrotropical* (*Mauritania to South Africa*). Almost throughout, at all elevations, usually commensal. *Alt.* 330-2200 m (very sparse at low levels).

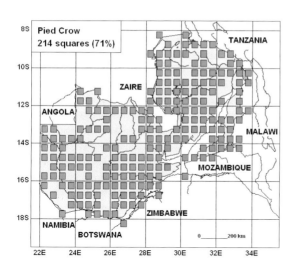

Ecology In open country with some tall trees, especially cultivation and townships: almost entirely commensal and a common scavenger everywhere. Avoids pure stands of dense woodland or forest. Nests mainly in tall trees, on pylons and in exotic plantations, which around cities also attract large numbers (up to 200)[1] for roosting in the non-breeding season. **Status** A 2-year survey showed it to be resident, but with seasonal flocking and some local wandering. This crow was very locally distributed in the late 19th and early 20th century[2,3], but it has subsequently benefited greatly from man's activities (fishing and domestic waste in particular).

Breeding	May	Jul	Aug	Sep	Oct	Nov	Dec
(n=67)	1	1	12	31	19	2	1

Clutch: C/1 (2); C/2 (1); C/3 (4); C/4 (8); C/5 (9); C/6 (12); C/7 (1).
Host to *Clamator glandarius*[1].
Taxonomy No races recognized.
References [1]Dowsett (in press a); [2]Neave (1910); [3]Pitman (1934).

Black Crow *Corvus capensis*   B384 **RB**

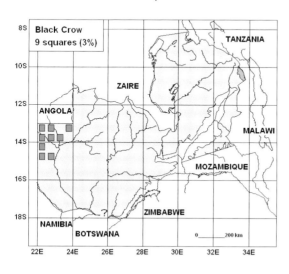

Distribution *Afrotropical* (*Ethiopia to South Africa*). Confined to the plains of W. Zambia, south to the Mbanda and Liuwa Plains[2], and east of the Zambezi only to Konkano Plain[1]. Usually uncommon, but fairly common on Minyanya Plain. One in a garden in Livingstone ("?" on map) was likely an escape from captivity[3]. [The following sight records have been rejected, though ought to be borne in mind: Kalambo Falls[2,5] and Mulolobela Falls, Ibwe Munyama[4].] *Alt.* 1000-1150 m.
Ecology Open plains, nesting in isolated groups of trees. In small groups of up to 7.
Status Resident.

Breeding	Aug	Sep
(n=11)	4	7

Clutch: C/1 (3); C/4 (4); C/6 (2).

Taxonomy *C. c. capensis.*
References [1]Benson (1962a); [2]Benson & Irwin (1967b); [3]Benson *et al.* (1970); [4]Dowsett (in press a); [5]Jones (1946).

White-necked Raven *Corvus albicollis*   B385 **RB**

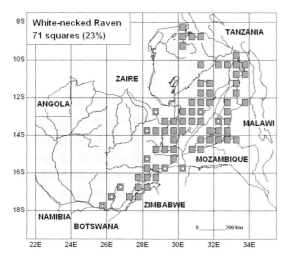

Distribution *Afrotropical (Kenya to South Africa).* On rocky hills associated with the Rift Valley, from Kashinda and Kasaba Bay[2] on L. Tanganyika, throughout the Eastern Province plateau, and down the Muchinga escarpment to the Copperbelt (at least as a wanderer)[1]. Onwards down the Middle Zambezi escarpment west to Masuku[1]. Occasionally wanders (open squares) away from rocky hills and escarpments to "line of rail" and the Southern Province plateau (e.g. Livingstone[2]). Even to the low-lying Middle Zambezi Valley opposite Mana Pools[3] and Luangwa town (Feira)[1]. *Alt.* 650-2200 m, rarely down to 330 m.

Ecology In open country around rocky hills. Nests on ledges of rock faces.

Status Resident, but with local wandering. In pairs or small flocks, with assemblages of 20-30 at times[1].

Breeding   Aug   Sep
(n=5)   1   4   *Clutch*: C/5 (2).

Taxonomy No races recognized.

References [1]Dowsett (in press a); [2]Dowsett & Dowsett-Lemaire (1978b); [3]Morris (1981).

Sturnidae

Waller's (Red-winged) Starling *Onychognathus walleri*   B573 **RB**

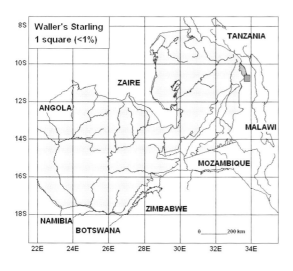

Distribution *Afromontane endemic (E. Nigeria/Cameroon to N. Malawi).* Known from montane forest on the Nyika Plateau only. *Alt.* 1970-2200 m.

Ecology Foliage and bark gleaner in canopy of montane rain forest; also flycatches, and takes fruit regularly[2]. A maximum of 12 pairs bred in 160 ha of forest patches on SW Nyika in 1980-81, with *c.* 6 pairs in Chowo forest (90 ha), but non-breeders are more numerous. Both food and nest sites (tree holes) are limiting factors[1,3].

Status Resident, but subject to local wandering. Gregarious when not breeding, in flocks of up to 60.

Breeding   Aug   Sep   Oct   Nov
(n=30)   2   12   13   3

(Including the Malawi side of SW Nyika.) Normally single-brooded[1].
Clutch: up to N/3. The eggs are undescribed.

Taxonomy *O. w. walleri.*
References [1]Dowsett-Lemaire (1983d); [2]Dowsett-Lemaire (1988b); [3]Dowsett-Lemaire (1989b).

African Red-winged Starling *Onychognathus morio*   B574 **RB**

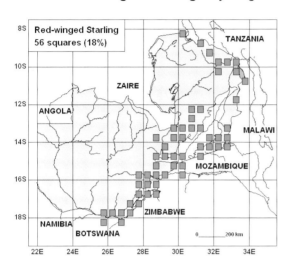

Distribution *Afrotropical (mainly Mali to South Africa).* Confined to rocky hills in the eastern half of the country, where locally common. In the north-east, from near Congo Point on L. Tanganyika, south and east to Nyika. Further south on the Eastern Province plateau in the Chama area, and widespread from 13°S southwards[3]. West of the Luangwa Valley reappears in Lavushi Manda[1]. Ranges southwards along the Muchinga escarpment and westwards to the Kapiri Mposhi area[3], in the Kafue basin to Mazabuka[6], and westwards along the Zambezi escarpment to Livingstone and the Victoria Falls[2] and Rapid 23 in the Batoka Gorge[3]. *Alt.* 330-2200 m (Nyika).

Ecology Around cliffs and boulders, rocky hills in woodland, even suburban gardens. Appears much more common in the Mafingas than on the Nyika, possibly as a consequence of the absence of *O. tenuirostris* in the former. Largely insectivorous, also takes some fruit[4]. Nests in rock crevices, also in the roofs of buildings (e.g. Livingstone) and on bridges (Gwembe Dist.)[3].

Status Essentially resident, but occurs in large groups in the non-breeding season: flocks of up to 80 at Livingstone[3], and 60 observed in the Mafingas[4].

Breeding	Sep	Oct	Nov	Dec	Jan	Feb	Mar	
(n=20)	1	1	5	5	4	1	3	*Clutch*: C/3 (6).

Taxonomy[5] *O. m. shelleyi.*
References [1]Benson (1956f); [2]Benson & Pitman (1961); [3]Dowsett (in press a); [4]Dowsett & Stjernstedt (1973); [5]Irwin (1981a); [6]Winterbottom (1936).

Slender-billed (Chestnut-winged) Starling *Onychognathus tenuirostris*   B575 **RB**

Distribution *Afromontane endemic (Ethiopia to N. Malawi).* Breeds on the Nyika Plateau, with one observation (wanderer?) at Nyikamwaka[1]. *Alt.* 1900-2200 m (higher on the Malawi side of Nyika).

Ecology Montane grassland with rocky streams, feeding also in nearby montane rain forest (where takes both insects and fruit). Breeds on rock faces along streams, often on the side of waterfalls, as on the Chire stream below Chowo[2].

Status Resident, with local wandering. Non-breeding birds are gregarious, the largest flock observed on the Zambian side being of 30 birds (Jul)[2].

Breeding	Sep	Dec
(n=4)	1	3

Clutch: N/3 known from the Malawi Nyika.
Taxonomy *O. t. theresae.*
References [1]Dowsett (in press a); [2]Dowsett-Lemaire (2006a).

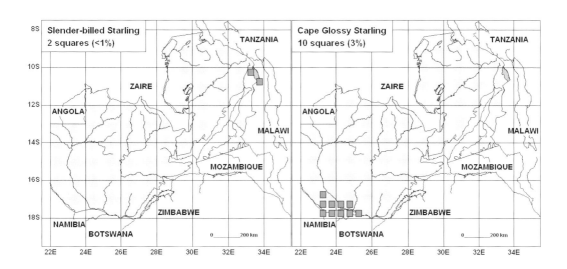

Cape Glossy Starling *Lamprotornis nitens*   B580 **R(B)**

Distribution *Afrotropical* (*S. Congo-Brazzaville to South Africa*). Confined to SW Zambia (in very small numbers), north to Mulele[2], and down the Zambezi to Kazungula[1]. *Alt*. 950-1000 m.

Ecology Typically in *Acacia* parkland, where it feeds on the ground, often with other starlings. Food has included termites, ants and beetles.

Status Perhaps resident, though east of the Zambezi recorded only irregularly, and only once in the rains (early Jan)[3]. Never in large groups, usually 2-3 together.

Breeding No records.

Taxonomy *L. n. phoenicopterus*.

References [1]Aspinwall (1972c); [2]Bruce-Miller & Dowsett (1977); [3]Dowsett (in press a).

Greater Blue-eared Starling *Lamprotornis chalybaeus*   B579 **RB**

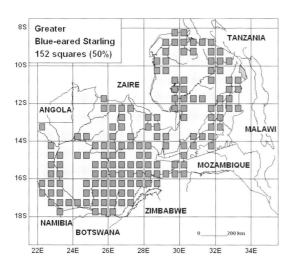

Distribution *Afrotropical* (*Mauritania to South Africa*). Throughout those plateau and valley areas in which *Acacia* dominates, and locally common (e.g. Kafue Flats and Southern Province). Thus unknown only in parts of Northern Province, the upper Luapula Valley and most of North-Western Province – exceptionally north to Nguvu and Minyanya[1]. Westwards from the Copperbelt to Solwezi[3] and near Jivundu Swamp[4]. *Alt*. 330-1600 m.

Ecology In various open woodlands, wooded grassland or thicket-clump savanna, especially in *Acacia*. Also in mopane, but not in pure miombo, and generally avoiding closed woodland.

Status Resident, in groups of up to 20 or so

when not breeding, exceptionally 150-200 roosting with other starlings (Lochinvar and Muckle Neuk, Apr)[4].

Breeding   Sep   Oct   Nov   Dec
(n=18)   1   9   7   1   *Clutch*: C/2 (3); C/3 (6); C/4 (1) & N/4 (1).
Moult: adults start late Nov and finish Mar or Apr[4].
Taxonomy[2,5] *L. c. nordmanni*, replaced by *L. c. sycobius* in the east (shoulder patch violet, not coppery).
References [1]Aspinwall (1979b); [2]Benson (1956f); [3]Benson & Irwin (1964b); [4]Dowsett (in press a); [5]Irwin & Benson (1967a).

Lesser Blue-eared Starling *Lamprotornis chloropterus*   B577 **RB**

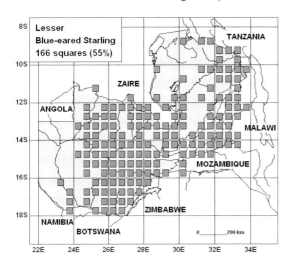

Distribution *Afrotropical* (*Senegal to Zimbabwe*). Common in miombo and mopane woodlands over much of Zambia, but largely replaced by *L. acuticaudus* in the west and north-west, and sparser in areas of overlap (e.g. west to Chishela Plain[3], exceptionally on the Luapula at Mwense[2]). Ranges west to Kaoma Dist.[1], and beyond the Zambezi to 15 km west of Nangweshi[4], and east of Imusho[5]. *Alt.* 330-1650 m (Mbala area).

Ecology In miombo woodland, also in mopane, wandering into any other woodland and suburban gardens. Highly gregarious (see below) and generally more common than *L. chalybaeus*, except in the low-lying valleys, where the reverse applies. Often with other species of starling, even with *L. acuticaudus* in much of the south-west[5].

Status Present in all months, a preponderance of records Mar-Jul (during a 2-year survey) and some local seasonal absences being probably the result of the greater visibility of this frugivorous species when in flocks after breeding, together with some local wandering. Numbers increase from early Jan, but especially at the start of the dry season. Flocks can be extremely large, often thousands, with up to 10-20,000 roosting together in the Choma area in Apr-Aug[5].

Breeding   Sep   Oct
(n=54)   35   19   *Clutch*: C/2 (8); C/3 (11); C/4 (21); C/5 (5).
Taxonomy[3] *L. c. elisabeth*.
References [1]Aspinwall (1973f); [2]Aspinwall (1974); [3]Benson (1956f); [4]Bruce-Miller & Dowsett (1977); [5]Dowsett (in press a).

Sharp-tailed Starling *Lamprotornis acuticaudus*   B578 **RB**

Distribution *Zambezian endemic* (*NW Angola to N. Botswana*). Largely those plateau woodland areas of the north and west, whence *L. chloropterus* scarce or absent, and usually common. In the north-east, east to Kowa[2] and Malole, south to Kasanka and the Copperbelt. More widespread to the west, throughout the Upper Zambezi Valley to Sesheke, and east of the Zambezi at Kaoma[1], wandering to Hippo

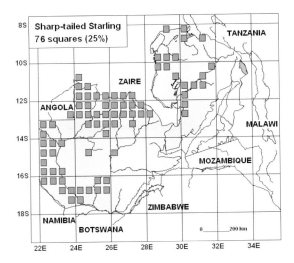

camp on the Kafue (Sep-Oct)[5]. In the Machile area east to Nanzhila camp and Dimba Dambo. Unknown from the Mashi area south of Shangombo[3]. *Alt.* 950-1730 m (Kowa).

Ecology Most often in miombo or *Baikiaea* forest, of the drier, more open types, and other broad-leaved woodlands (*Burkea* etc.). Often with other starlings, especially *L. chloropterus*.

Status Resident, though there is some wandering, in small groups of up to 50, even more than 70, after breeding[4].

Breeding   Oct
(n=1)   1   *Clutch*: no data.
The eggs have not been described.
Moult: by early Dec all were in moult[6].

Taxonomy No races recognized.

References [1]Aspinwall (1973f); [2]Aspinwall (1978a); [3]Benson (1956f); [4]Dowsett (in press a); [5]Fleming (1999); [6]Traylor (1965b).

Splendid Glossy Starling *Lamprotornis splendidus*   B576 **AMB**

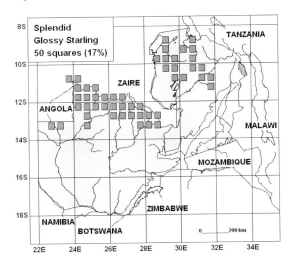

Distribution *Afrotropical (Senegal to N. Zambia)*. Seasonally common in forests of the north, in the east south to Shiwa Ngandu[1] and the Copperbelt. Throughout Mwinilunga Dist., and in the west south to Lungundu[3] and Kambizana stream[7]. These are the most southerly records of the species. *Alt.* 950-1550 m.

Ecology Evergreen forest, especially riparian or large, moist mushitu patches. Feeds in the canopy on fruits.

Status[4-6] An intra-African migrant and breeding visitor, moving northwards towards the Equator after breeding in Zambia and neighbouring areas. Records are for the period 28 May to 17 Jan. The average first date over 26 years was 5 Aug, the average last (in 21 years) 14 Dec[2]. First arrivals in N. Mwinilunga are usually during Jul, but at the boma in Aug and on the Copperbelt usually Sep. These movements are probably related to the timing of fruiting of certain trees, but this remains to be studied. Large flocks (400 or more) are recorded throughout the period Aug-Dec[2], which suggests that a large part of the population does not breed.

Breeding   Sep Oct Nov
(n=8)   4   3   1   *Clutch*: C/2 (3) & N/2 (2).

Taxonomy[1] *L. s. bailundensis*.

References [1]Benson (1956f); [2]Dowsett & Leonard (in press a); [3]Leonard (1998b); [4]Penry (1979c); [5]Prigogine (1983); [6]Prigogine & Benson (1980); [7]White (1945-46).

Burchell's Starling *Lamprotornis australis*   B582 **RB**

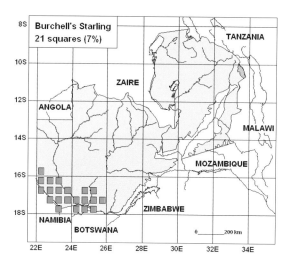

Distribution *Kalahari-Highveld near-endemic (S. Angola to South Africa).* As with *L. nitens*, confined to the south-west, but it does range up the Mashi River to the Chisangu Plain[3], and up the Zambezi to 40 km west of Nangweshi and the Matabele Plain[2,3]. Further east, occurs north to the Machile forest[3] and east to Kazungula, and even Mutwanjili[1]. *Alt.* 950-1150 m.

Ecology Occurs in a variety of habitats, from open *Acacia* or *Burkea*, occasionally mopane and even fields and treeless plains, less often fairly closed *Baikiaea* forest. Often in association with other starlings, in particular *L. chalybaeus*.

Status Resident; not known to form large flocks.

Breeding   Mar
(n=2)   2   *Clutch*: N/2 (1); C/3 (1).
Taxonomy No races recognized. Formerly considered conspecific with the much smaller *L. mevesii*.
References [1]Dowsett (in press a); [2]Smithers (1956); [3]Traylor & Hart (1965).

Southern Long-tailed Starling *Lamprotornis mevesii*   B581 **RB**

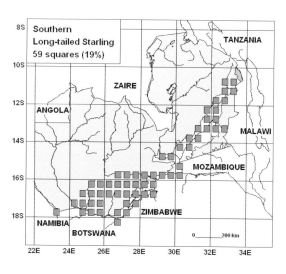

Distribution *Zambezian endemic (NE Zambia to South Africa).* Very common throughout the dry woodlands of the Luangwa and Middle Zambezi Valleys, from north and west of Chama[4], along the Luano Valley to Chembe[4,6], and the whole of the Zambezi Valley west to Sesheke and Katima Mulilo[7]. Unknown west of the Zambezi, except marginally near Imusho[4]. Occurs throughout much of the Southern Province plateau (though only a seasonal wanderer away from mopane, as around Choma and to Chilanga)[1,4], west along the southern side of the Kafue Flats to the Nanzhila area[8]. *Alt.* 330-1300 m.

Ecology In mopane woodland and secondarily *Acacia*-dominated savanna. In some places alongside the larger *L. australis*, which prefers more open *Acacia*-dominated habitats. A nest was in a hole in a live *Trichilia emetica* tree, 2.5 m high.

Status Resident, often in flocks of up to 150 outside the breeding season, and with "hundreds" roosting in *Acacia nilotica* trees in the Middle Zambezi Valley (Jul)[4].

Breeding   Feb   Mar
(n=8)   4   4   *Clutch*: C/3 (3).

Moult: adults from late Sep to Feb, before breeding. Partial post-juvenile moult May-Jun, first complete moult of young birds Jul-Nov[2,3,4].

Taxonomy[5] *L. m. mevesii.* Formerly considered conspecific with the much larger *L. australis*, with which there is some geographical overlap. Partial albinos have been reported occasionally.

References [1]Benson (1960d); [2]Brooke (1967a); [3]Dowsett (1967); [4]Dowsett (in press a); [5]Irwin & Benson (1967b); [6]White (1943d); [7]Winterbottom (1942a); [8]Winterbottom (1942b).

Amethyst (Plum-coloured) Starling *Cinnyricinclus leucogaster*   B583 **AMB**

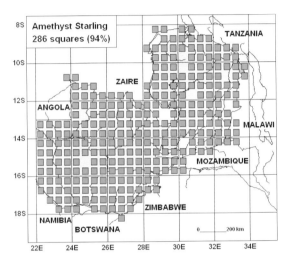

Distribution *Afrotropical (Mauritania to South Africa).* Seasonally common throughout, in most woodland and forest types. *Alt.* 330-2200 m (Nyika).

Ecology Most common in miombo woodland, also in thickets, deciduous and evergreen forest (where it breeds locally, up to 2200 m)[4] and wandering into any other kind of woodland and savanna, including suburban gardens. Feeds in trees as well as on the ground in open situations, and has a mixed insectivorous and frugivorous diet[3]. On SW Nyika breeds in some years and not others, depending on amount of fruit available[4].

Status Largely an intra-African migrant and breeding visitor[5]. There are records throughout the year, although overall frequency is significantly less Apr-Aug than Sep-Mar. On the other hand, in some places the species is far more frequent in the winter (Apr-Aug), e.g. Mongu and Livingstone[2]. Possibly there are two different populations visiting Zambia, one breeding and the other wintering[5].

Breeding   Sep   Oct   Nov   Dec
(n=93)   2   62   27   2   *Clutch*: C/1 (1); C/2 (19); C/3 (41); C/4 (1); C/5 (1).

Moult: between Dec and May, with some birds suspending moult while migrating. Body moult follows completion of wing moult. Juveniles have a first complete moult at 13-14 months, when males acquire adult plumage[2,5].

Taxonomy[1] *C. l. verreauxi.*

References [1]Benson (1956f); [2]Dowsett & Leonard (in press a); [3]Dowsett-Lemaire (1988b); [4]Dowsett-Lemaire (1989b); [5]Traylor (1971).

Sharpe's Starling *Cinnyricinclus sharpii*   B - **AV**

Distribution and Status *Afromontane endemic (Ethiopia to Tanzania).* A group of four on the edge of forest in the Mafinga Mts (0933C) 21 Nov 2002 is the only record; this was at the headwaters of the Luangwa River at 1970 m. The nearest population is in S. Tanzania, Mount Rungwe, itself far to the south of the main range of the species[1], and where it may be only a seasonal visitor. It is unknown from N. Malawi.

Taxonomy No races recognized. Molecular analysis suggests it may be best placed in the genus

Poeoptera[2].
References [1]Dowsett *et al.* (2003); [2]Lovette & Rubenstein (2007).

White-winged Starling *Neocichla gutturalis*   B584 **RB**

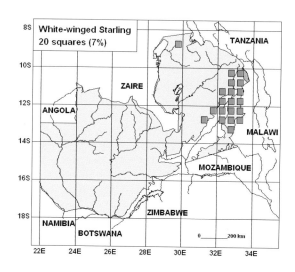

Distribution *Zambezian endemic (isolated populations centred on SW Angola and NE Zambia-Tanzania).* A strange distribution, essentially the miombo and tall mopane woodlands of the northern part of Eastern Province plateau, in the Lundazi and Chama Dists[4], and usually common, as on the Malawi side in Vwaza Marsh. It has occurred south on the plateau to the Chipengali area[3] (where very scarce), west across the Luangwa Valley to near Kapiri Kasweta at the foot of the Muchinga escarpment[5], and north to the Nyungwe area on the upper Luangwa. There is a very isolated population in the Kampinda area (0829D), centred on woodland 10-20 km north of Nsama[1], where still common in 2005[5]. *Alt.* 650-1500 m.

Ecology In tall miombo and mixed "cathedral" mopane-miombo woodland, feeding from the canopy to the ground and rather gregarious. It is more common in plateau woodlands than on the floor of the Luangwa Valley. Feeds on termites, small beetles, other insects and berries, and seen probing the large flowers of a *Protea*[3]. Nests in tree holes (e.g. a nest was 8 m up in a hole in a dead branch in tall miombo[1]).
Status Resident. Occurs in large groups of up to 20 or 30 when not breeding, and is at times in mixed bird parties.
Conservation The Kampinda population appears vulnerable, although the habitat there remains mostly untouched. Elsewhere (in the Lundazi area) there has been extensive clearing of miombo woodland for subsistence cultivation and the survival of the species is not assured. North Luangwa N.P. is important for this starling, especially as destruction of mopane by Elephants (a feature of parts of the Luangwa Valley), has not affected those areas favoured by this species.
Breeding   Oct   Nov
(n=4)   3   1   *Clutch*: C/2 (1); C/3 (2).
Taxonomy *N. g. angusta.*
References [1]Benson (1956d); [2]Benson *et al.* (1971a); [3]Berry (1983); [4]Dowsett (1973e); [5]Dowsett (in press a).

Wattled Starling *Creatophora cinerea*   B585 **AM(B?)**

Distribution *Afrotropical (Ethiopia to South Africa).* A highly nomadic species that can turn up anywhere in open country. *Alt.* 370-1700 m.
Ecology In various woodlands and wooded grassland (especially *Acacia*) and on the edge of floodplains. Accompanies cattle or game animals to feed on insects flushed, also eats fruit (e.g. *Ficus* spp.).
Status Highly erratic, although there are records for all months, large numbers are noted only Apr to

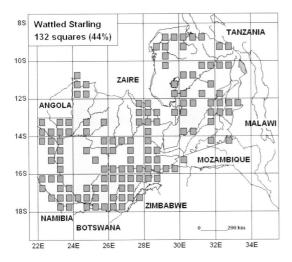

Nov. These large flocks (usually up to 300 birds, but totalling 1000s at Blue Lagoon in Jul 1998)[2] are probably post-breeding groups – whether from undiscovered colonies in Zambia or from outside cannot be said. There has possibly been an increase in numbers since the drought years of the 1990s, as observed in Malawi[3].

Breeding No records, but a male collected showed gonad activity in Feb[1], and birds with well-developed wattles are occasionally seen during the rains.

Taxonomy No races recognized.

References [1]Benson (1956f); [2]Dowsett (in press a); [3]Dowsett-Lemaire & Dowsett (2006).

Yellow-billed Oxpecker *Buphagus africanus*   B586 **RB**

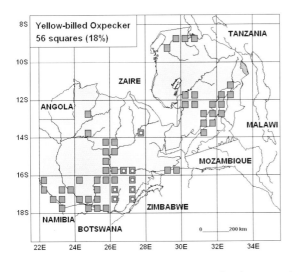

Distribution *Afrotropical* (*Mauritania to South Africa*). Confined mainly to game areas, and thus in the north-west reaches only West Lunga N.P.[5] Otherwise, the Mashi and Zambezi Rivers from Shangombo[1], and the Kafue basin from Pwira Pan[7] and the Busanga Plain south to Lochinvar and much of the Southern Province plateau (before extensive cattle dipping caused a great decline in the 1970s). Although no longer present on the Zambian side of L. Kariba (doubtless it was there before the lake was flooded), occurs in the Lower Zambezi N.P., and throughout the Luangwa Valley, northwards from the Chilongozi sector. On the northern plateau in the Kasanka area, Lusenga Plain, Mweru Wantipa[1] and Sumbu N.P. *Alt.* 370-1500 m.

Ecology In any wooded habitat, except the densest, where groups can detect their host animals. In the Luangwa Valley 11 host species have been recorded, in particular Buffalo, Kudu and (before its local extermination) Black Rhinoceros[4]. This species is more of a flesh-eater than *B. erythrorhynchus*, having a heavier bill and different feeding technique. Sometimes roost on their hosts at night[3].

Status[1,4] Resident.

Conservation Both species of oxpecker have become rare in recent decades in farming areas where cattle are treated with insecticides. "Oxpecker-friendly" dips are now available in Zambia, but the extent to which they are used, and their influence on oxpecker numbers, is unknown. Localities from which the last known reports were in the 1970s are shown by open squares (but recent information is lacking for many squares). Both oxpeckers remain common in national parks with good populations of favoured hosts, but in those where poaching has greatly reduced game numbers there may be cause for concern.

Breeding   Dec

(n=1)   1   At this nest in Kafue N.P. more than one pair was present, suggesting there may be cooperative breeding[2]. *Clutch*: N/3 (1).

Taxonomy[6] Perhaps *B. a. haematophagus*, but not very distinct from the nominate race.

References [1]Attwell (1966); [2]Dowsett (1965a); [3]Dowsett (1968); [4]Dowsett & Berry (in prep.); [5]Dowsett & Dowsett-Lemaire (1978d); [6]Irwin (1981a); [7]Tree (1966a).

Red-billed Oxpecker *Buphagus erythrorhynchus*   B587 **RB**

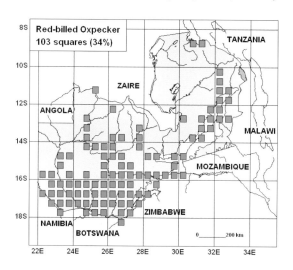

Distribution *Afrotropical* (*Ethiopia to South Africa*). More widespread than *B. africanus*, and as well as on game frequently on cattle and occasionally goats and other domestic stock. Thus it occurs up the Zambezi to the Sikongo area (Lukulu Dist.)[6] (although so far unrecorded from the Liuwa Plain N.P.), and further north to West Lunga N.P.[7], Kakoma and Solwezi[10]. Throughout the Kafue basin from Ndubeni[9], south to the Gwembe Valley, the Middle Zambezi and the entire Luangwa Valley north to Mubanga[4]. In the north recorded so far only from Sumbu N.P. (and not from Mweru Wantipa, cf. *B. africanus*); there are also remarkably few records from neighbouring Zaire[8]. *Alt.* 330-1700 m.

Ecology[1,6] In any wooded habitat, except the densest, where groups can detect their host animals. Large groups occur on host animals, up to 30-40 regularly on favoured species such as Impala, Giraffe, Hippopotamus and Zebra (of 12 host species known in the Luangwa Valley)[6]. Long-haired mammals such as Waterbuck and Bushbuck are intolerant of oxpeckers and are rarely hosts, though they may carry substantial numbers of ticks[6]. Sometimes roost on their hosts at night[5].

Status Resident, with some wandering (e.g. one ringed bird moved 50 km)[3].

Conservation Both oxpecker species became scarce where cattle dipping was undertaken, but since the 1990s "oxpecker-friendly" dips have been used in places. The population of the Choma area was exterminated in the 1970s, but in recent years there have been a few reports (including a breeding attempt in 1999), as well as records of this species during the 1990s at scattered localities throughout S. Zambia. Populations remain healthy in those national parks which still have good populations of the favoured hosts.

Breeding   Dec   Feb

(n=3)   2   1   *Clutch*: C/1 (1).

Taxonomy[2] *B. e. caffer*, with *B. e. angolensis* in the extreme south-west (larger, greyer above and lacking a brown collar).

References [1]Attwell (1966); [2]Benson *et al.* (1970); [3]Benson *et al.* (1971a); [4]Brelsford (1942); [5]Dowsett (1968); [6]Dowsett & Berry (in prep.); [7]Dowsett & Dowsett-Lemaire (1978d); [8]Schouteden (1971); [9]Tree (1966a); [10]White (1945-46).

Passeridae

House Sparrow *Passer domesticus*   B647 **RB**

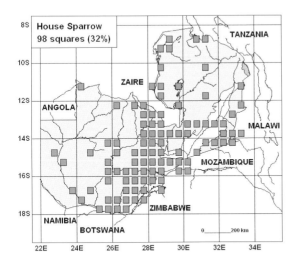

Distribution *Cosmopolitan (in the Afrotropics, mainly Somalia to South Africa, but spreading in West Africa)*. The spread of this species (introduced into South Africa) has been from the south[1,2]. It was first noticed in Zambia at Livingstone in Feb or Mar 1965 (breeding by early 1966), and later in 1965 was at Kalomo and Lusaka. These arrivals reflect the timing of its spread to N. Zimbabwe, to Karoi in 1961 and Wankie town in 1965[4]. It was soon on the Copperbelt (Ndola in 1966, Kitwe in 1967), two at Ngoma (Kafue N.P.) in Dec 1966 being the first of several examples of individuals turning up at localities and then disappearing, in advance of a later colonisation. *P. domesticus* had reached the far north-east by 1971 (Mbala), the same year it reached Eastern Province (Chadiza) and Lilongwe in Malawi[1]. The spread into W. Zambia appears to have been much slower, the first reports from Solwezi (1975) and Kalabo (1977) being long before the first from Mwinilunga Dist. (1993 at Hillwood)[3]. Its present distribution on the Eastern Province plateau is north to Chama. *Alt.* 330-1670 m.

Ecology Purely commensal, including bush-camps and very small villages, nesting on brick buildings; has come into contact with *P. griseus* in many places, but there is no direct evidence of the one replacing the other[5]. It is found on the whole in more densely-populated areas than its congener.

Status Resident in pairs and small groups usually, but assembling in several hundreds to roost in Lusaka in Feb 1980[3].

Breeding (n=144)

	Jan	Feb	Mar	Apr	May	Jun	Jul	Aug	Sep	Oct	Nov	Dec
	3	2	12	10	13	2	13	22	19	29	11	8

Clutch: C/1 (8); C/2 (9); C/3 (26); C/4 (35); C/5 (11). Multiple-brooded[3].

Moult: an adult started moult (after breeding) in Jan[3].

Taxonomy *P. d. indicus*.

References [1]Dowsett (1971a); [2]Dowsett (1976a); [3]Dowsett (in press a); [4]Harwin & Irwin (1966); [5]Penry (1978a).

[Great Sparrow *Passer motitensis*
Afrotropical (W. Angola to South Africa). Mapped as occurring in the Caprivi Strip (1822A), adjacent to SW Zambia[2], but this is perhaps a misidentification. It is unknown in NE Botswana beyond 18°50'S and is unlikely to occur further north[1]. **References** [1]Dowsett *et al.* (in prep.); [2]Herremans in Harrison *et al.* (1997).]

Northern Grey-headed Sparrow *Passer griseus*   B648 **RB**

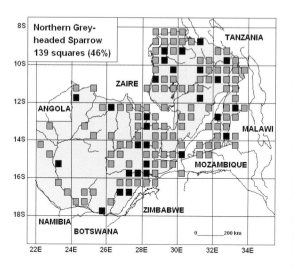

Distribution *Afrotropical* (*Mauritania to Zimbabwe*). (Black squares on the map indicate specimens examined). As with *P. domesticus*, this is a species which has arrived relatively recently in Zambia (but apparently from the north-east rather than the south): by the 1930s it was known with certainty south only to Chipata and Chiwefwe (Mkushi Dist.). Its range is still expanding[4]; at present it is unknown from much of the western half of the country (although in this case the sibling *P. diffusus* does occur in the woodland there). Its current range is down the Zambezi from Chavuma to Livingstone. It has spread in recent years to Mwinilunga Dist., reaching Mwinilunga town in 1980 and even Hillwood farm in 1992. Recorded from the Zambian side of the Middle Zambezi Valley at Feira (Luangwa town) and Chirundu; common in the Luangwa Valley in those few places with permanent buildings, and on the Eastern Province plateau[2]. *Alt.* 330-1700 m.

Ecology Generally commensal. Nest sites are more varied than in *P. domesticus*, including brick buildings, grass roofs, electric light poles, other species's nests (*Motacilla aguimp*)[1] and hollows in trees[2]. Has come into contact with *P. domesticus* through its congener spreading in the last 30 years. It seems unlikely these two sparrows are seriously competing[6]: in towns *P. griseus* tends to be in less populated areas than *P. domesticus*.

Status A 2-year survey of *P. griseus* and *P. diffusus* together showed no evidence of any movements[2].

Breeding	Dec	Jan	Feb	Mar	Apr	May	Jul	Aug	Sep
(n=51)	2	9	9	12	10	2	1	1	5

Clutch: C/2 (1); C/3 (3); C/4 (2); C/7 (1).

Taxonomy[3,5] This is now considered to be specifically distinct from *P. diffusus*, but their individual distributions and the extent to which they hybridize are not clear. The form concerned is *P. g. ugandae*.

References [1]Benson (1956b); [2]Dowsett (in press a); [3]Irwin (1981a); [4]Irwin (2002); [5]Irwin & Benson (1967b); [6]Penry (1978a).

Southern Grey-headed Sparrow *Passer diffusus*   B648 (part) **RB**

Distribution *Afrotropical* (*Tanzania to South Africa*). (Black squares on the map indicate specimens examined). Unlike *P. griseus*, mainly in woodland, where usually very common. Essentially the Luangwa Valley, from the Zinza stream (10°S)[3] southwards throughout the Zambezi Valley and Southern Province plateau (in parts of the latter a fairly recent arrival, perhaps from the 1940s)[5], north to about 15°S in the former, perhaps to 14°S in the latter, but definite identifications lacking north of the Kalabo area. *Alt.* 330-1300 m.

Ecology Open woodland, especially mopane and mixed *Acacia-Combretum*, also in thicket-clump savanna. In pairs when nesting, may flock in large numbers in the off-season. Nest sites are hollows in trees.

Status Resident, seasonally in flocks of several hundreds.

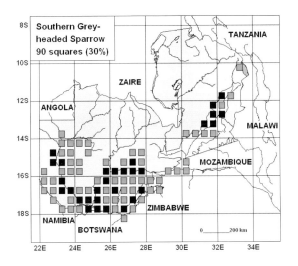

Breeding Jan Feb Mar
(n=6) 1 3 2
Clutch: C/4 (2); C/7 (1).
Moult: two birds in Mar had recently started[3].
Taxonomy[2,4] See discussion under *P. griseus*.
P. d. luangwae (type locality Mupamadzi
River; *NHM*)[1] is certainly the form in the
Luangwa Valley. It intergrades in the Middle
Zambezi with *P. d. stygiceps* (larger, but still
small-billed), the race in the rest of the
Southern Province plateau, being replaced
west of Victoria Falls by the paler *P. d. diffusus*.
References [1]Benson (1956b: 40); [2]Benson &
Benson (1975); [3]Dowsett (in press a); [4]Irwin
(1981a); [5]Irwin (2002).

Yellow-throated Petronia *Petronia superciliaris* B649 **RB**

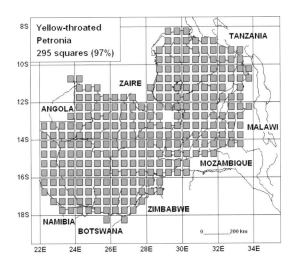

Distribution *Afrotropical (SE Gabon to South
Africa; mainly Zambezian)*. Locally very com-
mon in broad-leaved woodland throughout.
Alt. 330-1950 m (Mafingas)[3], though only
rarely to 1900 m on the Nyika[4].
Ecology In various types of woodland, mainly
miombo and mopane, also *Burkea*,
Combretum but usually avoiding *Acacia*.
Searches bark crevices for insects. Breeds in
tree holes, including old woodpeckers' nests.
Status A 2-year survey produced no evidence
of any movements[2].

Breeding	Jul	Aug	Sep	Oct
(n=53)	1	8	31	10
	Nov	Mar	Apr	
	1	1	1	

Clutch: C/1 (1); C/2 (11); C/3 (25); C/4 (7)

Moult: a juvenile just starting early Dec[6].
Taxonomy[5] *P. s. flavigula*, replaced in the north and north-west by *P. s. rufitergum* (type locality
Kabompo; *NMZB*)[1], which is darker above, greyer below.
References [1]Clancey (1964b: 136); [2]Dowsett (in press a); [3]Dowsett & Stjernstedt (1973); [4]Dowsett-
Lemaire (2006a); [5]Irwin & Benson (1967a); [6]Traylor (1965b).

Ploceidae

Red-billed Buffalo Weaver *Bubalornis niger* B644 **RB**

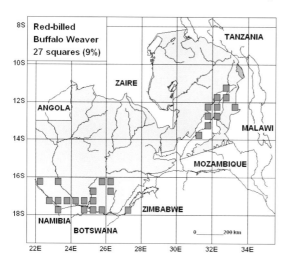

8S Red-billed
Buffalo Weaver
27 squares (9%)

Distribution *Afrotropical* (*Ethiopia to South Africa*). From the upper Luangwa Valley at the Musalangwa/Luangwa River confluence[4] south to about the Mtipwazi confluence[2]. Exceptionally has wandered to the Eastern Province plateau near Lundazi[4]. In the Middle Zambezi Valley near Sianzovu, then reappears above the Victoria Falls at Livingstone (where rare), up the Zambezi and the Mashi to the Matabele Plain and Shangombo[1] respectively, and on the Southern Province plateau to the Nanzhila area. Locally quite common, though easily overlooked away from nests. *Alt.* 500-1200 m.

Ecology Mopane and *Acacia* woodland, feeding on seeds on the ground (and seasonally on flying termites). Nests have been in Baobabs and *Acacia albida*, even in the base of stork (*Mycteria ibis*) nests.

Status Resident. Flocks of up to 20 when not breeding, but unlikely to move far from nest sites.

Breeding   Jan   Feb   Mar   Apr
(n=51)   8   15   20   8   *Clutch*: C/1 (2); C/2 (11); C/3 (22); C/4 (5); C/5 (1).

Taxonomy[5] *B. n. niger* in the south-west, replaced in the Luangwa Valley by *B. n. militaris* (type locality Mwaleshi River at *c.* 11°45'S, 32°15'E; *NMZB*)[3], female browner, less greyish, with little mottling.

References [1]Benson & Irwin (1967b); [2]Benson *et al.* (1971a); [3]Clancey (1977d: 234); [4]Dowsett (in press a); [5]Irwin (1981a).

Scaly-feathered Finch *Sporopipes squamifrons* B - **RB**

Distribution *Afrotropical* (*W. Angola to South Africa*). In 1994 and 1995 found at two localities in the south-west: Kazwili village (along the Livingstone-Sesheke road), and Limpumpu school, Loanja River (on the Simungoma-Machile road)[3]. In 1999 it was common in the Simungoma area, and also seen at Sekute, while in 2002 it appeared in the Ngwezi station area, and in 2007 at Livingstone[2]. Now nests annually in the Simungoma area (black square). *Alt.* 900-1000 m.

Ecology Degraded *Acacia* savanna, with scattered bushes and trees, often in heavily-grazed areas.

Status Undoubtedly a recent arrival, perhaps as a result of drought conditions in southern Africa. Probably resident now, although there are no records yet from Nov to Jan.

Breeding   Feb   Mar
(n=9)   6   3   Males in song and juveniles noted in Apr.
Clutch: C/2 (1); C/4 (2); C/5 (4) & N/5 (1); C/6 (1).

Taxonomy *S. s. squamifrons*[1].

References [1]Clancey (1968c); [2]Dowsett (in press a); [3]Dowsett *et al.* (1999a).

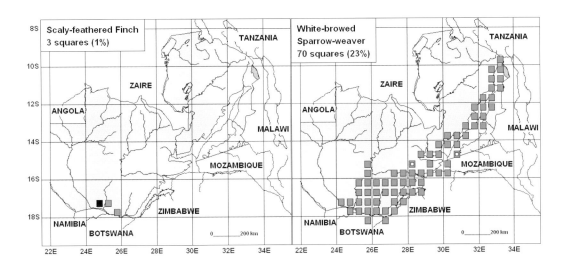

White-browed Sparrow-weaver *Plocepasser mahali*   B645 **RB**

Distribution *Afrotropical (Ethiopia to South Africa).* Throughout the Luangwa Valley from the Mafinga foothills[2] south to Luembe, and the Luano Valley to Chembe. Thence south to Feira (Luangwa town) and throughout the Middle Zambezi Valley, west to near Sesheke. Absent west of the Zambezi, even though there is some mopane in Sioma-Ngwezi N.P. North up the Kafue drainage to near Mwengwa[3], south of Chunga, and the southern edge of the Kafue Flats. Very common in its main range. Local in pockets of mopane on the Southern Province plateau (e.g. Lochinvar, Magoye River Bridge, Muckle Neuk). *Alt.* 330-1300 m.

Ecology Breeds gregariously, mostly in mopane but locally in *Sclerocarya caffra* and *Acacia* (e.g. *A. nigrescens*) amongst other species; where tall trees are available, nests are more than 4 m high[7]. Each bird has access to several nests, and several birds help with feeding young. Food in the dry season is predominantly seeds, with termite workers favoured early in the rains[6].

Status Resident, with some wandering outside the breeding season, e.g. to near Nyimba on the Eastern Province plateau (25 Mar) and to miombo near Lusaka (dry season, to Oct) (open squares)[3].

Breeding[5,6]   Sep   Oct   Nov   Dec   Jan   Feb   Mar
(n=58)   1   3   8   14   11   5   16
Clutch: C/1 (52); C/2 (52); C/3 (8). *Moult*: starting Apr or May[3].

Taxonomy[1,4] *P. m. pectoralis*, but *P. m. terricolor* is possible in the south-west.

References [1]Benson *et al.* (1970); [2]Clay (1953); [3]Dowsett (in press a); [4]Irwin (1981a); [5]Lewis (1982a); [6]Lewis (1982b); [7]Mitchell (1966).

Chestnut-mantled Sparrow-weaver *Plocepasser rufoscapulatus*   B646 **RB**

Distribution *Zambezian endemic (Angola east to Malawi).* Small numbers in the miombo woodlands of the northern plateau and escarpment, though unrecorded between Mporokoso Dist. and Chinsali Dist. (near Mukanga)[1]. South on the Eastern Province plateau to the Msoro escarpment[6] and Chipata[5]; down the Luangwa escarpment to near Mkunkunya, and in the Kafue drainage, south to about 14°30'S and the Luamala River[2]. Throughout the Copperbelt, while further west, it ranges to Chavuma and south on the Zambezi to Zambezi town (Balovale)[3], west to Nyatanda[4]. Present at lower levels in the Luangwa

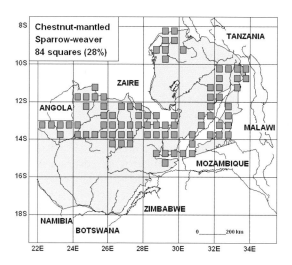

and Luano Valleys, where pockets of miombo occur, even to Frank's Lakes in the former[4]. Somewhat unobtrusive when not breeding, but the bulky nests are very conspicuous. *Alt.* 600-1500 m.

Ecology Usually in tall, dry, unspoilt miombo woodland, also where mixed with tall mopane. Often in escarpment woodlands, even the thinner types, and occasionally where there is a slight thicket understorey. Occasionally joins mixed bird parties. Nests occur in small clusters, up to 5 m up, even in spindly saplings.

Status Apparently resident.

Breeding	Sep	Oct	Nov
(n=12)	9	1	2

Clutch: C/2 (5); N/4 (1).

Taxonomy No races recognized.

References [1]Aspinwall (1973a); [2]Benson (1956f); [3]Britton (1970); [4]Dowsett (in press a); [5]Lynes (1938); [6]Winterbottom (1939b).

Baglafecht Weaver *Ploceus baglafecht*

B614 **RB**

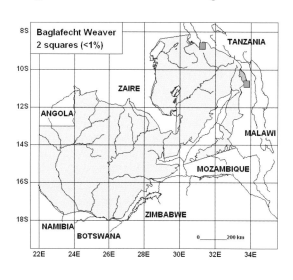

Distribution *Afromontane near-endemic (E. Nigeria/Cameroon and Ethiopia to N. Malawi)*. Essentially confined to the Nyika plateau, where fairly common (1900-2200 m, to 2450 m on the Malawi side)[4]. A pair at Uningi Pans near Mbala (1670 m)[5] in Dec 1999 were presumably wanderers from the Tanzanian Ufipa Plateau (where it breeds as near as Tatanda)[2]. The species is also quite common in SE Zaire, in the Marungu highlands[3].

Ecology Primarily an insectivorous species, in isolated clumps of trees in grassland, at forest edges and riparian scrub[4], sometimes on the edge of pine plantation. In pairs or small family groups.

Status Resident, with local wandering.

Breeding	Oct	Dec
(n=4)	1	3

(Including Malawi side of SW Nyika; breeds overall Oct to Feb[4].) Nest-building Jan. *Clutch*: C/2 (1).

Moult: both sexes have a non-breeding dress[6], but this aspect has not been examined in Zambia.

Taxonomy *P. b. nyikae* (type locality Nyika Plateau, Malawi)[1]. The Ufipa population is *P. b. sharpii* (differing from *P. b. nyikae* in having the belly lemon yellow rather than grey).

References [1]Benson (1938); [2]Dowsett (in press a); [3]Dowsett & Prigogine (1974); [4]Dowsett-Lemaire (2006a); [5]Leonard & Van Daele (2001b); [6]Mackworth-Praed & Grant (1949).

Bertram's Weaver *Ploceus bertrandi* B615 **RB**

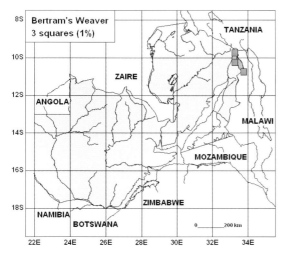

Distribution *Afromontane endemic (Tanzania to S. Malawi)*. Fairly common throughout the eastern highlands, from the Mafingas (1550-1950 m)[3,5], Makutu (2070 m)[2] to Nyika (1900-2200 m)[4].

Ecology Usually on forest edge, in riparian growth (including *Acacia abyssinica*) or in isolated clumps of trees in grassland, occasionally on the edge of pine plantation. Appears to fill the same ecological niche as the similar-sized *P. baglafecht*. Mostly insectivorous (and nectarivorous), in pairs or small family parties.

Status Resident.

Breeding   Nov   Dec
(n=2)   1   1
Occupied nests Apr-May[1]. *Clutch*: N/1 (1).

Taxonomy No races recognized.

References [1]Aspinwall (1971a); [2]Dowsett (1971h); [3]Dowsett & Stjernstedt (1973); [4]Dowsett-Lemaire (2006a); [5]Leonard *et al.* (2001a).

Slender-billed Weaver *Ploceus pelzelni* B616 **RB**

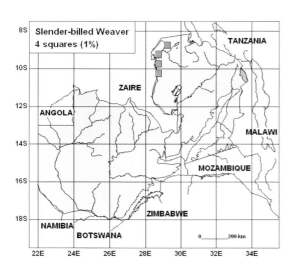

Distribution *Afrotropical (Sierra Leone to N. Zambia)*. Present only in the L. Mweru area, from near Chiengi[1] south to Chabilikila (where reported in 1998)[2] and Kasenga on the Luapula River[3] (the most southerly records of the species). In very small numbers, and easily overlooked. *Alt*. 920-960 m.

Ecology Reedbeds and Papyrus on the shores of L. Mweru and the Luapula River. A very small, insectivorous weaver, with no obvious counterpart in this habitat.

Status Resident.

Breeding   Feb
(n=1)   1   In addition copulation has been observed in late Dec and nest-building in Jan. *Clutch*: no data.

Taxonomy *P. p. monachus*.

References [1]Benson (1956d); [2]Dowsett (in press a); [3]Lynes (1938).

[Black-necked Weaver *Ploceus nigricollis*
Afrotropical (Senegal to S. Zaire). A species of forest edge and secondary habitats, known from Kasaji in Katanga[1], which might occur further south in N. Mwinilunga. **References** [1]Schouteden (1971).]

Spectacled Weaver *Ploceus ocularis* B626 **RB**

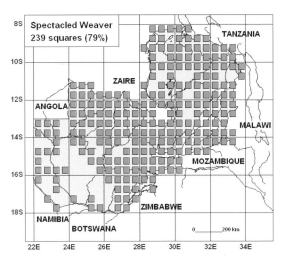

Distribution *Afrotropical* (*Nigeria to South Africa*). Common in rank growth, almost throughout at all elevations, including much of the Southern Province plateau (where previously thought to be absent)[1]. Scarce in the dry south-west, and unrecorded from a large area of wooded country between the Kafue and Zambezi drainages. *Alt.* 330 m at Luangwa town (Feira) to 2200 m on the Nyika Plateau[3].

Ecology Usually on the edge of riparian forest or thicket; it does occur away from water, though not in extensive dry forest or thicket such as *Cryptosepalum*. Insectivorous, foraging in dense vegetation and on bark, in pairs or small (presumably family) groups. One nest was made entirely of pine needles[5].

Status Resident. A ringed bird was retrapped when at least 11 years of age[2].

Breeding Sep Oct Nov Dec Jan Feb Mar
(n=64) 12 12 7 12 5 11 5 *Clutch*: C/1 (5); C/2 (34); C/3 (4).
Moult: there is no eclipse plumage. Adults usually start in Feb and finish about May-Jun[1].

Taxonomy[4,6,7] *P. o. crocatus*, replaced in the east by *P. o. suahelicus* (males with a more chestnut, less golden, wash on the forehead and surrounding the black throat) and in the Mambova and Kazungula areas by *P. o. tenuirostris*[1] (like *crocatus* in colour, differing from it and *suahelicus* by a more slender bill).

References [1]Dowsett (in press a); [2]Dowsett & Leonard (2001); [3]Dowsett-Lemaire (2006a); [4]Irwin & Benson (1967a); [5]Madge (1972g); [6]Traylor (1964); [7]Traylor (1965a).

Bocage's Weaver *Ploceus temporalis* B617 **RB**

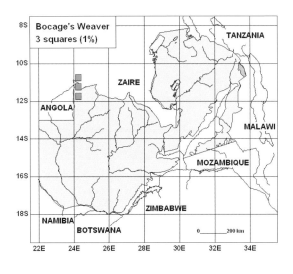

Distribution *Zambezian endemic* (*S. Zaire to south-central Angola*). Confined in Zambia to N. Mwinilunga Dist. Ranges from the Luakela/Chitunta stream confluence northwards, particularly in the Chitunta Plain area[2]. Very local, but when nesting may be present in moderate numbers. *Alt.* 1200-1400 m. The colony reported in 1956 on the Chisoko stream, Sakeji[1], may no longer exist[3].

Ecology Edge of thin riparian scrub, always nesting in bushes and trees over running water[2]. Colonies consist of up to 50 nests.

Status Presumably resident, but few observations outside the breeding season.

Breeding Aug Sep Oct
(n=86) 21 52 13

Nests are lined from Jun onwards. *Clutch*: C/1 (12); C/2 (41) & N/2 (11); C/3 (2).
Taxonomy No races (but in the past considered a subspecies of the Cape Weaver *P. capensis*).
References [1]Benson & Irwin (1964b); [2]Colebrook-Robjent (1984); [3]Dowsett (in press a).

Large Golden Weaver *Ploceus xanthops*   B618 **RB**

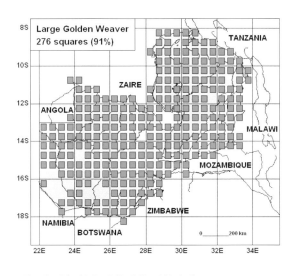

Distribution *Afrotropical (SE Gabon to South Africa).* Throughout and locally common, but so far few records from the south-west, apart from Shangombo[1] and a few other places[3]. At all altitudes, from 330 m in the lower Luangwa, up to 2050 m on the Nyika Plateau[4].
Ecology Usually near water, on the edge of forest, thicket and scrub, and small reedbeds. Locally also in gardens, abandoned cultivation and edges of any woodland. Only in small groups and does not flock. Not known to nest colonially.
Status Resident.

Breeding (n=219)	Aug	Sep	Oct	Nov	Dec
	1	17	30	13	16
	Jan	Feb	Mar	Apr	
	55	65	20	2	

Clutch: C/1 (24); C/2 (99); C/3 (19).
Moult: adults start at various times from late Feb onwards[3].
Taxonomy *P. x. xanthops* (*P. x. jamesoni*, greenish-yellow below, perhaps in the south-east[2]).
References [1]Benson & White (1957); [2]Clancey (1980d); [3]Dowsett (in press a); [4]Dowsett-Lemaire (2006a).

Southern Brown-throated Weaver *Ploceus xanthopterus*   B619 **RB**

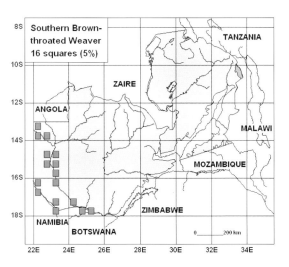

Distribution *Zambezian/Eastern (Tanzania to South Africa).* Along the Zambezi and Mashi Rivers, from near Chinyama Litapi[1], south-east to Mambova[4] and Kazungula[2]. Locally in large colonies, and doubtless easily overlooked because its habitat is often inaccessible. Scarce in the upper regions of the Zambezi, but common further south in the Kazungula area. There is no evidence that it occurs in Zambia outside this limited area (visually, it has been confused with other weavers, e.g. *P. xanthops*)[3]. *Alt.* 950-1050 m.
Ecology Along rivers, often over deep water. Breeds colonially in reedbeds, feeding in nearby grassland, scrub and thicket.
Status Resident.

Breeding   Feb   Mar
(n=12)   9   3   Nest-building mid-Dec. *Clutch*: C/1 (2); C/2 (1); C/3 (9).
Taxonomy *P. x. castaneigula*[3].
References [1]Aspinwall (1979b); [2]Dowsett (in press a); [3]Irwin (1978); [4]Irwin & Benson (1966b).

Lesser Masked Weaver *Ploceus intermedius*   B620 **RB**

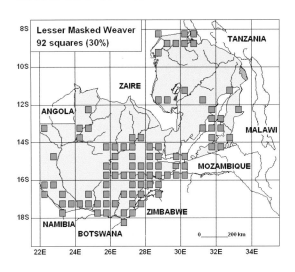

Distribution *Afrotropical* (*Ethiopia to South Africa*). A very patchy distribution, with small numbers essentially in the drier woodlands of Southern, Central and Eastern Provinces, with an isolated population between Lakes Mweru and Tanganyika (between Nchelenge[7] and Nkamba), where it is abundant. Occurs otherwise north to Monongwa (L. Bangweulu)[3], the Luangwa Valley to Tembwe, and Eastern Province plateau to Membe stream[6]. In W. Zambia few north of 14°S, to Nguvu[1], Ntambu[5], the Kabompo area[2], and in the Kafue basin to Munkumpu[3]. *Alt.* 330-1350 m.
Ecology Most often associated with dry, open woodland, especially *Acacia*, though usually not far from water. Its abundance in the far north may be due to the fact that *P. velatus* there occurs in a different habitat (see below). Has a mixed diet including fruit (such as mulberries) and insects. Its finer bill suggests it does not compete directly with its larger associates, *P. velatus* and *P. cucullatus*. Often nests in the colonies of other, more numerous, weavers (*P. velatus, P. cucullatus*). Usually in *Acacia*, but has nested in *Borassus* palms and exotic bamboos (*Bambusa vulgaris*), and even in an ambatch (*Aeschynomene elaphroxylon*) tree by L. Mweru[4]. As with other weavers, nests are sometimes built near those of *Belonogaster* wasps.
Status Present all months, and presumed mainly resident; one bird ringed at Lochinvar in Jan was recovered 20 km south the following Dec[5].

Breeding   Aug   Sep   Oct   Nov   Dec   Jan   Feb   Mar   Apr
(n=184)   3   22   7   14   25   49   50   13   1
In breeding dress from early Sep (the earliest weaver in the Luangwa Valley in this respect), but may work on its nest as early as May, when in non-breeding dress[5].
Clutch: C/1 (20); C/2 (69); C/3 (8) & N/3 (2). (Two C/1 were parasitized by *Chrysococcyx caprius*, as were several of the other clutches).
Taxonomy *P. i. cabanisii*.
References [1]Aspinwall (1979b); [2]Benson (1960c); [3]Benson & Irwin (1967b); [4]Benson & Pitman (1956-57); [5]Dowsett (in press a); [6]Meyer de Schauensee (1951); [7]White (1951b).

African Masked Weaver *Ploceus velatus*   B621 **RB**

Distribution *Afrotropical* (*Mauritania to South Africa*). There are two distinct populations in Zambia. (1) *P. v. velatus* (solid squares): the southern half of the country, northwards throughout the Luangwa Valley, the Kafue drainage to the Luswishi River confluence[1] and the whole of the Zambezi drainage

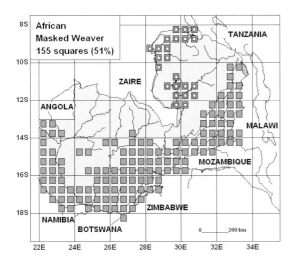

within Zambia; locally very common, even abundant. (2) *P. v. katangae* (open squares): in the L. Bangweulu area, from Mukuku and Kopa northwards up the Luapula to L. Mweru, and across to the Nkamba area[3]; quite numerous. The two forms occur within about 100 km of each other, but no specimens are available from the southern Bangweulu-Muchinga escarpment area to see if they are genetically isolated. [There are unconfirmed sight records from the Copperbelt[3] (if correct, it would be important to establish the taxon involved).] The area between L. Tanganyika and the upper Luangwa Valley, whence there is no record, is inhabited in part by another allopatric *Ploceus* weaver, *P. reichardi. Alt.* 330-1600 m.

Ecology The nominate race is a bird typically of dry, open woodland, especially thornbush and neglected cultivation, nesting almost exclusively in *Acacia*, usually in small colonies, but exceptionally of up to 1000 nests together in the Luangwa Valley[3]. It also occurs in Papyrus swamp in the Lukanga, a habitat similar to that of *P. v. katangae*, and it nests locally in reeds in Malawi[4]. *P. v. katangae* is associated with swamps, and nests mainly in reedbeds and Papyrus (e.g. on Chisenga Is.), but also in bush clumps (Katema Is.)[2] and a mango tree[3]. This difference in habitat has prompted some people to think there might be two species, but both taxa are more catholic than supposed. Flocks of *P. v. katangae* have been noted in dry woodland, up to 7 km from water. *P. v. velatus* may breed alongside other weavers (*P. intermedius, P. cucullatus*) and flock with them in the off-season.

Status Present all months, and presumed mainly resident, but one bird ringed at Lochinvar in Jan was recovered 55 km east the following Jun[3]. Roosts of non-breeding *velatus* (usually in reedbeds) often exceed 1000 birds.

Breeding   Aug   Sep   Oct   Nov   Dec   Jan   Feb   Mar
(n=491)   1   17   19   55   71   172   134   22

These figures include both races – the limited data for *P. v. katangae*, whose egg colour is distinctive, being for the months of Sep (1), Oct (2) and Mar (8)[3].
Clutch: C/1 (41); C/2 (139); C/3 (162); C/4 (13).
Moult: there is a partial pre-nuptial moult, with some birds in breeding dress late Jul and all by Nov, and a complete post-breeding moult from mid-Feb onwards[3].
Taxonomy *P. v. velatus/shelleyi*, replaced in the north by *P. v. katangae* (which some authorities consider a separate species)[5]. The male of *katangae* is smaller (wing 60-65 mm, as opposed to 73-81), and greener above in breeding dress, with the black of the sides of the head more restricted.
References [1]Benson & Irwin (1967b); [2]Benson & Pitman (1956-57); [3]Dowsett (in press a); [4]Dowsett-Lemaire & Dowsett (2006); [5]Louette & Benson (1982).

Lake Tanganyika Weaver *Ploceus reichardi*   B - **AV?**

Distribution and Status *Zambezian endemic* (*SW Tanzania to S. Zaire*). Known so far only from Kaka, Mbala Dist. (0831D), where found in Jan 1996[2], in Papyrus and other vegetation along the Saise River (which flows into the L. Rukwa system), and also in the trees and thicket clumps in the floodplain termitaria. Found again in the area in Dec 1999[3]. *Alt. c.* 1550 m. This species appears to form a superspecies with last, i.e. allopatric, and unlikely to occur together. No breeding data, but juveniles were present in Jan, and of 30-40 in mid-Dec, most were moulting into breeding dress.

Taxonomy *P. r. reichardi* (if the taxon *ruweti* is conspecific[1], and confined to S. Zaire).

References [1]Dowsett & Dowsett-Lemaire (1993); [2]Leonard & Beel (1999); [3]Leonard *et al.* (2001c).

Spotted-backed (Village) Weaver *Ploceus cucullatus*   B622 **RB**

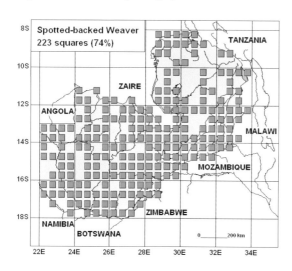

Distribution *Afrotropical* (*Mauritania to South Africa*). Almost throughout, but partial to water, and absent from higher altitudes. Although unexpectedly sparse in some areas, it is present in very large colonies in lower-lying areas as between Lakes Mweru and Tanganyika, and smaller colonies (usually up to 50 nests) at low altitude elsewhere. *Alt.* 330 to about 1450 m.

Ecology Usually near water, but often wandering into woodland. Unlike the situation in most of central and western Africa, where it is abundant around habitation, it is rarely commensal in Zambia. Breeds colonially in reeds or trees near water, occasionally in open woodland. Forages at all levels on the edge of thicket, riparian growth, in long grass or reeds, abandoned cultivation and (especially in the non-breeding season) in open woodland. Nests are sometimes in or near raptors' nests (e.g. *Terathopius ecaudatus*)[1].

Status Resident, with wandering in the off-season, often with other weavers (especially *P. velatus*).

Breeding	Sep	Oct	Nov	Dec	Jan	Feb	Mar	
(n=475)	35	47	12	4	63	272	42	*Clutch*: C/1 (21); C/2 (125); C/3 (78).

Moult: in S. Zambia may start as early as late Jan[4].

Taxonomy *P. c. nigriceps*, replaced by *P. c. paroptus* (brighter yellow above and below) in the east and north-east[2,3].

References [1]Benson (1956c); [2]Benson (1956f); [3]Clancey (1970e); [4]Dowsett (in press a).

Yellow-backed Weaver *Ploceus melanocephalus*   B623 **RB**

Distribution *Afrotropical* (*Mauritania to S. Zaire*). Locally common in swamps, from Bulaya, west through Mweru Wantipa to L. Mweru[1], and up the Luapula River to Johnston Falls[3]. [A sighting further south, from Bangweulu at Kalasa Mukoso, requires confirmation[2].] *Alt.* 950-1100 m.

Ecology Nests in small colonies in Papyrus swamp and reedbeds, wandering into nearby thicket.

Status Resident.

Breeding	Feb	Mar	
(n=17)	6	11	Also nest-building from late Dec. *Clutch*: C/1 (6); C/2 (7) & N/2 (3).

Breeding dress Dec to mid-Jun.

Taxonomy *P. m. duboisi*.

References [1]Benson & Pitman (1956-57); [2]Dowsett (in press a); [3]White (1951b).

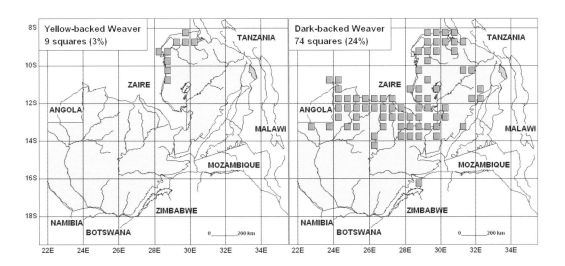

Dark-backed (Forest) Weaver *Ploceus bicolor* B625 **RB**

Distribution *Afrotropical* (*E. Nigeria to South Africa*). The main population is in the evergreen forests and thickets of the northern Zambian plateau, east to Muzyatama[2] and along the Muchinga escarpment to Masase and Chengelo[3]. Thence throughout the Copperbelt and continuously across to Mwinilunga[3], west to Lukolwe[4]. On the Copperbelt it ranges south to Imanda[7], and in the Kafue basin to the East Lunga pontoon and Moshi[3]. Generally common in its main range. An isolated breeding population exists in the dry thickets of the low-lying Middle Zambezi Valley around Mbendele, near Siavonga[1]. [Further downriver there is a sighting from Ruckomechi (1529C), on the Zimbabwean side of the Zambezi[6].] *Alt.* 930-1770 m (Danger Hill), with the Zambezi Valley population at 430 m.

Ecology Inhabits evergreen forest, both wet and dry, including *Cryptosepalum* (very common); and in the Zambezi Valley it is in dry, mainly deciduous thicket. Has adapted to gardens where there are suitable tall trees and shrubs. Present in rich, fire-protected miombo, turning into forest, at Ndola[5], and wanders into more open miombo with bird parties. An insectivorous species, in pairs or family groups, feeding by gleaning. Probes bark and vegetation debris.

Status Resident.

Breeding Sep Oct Dec Jan
(n=18) 12   3   1   2   Also nest-building early Apr. The 2 Jan records are from the Zambezi Valley.

Clutch: C/1 (1); C/2 (2); C/3 (4) & N/3 (1).

Taxonomy *P. b. kigomaensis*. The population in the Middle Zambezi appears to be *P. b. stictifrons*[1,6] (differing in having the crown and all upperparts dusky brown, lacking the contrast between the blackish brown crown and brownish upperparts of *P. b. kigomaensis*).

References [1]Aspinwall (1972a,b); [2]Benson (1949a); [3]Dowsett (in press a); [4]Leonard (1998b); [5]Madge (1972b); [6]Riddell (1995); [7]Tree (1966a).

Compact Weaver *Ploceus superciliosus* B624 **AV (R?)**

Distribution and Status *Afrotropical* (*Senegal to NW Zambia*). Jali Makawa collected three at Salujinga (1024C) 18 Sep 1962[1], none of them in breeding dress. It was not until 1998 that the species was found again, when between 10 Oct and 24 Nov up to 5 were present (at times with *Euplectes ardens*) in two areas of short grass dambo near the Jimbe and Kanyengele Rivers (also 1024C)[2]. These records are at the southern limit of its range. *Alt.* 1220-1280 m. Possibly this bird is just an occasional visitor to NW Zambia, although males in Nov were in breeding plumage and calling[2]. Further north at Kasaji in Zaire there are records for most months[4].

Taxonomy[3] No races, but this population is supposedly of the southern, monomorphic type. The species might be better placed in its own genus, *Pachyphantes*.

References [1]Benson & Irwin (1964b); [2]Leonard & Peters (1999); [3]Louette (1988a); [4]Schouteden (1971).

Bar-winged Weaver *Ploceus angolensis*   B627 **RB**

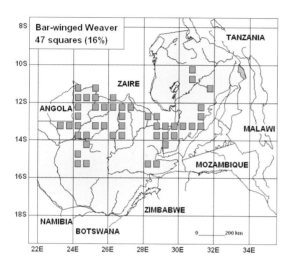

Distribution *Zambezian endemic (NE Zambia to W. Angola).* Usually uncommon, in mature, mossy miombo woodland. On the northern Zambian plateau, in a very limited area from Ngitwa[1] south-east to Shiwa Ngandu[3]. Further south, ranges along the Muchinga escarpment from Mutinondo Wilderness to Mita Hills Dam[2]. There is an isolated population in the Lusaka area[3] (protected in a private reserve on Lazy J ranch in the Leopardshill road area, but perhaps no longer near Chinkuli, where miombo largely destroyed). Locally on the Copperbelt, west almost to Zambezi (near Dipalata)[2] and south to the Luampa area[3]. *Alt.* 1000-1600 m.

Ecology Almost endemic to miombo woodland, but also in the canopy of *Cryptosepalum* forest (uncommon), where there is *Usnea* lichen ("Old man's beard"). Insectivorous, feeds by gleaning on the trunk and main branches, and into *Usnea* (in which it also constructs its nest)[3]. Does not flock, but often joins mixed bird parties.

Status Resident.

Breeding   Aug   Sep   Oct   Nov
(n=15)   1   9   4   1   Nest-building may start from end May.
Clutch: C/1 (1); C/2 (4) & N/2 (2); C/3 (2) & N/3 (1).

Taxonomy No races recognized. Related to the allopatric, and ecologically similar, *P. olivaceiceps*.

References [1]Aspinwall (1979a); [2]Dowsett (in press a); [3]Stjernstedt & Aspinwall (1979).

Olive-headed Weaver *Ploceus olivaceiceps*   B - **RB**

Distribution *Zambezian endemic (S. Tanzania to central Mozambique).* First found in 1979, it replaces the last species east of the Rift, in a limited area of the Eastern Province plateau, between the Lundazi area and Chimaliro F.R.[1] south to Misale[2], west to the Chipengali area[4]. Local and uncommon. *Alt.* 1150-1400 m.

Ecology Miombo woodland with *Usnea* lichen, in the canopy and mid-levels, feeding like *P. angolensis*.
Status Resident.

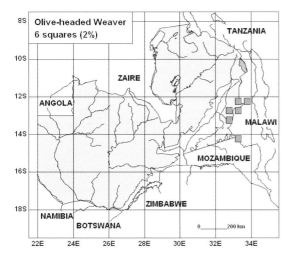

Olive-headed Weaver
6 squares (2%)

Conservation Classified as "Near Threatened"[3]. Suspected to occur in only one national park (Lukusuzi); present in a few forest reserves (but under heavy human pressure), such as Chimaliro.

Breeding   Oct
(n=1)   1   In addition 2 nests in Oct were ready for laying. *Clutch*: C/1 (1).

Taxonomy No races recognized (since the form in highland areas of Tanzania, *nicolli*, has been given specific status)[5].

References [1]Aspinwall (1979a); [2]Aspinwall (1984b); [3]BirdLife International (2000, 2004a); [4]Dowsett (in press a); [5]Franzmann (1983).

Red-headed Weaver *Anaplectes melanotis*   B628 **RB**

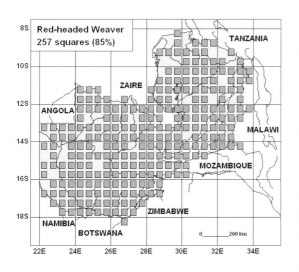

Red-headed Weaver
257 squares (85%)

Distribution *Afrotropical (Senegal to South Africa)*. Common in broad-leaved woodland almost throughout at low and medium altitudes. *Alt.* 330-1600 m.

Ecology Inhabits open, rather than closed, woodland of all types (except rare in *Acacia*). Regular in thin miombo, mopane, *Burkea*, and other woodlands of similar structure, even in the open canopy of *Cryptosepalum* forest (quite common in places). In family parties (not large flocks), often associated with mixed-species groups. Mainly insectivorous, gleaning from leaves and the tips of branches, in bushes, saplings, small and large trees. In the Lusaka area it is sometimes alongside another insectivore *P. angolensis*, of similar size, but with a different feeding ecology[5]. Nests (singly or in small groups) usually in trees (including eucalyptus), but also on pylons, telephone wires etc[2].

Status Resident, with no more than limited wandering. Monthly indices from a 2-year survey showed no seasonal fluctuations[2].

Breeding   Aug   Sep   Oct   Nov   Dec
(n=125)   5   56   35   24   5   *Clutch*: C/1 (2); C/2 (19); C/3 (62); C/4 (8).
Begins moulting into breeding dress in Jul, and may be in full plumage by the end of that month. Non-breeding dress mainly Mar-Jun[2].

Taxonomy[1] *A. m. rubriceps* (completely red head in male), but in N. Zambia individuals sometimes occur with some black on the face, thus tending towards *leuconotus* (but with yellow, rather than red, wings). Such birds ("*gurneyi*") have been reported south to Mansa Dist. and Bangweulu[4], and even once at Nkana[3]. The name *rubriceps* is pre-dated by *A. melanotis*.

References [1]Benson (1956f); [2]Dowsett (in press a); [3]Jones (1945); [4]Neave (1910); [5]Stjernstedt & Aspinwall (1979).

[Red-headed Malimbe *Malimbus rubricollis*

Guineo-Congolian near-endemic (*Sierra Leone to W. Kenya and S. Zaire*). There is a specimen from forest in the Kundelungu Mts of Katanga, far removed from the previously known range of the species[1]. **References** [1]Louette (1988a).]

Thick-billed Weaver *Amblyospiza albifrons*   B613 **RB**

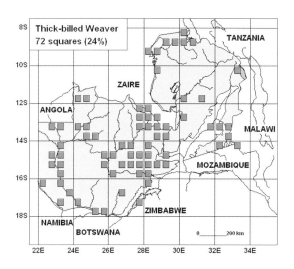

Thick-billed Weaver
72 squares (24%)

Distribution *Afrotropical* (*mainly Guinea to South Africa*). Fairly widespread in small reedbeds on the plateau. There are scattered breeding records from the whole of the range, except the extreme north-east and north-west. Does wander to dry riparian vegetation, including a few records from the low-lying Luangwa Valley (Masumba[6], Jan) and the Middle Zambezi Valley (near Sinamalima[6], Dec). Major concentrations occur in the Mweru-Luapula area (from Nkamba south to about Mwense), the Copperbelt and Kafue basin (south to Itezhi-Tezhi and Mchito Gorge), and the Upper Zambezi, from Jivundu camp down to the Victoria Falls. In Eastern Province there are a few records between the Kalichero area and Katete. In the north-east the only records are from Mpika[1] and near Mulekatembo, while in the north-west there are just two records (Mwinilunga[3] and Mundwiji Plain[5]), and it is unknown from Kasaji in neighbouring Zaire[7]. *Alt.* 900 to 1700 m, exceptionally down to 500 m in the Middle Zambezi and Luangwa Valleys.

Ecology Essentially a species of reedbeds and riparian forest on plateau streams and dams, or of *Typha* and Papyrus in floodplains. Its apparent absence from Bangweulu and the wetlands between Mwinilunga and Chililabombwe cannot be explained. Outside the breeding season it is also mainly in reedbeds, but wanders at times into cultivation (e.g. maize fields), thickets, riparian forest and even miombo woodland. Its large size and in particular its large bill probably preclude competition with other granivores. Nests in isolation or often in small groups (in reeds), up to 10.

Status Resident, with evidence of no more than local movements. In Apr-Oct (when not breeding) can occur in large groups, in flocks of up to 50, even to 300 at Ndola[6]. While the nest is conspicuous, the bird itself is discreet, and easily overlooked; nevertheless the impression that it has spread since the 1970s may be correct, favoured by the construction of new farm dams.

Breeding   Nov   Dec   Jan   Feb   Mar
(n=45)   1   1   13   25   5   Nest-building has been reported as early as the end of Sep. *Clutch*: C/1 (2); C/2 (5); C/3 (15); C/4 (4).
Moult: one completing moult end Jul[6].

Taxonomy *A. a. montana* (male with crown and nape black, little contrast with back), replaced by *A. a. maxima* (larger) in the Zambezi drainage (from Kabompo Dist. down to Victoria Falls)[2,4].

References [1]Benson (1956f); [2]Benson & White (1957); [3]Bowen (1983j); [4]Clancey (1972b); [5]Dowsett

(1973b); [6]Dowsett (in press a); [7]Schouteden (1971).

Cardinal Quelea *Quelea cardinalis*   B629 **AMB/R?**

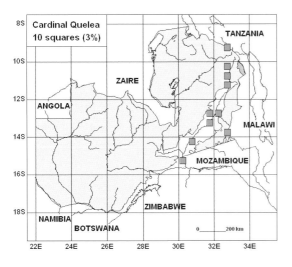

Distribution *Afrotropical* (*Ethiopia to Zambia-Malawi*). Distribution centred on dry, low-lying wooded savanna in the Luangwa Valley: from Kanyani[10] and Probert's Point[1], then Mulilo's[7,8] and scattered localities northwards to Mirongo[9]. Noted on a very few occasions on the Eastern Province plateau near Chipata[5] (and it has bred in similar habitat over the Malawi border near Lilongwe[6]). Exceptionally a male (in breeding dress) was seen in Apr near Mwenzo, on the Tanzanian border[5]. It should be sought in the Middle Zambezi Valley, as known from Mana Pools on the Zimbabwe side[11]. *Alt.* 370-1140 m, exceptionally to 1650 m (at Mwenzo).

Ecology Rank grassland and scrub, tall grass among trees in abandoned cultivation.

Status Difficult to assess, for even in breeding dress this species is not easily separated from *Q. erythrops.* The few records are for the period 23 Jan to 3 Jun, and it may be there is some migration (although in non-breeding dress the species could easily be overlooked). Usually in small groups, totalling 100 in one instance (Chiwale, 26 Feb 1980)[5].

Breeding   Feb
(n=1)   1   *Clutch*: C/3 (1). The one record from near Kakumbi[2,3].
Breeding dress Jan-late May[5].

Taxonomy *Q. c. rhodesiae* (type locality Mulilo's, near Old Petauke; *NHM*)[4,7].

References [1]Aspinwall (1975b); [2]Benson & Pitman (1956-57); [3]Benson & White (1957); [4]Dowsett (1980b); [5]Dowsett & Leonard (in press a); [6]Dowsett-Lemaire & Dowsett (2006); [7]Grant & Mackworth-Praed (1944: 65); [8]Neave (1907); [9]Neave (1910); [10]Stoehr & Sclater (1906); [11]Varden (1999a).

Red-headed Quelea *Quelea erythrops*   B630 **AMB**

Distribution *Afrotropical* (*Senegal to South Africa*). In general, allopatric with the last (from which it needs to be separated with great care in the field), and typically a bird of dambos and other wet plateau grasslands. It does occur sparsely on the Eastern Province plateau (as does *Q. cardinalis*), south to Chadiza Dist[4]. Otherwise, throughout the northern half of the country, southwards on the Southern Province plateau (where sparse) to Kalomo[1]. West of the Zambezi, south to Suu and Kalobolelwa[4], though so far unrecorded along the Mashi. Locally very numerous, especially in the north and north-west. *Alt.* 760-1670 m.

Ecology Damp grassland in general, particularly in dambos. Feeds also in rice fields, and at times in miombo woodland. Breeds in *Phragmites* reedbeds, in colonies of up to 100-150 nests (Mpulungu, Chalimbana, Bilili Hot Springs)[4].

Status Intra-African migrant and breeding visitor[5], present 11 Sep to 12 May, once 20 May (Ndubeni)[5].

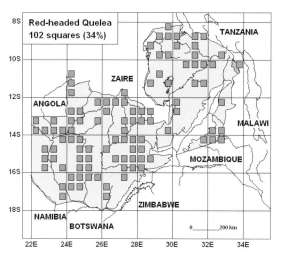

The average first date over 17 years was 11 Dec, the average last (in 21 years) 10 Apr[4]. Numbers are particularly noticeable mid-Jan to early Apr, when flocks of 100 or more occur[4]. Roosts with other seed-eaters such as *Quelea quelea* and *Euplectes* spp.

Breeding

	Jan	Feb	Mar
(n=8)	4	1	3

In addition, in 5 colonies egg-laying probably started in Jan. Breeding dress late Nov to 4 May[4]. *Clutch*: C/2 (2); C/3 (1).

Moult: no data on complete moult, although suggested it is probably mid-Apr to mid-Jun[5], and so possibly undertaken extralimitally.

Taxonomy No races recognized[3], although *Q. e. viniceps* has been proposed from S. Tanzania[2].

References [1]Aspinwall (1973f); [2]Clancey (1986); [3]Craig (1987); [4]Dowsett & Leonard (in press a); [5]Tree (1965).

Red-billed Quelea *Quelea quelea*

B631 **AMB**

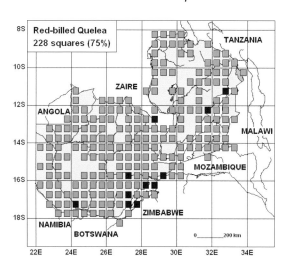

Distribution *Afrotropical* (*Mauritania to South Africa*). Throughout at low and medium elevations, and locally abundant (particularly at low levels). Sparse in well-wooded, high-rainfall areas, and absent from parts of the north and north-east over about 1400 m altitude. Localities from which breeding has been proven (black squares) are mainly below 1000 m, in the Middle Zambezi and Luangwa Valleys and immediately adjacent plateau areas[2]. Some small breeding colonies may have been overlooked in other dry areas, especially *Acacia*-dominated. Birds in much of the Zambian plateau may have wandered great distances. *Alt.* 330-1700 m.

Ecology Most numerous in areas where there are abundant grass seeds, whether natural (such as *Pennisetum typhoides*) or cultivated crops (especially millet)[3]. Away from farming areas most often in drier, more open woodlands such as *Acacia*. Nests colonially (at times abundant) in bushes, trees or reeds[3]. In 1992 a colony at Nabwalya covered 5 km, and each *Acacia* tree contained 100-500 nests[1].

Status Undoubtedly highly nomadic, probably with no regular migration. Locally abundant in the dry season, in flocks of 10,000s at times, and it is then that two birds ringed in Zimbabwe were recovered in S. Zambia (Appendix 1). May be a pest in rice-growing areas. Nestlings and adults may be captured for food at breeding colonies.

Breeding   Jan Feb Apr
(n=47)   1   1   45   The Apr records were all from one colony. In addition, egg-laying
started in Feb in 3 colonies, Mar in 5 others. The earliest signs of breeding dress are mid-Oct.
Clutch: N/3 (45).
Moult: usually completed by Sep[1].
Taxonomy[2] *Q. q. lathamii* is the breeding form, and has been found throughout Zambia. *Q. q. aethiopi-ca* has also been collected in the north; in breeding dress the black of its mask is confined to the fore-head (not extending onto the crown), but both forms are extremely variable (and some breeding males have pale fawn cheeks). *Q. q. spoliator* probably occurs too, as birds ringed within its breeding range in South Africa have been recovered north to Malawi and Zaire.
References [1]Dowsett & Leonard (in press a); [2]Irwin & Benson (1967a); [3]Stewart (1959).

Yellow-crowned Bishop *Euplectes afer*   B634 **RB**

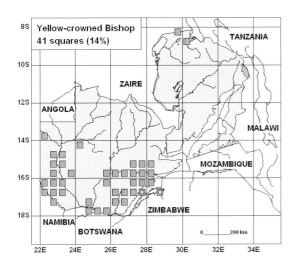

Distribution *Afrotropical* (*Mauritania to South Africa*). The main population is in S. and W. Zambia, up the Zambezi Valley to the Litapi Floodplain, east to Mayukwayukwa, and through the Kafue Flats north and east to the Chisamba area. It is generally common there, and even abundant on Liuwa Plain and the Kafue Flats[3]. The only records from the Middle Zambezi Valley are a specimen from Chipepo (24 Nov)[4] and a sighting at Siavonga (Dec)[3], probably wanderers (open squares). [Records claimed from the Copperbelt and Bangweulu are in need of confirmation[3].] The species reappears (a smaller population) in Mweru Wantipa, in the Mwawe[1] and Bulaya[2] areas. *Alt.* 760-1300 m (exceptionally down to 490 m at Chipepo).

Ecology Short grass floodplains and pans, seasonally inundated, nesting in low vegetation just above the water. This habitat is not used by other *Euplectes* spp.
Status Most are probably resident; in some areas (such as the Kafue Flats and Liuwa) large flocks occur after breeding, with groups in excess of 500 birds in Apr[3].
Breeding   Jan Feb Mar
(n=26)   6   19   1   Breeding dress from about Christmas to Mar (first signs appear late Nov). *Clutch*: C/1 (1); C/2 (4); C/3 (10); C/4 (6); C/5 (1).
Moult: starts mid-Mar[3].
Taxonomy *E. a. taha*.
References [1]Benson (1956d); [2]Benson & Irwin (1967b); [3]Dowsett (in press a); [4]Irwin & Benson (1981).

Black-winged (Fire-crowned) Bishop *Euplectes hordeaceus* B633 **RB**

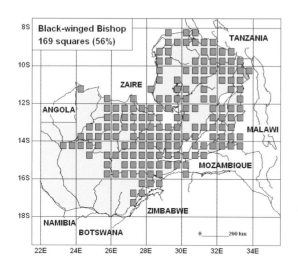

Black-winged Bishop
169 squares (56%)

Distribution *Afrotropical (Senegal to Zimbabwe)*. Ranges throughout most of the plateau and valley areas of the north and east, south along the Middle Zambezi escarpment to the Poliya stream (at 1000 m)[5], west along the Kafue Flats to Ngoma[2]. Further west to as far as the Kabompo/Zambezi River confluence[1,6,7]. Merely a vagrant to Mwinilunga Dist. (sighted twice, Kalene Hill and Zambezi Rapids)[4]. Generally common, but in the extreme north of the country it is sparse in areas between Mbala and the Luapula Valley. *Alt.* 330-1600 m.

Ecology Occurs in any rank grass and scrub on the edge of woodland or cultivation, often away from water. This bishop's distribution suggests it in part prefers higher-rainfall areas. Where it occurs in the same regions as *E. orix* and *E. capensis* it is overall in taller, lusher growth than them and (unlike *E. orix*) not in swamps.

Status Apparently resident, flocking in the off-season (two ringed birds moved up to 40 km)[3].

Breeding   Dec   Jan   Feb   Mar   Apr
(n=123)   1   17   49   42   14   Breeding dress from mid-Dec to mid-May, exceptionally to the end of that month[5]. *Clutch*: C/1 (2); C/2 (24); C/3 (32); C/4 (2).

Taxonomy *E. h. hordeaceus.*

References [1]Aspinwall (1973f); [2]Benson & Irwin (1967b); [3]Benson *et al.* (1971a); [4]Bowen (1983a); [5]Dowsett (in press a); [6]White (1945-46); [7]Winterbottom (1942a).

Red Bishop *Euplectes orix* B632 **RB**

Distribution *Afrotropical (Kenya to South Africa)*. Typically near water at low and medium altitudes, in a series of disjunct, isolated populations. Absent from much of Northern Province between the low-lying Luapula Valley and Malole in the Chambeshi Valley to the east[5], but present between Lakes Mweru and Tanganyika. Absent too from the Copperbelt (although recorded in neighbouring Zaire in the Lubumbashi area)[7]. Scarce in the Luangwa Valley. In south-central Zambia (where locally numerous), ranges up the Kafue drainage to the Luswishi River confluence[2], and on the Barotse Floodplain in the west noted as far north as the Litapi River, south of L. Mwange[5]. *Alt.* 330-1300 m.

Ecology Breeds gregariously near water, in long rank grass or *Phragmites,* more often in permanent swamps than seasonal floodplains. Usually in wetter situations than similar-sized *Euplectes*. Non-breeding flocks wander extensively into dry savanna. Breeds locally alongside *Quelea erythrops*[2].

Status Largely resident (one ringed bird moved 40 km)[6]. Occurs in large flocks when not breeding, often with other seed-eaters.

Breeding   Dec   Jan   Feb   Mar   Apr
(n=858)   23   402   304   114   15
Breeding dress from mid-Nov to mid-May (timing probably dependent upon local rains).
Clutch: C/1 (38); C/2 (247); C/3 (351); C/4 (59); C/5 (3).
Moult: starts late Mar or early Apr[5].

Taxonomy[1,3] *E. o. orix*, with some approach to *E. o. nigrifrons* (with the black on the forehead less extensive) in the north and east. An albino was seen in Monze Dist[4].
References [1]Benson (1956f); [2]Benson & Irwin (1967b); [3]Benson *et al.* (1971a); [4]Dowsett (1975c); [5]Dowsett (in press a); [6]Dowsett & Leonard (2001); [7]Schouteden (1971).

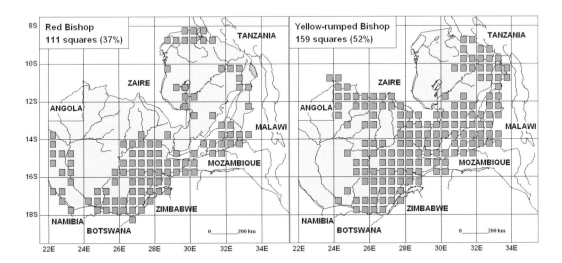

Yellow-rumped (Yellow) Bishop *Euplectes capensis*   B635 **RB**

Distribution *Afrotropical* (*E. Nigeria to South Africa*). Common throughout central and E. Zambia (but scarce in the valleys), and through the Copperbelt to Mwinilunga Dist., ranging south-west only to Mayau[4]. Absent from the Luapula basin: unknown westwards from Mbala[1], Chilubula[4] and SE Bangweulu[6]. [It is, though, present in the Marungu highlands in SE Zaire[7].] Absent from W. Zambia, barely reaching the Zambezi in the Katima Mulilo area[2]. *Alt.* 330-1700 m (rarely up to 1950 m on the Nyika[5]).
Ecology In rank grass with scattered bushes and on the edge of woodland, usually in drier situations than the similar-sized *E. hordeaceus*, with which it may be in competition locally[3]. Often in neglected cultivation.
Status Resident, occurring in large flocks when not breeding, often with other granivores.
Breeding   Dec   Jan   Feb   Mar   Apr
(n=349)   20   158   120   38   13   Breeding dress early Nov to mid-May (exceptionally from late Sep in S. Zambia)[4].
Clutch: C/1 (15); C/2 (87); C/3 (109); C/4 (3); C/5 (1).
Taxonomy *E. c. crassirostris*.
References [1]Benson (1956f); [2]Benson & White (1957); [3]Benson *et al.* (1971a); [4]Dowsett (in press a); [5]Dowsett-Lemaire (2006a); [6]Pitman (1934); [7]Schouteden (1971).

Red-shouldered Whydah *Euplectes axillaris*   B637 **RB**

Distribution *Afrotropical* (*E. Nigeria to South Africa*). In permanent swamps throughout the western half of the country, and much of the north. Locally very numerous (for example, 1000+ counted over

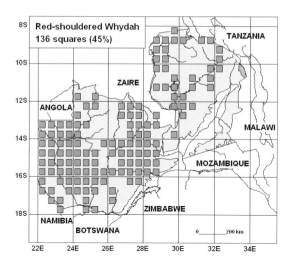

15 km of river on the Kafue Flats). In the south, occurs down the Zambezi to the Kazungula area[2], and locally on the Southern Province plateau to Kalomo[1]. In central Zambia, east to the edge of the Luano Valley and Muchinga escarpments, and in Northern Province not east of a line from Shiwa Ngandu, the Mbesuma area[4] and Sumbi (Mbala Dist.)[3]. *Alt.* 950-1600 m, mainly below 1300 m.

Ecology In tall swamp vegetation in permanent marshes, or the centre of dambos and wet floodplains; also in rice fields in the north and irrigated sugar-cane (Nakambala). Extensive swamps are preferred, and thus it is scarce on the Copperbelt and much of the higher plateau, and absent from Eastern Province.

Often alongside the smaller *E. orix*.

Status Resident, but with evidence of local wandering, for example apparently absent from the Kabwe area in the dry season. In the non-breeding season flocks are normally 30-50, but occasionally 200.

Breeding   Jan   Feb   Mar

(n=15)   5   5   5   Breeding dress from mid-Nov or early Dec to mid-Apr[3].

Clutch: C/1 (2); C/2 (5); C/3 (4) & N/3 (1).

Taxonomy *E. a. bocagei* (male breeding dress with lesser wing coverts orange, greater coverts orange buff), replaced in parts of the south by *E. a. axillaris* (lesser wing coverts red, greater cinnamon brown), and in the extreme north-east by the poorly-marked, intermediate *E. a. phoeniceus*[1].

References [1]Benson (1961a); [2]Benson & Irwin (1967b); [3]Dowsett (in press a); [4]Neave (1910).

Yellow-mantled Whydah *Euplectes macroura*   B636 **RB**

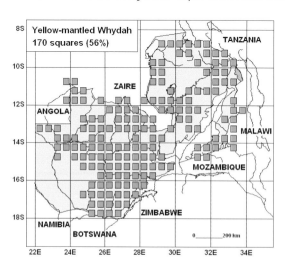

Distribution *Afrotropical (Senegal to Zimbabwe).* A bird of plateau grasslands, throughout except for the south-west and for parts of Northern Province; locally common. Occurs west of the Zambezi only in the north, west of Chavuma[2,3], thence south to Silonga[3]. Further south present to west of Mulobezi[1] and up the Zambezi to Mambova[1]. Absent from the low-lying Luangwa and Middle Zambezi Valleys, in each area reaching just the escarpment. Surprisingly unrecorded from a large part of Northern Province, north and east of Bangweulu. *Alt.* 900-1600 m.

Ecology Dambos and other areas of moist, short grassland, often alongside the larger *E. hartlaubi* in the northern half of its range. Avoids treeless, open plains. Where coexists with *E. hartlaubi*, occupies the drier periphery of the dambo.

Status Resident, forming small flocks in the non-breeding season.

Breeding   Dec   Jan   Feb   Mar

(n=113)   10   43   41   19   Breeding dress mid-Oct (mostly Nov) to mid-Apr, occasionally to early May[1]. *Clutch*: C/1 (1); C/2 (34); C/3 (36).

Taxonomy *E. m. macroura*. This (type species of the genus *Euplectes*) was first described from Ouidah (or "Whydah") in Dahomey (Benin), hence the name whydah should be applied to the long-tailed *Euplectes* and not to species of *Vidua*.

References [1]Dowsett (in press a); [2]White (1945-46); [3]Winterbottom (1942a).

White-winged Whydah *Euplectes albonotatus*   B640 **RB**

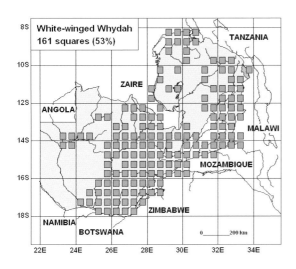

Distribution *Afrotropical (Ethiopia to South Africa).* Locally common in *Acacia* and other light woodland in south-central Zambia, the drier parts of the eastern half of the country and the far north. Westwards up the Zambezi Valley to Katongo[1], and across the Copperbelt to the area of Zambezi town (Balovale)[2] and Mpili, Namboma Rapids[6]. Its absence from the dry country in most of W. Zambia is at present inexplicable. It is similarly unknown from the whole of E. Angola[3,5]. *Alt.* 330-1600 m.

Ecology Drier country than the other *Euplectes*, in rank grass with scattered bushes, especially in *Acacia*, also on the edge of other woodland and in neglected cultivation.

Status Resident, in flocks of up to 60 when not breeding.

Breeding   Jan   Feb   Mar   Apr

(n=273)   57   140   64   12   First signs of breeding dress are noted Nov-Dec, full dress early Jan to early Apr.

Clutch: C/1 (20); C/2 (74); C/3 (96); C/4 (2); C/6 (1). The C/6 was perhaps laid by two females.

Moult: from Apr onwards, into an eclipse plumage[5].

Taxonomy *E. a. albonotatus*. A leucistic bird has been reported[4].

References [1]Benson & Irwin (1967b); [2]Britton (1970); [3]Dean (2000); [4]Dowsett (1974b); [5]Dowsett (in press a); [6]Winterbottom (1942a).

Red-collared Whydah *Euplectes ardens*   B641 **RB**

Distribution *Afrotropical (mainly Guinea to South Africa).* Particularly common in rank grass at medium and high elevations: essentially a bird of the northern and eastern plateau dambos, but locally even in the Luangwa Valley, where not rare. Absent from the lower Luangwa and Middle Zambezi Valleys, and very scarce on the Southern Province plateau, southwards down the Zambezi escarpment to Poliya stream[3]. Present in the Upper Zambezi Valley, south to Silonga[1] and Nawinda[3]. *Alt.* 550-2200 m (on the Nyika Plateau)[4].

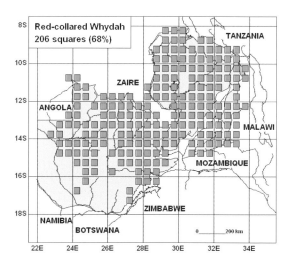

Ecology In a variety of situations, both wet and dry: dambos or any ground with lush rank grass and scattered bushes, at higher altitudes frequent in patches of bracken-briar and montane grassland. Also in neglected cultivation.

Status Resident everywhere, in large flocks when not breeding.

Breeding

	Jan	Feb	Mar	Apr
(n=153)	31	82	33	7

Breeding dress from late Dec to (exceptionally) late May, sometimes as early as late Nov, even from early Oct[3].

Clutch: C/1 (5); C/2 (41); C/3 (17); C/4 (2).

Taxonomy[2] *E. a. tropicus*, although males similar to *E. a. concolor* (lacking the red collar) have been reported on occasion from Mbala, Kitwe[5] and Chipata[3].

References [1]Benson & Irwin (1967b); [2]Clancey (1980d); [3]Dowsett (in press a); [4]Dowsett-Lemaire (2006a); [5]Tree (1972).

Long-tailed Whydah *Euplectes progne* B642 **RB**

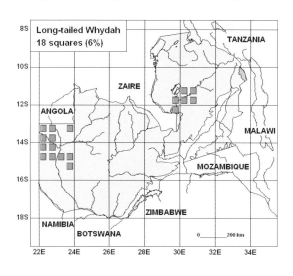

Distribution *Afrotropical (Kenya to South Africa)*. There are two populations. In the open plains of the Upper Zambezi, ranges south to some 60 km east of Mongu[7] and north-east to Kansalya[7] (perhaps even to Konkano Plain[3], though no record from there has been traced); overall common, and especially abundant on Liuwa Plain[7,9]. Reappears as an extreme isolate around L. Bangweulu (where locally common), from east of L. Chaya[4] south to Mukuku[7]. [There is a possible record from 15 km north of Nchelenge, a flock being reported 24 Aug 1976[7]. The observer was unaware that this species was recorded from Lukonzolwa[10], on the Zaire side of L. Mweru, although the specimen concerned was perhaps from higher altitude[5]. The occasional occurrence of this bird in the L. Mweru area should be borne in mind as a possibility. It also occurs in the Marungu highlands[8].] *Alt.* 1050-1150 m.

Ecology On the Liuwa Floodplain it is found in grass around pans, rather than on the extensive floodplain (which is occupied by *E. axillaris*)[9]. Similarly in Bangweulu it is in short-medium grass, only slightly damp.

Status Resident.

Breeding Mar

(n=1) 1 *Clutch*: C/3 (1).

Birds start to moult into breeding dress as early as Sep[1], and are in full plumage from Oct until at least

Mar[7]. Apparently first- and second-year males have a female-like plumage[11].

Taxonomy[2] *E. p. progne* (syn. *E. p. definita,* type locality between the Litapi and Kashiji Rivers; *DM*)[6].

References [1]Aspinwall (1979b); [2]Benson (1956f); [3]Benson *et al.* (1971a); [4]Brelsford (1943); [5]Chapin (1954: 17); [6]Clancey (1970b: 346); [7]Dowsett (in press a); [8]Dowsett & Prigogine (1974); [9]Osborne (1978); [10]Schouteden (1971); [11]Traylor (1965b).

Marsh Whydah *Euplectes hartlaubi*   B638 **RB**

Distribution *Afrotropical (E. Nigeria to central Zambia).* Throughout most of the northern plateau dambos, where locally quite common. Almost absent from lower elevations between Lakes Tanganyika and Mweru (except in the Kaputa area), otherwise southwards from Chitimbwa[4] and Kalungwishi[5], east to Isoka town[3]. Thence it ranges south along the Muchinga escarpment to Chingombe and Kabwe Dist. (1428D, the most southerly records of the species), then west to the Luamala River[1], and across the Copperbelt to Nyatanda[4], Sanjongo[2] and the South Kashiji River[1]. *Alt.* 1100-1770 m (Danger Hill), rarely down to 930 m (Kaputa).

Ecology Larger moist dambos, alongside the smaller *E. ardens* in particular. Often next to *E. macroura,* but on wetter ground.

Status Resident, with flocks (usually monospecific) of up to 60.

Breeding   Dec   Jan   Feb   Mar
(n=30)   9   10   7   4   Territories are reoccupied from early Oct, and breeding dress attained earlier than in other *Euplectes*, from 24 Oct to late Apr (the odd bird still in faded breeding dress late Jun or late Jul). *Clutch:* C/1 (1); C/2 (13); C/3 (7); C/4 (1).

Moult: one half-way through mid-Aug[4].

Taxonomy *E. h. hartlaubi.*

References [1]Benson (1962a); [2]Britton (1970); [3]Clay (1953); [4]Dowsett (in press a); [5]Neave (1910).

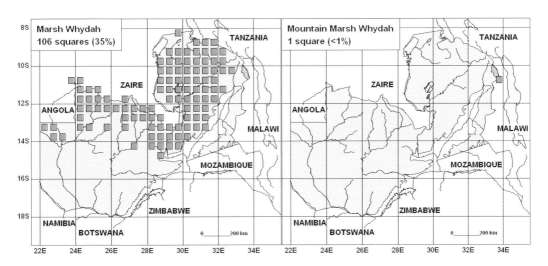

Mountain Marsh Whydah *Euplectes psammocromius*   B639 **RB**

Distribution *Afromontane endemic (SW Tanzania to N. Malawi).* Occurs only in the wetter montane grasslands of the Nyika Plateau, from 2000 m[1] up to 2200 m (higher on the Malawi side), but common only above 2100 m.

Ecology Rank grass in dambos and streamside vegetation.

Status Resident, in flocks of up to 50 when not breeding.

Breeding No detailed records, but an occupied nest in Jan[2], and egg-laying on the Malawi side Oct and Nov[3]. Assumes breeding dress by late Sep or early Oct, until Feb-Mar (latest early Apr)[2].

Taxonomy No races recognized. Generally considered to be specifically distinct from *E. hartlaubi*[1].

References [1]Benson & Irwin (1967b); [2]Dowsett-Lemaire (2006a); [3]Dowsett-Lemaire & Dowsett (2006).

Estrildidae

Green-winged Pytilia (Melba Finch) *Pytilia melba*   B658 **RB**

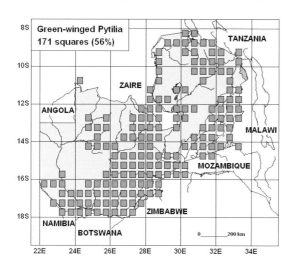

Green-winged Pytilia
171 squares (56%)

Distribution *Afrotropical* (*Mauritania to South Africa*). Locally common in thickets in lower-rainfall areas, throughout the south and east, and parts of the north and west. The Kafue basin and upper Kabompo River, north to West Lunga N.P.[2], and the Zambezi and Mashi Rivers to Siandi[2] and Shangombo[1]. [Reports from Lukulu and Kaoma[6] have not been confirmed[1].] It reappears in the far north of Mwinilunga Dist., at Chilula[2] (although unknown in adjacent Zaire[4]). Scarce in high-rainfall areas (including the Copperbelt). *Alt.* 330-1500 m.

Ecology Deciduous (especially *Acacia*) and evergreen thickets and neglected cultivation, feeding on grasses in the understorey. Also on the edge of riparian forest.

Status Resident.

Breeding

	Oct	Dec	Jan	Feb	Mar	Apr	May
(n=119)	1	2	6	31	50	17	12

Clutch: C/1 (7); C/2 (12); C/3 (9); C/4 (34); C/5 (24); C/6 (3).

A frequent host to *Vidua paradisaea*.

Moult: from ringing studies, most have a complete moult Oct-Dec, but for a few it is post-breeding, Apr-May[2]. Some individuals may have 2 moults a year[5].

Taxonomy Variation is clinal, and differences rather slight. *P. m. melba*, replaced by the darker *P. m. hygrophila* (type locality Bulaya; *NMZB*)[3] in the north-east. There is some approach to *P. m. grotei* (the chest suffused reddish) in the Middle Zambezi and Luangwa Valleys, while birds in the dry south-west are *P. m. damarensis* (red on head, throat scarlet, and crown pale grey).

References [1]Benson & Irwin (1967b); [2]Dowsett (in press a); [3]Irwin & Benson (1967b: 21); [4]Schouteden (1971); [5]Traylor (1965b); [6]White (1945-46).

Orange-winged Pytilia *Pytilia afra*   B657 **RB**

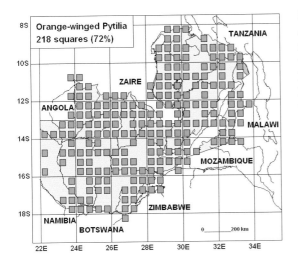

Distribution *Afrotropical (Ethiopia to South Africa)*. A catholic species, occurring almost throughout the country, though unrecorded west of the Zambezi between the South Lueti River[3] and Sinjembela[2]. *Alt.* 500-1600 m.

Ecology In the herbaceous understorey of any woodland. Most frequently in miombo and degraded *Baikiaea* (where it feeds on the ground, in ant-hill thickets or even in neglected cultivation, on the edge of woodland). Much less tied to thickets than the similar-sized *P. melba*, and rarely in *Acacia*.

Status Resident, but with local wandering outside the breeding season, in flocks of up to 30 or more in the Kafue area[3]. The extent of any movements is not known, this species being normally discreet and easily overlooked.

Breeding	Jan	Feb	Mar	Apr	May	Aug
(n=43)	4	11	11	7	8	2

A frequent host to *Vidua obtusa*.

Clutch: C/2 (3); C/3 (3); C/4 (17); C/5 (2).

Moult: recorded Jul (starting) and Nov[1,4].

Taxonomy No races recognized.

References [1]Dowsett (in press a); [2]Irwin & Benson (1967b); [3]Leonard (1998c); [4]Traylor (1965b).

Red-faced Crimsonwing *Cryptospiza reichenovii*   B660 **RB**

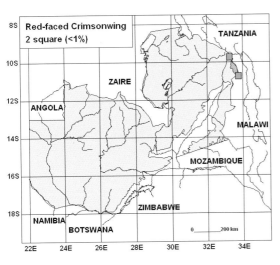

Distribution *Afromontane endemic (E. Nigeria/Cameroon to E. Zimbabwe)*. Known in Zambia only in the forests of the Nyika Plateau[3] and Mafinga Mts[2]. Extralimitally, it is known from Jembya (1033A) in N. Malawi[3], only 100-200 m from the Zambian border. It is also present on the Ufipa Plateau in SW Tanzania. Elusive, but not uncommon. *Alt.* 2000-2200 m.

Ecology The dense understorey of the forest interior, in shrubby thickets and herbaceous tangles, often near streams (it drinks frequently). Feeds on a variety of seeds, usually on or near the ground, rarely in the canopy[4]. Breeding territories are 1-4 ha in extent[3].

Status Resident, with at least local wandering in the non-breeding season; only 4 of 37 ringed adults were retrapped locally, and one of 45 ringed birds of all ages was recaught 3 km distant[1].

Breeding	Jun	Jul	Sep
(n=3)	1	1	1

(Including Malawi side of SW Nyika[4].) *Clutch*: no data.

Moult: two were completing moult in Nov[2].
Taxonomy *C. r. australis.*
References [1]Dowsett (1985a); [2]Dowsett (in press a); [3]Dowsett-Lemaire (1989b); [4]Dowsett-Lemaire (2006a).

Black-bellied Seedcracker *Pyrenestes ostrinus*   B661 **RB**

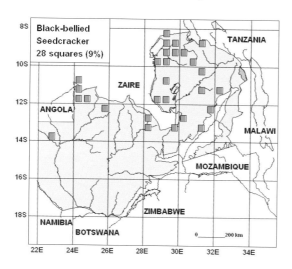

Distribution *Afrotropical (Ivory Coast to NE Zambia).* Locally at forest edges in N. Zambia, east to the Mbala area[6], and to the Muchinga escarpment near Muzyatama[2]. It occurs below the Muchingas on the upper Munyamadzi[3] and on the escarpment at Masase[6], then ranges westwards to the Copperbelt (south to the Luanshya area), and on to Mundwiji Plain[5] and N. Mwinilunga. Exceptionally it occurs further west at Kashiji (the most southerly record of the species)[1,4]. Very discreet and easily overlooked, but nevertheless does genuinely seem to be sparsely distributed. *Alt.* 900-1770 m (near Danger Hill), rarely down to 680 m (upper Munyamadzi).

Ecology In rank growth on the edge of moist evergreen and riparian forest, feeding on or near the ground (on larger seeds than sympatric firefinches and waxbills, as well as berries), and also in neglected cultivation (cassava).
Status Resident.

Breeding	Feb	Mar	
(n=4)	1	3	*Clutch*: no data.

Moult: three were half-way through moult Jul-Aug[6].
Taxonomy *P. o. frommi.*
References [1]Aspinwall (1979b); [2]Benson (1949a); [3]Benson (1955b); [4]Benson (1960c); [5]Benson & Irwin (1965b); [6]Dowsett (in press a).

Red-throated Twinspot *Hypargos niveoguttatus*   B662 **RB**

Distribution *Zambezian near-endemic (Rwanda and Kenya to South Africa).* Locally common in thickets and on forest edge in N. and E. Zambia, at low and medium elevations, though sparse on much of the Northern Province plateau. Southwards along the Zambezi Valley to the Victoria Falls area[5], where scarce. Throughout the eastern half of the Southern Province plateau, and all the Kafue basin, west to the Mumbeji/Kabompo River confluence[3] and Kayombo. Absent from the dry thickets in the west. *Alt.* 330-1500 m.
Ecology Dense understorey of thickets (even on termitaria in moist miombo), and various dry forests (riparian, evergreen *Cryptosepalum* and *Marquesia*).
Status Resident.

Breeding	Jan	Feb	Mar	Apr	May	
(n=9)	2	3	1	1	2	*Clutch*: C/1 (1); C/4 (1); C/5 (1).

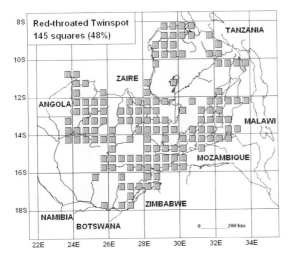

Host to *Vidua codringtoni*[7]. *Moult*: Jul-Nov[5].

Taxonomy[1,6] Subspecific differences in colour intensity are not great, and are on the whole clinal. *H. n. niveoguttatus*, replaced by *H. n. centralis* in the north-east, *H. n. macrospilotus* the north-west, and *H. n. interior* from the Middle Zambezi westwards. For plumage differences, see ref. 2, and for an alternative arrangement ref. 4.

References [1]Benson & Irwin (1967b); [2]Benson *et al.* (1971a); [3]Britton (1970); [4]Clancey (1968c); [5]Dowsett (in press a); [6]Irwin (1981a); [7]Payne *et al.* (1992).

Green Twinspot *Mandingoa nitidula*   B659 **R(B)**

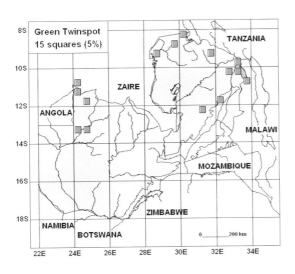

Distribution *Afrotropical (Guinea to South Africa).* Apparently very scarce and local. In the extreme north of the country, in the east south to the Nyika (rare)[5] and along the Muchinga escarpment to the Mwaleshi River at Mano and Mutinondo Wilderness[3], but in Luapula not beyond Nchelenge[1]. Absent from the Copperbelt, but reappears in Mwinilunga Dist., south to Mundwiji Plain, and further south also in the area of Manyinga and Jivundu camp[3]. Unrecorded from the forest patches west of the Zambezi. *Alt.* 930 m (Nchelenge) to 1950 m on Makutu and the Mafingas (where small numbers)[2,4], rarely wandering to 2150 m on the Nyika[5].

Ecology In the herbaceous understorey of evergreen forest, at edges and (occasionally) in the canopy. Feeds mainly on grass seeds.

Status Resident, except at high altitude (Nyika) where it appears to be a vagrant (4 records in all from the Zambian side)[5].

Breeding No detailed records. Juveniles in Aug suggest that, as in Malawi, breeding is during the first half of the year.

Taxonomy *M. n. chubbi.*

References [1]Aspinwall (1974); [2]Dowsett (1971h); [3]Dowsett (in press a); [4]Dowsett & Stjernstedt (1973); [5]Dowsett-Lemaire (2006a).

Brown Firefinch *Lagonosticta rufopicta*   B663 **RB**

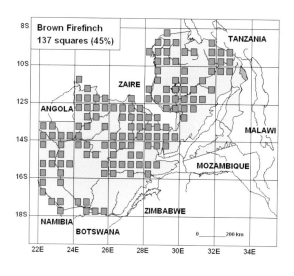

Distribution *Afrotropical (Senegal to N. Zimbabwe).* Locally common in riparian vegetation on the Zambian plateau, west of the Rift, from the Ilonda Hills[3] south-westwards along the Muchinga escarpment to the Kafue Gorge[1]. From there it ranges throughout the Kafue drainage, the Mashi[3], and down the Upper Zambezi to Livingstone[3,7]. Absent east of the Luangwa Rift (and from the whole of Malawi). *Alt.* 880-1750 m (Kawimbe).

Ecology Feeds on the ground, on the edge of forest or thicket (evergreen in the north of the country, more deciduous or dry riparian in the south). Uses old nests of weavers[5]. Often alongside other firefinches and small granivores[2].

Status Resident.

Breeding   Jan   Feb   Mar   Apr   May   Jun   Jul   Sep   Oct   Dec
(n=25)   2   7   2   4   3   3   1   1   1   1
Clutch: C/1 (2); C/2 (2); C/3 (4); C/4 (5); C/5 (1).
Moult: completed during Nov[3,6].
Taxonomy *L. r. nitidula*, with *L. r. plumbaria* in the south-west (more greyish brown above, lacking pale buff in centre of abdomen)[2]. There are reasons for considering *nitidula* to be conspecific with the northern *rufopicta*[4]; were they to be separated, *L. nitidula* would be a Zambezian endemic.
References [1]Benson (1959c); [2]Benson *et al.* (1971a); [3]Dowsett (in press a); [4]Dowsett & Dowsett-Lemaire (1993); [5]Madge (1972i); [6]Traylor (1965b); [7]Winterbottom (1956b).

Red-billed Firefinch *Lagonosticta senegala*   B664 **RB**

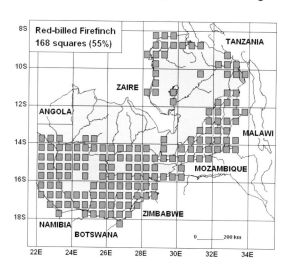

Distribution *Afrotropical (Mauritania to South Africa).* A species of *Acacia* or dry secondary habitats, in the west of the country not known for certain north of the South Kashiji River[8] and Zambezi town (Balovale)[3]. [Sight records from West Lunga N.P. and Kalilele require confirmation[4], while a specimen from "Ndola"[5] is possibly mislabelled, as there is otherwise no record from the well-explored Copperbelt[4]. It is absent from neighbouring parts of Zaire too[7].] It occurs as near to the Copperbelt as the Mkushi farming block. It ranges throughout the Luangwa Valley and Eastern Province plateau, and loops around the upper Chambeshi[4] (exceptionally to Kasama[1]) to the low-lying country between Lakes Tanganyika and Mweru, and

up the Luapula Valley to Samfya and Miloki[1]. Usually very common to abundant. *Alt.* 330-1700 m.
Ecology In patches of thicket and scrub next to some bare ground where much feeding takes place; and in similar situations around human settlements and in suburban gardens. Frequently breeds in or near habitation (e.g. thatch roofs). Often alongside other granivores, especially *Uraeginthus angolensis*.
Status Resident.

Breeding	Jan	Feb	Mar	Apr	May	Jul	Aug	Sep
(n=82)	8	23	31	8	3	3	4	2

Clutch: C/1 (2); C/2 (4); C/3 (13); C/4 (30); C/5 (3); C/6 (2); C/7 (1); C/9 (2). Host to *Vidua chalybeata*.
Moult: most adults have a complete moult Oct-Feb, but a few are just starting in Jan. Moulting birds in other months may be mainly juveniles. Moult takes *c.* 4 months in both age groups[4,6].
Taxonomy Variation is clinal, and not well-marked[2]. *L. s. pallidicrissa* (syn. *L. s. dilutior*, type locality Zambezi town (Balovale); *OUM*)[9], replaced by *L. s. ruberrima* (male with redder upperparts) in the north-east and by *L. s. rendalli* (pinker below) in the east.
References [1]Benson & White (1957); [2]Benson *et al.* (1971a); [3]Britton (1970); [4]Dowsett (in press a); [5]Payne (1973); [6]Payne (1980b); [7]Schouteden (1971); [8]White (1945-46); [9]White (1946a: 10).

Blue-billed Firefinch *Lagonosticta rubricata*   B665 **RB**

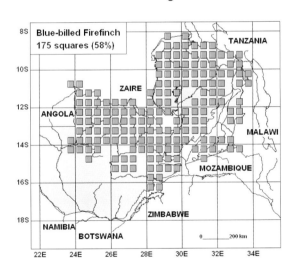

Distribution *Afrotropical (Guinea-Bissau to South Africa).* Common in rank growth throughout the northern Zambian plateau, south on the Zambezi escarpment to near Chirundu, and in central Zambia to Myooye (Mumbwa Dist.), Kafue Hook[2] and Kaoma[4]. It occurs west to the Mumbeji-Kabompo area[2]. It is present in the Luangwa Valley only in hilly woodland, as in the Mterize area[3]. *Alt.* 600-2200 m (Nyika, higher on the Malawi side).
Ecology In patches of thicket, rank grass in gullies (in woodland), edges of evergreen forest (including *Cryptosepalum*), and montane bracken-briar; also in neglected cultivation next to cover.
Status Resident.

Breeding	Jan	Feb	Mar	Apr	May
(n=15)	2	2	5	1	5

Clutch: C/1 (1); C/3 (1); C/4 (1).
Host to *Vidua funerea*. *Moult*: noted Jul and Oct-Dec[2].
Taxonomy *L. r. haematocephala*, with *congica* in the extreme north-west[1] (male with crown dull, not bright, pink).
References [1]Benson & Irwin (1967b); [2]Dowsett (in press a); [3]Neave (1907); [4]Payne (1973).

Jameson's Firefinch *Lagonosticta rhodopareia*   B666 **RB**

Distribution *Afrotropical (Ethiopia to South Africa).* A species of drier scrub than *L. rubricata*, in the south of the country north to 14°S (e.g. the Kabwe area)[3] but west of the Zambezi only to Mfubakazi[5], further north to near Watopa. From the upper Luangwa it loops round through the dry country between

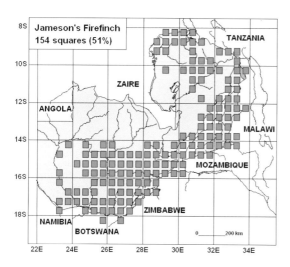

Lakes Tanganyika and Mweru, to Mwenda[3]. [It is reported from further south in the Luapula drainage at Kasenga and Masombwe, in Zaire[6].] Locally very common. *Alt.* 330-1400 m, reported exceptionally to 1670 m (Mbala)[5].

Ecology In various types of thicket, rank grass or scrub in gullies (in woodland) and at edges of riparian forest, and neglected cultivation next to cover. Often with other small granivores, alongside *L. senegala* in many places. In the same localities as its sibling *L. rubricata* in parts of E. and central Zambia, usually in drier vegetation: e.g. both are present at Kasama, *L. rubricata* in bracken-briar on the edge of forest, *L. rhodopareia* in thickets on rocky hills[1].

Status Resident.

Breeding	Jan	Feb	Mar	Apr	May	Sep
(n=70)	14	24	17	10	4	1

Clutch: C/1 (1); C/2 (4); C/3 (12); C/4 (29); C/5 (13); C/6 (2). Host to *Vidua purpurascens*.
Moult: from about Sep or Oct to Jan; retraps suggest 3-4 months needed[3].
Taxonomy[2,4] *L. r. jamesoni*, perhaps replaced in the Middle Zambezi Valley and west of the Victoria Falls by *L. r. taruensis* (female darker, more reddish brown above).
References [1]Benson (1956f); [2]Clancey (1970c); [3]Dowsett (in press a); [4]Irwin (1981a); [5]Payne (1973); [6]Schouteden (1971).

Swee Waxbill *Coccopygia melanotis*   B671 **RB**

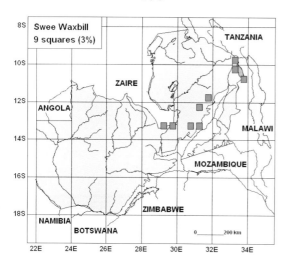

Distribution *Afromontane near-endemic (Ethiopia to South Africa)*. Very common in the eastern highlands (the Mafingas[8] and Makutu[4] south to the Nyika[9]), then in isolated pockets down the Muchinga escarpment (locally numerous) from Danger Hill[1] to Kundalila Falls[11] and Musense[2], west to Changwena Falls and north of Mkushi. Extralimitally, it occurs north of Mbala in the Marungu highlands and on the Ufipa Plateau[7]. *Alt.* mostly 1620-1800 m on the Northern Province plateau, up to 2200 m in the eastern highlands (Nyika, higher on the Malawi side); down to 1200 m near Musense, on the upper Lusiwashi River (Muchinga escarpment)[5].

Ecology In bracken-briar and dense herbaceous growth at edges of forest and along streams, scrub on rocky hills, also in small forest clearings and penetrating inside forest to drink.
Status Resident, in small flocks for much of the year, up to 50 in the off-season (Nyika).

Breeding Jan
(n=1) 1 *Clutch*: C/3 (1).
Taxonomy *C. m. stuartirwini*, with some tendency towards *C. m. kilimensis* (darker olive on mantle, darker grey on chest) on the Mafingas and Makutu[3]. Often placed in the genus *Estrilda*, but *Coccopygia* is distinct, according to DNA analysis[10]. Zambian and other populations have been separated specifically (as *C. quartinia*) from black-faced birds of the nominate group, but we retain them as one[6].
References [1]Benson (1956d); [2]Benson *et al.* (1961); [3]Benson *et al.* (1970); [4]Dowsett (1971h); [5]Dowsett (in press a); [6]Dowsett & Dowsett-Lemaire (1993); [7]Dowsett & Prigogine (1974); [8]Dowsett & Stjernstedt (1973); [9]Dowsett-Lemaire (2006a); [10]Payne (2005); [11]Taylor (1978c).

Black-tailed Grey Waxbill *Estrilda perreini* B670 **RB**

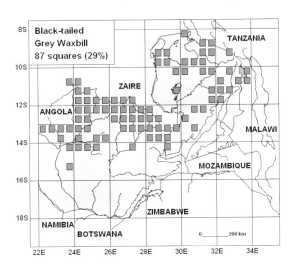

Distribution *Zambezian/Eastern* (*SE Gabon to South Africa*). Forests of the northern plateau, south in the east to Mwanda Mtn[3] (an outlier of the Nyika Plateau), through the Copperbelt (where locally common) south to Mita Hills Dam and in the Kafue drainage to the Luamala River[4]. (Unrecorded from the upper Luapula drainage, west of Lukulu Dist.). It ranges west to the Upper Zambezi River, and across the river to Nguvu[2] and Muyeke[6], and thence south to Kanda forest (some 75 km east of Mongu)[1]. *Alt.* 950-1950 m.
Ecology Normally associated with dense dry evergreen forest or thicket, including *Cryptosepalum* forest (where common) and bamboo thickets. Often in disturbed and secondary situations, even light miombo on rocks (near riparian). It feeds normally on the edge, near the ground, but at times forages at higher levels, even in the canopy, often feeding at flowers (including those of eucalyptus)[5]. Occasionally in small flocks.
Status Resident.
Breeding Dec Jan Feb Apr May
(n=8) 2 3 1 1 1 *Clutch*: C/3 (1); C/5 (1).
Moult: one bird half-way through mid-Jul[5].
Taxonomy *E. p. perreini*. Has at times been considered conspecific with the northern sibling *E. caerulescens*.
References [1]Aspinwall (1973f); [2]Aspinwall (1979b); [3]Benson (1951); [4]Benson (1958a); [5]Dowsett (in press a); [6]Leonard (1998b).

Fawn-breasted Waxbill *Estrilda paludicola* B672 **RB**

Distribution *Afrotropical* (*Ethiopia to S. Angola*). Common in the dambos of N. Zambia, west of the Muchinga escarpment – exceptionally east of the Luangwa Valley at Muyombe[6]. It ranges south-west along the edge of the Rift to the Kabwe area (Maplehurst and Viljoen's Drift on the Mteteshi River)[5], while single wanderers have been reported from Chisamba[2] [and possibly at Munali (Lusaka), not

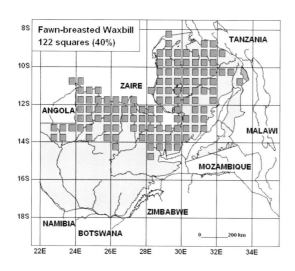

mapped[1].] In the upper Kafue basin south to Ndulumina[3], and in the Upper Zambezi south and west to Lukolwe, the South Kashiji River[4] and Zambezi town (Balovale)[7]. *Alt.* 950-1770 m (Danger Hill).

Ecology Dambos and other marshy ground, rank grass on the edge of evergreen forest, occasionally even in clearings in miombo woodland. In small flocks, exceptionally as many as 50.

Status Resident.

Breeding | Nov | Dec | Jan | Feb | Apr
(n=6) | 1 | 1 | 2 | 1 | 1
Clutch: N/4 (1).

Taxonomy *E. p. benguellensis.*

References [1]Aspinwall (1973f); [2]Aspinwall (1975b); [3]Benson & Irwin (1964b); [4]Britton (1970); [5]Dowsett (in press a); [6]Dowsett & Dowsett-Lemaire (1978c); [7]White (1945-46).

Orange-cheeked Waxbill *Estrilda melpoda* B673 **R(B)**

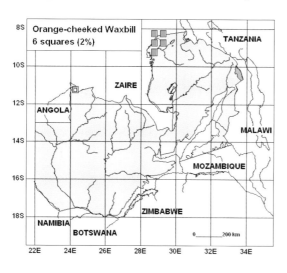

Distribution *Afrotropical (Senegal to N. Zambia).* Known mainly from L. Mweru and the lower Luapula Valley, east to Chiengi[2], and no further south than the mouth of the Luapula[2] and the Mwatishi River[4]. It has also been found once in N. Mwinilunga, at the Zambezi Rapids (open square)[3]. Common in the Chiengi area[1], less often reported elsewhere. *Alt.* 920-1200 m.

Ecology In cultivation and rank growth on the edge of thickets or forest, usually near water, feeding on grass seeds.

Status Resident, in small parties. The record from NW Zambia was of two birds with *E. paludicola* on 21 Nov 1998[3], perhaps vagrants (it is quite common at Kasaji, Katanga, some 120 km to the north)[5].

Breeding No records.

Taxonomy *E. m. fucata* (sic).

References [1]Dowsett (in press a); [2]Keith & Vernon (1969); [3]Leonard & Peters (1999); [4]Leonard *et al.* (2001c); [5]Schouteden (1971).

Common Waxbill *Estrilda astrild*   B674 **RB**

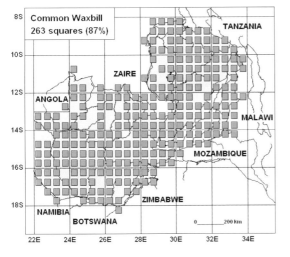

Distribution *Afrotropical (mainly Guinea to South Africa).* Common in grassland and swamps throughout the country, from the low-lying valleys to the high Nyika. *Alt.* 350-2200 m (Nyika, higher on the Malawi side).

Ecology In rank grass of floodplains and dambos, in swamps, around dams and sewage ponds, in neglected cultivation, suburban gardens, and montane grassland.

Status Resident, highly gregarious and often in large flocks, wandering locally.

Breeding	Dec	Jan	Feb	Mar	Apr
(n=30)	2	10	11	4	3

Clutch: C/1 (3); C/2 (2); C/3 (2); C/4 (3); C/5 (4); C/6 (6).

Main host to *Vidua macroura*.

Moult: finishing mid-Nov[2].

Taxonomy *E. a. cavendishi*, replaced in the west by *E. a. niediecki* (type locality Namwala; *type specimen not traced*; named for the German big game hunter Paul Niedieck)[1], which differs in being paler above, and less pink on the throat and face.

References [1]Reichenow (1916: 168); [2]Traylor (1965b).

[Black-lored Waxbill *Estrilda nigriloris*

This taxon is perhaps a form of *E. astrild*[2], but some authors consider it to be a very rare endemic species of S. Zaire; it is known from as near to N. Zambia as the Upemba area[1]. The two waxbills appear to be allopatric. **References** [1]Collar & Stuart (1985); [2]Dowsett & Dowsett-Lemaire (1993).]

Black-cheeked Waxbill *Estrilda erythronotos*   B675 **RB**

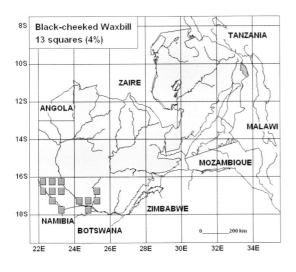

Distribution *Afrotropical (Kenya to South Africa).* Locally not uncommon in *Acacia* country in the extreme south-west, north to Shangombo[1] on the Mashi and 25 km west of Nangweshi[2] on the Zambezi east to Simungoma. There are a few records further east still to the Machile area[2] and Buwe Pool, with one possible sight record of two vagrants near Lochinvar 17 Sep 1973[3] ("?" on map). Unrecorded from the Middle Zambezi Valley [but in Zimbabwe occurs in the mid-altitude escarpment, as far east as the Sengwa Wildlife Research Area (1828A)[5]]. *Alt.* 950-1050 m.

Ecology Feeds on the ground in *Acacia* scrub and on the edge of thicket.

Status Resident, sometimes in small groups.

Records to the east of Simungoma and Mwandi are Jul-Oct only, and may represent post-breeding wandering in extreme cold seasons.
Breeding   Jan   Feb
(n=9)   1   8   A female specimen showed slight gonad activity Nov[2].
Clutch: C/1 (1); C/3 (2); C/5 (1); C/6 (4).
Taxonomy[4] *E. e. erythronotus*.
References [1]Benson (1956d); [2]Benson & Irwin (1967b); [3]Dowsett (in press a); [4]Irwin & Benson (1967b); [5]Salewski *et al.* (2001).

Blue Waxbill *Uraeginthus angolensis*   B667 **RB**

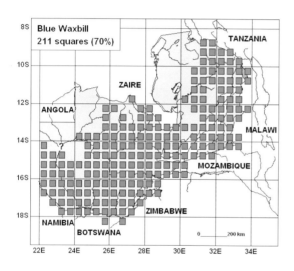

Distribution *Afrotropical (S. Congo-Brazzaville and Zaire to South Africa)*. Very common in any small thicket and rank growth in S. and E. Zambia. In the north-east it ranges west to Chishimba Falls[2] and Chikuni. Throughout the Copperbelt, west to the Matebo area, and in the west, north to the upper Luanginga River [and perhaps Lukulu, "?" on map, where a possible hybrid with the parapatric sibling *U. bengalus* has been reported][4]. *Alt.* 330-1800 m, even wandering once to 2150 m on the Nyika[1].
Ecology In any kind of thicket, scrubby understorey of open woodland or clearings, edges of plantations, neglected cultivation and particularly common around rural settlements and in gardens. Feeds alongside firefinches *Lagonosticta* spp. and other small granivores. Its nests are often associated with those of wasps.
Status Resident.
Breeding   Dec   Jan   Feb   Mar   Apr   May   Jun
(n=180)   7   41   35   60   33   3   1
Clutch: C/1 (4); C/2 (7); C/3 (23); C/4 (33); C/5 (42); C/6 (13); C/7 (1).
Moult: noted during two periods, Oct-Nov and Feb-May, but whether individual birds moult twice each year is not clear[4].
Taxonomy *U. a. niassensis*, replaced in the west by *U. a. cyanopleurus* (paler, less richly coloured above)[3,7]. Birds with the characters of hybrids with *U. bengalus* have been reported far from the normal range of the latter (Lusaka[4,5] and Lochinvar[6]).
References [1]Aspinwall (1971a); [2]Benson (1956f); [3]Clancey (1968c); [4]Dowsett (in press a); [5]Francis (1975); [6]Kelsey & Barnard (1988); [7]Traylor (1965b).

Red-cheeked Cordon-bleu *Uraeginthus bengalus*   B668 **RB**

Distribution *Afrotropical (Mauritania to W. Zambia)*. Replaces the last species in parts of the north and north-west, where never as common as *U. angolensis*. In the north, east only to the Mbala area (0831C being one of only two squares in which both are reported)[3]; thence throughout Luapula [a record of *U.*

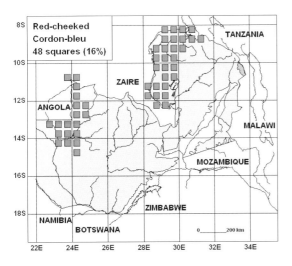

angolensis from Kilwa[4] was probably misidentified]. It occurs no nearer the Copperbelt than the lower Mabila and Kapashi. Reappears in the Upper Zambezi drainage, from N. Mwinilunga (where very scarce)[3], east to Ntambu[2]. Then south to Nabowa[3] (the most southerly record of the species) and west to Chingi, north of Chavuma[6] (both species being reported from the Kabompo square, 1324C, and perhaps Lukulu 1423A[3]). *Alt.* 760-1670 m.

Ecology Feeds on the ground in cultivation, on the edge of thicket, grass under miombo, usually in higher-rainfall areas than most populations of the sibling *U. angolensis.*

Status Resident.

Breeding   Dec   Jan   Apr
(n=3)   1   1   1

Clutch: N/4 (1).

Taxonomy[1] *U. b. katangae* (syn. *U. b. semotus*, type locality Chingi, Chavuma; *OUM*)[5]. Forms a superspecies with *U. angolensis.*

References [1]Benson (1956f); [2]Benson (1962a); [3]Dowsett (in press a); [4]Schouteden (1971); [5]White (1944c: 7); [6]White (1945-46).

Violet-eared Waxbill *Uraeginthus granatinus*   B669 **RB**

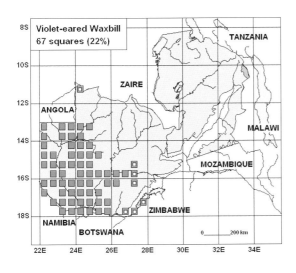

Distribution   *Kalahari/Zambezian (NW Angola to South Africa).* Small numbers in dry country in W. Zambia, down the Zambezi, east to Nyawa, the Namwala area and Dambwa F.R., Livingstone[2,3]. It is resident north only to 13°S, east to Manyinga[5] and Jivundu[6]. Vagrants (open squares) occur in some years further afield than usual in Southern Province (both plateau and valley), north to Kapyanga[6], and east to the Sianzovu-Sinamalima area of the Middle Zambezi Valley. These appear mainly to be in the cold season, after breeding. Exceptionally it has wandered to N. Mwinilunga at Hillwood farm (6 in mid-Sep 1992, a very dry year)[6]. [A specimen from Kitwe (1228C) in 1959 has been rejected as being an escape from captivity[1], although what is now known of the wanderings of non-breeding birds in some years suggests it could have been wild. Moreover, another species of the southern *Acacia, Urolestes melanoleucus,* was collected at Kitwe the same year, in Mar[1].] *Alt.* 500-1200 m.

Ecology Feeds on the ground in *Acacia* thicket and scrub (including the understorey of regenerating *Baikiaea* forest), and very common on the edge of *Cryptosepalum* forest in the Luena area[3]. Also often in cultivation.

Status Mainly resident and usually in pairs, though small groups form outside the breeding season, when it may join other seed-eaters. Occasionally wanders out of its usual range in cold years of low rainfall (see above).

Breeding   Dec   Jan   Feb   Mar   Apr
(n=16)   1   3   5   4   3   *Clutch*: C/2 (3); C/3 (3); C/4 (3); C/5 (1).
Host to *Vidua regia*.
Moult: in body moult mid-Nov[7].
Taxonomy *U. g. granatinus*[2].
References [1]Benson (1962a); [2]Benson & Irwin (1964b); [3]Benson & Irwin (1965a); [4]Benson & Irwin (1967b); [5]Benson *et al.* (1971a); [6]Dowsett (in press a); [7]Traylor (1965b).

Zebra (Orange) Waxbill *Amandava subflava*   B676 **RB**

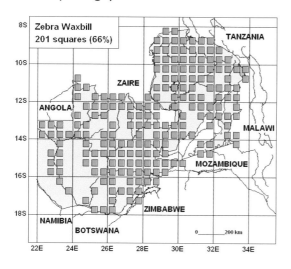

Distribution *Afrotropical* (*Senegal to South Africa*). Almost throughout, in moist grassland, although unrecorded from the Mashi River. Very local at lower levels, and absent from the eastern highlands. *Alt.* 350-1670 m.

Ecology In grass of dambos and floodplains, rank secondary growth along streams or edges of swamps; moves into drier types of grassland in the rains. Frequently uses old nests of *Ploceus* and *Euplectes* spp[2].

Status Present in all months, though a 2-year survey did suggest sightings were somewhat more frequent Sep-Dec[1]. This is the time of year that they flock (up to 50, prior to breeding), and are thus more conspicuous, and it is not clear if there are any real movements.

Breeding   Dec   Feb   Mar   Apr   May   Jun   Jul
(n=80)   2   4   41   20   11   1   1
Clutch: C/1 (3); C/2 (7); C/3 (12); C/4 (21); C/5 (19); C/6 (3); C/7 (1).
Taxonomy *A. s. clarkei*.
References [1]Dowsett (in press a); [2]Pitman (1934).

Locust Finch *Paludipasser locustella*   B679 **RB**

Distribution *Afrotropical* (*Nigeria to Zimbabwe*). In small numbers throughout the plateau dambos, south along the Zambezi escarpment to Masuku Mission[8], on the Upper Zambezi to Nawinda[3] and in the far west, south to the South Lueti River[7]. *Alt.* 950-1670 m.

Ecology In short moist grass of dambos, also on the edge of swamp and seasonal floodplain. Often alongside quail finches *Ortygospiza* spp.[4].

Status Present in all months, in pairs or small groups, with no suggestion of any movements[3].

Conservation Surprisingly classified as "Near Threatened" by BirdLife[1]; this appears unjustified in view of the wide distribution and availability of habitat.

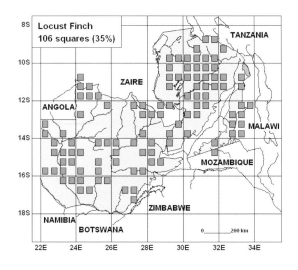

Breeding   Jan   Feb   Mar   Apr   May
(n=12)   3   2   2   3   2
Clutch: C/3 (1); C/4 (2); C/5 (4); C/6 (1); C/8 (1).
Moult: completed early Dec[7], a bird examined Jul being very worn[3].
Taxonomy *P. l. locustella* (type locality Lubansenshi River; *NHM*)[2,5]. Often treated as an *Ortygospiza*, but molecular studies show that this species is better placed in the mono-typic genus *Paludipasser*[6].
References [1]BirdLife International (2004a); [2]Dowsett (1980b); [3]Dowsett (in press a); [4]Madge (1972h); [5]Neave (1909: 25); [6]Payne & Sorenson (2003); [7]Traylor (1965b); [8]Winterbottom (1951-52).

African Quail Finch *Ortygospiza atricollis*   B677 **RB**

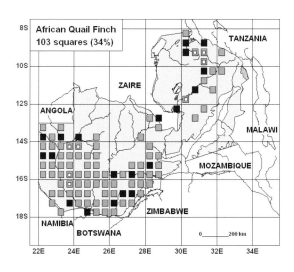

Distribution *Afrotropical* (*Mauritania to South Africa*). Common in the short grasslands of the south-west, rather local elsewhere. In the west north to the Makondu River[7] and Kabompo[4], and east throughout the Southern Province to Leopardshill[5]. Sparingly on the Copperbelt (e.g. Ndola[4]), to Bangweulu, throughout the Chambeshi to Mbesuma and Chozi, then to Mweru Wantipa[1]. (Black squares are specimen records, open ones sightings uncertain as to species). Overlaps widely with its close relative *O. gabonensis* in the west and the north; there are specimen records of both species from as many as 7 squares, from Liuwa Plain (1422D) to Mbala (0831C). *Alt.* 640-1780 m.
Ecology In short, dry grassland at edges of dambos, treeless floodplains, airfields and well adapted to cattle pastures. Has been recorded alongside *O. gabonensis* and *Paludipasser locustella* at Ndola[3]. In pairs or small flocks, of up to *c.* 20.
Status Resident: no evidence of movements other than local, especially well studied on the Kafue Flats, and in a 2-year national survey[2].
Breeding   Jan   Feb   Mar   Apr   May   Jun
(n=42)   15   7   12   1   6   1
Clutch: C/1 (1); C/2 (1); C/3 (3); C/4 (17); C/5 (14); C/6 (1).   *Moult*: ending Nov or Dec[2].
Taxonomy[4] *O. a. muelleri* (syn. *O. a. minuscula*, type locality Zambezi town (Balovale); *type specimen lost*)[6], replaced in much of Northern Province by *O. a. smithersi* (type locality Mpasa; *NHM*; named for R.H.N. Smithers)[1]; the latter differs in its darker, more streaked, back, the black of throat more extensive.

References [1]Benson (1955a: 106); [2]Dowsett (in press a); [3]Madge (1972h); [4]Traylor (1963); [5]Tree (1962b); [6]White (1945-46: 218); [7]Winterbottom (1942a).

Black-chinned (Red-billed) Quail Finch *Ortygospiza gabonensis*   B678 **RB**

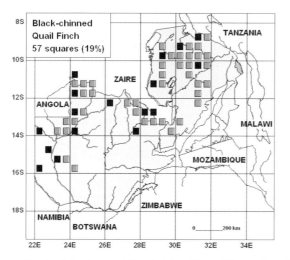

Black-chinned
Quail Finch
57 squares (19%)

Distribution *Afrotropical* (*Equatorial Guinea to W. Zambia*). Locally distributed in the dambos of the north and north-west; in the west south to the South Lueti River[9] and square 1524C[3] (the most southerly records of the species), and in the upper Kafue to Pwira Pan[2]. Throughout the Copperbelt to Mkushi River (Chalata), up the Muchinga escarpment to Shiwa Ngandu, thence to Mbala[3] and Kawambwa[1]. The two quail finch species are separable in the field only with difficulty, and their exact distribution limits remain to be determined. (Black squares are specimen records.) For overlap with *O. atricollis* see that species. *Alt.* 1050-1700 m.

Ecology[6] Usually in short, moist grass (or low sedges) of dambos and floodplains. Overall in wetter situations than *O. atricollis*, although sometimes in the same area, and also frequently alongside *Paludipasser locustella*.

Status Resident.

Breeding   Feb   Mar   Apr
(n=8)   4   3   1   *Clutch*: C/3 (2); C/4 (2).
Moult: ending Nov[9].

Taxonomy[8] *O. g. fuscata* (type locality Kawambwa; *NHM*)[7]. Considered by some authors to be conspecific with *O. atricollis*[5], but they are sympatric in some places. A possible hybrid specimen was reported from Kalabo[2].

References [1]Benson (1955a); [2]Benson & Irwin (1967b); [3]Dowsett (in press a); [4]Madge (1972h); [5]Payne (2005); [6]Penry (1986); [7]Sclater (1932: 142); [8]Traylor (1963); [9]Traylor (1965b).

Bronze Mannikin *Spermestes cucullata*   B680 **RB**

Distribution *Afrotropical* (*Senegal to South Africa*). Very common in any open savanna throughout the country. *Alt.* 330-1900 m, rarely wandering to 2100 m (Nyika)[3].

Ecology In any open or wooded grassland, on the edge of dambos, woodland or thicket, at swamp margins, around cultivation and frequently in gardens. Highly gregarious, sometimes even when breeding. Nests can be placed close to those of wasps.

Status Resident, with local wandering.

Breeding   Oct   Dec   Jan   Feb   Mar   Apr   May
(n=84)   1   5   27   22   15   8   6
Clutch: C/1 (1); C/2 (4); C/3 (4); C/4 (7); C/5 (15); C/6 (11); C/7 (2).
Moult: Jul and Aug, finishing Nov[2].

Taxonomy[1,4] *S. c. scutata*, with *S. c. tessellata* in the south-west (somewhat less brown above), the two

intergrading widely. Molecular studies suggest that the Afrotropical species of *Lonchura* are now best placed in the genus *Spermestes*[5].
References [1]Clancey (1968c); [2]Dowsett (in press a); [3]Dowsett-Lemaire (2006a); [4]Irwin (1981a); [5]Payne & Sorenson (2003).

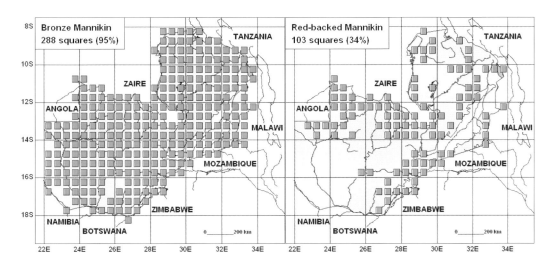

Red-backed Mannikin *Spermestes bicolor*   B681 **RB**

Distribution *Afrotropical (Guinea-Bissau to South Africa).* Tall woodland and riparian vegetation through the northern half of the Zambian plateau, including Eastern Province (Fungwe F.R.[4], south to east of Lundazi and in the Chipata area). Unknown from low altitude in the Luangwa Valley north of 14°30'S, although widespread in the Middle Zambezi. It reappears in the Nyimba area, thence ranges down the Zambezi escarpment to Sianzovu, and west along the middle Kafue to Kalala Is.[3]. Further west, ranges south only to Lutali[2], and west to the Chavuma area[4] (being unrecorded from across the Zambezi)[5]. Locally common in Eastern Province and on the Copperbelt. *Alt.* 370-1800 m.
Ecology On the edge of evergreen forest and dense thicket (mostly riparian), and in rich woodland, particularly miombo outside the breeding season. Often probes at flowers high in the canopy; otherwise feeds mainly on small seeds of long grass and sedges, gregarious and mixing occasionally with *S. cucullata.*
Status Probably resident in most parts of its range, though often more noticeable in the rains, and with some dispersal after breeding. Small groups of up to a dozen, rarely 20-40.
Breeding   Jan   Feb   Mar   Apr   May
(n=6)   1   2   1   1   1   Nest-building has been observed from mid-Nov.
Clutch: N/4 (1).
Taxonomy[1] *S. b. nigriceps*, with *S. b. woltersi* in the north-west (mantle blackish brown, not chestnut).
References [1]Benson & Irwin (1964b); [2]Britton (1970); [3]Brooke (1966c); [4]Dowsett (in press a); [5]Leonard (1998b).

Pied (Magpie) Mannikin *Spermestes fringilloides* B682 **RB**

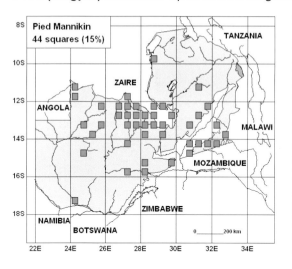

Distribution *Afrotropical* (*Senegal to South Africa*). There are two main centres of distribution in Zambia, the Copperbelt and the Eastern Province plateau and adjacent Luangwa Valley. It ranges throughout the Copperbelt, from the upper Luapula westwards, with a few reaching Mwinilunga Dist.[7]. In the Kafue drainage can be quite common south to the Imanda area[1], the Luamala River[3], and west to Kaoma. Further south it is irregular in the Lusaka area, with single records from Chilanga[4] and Lochinvar[6]. The only record from the Upper Zambezi is from Ngambwe Rapids[13]. In the east it is known on the plateau, from Kachalola[5] north to Chipata[2], and in the valley from Chipekete[8], the Niamadzi River[10] north to the escarpment at Jumbe[8] and the Munyamadzi River[2]. There are single records on the Northern Province plateau at Chalabesa[8] and in the lower Luapula at Mbereshi[8]. *Alt.* 600-1500 m.

Ecology Principally in thickets or riparian woodland with bamboo *Oxytenanthera abyssinica* (the seeds of which constitute the staple diet of this bird). Occasionally recorded in other habitat when on the move, especially reeds or marsh, or well-irrigated gardens. Even though it has been suggested that *Oxytenanthera* has a life-cycle of 20-30 years[9], observations in Malawi show this to be much shorter. It is not known whether the mannikin can take advantage of the exotic *Bambusa vulgaris*, planted or feral. In Jul 1982 there were many in *Oxytenanthera* bamboo that had flowered at Mambo, Nyimba Dist. Numerous, even abundant, in the Miengwe area Aug-Nov 1991, where bamboos were seeding, after flowering earlier that year. At Kafubu bamboos flowered Oct 1992, and mannikins were numerous there the following Apr-Nov, with nest-building observed[8]. Two adults found in the stomach of a nocturnal snake (*Dipsadoboa shrevei*) killed near Chingola, Jan, were perhaps roosting together in a nest[12].

Status Gregarious at all seasons (usually up to 8), and can be numerous at seeding bamboos (where resident for periods).

Breeding Feb Mar
(n=2) 1 1 Nest-building noted in the Kafubu area Apr, Sep and Nov[8].
Clutch: no data. The two breeding records are of females collected when about to lay (Chipata[2], St Anthony's Mission[11]).

Taxonomy No races recognized.

References [1]Aspinwall (1975b); [2]Benson (1956d); [3]Benson (1958a); [4]Benson (1958b); [5]Benson *et al.* (1970); [6]Dowsett (1966b); [7]Dowsett (1973b); [8]Dowsett (in press a); [9]Jackson (1972); [10]Neave (1907); [11]Tree (1966a); [12]Vernon (1993); [13]Winterbottom (1954).

Cut-throat Finch *Amadina fasciata* B683 **RB**

Distribution *Afrotropical* (*Mauritania to South Africa*). Prior to 1970, this species was confined to the Southern Province plateau and Zambezi Valley west to Livingstone[6], apart from rare sightings in the Luangwa Valley[3]. Since then, the species has become widespread in the south, possibly as a result of

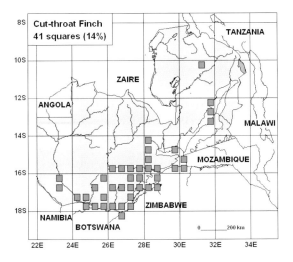

Cut-throat Finch
41 squares (14%)

increasingly dry conditions in southern Africa. It has occurred north to Kabwe[4], along the Kafue west to Itezhi-Tezhi[4], and up the Zambezi to the Matabele Plain[1]. The Luangwa Valley population is now more in evidence, from Chichele Lodge northwards. In Sep 1994 (a dry year) one (vagrant?) even appeared as far north as Kasama[4]. *Alt.* 330-1450 m.

Ecology In scrub in dry open woodland, mainly with *Acacia* or mopane, but also in degraded miombo and mixed *Acacia-Combretum*. One brood was in an old nest of *Plocepasser mahali* at Livingstone[2], and several birds have been known to take over nests in *Ploceus cucullatus* colonies[4].

Status Subject to at least local movements. Originally observed only infrequently, in pairs or small family groups. The first large numbers to be seen were 30 in a flock with *Quelea quelea* near Livingstone 18 Jan 1985[4]. Exceptional numbers of sightings and large flocks were evident from 1992. Individual flocks of over 100, and local concentrations of 200 or more, have been reported in the months of Jul to early Nov, decreasing with the advent of the rains that month. These are presumably post-breeding flocks, and have been reported from Lusaka to Livingstone. A group of 20 roosted in the nests of *Ploceus cucullatus* at Lusaka Sep-Jan[4].

Breeding   Mar   May   Jun
(n=3)   1   1   1   Also copulation Lusaka Apr, nest-building Livingstone Jan and Jul-Aug. *Clutch*: N/2 (2); C/3 (1) & N/3 (1).

Taxonomy *A. f. meridionalis* (type locality Livingstone; *type specimen not traced*)[5].

References [1]Aspinwall (1973f); [2]Benson & Irwin (1967b); [3]Benson *et al.* (1970); [4]Dowsett (in press a); [5]Neunzig (1910: 198); [6]Winterbottom (1951-52).

[Red-headed Finch *Amadina erythrocephala*
Afrotropical (*W. Angola to South Africa*). Mapped as occurring in the Caprivi Strip (1724A,C, 1725C), adjacent to SW Zambia[2], but confirmation desirable. This nomadic species might perhaps range this far north in dry years[1]. **References** [1]Dowsett *et al.* (in prep.); [2]Herremans in Harrison *et al.* (1997).]

Viduidae

Parasitic Weaver *Anomalospiza imberbis*   B643 **RB**

Distribution *Afrotropical* (*mainly Guinea to South Africa*). In grassland throughout most of the Zambian plateau, except in the north-east unrecorded between Chozi Floodplain[4] and Lundazi[9]. West of the Zambezi, known south to the Siloana Plains[4], and in the Mashi drainage to the South Lueti River[7]. There are few records at low altitude. In the upper Luangwa Valley perhaps only a rare visitor, with observations from Mfuwe (one 9 Apr) and Frank's Lakes (15 on 13 Sep)[4]. In the lower Luangwa seen once at Probert's Point (one 6 Mar)[4]. Apart from one report from Siavonga[4], there is no record from the Middle Zambezi, until Livingstone is reached[3]. *Alt.* 450-1650 m.

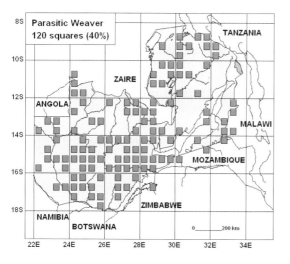

Ecology When breeding, found in open grassland, usually wet or at least rank, and in particular dambos, with scattered bushes. Although its hosts (*Prinia subflava* and *Cisticola* spp.) are widespread, *Anomalospiza* is more selective in its choice of habitat. After breeding large numbers roost in reedbeds.

Status Subject at least to local movements, and perhaps migratory. After breeding, flocks of 100-500 form Feb-Apr (often with *Euplectes* spp.), but in most areas they then disappear, and are not noted again before Nov or even Dec (when there are large pre-breeding flocks, e.g. 5-6000 in the third week of Nov in the Choma area). It is only at Itawa Swamp (Ndola) that large numbers have been reported throughout the dry season[4]. Indeed, there are only 3 other records for the months of Jun-Aug, involving 1-2 birds[2,4]. In some well-studied areas the species has been noted as essentially absent during the dry season, e.g. Lusaka[4] and Kafue fish farm[6]. It is possible that there is some long-distance movement after breeding, perhaps to the north of Zambia[1].

Breeding

	Nov	Dec	Jan	Feb	Mar	Apr
(n=80)	1	10	20	23	20	6

The bright breeding dress noted from 27 Sep, mostly from Nov[4,7]. A parasitic species, laying in the nests of *Prinia subflava* (34 cases), *Cisticola juncidis* (15), *C. aridulus* (4), *C. erythrops* (1), *C. natalensis* (4)[4]. Eggs have often been found in nests which contained no eggs of the host. Up to 4 eggs of *Anomalospiza* in one nest, frequently 2[4].

Taxonomy No races recognized (although *mukandakundae* has type locality Zambezi town (Balovale)[8]; *type specimen lost*). Formerly placed in the Ploceidae, but now shown to belong to the Viduidae[5].

References [1]Aspinwall (1983); [2]Benson & Irwin (1965b); [3]Benson & Pitman (1964); [4]Dowsett (in press a); [5]Lahti & Payne (2003); [6]Leonard (1999c); [7]Traylor (1965b); [8]White (1945-46: 219); [9]White (1947b).

Village Indigobird *Vidua chalybeata*   B654 **RB**

Distribution *Afrotropical* (*Mauritania to South Africa*). In *Acacia* and other dry vegetation types, and usually common. In the north from Kaputa[5] eastwards to Kaombwe[1], then throughout the Luangwa Valley and Eastern Province plateau to Chisomo and the Lusaka area. In the Kafue basin it occurs north to Ntomeshya pontoon and the Busanga Plain. Throughout the Middle Zambezi and Southern Province, and up the Zambezi to Zambezi town (Balovale)[2], west to Luachi[8]. *Alt.* 330-1450 m.

Ecology[6] In open savanna and woodland margins, partial to *Acacia* in many areas, but also around rural settlements generally (especially farms with livestock) and suburban gardens. In the breeding season males "lek", attracting several females to their song posts.

Status Probably resident (the only movement recorded by a ringed bird was *c.* 25 km)[3]. Post-breeding groups of both sexes and young may number scores. A ringed male at Lochinvar reached the age of at least 6 years[4].

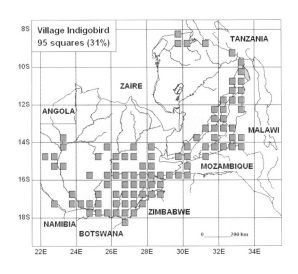

Breeding   Jan   Feb   Mar
(n=20)   3   6   5
                Apr   May   Jun
                 3   2   1

Breeding dress mid-Dec to Jun, even to late Aug. The male includes in its vocalisations imitations of the song of *Lagonosticta sene-gala*, and the female lays its eggs in its nest, the young all being raised together by the fire-finches. Exceptionally, some birds in the Livingstone-Katombora area mimic *L. rufopicta* (rather than *L. senegala*), and to add to the confusion, have a white bill[7].

Clutch: most records are of single eggs with clutches of the host, but up to 3 parasite eggs have been found in a nest[3].

Moult: a bird was completing moult late Oct[3].

Taxonomy *V. c. amauropteryx*. White-billed birds of the subspecies *centralis* may occur in N. Zambia[5], but more investigation needed.

References [1]Aspinwall (1975b); [2]Benson & White (1957); [3]Dowsett (in press a); [4]Payne in Fry & Keith (2004); [5]Payne (1973); [6]Payne (1987); [7]Payne *et al.* (2002); [8]Traylor (1965b).

Dusky Indigobird *Vidua purpurascens*   B652 **RB**

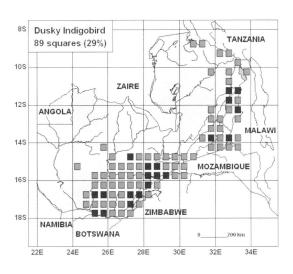

Distribution *Afrotropical (Kenya to South Africa)*. Black squares are specimens. Its range is much like that of *V. chalybeata*, but it occurs in smaller numbers and it extends west only to near Luampa (perhaps to Kalongola and Senanga, "?" on map)[1], north in the Kafue basin to the Busanga area[1]. Throughout the Middle Zambezi and Luangwa Valleys and Eastern Province, westwards in the north to the Chambeshi River and Kambole[1]. [The ranges of this species and *V. funerea* are incompletely known owing to the difficulty of separating them in the field.] *Alt.* 330-1600 m.

Ecology In open woodland, edges of thicket and riparian forest or woodland.

Status Gregarious in the off-season like other indigobirds, extent of movements unknown.

Two colour-ringed males sang at the same call-sites at Lochinvar for 4 successive years[2].

Breeding   Jan   Feb   Mar   Apr   May
(n=8)   1   2   2   2   1

Breeding dress late Dec to early Jul[1]. Parasitizes *Lagonosticta rhodopareia*[4].

Clutch: there are 6 records of single eggs or young in the host nests[1].

Taxonomy No races recognized[2]. Two male *Vidua* spp. were believed to be hybrids between a male *V. purpurascens* and female *V. paradisaea*; they were superficially like the East African endemic species

Steel-blue Widow *V. hypocherina*[3].
References [1]Dowsett (in press a); [2]Payne in Fry & Keith (2004); [3]Payne (1980a); [4]Payne (1987).

Variable Indigobird *Vidua funerea*   B653 (part) **R(B)**

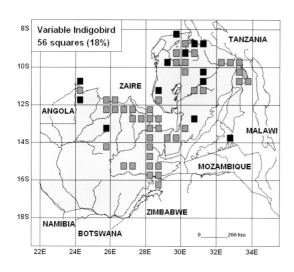

Distribution *Afrotropical (Nigeria to South Africa)*. Black squares are specimens. Occurs rather uncommonly on the northern plateau (in the same habitat as its host, *Lagonosticta rubricata*), in the east to the Nyika Plateau and south to Chipata[2]. Then from the Copperbelt, south to Ibwe Munyama on the Zambezi escarpment, and in the west to Kasempa and Mwinilunga town[2,4]. *Alt.* 940-2000 m (Nyika).
Ecology In grassland with scattered bushes, on the edge of woodland, thicket and plantations.
Status Gregarious in the off-season like other indigobirds (exceptionally 80 together, 22 Apr, Mwinilunga Dist.)[1]; extent of movements unknown.
Breeding No records. Full breeding dress from Jan to late Jun[1]. Host is known to be *Lagonosticta rubricata*[2].
Taxonomy[3] *V. f. nigerrima*.
References [1]Dowsett (in press a); [2]Payne (1973); [3]Payne *et al.* (1993); [4]White (1945-46).

Green Indigobird *Vidua codringtoni*   B653 (part) **R(B)**

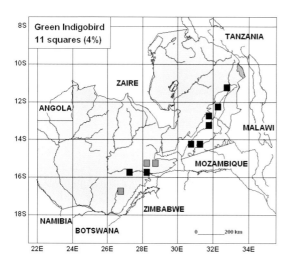

Distribution *Zambezian endemic (Zambia to Zimbabwe)*. Black squares are specimens. The Luangwa Valley from Katangalika southwards (a specimen originally attributed to *V. funerea*[3]) to Mulilo's, the Lusaka area, Lochinvar and Choma[1,4]. *Alt.* 550-1300 m. Likely more widespread (as is its host, *Hypargos niveoguttatus*).
Ecology In open woodland, on the edge of thicket and riparian vegetation.
Status Probably resident. Apparently very sparse, but status unclear owing to difficulty in recognizing it in the field (the distinctive imitations in its song are of very short duration).
Breeding No records. Breeding dress and song noted late Jan to end May[1] (with song again reported 22 Oct)[1].
Taxonomy No races: *V. codringtoni* (type locality Mulilo; *NHM*; named for R.E. Codrington [1869-

1908], Deputy Administrator of North Eastern Rhodesia)[2]. Originally described as a race of *V. funerea*, but now known to be a distinct species, parasitizing *Hypargos niveoguttatus*[4].
References [1]Dowsett (in press a); [2]Neave (1907: 94); [3]Payne (1973); [4]Payne *et al.* (1992).

Pin-tailed Widow *Vidua macroura*   B650 **RB**

Distribution *Afrotropical* (*Mauritania to South Africa*). Locally common throughout the country in any grassland. *Alt.* 330-2200 m.
Ecology In a variety of open situations such as wooded grassland, dambo margins, floodplains, edges of any woodland, roadsides, neglected cultivation and gardens. Polygamous, as other *Vidua* spp., usually one male associating with a number of females.
Status Resident. Forms small flocks in the off-season, often mixing with other *Vidua* finches.
Breeding   Dec   Jan   Feb   Mar
(n=12)   1   4   5   2   Breeding dress early Oct to end Apr, occasionally to mid-
May[2]. Has parasitized *Estrilda astrild* (7) and *Spermestes cucullata* (2)[2].
Clutch: C/1 or N/1 with host's eggs, but once 3 eggs of parasite[2].
Taxonomy No races recognized[3] (*contra* ref. 1).
References [1]Clancey (1980d); [2]Dowsett (in press a); [3]Payne in Fry & Keith (2004).

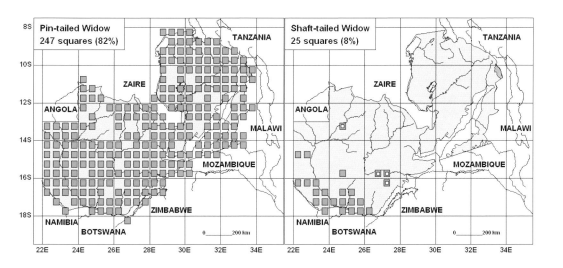

Shaft-tailed Widow *Vidua regia*   B651 **RB**

Distribution *Kalahari/Zambezian* (*mainly SW Angola to South Africa*). Fairly common in the south-west, north to 16°S along the Mashi and Zambezi Rivers, to 60 km west of Kalabo[1], and east to Afumba[3]. It ranges south-eastwards to the Machile area, to Nyawa, Livingstone[8] and Kalomo River[4]. In some years, wanderers (open squares) appear further north, to the Kafue Flats at Kabulamwanda[2], Kawehi and Lochinvar, exceptionally further north at Jivundu (1324B)[4]. [Unrecorded from the Middle Zambezi Valley[7], although a plot in square 1727C[6] suggests otherwise.] *Alt.* 950-1200 m.
Ecology *Acacia* bush, where it feeds on the ground, often in association with other granivores.
Status Resident in its main range, in small groups, but wanders at times further north and east. In early

2006 there was an influx in the Livingstone area, with flocks moulting out of breeding dress late Apr-May[4].

Breeding Feb Mar Apr
(n=5) 2 1 2 Breeding dress from 25 Nov to late Apr[4]. Parasitizes *Uraeginthus granatinus* (5) with up to 3 eggs per nest[4].

Taxonomy No races recognized[5].

References [1]Benson & Irwin (1967b); [2]Bruce-Miller & Bruce-Miller (1972); [3]Bruce-Miller & Dowsett (1977); [4]Dowsett (in press a); [5]Payne in Fry & Keith (2004); [6]Barnard in Harrison *et al.* (1997); [7]Irwin (1981a); [8]Winterbottom (1951-52).

Long-tailed Paradise Widow *Vidua paradisaea* B655 **RB**

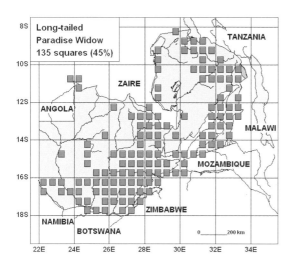

Distribution *Afrotropical* (*Sudan to South Africa*). Has the same range as its host *Pytilia melba* (but usually in more open woodland than the thickets of its host), and locally common. In the south-west, north to the Shangombo area and south of Lukulu. Throughout the south and east, in the *Acacia*-country loop around the north-east, down the Luapula to the Copperbelt, and west to Mutanda[3]. There is an isolated population (as of its host) in the north of Mwinilunga, exact limits not known. *Alt.* 330-1500 m.

Ecology Partial to open *Acacia* woodland or wooded grassland, also in undifferentiated woodland, mopane and drier types of miombo (especially in the non-breeding season).

Status Resident. As with others of the genus, usually a male with several females in the breeding season, several such groups flocking together at other times, often mixed with other *Vidua* finches.

Breeding Jan Feb Mar Apr May
(n=15) 1 5 5 3 1 (There is an unconfirmed record of egg-laying Oct[1]). Breeding dress from Dec, mainly early Jan to late Jul[2]. Parasitizes *Pytilia melba*[2].
Clutch: up to 3 *Vidua* eggs in each nest[2].

Taxonomy No races recognized now that Sahel *V. orientalis* treated as a distinct species. Two male *Vidua* spp. at Lochinvar were believed to be hybrids between a male *V. purpurascens* and female *V. paradisaea*; they were superficially like the East African endemic species *V. hypocherina*[4].

References [1]Benson *et al.* (1971a); [2]Dowsett (in press a); [3]Irwin & Benson (1967b); [4]Payne (1980a).

Broad-tailed Paradise Widow *Vidua obtusa* B656 **RB**

Distribution *Zambezian near-endemic* (*Burundi to South Africa*). Locally common in open woodland, though not usually mopane (and thus rare in the Luangwa and Middle Zambezi Valleys). In the south-west occurs as far as Sinjembela[3], and further north west to the Luachi River and Sikongo (Kalabo Dist.)[5]. *Alt.* 350-1670 m (Mbala).

Ecology In various types of woodland and wooded grassland, but rarely in mopane.

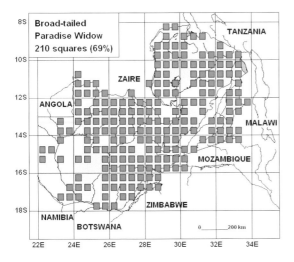

Status Resident. As with others of the genus, usually a male with several females in the breeding season, several such groups flocking together at other times.

Breeding

	Feb	Mar	Apr	Aug	Sep
(n=7)	2	2	1	1	1

Breeding dress late Mar to early Sep (Mwinilunga), late Jan to mid-Jul (southern and central areas)[2].

Parasitizes *Pytilia afra*[1].

Clutch: up to 4 eggs have been laid in a nest[2].

Moult: in W. Zambia finishing Nov[5].

Taxonomy No races recognized, now that it is separated from *V. paradisaea s.l.*[4].

References [1]Colebrook-Robjent (1975b); [2]Dowsett (in press a); [3]Irwin & Benson (1967b); [4]Payne (1971); [5]Traylor (1965b).

Fringillidae

Cape Canary *Serinus canicollis*   B693 **RB**

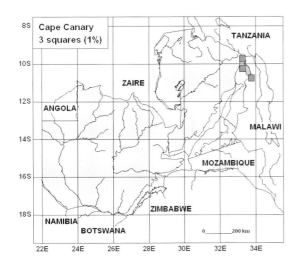

Distribution *Afromontane near-endemic* (*Ethiopia to South Africa*). Locally common in the eastern highlands, on the Mafingas[1] and the Nyika Plateau[2]. *Alt.* 1700-2200 m (higher on the Malawi side of the Nyika).

Ecology Montane grassland with scattered bushes; also at forest edges.

Status Resident, as seen year-round (Nyika), with some local wandering in flocks.

Breeding

	Sep	Oct
(n=7)	4	3

(Including Malawi side of SW Nyika.)

Clutch: C/2 (2); C/3 (2).

Taxonomy *S. c. sassii*.

References [1]Clay (1953); [2]Dowsett-Lemaire (2006a).

African Citril *Serinus citrinelloides*   B695 **RB**

Distribution *Afromontane near-endemic* (*Ethiopia to S. Malawi*). A submontane species, confined to the north and east, from Mbala[2] and Kamuswazi stream[3], south to the Mafingas[6], Vipama stream[1] and the Nyika Plateau[5]. Reappears in the Chipata area, at Chipata[9] and Mtenguleni, near Kazimuli. *Alt.* 1140 m (Chipata) to 2200 m (Nyika)[5].

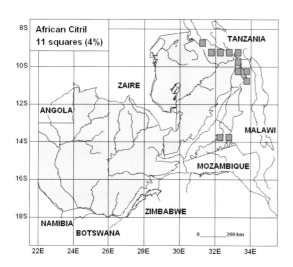

Ecology Common at forest edges, and in various stages of forest regrowth, often near streams; occasional in miombo woodland. On the Nyika has been seen taking seeds of *Hagenia abyssinica* and *Cussonia spicata*.

Status Essentially resident, usually in small family groups. Some records at low altitude in the Mafingas-Nyika area and parts of Isoka Dist. may represent non-breeding dispersal Apr-Aug when there are rather fewer high-altitude observations, or it may be resident at medium altitude, as at Chipata and in neighbouring Malawi.

Breeding   Jun   Oct
(n=2)   1   1   Lays Sep-Mar in Malawi. *Clutch*: no data.

Taxonomy *S. c. hypostictus* (male lacking yellow eye-stripe, cheeks sooty grey), from Chipata to the Nyika, with sight records from Kaombwe and square 0932A[3]; *S. c. frontalis* (male with yellow forehead and eye-stripe, cheeks black) at Mbala. It is not clear whether the two taxa come into contact. Treated as different species by some authors, but this does not appear to be justified[4,8]. Preliminary molecular studies suggest all Zambian *"Serinus"* except *S. canicollis* should be in the genus *Crithagra*[7], but further study needed.

References [1]Aspinwall (1975b); [2]Benson (1956d); [3]Dowsett (in press a); [4]Dowsett & Dowsett-Lemaire (1993); [5]Dowsett-Lemaire (2006a); [6]Leonard *et al.* (2001a); [7]Ryan *et al.* (2004); [8]Short *et al.* (1990); [9]Winterbottom (1936).

Black-faced Canary *Serinus capistratus*   B694 **RB**

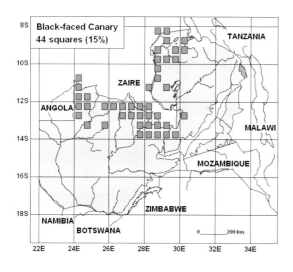

Distribution *Zambezian near-endemic (S. Gabon to N. Zambia)*. In the higher-rainfall region of the north, but absent from areas where *S. citrinelloides* occurs. Thus east only to Bulaya and Mporokoso[1]. Widespread in the Luapula Valley, down to the Copperbelt (most regularly noted at Itawa and Miengwe)[3], and east to Kasanka[3], Musofu[3] and Mkushi River (Chalata) (the most southerly records of the species). Distribution is continuous towards the west, throughout Mwinilunga Dist. (though rare in the north), south along the upper Kabompo River to Ngalula[2]. Generally uncommon. *Alt.* 920-1430 m.

Ecology Edge of evergreen forest, especially riparian. Also on the edge of thickets near water or in dambos, and at times even in rich miombo woodland.

Status Mainly resident, in pairs or (when not breeding) small groups of up to 12, rarely 20. On the Copperbelt there are remarkably few records Apr-Jun, and often reports of birds "reappearing" from about mid-Jul. However, such movements are unlikely to be distant, and there are May records from Mkushi Dist. and the Luapula Valley (in both Zambia and Zaire)[4]. It is possible, too, that birds become unobtrusive during a post-breeding moult.

Breeding   Dec
(n=2)   2   *Clutch*: no data. The nest and eggs are undescribed.
Taxonomy *S. c. capistratus*.
References [1]Benson (1956d); [2]Benson & Holliday (1964); [3]Dowsett (in press a); [4]Schouteden (1971).

Black-throated Canary *Serinus atrogularis*   B690 **RB**

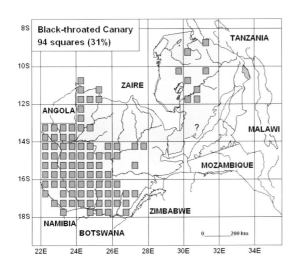

Distribution *Afrotropical* (*W. Kenya to South Africa*). There are two populations in Zambia. (1) Occurs commonly on the Kalahari sands of the south-west, east to the Zambezi escarpment in Kalomo Dist., Choma, and the Lukanga Swamp[1] in the Kafue drainage, exceptionally to Blue Lagoon[3]. In the north-west it reaches the plains in N. Mwinilunga, east to the West Lumwana[4]. (2) Smaller numbers reappear on the plains of Northern Province, from the Bangweulu area, east to Kasama[1] and north to Uningi Pans and the Mbala area[4,7]. [A specimen record from "Serenje"[8] dates from the time when the boma of that name was at the locality called Old Serenje ("?" on map), but the canary is likely to have come from further north, around Bangweulu.] *Alt.* 950-1450 m (exceptionally to 1800 m at Uningi Pans).

Ecology Usually in open grasslands or lightly-wooded savanna (*Burkea, Terminalia*), but also at times in rank grass under miombo woodland. In the north-east often associated with dambos and plains.

Status Resident, in small groups, and in flocks of up to 40 in the non-breeding season. There is some post-breeding wandering, usually of no great distance; two flocks of 15-20 each at Blue Lagoon mid-Aug[3] were some way from the nearest known breeding areas, in the Choma area and Supuni ferry in the upper Kafue[2], but the W. Kafue Flats have been under-explored.

Breeding   Dec   Jan   Feb   Mar   Apr   May
(n=22)   4   6   2   4   5   1   *Clutch*: C/2 (6); C/3 (8); C/4 (2).
Moult: finishing late Oct-early Nov[9].

Taxonomy[6,7] *S. a. lwenarum* (type locality Zambezi town (Balovale); *SAM*)[10], syn. *S. a. kasamaensis* (type locality Kasama; *NHM*)[1]; replaced in the south by *S. a. semideserti* (colder and greyer above), syn. *S. a. seshekeensis* (type locality Chunga Pool; *NHM*)[5]. Some eastern African populations are now treated as a separate species, *S. reichenowi*[11].

References [1]Benson (1955a: 108); [2]Benson (1959c); [3]Dowsett (1965c); [4]Dowsett (in press a); [5]Grant & Mackworth-Praed (1958: 17); [6]Irwin (1981a); [7]Irwin & Benson (1967b); [8]Stoehr & Sclater (1906); [9]Traylor (1965b); [10]White (1944a: 40); [11]Zimmerman *et al.* (1996).

[Lemon-breasted Canary *Serinus citrinipectus*

Eastern endemic (S. Malawi to Natal). The suggestion that it "ranges upstream in the Middle Zambezi Valley where it has been recorded in south-eastern Zambia"[2] is without foundation, even though the low-lying habitat may seem suitable. The only claim from Zambia was from Chipata, in atypical habitat, was not satisfactorily proven and was not published[1]. **References** [1]Dowsett (in press a); [2]Williams & Varden (1994).]

Yellow-eyed (Yellow-fronted) Canary *Serinus mozambicus*   B689 **RB**

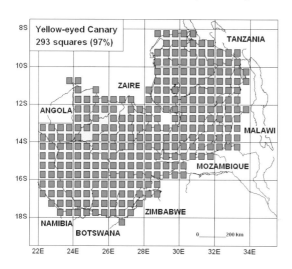

8S Yellow-eyed Canary
293 squares (97%)
TANZANIA
10S
ZAIRE
12S
ANGOLA
MALAWI
14S
MOZAMBIQUE
16S
ZIMBABWE
18S
NAMIBIA
BOTSWANA   0_____200 km
22E   24E   26E   28E   30E   32E   34E

Distribution *Afrotropical (Mauritania to South Africa).* Very common throughout, in any lightly-wooded country. *Alt.* 330-1800 m (Uningi Pans).

Ecology In any open woodland or wooded savanna, riparian growth, edge of marsh, cultivation and gardens.

Status Resident. Forms flocks in the off-season.

Breeding	Aug	Sep	Dec	Jan
(n=98)	6	2	13	37
	Feb	Mar	Apr	
	19	17	4	

Clutch: C/1 (3); C/2 (20); C/3 (44); C/4 (2). *Moult*: there is some evidence of a pre-nuptial moult, finishing Nov, and a complete post-breeding moult, late Feb onwards[2].

Taxonomy[1] *S. m. mozambicus* (deep green above, heavily streaked), syn. *S. m. madaraszi* (type locality Muyombe[3]; *type specimen destroyed, Budapest 1956*, named for the Hungarian ornithologist J. von Madarász [1858-1931]. It is replaced in the extreme north and north-west by *S. m. samaliyae* (brighter green, more lightly streaked), and in the west by *S. m. vansoni* (as last, but paler above and below). [*S. m. intensus* is an invalid name.]

References [1]Benson & Irwin (1967b); [2]Dowsett (in press a); [3]Reichenow (1902: 8).

Yellow Canary *Serinus flaviventris*   B691 **AV**

Distribution and Status *Afrotropical (essentially SW Angola to South Africa).* A very rare vagrant to plains in W. Zambia, with a specimen record from Sinjembela (1723A, 1000 m, dated 9 Oct 1964)[1] and a sight record from the Chitunta Plain (1124A, 1370 m, on 13 Nov 1978)[3]. Both were probably post-breeding vagrants from breeding areas to the south-west. [Extralimitally, a plot mapped in error in 1724A[4], presumably meaning the Caprivi Strip, lacks details and requires confirmation[2], as does a Zimbabwe plot in the Kazungula square (1725C)[5].]

Taxonomy The race of the single Zambian specimen is uncertain, being slightly more greenish, less golden, below than *S. f. damarensis* (the form that occurs nearest)[1]. On the other hand, the bird seen on Chitunta Plain corresponded best to *S. f. damarensis*[3].

References [1]Benson & Irwin (1967b); [2]Dowsett *et al.* (in prep.); [3]Dowsett & Dowsett-Lemaire (1979b); [4]Dean in Harrison *et al.* (1997); [5]Hustler (1998).

Bully Canary *Serinus sulphuratus* B692 **RB**

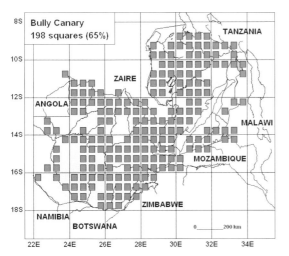

Distribution *Afrotropical* (*Kenya to South Africa*). Through most of the plateau areas (where generally not uncommon), absent from the low-lying Luangwa Valley and between Lakes Mweru and Tanganyika. Fairly regular in the Middle Zambezi Valley, but only exceptionally west of the Zambezi, to some 55 km south of the South Lueti River, at 16°10'S, 22°07'E[2]. *Alt.* 330-2200 m (Nyika, higher on the Malawi side).

Ecology A species of ecotone, found on fringes of woodland, forest, thickets; in montane areas it favours wooded grassland and bracken-briar; also in gardens and at the edge of plantations.

Status Present in all months, but a 2-year survey did suggest it was more frequent Oct-Mar. This is after the breeding season, and although the species does not gather into large flocks (up to 12 as a rule), it may be more conspicuous then. There are probably no movements, other than local[3].

Breeding

	Jan	Mar	Apr	Jul	Aug	Sep	Oct	Nov
(n=93)	3	12	5	2	20	33	17	1

Clutch: C/1 (2); C/2 (13); C/3 (40); C/4 (9).

Moult: starting Dec[3].

Taxonomy Tentatively: *S. s. frommi*, replaced in the south by the paler yellow *S. s. languens*[1,4].

References [1]Benson & Benson (1977); [2]Benson & Irwin (1967b); [3]Dowsett (in press a); [4]Irwin (1981a).

Black-eared Seedeater *Serinus mennelli* B699 **RB**

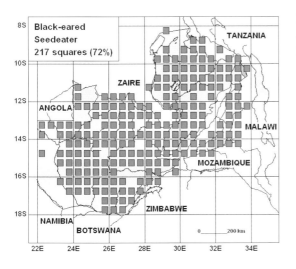

Distribution *Zambezian endemic* (*SE Zaire to Zimbabwe*). Locally common throughout the plateau miombo woodlands. Absent from most of the *Baikiaea* forests on the Kalahari sands, thus not immediately west of Livingstone[2]. West of the Zambezi, not south of Liumba, Kalabo Dist., except marginally near Nyambisi Pool[1]. [A sight record from Sioma-Ngwezi N.P. requires confirmation[4].] Also absent from the low-lying Luangwa Valley and the drier country between Lakes Mweru and Tanganyika. *Alt.* 550-1780 m, as high as 1950 m on the Mafingas[5] and 2070 m (Makutu)[3].

Ecology Mainly in miombo woodland, where found frequently alongside *S. reichardi* (it is usually more numerous), overall preferring drier types than its congener. Also on the edge of *Cryptosepalum.* Rarely in other woodland (e.g. mopane, *Baikiaea*). Normally feeding on grass seeds.

Status Resident. Usually in small family groups, but flocks of up to 20 post-breeding.

Breeding   Nov   Dec   Jan   Feb   Mar   Apr
(n=12)   1   1   1   3   5   1   *Clutch*: C/1 (1); C/2 (7); C/3 (1).
Moult: one bird was half-way through end Jul[4].

Taxonomy No races recognized.

References [1]Aspinwall (1973f); [2]Benson & Irwin (1967b); [3]Dowsett (1971h); [4]Dowsett (in press a); [5]Dowsett & Stjernstedt (1973).

Streaky-headed Seedeater *Serinus gularis*   B697 **AM?**

Distribution *Afrotropical* (*Guinea to South Africa*). In the dry south-west, west of the Zambezi, perhaps a sparse resident, rather than an irregular visitor. From Liande Plain south to Kaungo, and exceptionally down the Zambezi to Lusu Hill[1] and Simungoma[2]. [Despite reports to the contrary, there is no proof that it occurs further east, near to Livingstone, on the southern bank of the Zambezi. Although a map of distribution in Zimbabwe gives the impression that it is throughout much of the Middle Zambezi Valley[3], this is considered erroneous[5], and it does not in fact occur below the escarpment[4].] There are three specimens from the South Lueti River[6], other records are considered reliable sightings. *Alt.* 950-1050 m.

Ecology Reported from light broad-leaved woodland, in one instance rocky.

Status Probably resident, though for the moment the few Zambian records fall between 4 Sep and 24 Dec.

Breeding No records, but specimens were in fresh plumage late Nov[6] and males in song early Dec[2].

Taxonomy *S. g. benguellensis.*

References [1]Aspinwall (1973f); [2]Dowsett & Leonard (in press a); [3]Nuttall in Harrison *et al.* (1997); [4]Irwin (1981a); [5]Riddell (2004a); [6]Traylor (1965b).

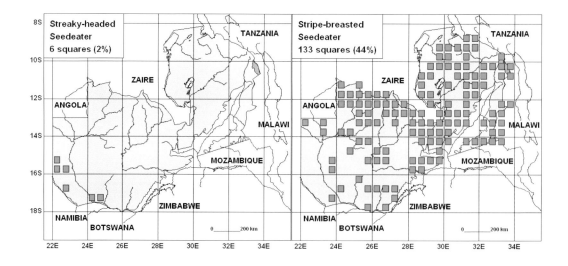

Stripe-breasted Seedeater *Serinus reichardi* B698 **RB**

Distribution *Afrotropical* (*Ethiopia to Mozambique and Zambia*). Locally common in the plateau miombo woodlands of the north and east, but scarce on the Southern Province plateau – west to the Kataba area (1625A)[4]. Absent from the low-lying valleys, between Lakes Tanganyika and Mweru, from the lower Luapula Valley and most of the south-west. In NW Zambia, ranges south to the Upper Zambezi at Zambezi town (Balovale)[3] and to the west at Nyatanda[5]. There are isolated records from Mongu Dist., Katoti[1] and Litungi. Collected once west of the Zambezi further south, at Cholola[2]. It reaches its southern limit in the Livingstone area, being absent south of the Zambezi. *Alt.* 1000-1900 m.
Ecology Well-developed miombo woodland (as in higher-rainfall areas), locally around rocks, also on the edge of riparian forest. Records west of the Zambezi are from *Burkea* woodland. Often alongside the commoner *S. mennelli*.
Status Resident, in small groups usually, though exceptionally 25 feeding on dry flower heads.
Breeding   Sep   Oct   Mar
(n=8)   6   1   1   *Clutch*: C/1 (1); C/2 (1) & N/2 (1); C/3 (1).
Taxonomy *S. r. reichardi*. If, as seems likely, the form *striatipectus* of E. Africa proves to be a separate species, then *S. reichardi* is a Zambezian endemic.
References [1]Aspinwall (1973f); [2]Benson & Irwin (1967b); [3]Britton (1970); [4]Bruce-Miller & Dowsett (1977); [5]Dowsett (in press a).

Streaky Seedeater *Serinus striolatus* B696 **RB**

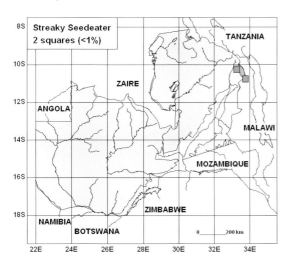

Distribution *Afromontane endemic* (*Ethiopia to N. Malawi*). In the eastern highlands only, from the Mafingas (scarce) and the Nyika Plateau (common)[2]. *Alt.* 1900-2200 m (2400 m on the Malawi side of Nyika).
Ecology Inhabits forest edges, montane shrubland and locally the dense understorey of riparian forest.
Status Resident, not seen to flock.
Breeding   Sep   Oct   Nov   Dec
(n=6)   1   3   1   1
(Including the Malawi side of SW Nyika.)
Clutch: C/2 (1). *Moult*: from Nov onwards[1].
Taxonomy *S. s. whytii* (type locality Nyika Plateau, Malawi)[3]. This form is given specific status by some authors, but we find no justification for this.
References [1]Dowsett (in press a); [2]Dowsett-Lemaire (2006a); [3]Shelley in Shelley & Sclater (1897).

Emberizidae

Lark-like Bunting *Emberiza impetuani*   B687 **AV**

Distribution and Status *Afrotropical* (*breeds perhaps Angola, to South Africa*). An irruptive vagrant from arid SW Africa. In 1964-65 (a cold year) there were three records in S. Zambia of 1-2 birds (one collected) from Lochinvar (1527C: 2 Jul), the Kariba Dam wall (1628D: 29 Nov) and Livingstone (1725D: 17 Apr)[1]. The species has twice been observed in N. Mwinilunga at the Zambezi Rapids (1124A: one 25 Feb 1978 and two parties of 5-6 birds 7 Jul 1980)[2]. Vagrants have occurred at similar latitude and even further north in neighbouring countries, to L. Cameia (Angola) 10 Aug (possibly a resident population)[4] and Kananga (Zaire) 23-30 Sep[3]. In Aug 1993 large numbers reached the Kariba area (Zimbabwe, 1628B)[5]. *Alt.* 550 m (Kariba) to 1190 m (Zambezi Rapids). In mopane, *Acacia* and rocks with scattered grass.
Taxonomy *E. i. impetuani.*
References [1]Benson & Irwin (1967b); [2]Bowen (1983g); [3]Chapin (1954); [4]Dean (2000); [5]Jones (1994).

Cinnamon-breasted Rock Bunting *Emberiza tahapisi*   B686 **AMB**

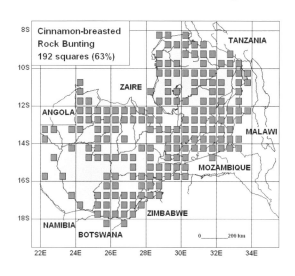

Distribution *Afrotropical* (*Mauritania to South Africa*). Almost throughout, often associated with rocks and sparse in areas of Kalahari sand in the south-west. West of the Zambezi, not known south of the South Lueti River[3], where perhaps on passage. *Alt.* 330-2200 m.
Ecology Around rocky outcrops and lightly-wooded hillsides or escarpments with stony or scantily grassed ground; disperses to any open country including cultivation and dirt roads.
Status Is largely an intra-African breeding migrant. Although there are records in all months, a survey over 4 years showed that frequency was less Sep-Mar, and increased Apr-Aug. Arrives in the extreme south Feb-Mar, on the Copperbelt in Apr. Very few remain during the rains[1].

Breeding[2]   Apr   May   Jun   Jul   Aug
(n=32)   2   9   15   4   2   *Clutch*: C/1 (1); C/2 (11); C/3 (14).
Moult: one bird completing moult late Oct[3], while an adult was half-way through (perhaps suspended) mid-Mar[1].
Taxonomy *E. t. tahapisi.*
References [1]Dowsett & Leonard (in press a); [2]Haydock (1949b); [3]Traylor (1965b).

Cape Bunting *Emberiza capensis*   B688 **R(B)**

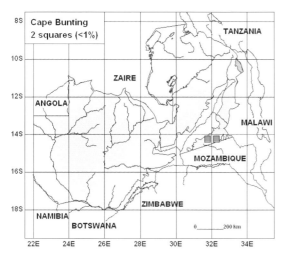

Distribution *Afrotropical (S. Tanzania to South Africa)*. Confined to a small area of rocky koppjes on the Eastern Province plateau, in the Nyanje and Chadiza region[3], such as Mbewa Hill[1,2]. *Alt.* 1070-1320 m.

Ecology Areas of bare rock, especially large boulders or inselbergs, where may be seen alongside its smaller congener *E. tahapisi*.

Status A very scarce and retiring bird, easily overlooked if not in song. Presumably resident, but the few dated records are 28 Mar to 17 Aug[3], and most visitors to the area have failed to find it.

Breeding No records, but males were in gonad activity late Mar[3], and the one breeding record in Malawi is of egg-laying Apr[4].

Taxonomy *E. c. vincenti.* This, the darkest form, has been separated as a distinct species by Fry[5], but Lowe[6] gave good reasons against a split; in fact the geographically nearest race (*E. c. smithersii* of E. Zimbabwe) is also dark[7], and is a link in a broken cline. Moreover, the song and call notes of *E. c. vincenti* are identical to those of South African birds.

References [1]Benson (1956d); [2]Benson (1958c); [3]Dowsett (in press a); [4]Dowsett-Lemaire & Dowsett (2006); [5]Fry in Fry & Keith (2004); [6]Lowe (1932); [7]Plowes (1951).

Golden-breasted Bunting *Emberiza flaviventris*   B685 **RB**

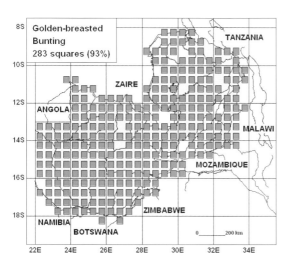

Distribution *Afrotropical (Mauritania to South Africa)*. Common throughout, in any open woodland. *Alt.* 330 to 1950 m (Mafingas)[3] and 2000 m (Nyika)[4].

Ecology In any woodland, miombo, mopane, *Acacia, Combretum* and other mixed types; also in scattered trees on rocky hills.

Status Resident. A 2-year survey produced no evidence of any clear movements, although the species can be extremely common at times locally[2].

Breeding

(n=135)	Sep	Oct	Nov	Dec
	21	49	33	19
	Jan	Feb	Mar	May
	7	4	1	1

Clutch: C/1 (15); C/2 (80); C/3 (8).

Taxonomy *E. f. kalaharica*, perhaps tending to nominate *flaviventris* (less reddish above, darker below) in the east[1,5].

References [1]Benson & Benson (1977); [2]Dowsett (in press a); [3]Dowsett & Stjernstedt (1973); [4]Dowsett-Lemaire (2006a); [5]White (1963).

Cabanis's Bunting *Emberiza cabanisi* B684 **RB**

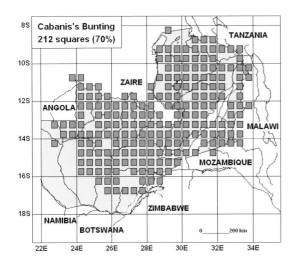

Distribution *Afrotropical* (*Guinea to Zimbabwe*). Fairly common throughout the miombo belt of the country; scarce at low altitude. Ranges on the Southern Province plateau to Choma and Gwembe Dists, westwards to the upper Lumbe River. In the Upper Zambezi, south and west to Chavuma[1] and the Muchicha River[6] (the only locality west of the Zambezi). *Alt.* 500 to 1950 m (Mafingas)[3] and 2150 m (Nyika)[4].

Ecology Most common in miombo woodland (including the poorer types), rarely wandering into mopane or *Acacia*, as in the Luangwa Valley (May to late Oct)[2]. Overlaps widely with *E. flaviventris*.

Status Resident, with local wandering to lower levels.

Breeding   Oct Nov Dec Jan Feb
(n=28)   7   10   8   2   1   *Clutch*: C/2 (9); C/3 (7).

Taxonomy[5] *E. c. orientalis*, replaced in the west by *E. c. cognominata* (mantle washed reddish brown, not black).

References [1]Britton (1970); [2]Dowsett (in press a); [3]Dowsett & Stjernstedt (1973); [4]Dowsett-Lemaire (2006a); [5]Irwin & Benson (1967a); [6]Osborne (1978).

Appendix 1

Ringing recoveries

There has been an irregular, at times substantial, ringing effort in Zambia since the 1960s. Ringing totals, details of local recoveries and longevity have been presented by Dowsett & Leonard (2001). Ringers in the 1970s used rings with a Livingstone Museum address (for many of the waterfowl and Palaearctic migrants), but that scheme is unlikely to be continued, and most ringing has otherwise been with South African rings.

Some 88 foreign recoveries have been reported of birds ringed in Zambia, and at least 223 birds ringed elsewhere have been recovered in this country; these are mapped or detailed below. Black symbols denote ringing localities, and blue symbols recovery sites. For coordinates of Zambian localities, see the gazetteer. Distances given are straight-line measurements. Purely local recoveries are excluded, and major longevity records are mentioned under the species' accounts in this book. Fuller details of any recovery can be requested from the authors' *Tauraco* databank.

White-breasted Cormorant *Phalacrocorax carbo*
A nestling ringed 8 Jan 1969 at Barberspan (26°37'S, 25°36'E) **South Africa** was found dead Oct 1970 at Kazungula (980 km N).

Reed Cormorant *Phalacrocorax africanus*
A nestling ringed 13 Mar 1974 at Barberspan (26°37'S, 25°36'E) **South Africa** was found dead 12 Oct 1990 at Katala (1300 km NNW).

Cattle Egret *Bubulcus ibis*
Thirteen birds ringed as nestlings in **South Africa** (between Nov and Feb) have been recovered in Zambia (Map 1), most Apr-May and Aug-Dec (5 in their first year). Maximum displacement 1900 km N.

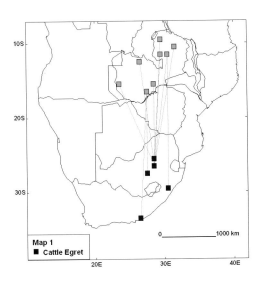

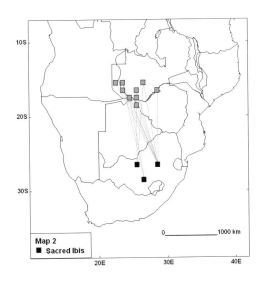

Black Egret *Egretta ardesiaca*
A nestling ringed Aug 1975 on the Lukulu River, Bangweulu (@ 12°10'S, 30°35'E) was recovered 23 Jan 1976 at Norton (17°50'S, 30°40'E) **Zimbabwe** (630 km S).

Yellow-billed Egret *Egretta intermedia*
A nestling ringed 3 Nov 1956 at Rondevlei, Cape (34°05'S, 18°30'E) **South Africa** was found dead 26 May 1957 at Mongu (2120 km NNE).

Grey Heron *Ardea cinerea*
A nestling ringed 15 May 1974 on the Kafue Flats (@ 15°50'S, 27°21'E) was recovered Sep 1975 at Plumtree (20°35'S, 27°50'E) **Zimbabwe** (530 km S).

Openbill Stork *Anastomus lamelligerus*
A nestling ringed 30 Jul 1974 on the Kafue Flats (15°50'S, 27°21'E) was killed 15 Jan 1975 in southern Ovamboland (*c.* 17°45'S, 16°30'E) **Namibia** (*c.* 1180 km WSW).

White Stork *Ciconia ciconia*
There have been at least 66 recoveries in Zambia (Map 3) of nestlings ringed in **Germany** (26), **Poland** (16), **Russia** (4), **Greece** and **Lithuania** (3 each), **Denmark** and **Jugoslavia** (2 each), **France**, **Spain**, **Austria**, **Bulgaria**, **Czech Rep.**, **Slovakia**, **Croatia**, **Ukraine**, **Hungary** and **South Africa** (1 each). No fewer than 48 were recovered in their first year (mostly killed). In addition a number of satellite-tracked birds (from Europe and the small South African-breeding population) have been traced to Zambia. Maximum displacement *c.* 8180 km SSE.

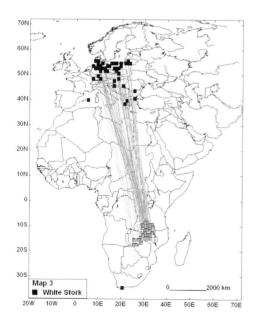

Map 3
■ White Stork

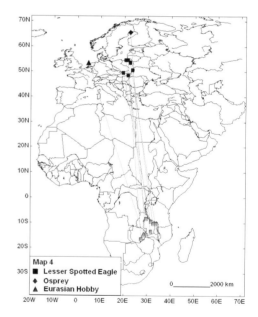

Map 4
■ Lesser Spotted Eagle
♦ Osprey
▲ Eurasian Hobby

Sacred Ibis *Threskiornis aethiopicus*
There have been at least 57 recoveries in W. Zambia of birds ringed as nestlings (Sep-Mar) in **South Africa**, recovered mostly Apr-Oct (Map 2), up to 1470 km NW. 26 were recovered in their first year (mostly killed).

Glossy Ibis *Plegadis falcinellus*
A nestling ringed 21 Nov 1970 at Benoni, Transvaal (26°13'S, 28°18'E) **South Africa** was killed 15 Aug 1973 in Senanga Dist. (15°39'S, 23°02'E), 1300 km NW.

African Spoonbill *Platalea alba*
A nestling ringed 3 Oct 1953 at Benoni, Transvaal (26°13'S, 28°18'E) **South Africa** was killed 23 Sep 1954 at Mwandi (1040 km NW).

Fulvous Tree Duck *Dendrocygna bicolor*
One ringed 5 Dec 1974 at Lochinvar was killed 18 Jul 1976 at Malakal, upper Nile (9°31'N, 31°40'E) **Sudan** (2900 km NE).

White-faced Tree Duck *Dendrocygna viduata*
Four birds ringed in S. **Zimbabwe** (Oct, Dec, Feb, Mar) were recovered in S. Zambia (Jun, Sep, Dec). One ringed 4 May 1974 at Lochinvar was killed Feb 1975 at Plumtree (20°30'S, 27°50'E) **Zimbabwe** (maximum movement 530 km S).

White-backed Duck *Thalassornis leuconotus*
One ringed 20 Jul 1971 at Lochinvar was killed May 1973 in the Lukanga Swamp (*c.* 14°20'S, 27°40'E), 180 km NE.

Knob-billed Duck *Sarkidiornis melanotos*
Three birds ringed in S. **Zimbabwe** (Nov, Mar) were recovered in S. Zambia (Nov, Jan, Apr) (Map 6), maximum displacement 710 km NW.

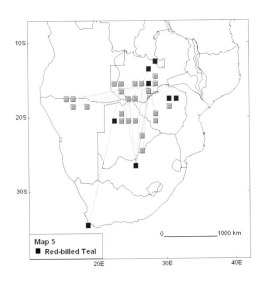

Map 5
■ Red-billed Teal

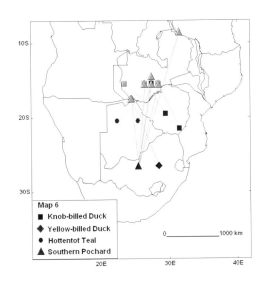

Map 6
■ Knob-billed Duck
◆ Yellow-billed Duck
● Hottentot Teal
▲ Southern Pochard

African Pygmy Goose *Nettapus auritus*
One ringed 4 May 1973 at Lochinvar was recovered 2 years later in the Lukanga Swamp (*c.* 14°20'S, 27°40'E), 180 km NE.

Yellow-billed Duck *Anas undulata*
One ringed 1 Oct 1965 at Leeukop, Johannesburg (26°00'S, 28°03'E) **South Africa** was recovered the following year at Mwandi (Map 6), 1020 km NNW.

Red-billed Teal *Anas erythrorhyncha*
There have been 26 foreign recoveries of birds ringed in Zambia: **Zimbabwe** (11), **Botswana** (7), **Namibia** (5) and **South Africa** (3). There have also been the following 14 recoveries in Zambia of foreign-ringed birds: **South Africa** (11), **Zimbabwe** (2) and **Botswana** (1) (Map 5). Most birds have been in Zambia May-Nov, and outside the country Oct-Jan. Maximum distance moved, 2130 km NNE.

Hottentot Teal *Anas hottentota*
Two ringed in Oct at Lochinvar were recovered in N. **Botswana** in Jan and Mar (Map 6), up to 680 km SW.

Southern Pochard *Netta erythrophthalma*
Six ringed at Barberspan (26°37'S, 25°36'E) **South Africa** (Jul-Sep, Dec, Mar) have been recovered in Zambia (Map 6) (Apr, Jun-Aug, Oct); maximum displacement 2080 km NE.

Yellow-billed Kite *Milvus migrans parasitus*
One ringed 22 Nov 1957 at Ngwezi Pools was recovered 29 Oct 1960 at Nana Candundo (11°31'S, 23°03'E) **Angola** (630 km NNW); one ringed 13 Oct 1948 at Luanshya was recovered 20 Dec 1948 some 80 km north of Bulawayo (*c* 19°20'S, 28°45'E) **Zimbabwe** (680 km S).

Lappet-faced Vulture *Torgos tracheliotus*
A nestling ringed 8 Nov 1993 in the Kruger N.P. (22°52'S, 31°20'E) **South Africa** was seen 23 Oct 1994 at Nsefu, Luangwa Valley (1120 km N).

Steppe Buzzard *Buteo buteo*
Two nestlings ringed in **Finland** have been recovered in E. Zambia (13 Oct and 18 Dec), 8340 km S.

Wahlberg's Eagle *Aquila wahlbergi*
One ringed 3 Nov 1989 in the Transvaal (24°50'S, 31°25'E) **South Africa** was killed 16 Mar 1990 near Kaoma (1300 km NW).

Lesser Spotted Eagle *Aquila pomarina*
Five ringed on the breeding grounds **Russia** (1), **Poland** and **Slovakia** (2 each) have been recovered in E. Zambia (Map 4) (27 Oct, Jan-early Mar). In addition at least 9 birds have been tracked by satellite from **Germany** and **Poland** to S. Zambia, wintering or on passage, between 22 Oct and 11 Mar. Maximum displacement *c*. 7800 km SSE.

[Greater Spotted Eagle *Aquila clanga*
A satellite-tracked bird from Biebrzanski N.P. (*c*. 53°29'N, 22°59'E) in **Poland** wintered in two successive years in the Luangwa Valley (*c*. 12°00'S, 31°00'E), having moved 7470 km SSE, and a second bird was tracked to Zambia later. But the possibility they were hybrid *A. clanga x A. pomarina* cannot be ruled out.]

Tawny Eagle *Aquila rapax*
A nestling ringed 18 Aug 1974 at Lochinvar was recovered 14 Aug 1978 in the Gwaai Valley (18°45'S, 27°20'E) **Zimbabwe** (330 km S).

Osprey *Pandion haliaetus*
A nestling ringed 21 Jul 1979 at Lulea, Sundom (65°47'N, 22°16'E) **Sweden** was found dead 20 Jan 1996 at Chikupili, Lunsemfwa River (Map 4), 8870 km SSE.

Eurasian Hobby *Falco subbuteo*
A nestling ringed 26 Jul 1982 at Westermient, Texel (53°03'N, 4°43'E) **Holland** was found dead 26 Nov 1992 at Memaco, near Kabwe (Map 4), 7820 km SE.

Lanner Falcon *Falco biarmicus*
An adult ringed 7 Mar 1991 in the Kalahari Gemsbok N.P. (25°41'S, 20°20'E) **South Africa** was found dead 9 Jun 1992 in Choma Dist., having moved *c.* 1200 km NE.

African Jacana *Actophilornis africanus*
Two ringed in Oct (1969) and Jan (1974) at Lochinvar were recovered, respectively, 28 Oct 1973 at Lake Chilondo (170 km NE) and 25 Sep 1982 near Mukonchi (230 km NE).

Bronze-winged Courser *Rhinoptilus chalcopterus*
One ringed 1 Apr 1996 at Mbuzana, Umfolozi G.R. (28°19'S, 31°50'E) **South Africa** was killed 26 Oct 1997 on the Lumezi River, Lundazi Dist. (1760 km N).

Long-toed Plover *Vanellus crassirostris*
An adult ringed 29 Nov 1966 at Blue Lagoon was recovered 26 Jul 1983 in the Lukanga Swamp (*c.* 120 km N).

Greenshank *Tringa nebularia*
One ringed 13 Jan 1982 at Gwebi Dam, Harare (17°52'S, 30°31'E) **Zimbabwe** was found dead 7 Mar 1984 at Mufulira (640 km NW).

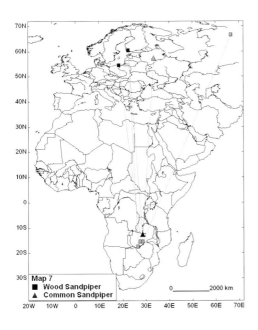

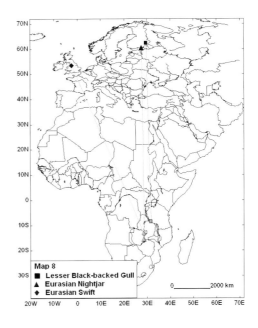

Wood Sandpiper *Tringa glareola*
Two ringed in **Finland** and one in **Poland** have been recovered in S. Zambia (two dated 31 Jan and 23 Mar), while one ringed 31 Jan 1975 at Lusaka was killed 5 Jun 1976 at Salekhard, Tyumen (66°34'N, 66°40'E) **Russia** (Map 7), this last 9610 km NE.

Common Sandpiper *Actitis hypoleucos*
One ringed 25 Aug 1962 at Kitwe was reported 1 Sep 1963 at Selyei, Ostashkov (57°09'N, 33°10'E) **Russia** (Map 7), 7740 km N.

Little Stint *Calidris minuta*
One ringed 1 Dec 1966 at Blue Lagoon was retrapped 25 Mar 1968 at Lake Nakuru (0°20'S, 36°06'E) **Kenya** (1940 km NE).

Lesser Black-backed Gull *Larus fuscus*
A nestling ringed 5 Jul 1995 at Polvijärvi (62°44'N, 29°19'E) **Finland** was killed 5 Mar 1996 near Mbala (presumably on L. Tanganyika, Map 8, 7920 km S).

Grey-headed Gull *Larus cirrocephalus*
Two ringed at Benoni, Transvaal (26°13'S, 28°18'E) **South Africa** (18 May 1963 and 5 Jun 1965) were recovered 15 Sep 1963 at Senanga and 18 Jul 1966 at Mwandi, respectively, 1230 and 1040 km NW.

Eurasian Nightjar *Caprimulgus europaeus*
One ringed 29 May 1981 in Kymi Dept. (60°18'N, 27°24'E) **Finland** was found dead 22 Nov 1981 in the Chibombo area (*c.* 15°03'S, 28°44'E, 8340 km S, Map 8).

Eurasian Swift *Apus apus*
One ringed 26 Jun 1969 at Tyldesley, Leigh (53°31'N, 02°28'W) **Britain** was recovered 25 Nov 1976 at Luanshya, 7940 km SSE (Map 8).

Eurasian Sand Martin *Riparia riparia*
One ringed 15 Dec 1974 at Muckle Neuk, Choma was recovered 12 Jun 1976 at Nizhnyaya Toyma (62°14'N, 45°00'E) **Russia** (8880 km NE, Map 10).

Eurasian Swallow *Hirundo rustica*
There have been 45 recoveries abroad of Swallows ringed in Zambia, and 20 foreign-ringed birds recovered here (Map 9); the countries involved are **Russia** and **Ukraine** (14 each), **Poland** (10), **Finland** (8), **Czech Rep.** (3), **Bulgaria**, **France** and **South Africa** (2 each), **Britain**, **Holland**, **Denmark**, **Sweden**, **Slovakia**, **Lithuania**, **Hungary**, **Georgia**, **Beylorussia**, **Israel** (1 each). Maximum distance, *c.* 9200 km NE.

Eurasian House Martin *Delichon urbicum*
Three ringed in Europe have been recovered in Zambia (Map 10): from Rietschen (51°23'N, 14°47'E) **Germany** to Lusaka (1962), from Ottenby, Oland (56°12'N, 16°24'E) **Sweden** to Petauke Dist. (1949) and Wolfsburg (52°26'N, 10°42'E) **Germany** to Zimba (18 Dec 1980). The Swedish bird moved 7920 km SE.

Sedge Warbler *Acrocephalus schoenobaenus*
One ringed 21 Aug 1986 near Helsinki (60°12'N, 24°49'E) **Finland** was killed 16 Mar 1987 near Chipepo (Kabwe Dist.), having moved 8270 km S (Map 11).

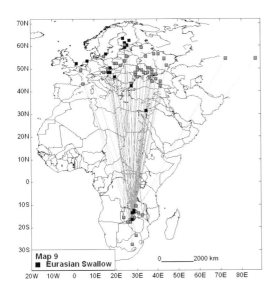

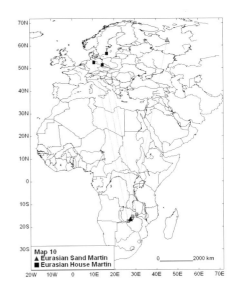

(European) Marsh Warbler *Acrocephalus palustris*
Two ringed on passage at Ngulia, Tsavo (3°00'S, 38°13'E) **Kenya** (15 Dec 1991 and 11 Dec 1993) were recovered respectively 25 Jan 1992 near Kabwe and 15 Feb 1994 in the Lake Bangweulu area (Map 11). They had moved up to 1650 km SW.

Willow Warbler *Phylloscopus trochilus*
Five ringed in Scandinavia have been recovered in Zambia (Map 11), from **Sweden** (2) and **Norway**, **Finland** and **Estonia** (1 each). Three were recovered 1-20 Apr, the others 26 Oct and 6 Jan; maximum movement 8750 km S.

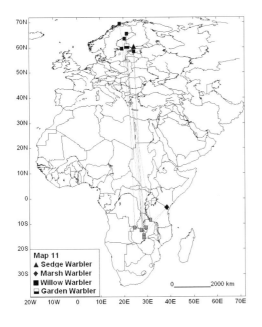

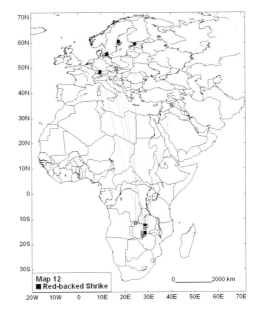

Garden Warbler *Sylvia borin*
One ringed 28 Aug 1962 at Korpo (60°09'N, 21°33'E) **Finland** found 9 Feb 1963 at Lusaka, some 8390 km S (Map 11).

Red-backed Shrike *Lanius collurio*
There have been recoveries of 2 ringed in Zambia and 5 ringed in N. Europe (Map 12). One ringed 15 Dec 1962 at Kitwe was breeding Jun 1970 near Brno (49°22'N, 16°26'E) **Czech Rep.**, and one ringed 7 Dec 1974 at Lusaka was on passage 2 May 1977 at Deir el Zor (35°20'N, 40°08'E) **Syria**. Birds ringed in **Germany** (2) and **Sweden**, **Finland** and **Denmark** (1 each) were recovered in Zambia on 13 Nov, 4 Feb and mid-Mar to 8 Apr (3). Maximum movement was 8520 km SSE.

Red-billed Quelea *Quelea quelea*
Two ringed at Nyamandhlovu (19°52'S, 28°15'E) **Zimbabwe** (26 Jul 1951, 18 Oct 1953) were recovered in S. Zambia (22 Sep 1952, Sep 1954 respectively), some 660 km N.

Appendix 2

Gazetteer of localities

This gazetteer includes all Zambian localities mentioned in the text (and significant extra-limital ones), with their coordinates determined usually from the best available maps (only in recent years have GPS readings been reported for a few). Where coordinates are not available, the map square will enable an approximate location. Map squares are determined as follows (e.g. Afumba):

Altitudes are included wherever possible, but they have not usually been recorded by observers in Zambia; not all available maps are accurately contoured, and thus many of the altitudes given are approximations.

For localities that are Important Bird Areas (Leonard 2005) the reference number is given (e.g. "IBA 28"). Some alternative names are given in brackets. Dates are given for abandoned "bomas" (including former District HQs).

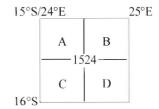

Locality ....Alt. (m) ....Square ....Coordinates

Locality	Alt. (m)	Square	Coordinates
Afumba, Kaoma Dist.	1220	1524D	15°38'S, 24°56'E
Alala Plateau, Mkushi Dist.	1429A		
Bakabaka lagoon, Nsefu, South Luangwa N.P.	530	1231D	12°58'S, 31°55'E
Balovale (now Zambezi) (Dist. H.Q.) (*Map*, p. 1)	1078	1323C	13°33'S, 23°07'E
Bangweulu, Lake & Swamps (*Map*, p. 2) (IBA 28)	1029-1129	1129B,D etc.	
Barker's, Sesheke/Kazungula Dists	960	1725A	17°07'S, 25°07'E
Barotse Floodplain (*Map*, p. 2) (IBA 9)			
Batoka Gorge (lower) (IBA 13)	1726D		
Batoka Plateau, Choma Dist.	mainly 1626D		
Batoka town, Choma Dist.	1240	1627C	16°46'S, 27°14'E
Bilili Hot Springs, Kalomo Dist.	1090	1626C	16°39'S, 26°09'E
Bimbi (Bwimbi) Hot Springs, Sinazongwe Dist.	630	1826B	18°01'S, 26°45'E
Blue Lagoon N.P. (IBA 15)	980	1527A	15°27'S, 27°27'E
Bovu, Kazungula Dist.	990	1725D	17°42'S, 25°33'E
Bovu River, Kazungula Dist.	1020	1725C	17°47'S, 25°17'E
Broken Hill (now Kabwe) (Dist. H.Q.) (*Map*, p. 1)	1180	1428A	14°27'S, 28°27'E
Bua River drainage, *Malawi*	*c.* 1050 m	1234C	*c.* 12°50'S, 34°10'E
Bulaya, Mweru Marsh, Kaputa Dist.	940	0830C	8°33'S, 30°07'E
Buluma school, Isoka Dist.	1380	1033B	10°25'S, 33°32'E
Busanga Plain (Swamps), Kafue N.P. (*Map*, p. 2)	1425B, 1426A		
Buwe Pool, Kazungula Dist.	990	1625C	16°52'S, 25°22'E
Bwina, Sesheke Dist.	1150	1624B	16°27'S, 24°58'E
Cameia, Lake, *Angola*	1130	1120D	11°43'S, 20°48'E
Caprivi Strip, *Namibia* (*Map*, p. 2)	1724D, 1725C		
Chabilikila, Nchelenge Dist.	940	0928D	9°32'S, 28°44'E
Chaboboma, Gwembe Dist.	520	1627D	16°46'S, 27°48'E

Locality ....**Alt. (m)** ....**Square** ....**Coordinates**

Chadiza (Dist. H.Q.)...1070...............1432A ....14°04'S, 32°26'E

Chalabesa, Mpika Dist. ....1300...............1131A ....11°23'S, 31°01'E

Chalamba River, Solwezi Dist. ....1290...............1225B ....12°15'S, 25°34'E

Chalata (ex-Mkushi River), Mkushi Dist. ....1400...............1329D ....13°33'S, 29°41'E

Chalimbana, Chongwe Dist...1140...............1528B ....15°20'S, 28°35'E

Chama (Dist. H.Q.) ....760...............1133A ....11°12'S, 33°09'E

Chambeshi pontoon or bridge, Mpika Dist. ....1240...............1031C ....10°58'S, 31°03'E

Chambeshi River (*Map*, p. 2)

Chana Chamuhina Plain, Mwinilunga Dist. ....1280...............1024C ....10°55'S, 24°08'E

Chanachanyidi Plain, Mwinilunga Dist. ....1410...............1124C ....11°42'S, 24°12'E

Changa (Chaanga), Siavonga Dist. ....780...............1628A ....16°18'S, 28°24'E

Changwena Falls (Gurney's mine), Mkushi Dist..................1350...............1329B ....13°23'S, 29°33'E

Chasefu, Lundazi Dist..1070...............1133C ....11°55'S, 33°05'E

Chassa, Petauke Dist. ....1090...............1431B ....14°14'S, 31°47'E

Chavuma Hill, Chavuma Dist. ....1160...............1322B ....13°05'S, 22°41'E

Chavuma (Dist. H.Q.) ....1080...............1322B ....13°05'S, 22°41'E

Chaya, Lake, Mpika Dist. ....1170...............1130B ....11°28'S, 30°33'E

Chembe bird sanctuary, Chingola Dist. ....1260...............1227D ....12°50'S, 28°00'E

Chembe ferry, Luapula River, Mansa Dist. ....1050...............1128D ....11°58'S, 28°44'E

Chembe, Luano Valley, Mkushi Dist. ....470...............1429C ....14°51'S, 29°23'E

Chengelo, Mkushi Dist. ....1390...............1329D ....13°38'S, 29°36'E

Chewore escarpment, *Zimbabwe* ....c. 1250...............1629B ....16°05'S, 29°41'E

Chewore Safari Area, *Zimbabwe* ....370...............1529D ....15°45'S, 30°00'E

Chiawa, Kafue Dist. ....370...............1529C ....15°53'S, 29°02'E

Chibale, Serenje Dist..1410...............1330C ....13°35'S, 30°08'E

Chibembe camp, Luangwa Valley, Mambwe Dist................540...............1232C ....12°47'S, 32°04'E

Chibesakunda, Chinsali Dist. ....1310...............1132A ....11°03'S, 32°09'E

Chibombo (Dist. H.Q.)..1160...............1428C ....14°39'S, 28°04'E

Chichele Lodge, South Luangwa N.P. ....540...............1331B ....13°10'S, 31°42'E

Chidonga (Chidongo), Lundazi Dist.....................................1080...............1232D ....12°56'S, 32°58'E

Chiengi, Lake Mweru (Dist. H.Q.) ....940...............0829C ....8°39'S, 29°09'E

Chifoma, Chinsali Dist...1530...............1031D ....10°59'S, 31°45'E

Chifunda, Chama Dist..670...............1132D ....11°54'S, 32°38'E

Chifungwe Plain, South Luangwa N.P..................................650...............1231B ....12°22'S, 31°44'E

Chifuwe/Kabompo River confl., Solwezi/Mufumbwe Dists. ....1140...............1225C ....12°58'S, 25°00'E

Chifwembe, Isoka Dist...1350...............0932D ....9°44'S, 32°57'E

Chijalile (Malabo) Hills, Kalomo Dist..................................1130...............1726D ....17°41'S, 26°47'E

Chikana, Chibombo Dist. ....1170...............1427D ....14°49'S, 27°38'E

Chikankata, Choma Dist. ....1220...............1628A ....16°15'S, 28°05'E

Chikata Rapids, Kabompo Dist...1130...............1324C ....13°35'S, 24°14'E

Chikaya Plain, South Luangwa N.P. ....590...............1231D ....12°37'S, 31°53'E

Chikonkwelo stream, Kabompo Dist. ....1130...............1324A ....13°18'S, 24°05'E

Chikonta, Isoka Dist...930...............1033C ....10°35'S, 33°06'E

Locality ....Alt. (m) ....Square ....Coordinates

Chikuni (Bangweulu), Mpika Dist. ....1160 ....1130C ....11°57'S, 30°15'E
Chikupili, Lunsemfwa River, Mkushi Dist. ....1210..............1429A ....14°03'S, 29°13'E
Chikwenya, Zambezi River, *Zimbabwe* ....370 ....1529D ....15°46'S, 29°35'E
Chila, Lake, Mbala Dist. ....1660 ....0831C ....8°50'S, 31°23'E
Chilanga, Kafue Dist. ....1270 ....1528C ....15°33'S, 28°16'E
Chilaunga Hill, Chakwenga, Chongwe Dist. ....1490 ....1529A ....15°14'S, 29°29'E
Chilenga, Kafue River, Kapiri Mposhi Dist. ....1130 ....1427A ....14°06'S, 27°25'E
Chililabombwe (ex-Bancroft) (Dist. H.Q.) ....1340 ....1227B ....12°22'S, 27°51'E
Chilola/Zongwe stream confl., Choma Dist. ....600 ....1627D ....16°56'S, 27°42'E
Chilondo, Lake, Chibombo Dist. ....1120 ....1427B ....14°25'S, 27°58'E
Chilonga, Mpika Dist. ....1440 ....1231A ....12°02'S, 31°21'E
Chilongozi camp, South Luangwa N.P. ....530 ....1331B ....13°27'S, 31°34'E
Chilongozi sector, South Luangwa N.P. ....530 ....1331B,C
Chilubi (Dist. H.Q.) ....1160 ....1130A ....11°08'S, 30°01'E
Chilubi (Chirui) Is., Bangweulu ....1160 ..1129B-1130A
Chilubula Mission, Kasama Dist. ....1250 ....1030B ....10°08'S, 30°57'E
Chilufya, Kasama Dist. ....1220 ....1030D ....10°45'S, 30°48'E
Chilula River, Mwinilunga Dist. ....1300 ....1024C ....10°54'S, 24°05'E
Chimaliro National Forest, Lundazi Dist. ....1310-1636 ....1233B ....12°22'S, 33°32'E
Chimene (Zhimu) stream, Gwembe Dist. ....500 ....1727C ....@ 17°34'S, 27°10'E
Chimwange, Lake, Zambezi Dist. ....1070 ....1322B ....13°19'S, 22°53'E
Chingi, Chavuma Dist. ....1090 ....1322B ....13°01'S, 22°44'E
Chingola (Dist. H.Q.) ....1340 ....1227D ....12°31'S, 27°51'E
Chingombe Mission, Mkushi Dist. ....530 ....1429B ....14°25'S, 29°58'E
Chinkuli, Chongwe Dist. ....1120 ....1528B ....15°15'S, 28°32'E
Chinsali (Dist. H.Q.) ....1290 ....1032C ....10°35'S, 32°07'E
Chinyama Litapi, Zambezi Dist. ....1070 ....1322A ....13°29'S, 22°19'E
Chinyingi, Zambezi Dist. ....1090 ....1323A ....13°22'S, 23°00'E
Chinyunyu Hot Springs, Chongwe Dist. ....1000 ....1529A ....15°16'S, 29°01'E
Chinzewe, Mambwe Dist. ....660 ....1331D ....13°39'S, 31°54'E
Chinzombo, Luangwa Valley, Mambwe Dist. ....530 ....1331B ....13°06'S, 31°47'E
Chipata (ex-Fort Jameson) (Dist. H.Q.) (*Map*, p. 1)................1140 ....1332D ....13°38'S, 32°38'E
Chipekete, Chongwe Dist. ....770 ....1529B ....15°12'S, 29°57'E
Chipengali (Chipangali), Chipata Dist. ....1020 ....1332B ....13°25'S, 32°40'E
Chipepo, Gwembe Dist ....490 ....1627D ....16°49'S, 27°49'E
Chipepo (Kapopo), Kapiri Mposhi Dist. ....1170 ....1428A ....14°12'S, 28°13'E
Chipungu, Nchelenge Dist. ....930 ....0828B ....8°30'S, 28°59'E
Chire Bridge, Chama/Isoka Dist. ....1330 ....1033C ....10°47'S, 33°28'E
Chiriwe, Luangwa Dist. ....430 ....1530A ....15°19'S, 30°20'E
Chiromwe Hill, Luangwa Dist. ....990 ....1530C ....15°37'S, 30°20'E
Chirundu, Siavonga Dist. ....400 ....1628B ....16°02'S, 28°50'E
Chisamba, Chibombo Dist. (IBA 19)..1120 ....1428C ....14°58'S, 28°29'E
Chisangu Plain, Kalabo Dist. ....1050 ....1522C ....15°53'S, 22°09'E

Locality ....**Alt. (m)** ....**Square** ....**Coordinates**

Locality	Alt. (m)	Square	Coordinates
Chisasa (Chissasa), Solwezi Dist.	1370	1225A	12°07'S, 25°30'E
Chisekesi, Monze Dist.	1180	1627A	16°27'S, 27°29'E
Chisenga Is., Lake Mweru, Nchelenge Dist.	920	0928B	9°28'S, 28°34'E
Chishela (Chishera) Plain, Kaputa Dist.	910	0830C	8°31'S, 30°07'E
Chishi (Cheshi), Lake, Mweru Wantipa N.P.	930	0829D	8°56'S, 29°44'E
Chishimba (Chisimba) Falls, Kasama Dist.	1360	1030B	10°06'S, 30°54'E
Chishinga Swamp, Mbala Dist.	1460	0931C	9°32'S, 31°06'E
Chisoko stream, Sakeji, Mwinilunga Dist.	1430	1124A	11°22'S, 24°15'E
Chisomo, Serenje Dist.	660	1330D	13°37'S, 30°40'E
Chitambo (Livingstone memorial), Serenje Dist.	1190	1230A	12°18'S, 30°17'E
Chitambo Mission, Serenje Dist.	1510	1230D	12°53'S, 30°36'E
Chitimbwa, Mpulungu Dist.	1590	0830D	8°50'S, 30°50'E
Chitimukulu, Mungwi Dist.	1300	1031B	10°01'S, 31°37'E
Chitipa (ex-Fort Hill), *Malawi*	1300	0933C	9°43'S, 33°16'E
Chitokoloki, Zambezi Dist.	1040	1323C	13°50'S, 23°14'E
Chitongo (Chitombo), Namwala Dist.	1030	1626B	16°03'S, 26°56'E
Chitunda (Kasangu), Nchelenge Dist.	1200	0829A	8°27'S, 29°22'E
Chitungulu (Chitingulu), Mambwe Dist.	580	1232A	12°26'S, 32°15'E
Chitunta Bridge & Plain, Mwinilunga Dist. (IBA 3)	1360-1390	1124A,C	11°30'S, 24°23'E
Chiwale (Chibale), Chama Dist.	750	1032D	10°33'S, 32°47'E
Chiwefwe, Mkushi Dist.	1320	1329C	13°38'S, 29°27'E
Chiwemupala Hill, Kalulushi Dist.	1380	1227D	12°47'S, 27°50'E
Chizera, Mufumbwe Dist.	1180	1325A	13°05'S, 25°00'E
Chobe/Zambesi River confl., Kazungula Dist.	970	1725C	17°47'S, 25°17'E
Chocha, Mweru Wantipa, Kaputa Dist.	1000	0829B	8°26'S, 29°48'E
Cholola, Sesheke Dist.	1020	1723B	17°14'S, 23°51'E
Choma (Dist. H.Q.) (*Map*, p. 1)	1270	1626D	16°48'S, 26°59'E
Choma, Mweru Wantipa, Kaputa Dist.	920	0829B	8°28'S, 29°40'E
Chongwe (Dist. H.Q.)	1090	1528B	15°20'S, 28°41'E
Chongwe/Zambezi River confl., Kafue Dist.	730	1529C	15°42'S, 29°20'E
Chowo forest & Rocks, Nyika N.P.	2070-2200	1033D	10°35'S, 33°41'E
Chozi, Nakonde Dist.	1250	0932A	9°23'S, 32°14'E
Chozi Floodplain, Mungwi Dist.	1200	0932C	9°45'S, 32°21'E
Chulwe Lagoon, Kafue Flats, Mumbwa Dist.	980	1527C	15°43'S, 27°17'E
Chundu, Livingstone Dist.	1010	1725D	17°49'S, 25°40'E
Chunga, Kafue N.P.	1080	1525B,1526A	15°03'S, 26°00'E
Chunga Pool, Sesheke Dist.	1020	1723B	*c.* 17°00'S, 23°45'E
Chusa Falls, Manshya River, Mpika Dist.	1240	1031C	10°57'S, 31°04'E
Combrinck's farm, near Senkobo, Livingstone Dist.	1090	1726C	17°40'S, 26°01'E
Congo Point, Kaputa Dist.	900	0830B	8°18'S, 30°33'E
Copperbelt (= Chililabombwe S to Ndola) (*Map*, p. 1)		1277D-1228D	
Dambwa Forest Reserve, Livingstone Dist.	1000	1725D	17°47'S, 25°50'E
Danger Hill (Bwingimfumu), Chinsali Dist. (*Map*, p. 2)	1770	1131D	11°32'S, 31°36'E

Locality ....**Alt. (m)** ....**Square** ....**Coordinates**

Locality	Alt. (m)	Square	Coordinates
Dengwe River, Kasempa Dist.	1280	1325B	13°19'S, 25°51'E
Devil's Gorge, Sinazongwe Dist.	550	1726D	17°58'S, 26°57'E
Dimba Dambo, Kazungula Dist.	1050	1625D	16°41'S, 25°48'E
Dimbwe, Kalomo Dist.	1290	1726B	17°10'S, 26°56'E
Dipalata, Zambezi Dist.	1110	1323A	13°19'S, 23°13'E
Diwa Hill, Chipata Dist.	1130	1332B	13°03'S, 32°57'E
East Four, Mkushi Dist.	610	1429C	14°44'S, 29°06'E
East Lunga pontoon, Kasempa Dist.	1140	1326C	13°59'S, 26°20'E
East Lunga River (*Map*, p. 2)			
80-mile Dambo, Chongwe Dist.	930	1529A	15°08'S, 29°21'E
Feira (now Luangwa town) (Dist. H.Q.)	330	1530C	15°37'S, 30°24'E
Fife (= Old Fife), Nakonde Dist.	1540	0932B	9°19'S, 32°38'E
Filolo, Isoka Dist.	1390	1032B	10°07'S, 32°32'E
Fitula Dambo, Chingola Dist.	1300	1227D	12°39'S, 27°53'E
Forest Inn, Mkushi Dist.	1230	1329C	13°43'S, 29°09'E
Fothergill Is., Lake Kariba, *Zimbabwe*	500	1628D	16°42'S, 28°40'E
Frank's Lakes, South Luangwa N.P.	630	1231D	12°38'S, 31°47'E
Funda Dambo, Mpongwe Dist.	1190	1327A	13°16'S, 27°26'E
Fungwe National Forest, Isoka Dist.	1270	1033A	10°22'S, 33°11'E
Gabela, *Angola*	630-790	1014C	10°51'S, 14°22'E
Gokora (Kokori) Pan, *Botswana*	c. 970	1824B	18°21'S, 24°50'E
Gwaai/Zambezi River confl., *Zimbabwe*	600	1726D	17°58'S, 26°55'E
Greystone, Kitwe Dist.	1240	1228C	12°53'S, 28°14'E
Gwabi, Siavonga Dist.	450	1528D	15°57'S, 28°45'E
Gwembe, Gwembe Dist.	1230	1627B	16°29'S, 27°36'E
Gwembe Valley (= Zambezi Valley, Lake Kariba section)		1628B-1727C	
Hillwood farm, Mwinilunga Dist. (IBA 1)	1350-1430	1124A	11°15'S, 24°19'E
Hippo camp, Kafue N.P.	1090	1426C	14°41'S, 26°23'E
Homani, Chama Dist.	830	1133A	11°14'S, 33°11'E
Huntley farm, Chibombo Dist.	1150	1528A	15°01'S, 28°06'E
Hwange (Wankie) N.P. (Main camp), *Zimbabwe*	930-1070	1826D	18°44'S, 26°57'E
Ibwe Munyama (Old boma, 1908-22), Siavonga Dist.	1100	1628B	16°09'S, 28°32'E
Ikawa (?1890-1921), Nakonde Dist.	1680	0932B	9°20'S, 32°45'E
Ikelenge (Ikelengi), Mwinilunga Dist.	1400	1124A	11°14'S, 24°16'E
Ilonda Hills, Isoka Dist.	1550	0932D	9°33'S, 32°41'E
Ilondola Mission, Chinsali Dist.	1330	1031D	10°43'S, 31°48'E
Ilowa, Lake, Senanga Dist.		1523C	
Imanda mushitu, Mpongwe Dist. (IBA 21)	1180	1327B	13°29'S, 27°56'E
Imusho, Sesheke Dist.	980	1723C	17°34'S, 23°23'E
Inangu peninsula, Sumbu N.P.	800	0830B	8°29'S, 30°40'E
Ipumbu (Lipumbu) Plain, Lufwanyama Dist.	1190	1327D	13°39'S, 27°50'E
Isoka (Dist. H.Q.) (*Map*, p. 1)	1330	1032B	10°05'S, 32°42'E
Isoko, *Tanzania*	1610	0933A	9°29'S, 33°30'E

Locality ....Alt. (m) ....Square ....Coordinates

Isombu (Lisombo, Kasombo), Mwinilunga Dist. ....1250 ....1124A ....11°16'S, 24°06'E

Itawa Swamp, Ndola Dist. ....1250 ....1228D ....12°57'S, 28°41'E

Itezhi-Tezhi (Meshiteshi) Dam & Dist. H.Q. ....1040 ....1526C ....15°46'S, 26°01'E

Jeki, Lower Zambezi N.P. ....360 ....1529D ....15°38'S, 29°34'E

Jembya Plateau, *Malawi* ....1900 ....1033A ....10°09'S, 33°28'E

Jimbe stream, Mwinilunga Dist. ....1220 ....1024C ....@ 10°57'S, 24°05'E

Jimbe, or Jimbe Bridge, Malungu stream, Mwinilunga Dist..........1240 ....1124A ....11°06'S, 24°01'E

Jimbe/Chilula stream confl., Mwinilunga Dist. (IBA 4) ....1250 ....1024C ....10°57'S, 24°04'E

Jivundu (Jiwundu) River, Solwezi Dist. ....1300 ....1225B ....12°13'S, 25°35'E

Jivundu camp, West Lunga N.P. ....1190 ....1324B ....13°07'S, 24°42'E

Jivundu Swamp, Solwezi Dist. ....1300 ....1125D ....11°55'S, 25°33'E

Johnston (Mambilima) Falls, Luapula River, Mwense Dist. ....990 ....1028D ....10°33'S, 28°40'E

Jombo, Isoka Dist. ....1470 ....1033A ....10°27'S, 33°17'E

Julius (Old camp site), South Luangwa N.P. ....680 ....1231C ....12°57'S, 31°22'E

Jumbe (Mambwe Dist. H.Q.) ....790 ....1332A ....13°16'S, 32°07'E

Kaaba (Kaba) Hill, Mongu Dist...1050 ....1423D ....14°42'S, 23°39'E

Kabanga, Kalomo Dist. ....1220 ....1726D ....17°32'S, 26°47'E

Kabanga Dambo, Kafue N.P. ....1120 ....1426A ....14°07'S, 26°06'E

Kabendwe, Nchelenge Dist. ....1120 ....0829A ....8°28'S, 29°17'E

Kabompo (Dist. H.Q.) (*Map*, p. 1) ....1080 ....1324C ....13°36'S, 24°12'E

Kabompo Bridge, Mwinilunga/Kabompo Dists. ....1410 ....1125C ....11°53'S, 25°15'E

Kabompo Bridge, Kabompo Dist...1120 ....1324A ....13°17'S, 24°13'E

Kabompo Gorge, Mwinilunga/Solwezi Dists ....1300 ....1225A ....12°03'S, 25°10'E

Kabompo River headwaters, Mwinilunga Dist. 1125C

Kabompo/Zambezi River confl., Zambezi Dist. (*Map*, p. 2)..........1040 ....1423A ....14°11'S, 23°11'E

Kabonde Swamp, Kawambwa Dist. 0929C

Kabulamwanda, Namwala Dist..990 ....1526D ....15°53'S, 26°53'E

Kabuyu, Sesheke Dist. ....1010 ....1723B ....17°21'S, 23°33'E

Kabuyu, Livingstone Dist. ....1120 ....1726C ....17°31'S, 26°00'E

Kabuzu Pool, Kazungula Dist..1070 ....1625D ....16°38'S, 25°44'E

Kabwe (ex-Broken Hill) (Dist. H.Q.) (*Map*, p. 1) ....1210 ....1428A ....14°27'S, 28°27'E

Kabwe Swamp, Chinsali Dist. ....1230 ....1031D ....10°35'S, 31°40'E

Kachalola, Nyimba Dist. ....920 ....1430D ....14°45'S, 30°35'E

Kadata River, Mwinilunga Dist. ....1260 ....1023D ....10°54'S, 23°59'E

Kafubu Dam & stream, Ndola Dist. ....1260 ....1328B ....13°03'S, 28°35'E

Kafue town (Dist. H.Q.) & Bridge ....980 ....1528C ....15°47'S, 28°11'E

Kafue Fisheries, Kafue Dist. ....1000 ....1528C ....15°44'S, 28°05'E

Kafue Flats (*Map*, p. 2) (IBA 15)..1526C-1528C

Kafue Gorge, Kafue Dist. ....960 ....1528C ....15°48'S, 28°24'E

Kafue Hook, Kafue N.P. (IBA 14)..1090 ....1426C ....14°59'S, 26°00'E

Kafulafuta River, near Ndola, Masaiti Dist. ....1230 ....1328A ....@ 13°16'S, 28°20'E

Kafunta River Lodge, Luangwa Valley, Mambwe Dist..................520 ....1331B ....13°09'S, 31°44'E

Kafwa River, Mkushi Dist. ....1420 ....1329D ....13°33'S, 29°40'E

Locality ....Alt. (m) ....Square ....Coordinates

Locality	Alt. (m)	Square	Coordinates
Kafwala camp, Kafue N.P.	1100	1426C	14°48'S, 26°11'E
Kafwambila, Namazambwe stream, Kalomo Dist.	c. 750	1726D	c. 17°50'S, 26°55'E
Kahutu (Chihutu), Kabompo Dist.	1130	1324A	13°15'S, 24°04'E
Kaindabaila Hill, Kafue N.P.	1090	1525B	15°28'S, 25°56'E
Kaingo camp, South Luangwa N.P.	530	1231D	12°54'S, 31°57'E
Kajilisha, Zambezi Dist.	1090	1323A	13°30'S, 23°07'E
Kaka, Mbala Dist.	1550	0831D	8°57'S, 31°44'E
Kakeka (Kakeke), Zambezi Dist.	1110	1323A	13°15'S, 23°30'E
Kakenge River, Senanga Dist.	1040	1623B	@ 16°17'S, 23°40'E
Kako, Lake, Kaputa Dist.	960	0830C	8°40'S, 30°15'E
Kakoma (ex-Caenby), Mwinilunga Dist.	1450	1125A	11°20'S, 25°14'E
Kakumbi, Luangwa Valley, Mambwe Dist.	530	1331B	13°06'S, 31°49'E
Kalabo (Dist. H.Q.) (*Map*, p. 1)	1050	1422D	14°58'S, 22°42'E
Kalabwe, Mporokoso Dist.	1380	0929B	9°29'S, 29°50'E
Kalala Is., Kafue N.P.	1030	1525D	15°43'S, 25°59'E
Kalambo Falls, Mbala Dist.	1480	0831C	8°36'S, 31°15'E
Kalasa Mukoso, Samfya Dist.	1170	1129D	11°48'S, 29°36'E
Kalaye escarpment, Kaputa Dist.	1130	0829D	8°57'S, 29°42'E
Kalene Hill, Mwinilunga Dist.	1280-1420	1124A	11°11'S, 24°12'E
Kalenje, Kafue N.P.	1010	1625B	16°12'S, 26°00'E
Kalichero, Chipata Dist.	940	1332A	13°30'S, 32°30'E
Kalikali, Chipata Dist.	1010	1332B	13°08'S, 32°46'E
Kalilele Dambo, Solwezi Dist.	1320	1227A	12°20'S, 27°10'E
Kalinku, Chama Dist.	820	1133A	11°07'S, 33°11'E
Kalobolelwa, Sesheke Dist.	1000	1723B	17°04'S, 23°59'E
Kalomo (Dist. H.Q.) & River (*Map*, p. 1)	1220	1726A	17°01'S, 26°29'E
Kalonda, Isoka Dist.	1400	0932D	9°33'S, 32°58'E
Kalongola ferry & F.R., Senanga/Shangombo Dists	1000	1623A	16°17'S, 23°15'E
Kalulushi (Dist. H.Q.)	1280	1228C	12°50'S, 28°06'E
Kalungu River, Isoka Dist.	c. 1600	0932D	@ 9°38'S, 32°59'E
Kalungwishi (Old boma), Nchelenge Dist.	950	0929A	9°02'S, 29°02'E
Kalungwishi plateau, Mporokoso Dist.	1500-1600	0829D-0930C	
Kalungwishi ranch, Mporokoso Dist. (IBA 33)	1500-1600	0930C	9°52'S, 30°20'E
Kalungwishi River, Mporokoso Dist.	1250	0929C	@ 9°32'S, 29°27'E
Kamakawu, Lake, Mwinilunga Dist.	1420	1124D	11°42'S, 24°35'E
Kamando, Kaoma Dist.	1150	1524B	15°12'S, 24°38'E
Kamapanda Plain, Mwinilunga Dist.	1470	1224A	12°04'S, 24°05'E
Kambe Plain, Sesheke Dist.	1080	1624A	16°20'S, 24°18'E
Kambizana stream, Zambezi Dist.	1070	1323A	13°29'S, 23°03'E
Kambole Mission, Mpulungu Dist.	1620	0830D	8°46'S, 30°46'E
Kambuyu (Kambuya) Plains, Chavuma Dist.	1080	1322A,B	13°08'S, 22°30'E
Kamekunga, Chavuma Dist.	1080	1322A	13°28'S, 22°07'E
Kamilende, Lukulu Dist.	1060	1423B	14°08'S, 23°32'E

Locality ....**Alt. (m)** ....**Square** ....**Coordinates**

Kampemba, Luapula River, Mwense Dist. ....950 ....1028B ....10°16'S, 28°43'E

Kampinda, Mweru Wantipa, Kaputa Dist. ....930 ....0829D ....8°47'S, 29°46'E

Kampumbu, Isoka Dist. ....820 ....1033A ....10°12'S, 33°03'E

Kamunoka Plain, Zambezi Dist. 1322B

Kamuswazi stream, Mbala Dist. ....1650 ....0931B ....9°07'S, 31°34'E

Kananga (Luluaburg), *Zaire* ....720 ....0522C ....5°53'S, 22°26'E

Kanchibya River, Mporokoso Dist. ....1250 ....0929C ....@ 9°32'S, 29°27'E

Kanchibya River, Mpika Dist. ....1330 ....1131A............@ 11°30'S, 31°17'E

Kanchindu, Sinazongwe Dist. ....500 ....1727C ....17°37'S, 27°16'E

Kanda forest, Mongu Dist. ....1080 ....1523B ....15°04'S, 23°40'E

Kande, Mongu Dist. ....1070 ....1523A ....15°13'S, 23°13'E

Kanini, Ndola Dist. ....1300 ....1228D ....12°58'S, 28°38'E

Kanona, Serenje Dist..1610 ....1330B ....13°04'S, 30°38'E

Kansalya, Kabompo Dist..1120 ....1323B ....13°23'S, 23°59'E

Kansoko (Kansoku) stream, Mwinilunga Dist. ....1310 ....1224A ....12°22'S, 24°05'E

Kansoku stream, Chilula, Mwinilunga Dist. ....1290 ....1024C ....10°54'S, 24°04'E

Kansombo stream, Chilula, Mwinilunga Dist. ....1300 ....1024C ....10°54'S, 24°05'E

Kantolo, Masaiti Dist. ....1230 ....1328A,C ....13°30'S, 28°28'E

Kanyama Bridge, West Lunga River, Mwinilunga Dist. ....1410 ....1124B ....11°27'S, 24°45'E

Kanyani (Kanyamwe), Luangwa Dist..370 ....1530A ....15°14'S, 30°15'E

Kanyengele/Jimbe stream confl. (Mad Man's crossing)................1220 ....1024C ....10°57'S, 24°05'E

Kaoma (ex-Mankoya) (Dist. H.Q.) ....1150 ....1424D ....14°48'S, 24°48'E

Kaombwe (Kawombwe), Nakonde Dist. ....1450 ....0932B ....9°28'S, 32°53'E

Kapamba/Luangwa River confl, South Luangwa N.P. ....510 ....1331B ....13°24'S, 31°33'E

Kapanda Bridge, Kazungula Dist. ....980 ....1725C ....17°47'S, 25°21'E

Kapashi, Mansa Dist. ....1130 ....1228B ....12°14'S, 28°58'E

Kapiri Kamfumu, South Luangwa N.P. ....600 ....1331B ....13°05'S, 31°40'E

Kapiri Kasweta, South Luangwa N.P..790 ....1231C ....12°44'S, 31°28'E

Kapiri Mposhi (Dist. H.Q.) ....1260 ....1328D ....13°58'S, 28°40'E

Kapisya, Mwambwa River, Chama Dist...960 ....1032D ....10°50'S, 32°35'E

Kapoche, Luangwa Dist..380 ....1530A ....15°25'S, 30°21'E

Kapolowe, *Zaire* ....1150 ....1126B ....11°02'S, 26°58'E

Kaputa (Dist. H.Q.) ....930 ....0829B ....8°28'S, 29°40'E

Kapweletete Plain, Lukulu Dist. ....1090 ....1423B ....14°17'S, 23°54'E

Kapweshi Forest Reserve, Kawambwa Dist. ....1410 ....0928D ....9°49'S, 28°56'E

Kapwila River, Nakonde Dist. ....1300 ....0932A ....9°17'S, 32°27'E

Kapyanga, Mumbwa Dist. ....1110 ....1527A ....15°10'S, 27°30'E

Kariba Dam wall, Siavonga Dist. ....550 ....1628D ....16°32'S, 28°45'E

Kariba Gorge, Siavonga Dist...*c.* 430-600 ....1628B

Kariba, Lake (*Map*, p. 1)..500 ....1727B

Kariba town, *Zimbabwe* ....520 ....1628D ....16°31'S, 28°47'E

Karoi, *Zimbabwe* ....1280 ....1629D ....16°49'S, 29°41'E

Karubwe, Chibombo Dist...1170 ....1528A ....15°09'S, 28°20'E

Locality	Alt. (m)	Square	Coordinates
Kasaba Bay, Sumbu N.P.	760	0830D	8°31'S, 30°40'E
Kasaji, Katanga, *Zaire*	c. 1100	1023A	10°23'S, 23°28'E
Kasama (Dist. H.Q.) (*Map*, p. 1)	1460	1031A	10°12'S, 31°11'E
Kasane, *Botswana*	930	1725C	17°51'S, 25°08'E
Kasangu (Chitunda), Nchelenge Dist.	1200	0829A	8°27'S, 29°22'E
Kasanka N.P. (IBA 25)	1190	1230C	12°38'S, 30°14'E
Kasempa (Dist. H.Q.) (*Map*, p. 1)	1230	1325B	13°27'S, 25°50'E
Kasenga, Luapula River, *Zaire*	960	1028B	10°23'S, 28°36'E
Kashiba (Kashiwa), Lake, Masaiti Dist.	1180	1328A	c. 13°20'S, 28°10'E
Kashiba, Mwense Dist	960	1028B	10°26'S, 28°40'E
Kashiji, Zambezi Dist.	1070	1322D	13°36'S, 22°47'E
Kashikishi, Nchelenge Dist.	960	0928B	9°18'S, 28°45'E
Kashima stream, Zambezi Dist.	1080	1323A	@ 13°29'S, 23°04'E
Kashinda, Mporokoso Dist.	1430	0930A	9°21'S, 30°07'E
Kashinji (Kashingi), Chavuma Dist.	1070	1322A	13°27'S, 22°27'E
Kasikezi Lagoon, South Luangwa N.P.	530	1231D	12°56'S, 31°54'E
Kasisi Mission, Chongwe Dist.	1110	1528A	15°16'S, 28°28'E
Kasoma forest, Nyika N.P.	1980-2050	1033D	10°37'S, 33°40'E
Kasungu N.P., *Malawi*	1050	1333A	13°05'S, 33°08'E
Kasusu, Kalomo Dist.	1250	1626C	16°50'S, 26°18'E
Kataba, Kazungula Dist.	1180	1625A	16°05'S, 25°06'E
Kataba, Mongu Dist	1040	1523A	15°26'S, 23°18'E
Katala, Kaoma Dist.	1100	1423D	14°50'S, 23°50'E
Katangalika, Chama Dist.	650	1132B	11°29'S, 32°50'E
Katanino, Masaiti Dist.	1280	1328D	13°34'S, 28°43'E
Katayauchi Hill, Petauke Dist.	1030	1431C	14°32'S, 31°26'E
Katema Is., Mweru Wantipa N.P.	950	0829D	8°48'S, 29°41'E
Katete (Dist. H.Q.) & River	1040	1432A	14°05'S, 32°04'E
Katima Mulilo, Sesheke Dist.	990	1724A	17°28'S, 24°14'E
Katombora Rapids, Kazungula Dist.	1000	1725C	17°50'S, 25°24'E
Katondwe Mission, Luangwa Dist.	440	1530A	15°15'S, 30°14'E
Katongo, Sesheke Dist.	990	1724A	17°25'S, 24°28'E
Katoti, Mongu Dist.	1070	1523B	15°27'S, 23°31'E
Katumba stream, Isoka Dist.	800	1033A	10°15'S, 33°01'E
Katuta, Mwense Dist.	1050	1028D	10°49'S, 28°36'E
Kaunga stream, Chama Dist.	710	1032D	10°37'S, 32°51'E
Kaunga, Kafue N.P.	1130	1625B	16°09'S, 25°42'E
Kaungashi River, Kasempa Dist.	1210	1326D	@ 13°54'S, 26°38'E
Kaungo, Shangombo Dist.	1000	1622D	16°58'S, 22°38'E
Kaungulu (Kungulu), Mumbwa Dist.	1110	1526B	15°04'S, 26°52'E
Kawambwa (Dist. H.Q.) (*Map*, p. 1)	1300	0929C	9°45'S, 29°10'E
Kawehi, Monze Dist.		1627A	
Kawimbe, Mbala Dist.	1750	0831D	8°50'S, 31°31'E

Locality ....**Alt. (m)** ....**Square** ....**Coordinates**

Kayombo, Kabombo Dist...1150 ....1323B ....13°03'S, 23°51'E

Kazembe, Mutinondo River, Mpika Dist........................630 ....1231B ....12°18'S, 31°44'E

Kazikizi stream, Serenje Dist..470 ....1330D ....13°52'S, 30°58'E

Kazimuli, Chipata Dist...1060 ....1332C ....13°54'S, 32°24'E

Kazuma Pan, Hwange N.P., *Zimbabwe* ....1070 ....1825B ....18°22'S, 25°31'E

Kazungula (Dist. H.Q.)...1020 ....1725C ....17°47'S, 25°17'E

Kazwili village, Sesheke Dist..940 ....1724B ....17°29'S, 24°52'E

Keembe, Chibombo Dist..1130 ....1427D ....14°55'S, 27°50'E

Khulamayembe, Lundazi Dist..1150 ....1133C ....11°38'S, 33°13'E

Kifubwa (Chifubwa) Gorge, Solwezi Dist.......................1350 ....1226A ....12°11'S, 26°27'E

Kilwa Is., Lake Mweru, Nchelenge Dist...........................930 ....0928A ....9°16'S, 28°27'E

Kipopo, Katanga, *Zaire*..970 ....1027C ....10°40'S, 27°28'E

Kitwe (Dist. H.Q.) (*Map*, p. 1)......................................1220 ....1228C ....12°48'S, 28°14'E

Konkano Plain, Kabombo Dist. ....1140 ....1323B ....13°15'S, 24°00'E

Kopa, Bangweulu, Mpika Dist..1210 ....1130D ....11°43'S, 30°46'E

Kowa, Mbala Dist. ....1730 ....0831C ....8°50'S, 31°28'E

Kukwe Hill, Chipata Dist..1140 ....1332D ....13°35'S, 32°43'E

Kumanu Plain, Zambezi Dist..1060 ....1322D ....13°38'S, 22°49'E

Kundabwika Falls, Kawambwa Dist. ....1040 ....0929A ....9°13'S, 29°18'E

Kundalila (Kondolilo) Falls, Serenje Dist. ....1510 ....1330B ....13°09'S, 30°42'E

Kundelungu Mts, Katanga, *Zaire*................................*c.* 1700 ....1027B ....10°00'S, 27°50'E

Kungulu Hill, Muchinga escarpment, Mpika Dist. ....1340-1520 ....1231A ....12°17'S, 31°27'E

Kungwala Hill, Manyenjere, Nyika N.P. ....2020 ....1033D ....10°35'S, 33°40'E

Kyimbwe salt pan, Kasempa Dist....................................1320 ....1325B ....13°04'S, 25°57'E

Lalafuta River, Kaoma/Mufumbwe Dists ....1180 ....1424B .... @ 14°12'S, 24°59'E

Lambwe Chikwama, Nchelenge Dist. ....1050 ....0829A ....8°27'S, 29°19'E

Lavushi Manda N.P. (IBA 26) ....1100-1800 ....1230B ....12°22'S, 30°52'E

Lazy J ranch (Jellises' farm) (South), Kafue Dist...........1260 ....1528C ....15°30'S, 28°27'E

Leopardshill ranch, Kafue Dist. ....1130 ....1528D ....15°36'S, 28°42'E

Liande Plain (West), Kalabo Dist. ....1050 ....1522A ....15°26'S, 22°30'E

Libonda, Kalabo Dist. ....1020 ....1422D ....14°55'S, 23°00'E

Lilayi Lodge, Kafue Dist. ....1300 ....1528C ....15°33'S, 28°19'E

Lilondo Plain, Shangombo Dist. ....1020 ....1622A ....16°29'S, 22°09'E

Lilongwe, *Malawi* ....1100 ....1333D ....13°58'S, 33°47'E

Limpumpu school, Loanja River, Sesheke Dist..............990 ....1724B ....17°14'S, 24°39'E

"Line of rail" = Copperbelt to Livingstone

Litapi Floodplain, Zambezi Dist......................................1322C

Litapi River headwaters, Chavuma Dist..........................1090 ....1322A ....13°20'S, 22°04'E

Litoma Plain, Sesheke Dist. ....1180 ....1525C ....15°58'S, 25°02'E

Litungi, Mongu Dist..1070 ....1523B ....*c.* 15°32'S, 23°47'E

Liumba (Lyumba) Hill & Mission, Kalabo Dist...............1040 ....1422C ....14°59'S, 22°28'E

Liuwa Plain N.P. (*Map*, p. 2) (IBA 8)............................1050 ....1422D ....@ 14°25'S, 22°40'E

Livingstone (Dist. H.Q.) (*Map*, p. 1) ....970 ....1725D ....17°50'S, 25°51'E

Locality ....**Alt. (m)** ....**Square** ....**Coordinates**

Loanja River, Sesheke Dist. ....1060..............1724A ....@ 17°00'S, 24°30'E
Lochinvar N.P. (lodge) (*Map*, p. 2) ....1000..............1527C ....15°59'S, 27°15'E
Lofu (Lufubu) River, Mpulungu Dist...0831C
Loma Plain, Mongu Dist...1080..............1523B ....15°07'S, 23°39'E
Lower Zambezi N.P. (IBA 18)..1529C,D
Luachi (Lwati) River, Kalabo Dist. ....1040..............1422C ....@ 14°50'S, 22°22'E
Luakela Bridge & River, Mwinilunga Dist................................1430..............1124C ....11°31'S, 24°24'E
Luakela/Chitunta stream confl., Mwinilunga Dist..................1430 ....1124A,C ....11°30'S, 24°22'E
Luamala River, Kapiri Mposhi Dist. ....1160..............1427A ....@ 14°06'S, 27°08'E
Luamala/Kafue River confl., Kapiri Mposhi Dist. ....1120..............1427A ....14°10'S, 27°25'E
Luambe N.P. ....560..............1232A,C ....12°28'S, 32°08'E
Luambimba River, Kalabo Dist. ....1030..............1422D ....*c.* 15°00'S, 22°47'E
Luamfwa, South Luangwa N.P. ....500..............1331A ....13°28'S, 31°22'E
Luampa Mission, Kaoma Dist. ....1220..............1524A ....15°03'S, 24°27'E
Luamuloba Dambo, Sesheke Dist. ....1170..............1625A ....16°20'S, 25°01'E
Luanginga River (upper), Kalabo Dist...................................1040..............1422A ....@ 14°25'S, 22°10'E
Luangwa town (ex-Feira) (Dist. H.Q.)....................................330..............1530C ....15°37'S, 30°24'E
Luangwa Bridge, Chongwe/Nyimba Dists ....760..............1430C ....14°58'S, 30°13'E
Luano Valley (= Lunsemfwa Valley) (*Map*, p. 2)
Luanshya (Dist. H.Q.) ....1230..............1328A ....13°08'S, 28°25'E
Luansobe (Lwansobe), Masaiti Dist. ....1240..............1328C ....13°31'S, 28°30'E
Luao River, Nchelenge Dist. ....1000..............0829C ....*c.* 8°32'S, 29°07'E
Luapula River mouth, Nchelenge Dist. (IBA 31) (*Map*, p. 1)..........920 ....0928B ....9°25'S, 28°30'E
Luau River, *Angola* ....*c.* 1050..............1022C ....*c.* 10°40'S, 22°15'E
Lubansenshi (Luansenshi) River, Lake Bangweulu, Kasama Dist. ....1030D ....*c.* 10°33'S, 30°33'E
Lubumbashi (ex-Elisabethville), *Zaire* ....1240..............1127C ....11°40'S, 27°28'E
Lubungu pontoon, Kafue N.P...1100..............1426C ....14°33'S, 26°27'E
Luchinde stream, Nakonde Dist...1300..............0932A ....@ 9°08'S, 32°16'E
Luembe, Nyimba Dist. ....500..............1430A ....14°26'S, 30°27'E
Luena (Lwena) (1902-1909), Lake Bangweulu, Chilubi Dist........1240..............1030C ....10°38'S, 30°12'E
Luena Flats, Lukulu Dist...1000..............1423C
Luena River (now Kashamba), Lukulu Dist. ....1130..............1424A ....@ 14°28'S, 24°10'E
Luena River (upper), Mwense Dist. 1029A
Lueti (Luete, Lwati) River, (South), Kalabo Dist ....1050..............1522C ....@ 15°38'S, 22°14'E
Lufila River (upper), Mpika Dist. ....1140..............1132A ....11°25'S, 32°07'E
Lufila/Luangwa River confl., Mpika Dist................................600..............1132D ....11°41'S, 32°36'E
Lufubu (Lufupa) River mouth, Mpulungu Dist. ....790..............0830D ....8°34'S, 30°44'E
Lufupa/Kafue River confl., Kafue N.P.....................................1100..............1426C ....14°37'S, 26°11'E
Lufwanyama town (Dist.H.Q.) & River ....1140..............1327B ....13°26'S, 27°45'E
Luinga (Luianga) River source, Mwinilunga Dist...................1340..............1124A ....11°14'S, 24°15'E
Lukanda Hills, Kapiri Mposhi Dist...1400..............1328D ....13°53'S, 28°40'E
Lukanga/Kafue River confl., Kapiri Mposhi Dist...................1110..............1427A ....14°22'S, 27°11'E
Lukanga Swamp (*Map*, p. 2) (IBA 20)..................................1100..............1427B

Locality ....**Alt. (m)** ....**Square** ....**Coordinates**

Locality	Alt. (m)	Square	Coordinates
Lukolwe, Zambezi Dist.	1060	1322B	13°11'S, 22°43'E
Lukonzolwa, *Zaire*	980	0828D	8°47'S, 28°38'E
Lukulu (Dist. H.Q.)	1050	1423A	14°20'S, 23°17'E
Lukulu Bridge, Kasama Dist.	1290	1030B	10°11'S, 30°57'E
Lukulu River headwaters, Mporokoso Dist.	1470	0930C	9°57'S, 30°27'E
Lukulu River, Lavusi Manda N.P.	1290	1230B	@ 12°12'S, 30°50'E
Lukusashi/Lunsemfwa River confl., Mkushi/Nyimba Dists	640	1430C	14°39'S, 30°01'E
Lukusashi (Lukasashi) River (upper), Serenje Dist.		1330B	
Lukusuzi N.P. & River (IBA 41)		mainly 1232D	
Lulingi, Katanga, *Zaire*	c. 1500	0927B	9°20'S, 27°36'E
Lumbe River (upper), Senanga Dist.	1100	1524C	c. 16°00'S, 24°15'E
Lumezi Mission, Lundazi Dist.	1150	1233C	12°32'S, 33°02'E
Lunchinda (Lunkinda) River, Nchelenge Dist.	950	0829C	@ 8°31'S, 29°00'E
Lundazi (Dist. H.Q.) (*Map*, p. 1)	1140	1233A	12°17'S, 33°10'E
Lundazi River (lower)		1232A	
Lunga, Gwembe Dist.	710	1627D	16°50'S, 27°40'E
Lunga-Muzela Swamp, Mwinilunga Dist.	1400	1124B	11°17'S, 24°58'E
Lungundu, Zambezi Dist.	1060	1322B	13°15'S, 22°52'E
Lungwebungu River, Zambezi Dist.		1322C-1423A	
Lunsemfwa/Luangwa River confl., Chongwe/Nyimba Dists	760	1430C	14°54'S, 30°12'E
Lupamadzi River, Chama Dist.	760	1133A	@ 11°21'S, 33°04'E
Lupande/Luangwa River confl., Mambwe Dist.	530	1331B	13°06'S, 31°49'E
Lupuka, Shangombo Dist.	1000	1622C	16°48'S, 22°28'E
Lusaka (Dist. H.Q.) (*Map*, p. 1)	1260	1528A	15°24'S, 28°17'E
Lusenga Plain N.P. (IBA 32)	1000	0929A,C	9°30'S, 29°10'E
Lushushwa Plain, Senanga Dist.	1050	1522D	15°40'S, 22°50'E
Lusitu stream, Siavonga Dist.	410	1628B	@ 16°10'S, 28°45'E
Lusiwashi, Lake, Serenje Dist.	1570	1230D	12°58'S, 30°42'E
Lusiwashi River (upper), Serenje Dist.		1331A	
Lusokosoko (Lusakasaka) stream, Kafue N.P.	1160	1426A	@ 14°13'S, 26°28'E
Lusongwa River, Kabompo Dist.	1150	1324A	13°03'S, 24°03'E
Lusu Hill, Sesheke Dist.	1030	1724A	17°16'S, 24°08'E
Luswishi River @ wooden Bridge, Mpongwe Dist.	1160	1327A	13°13'S, 27°18'E
Luswishi/Kafue River confl., Mpongwe/Kapiri Mposhi Dists	1130	1327C	@ 13°55'S, 27°24'E
Lutali, Zambezi Dist.	1090	1323C	13°43'S, 23°27'E
Lutembwe River, Mambwe Dist.	760	1332A	@ 13°24'S, 32°17'E
Lutembwe/Lungwebungu River confl., Zambezi Dist.		1322D	13°57'S, 22°37'E
Luwingu (Dist. H.Q.)	1420	1029B	10°15'S, 29°56'E
Luzu, Zambezi Dist.	1050	1322B	13°14'S, 22°53'E
Lwamakunyi stream, Mwinilunga Dist.	1320	1224A	12°00'S, 24°19'E
Lwampungu/Njoko stream confl., Sesheke Dist.	1030	1624C	16°40'S, 24°19'E
Lwela, Mansa Dist.	1170	1129C	11°44'S, 29°07'E
Lweti (Lueti) school, Kalabo Dist.	1040	1522C	15°41'S, 22°24'E

Locality ....Alt. (m) ....Square ....Coordinates

Maala, Namwala Dist. ....990 ....1526D ....15°44'S, 26°44'E

Mabila River (lower), Mansa Dist. ....1100 ....1128C ....11°30'S, 28°23'E

Mabwingombe Hills, Gwembe Dist. ....1170 ....1627D ....16°58'S, 27°18'E

Machechete Hills, Chongwe Dist. ....990 ....1429D ....14°59'S, 29°54'E

Machile (Machili) forest, Sesheke Dist. (IBA 12) ....1000 ....1625C ....@ 16°51'S, 25°02'E

Machile, Sesheke Dist. ....930 ....1724B ....17°29'S, 24°58'E

Machile River system (upper), Sesheke/Kazungula Dists 1624B, 1625A

Machile/Zambezi River confl., Sesheke Dist. ....930 ....1724D ....17°33'S, 24°58'E

Mafinga Mts, Isoka Dist. (*Map*, p. 2) (IBA 39) ....1750-2200 ..0933C,1033A ....10°00'S, 33°20'E

Magoye River & Bridge, Mazabuka Dist. ....1000 ....1527D ....15°58'S, 27°36'E

Mahobe (Mahowe), Isoka Dist. ....1460 ....1033B ....10°28'S, 33°40'E

Makapaela, Lake, Mongu Dist. ....1050 ....1523A ....15°02'S, 23°13'E

Makoche, Siavonga Dist. ....450 ....1628B ....*c.* 16°02'S, 28°52'E

Makondu River, Zambezi Dist. ....1323A ....@ 13°22'S, 23°04'E

Makutu (Mukutu) Plateau, Isoka Dist. ....1900-2119 ....1033A ....10°25'S, 33°18'E

Makuwa Kuwa forest, Zambezi Dist. ....1060 ....1322B ....13°18'S, 22°56'E

Malambanyama, Chibombo Dist. ....1150 ....1427D ....14°52'S, 27°42'E

Malole, Mungwi Dist. ....1290 ....1031B ....10°07'S, 31°35'E

Mambo, Nyimba Dist. ....810 ....1430B ....14°28'S, 30°52'E

Mambova, Kazungula Dist. ....940 ....1725C ....17°44'S, 25°11'E

Mambwe Dist. (see Jumbe, Dist. H.Q.)

Mana Pools N.P., *Zimbabwe* ....370 ....1529C ....15°43'S, 29°22'E

Manchamvwa, Gwembe Dist. ....640 ....1628C ....*c.* 16°35'S, 28°05'E

Manda Hill, Chama Dist. ....1370 ....1133C ....11°35'S, 33°13'E

Manenekera escarpment, Chongwe Dist. ....930 ....1529B ....15°04'S, 29°50'E

Manenekera, Chongwe Dist. ....930 ....1529B ....15°04'S, 29°44'E

Mangalala/Luangwa River confl., Mpika Dist. ....540 ....1132D ....11°40'S, 32°35'E

Mano camp, North Luangwa N.P. ....1170 ....1132C ....11°36'S, 32°01'E

Mansa (ex-Fort Rosebery) (Dist. H.Q.) (*Map*, p. 1) ....1260 ....1128B ....11°12'S, 28°53'E

Manyani, Nyimba Dist. ....1000 ....1431C ....14°38'S, 31°08'E

Manyenjere forest, Nyika N.P. ....1970-2070 ....1033D ....10°35'S, 33°39'E

Manyinga, Kabompo Dist. ....1120 ....1324A ....13°17'S, 24°13'E

Manyinga/Kabompo River confl., Kabompo Dist. ....1130 ....1324A ....@ 13°27'S, 24°20'E

Manze (Manzi) River, South Luangwa N.P. ....520 ....1331B ....13°12'S, 31°42'E

Mapanza, Choma Dist. ....1060 ....1626B ....16°15'S, 26°55'E

Maplehurst farm, Kabwe Dist. ....1180 ....1428A ....14°29'S, 28°23'E

Mapungu (Mapungo), Kalabo Dist. ....1040 ....1522B ....15°02'S, 22°45'E

Marble Hill, Kafue Dist. ....1110 ....1528D ....15°40'S, 28°37'E

Marungu highlands, *Zaire* ....1900-2100 ....0729D etc. .... *c.* 7°45'S, 29°45'E

Masaiti (Dist. H.Q.) ....1200 ....1328A ....13°16'S, 28°25'E

Masase (Musense), Serenje Dist. ....1490 ....1331A ....13°11'S, 31°05'E

Masese, Sesheke Dist. ....980 ....1724B ....17°17'S, 24°40'E

Mashi (Kwando) River, *Angola/Zambia* (*Map*, p. 1)

Locality ....**Alt. (m)** ....**Square** ....**Coordinates**

Masombwe, Luapula, *Zaire* ....1340 ....0927A ....9°05'S, 27°12'E
Masuku Mission, Choma Dist..1310 ....1727A ....17°12'S, 27°07'E
Masumba, Luangwa Valley, Mambwe Dist.. ....560 ....1331B ....13°13'S, 31°57'E
Matabele Plain, Shangombo Dist..1000 ....1623A ....16°20'S, 23°08'E
Matakala, Lungwebungu River, Zambezi Dist. ....1070 ....1322C ....13°40'S, 22°19'E
Matanda, Mansa Dist. ....1070 ....1128A ....11°21'S, 28°28'E
Matebo, Solwezi Dist..1230 ....1225D ....12°48'S, 25°48'E
Matetsi, *Zimbabwe* ....1060 ....1825B ....18°17'S, 25°56'E
Matinangala, Siavonga Dist. ....490 ....1628D ....*c.* 16°32'S, 28°32'E
Matipa, Chilubi Dist..1190 ....1030C ....10°50'S, 30°18'E
Matongo Is., Samfya Dist. ....1170 ....1130C ....11°35'S, 30°15'E
Mayau (Mayowo), Kabompo Dist. ....1130 ....1224C ....12°43'S, 24°16'E
Mayuka, Mpika Dist. ....1180 ....1130B ....11°28'S, 30°40'E
Mayukwayukwa, Luena Flats, Lukulu Dist. ....1150 ....1424A
Mazabuka (Dist. H.Q.)...1040 ....1527D ....15°51'S, 27°45'E
Mbala (ex-Abercorn) (Dist. H.Q.) (*Map*, p. 1) ....1650 ....0831C ....8°50'S, 31°22'E
Mbanda Plain, Kalabo Dist. ....1040 ....1422C ....14°40'S, 22°10'E
Mbati, Mpika Dist. ....1200 ....1130B ....11°11'S, 30°47'E
Mbendele, Siavonga Dist. ....450 ....1628B ....16°20'S, 28°43'E
Mbereshi causeway, Kawambwa Dist. ....990 ....0928D ....9°43'S, 28°47'E
Mbesuma, Chinsali Dist. ....1230 ....1032A ....10°02'S, 32°04'E
Mbewa Hill, Nyanje, Petauke Dist. (IBA 42) ....1320 ....1431B ....14°24'S, 31°46'E
Mbulo forest, Zambezi Dist. (IBA 7)..1050 ....1322B ....13°13'S, 22°50'E
Mbulungu/Zambezi River confl., Mwinilunga Dist.....................1170 ....1124A ....11°07'S, 24°05'E
Mchimadzi, Nyimba Dist...880 ....1430D ....14°42'S, 30°46'E
Mchinji, *Malawi*..1200 ....1332D ....13°43'S, 32°54'E
Mchito (Mchuto) Gorge, Kafue Dist. ....1040 ....1528C ....15°48'S, 28°15'E
Membe stream, Lundazi Dist. ....1150 ....1233A ....12°13'S, 33°10'E
Mfubakazi, Shangombo Dist..1000 ....1723A ....17°09'S, 23°04'E
Mfuwe (Old), South Luangwa N.P. ....530 ....1331B ....13°05'S, 31°47'E
Miengwe, Masaiti Dist. ....1280 ....1328B ....13°24'S, 28°46'E
Milenge (Dist. H.Q.) ....1060 ....1128D ....11°57'S, 28°52'E
Miloki, Samfya Dist. ....1160 ....1129D ....11°36'S, 29°45'E
Minga Mission, Petauke Dist. ....880 ....1431A ....14°21'S, 31°09'E
Minyanya Plain, Chavuma Dist. (*Map*, p. 2) (IBA 6) ....1070 ....1322A ....13°09'S, 22°23'E
Mirongo (Mwini-Mirongo) (1897-1907), Isoka Dist. ....1070 ....1032B ....10°18'S, 32°44'E
Misaka F.R., Ndola Dist..1280 ....1228C ....*c.* 12°55'S, 28°25'E
Misale (Sinda Missale), Chiwali River, Chadiza Dist. ....1100 ....1433A ....14°02'S, 33°03'E
Misuku Hills, *Malawi* ....2050 ......0933C2,D1
Miswa, Chibombo Dist. ....1140 ....1428C ....14°53'S, 28°21'E
Mita Hills Dam, Mkushi Dist..1100 ....1429A ....14°14'S, 29°08'E
Mitashi Plain, Zambezi Dist. ....1070 ....1322D ....13°35'S, 22°50'E
Mize (Ndungu), Zambezi Dist. ....1080 ....1323C ....13°33'S, 23°05'E

Locality ....Alt. (m) ....Square ....Coordinates

Mkunkunya, Chongwe Dist. ....670 ....1430C ....14°58'S, 30°09'E
Mkushi (Dist. H.Q.) (*Map*, p. 1) ....1250 ....1329C ....13°36'S, 29°23'E
Mkushi River town (now Chalata), Mkushi Dist...........1400 ....1329D ....13°33'S, 29°41'E
Mkushi, Old (= Old Mkushi III), Mkushi Dist. ....1150 ....1429A ....14°22'S, 29°22'E
Mkuzye/Luangwa River confl., South Luangwa N.P. ......540 ....1331C ....13°35'S, 31°11'E
Mkwisi (Makwishi) Hill, Kafue Dist. ....700 ....1528D ....15°54'S, 28°36'E
Mlembo River, Serenje Dist...1240 ....1230C ....@ 12°33'S, 30°20'E
Mofwe Dambo, Kaputa Dist. ....930 ....0829C ....8°55'S, 29°27'E
Monga, Mansa Dist. ....1240 ....1129A ....11°12'S, 29°06'E
Mongu (Dist. H.Q.) (*Map*, p. 1).................................1060 ....1523A ....15°16'S, 23°08'E
Monongwa, Chilubi Dist. ....1190 ....1130A ....11°03'S, 30°28'E
Monze (Dist. H.Q.)...1130 ....1627A ....16°16'S, 27°28'E
Mopala, Katanga, *Zaire*...1330 ....1229D ....12°58'S, 29°41'E
Moshi, Kafue N.P..1100 ....1426A ....14°25'S, 26°09'E
Mount Makulu, Chilanga, Kafue Dist. ....1210 ....1528C ....15°33'S, 28°15'E
Mount Moco, *Angola* ....2620 ....1215A ....12°25'S, 15°16'E
Moxico, *Angola*..1280 ....1120C ....11°51'S, 20°03'E
Mpandapanda pan, Kabompo Dist................................1120 ....1323D ....13°46'S, 23°59'E
Mpanyakunda, Chama Dist...680 ....1132B ....11°24'S, 32°44'E
Mpasa, Bangweulu, Chilubi Dist. ....1190 ....1130B ....11°00'S, 30°30'E
Mpata Gorge, Luangwa Dist...480 ....1530C ....15°37'S, 30°08'E
Mpika (District H.Q.) (*Map*, p. 1).............................1400 ....1131C ....11°52'S, 31°26'E
Mpili, Namboma Rapids, Zambezi Dist. ....1050 ....1423A ....14°05'S, 23°14'E
Mpomwa Hills, Mambwe Dist.......................................800 ....1332A ....13°27'S, 32°19'E
Mpongwe (Dist. H.Q.) ....1200 ....1328C ....13°30'S, 28°09'E
Mporokoso (Dist. H.Q.) ....1430 ....0930A ....9°22'S, 30°06'E
Mpudi (Mbudi) River, Mwinilunga Dist. ....1440 ....1124A ....11°27'S, 24°26'E
Mpulungu (Dist. H.Q.), Lake Tanganyika ....1520 ....0831C ....8°45'S, 31°06'E
Msoro, Mambwe Dist. ....640 ....1331D ....13°35'S, 31°53'E
Mswebe (Mswebi, Msweba), Mumbwa Dist. ....1130 ....1426B ....14°28'S, 26°58'E
Mtenguleni, Chipata Dist. ....1060 ....1332C ....*c.* 13°54'S, 32°24'E
Mterize/Mvuvye River confl., Luangwa Valley, Nyimba Dist. ....710 ....1430B ....14°15'S, 30°52'E
Mtipwazi/Luangwa River confl., South Luangwa N.P. ....490 ....1331C ....13°43'S, 31°06'E
Mubanga, Chinsali Dist; ....1310 ....1032A ....10°08'S, 32°20'E
Mubi Pools, Kafue N.P...1010 ....1625B ....16°22'S, 25°54'E
Muchenja (Mchenja) camp, South Luangwa N.P. ....530 ....1231D ....12°56'S, 31°54'E
Muchicha (Omboya) River, Liuwa N.P. ....1040 ....1422B ....@ 14°25'S, 22°40'E
Muchinga Escarpment (*Map*, p. 2)
Muckle Neuk, Choma Dist. ....1200 ....1627C ....16°37'S, 27°01'E
Mudileji River, Mwinilunga Dist.................................1300 ....1124A ....@ 11°15'S, 24°08'E
Mudyanyama River, Mwinilunga Dist..........................1360 ....1124C ....11°45'S, 24°26'E
Mufulira (Dist. H.Q.) ....1310 ....1228C ....12°32'S, 28°15'E
Mufumbwe (Dist. H.Q.) ....1150 ....1324D ....13°41'S, 24°48'E

Locality ....Alt. (m) ....Square ....Coordinates

Mufumbwe/Dongwe River confl., Mufumbwe Dist. ....1110 ....1324D ....@ 13°54'S, 24°48'E

Mufundwa Bridge, Mwinilunga Dist. ....1500 ....1125C ....11°41'S, 25°15'E

Mujimbeji Mission & Hill, Mwinilunga Dist. ....1340 ....1224B ....12°08'S, 24°56'E

Mukanga, Chinsali Dist. ....*c.* 1600 ....1032A ....10°02'S, 32°18'E

Mukonchi, Mkushi Dist. ....1200 ....1428B ....14°12'S, 28°47'E

Mukonje Hill, Livingstone Dist. ....1160 ....1726C ....17°36'S, 26°02'E

Mukopa, Serenje Dist. ....1180 ....1330C ....13°45'S, 30°10'E

Mukuku Bridge, Luapula River, Samfya Dist. ....1160 ....1229B ....12°08'S, 29°50'E

Mukuni Pool, Kazungula Dist. ....1100 ....1625D ....16°35'S, 25°43'E

Mulanga, Kazungula Dist. ....980 ....1625C ....16°55'S, 25°18'E

Mulanga, Chinsali Dist. ....1300 ....1032C ....10°59'S, 32°09'E

Mulangale forest, Mafinga Mts, Isoka Dist. ....1950-2130 ....0933C ....9°59'S, 33°18'E

Mulekatembo (Mlekatembo), Isoka Dist. ....1440 ....1033A ....10°07'S, 33°19'E

Mulele, Shangombo Dist. ....1010 ....1623C ....16°36'S, 23°06'E

Mulilansoro, Chiawa-Chongwe River mouth, Kafue Dist. ....390 ....1529C ....15°45'S, 29°15'E

Mulilo's (Muliro), Nyimba Dist. ....580 ....1430B ....14°03'S, 30°58'E

Mulobezi, Sesheke Dist. ....1000 ....1625C ....16°47'S, 25°10'E

Mulolobela Falls, Ibwe Munyama, Siavonga Dist. ....780 ....1628B ....16°11'S, 28°33'E

Mulungushi Dam, Chibombo/Mkushi Dist. ....1070 ....1428D ....14°42'S, 28°50'E

Mumbeji, Kabompo Dist. ....1090 ....1323D ....13°52'S, 23°41'E

Mumbeji/Kabompo River confl., Kabompo Dist. ....1140 ....1323B ....@ 13°15'S, 23°45'E

Mumbi stream, Mpika Dist. ....1260 ....1132A ....*c.* 11°15'S, 32°05'E

Mumbwa (Dist. H.Q.) ....1190 ....1427C ....15°00'S, 27°01'E

Mumbwe, Isoka Dist. ....*c.* 1400 ....1032B ....10°15'S, 32°50'E

Munali Hills, Mazabuka Dist. ....1090 ....1528C ....15°56'S, 28°10'E

Mundwiji Plain, Mwinilunga Dist. ....1420 ....1124D ....11°44'S, 24°44'E

Mungwi (Dist. H.Q.) ....1370 ....1031A ....10°10'S, 31°23'E

Munkonje, Kasama Dist. ....1340 ....1030B ....10°19'S, 30°41'E

Munkonko, Chingola Dist. ....1270 ....1227D ....12°53'S, 27°45'E

Munkumpu farm, Kafue River, Mpongwe Dist. ....1150 ....1327D ....13°31'S, 27°43'E

Mununga, Nchelenge Dist. ....960 ....0929A ....9°02'S, 29°02'E

Mununga station, Mpika Dist. ....1480 ....1231C ....*c.* 12°38'S, 31°01'E

Munwa F.R., Kasama Dist. ....1230 ....1030D ....10°42'S, 30°42'E

Munyakeshi (Munyakawezi) River & Plain, Mwinilunga Dist. ......1400 ....1124B ....11°22'S, 24°42'E

Munyamadzi River (upper), Luangwa Valley, Mpika Dist. ......640-680 ....1231B ......@ 12°05'S, 31°40-43'E

Munyumbwe (Gwembe Dist. H.Q.) ....640 ....1627D ....16°38'S, 27°47'E

Mupamadzi River, Mpika Dist. ....550 ....1232C .... @ 12°37'S, 32°07'E

Mupamadzi village, Mpika Dist. ....1480 ....1231C ....12°50'S, 31°05'E

Mupemba, Mansa Dist. ....1300 ....1128B ....11°28'S, 28°40'E

Musa (Muso) Hills, Mpika Dist. ....1490 ....1230D ....12°46'S, 30°56'E

Musa/Kafue River confl., Kafue N.P. ....990 ....1526C ....15°47'S, 26°01'E

Musalangwa/Luangwa River confl., Chama Dist. ....660 ....1132B ....11°17'S, 32°53'E

Musense Hill, see Nsense, Serenje Dist. ....1270 ....1331A ....13°14'S, 31°06'E

Locality ....**Alt. (m)** ....**Square** ....**Coordinates**

Mushika, Lower Zambezi N.P. ....370 ....1529D ....15°37'S, 29°46'E

Mushima, Mufumbwe Dist. ....1180 ....1325C ....13°40'S, 25°20'E

Mushota, Kawambwa Dist. ....1230 ....0929C ....9°49'S, 29°24'E

Mushukula, Sesheke Dist.. 1060 ....1624C ....16°59'S, 24°30'E

Musi (Muzi) River, Chama Dist. ....710 ....1032D ....10°44'S, 32°50'E

Musofu Mission, Mkushi Dist. ....1310 ....1329C ....13°32'S, 29°02'E

Musola River, Serenje Dist. ....1220 ....1230C ....@ 12°35'S, 30°16'E

Musombwe, Kaputa Dist. ....930 ....0829D ....8°44'S, 29°34'E

Musonda Falls, Mansa Dist..1160 ....1028D ....10°44'S, 28°49'E

Musosa, Katanga, *Zaire* ....1060 ....0829B ....8°22'S, 29°36'E

Mutala Plain, Kalabo Dist...1040 ....1422C ....14°45'S, 22°15'E

Mutanda Bridge, Solwezi Dist...1330 ....1226A ....12°23'S, 26°14'E

Mutinondo River, Mpika Dist. ....640 ....1231B ....@ 12°18'S, 31°43'E

Mutinondo Wilderness, Mpika Dist. (IBA 27) ....1360-1685 ....1231A ....12°25'S, 31°17'E

Mutondo River (upper), Senanga Dist. ....1110 ....1524C .....*c.* 15°35'S, 24°05'E

Mutulanganga Bridge, Siavonga Dist. (IBA 17)..........................430 ....1628B ....16°14'S, 28°43'E

Mutwanjili, Kazungula Dist..1000 ....1725B ....17°28'S, 25°30'E

Muyeke River forest, Zambezi Dist..1070 ....1322B ....13°10'S, 22°39'E

Muyombe, Isoka Dist. ....1350 ....1033C ....10°40'S, 33°30'E

Muzi (Musi) River, Chama Dist. ....710 ....1032D ....10°44'S, 32°50'E

Muzyatama, Chinsali Dist. ....1140 ....1132A ....11°01'S, 32°27'E

Mvuvye River (upper), Nyimba Dist. ....510 ....1430B ....14°03'S, 30°48'E

Mwaleshi/Luangwa River confl., North Luangwa N.P...................600 ....1232A ....12°02'S, 32°20'E

Mwanda Mountain, Nyika N.P..2150 ....1033D ....10°42'S, 33°34'E

Mwandi (Old Sesheke, 1878-1945), Sesheke Dist. ....940 ....1724D ....17°30'S, 24°48'E

Mwangazi, Chadiza Dist...990 ....1432B ....14°08'S, 32°39'E

Mwange, Lake, Zambezi Dist..1070 ....1322C ....13°35'S, 22°25'E

Mwape, Nyimba Dist. ....560 ....1430B ....14°08'S, 30°50'E

Mwapula Gorge, Chongwe Dist. ....740 ....1529A ....15°10'S, 29°05'E

Mwase Lundazi, Lundazi Dist. ....1250 ....1233A ....12°25'S, 33°20'E

Mwatishi River & causeway, Nchelenge Dist. ....960 ....0928B ....9°15'S, 28°47'E

Mwavumwe River, Isoka Dist...1580 ....1033D ....10°35'S, 33°38'E

Mwawe, Kaputa Dist. ....930 ....0829B ....8°28'S, 29°51'E

Mwekera, Kitwe Dist. ....1200 ....1228C ....12°49'S, 28°23'E

Mwembeshi River, Lusaka Dist. ....1130 ....1527B ....@ 15°28'S, 27°49'E

Mwenda, Chibalashi River, Mwense Dist. ....1280 ....1029A ....10°28'S, 29°10'E

Mwendengombe/Luangwa River confl., South Luangwa N.P.........550 ....1331C ....13°37'S, 31°08'E

Mwenembwe, Nyika N.P., *Malawi* ....2000-2350 ....1034C ....10°40'S, 34°01'E

Mwengwa/Kafue River confl., Itezhi-tezhi Dist. ....1110 ....1525B ....15°17'S, 25°59'E

Mwense (Dist. H.Q.) ....950 ....1028B ....10°23'S, 28°42'E

Mwenzo, Nakonde Dist. ....1650 ....0932B ....9°19'S, 32°40'E

Mweru (Moero), Lake (*Map*, p. 1)...920 ....0928B

Mweru Wantipa N.P. (*Map*, p. 2) (IBA 34) ....920 ....0829D ....8°48'S, 29°41'E

Locality ....Alt. (m) ....Square ....Coordinates

Mwilozi (Mwilosi) Dambo, Mbala Dist. ....1550..............0931A ....9°29'S, 31°13'E

Mwinilunga (Dist. H.Q.) ....1390 ....1124C ....11°44'S, 24°26'E

Mwombezhi River, Solwezi Dist. ....1220 ....1225B ....@ 12°14'S, 25°34'E

Myooye, Mumbwa Dist. ....1060 ....1527A ....15°12'S, 27°20'E

Nabowa, Kaoma Dist. ....1140 ....1424C ....14°31'S, 24°14'E

Nabwalya, Mpika Dist. ....580 ....1231B ....12°25'S, 31°59'E

Nakambala, Mazabuka Dist. ....1000 ....1527D ....15°49'S, 27°42'E

Nakasalwa (Nakasolwo) Hill, Serenje Dist. ....1080 ....1330D ....13°37'S, 30°51'E

Nakonde (Dist. H.Q.) ....1610 ....0932B ....9°20'S, 32°45'E

Nalusanga, Mumbwa Dist. ....1160 ....1426D ....14°58'S, 26°42'E

Namando, Kaoma Dist. ....1150 ....1524B ....15°12'S, 24°37'E

Namatelo Gorge, Siavonga Dist...520 ....1628C ....16°30'S, 28°26'E

Namayonga, Kwemba River, Sesheke Dist. ....1060 ....1624A ....16°28'S, 24°24'E

Nambala Hill & Mission, Mumbwa Dist. ....1100 ....1527A ....15°05'S, 27°01'E

Nampini Ranch, *Zimbabwe* ....1000 ....1725C ....17°52'S, 25°18'E

Namushakende, Mongu Dist..1020 ....1523A ....15°26'S, 23°12'E

Namwala (Dist. H.Q.) (*Map*, p. 1) ....980 ....1526C ....15°44'S, 26°26'E

Namwiwe (Namwewe), Isoka Dist. ....1560 ....1033A ....10°06'S, 33°22'E

Nanga, Mazabuka Dist. ....1000 ....1527D ....15°46'S, 27°56'E

Nangweshi, Shangombo Dist. ....1010 ....1623A ....16°22'S, 23°18'E

Nankoli stream, Gwembe Dist. ....740 ....1627D ....16°38'S, 27°47'E

Nanzhila camp, Kafue N.P. ....1030 ....1625B ....16°17'S, 25°54'E

Nanzhila Mission, Itezhi-tezhi Dist. ....1010 ....1626A ....16°04'S, 26°05'E

Nasilele, Kalabo Dist. ....1040 ....1422C ....14°51'S, 22°11'E

Nasiongo (= Mashi I), Shangombo Dist. ....1010 ....1623A ....16°29'S, 23°09'E

Natukoma, Shangombo Dist. ....1010 ....1622B ....*c.* 16°25'S, 22°40'E

Natwange, Mwaleshi River, Mpika Dist......................................1370 ....1132C ....11°36'S, 32°01'E

Nawinda, Njoko River, Sesheke Dist...1090 ....1624C ....16°33'S, 24°29'E

Nchanga farm, near Sunzu Mtn, Mbala Dist. ....1550..............0831D ....8°58'S, 31°32'E

Nchelenge (Dist. H.Q.)..930 ....0928B ....9°20'S, 28°44'E

Nchenachena, *Malawi* ....1200 ....1034C ....10°44'S, 34°00'E

Ncheta Is., Bangweulu, Samfya Dist.. ....1170 ....1130C ....11°40'S, 30°04'E

Nchete Is., Lake Kariba, Sinazongwe Dist ....510 ....1727B ....17°21'S, 27°35'E

Nchila Wildlife Sanctuary, Hillwood (IBA 1), Mwinilunga Dist. ...1400 ....1124A ....11°15'S, 24°20'E

Ndanda Plain, Mongu Dist..1040 ....1423C ....14°53'S, 23°22'E

Ndeke sewage ponds, Kitwe Dist. ....1230 ....1228C ....12°53'S, 28°15'E

Ndola (Dist. H.Q.) (*Map*, p. 1)..1300 ....1228D ....12°58'S, 28°38'E

Ndola forestry plots, Ndola Dist. ....1270 ....1228D ....12°58'S, 28°38'E

Ndubeni, Kafue River, Lufwanyama Dist....................................1170 ....1327B ....13°24'S, 27°49'E

Ndulumina, Kafue N.P. ....1130 ....1426A ....14°06'S, 26°08'E

Ndumdumwense (Dundumwenze), Kazungula Dist....................1220 ....1626C ....16°43'S, 26°02'E

Ndungu, Lake, Mwinilunga Dist. ....1380 ....1124C ....11°41'S, 24°25'E

Ngalula, Mufumbwe Dist..1170 ....1324B ....13°24'S, 24°51'E

Locality ....Alt. (m) ....Square ....Coordinates

Ngambwe Rapids, Sesheke Dist. ....1030..............1724A ....17°15'S, 24°08'E
Nganjo (Ng'anjo), Chama Dist..760..............1032D ....10°36'S, 32°57'E
Ngitwa, Kasama Dist. ....1380 ..0930D,1030B ....10°00'S, 30°48'E
Ngoma, Kafue N.P. ....1020..............1525D ....15°54'S, 25°57'E
Nguma (Ngoma) Plain, Senanga Dist...1040..............1522D ....15°40'S, 22°41'E
Ngunda stream, Kaoma Dist. ....1150..............1524B ....15°18'S, 24°36'E
Nguvu, Chavuma Dist. ....1090..............1322A ....13°27'S, 22°02'E
Ngwezi River, Kazungula Dist. ....940..............1725C..........@ 17°34'S, 25°11'E
Ngwezi station, Kazungula Dist. ....990..............1725A ....17°26'S, 25°28'E
Niamadzi (Nyamadzi)/Luangwa River confl., Nyimba Dist. ....470..............1430B ....14°08'S, 30°42'E
Ninda, *Angola*..1150..............1421C ....14°51'S, 21°20'E
Njalamimba (Nialamimba), Mporokoso Dist. ....1430..............0929B ....9°17'S, 29°56'E
Njoko, Kasama Dist. ....1220..............1030D ....10°46'S, 30°49'E
Njoko River, Seseke Dist. ....990..............1724A ....@ 17°08'S, 24°04'E
Nkamba (Kamba) Bay, Sumbu N.P. ....760..............0830D ....8°35'S, 30°32'E
Nkana, Kitwe Dist..1260..............1228C ....12°50'S, 28°12'E
Nkanga River Conservation Area, Choma Dist. (IBA 16) ....1180-1280..............1627C ....16°38'S, 27°02'E
Nkumbula Is., Lake Tanganyika, Mpukungu Dist. ....840..............0831C ....8°45'S, 31°06'E
Nondo, Mbala Dist. ....1520..............0931C ....9°33'S, 31°11'E
North Kashiji River 1322A
North Luangwa N.P. (IBA 29) ....600-1310..mainly 1032C
Nsama, Kaputa Dist. ....1050..............0829D ....8°54'S, 29°57'E
Nsefu camp, South Luangwa N.P. ....530..............1231D ....12°56'S, 31°54'E
Nsombo, Chilubi Dist..1190..............1029D ....10°49'S, 29°56'E
Ntambu, Mwinilunga Dist...1190..............1224B ....12°24'S, 24°59'E
Ntatumbila, Nakonde Dist. ....1300..............0932A ....9°13'S, 32°16'E
Ntemwa camp, Kafue N.P. ....1100..............1426A ....14°25'S, 26°03'E
Ntomeshya pontoon, Kapiri Mposhi Dist. ....1130..............1427A ....14°07'S, 27°25'E
Nyakaseya Bridge, Chinyashi River, Mwinilunga Dist.................1220..............1124A ....11°10'S, 24°10'E
Nyakotoko Lagoon, South Luangwa N.P..540..............1232C ....12°47'S, 32°04'E
Nyamaluma, Luangwa Valley, Mambwe Dist. ....530..............1331B ....13°22'S, 31°38'E
Nyambela Plain & stream, Mwinilunga Dist. ....1430..............1124A ....11°18'S, 24°16'E
Nyambisi Pool, Shangombo Dist...1010..............1623D ....16°44'S, 23°36'E
Nyamuomba Hot Springs, Siavonga Dist. ....420..............1628B ....16°21'S, 28°49'E
Nyanje Mission, Petauke Dist..1280..............1431B ....14°23'S, 31°48'E
Nyatanda, Chavuma Dist. ....1090..............1322A ....13°10'S, 22°10'E
Nyawa, Kazungula Dist. ....1150..............1725B ....17°11'S, 25°53'E
Nyidi Plain, Mwinilunga Dist. ....1420..............1124C ....11°42'S, 24°10'E
Nyika Plateau (Nyika N.P.) (*Map*, p. 2) (IBA 38)................1600-2200..............1033D ....10°35'S, 33°41'E
Nyikamwaka, Isoka Dist...1900-1950..............1033A ....10°10'S, 33°28'E
Nyimba (Dist. H.Q.)..700..............1430D ....14°33'S, 30°48'E
Nyungwe, Isoka Dist...810..............1033A ....10°15'S, 33°01'E
Old Fife (?1898-1911), Nakonde Dist. ....1540..............0932B ....9°19'S, 32°38'E

Locality ....**Alt. (m)** ....**Square** ....**Coordinates**

Old Kalungwishi (1892-1908), Nchelenge Dist. ....940..............0929A ....9°02'S, 29°02'E

Old Mabenga, Luamuloba Dambo, Sesheke Dist.........................1170..............1625A ....16°20'S, 25°01'E

Old Mwengwa (1911-21), Itezhi-Tezhi Dist. ....1110..............1525B ....15°17'S, 25°59'E

Old Mkushi III (1909-1954), Mkushi Dist. ....1130..............1429A ....14°22'S, 29°22'E

Old Mkushi mine, Mkushi Dist..1140..............1329C ....13°57'S, 29°07'E

Old Petauke (1901-44), Petauke Dist. ....760..............1431A ....14°03'S, 31°05'E

Old Serenje (1900-1953), Serenje Dist..1390..............1330B ....13°10'S, 30°46'E

Old Sesheke (Mwandi) (1878-1945), Sesheke Dist........................940..............1724D ....17°30'S, 24°48'E

Paradise Rocks, Zambezi escarpment 1627B

Pemba, Monze Dist. ....1230..............1627C ....16°31'S, 27°22'E

Petauke (Dist. H.Q.) (*Map*, p. 1)...1040..............1431A ....14°15'S, 31°20'E

Petauke (=Old Petauke, 1901-44) ....760..............1431A ....14°03'S, 31°05'E

Poliya stream, Choma Dist..1130..............1727A ....17°01'S, 27°18'E

Probert's Point, Luangwa Dist. ....450..............1530A ....15°02'S, 30°14'E

Pumpa, Mbala Dist..1580..............0931B ....9°02'S, 31°34'E

Pwira (Mpulila) Pan, Kapiri Mposhi Dist....................................1200..............1327D ....13°44'S, 27°52'E

Rapid 23, Batoka Gorge, Kazungula Dist. 1825B

Ruckomechi (Rukomechi)/Zambezi River confl., *Zimbabwe* ....370 ....1529C ....15°50'S, 29°09'E

Rufunsa, Chongwe Dist. ....780..............1529B ....15°04'S, 29°38'E

Rufunsa Valley, Chongwe Dist...1429D

Rukuzye Dam, Chipata Dist. ....1010..............1332B ....13°21'S, 32°49'E

Rukuzye/Luangwa River confl, Lundazi Dist. ....540..............1232C ....@ 12°47'S, 32°02'E

Rukwa Valley, *Tanzania* ....*c.* 790..............0832A ....*c.* 8°20'S, 32°20'E

Rungwe Mtn, *Tanzania* ....2950..............0933B ....9°08'S, 33°40'E

Sachibonda (Sachibondu), Mwinilunga Dist. ....1420..............1124C ....11°31'S, 24°27'E

Sailunga, Mwinilunga Dist. ....1390..............1224B ....12°02'S, 24°53'E

Saise River, Mbala Dist. (IBA 36)..1520..............0831D ....8°58'S, 31°40'E

Sakala, Chongwe Dist. ....1090..............1528B ....15°14'S, 28°46'E

Sakeji airfield, Mwinilunga Dist...1360..............1124A ....11°14'S, 24°18'E

Sakeji stream (source), Mwinilunga Dist. ....1430..............1124A ....11°21'S, 24°16'E

Salujinga, Mwinilunga Dist. ....1280..............1024C ....10°58'S, 24°07'E

Samfya (Dist. H.Q.)..1180..............1129B ....11°22'S, 29°33'E

Sanjika Dambo, Chipata Dist..1210..............1332D ....13°43'S, 32°46'E

Sanjongo, Chavuma Dist...1080..............1322B ....13°05'S, 22°40'E

Savuti, Chobe N.P., *Botswana* ....960..............1824C ....18°32'S, 24°04'E

Sefula, Mongu Dist. ....1050..............1523A ....15°21'S, 23°12'E

Sekute (Kamangoza Sekute), Kazungula Dist. ....1020..............1725D ....17°35'S, 25°34'E

Semende, Sesheke Dist. ....990..............1723A ....17°26'S, 23°09'E

Sena, Zambezi River, *Mozambique* ....60..............1735A ....17°25'S, 35°01'E

Senanga (Dist. H.Q.) (*Map*, p. 1)..1050..............1623A ....16°07'S, 23°16'E

Senga Hill, Mbala Dist. ....1600-1780..............0931A ....9°25'S, 31°14'E

Sengwa Wildlife Research Area, *Zimbabwe*...........................800-950..............1828A ....18°10'S, 28°14'E

Senkobo, Livingstone Dist. ....1090..............1725D ....17°37'S, 25°56'E

Locality ....Alt. (m) ....Square ....Coordinates

Serenje (Dist. H.Q.) (*Map*, p. 1) ....1430...............1330A ....13°14'S, 30°14'E

Serenje (Old Serenje, 1900-1953), Serenje Dist. ....1390...............1330B ....13°10'S, 30°46'E

Sesheke (Dist. H.Q., from 1945) (*Map*, p. 1) ....950...............1724A ....17°28'S, 24°17'E

Sesheke (Old Sesheke=Mwandi, to 1945), Sesheke Dist. ....940...............1724D ....17°30'S, 24°48'E

Shangombo (Dist. H.Q.) ....1030...............1622A ....16°19'S, 22°05'E

Shebene (Shebele), Kawambwa Dist. ....1230...............1029A ....10°14'S, 29°20'E

Shikabeta (Shikaweta), Chongwe Dist. ....670...............1429D ....14°54'S, 29°43'E

Shitwe stream, Masaiti Dist. ....1330...............1328D ....*c.* 13°32'S, 28°51'E

Shiwa Ngandu (Lake Young), Chinsali Dist. (IBA 30) ....1400 ....1131B ....11°15'S, 31°46'E

Shoebill Is. (Bangweulu), Mpika Dist. ....1170...............1130C ....11°57'S, 30°11'E

Siameja, Sinazongwe Dist. ....500...............1727B ....17°06'S, 27°32'E

Siandi (Sianda) Mission, Senanga Dist. ....1030...............1523C ....15°34'S, 23°16'E

Sianzovu, Siavonga Dist. ....700...............1726D ....17°47'S, 26°54'E

Siavonga (Dist. H.Q.) ....490...............1628D ....16°32'S, 28°43'E

Sichifula River, Kazungula Dist. 1626C-1724D

Sichili, Sesheke Dist. ....1060...............1624D ....16°43'S, 24°57'E

Sihole, Kalabo Dist. ....1060...............1522B ....15°19'S, 22°34'E

Sikongo, Lukulu Dist. ....1030...............1423C ....14°45'S, 23°10'E

Sikongo, Kalabo Dist. ....1040...............1522A ....15°01'S, 22°10'E

Sililo, Kalabo Dist. ....1050...............1422A ....14°16'S, 22°29'E

Sililo, Sesheke Dist. ....980...............1724A ....17°28'S, 24°25'E

Silita, Lake, Senanga Dist. ....1040...............1523C ....15°37'S, 23°18'E

Siloana Plains, Shangombo Dist. ....1010...............1623C ....*c.* 16°48'S, 23°10'E

Silolo, Sesheke Dist. ....1030...............1724A ....17°23'S, 24°10'E

Silonga, Lukulu Dist. ....1020...............1423C ....14°44'S, 23°03'E

Simamba, Siavonga Dist. ....1050...............1625D ....16°40'S, 25°38'E

Simonga (Simoonga), Livingstone ....1020...............1725D ....17°48'S, 25°43'E

Simuhanga, Kalabo Dist. ....1040...............1522C ....15°32'S, 22°28'E

Simungoma, Sesheke Dist. (IBA 11) ....970...............1724B ....17°24'S, 24°41'E

Simwami, Kalomo Dist. ....1220...............1726A ....17°21'S, 26°11'E

Sinamalima, Sinazongwe Dist. ....520...............1727B ....17°02'S, 27°36'E

Sinazeze, Sinazongwe Dist. ....500...............1727A ....17°13'S, 27°25'E

Sinazongwe (Dist. H.Q.) ....540...............1727A ....17°16'S, 27°27'E

Sinde Mission, Kazungula Dist. ....1060...............1725D ....17°37'S, 25°50'E

Sinde/Zambezi River confl., Livingstone Dist. ....1030...............1725D ....17°50'S, 25°44'E

Sinjembela (Sinjembele), Shangombo Dist. ....990...............1723A ....17°19'S, 23°03'E

Sioma Falls, Shangombo Dist. ....1010...............1623D ....16°39'S, 23°34'E

Sioma-Ngwezi N.P. (IBA 10) ....970-1000...............1723A ....17°17'S, 23°27'E

Sitoti, Shangombo Dist. ....1010...............1623A ....16°20'S, 23°16'E

Sitoya, Lukulu Dist. ....1040...............1423C ....14°46'S, 23°29'E

Solwezi (Dist. H.Q.) (*Map*, p. 1) ....1330...............1226A ....12°10'S, 26°24'E

Songwe/Zambezi River confl., Livingstone Dist. ....970...............1725D ....17°58'S, 25°52'E

Sonso River, Sesheke Dist. ....1130...............1624A ....@ 16°03'S, 24°29'E

Locality ....**Alt. (m)** ....**Square** ....**Coordinates**

South Kashiji (Kasisi, Kasiji) River, Zambezi Dist. ....1060..............1322D ....@ 13°32'S, 22°39'E
South Luangwa N.P. (IBA 40) ....1231D, 1331B etc.
South Lueti River, Kalabo Dist. ....1040 ....1522C ....@ 15°38'S, 22°14'E
St Anthony's Mission, Mpongwe Dist...1160 ....1327B ....13°27'S, 27°56'E
Sumbi, Mbala Dist. ....1300..............0932A ....9°25'S, 32°05'E
Sumbu, Mpulungu Dist. ....760 ....0830C ....8°31'S, 30°29'E
Sumbu N.P. (IBA 35) 0830C,D
Sunzu Mtn, Mbala Dist. ....1770..............0931A ....9°03'S, 31°30'E
Supuni ferry, Kapiri Mposhi Dist...1120..............1427A ....14°18'S, 27°16'E
Suu, Senanga Dist. ....1050..............1522D ....15°48'S, 22°52'E
Suye, Lake, Lukanga Swamp, Kapiri Mposhi Dist. ....1120..............1427B ....14°16'S, 27°41'E
Swanandumba (Swanadongo), Kabompo Dist. ....1130..............1224D ....12°36'S, 24°33'E
Talabuku, Chongwe Dist..970..............1529B ....15°03'S, 29°51'E
Tatanda, *Tanzania*...1750..............0831C ....8°31'S, 31°30'E
Tatayoyo, Kafue N.P...1170..............1425C ....14°54'S, 25°28'E
Tembwe, Chama Dist. ....660..............1132B ....11°21'S, 32°53'E
Tena-tena camp, South Luangwa N.P. ....530..............1231D ....12°59'S, 31°55'E
Tiger camp, Lukulu Dist. ....1020..............1423C ....14°46'S, 23°01'E
Tondwa, Lake, Kaputa Dist. (IBA 35)...970..............0830C ....8°39'S, 30°08'E
Tongabezi, Livingstone Dist. ....1010..............1725D ....17°47'S, 25°42'E
Treetops school camp, Kafue N.P. ....1100..............1426A ....14°24'S, 26°02'E
Trotover farm, Leopardshill, Chongwe Dist. ....1250..............1528A ....15°26'S, 28°23'E
Tunduma, *Tanzania* ....1600..............0932B ....9°18'S, 32°46'E
Ufipa Plateau, *Tanzania* ....2260..............0731D ....7°58'S, 31°38'E
Uningi Pans, Mbala Dist. (IBA 37) ....1700-1800 ....0831C ....8°56'S, 31°22'E
Upemba, *Zaire*..540..............0826C ....*c.* 8°45'S, 26°30'E
Victoria Falls (Mosi-oa-Tunya N.P.) (IBA 13) ....880..............1725D ....17°55'S, 25°51'E
Viljoen's drift, Mteteshi River, Kabwe Dist. ....1160..............1428B ....14°16'S, 28°35'E
Vipama stream, Isoka Dist. ....1240 ....1033C,D ....10°43'S, 33°30'E
Viphya Plateau (South), *Malawi*..900-1950 ....1133D ....*c.* 11°50'S, 33°50'E
Vubwi (Vubwe), Chadiza Dist. ....890..............1432B ....14°02'S, 32°52'E
Vwaza Marsh, *Malawi* ....1100-1200 ....1133A ....*c.* 11°00'S, 33°30'E
Wasa, Lake, Kasanka N.P...1270..............1230C ....12°34'S, 30°17'E
Watopa, Lukulu/Kabompo Dists..1070..............1423B ....14°02'S, 23°38'E
West Lumwana River & Mission, Mwinilunga Dist. ....1460 ....1125C ....11°49'S, 25°08'E
West Lunga N.P. (IBA 5) ....1100-1400..............1224D
West Lunga River (*Map*, p. 2)
Wonder Gorge, Mkushi Dist. (IBA 24) ....500-1150..............1429C ....14°35'S, 29°05'E
Yakobe, Mambwe Dist...550..............1232C ....12°41'S, 32°08'E
Young, Lake, Shiwa Ngandu, Chinsali Dist. ....1560..............1131B ....11°15'S, 31°46'E
Yowela, Solwezi Dist. ....1340..............1127C ....11°48'S, 27°10'E
Zambezi River source, Mwinilunga Dist. (IBA 2)................1445-1490..............1124A ....11°22'S, 24°18'E
Zambezi Rapids, Mwinilunga Dist. ....1190..............1124A ....11°08'S, 24°10'E

Locality	Alt. (m)	Square	Coordinates
Zambezi (ex-Balovale) (Dist. H.Q.) (*Map*, p. 1)	1080	1323C	13°33'S, 23°07'E
Zambezi/Kafue River confl., Kafue/Siavonga Dists .	370	1528D	15°57'S, 28°54'E
Zambezi, Middle = from Luangwa town (Feira) to Victoria Falls			
Zambezi, Upper = from Livingstone upriver			
Zibamenda Pan, Siavonga Dist.	500	1628B	16°14'S, 28°36'E
Zimba, Kalomo Dist.	1220	1726A	17°19'S, 26°12'E
Zinza (Zinsa) stream, Mafinga Mts, Isoka Dist.	*c.* 1750	0933C	*c.* 9°58'S, 33°17'E
Zongwe River, Sinazongwe Dist.	520	1727A	17°16'S, 27°27'E
Zovochipolo, Nyika, *Malawi*	2200	1033D	10°35'S, 33°43'E

References

Alexander B. 1899. *Cinnyris shelleyi*, sp. n. *Bull. Brit. Orn. Club* 8: 54-55.
Alexander B. 1899-1900. An ornithological expedition to the Zambesi River. *Ibis* (7) 5: 549-583; 6: 70-109, 424-458.
Allen L.D.C. & Ansell W.F.H. 1966. The Secretary Bird (*Sagittarius serpentarius*) in the Luangwa Valley. *Puku* 4: 187-188.
Amadon D. 1954. A new race of *Chloropeta gracilirostris* Ogilvie-Grant. *Ostrich* 25: 140-141.
American Ornithologists' Union. 2007. Committee on Classification and Nomenclature of Birds (Middle and North America) Policy on English names of birds. *Auk* 124 (in press).
Angus A. & Wilson K.J. 1964. Observations on the diet of some game birds and Columbidae in Northern Rhodesia. I. The Helmeted Guineafowl (*Numida meleagris*). *Puku* 2: 1-9.
Anon. 1957. Alfred Sharpe's travels in the Northern Province and Katanga. *N. Rhod. J.* 3: 210-219.
Anon. (W.V. Brelsford) 1965. Chiengi-Rhodesia-Kalungwishi. *N. Rhod. J.* 6: 104-105.
Anon. 1971. *Meteorological Department Climatological summaries for Zambia*. Lusaka: Govt Printer.
Anon. 2006. Steppe waders faring better than expected. *WorldBirdwatch* 28 (4): 6.
Ansell W.F.H. 1978. *The mammals of Zambia*. Chilanga: Nat. Parks & Wildlife Service.
Ansell W.F.H. 1987. T.G.C. Vaughan-Jones, OBE, 1907-1986. *Oryx* 21: 134.
Aspinwall D.R. 1971a. Further records from the Nyika Plateau. *Bull. Zambian Orn. Soc.* 3: 5-8.
Aspinwall D.R. 1971b. Records from Mwinilunga District. *Bull. Zambian Orn. Soc.* 3: 29-35.
Aspinwall D.R. 1971c. Bird notes from the Luangwa Valley. *Bull. Zambian Orn. Soc.* 3: 57.
Aspinwall D.R. 1972a. Some sight records from the Middle Zambezi Valley. *Bull. Zambian Orn. Soc.* 4: 6-9.
Aspinwall D.R. 1972b. A Dark-backed Weaver population in the Zambezi Valley. *Bull. Zambian Orn. Soc.* 4: 19-20.
Aspinwall D.R. 1972c. Starlings in western Kalomo District. *Bull. Zambian Orn. Soc.* 4: 20-21.
Aspinwall D.R. 1973a. Notes from Northern Province. *Bull. Zambian Orn. Soc.* 5: 4-9.
Aspinwall D.R. 1973b. Sight record of a Great Sandplover *Charadrius leschenaultii*: a species new to Zambia. *Bull. Zambian Orn. Soc.* 5: 29.
Aspinwall D.R. 1973c. Spotted-flanked Barbet *Tricholaema lacrymosum*: a species new to Zambia. *Bull. Zambian Orn. Soc.* 5: 32.
Aspinwall D.R. 1973d. Sight records of Sharpe's Akalat *Sheppardia sharpei*. *Bull. Zambian Orn. Soc.* 5: 34.
Aspinwall D.R. 1973e. Sight record of a Bushveld Pipit *Anthus caffer*. *Bull. Zambian Orn. Soc.* 5: 36.
Aspinwall D.R. 1973f. Bird notes from five provinces. *Bull. Zambian Orn. Soc.* 5: 43-63.
Aspinwall D.R. 1974. Bird notes from Luapula Province. *Bull. Zambian Orn. Soc.* 6: 2-14.
Aspinwall D.R. 1975a. A record of overwintering *Oenanthe oenanthe* from Lusaka, Zambia. *Bull. Brit. Orn. Club* 95: 46-48.

Aspinwall D.R. 1975b. Notes on some birds in Zambia. *Bull. Zambian Orn. Soc.* 7: 39-67.

Aspinwall D.R. 1975c. Great Sandplover (*Charadrius leschenaultii*) and Eastern Golden Plovers (*Pluvialis dominicus*) at Lusaka. *Bull. Zambian Orn. Soc.* 7: 101-102.

Aspinwall D.R. 1976a. White-tailed Bush Lark in Gwembe District. *Bull. Zambian Orn. Soc.* 8: 23-24.

Aspinwall D.R. 1976b. Notes from the Mafinga Mountains. *Bull. Zambian Orn. Soc.* 8: 38-40.

Aspinwall D.R. 1976c. First records of Chestnut Wattle-eye (*Platysteira castanea*) in Zambia. *Bull. Zambian Orn. Soc.* 8: 65-66.

Aspinwall D.R. 1977a. The Rock Kestrel (*Falco tinnunculus*) in Zambia. *Bull. Zambian Orn. Soc.* 9: 1-10.

Aspinwall D.R. 1977b. First records of Fischer's Finch Lark *Eremopterix leucopareia* in Zambia. *Bull. Zambian Orn. Soc.* 9: 21-22.

Aspinwall D.R. 1977c. The Silvery-cheeked Hornbill (*Bycanistes brevis*) in Zambia. *Bull. Zambian Orn. Soc.* 9: 23-25.

Aspinwall D.R. 1977d. European Rockthrush at Mbala. *Bull. Zambian Orn. Soc.* 9: 25-26

Aspinwall D.R. 1977e. Isabelline Wheatears in eastern Zambia. *Bull. Zambian Orn. Soc.* 9: 26-28.

Aspinwall D.R. 1977f. Bird notes from Isoka District and adjacent areas. *Bull. Zambian Orn. Soc.* 9: 37-41.

Aspinwall D.R. 1977g. Black-winged Pratincoles (*Glareola nordmanni*) at Mwinilunga and Liuwa Plain. *Bull. Zambian Orn. Soc.* 9: 58-59.

Aspinwall D.R. 1977h. Palm-nut Vulture (*Gypohierax angolensis*) at Chipata. *Bull. Zambian Orn. Soc.* 9: 59-60.

Aspinwall D.R. 1978a. Bird notes from northern Nchelenge District. *Bull. Zambian Orn. Soc.* 10: 1-4.

Aspinwall D.R. 1978b. Lesser Black-backed Cisticolas in western Kaoma District. *Bull. Zambian Orn. Soc.* 10: 28-29.

Aspinwall D.R. 1978c. Striped Crakes and some other dambo birds near Lusaka. *Bull. Zambian Orn. Soc.* 10: 52-56.

Aspinwall D.R. 1979a. The Olive-headed Weaver (*Ploceus olivaceiceps*) in Zambia. *Bull. Zambian Orn. Soc.* 11 (1): 23.

Aspinwall D.R. 1979b. Bird notes from Zambezi District, North-Western Province. *Occ. Pap. Zambian Orn. Soc.* 2: 1-60.

Aspinwall D.R. 1980. Further tree nests of the Lesser Striped Swallow *Hirundo abyssinica*. *Bull. Zambian Orn. Soc.* 12: 32-33.

Aspinwall D.R. 1981. Grey Wagtail sighting in Zambia. *Ostrich* 52: 128.

Aspinwall D.R. 1983. Movement analysis charts. Comments on Cuckoo Weaver. *Zambian Orn. Soc. Newsl.* 13: 3-5.

Aspinwall D.R. 1984a. A record of three marsh cisticola species, *Cisticola galactotes, C. pipiens* and *C. tinniens* together in Western Province. *Bull. Zambian Orn. Soc.* 16: 15-16.

Aspinwall D.R. 1984b. Further records of Olive-headed Weaver *Ploceus olivaceiceps* in Zambia. *Bull. Zambian Orn. Soc.* 16: 17.

Aspinwall D. 1989. Spurwinged Plover *Vanellus spinosus* in northern Botswana. *Babbler* 18: 34-35.

Aspinwall D.R. ["D.R.A."] 1990. The Bushveld (or Little Tawny) Pipit *Anthus caffer* in Zambia. *Zambian Orn. Soc. Newsl.* 20: 58-61.

Aspinwall D.R. 1993a. Which White-bellied Sunbird occurs in plateau Mpika District? *Zambian Orn. Soc. Newsl.* 23: 18.

Aspinwall D.R. 1993b. Important Bird Areas. *Zambian Orn. Soc. Newsl.* 23: 151-153.

Aspinwall D.R. & Atkins J.D. 1978. July record of Didric Cuckoo (*Chrysococcyx caprius*). *Bull. Zambian Orn. Soc.* 10: 71.

Aspinwall D. & Hustler K. 1997. Status of the Madagascar Bee-eater in Zambia and Zimbabwe. *Honeyguide* 43: 153-163.

Aspinwall D.R., Madge S.G. & Tucker J.J. 1973. Further records from the Nyika Plateau. *Bull. Zambian Orn. Soc.* 5: 10-16.

Aspinwall D.R., Moulton J.P. & Stjernstedt R. 1995. Record of Solitary Sandpiper in Zambia. *Bull. Afr. Bird Club* 2: 106-107.

Atkins J.D. 1977. A Palm-nut Vulture in Lusaka Province. *Bull. Zambian Orn. Soc.* 9: 60-61.

Attwell R.I.G. 1959. The African Skimmer *Rhynchops flavirostris*: population counts and breeding in the Nsefu Game Reserve. *Ostrich* 30: 69-72.

Attwell R.I.G. 1963. Some observations on feeding habits, behaviour and inter-relationships of Northern Rhodesian vultures. *Ostrich* 34: 235-247.

Attwell R.I.G. 1966. Oxpeckers, and their associations with mammals in Zambia. *Puku* 4: 17-48.

Austin G.T. 1978. Pattern and timing of moult in penduline tits (*Anthoscopus*). *Ostrich* 49: 168-173.

Avian Demography Unit. 2001. White Storks: "Saturn" satellite tracking map. http://web. uct.ac.za/ depts/stats/ adu/wstork07.htm.

Baillie V.W. 1983. Additional comments on diving behaviour in Carmine Bee-eaters *Merops nubicus* from observations in the Luangwa Valley. *Bull. Zambian Orn. Soc.* 13/15: 128-129.

Baker N.E. 1994. The Spur-winged Plover *Vanellus spinosus* in Tanzania. *Scopus* 18: 130-132.

Becking J.H. 1988. The taxonomic status of the Madagascar Cuckoo *Cuculus* (*poliocephalus*) *rochii* and its occurrence on the African mainland, including southern Africa. *Bull. Brit. Orn. Club* 108: 195-206.

Beel C. ["CB"] 1992a. Species new to the Angolan list. *Zambian Orn. Soc. Newsl.* 22: 2.

Beel C. ["CB"] 1992b. Margaret's Batis in Western Province. *Zambian Orn. Soc. Newsl.* 22: 50.

Beel C. ["CB"] 1992c. How widespread is the Black-tailed Cisticola. *Zambian Orn. Soc. Newsl.* 22: 92.

Beel C. ["CB"] 1993. Some notes on Oustalet's White-bellied Sunbird. *Zambian Orn. Soc. Newsl.* 23: 71-72.

Beel C. 1994. Longclaws in the Luangwa Valley. *Zambian Orn. Soc. Newsl.* 24: 98-99.

Beel C. 1995. Zambian bird list becomes shorter – Mwinilunga specialities under threat. *Zambian Orn. Soc. Newsl.* 25: 89-90.

Beeston Bancroft G.W. 1957. What's in a name. *Black Lechwe* 1 (2): 29-30.

Belcher C.F. 1930. *The birds of Nyasaland*. London: Technical Press Ltd.

Bennun L. & Njoroge P. 1999. *Important Bird Areas in Kenya*. Nairobi: Nature Kenya.

Benson C.W. 1938. [Two new races]. *Bull. Brit. Orn. Club* 58: 112-113.

Benson C.W. 1939. A new lark from Nyasaland. *Bull. Brit. Orn. Club* 59: 85-86.

Benson C.W. 1940-41a. Further notes on Nyasaland birds (with particular reference to those of the Northern Province). *Ibis* (14) 4: 257-298, 387-433, 583-629; 5: 1-55.

Benson C.W. 1941b. A new cisticola from the Nyika plateau, Nyasaland. *Ostrich* 12: 28-29.

Benson C.W. 1945. New name for *Cisticola lais nyikae* Benson. *Bull. Brit. Orn. Club* 66: 16.

Benson C.W. 1946. On a change of coloration in *Lybius zombae* (Shelley). *Bull. Brit. Orn. Club* 67: 33-35.

Benson C.W. 1948a. The Long-legged Buzzard in Northern Rhodesia. *Bull. Brit. Orn. Club* 68: 147.

Benson C.W. 1948b. A new race of sunbird from Nyasaland. *Bull. Brit. Orn. Club* 69: 19-20.

Benson C.W. 1949a. Notes from the Lundazi District, Northern Rhodesia. *Bull. Brit. Orn. Club* 69: 58-60.

Benson C.W. 1949b. The systematics and migrations of the Pearl-breasted Swallow *Hirundo dimidiata* Sundevall. *Ostrich* 20: 137-145.

Benson C.W. 1951. Breeding and other notes from Nyasaland and the Lundazi District of Northern Rhodesia. *Bull. Mus. Comp. Zool. Harvard* 106 (2): 69-114.

Benson C.W. 1952a. Further new or unusual records from Northern Rhodesia. *Bull. Brit. Orn. Club* 72: 81-85.

Benson C.W. 1952b. Notes from Nyasaland (preliminary to publication of a check-list). *Ostrich* 23: 144-159.

Benson C.W. 1953. *A check list of the birds of Nyasaland*. Blantyre & Lusaka: Nyasaland Soc. & Publications Bureau.

Benson C.W. 1954. A new race of warbler from Northern Rhodesia. *Bull. Brit. Orn. Club* 74: 77-79.

Benson C.W. 1955a. New forms of pipit, longclaw, robin-chat, grass-warbler, sunbird, quail-finch and canary from Central Africa. *Bull. Brit. Orn. Club* 75: 101-109.

Benson C.W. 1955b. A note on *Pirenestes* Swainson, and description of a new species. *Bull. Brit. Orn. Club* 75: 109-110.

Benson C.W. 1956a. Notes from Central Africa. *Bull. Brit. Orn. Club* 76: 31-32.

Benson C.W. 1956b. The relationship of *Passer griseus* (Vieillot) and *Passer diffusus* (Smith), with the description of a new race of the latter. *Bull. Brit. Orn. Club* 76: 38-42.

Benson C.W. 1956c. Correspondence: display by Bateleur Eagle. *Ibis* 98: 138-139.

Benson C.W. 1956d. New or unusual records from Northern Rhodesia. *Ibis* 98: 595-605.

Benson C.W. 1956e. Breeding of the White Pelican in the Mweru Marsh, Northern Rhodesia, and elsewhere in eastern tropical Africa. *J. E. Afr. Nat. Hist. Soc.* 23 (1) (98): 103-104.

Benson C.W. 1956f. A contribution to the ornithology of Northern Rhodesia. *Occ. Pap. Nat. Mus. Sth. Rhod.* 3 (21B): 1-51.

Benson C.W. 1956g. The Joyful Bulbul *Chlorocichla laetissima* (Sharpe) and other new birds from Northern Rhodesia. *Rev. Zool. Bot. Afr.* 54: 118-120.

Benson C.W. 1957. Migrants at the south end of Lake Tanganyika. *Bull. Brit. Orn. Club* 77: 88.

Benson C.W. 1958a. Notes from Northern Rhodesia. *Bull. Brit. Orn. Club* 78: 90-93.

Benson C.W. 1958b. Birds from the Mwinilunga District, Northern Rhodesia. *Ibis* 100: 281-285.

Benson C.W. 1958c. Some additions and corrections to a *Check list of the birds of Northern Rhodesia. Occ. Pap. Nat. Mus. S. Rhod.* 22B: 190-197.

Benson C.W. 1959a. *Turturoena iriditorques* in the Mwinilunga District, Northern Rhodesia. *Ibis* 101: 240.

Benson C.W. 1959b. Northern Rhodesia Schools Exploration. Report on the expedition to Sesheke 1959. *N. Rhod. School's Explor. Soc. Rep.* 1959: 18-20.

Benson C.W. 1959c. Some additions and corrections to a *Check list of the birds of Northern Rhodesia.* Number 2. *Occ. Pap. Nat. Mus. S. Rhod.* 23B: 257-285.

Benson C.W. 1959d. Kafue excursion. *Ostrich* suppl. 3: 8-9.

Benson C.W. 1960a. Breeding of White Pelicans. *Afr. Wild Life* 14 (1): 81-82.

Benson C.W. 1960b. Breeding seasons of some game and protected birds in Northern Rhodesia. *Black Lechwe* 2 (5): 149-158.

Benson C.W. 1960c. Recent records from north-western Northern Rhodesia. *Bull. Brit. Orn. Club* 80: 106-112, 114-119.

Benson C.W. 1960d. Some additions and corrections to a *Check list of the birds of Northern Rhodesia.* Number 3. *Occ. Pap. Nat. Mus. S. Rhod.* 3 (24B): 343-350.

Benson C.W. 1961a. A note on *Euplectes axillaris. Bull. Brit. Orn. Club* 81: 6-8.

Benson C.W. 1961b. Jacanas and other birds perching on hippo. *Bull. Brit. Orn. Club* 81: 85-86.

Benson C.W. 1961c. Some notes from Northern Rhodesia. *Bull. Brit. Orn. Club* 81: 145-147.

Benson C.W. 1961d. The breeding of the Whale-headed Stork or Shoe-bill in Northern Rhodesia. *N. Rhod. J.* 4: 557-560.

Benson C.W. 1962a. Some additions and corrections to a *Check list of the birds of Northern Rhodesia.* Number 4. *Occ. Pap. Nat. Mus. Sth. Rhod.* 3 (26B): 631-652.

Benson C.W. 1962b. The food of the Spotted Eagle-Owl *Bubo africanus. Ostrich* 33 (4): 35.

Benson C.W. 1963. Breeding seasons of game birds in the Federation of Rhodesia and Nyasaland. *Puku* 1: 51-69.

Benson C.W. 1964a. A further revision of the races of Whyte's Barbet, *Buccanodon whytii* Shelley. *Arnoldia (Rhod.)* 1 (6): 1-4.

Benson C.W. 1964b. The European and African races of Baillon's Crake, *Porzana pusilla. Bull. Brit. Orn. Club* 84: 2-5.

Benson C.W. 1964c. The species of *Cercococcyx* in Mwinilunga, Northern Rhodesia. *Bull. Brit. Orn. Club* 84: 5-7.

Benson C.W. 1964d. *Alcedo quadribrachys* and *A. semitorquata* in the North-Western Province of Northern Rhodesia. *Bull. Brit. Orn. Club* 84: 67-69.

Benson C.W. 1964e. A new subspecies of Pink-billed Lark, *Calandrella conirostris* from Barotseland, Northern Rhodesia. *Bull. Brit. Orn. Club* 84: 106-107.

Benson C.W. 1964f. Some further records from Barotseland. *Bull. Brit. Orn. Club* 84: 108.

Benson C.W. 1964g. Some intra-African migratory birds. *Puku* 2: 53-66.

Benson C.W. 1965. The Grass-Owl and the Marsh-Owl. *Puku* 3: 175-176.

Benson C.W. 1966. The Madagascar Bee-eater *Merops superciliosus. Puku* 4: 189.

Benson C.W. 1967. Recent records of the White Stork, *C. ciconia*, from Zambia (formerly Northern Rhodesia). *Vogelwarte* 24: 38-40.

Benson C.W. 1969. A breeding record of the African Broadbill. *Puku* 5: 217.

Benson C.W. 1970. An accomplished collector: Jali Makawa. *Honeyguide* 63: 30-31.

Benson C.W. 1976. A breeding record of the Short-tailed Pipit (*Anthus brachyurus*). *Bull. Zambian Orn. Soc.* 8: 67.

Benson C.W. 1977. *Telacanthura ussheri benguellensis* in Zambia. *Bull. Brit. Orn. Club* 97: 135-136.

Benson M.J. 1978. Livingstone and wildlife. *Black Lechwe* 12 (5): 21-29.

Benson C.W. 1982. Migrants in the Afrotropical Region south of the equator. *Ostrich* 53: 31-49.

Benson C.W. & Benson F.M. 1975. Studies of some Malawi birds. *Arnoldia Rhod.* 7 (32): 1-27.

Benson C.W. & Benson F.M. 1977. *The birds of Malawi.* Limbe, Malawi: Montfort Press.

Benson C.W. & Dowsett R.J. 1969. The Madagascar Squacco Heron, *Ardeola idae*, in Zambia. *Puku* 5: 217.

Benson C.W. & Holliday C.S. 1964. Some further records from the North-Western Province of Northern Rhodesia. *Bull. Brit. Orn. Club* 84: 69-70.

Benson C.W. & Irwin M.P.S. 1960. A new form of *Apus barbatus* from the Victoria Falls. *Bull. Brit. Orn. Club* 80: 98-99.

Benson C.W. & Irwin M.P.S. 1964a. The migrations of the Pitta of eastern Africa (*Pitta angolensis longipennis*

Reichenow). *N. Rhod. J.* 5: 465-475.

Benson C.W. & Irwin M.P.S. 1964b. Some additions and corrections to a *Check list of the birds of Northern Rhodesia.* Number 5. *Occ. Pap. Nat. Mus. S. Rhod.* 27B: 106-127.

Benson C.W. & Irwin M.P.S. 1965a. The birds of *Cryptosepalum* forests, Zambia. *Arnoldia (Rhod.)* 1 (28): 1-12.

Benson C.W. & Irwin M.P.S. 1965b. Some birds from the North-Western Province, Zambia. *Arnoldia (Rhod.)* 1 (29): 1-11.

Benson C.W. & Irwin M.P.S. 1965c. The birds of *Marquesia* thickets in northern Mwinilunga District, Zambia. *Arnoldia (Rhod.)* 1 (30): 1-4.

Benson C.W. & Irwin M.P.S. 1965d. The genus *Rhinopomastus* in Zambia and adjacent territory. *Arnoldia (Rhod.)* 1 (31): 1-5.

Benson C.W. & Irwin M.P.S. 1965e. The Grey-backed Sparrow-Lark, *Eremopterix verticalis* (Smith). *Arnoldia (Rhod.)* 1 (36): 1-9.

Benson C.W. & Irwin M.P.S. 1965f. A new subspecies of Clapper Lark, *Mirafra apiata* from Barotseland. *Arnoldia (Rhod.)* 1 (37): 1-3.

Benson C.W. & Irwin M.P.S. 1965g. A new species of tinker-barbet from Northern Rhodesia. *Bull. Brit. Orn. Club* 85: 5-9.

Benson C.W. & Irwin M.P.S. 1965h. The River Warbler *Locustella fluviatilis* (Wolf) in Barotseland, south-western Zambia. *Bull. Brit. Orn. Club* 85: 116.

Benson C.W. & Irwin M.P.S. 1965i. Some intra-African migratory birds II. *Puku* 3: 45-55.

Benson C.W. & Irwin M.P.S. 1966a. The Common Quail *Coturnix coturnix* in the Ethiopian and Malagasy regions. *Arnoldia (Rhod.)* 2 (13): 1-14.

Benson C.W. & Irwin M.P.S. 1966b. The sunbirds *Nectarinia bouvieri* and *batesi. Bull. Brit. Orn. Club* 86: 62-65.

Benson C.W. & Irwin M.P.S. 1966c. The *Brachystegia* avifauna. *Ostrich* suppl. 6: 297-321.

Benson C.W. & Irwin M.P.S. 1966d. Some intra-African migratory birds, III. *Puku* 4: 49-56.

Benson C.W. & Irwin M.P.S. 1967a. The distribution and systematics of *Bubo capensis* Smith (Aves). *Arnoldia (Rhod.)* 3 (19): 1-19.

Benson C.W. & Irwin M.P.S. 1967b. A contribution to the ornithology of Zambia. *Zambia Mus. Pap.* 1: 1-139.

Benson C.W. & Irwin M.P.S. 1972a. The Thick-billed Cuckoo *Pachycoccyx audeberti* (Schlegel) (Aves: Cuculidae). *Arnoldia (Rhod.)* 5 (33): 1-24.

Benson C.W. & Irwin M.P.S. 1972b. Variation in tarsal and other measurements in *Otis denhami*, with some distributional notes. *Bull. Brit. Orn. Club* 92: 70-77.

Benson C.W. & Irwin M.P.S. 1974. The significance of records of the Common Sandpiper breeding in East Africa. *Bull. Brit. Orn. Club* 94: 20-21.

Benson C.W. & Irwin M.P.S. 1983. The breeding season of Cassin's Grey Flycatcher *Muscicapa cassini. Bull. Zambian Orn. Soc.* 13/15: 15.

Benson C.W. & Pitman C.R.S. 1956-57. Some breeding records from Northern Rhodesia. *Ool. Rec.* 30: 7-11, 21-27, 37-43; 31: 9-10.

Benson C.W. & Pitman C.R.S. 1958-59. Further breeding records from Northern Rhodesia. *Bull. Brit. Orn. Club* 78: 164-166; 79: 14-16, 18-22.

Benson C.W. & Pitman C.R.S. 1961. Further breeding records from Northern Rhodesia (No. 2). *Bull. Brit. Orn. Club* 81: 156-163.

Benson C.W. & Pitman C.R.S. 1963. Further breeding records from Northern Rhodesia (No. 3). *Bull. Brit. Orn. Club* 83: 32-36.

Benson C.W. & Pitman C.R.S. 1964. Further breeding records from Northern Rhodesia (No. 4). *Bull. Brit. Orn. Club* 84: 54-60.

Benson C.W. & Pitman C.R.S. 1966. Further breeding records from Zambia (formerly Northern Rhodesia) (No. 5). *Bull. Brit. Orn. Club* 86: 21-33.

Benson C.W. & Serventy D.L. 1956. Breeding data from Katema Island, Northern Rhodesia. *Ostrich* 27: 171-172.

Benson C.W. & Smithers R.H.N. 1958. The Teita Falcon *Falco fasciinucha* Reichenow & Neumann at the Victoria Falls. *Ostrich* 29: 57-58.

Benson C.W. & White C.M.N. 1957. *Check list of the birds of Northern Rhodesia.* Lusaka: Govt Printer.

Benson C.W. & White C.M.N. 1960. Discontinuous distribution (Aves). *Proc. 1 Fed. Sci. Congr. (Salisbury)*: 195-216.

Benson C.W. & White C.M.N. 1962. *Erythropygia quadrivirgata* and allied species. *Bull. Brit. Orn. Club* 82: 72-75.

Benson C.W., Grimwood I.R. & Maclaren P.I.R. 1955. Further records of waders in Northern Rhodesia. *Bull. Brit. Orn. Club* 75: 80-81.

Benson C.W., Boulton R. & Irwin M.P.S. 1961. Some records from the Mpika and Serenje Districts, Northern Rhodesia. *Bull. Brit. Orn. Club* 81: 3-5.

Benson C.W., Irwin M.P.S. & White C.M.N. 1962. The significance of valleys as avian zoogeographical barriers. *Ann. Cape Prov. Mus.* 2: 155-189.

Benson C.W., Brooke R.K. & Vernon C.J. 1964 Bird breeding data for the Rhodesias and Nyasaland. *Occ. Pap. Nat. Mus. S. Rhod.* 27B: 30-105.

Benson C.W., Brooke R.K., Dowsett R.J. & Irwin M.P.S. 1970. Notes on the birds of Zambia: Part V. *Arnoldia (Rhod.)* 4 (40): 1-59.

Benson C.W., Brooke R.K., Dowsett R.J. & Irwin M.P.S. 1971a. *The birds of Zambia.* London: Collins.

Benson C.W., Brooke R.K. & Irwin M.P.S. 1971b. The Slatey Egret *Egretta vinaceigula* is a good species. *Bull. Brit. Orn. Club* 91: 131-133.

Beresford P., Barker F.K., Ryan P.G. & Crowe T.M. 2005. African endemics span the tree of songbirds (Passeri): molecular systematics of several evolutionary 'enigmas'. *Proc. R. Soc.* B 272: 849-858.

Berry P.S.M. 1972. White-backed Duck in the Middle Zambezi Valley. *Bull. Zambian Orn. Soc.* 4: 23.

Berry P.S.M. 1974. Slaty Egret (*Egretta vinaceigula*) in the Bangweulu Swamps. *Bull. Zambian Orn. Soc.* 6: 49.

Berry P.S.M. 1981a. More Luangwa Valley notes. *Bull. Zambian Orn. Soc.* 12: 55-61.

Berry P.S.M. 1981b. Cape and Long-tailed Wagtails in the Luangwa Valley. *Bull. Zambian Orn. Soc.* 12: 69-70.

Berry P.S.M. 1983. Additional Luangwa Valley records. *Bull. Zambian Orn. Soc.* 13/15: 129-134.

Berry P.S.M. 1984. Sex and age composition of an unusual gathering of Saddlebill Storks. *Bull. Zambian Orn. Soc.* 16: 13-14.

Berry P.S.M. 1994. Longclaws of the Luangwa Valley. *Zambian Orn. Soc. Newsl.* 24: 143.

Berry P.S.M. & Ansell P.D.H. 1978. African Pitta (*Pitta angolensis*) displaying in the upper Luangwa Valley. *Bull. Zambian Orn. Soc.* 10: 29.

Berry P.S.M. & Dowsett R.J. 2003. Pel's Fishing Owl, *Scotopelia peli*, preying on a small crocodile. *Ostrich* 74: 133.

Berry P.S.M. & Robinson G.P. 1979. Notes from the Luangwa Valley. *Bull. Zambian Orn. Soc.* 11 (1): 1-2.

Berwick D. 1954. "Mystery Isle", Mweru Marsh. *N. Rhod. J.* 2 (3): 56-59.

Bingham M. 2000. Protea Hill notes. *Zambian Orn. Soc. Newsl.* 30 (2): 2.

BirdLife International. 2000. *Threatened birds of the World.* Barcelona & Cambridge, UK: Lynx Edicions & BirdLife International.

BirdLife International. 2004a. *Threatened birds of the world.* CD-ROM. Cambridge, UK: BirdLife International.

BirdLife International. 2004b. *Birds in Europe: population estimates, trends and conservation status.* Cambridge, UK: BirdLife International.

Black H.L., Howard G. & Stjernstedt R. 1979. Observations on the feeding behavior of the Bat Hawk (*Macheiramphus alcinus*). *Biotropica* 11: 18-21.

Böhning-Gaese K., Schuda M.D. & Helbig A.J. 2003. Weak phylogenetic effects on ecological niches of *Sylvia* warblers. *J. Evol. Biol.* 16: 956-965.

Boileau E.R.F. 1899. The Nyasa-Tanganyika Plateau. *Geogr. J.* 13 (6): 577-595, map opp. p. 692.

Bourdin P. 1996. Frank's Lakes – South Luangwa National Park. *Zambian Orn. Soc. Newsl.* 26: 84.

Bowen P. St J. 1977a. European Swift mortality on migration. *Bull. Zambian Orn. Soc.* 9: 61.

Bowen P. St J. 1977b. Large-scale movements of Yellow-billed Kites – a cautionary note. *Bull. Zambian Orn. Soc.* 9: 62-63.

Bowen P. St J. 1977c. A large concentration of Pennant-winged Nightjars in Mwinilunga District. *Bull. Zambian Orn. Soc.* 9: 63-64.

Bowen P. St J. 1978. A large flock of Red-throated Cliff Swallow (*Hirundo rufigula*) at Mwinilunga. *Bull. Zambian Orn. Soc.* 10: 30.

Bowen P. St J. 1979a. An old August record of the European Hobby (*Falco subbuteo*) at Mwinilunga. *Bull. Zambian Orn. Soc.* 11 (1): 24.

Bowen P. St J. 1979b. The spread of the Red-throated Cliff Swallow (*Hirundo rufigula*) in North-Western Province. *Bull. Zambian Orn. Soc.* 11 (1): 24-25.

Bowen P. St J. 1979c. The African Rock Martin (*Hirundo rufigula*) at Kalene Hill, Mwinilunga District. *Bull.*

Zambian Orn. Soc. 11 (1): 28-29.

Bowen P. St J. 1979d. The rediscovery of Margaret's Batis (*Batis margaritae*) at Mwinilunga. *Bull. Zambian Orn. Soc.* 11 (1): 29.

Bowen P. St J. 1979e. Some notes on Margaret's Batis (*Batis margaritae*) in Zambia. *Bull. Zambian Orn. Soc.* 11 (2): 1-10.

Bowen P. St J. 1979f. Brown-chested Wattled Plover *Vanellus superciliosus* at Mwinilunga; a new species for Zambia. *Bull. Zambian Orn. Soc.* 11 (2): 33.

Bowen P. St J. 1979g. A large flock of Western Red-footed Falcons at Mwinilunga. *Bull. Zambian Orn. Soc.* 11 (2): 38-41.

Bowen P. St J. 1980a. Large movements of the Yellow-billed Kite *Milvus migrans parasitus* at Mwinilunga at the start of the rains. *Bull. Zambian Orn. Soc.* 12: 1-3.

Bowen P. St J. 1980b. Cassin's Grey Flycatcher *Muscicapa cassini* in Mwinilunga District. *Bull. Zambian Orn. Soc.* 12: 4-7.

Bowen P. St J. 1980c. The first records of the White Stork *Ciconia ciconia* from Mwinilunga. *Bull. Zambian Orn. Soc.* 12: 34-35.

Bowen P. St J. 1980d. A Red-backed Shrike *Lanius collurio* impaling prey on thorns in Zambia. *Bull. Zambian Orn. Soc.* 12: 36-37.

Bowen P. St J. 1980e. The birds of *Cryptosepalum* forest near Mwinilunga. *Bull. Zambian Orn. Soc.* 12: 48-54.

Bowen P. St J. 1983a. The first records of the Black-winged Bishop *Euplectes hordeaceus* from Mwinilunga District. *Bull. Zambian Orn. Soc.* 13/15: 2-3.

Bowen P. St J. 1983b. The Black-collared Bulbul *Neolestes torquatus* in Mwinilunga District and the first Zambian breeding record. *Bull. Zambian Orn. Soc.* 13/15: 7-15.

Bowen P. St J. 1983c. The White-chinned Prinia *Prinia leucopogon* in Mwinilunga District. *Bull. Zambian Orn. Soc.* 13/15: 16-22.

Bowen P. St J. 1983d. The status of the Namaqua Dove *Oena capensis* in Mwinilunga District. *Bull. Zambian Orn. Soc.* 13/15: 22.

Bowen P. St J. 1983e. Some observations on the Black-and-rufous Swallow *Hirundo nigrorufa* in Zambia. *Bull. Zambian Orn. Soc.* 13/15: 23-35.

Bowen P. St J. 1983f. The Red-breasted Wryneck *Jynx ruficollis* in Zambia. *Bull. Zambian Orn. Soc.* 13/15: 35-41.

Bowen P. St J. 1983g. The Larklike Bunting *Emberiza impetuani* in Mwinilunga District. *Bull. Zambian Orn. Soc.* 13/15: 41-43.

Bowen P. St J. 1983h. Palaearctic migrants in Mwinilunga District, North-Western Province. *Bull. Zambian Orn. Soc.* 13/15: 43-84.

Bowen P. St J. 1983i. Some first records from Mwinilunga District, North-Western Province. *Bull. Zambian Orn. Soc.* 13/15: 84-104.

Bowen P. St J. 1983j. Notes on the status of certain species in Mwinilunga District, North-Western Province. *Bull. Zambian Orn. Soc.* 13/15: 104-121.

Bowen P. St J. & Colebrook-Robjent J.F.R. 1984. The nest and eggs of the Black-and-rufous Swallow *Hirundo nigrorufa*. *Bull. Brit. Orn. Club* 104: 146-147.

Bowie R.C.K., Fjeldså J., Hackett S.J. & Crowe T.M. 2004. Molecular evolution in space and through time: mtDNA phylogeography of the Olive Sunbird (*Nectarinia olivacea/obscura*) throughout continental Africa. *Mol. Phylogenet. Evol.* 33: 56-74.

Bowmaker A.P. 1963. Cormorant predation on two Central African lakes. *Ostrich* 34: 2-26.

Brelsford V. 1941. Field-notes on some Northern Rhodesian birds. *Ibis* (14) 5: 161-172.

Brelsford W.V. 1942. Further field notes on Northern Rhodesian birds. *Ibis* (14) 6: 83-90.

Brelsford W.V. 1943. Field observations, Northern Province, Northern Rhodesia. *Ostrich* 14: 170-178.

Brelsford W.V. 1946. Ecological aspects of the bird life in the Bangweulu area. *Ostrich* 17: 165-171.

Brelsford V. 1947. Notes on the birds of the Lake Bangweulu area in Northern Rhodesia. *Ibis* 89: 57-77.

Brelsford W.V. 1955. The problem of Mweru-wantipa. *N. Rhod. J.* 2 (5): 3-15.

Brelsford W.V. ["Anon."] 1965. Chiengi-Rhodesia-Kulungwishi. *N. Rhod. J.* 6: 104-105.

Brewster C.A. 2007. Records of Melodious Lark *Mirafra cheniana*, Cloud Cisticola *Cisticola textrix* and Bokmakierie *Telophorus zeylonus* in the Pitsane grasslands, southeastern Botswana. *Babbler* 49: 55-57.

Britton P.L. 1968. Two African species pairs. *Bull. Brit. Orn. Club* 88: 163-166.

Britton P.L. 1969. Weights of the Pennant-winged Nightjar. *Bull. Brit. Orn. Club* 89: 21-24.

Britton P.L. 1970. Birds of the Balovale District of Zambia. *Ostrich* 41: 145-190.

Britton P.L. 1971. On the apparent movements of *Cossypha natalensis. Bull. Brit. Orn. Club* 91: 137-144.

Britton P.L. 1973. Seasonal movements of the black cuckoo-shrikes *Campephaga phoenicea* and *C. flava*, especially in eastern Africa. *Bull. Brit. Orn. Club* 93: 41-48.

Britton P.L. (Ed.). 1980. *Birds of East Africa.* Nairobi: E. Afr. Nat. Hist. Soc.

Britton P.L. & Dowsett R.J. 1969. More weights of the Carmine Bee-eater. *Bull. Brit. Orn. Club* 89: 85-86.

Brogger-Jensen S. 1977. First record of Temminck's Stint (*Calidris temminckii*) in Zambia. *Bull. Zambian Orn. Soc.* 9: 23.

Brooke R.K. 1963. Little and Palm Swifts breeding on man-made structures in Rhodesia. *Ostrich* 34: 27-35.

Brooke R.K. 1964. Avian observations on a journey across Central Africa and additional information on some of the species seen. *Ostrich* 35: 277-292.

Brooke R.K. 1965. Notes, chiefly distributional, on some birds in the Kafue National Park. *Puku* 3: 59-65.

Brooke R.K. 1966a. The Bat-like Spinetail *Chaetura boehmi* Schalow (Aves). *Arnoldia* (*Rhod.*) 2 (29): 1-18.

Brooke R.K. 1966b. Is *Schoenicola platyura brevirostris* (Sundevall) a migrant? *Ostrich* 37: 214-215.

Brooke R.K. 1966c. A preliminary list of the birds of the Kafue National Park. *Puku* 4: 57-86.

Brooke R.K. 1967a. On the moults and breeding season of the Long-tailed Starling *Lamprotornis mevesii* (Wahlberg). *Bull. Brit. Orn. Club* 87: 2-5.

Brooke R.K. 1967b. Further breeding records from Zambia (No. 6). *Bull. Brit. Orn. Club* 87: 120-122.

Brooke R.K. 1969. The African Hobby, *Falco cuvierii*, at Livingstone. *Puku* 5: 219.

Brooke R.K. 1970. An early ornithologist — L.B. Mouritz. *Honeyguide* 61: 30.

Brooke R.K. 1972a. An out of season breeding record of *Aquila wahlbergi* from Zambia. *Bull. Brit. Orn. Club* 92: 97.

Brooke R.K. 1972b. Geographical variation in Palm Swifts *Cypsiurus* spp. (Aves: Apodidae). *Durban Mus. Novit.* 9 (15): 217-231.

Brooke R.K. 1973. Distributional and biological notes on the Mottled Swift in Rhodesia. *Ostrich* 44: 106-110.

Brooke R.K. 1974a. The Spotted Crake *Porzana porzana* (Aves: Rallidae) in south-central and southern Africa. *Durban Mus. Novit.* 10 (3): 43-52.

Brooke R.K. 1974b. The migratory Black Kite *Milvus migrans migrans* (Aves: Accipitridae) of the Palaearctic in southern Africa. *Durban Mus. Novit.* 10 (4): 53-66.

Brooke R.K. 1982. Obituary. Constantine Walter Benson 1909-1982. *Ostrich* 53: 254-255.

Brooke R.K. & Herroelen P. 1988. The non-breeding range of southern African bred European Bee-eaters *Merops apiaster. Ostrich* 59: 63-66.

Brooke R.K. & Hougaard P. 1971. The Madagascar Bee-eater breeding in Rhodesia. *Ostrich* 42: 230.

Brooke R.K. & Kemp A.C. 1973. Specimen data on *Bucorvus leadbeateri. Bull. Brit. Orn. Club* 93: 89-92.

Brooke R.K. & Vernon C.J. 1961a. Aspects of the breeding biology of the Rock Martin. *Ostrich* 32: 51-52.

Brooke R.K. & Vernon C.J. ["J.C."] 1961b. The Little Swift and others at Kasama. *Ostrich* 32: 128-133.

Brooke R.K. & Vernon C.J. 1981. Early names and records of two small *Hieraaetus* eagles (Aves: Accipitridae) in the Cape Province of South Africa. *Ann. Cape Prov. Mus.* 13: 133-139.

Brooke R.K., Grobler J.H., Irwin M.P.S. & Steyn P. 1972. A study of the migratory eagles *Aquila nipalensis* and *A. pomarina* (Aves: Accipitridae) in southern Africa, with comparative notes on other large raptors. *Occ. Pap. Nat. Mus. Sth. Rhod.* B5 (2): 61-114.

Brosset A. & Erard C. 1986. *Les oiseaux des régions forestières du nord-est du Gabon.* Vol.1: Ecologie et comportement des espèces. Paris: Soc. Natl. Protection de la Nature.

Brown H.D. 1957. The breeding of the Lesser Flamingo in the Mweru Wantipa, Northern Rhodesia. *Ibis* 99: 688-692.

Browning M.R. 1992. Comments on the nomenclature and dates of publication of some taxa in Bucerotidae. *Bull. Brit. Orn. Club* 112: 22-27.

Bruce M.D. & Dowsett R.J. 2004. The correct name of the Afrotropical mainland subspecies of Barn Owl *Tyto alba. Bull. Brit. Orn. Club* 124: 184-187.

Bruce-Miller W.F. & Bruce-Miller M. 1972. Shaft-tailed Widow in Namwala District. *Bull. Zambian Orn. Soc.* 4: 23.

Bruce-Miller W.F. & Bruce-Miller M. 1975. Sombre Bulbul (*Andropadus importunus*) in Namwala District. *Bull. Zambian Orn. Soc.* 7: 24.

Bruce-Miller W.F. & Dowsett R.J. 1977. Observations from south-western Zambia. *Bull. Zambian Orn. Soc.* 9: 42-49.

Burton M. & Benson C.W. 1961. The Whale-headed Stork or Shoe-bill: legend and fact. *N. Rhod. J.* 4: 411-426.

Butler R. 1989. Chirping Cisticola in Zimbabwe. *Honeyguide* 35: 119.

Button E.L. ("J.") 1942. Grey Kestrel (*Dissodectes dickinsoni*). *Ostrich* 13: 169-172.

Button E. 1953. The Nyasa Rosy-cheeked Love Bird. *N. Rhod. J.* 2 (1): 37-42.

Button E.L. 1973. The Common Snipe *Gallinago gallinago* in Zambia. *Bull. Brit. Orn. Club* 93: 174.

Buxton L., Slater J. & Brown L.H. 1978. The breeding behaviour of the shoebill or whale-headed stork *Balaeniceps rex* in the Bangweulu Swamps, Zambia. *E. Afr. Wildl. J.* 16: 201-220.

Campbell N.A. 1965. Sight record of a Whimbrel in Zambia. *Ostrich* 36: 96-97.

Carcasson R.H. 1964. A preliminary survey of the zoogeography of African butterflies. *E. African Wildlife J.* 2: 122-157.

Carruthers J. 2001. *Wildlife & warfare. The life of James Stevenson-Hamilton.* Pietermaritzburg: Univ. Natal Press.

Carter C. 1973. A visit to Mwinilunga District. *Bull. Zambian Orn. Soc.* 5: 74.

Carter C. 1975. Some bird records from the Nyika Plateau. *Bull. Zambian Orn. Soc.* 7: 3-4.

Casalis de Pury R.J. 1979. Grey Wagtail *Motacilla cinerea* at Mwekera. *Bull. Zambian Orn. Soc.* 11 (2): 44-45.

Casalis de Pury R.J. & Taylor P.B. 1980. Exceptional numbers of Pintail *Anas acuta* at Luanshya, Zambia in 1979/1980. *Scopus* 4: 90-92.

Chapin J.P. 1932. The birds of the Belgian Congo. Part 1. *Bull. Amer. Mus. Nat. Hist.* 65: 1-756.

Chapin J.P. 1952. A new race of *Muscicapa aquatica* Heuglin, from Northern Rhodesia. *Bull. Brit. Orn. Club* 72: 21-22.

Chapin J.P. 1953. The birds of the Belgian Congo. Part 3. *Bull. Amer. Mus. Nat. Hist.* 75A: 1-821.

Chapin J.P. 1954. The birds of the Belgian Congo. Part 4. *Bull. Amer. Mus. Nat. Hist.* 75B: 1-846.

Chappuis C. 2000. *Oiseaux d'Afrique. 2. West and Central Africa.* (11 CDs). Paris: Société d'Etudes Ornithologiques de France.

Chappuis C., Erard C. & Morel G.J. 1979. Données comparatives sur la morphologie et les vocalisations des diverses formes d'*Eupodotis ruficrista* (Smith). *Malimbus* 1: 74-89.

Charge P. 1998. A Grey-winged Robin *Cossypha polioptera* nest. *Zambia Bird Rep.* 1997: 53.

Cibois A. 2003. *Sylvia* is a babbler: taxonomic implications for the families Sylviidae and Timaliidae. *Bull. Brit. Orn. Club* 123: 257-261.

Clancey P.A. 1951. Notes on birds of the South African subcontinent. *Ann. Natal Mus.* 12: 137-152.

Clancey P.A. 1954. Miscellaneous taxonomic notes on African birds 4. Three new geographical races of the African Fiscal Shrike *Lanius collaris* Linnaeus. *Durban Mus. Novit.* 4: 77-86.

Clancey P.A. 1962. A new race of *Myioparus plumbeus* (Hartlaub). *Bull. Brit. Orn. Club* 82: 61-63.

Clancey P.A. 1963a. Miscellaneous taxonomic notes on African birds XX. 1. The South African races of the broadbill *Smithornis capensis* (Smith). *Durban Mus. Novit.* 6 (19): 231-241.

Clancey P.A. 1963b. Taxonomic notes on southern African *Acrocephalus baeticatus* (Vieillot). *Ostrich* 34: 168-169.

Clancey P.A. 1964a. Miscellaneous taxonomic notes on African birds XXI. Geographical variation in the Goaway Bird *Corythaixoides concolor* (Smith). *Durban Mus. Novit.* 7 (5): 125-130.

Clancey P.A. 1964b. Miscellaneous taxonomic notes on African birds XXI. [3.] The geographical races of the Yellow-throated Sparrow *Petronia superciliaris* (Blyth). *Durban Mus. Novit.* 7 (5): 132-137.

Clancey P.A. 1966. A Catalogue of birds of the South African sub-region. (Part IV). *Durban Mus. Novit.* 7 (12): 465-544.

Clancey P.A. 1967. On variation in *Nectarinia talatala* (Smith). *Bull. Brit. Orn. Club* 87: 153-157.

Clancey P.A. 1968a. Variation in *Ardeola ralloides* (Scopoli) (Aves-Ardeidae). *Arnoldia* (*Rhod.*) 3 (37): 1-5.

Clancey P.A. 1968b. Seasonal movement and variation in the southern populations of the Dusky Lark *Pinarocorys nigricans* (Sundevall). *Bull. Brit. Orn. Club* 88: 166-171.

Clancey P.A. 1968c. Subspeciation in some birds from Rhodesia. *Durban Mus. Novit.* 8 (11): 115-152; (12) 153-182.

Clancey P.A. 1969a. A Catalogue of birds of the South African sub-region. Supplement No. 1. *Durban Mus. Novit.* 8 (16): 275-324.

Clancey P.A. 1969b. On the status of *Coracias weigalli* Dresser, 1890. *Ostrich* 40: 156-162.

Clancey P.A. 1970a. Miscellaneous taxonomic notes on African birds XXVIII. A further subspecies of *Lanius souzae* Bocage. *Durban Mus. Novit.* 8 (17): 340-344.

Clancey P.A. 1970b. Miscellaneous taxonomic notes on African birds XXVIII. On the status and range of *Euplectes progne delacouri* Wolters, 1953. *Durban Mus. Novit.* 8 (17): 344-348.

Clancey P.A. 1970c. Miscellaneous taxonomic notes on African birds XXVIII. The present taxon *Lagonosticta rhodopareia jamesoni* Shelley, a composite of two minor subspecies. *Durban Mus. Novit.* 8 (17): 348-351.

Clancey P.A. 1970d. Miscellaneous taxonomic notes on African birds XXIX. A name for a form of Greater Honeyguide. *Durban Mus. Novit.* 8 (20): 377-378.

Clancey P.A. 1970e. Miscellaneous taxonomic notes on African birds XXIX. Variation in weavers of the *Ploceus cucullatus spilonotus/nigriceps* complex. *Durban Mus. Novit.* 8 (20): 378-390.

Clancey P.A. 1970f. Miscellaneous taxonomic notes on African birds XXX. Variation in the southern African populations of the Laughing Dove *Streptopelia senegalensis* (Linnaeus). *Durban Mus. Novit.* 9 (1): 1-8.

Clancey P.A. 1971a. Miscellaneous taxonomic notes on African birds XXXII. On the present nominate subspecies of *Merops superciliosus* Linnaeus. *Durban Mus. Novit.* 9 (5): 39-44.

Clancey P.A. 1971b. Miscellaneous taxonomic notes on African birds XXXIII. Variation in Kittlitz's Sandplover *Charadrius pecuarius* Temminck. *Durban Mus. Novit.* 9 (9): 109-112.

Clancey P.A. 1971c. Miscellaneous taxonomic notes on African birds XXXIII. Comments on the Southern African Caspian terns *Hydroprogne caspia* (Pallas). *Durban Mus. Novit.* 9 (9): 118-120.

Clancey P.A. 1971d. On the South African race of the Little Spotted Woodpecker. *Ostrich* 42: 119-122.

Clancey P.A. 1972a. A catalogue of birds of the South African sub-region. Supplement No. 2. *Durban Mus. Novit.* 9 (12): 163-200.

Clancey P.A. 1972b. Miscellaneous taxonomic notes on African birds XXXV. On the range of *Amblyospiza albifrons albifrons* (Vigors), 1831. *Durban Mus. Novit.* 9 (16): 245-249.

Clancey P.A. 1973. Miscellaneous taxonomic notes of African birds XXXVII. The Great Spotted Cuckoo in southern Africa. *Durban Mus. Novit.* 10 (1): 1-11.

Clancey P.A. 1974a. Subspeciation studies in some Rhodesian birds. *Arnoldia Rhod.* 6 (28): 1-43.

Clancey P.A. 1974b. Miscellaneous taxonomic notes on African birds XXXIX. Subspeciation in *Trachyphonus vaillantii* Ranzani, 1821. *Durban Mus. Novit.* 10 (7): 87-95.

Clancey P.A. 1974c. Miscellaneous taxonomic notes on African birds XXXIX. Variation in the Bearded Scrub Robin *Erythropygia barbata* (Hartlaub and Finsch), 1870. *Durban Mus. Novit.* 10 (7): 95-98.

Clancey P.A. 1974d. Miscellaneous taxonomic notes on African birds XXXIX. Variation in *Eremomela atricollis* Bocage, 1894. *Durban Mus. Novit.* 10 (7): 98-101.

Clancey P.A. 1975. Miscellaneous taxonomic notes on African birds XLIII. Subspeciation in the Sharpbilled or Wahlberg's Honeyguide *Prodotiscus regulus* Sundevall. *Durban Mus. Novit.* 11 (1): 9-15.

Clancey P.A. 1977a. Miscellaneous taxonomic notes on African birds XLVII. The characters and range limits of the nominate subspecies of *Indicator minor* Stephens. *Durban Mus. Novit.* 11 (10): 181-187.

Clancey P.A. 1977b. Miscellaneous taxonomic notes on African birds XLVIII. On southern African *Indicator variegatus* Lesson. Durban Mus. Novit. 11 (11): 213-215.

Clancey P.A. 1977c. Miscellaneous taxonomic notes on African birds XLVIII. A further subspecies of *Indicator exilis* (Cassin). *Durban Mus. Novit.* 11 (11): 215-217.

Clancey P.A. 1977d. Miscellaneous taxonomic notes on African birds XLIX. Variation in the southern populations of *Bubalornis niger* A. Smith, 1836. *Durban Mus. Novit.* 11 (12): 229-238.

Clancey P.A. 1977e. Miscellaneous taxonomic notes on African birds L. The southern African races of the Redcapped Lark *Calandrella cinerea* (Gmelin). *Durban Mus. Novit.* 11 (14): 252-258.

Clancey P.A. 1978a. Miscellaneous taxonomic notes on African birds LI. Further comments on variation in *Alcedo semitorquata* Swainson, 1823. *Durban Mus. Novit.* 11 (16): 272-277.

Clancey P.A. 1978b. Miscellaneous taxonomic notes on African birds LII. The south-central and south-eastern populations of *Cisticola erythrops* (Hartlaub). *Durban Mus. Novit.* 11 (19): 312-317.

Clancey P.A. 1978c. Miscellaneous taxonomic notes on African birds LII. On the southern and eastern races of *Nectarinia olivacea* (Smith), 1840. *Durban Mus. Novit.* 11 (19): 317-327.

Clancey P.A. 1979. Miscellaneous taxonomic notes on African birds LIII. The subspecies of the Scalythroated Honeyguide *Indicator variegatus* Lesson. *Durban Mus. Novit.* 12 (1): 11-15.

Clancey P.A. 1980a. Miscellaneous taxonomic notes on African birds LVI. Variation in *Nicator gularis* Hartlaub and Finsch. *Durban Mus. Novit.* 12 (10): 129-134.

Clancey P.A. 1980b. Miscellaneous taxonomic notes on African birds LVIII. The mainland Afrotropical subspecies of the Little Swift *Apus affinis* (Gray). *Durban Mus. Novit.* 12 (13): 151-156.

Clancey P.A. 1980c. Miscellaneous taxonomic notes on African birds LVIII. On the Lesser Grey Shrike *Lanius* *minor* Gmelin in southern Africa. *Durban Mus. Novit.* 12 (13): 161-165.

Clancey P.A. (Ed.) 1980d. *SAOS Checklist of Southern African Birds.* Houghton: S. Afr. Orn. Soc.

Clancey P.A. 1981a. Miscellaneous taxonomic notes on African birds LIX. On geographical variation in the Terek Sandpiper *Xenus cinereus* (Güldenstaedt). *Durban Mus. Novit.* 12 (20): 223-224.

Clancey P.A. 1981b. Miscellaneous taxonomic notes on African birds LIX. Variation in the present nominate race of *Glareola nuchalis* Gray. *Durban Mus. Novit.* 12 (20): 224-227.

Clancey P.A. 1981c. The European Swift *Apus apus* (Linnaeus) in the southern Afrotropics. *Durban Mus. Novit.* 13 (2): 13-20.

Clancey P.A. 1982. Miscellaneous taxonomic notes on African birds LXIII. The Great Sandplover *Charadrius leschenaultii* Lesson in southern and eastern Africa. *Durban Mus. Novit.* 13 (10): 131-132.

Clancey P.A. 1984a. Miscellaneous taxonomic notes on African birds LXV. On the so-called Mountain Pipit of the Afrotropics. *Durban Mus. Novit.* 13 (15): 189-194.

Clancey P.A. 1984b. Geographical variation and post-breeding dispersal in Temminck's Courser of the Afrotropics. *Gerfaut* 74: 361-374.

Clancey P.A. 1985. Species limits in the long-billed pipits of the southern Afrotropics. *Ostrich* 56: 157-169.

Clancey P.A. 1986. Breeding season and subspecific variation in the Redheaded Quelea. *Ostrich* 57: 207-210.

Clancey P.A. 1987. The Tree Pipit *Anthus trivialis* (Linnaeus) in southern Africa. *Durban Mus. Novit.* 14 (3): 29-42.

Clancey P.A. 1989. The status of *Anthus caffer mzimbaensis* Benson, 1955. *Bull. Brit. Orn. Club* 109: 43-47.

Clancey P.A. 1994. The status of *Nectarinia olivacea* (Smith), 1840; a unitary species or two polytypic allospecies? *Gerfaut* 82-83 (1992-93): 25-29.

Clancey P.A. 1996. Further on subspeciation in the Red-billed Francolin *Pternistis adspersus* (Waterhouse), 1838. *Bull. Brit. Orn. Club* 116: 104-108.

Clancey P.A. 1997. The Cape Parrot: an additional valid species. *Honeyguide* 43: 61-62.

Clancey P.A. & Irwin M.P.S. 1978. Species limits in the *Nectarinia afra/N. chalybea* complex of African doublecollared sunbirds. *Durban Mus. Novit.* 11 (20): 331-351.

Clark A. 1977. Review of the records of three Palaearctic ducks in southern Africa. *Bull. Brit. Orn. Club* 97: 107-114.

Clark J.D. 1951. Bushmen hunters of the Barotse forests. *N. Rhod. J.* 1 (3): 56-65.

Clark W.S. 1999. Plumage differences and taxonomic status of three similar *Circaetus* snake-eagles. *Bull. Brit. Orn. Club* 119: 56-59.

Clark W.S. 2005. Steppe Eagle *Aquila nipalensis* is monotypic. *Bull. Brit. Orn. Club* 125: 149-153.

Clark J.D. & Clay G. 1963. David Livingstone: a chronology. *N. Rhod. J.* 5: 261-267.

Clarke J.E. & Loe I.D. 1974. *A guide to the National Parks of Zambia.* Lusaka: Anglo American Corporation.

Clarke S.R. 1920. [*Lybius chaplini*, sp. nov.] *Bull. Brit. Orn. Club* 41: 50-51.

Clarke S.R. 1921. An account of the birds met with during a two-months shooting trip in Northern Rhodesia. *Ibis* (11) 3: 611-621.

Clay G. 1943. Livingstone in North-eastern Rhodesia. *Ostrich* 13: 227-231.

Clay G. 1944. Game birds in Barotseland. *Ostrich* 15: 55-61.

Clay G. 1953. Some notes on the birds of the Isoka District of the Northern Province of Northern Rhodesia. *Ostrich* 24: 76-97.

Coates B. 1974. Notes on a pair of Lesser Black-winged Plovers in Sumbu National Park. *Bull. Zambian Orn. Soc.* 6: 23.

Colebrook-Robjent J.F.R. 1973. Nest of Crowned Eagle at Livingstone. *Bull. Zambian Orn. Soc.* 5: 32.

Colebrook-Robjent J.F.R. 1975a. *Chrysococcyx caprius*: a new biological host record for Zambia. *Ostrich* 46: 264-265.

Colebrook-Robjent J.F.R. 1975b. Some breeding records of birds in Zambia. *Zambia Mus. J.* 4 (1973): 7-18.

Colebrook-Robjent J.F.R. 1977. Cuckoos in Zambia. *Black Lechwe* 12 (3): 26-31.

Colebrook-Robjent J.F.R. 1980. Didric Cuckoo breeding in Mwinilunga. *Bull. Zambian Orn. Soc.* 12: 8-9.

Colebrook-Robjent J.F.R. 1984. The breeding of the Didric Cuckoo *Chrysococcyx caprius* in Zambia. *Proc. 5th Pan-Afr. Orn. Congr.*: 763-777.

Colebrook-Robjent J.F.R. & Aspinwall D.R. 1986. The nest and eggs of *Circaetus cinerascens* and other snake eagles in Zambia. *Bull. Brit. Orn. Club* 106: 5-9.

Colebrook-Robjent J.F.R. & Osborne T.O. 1973. Nesting of Verreaux's Eagle *Aquila verreauxi* in Zambia. *Bull. Brit. Orn. Club* 93: 166.

Colebrook-Robjent J.F.R. & Osborne T.O. 1974. High density breeding of the Red-necked Falcon *Falco chicquera* in Zambia. *Bull. Brit. Orn. Club* 94: 172-176.

Colebrook-Robjent J.F.R. & Spottiswoode C.N. In prep. Host use and parasitism rates of the brood parasitic Greater and Lesser Honeyguides (Indicatoridae) in Zambia.

Colebrook-Robjent J.F.R. & Stjernstedt R. 1976. Chaplin's Barbet *Lybius chaplini*: first description of eggs, a new host record for the Lesser Honeyguide *Indicator minor. Bull. Brit. Orn. Club* 96: 109-111.

Colebrook-Robjent J.F.R. & Tanner I.C. 1978. Observations at a Dickinson's Kestrel's nest in Zambia. *Proc. 1 Symp. Afr. Predatory Birds*: 62-70.

Collar N.J. & Fishpool L.D.C. 2006. What is *Pogoniulus makawai*? *Bull. Afr. Bird Club* 13: 18-27.

Collar N.J. & Stuart S.N. 1985. *Threatened birds of Africa and related islands*. Cambridge: I.C.B.P. & I.U.C.N.

Conant R.A. 1980. First breeding record of Whiskered Tern *Chlidonias hybrida* in Zambia. *Bull. Zambian Orn. Soc.* 12: 39-40.

Cooper J. 1972. A check list of the birds of the Zambezi Valley from Kariba to Zumbo. *S. Afr. Avifauna Ser.* 85: 1-44.

Cott H.B. & Benson C.W. 1971. The palatability of birds, mainly based upon observations of a tasting panel in Zambia. *Ostrich* suppl. 8: 357-384.

Cottrell J.A. 1938. Nesting of the Booted Eagle (*Hieraaetus pennatus*). *Ostrich* 9: 97-98.

Couto J.T. 1996. Illegal trade in Lilian's Lovebird. *Honeyguide* 42: 52-53.

Craig A.J.F.K. 1987. Redheaded Quelea subspecies and African bird taxonomy. *Ostrich* 58: 90-91.

Crook L. 1970. Dr F .O. Stöhr. *Honeyguide* 63: 34, 37.

Crowe T.M., Harley E.H., Jakutowicz M.B., Komen J. & Crowe A.A. 1992. Phylogenetic, taxonomic and bio-geographical implications of genetic, morphological and behavioral variation in francolins (Phasianidae: *Francolinus*). *Auk* 109: 24-42.

Danckwerts B. 1979. Observations at the nest of a Bateleur (*Terathopius ecaudatus*). *Bull. Zambian Orn. Soc.* 11 (1): 12-15.

Darling F.F. 1960. *Wild life in an African territory.* London: Oxford Univ. Press.

David N. & Gosselin M. 2002a. Gender agreement of avian species names. *Bull. Brit. Orn. Club* 122: 14-49.

David N. & Gosselin M. 2002b. The grammatical gender of avian genera. *Bull. Brit. Orn. Club* 122: 257-282.

Davis D.H. (Ed.) 1971. *Zambia in maps*. London: Univ. London Press.

Dawson J. 1967. [Letter: nest of Macclounie's Barbet]. *Bokmakierie* 19: 50.

Dean W.R.J. 1971. Breeding data for the birds of Natal and Zululand. *Durban Mus. Novit.* 9 (6): 59-91.

Dean W.R.J. 2000. *The birds of Angola: an annotated checklist*. Tring: B.O.U. Checklist n° 18.

Dean W.R.J. & Brooke R.K. 1991. Review of the Olive Bee-eater *Merops superciliosus* breeding in eastern Africa south of 14°S. *Ostrich* 62: 86-88.

Dean W. R. J., Dowsett R.J., Sakko A. & Simmons R.E. 2002. New records and amendments to the birds of Angola. *Bull. Brit. Orn. Club* 122: 180-184.

del Hoyo J., Elliott A. & Sargatal J. (Eds) 1996. *Handbook of the Birds of the World*. Vol. 3. (Hoatzin to auks). Barcelona: Lynx Edicions.

del Hoyo J., Elliott A. & Sargatal J. (Eds) 1997. *Handbook of the Birds of the World*. Vol. 4. (Sandgrouse to cuckoos). Barcelona: Lynx Edicions.

del Hoyo J., Elliott A. & Sargatal J. (Eds) 2001. *Handbook of the Birds of the World*. Vol. 6. (Mousebirds to hornbills). Barcelona: Lynx Edicions.

del Hoyo J., Elliott A. & Christie D.A. (Eds) 2004. *Handbook of the Birds of the World*. Vol. 9. (Cotingas to pipits and wagtails). Barcelona: Lynx Edicions.

del Hoyo J., Elliott A. & Christie D.A. (Eds) 2005. *Handbook of the Birds of the World*. Vol. 10. (Cuckoo-shrikes to thrushes). Barcelona: Lynx Edicions.

Delacour J. 1944. A revision of the family Nectariniidae (sunbirds). *Zoologica N.Y.* 29: 17-38.

Dodman T. N.d. (=1996) Status and distribution of the Black-cheeked Lovebird *Agapornis nigrigenis. R.S.P.B. Report*: 50 + xxxix pp.

Donnelly B.G. 1974. The Lesser Black-backed Gull *Larus fuscus* in southern and central Africa. *Bull. Brit. Orn. Club* 94: 63-68.

Donnelly B.G. & Donnelly A. 1983. The birds of the Lake Kariba basin, Zimbabwe. *Honeyguide* 114/115: 27-42.

Douglas G., Wenham C. & Mundy P.J. 2000. First Eurasian Turtle Dove in Zimbabwe. *Honeyguide* 46: 158-159.

Douthwaite R.J. 1972. A record of the Swamp Flycatcher from the Kafue Flats. *Bull. Zambian Orn. Soc.* 4: 23-24.

Douthwaite R.J. 1974. An endangered population of Wattled Cranes (*Grus carunculatus*). *Biol. Conserv.* 6: 134-142.

Douthwaite R.J. 1977. Filter-feeding ducks of the Kafue Flats, Zambia, 1971-1973. *Ibis* 119: 44-66.

Douthwaite R.J. 1978. Geese and Red-knobbed Coot on the Kafue Flats in Zambia, 1970-1974. *E. Afr. Wildl. J.* 16: 29-47.

Dowsett R.J. 1962. Eastern Province ornithological notes, September to November 1962. *Naturalist Soc. Centr. Afr.* 3: 89-91.

Dowsett R.J. 1965a. On a nest of the Yellow-billed Oxpecker *Buphagus africanus* in Zambia. *Bull. Brit. Orn. Club* 85: 133-135.

Dowsett R.J. 1965b. The occurrence of the Yellow Wagtail *Motacilla flava flavissima* in Central Africa. *Ostrich* 36: 32-33.

Dowsett R.J. 1965c. Some interesting birds from the northern Kafue Flats. *Puku* 3: 177.

Dowsett R.J. 1966a. The moulting pattern of European Swallows, *Hirundo rustica*, wintering in eastern Zambia. *Puku* 4: 91-100.

Dowsett R.J. 1966b. A preliminary list of the birds of the Kafue Flats. *Puku* 4: 101-124.

Dowsett R.J. 1966c. The status and distribution of the Hottentot Teal *Anas punctata* in Zambia. *Puku* 4: 125-127.

Dowsett R.J. 1966d. The status of four species of aquatic bird in Zambia as suggested by ringing recoveries. *Puku* 4: 129-133.

Dowsett R.J. 1967. Breeding biology of *Lamprotornis mevesii* (Wahlberg). *Bull. Brit. Orn. Club* 87: 157-164.

Dowsett R.J. 1968. Oxpeckers *Buphagus* spp. on game animals at night. *Bull. Brit. Orn. Club* 88: 130-132.

Dowsett R.J. 1969a. List of the birds of the Luangwa Valley game reserves. *Bull. Zambian Orn. Soc.* 1: 5-19.

Dowsett R.J. 1969b. Gull-billed Tern (*Gelochelidon nilotica*) and Crimson-wing (*Cryptospiza reichenovii*): species new to Zambia. *Bull. Zambian Orn. Soc.* 1: 43-44.

Dowsett R.J. 1969c. Ringed Sacred Ibis *Threskiornis aethiopica* recovered in Zambia. *Puku* 5: 59-63.

Dowsett R.J. 1969d. The call of the Three-banded Courser *Rhinoptilus cinctus*. *Puku* 5: 222.

Dowsett R.J. 1969e. The call and distribution of the Black-backed Barbet, *Lybius minor*. *Puku* 5: 222-223.

Dowsett R.J. 1970a. A collection of birds from the Nyika Plateau, Zambia. *Bull. Brit. Orn. Club* 90: 49-53.

Dowsett R.J. 1970b. Steppe Eagle *Aquila nipalensis*: a species new to the Zambian List. *Bull. Zambian Orn. Soc.* 2: 46.

Dowsett R.J. 1971a. The spread of the House Sparrow in Zambia. *Bull. Zambian Orn. Soc.* 3: 50-52.

Dowsett R.J. 1971b. Yellow-throated Warbler *Phylloscopus ruficapilla*: a species new to Zambia. *Bull. Zambian Orn. Soc.* 3: 53.

Dowsett R.J. 1971c. The Slatey Egret *Egretta vinaceigula*: a species new to the Zambian list. *Bull. Zambian Orn. Soc.* 3: 53-54.

Dowsett R.J. 1971d. Partial albino Laughing Dove at Lochinvar. *Bull. Zambian Orn. Soc.* 3: 55.

Dowsett R.J. 1971e. A preliminary survey of Zambia's wetlands and wildfowl. *I.W.R.B. Bull.* 32: 75-84.

Dowsett R.J. 1971f. The Lesser Grey Shrike *Lanius minor* in Africa. *Ostrich* 42: 259-270.

Dowsett R.J. 1971g. Growth of nestling Giant Kingfishers *Ceryle maxima*. *Ostrich* 42: 297-298.

Dowsett R.J. 1971h. The avifauna of the Makutu Plateau, Zambia. *Rev. Zool. Bot. Afr.* 84: 312-333.

Dowsett R.J. 1972a. The type locality of *Agapornis nigrigenis*. *Bull. Brit. Orn. Club* 92: 22-23.

Dowsett R.J. 1972b. Geographical variation in *Pseudhirundo griseopyga*. *Bull. Brit. Orn. Club* 92: 97-100.

Dowsett R.J. 1972c. Is the bulbul *Phyllastrephus placidus* a good species? *Bull. Brit. Orn. Club* 92: 132-138.

Dowsett R.J. 1972d. Races of the lark *Mirafra africana* in the Tanganyika-Nyasa montane group. *Bull. Brit. Orn. Club* 92: 156-159.

Dowsett R.J. ("Editor") 1973a. Records of the Black-tailed Godwit: a species new to Zambia. *Bull. Zambian Orn. Soc.* 5: 30.

Dowsett R.J. 1973b. New distributional records from North-Western Province. *Bull. Zambian Orn. Soc.* 5: 66-69.

Dowsett R.J. 1973c. Brown-eared Woodpeckers (*Campethera caroli*) in Mwinilunga: a species new to Zambia. *Bull. Zambian Orn. Soc.* 5: 72.

Dowsett R.J. 1973d. Olive-tree Warbler (*Hippolais olivetorum*) at Lochinvar: a species new to Zambia. *Bull. Zambian Orn. Soc.* 5: 72.

Dowsett R.J. 1973e. Observations from the Luangwa Valley. *Bull. Zambian Orn. Soc.* 5: 75-76.

Dowsett R.J. 1973f. Yellow-billed Duck (*Anas undulata*) near Victoria Falls. *Bull. Zambian Orn. Soc.* 5: 76.

Dowsett R.J. 1973g. The River Warbler *Locustella fluviatilis* in Africa. *Zambia Mus. J.* 3 (1972): 69-79.

Dowsett R.J. 1974a. Baillon's Crake (*Porzana pusilla*) near Choma. *Bull. Zambian Orn. Soc.* 6: 49.

Dowsett R.J. 1974b. A leucistic White-winged Whydah (*Euplectes albonotatus*). *Bull. Zambian Orn. Soc.* 6: 50-51.

Dowsett R.J. 1975a. Sight record of an Olive-tree Warbler near Mambova. *Bull. Zambian Orn. Soc.* 7: 19-20.

Dowsett R.J. 1975b. Red-winged Warbler (*Heliolais erythroptera*) in the Luangwa Valley. *Bull. Zambian Orn. Soc.* 7: 24.

Dowsett R.J. 1975c. Some records of colour abnormalities in Zambian birds. *Bull. Zambian Orn. Soc.* 7: 103-104.

Dowsett R.J. 1975d. Jali Makawa – a profile. *Zambia Mus. J.* 4 (1973): 39-42.

Dowsett R.J. 1976a. The further spread of the House Sparrow in Zambia. *Bull. Zambian Orn. Soc.* 8: 2-6.

Dowsett R.J. 1976b. Mottled Swifts (*Apus aequatorialis*) at the Victoria Falls gorges. *Bull. Zambian Orn. Soc.* 8: 67-68.

Dowsett R.J. 1977a. Marico Sunbird in Southern Province. *Bull. Zambian Orn. Soc.* 9: 30-31.

Dowsett R.J. 1977b. Feral Rock Doves. *Bull. Zambian Orn. Soc.* 9: 31-32.

Dowsett R.J. 1977c. Notes on the distribution of the Red-and-blue Sunbird. *Bull. Zambian Orn. Soc.* 9: 64-65.

Dowsett R.J. 1977d. Hunting methods of the Rufous-breasted Sparrowhawk. *Bull. Zambian Orn. Soc.* 9: 66.

Dowsett R.J. 1977e. The distribution and possible spread of the Little Swift. *Bull. Zambian Orn. Soc.* 9: 66.

Dowsett R.J. 1978a. A hybrid *Hirundo rustica* x *Delichon urbica* in Zambia. *Bull. Brit. Orn. Club* 98: 113-114.

Dowsett R.J. 1978b. The Booted Eagle (*Hieraaetus pennatus*) in Zambia. *Bull. Zambian Orn. Soc.* 10: 5-7.

Dowsett R.J. 1978c. The altitude of Julius, Luangwa Valley. *Bull. Zambian Orn. Soc.* 10: 32-33.

Dowsett R.J. 1978d. Obituary: C.M.N. White. *Bull. Zambian Orn. Soc.* 10: 82-83.

Dowsett R.J. 1979a. Recent additions to the Zambian List. *Bull. Brit. Orn. Club* 99: 94-98.

Dowsett R.J. 1979b. Sight record of a South African Cliff Swallow in Mwinilunga District. *Bull. Zambian Orn. Soc.* 11 (1): 32.

Dowsett R.J. 1979c. The status of the Broad-tailed Warbler *Schoenicola platyura* in Zambia. *Bull. Zambian Orn. Soc.* 11 (2): 11-13.

Dowsett R.J. 1980a. The migration of coastal waders from the Palaearctic across Africa. *Gerfaut* 70: 3-35.

Dowsett R.J. 1980b. Comments on some ornithological type-localities in Zambia. *Zambia Mus. J.* 5: 7-16.

Dowsett R.J. 1981. Breeding and other observations on the Slaty Egret *Egretta vinaceigula*. *Bull. Brit. Orn. Club* 101: 323-327.

Dowsett R.J. 1982. The population dynamics and seasonal dispersal of the Starred Robin *Pogonocichla stellata*. M.Sc. thesis, Univ. of Natal, Pietermaritzburg: 223 pp.

Dowsett R.J. 1983. Breeding and other observations on the Taita Falcon *Falco fasciinucha*. *Ibis* 125: 362-366.

Dowsett R.J. 1985a. Site fidelity and survival rates of some montane forest birds in Malawi, south-central Africa. *Biotropica* 17: 145-154.

Dowsett R.J. 1985b. Notes on white-eyes in the Cape Province and south-central Africa. *Safring News* 14: 13-18.

Dowsett R.J. 1988a. Intra-African migrant birds in south-central Africa. *Proc. XIX Int. orn. Congr.*: 778-790.

Dowsett R.J. 1988b. Ornithological exploration in the Afrotropics. 1. Boyd Alexander in Zambesia *Tauraco* 1: 105-109.

Dowsett R.J. 1997. Obituary: W.F.H. Ansell (1923-1996). *Mammalia* 61: 635-637.

Dowsett R.J. 2002. On a claimed specimen of White-throated Bee-eater, *Merops albicollis*, from Zambia. *Ostrich* 73: 180.

Dowsett R.J. in press a. The resident birds of Zambia: new data on distribution and status. *Tauraco Res. Rep.* 9.

Dowsett R.J. in press b. Palaearctic migrants in Zambia. *Tauraco Res. Rep.* 9.

Dowsett R.J. & Berry P.S.M. In prep. Host preferences of oxpeckers *Buphagus* spp. in Zambia and Malawi.

Dowsett R.J. & Dowsett-Lemaire F. 1978a. Mottled Swift (*Apus aequatorialis*) in Chinsali District. *Bull. Zambian Orn. Soc.* 10: 33.

Dowsett R.J. & Dowsett-Lemaire F. 1978b. Notes on the distribution of the White-necked Raven (*Corvus albicollis*). *Bull. Zambian Orn. Soc.* 10: 33-34.

Dowsett R.J. & Dowsett-Lemaire F. 1978c. Fuelleborn's Longclaw (*Macronyx fuelleborni*) in eastern Isoka District. *Bull. Zambian Orn. Soc.* 10: 77.

Dowsett R.J. & Dowsett-Lemaire F. 1978d. Oxpeckers (*Buphagus* sp.) in North-Western Province. *Bull. Zambian Orn. Soc.* 10: 78.

Dowsett R.J. & Dowsett-Lemaire F. 1979a. Boehm's Bee-eater (*Merops boehmi*) on the Kabompo River. *Bull. Zambian Orn. Soc.* 11 (1): 32-33.

Dowsett R.J. & Dowsett-Lemaire F. 1979b. A possible Yellow Canary (*Serinus flaviventris*) in Mwinilunga District. *Bull. Zambian Orn. Soc.* 11 (2): 45-46.

Dowsett R.J. & Dowsett-Lemaire F. 1979c. The Mountain Buzzard *Buteo tachardus* in central Africa. *Scopus* 3: 14-18.

Dowsett R.J. & Dowsett-Lemaire F. 1980. The systematic status of some Zambian birds. *Gerfaut* 70: 151-199.

Dowsett R.J. & Dowsett-Lemaire F. 1984. Breeding and moult cycles of some montane forest birds in south-central Africa. *Rev. Ecol. (Terre et Vie)* 39: 89-111.

Dowsett R.J. & Dowsett-Lemaire F. 1987. Longbilled Pipit systematics. *Ostrich* 58: 46.

Dowsett R.J. & Dowsett-Lemaire F. 1993. Comments on the taxonomy of some Afrotropical bird species. *Tauraco Res. Rep.* 5: 323-389.

Dowsett R.J. & Dowsett-Lemaire F. 2001. Book review. *The Atlas of Southern African Birds* (Harrison *et al.* 1997). *Ostrich* 72: 62, 100 & 108.

Dowsett R.J. & Forbes-Watson A.D. 1993. *Checklist of birds of the Afrotropical and Malagasy Regions*. Vol. 1. Liège: Tauraco Press.

Dowsett R.J. & Kemp A.C. 1988. The claimed occurrences of Long-legged Buzzards *Buteo rufinus* in Africa south of the equator. *Gabar* 3: 67-69.

Dowsett R.J. & Lemaire F. 1976. A second Zambian record of Mongolian Sandplover (*Charadrius mongolus*). *Bull. Zambian Orn. Soc.* 8: 68-69.

Dowsett R.J. & Leonard P.M. 2001. Results from Bird Ringing in Zambia. *Zambia Bird Rep.* 1999: 16-46.

Dowsett R.J. & Leonard P.M. in press a. Intra-African migrants in Zambia. *Tauraco Res. Rep.* 9.

Dowsett R.J. & Leonard P.M. in press b. Annotated lists of the birds of Zambia's national parks. *Tauraco Res. Rep.* 9.

Dowsett R.J. & Osborne T. 1971. A Gull-billed Tern near Choma. *Bull. Zambian Orn. Soc.* 3: 54.

Dowsett R.J. & Osborne T.O. 1973. A "Big Day" in Zambia. *Bull. Zambian Orn. Soc.* 5: 70-71.

Dowsett R.J. & Prigogine A. 1974. *The avifauna of the Marungu Highlands*. Exploration hydrobiologique du bassin du lac Bangweolo et du Luapula. Cercle Hydrobiologique de Bruxelles. 19: 67 pp.

Dowsett R.J. & Robjent J.C. 1972. Black Eagles in the Victoria Falls gorges. *Bull. Zambian Orn. Soc.* 4: 25.

Dowsett R.J. & Stjernstedt R. 1973. The birds of the Mafinga Mountains. *Puku* 7: 107-123.

Dowsett R.J. & Stjernstedt R. 1979. The *Bradypterus cinnamomeus-mariae* complex in Central Africa. *Bull. Brit. Orn. Club* 99: 86-94.

Dowsett R.J. & Tree A.J. 1964. The occurrence of *Neophron percnopterus* in Northern Rhodesia. *Bull. Brit. Orn. Club* 84: 52-54.

Dowsett R.J., Colebrook-Robjent J.F.R. & Osborne T.O. 1974. Further additions to the Nyika Plateau avifauna. *Bull. Zambian Orn. Soc.* 6: 40-43.

Dowsett R.J., Aspinwall D.R. & Leonard P.M. 1999a. Further additions to the avifauna of Zambia. *Bull. Brit. Orn. Club* 119: 94-103.

Dowsett R.J., Olson S.L , Roy M.S. & Dowsett-Lemaire F. 1999b. Systematic status of the Black-collared Bulbul *Neolestes torquatus*. *Ibis* 141: 22-28.

Dowsett R.J., Berry P.S.M. & Foot D. 2003. Sharpe's Starling *Cinnyricinclus sharpii* new to Zambia, and its status in eastern Africa. *Bull. Afr. Bird Club* 10: 125-126.

Dowsett R.J., Brewster C.A. & Hines C. In prep. Some bird distributional limits in the Upper Zambezi Valley.

Dowsett-Lemaire F. 1979. The imitative range of the song of the Marsh Warbler *Acrocephalus palustris*, with special reference to imitations of African birds. *Ibis* 121: 453-468.

Dowsett-Lemaire F. 1983a. Scaly-throated Honeyguide *Indicator variegatus* parasitizing Olive Woodpeckers *Dendropicos griseocephalus* in Malawi. *Bull. Brit. Orn. Club* 103: 71-75.

Dowsett-Lemaire F. 1983b. Studies of a breeding population of Olive Woodpeckers, *Dendropicos griseocephalus*, in montane forests of south-central Africa. *Gerfaut* 73: 221-237.

Dowsett-Lemaire F. 1983c. Ecological and territorial requirements of montane forest birds on the Nyika Plateau, south-central Africa. *Gerfaut* 73: 345-378.

Dowsett-Lemaire F. 1983d. Studies of a breeding population of Waller's Redwinged Starlings in montane forests of south-central Africa. *Ostrich* 54: 105-112.

Dowsett-Lemaire F. 1985a. Breeding productivity and the non-breeding element in some montane forest birds in Malawi, south-central Africa. *Biotropica* 17: 137-144.

Dowsett-Lemaire F. 1985b. The forest vegetation of the Nyika Plateau (Malawi-Zambia): ecological and phenological studies. *Bull. Jard. Bot. Nat. Belg.* 55: 301-392.

Dowsett-Lemaire F. 1987. On the distribution, ecology and voice of two *Alethe* species in Malawi. *Scopus* 11: 25-32.

Dowsett-Lemaire F. 1988a. The forest vegetation of Mt Mulanje (Malawi): a floristic and chorological study along an altitudinal gradient (650-1950 m). *Bull. Jard. Bot. Nat. Belg.* 58: 77-107.

Dowsett-Lemaire F. 1988b. Fruit choice and seed dissemination by birds and mammals in the evergreen forests of upland Malawi. *Rev. Ecol.* (*Terre et Vie*) 43: 251-285.

Dowsett-Lemaire F. 1988c. On the breeding behaviour of three montane sunbirds *Nectarinia* spp. in northern Malawi. *Scopus* 11: 79-86.

Dowsett-Lemaire F. 1989a. The flora and phytogeography of the evergreen forests of Malawi. I: Afromontane and mid-altitude forests. *Bull. Jard. Bot. Nat. Belg.* 59: 3-131.

Dowsett-Lemaire F. 1989b. Ecological and biogeographical aspects of forest bird communities in Malawi. *Scopus* 13: 1-80.

Dowsett-Lemaire F. 1989c. Food plants and the annual cycle in a montane community of sunbirds (*Nectarinia* spp.) in northern Malawi. *Tauraco* 1: 167-185.

Dowsett-Lemaire F. 1997. The avifauna of Odzala National Park, northern Congo. *Tauraco Res. Rep.* 6: 15-48.

Dowsett-Lemaire F. 2004. On the importance of the forest tree *Parinari excelsa* in the diet of Brown-necked Parrots *Poicephalus robustus* in Malawi-Zambia. *Bull. Afr. Bird Club* 11: 139-141.

Dowsett-Lemaire F. 2006a. An annotated list and life history of the birds of Nyika National Park, Malawi-Zambia. *Tauraco Res. Rep.* 8: 1-64.

Dowsett-Lemaire F. 2006b. Notes supplementary to *The Birds of Malawi* (2006). *Tauraco Res. Rep.* 8: 65-121.

Dowsett-Lemaire F. & Dowsett R.J. 1978a. Singing Cisticola (*Cisticola cantans*) in Mbala District. *Bull. Zambian Orn. Soc.* 10: 35-36.

Dowsett-Lemaire F. & Dowsett R.J. 1978b. White-throated Nicator in western Kalomo District. *Bull. Zambian Orn. Soc.* 10: 76.

Dowsett-Lemaire F. & Dowsett R.J. 1987a. European and African Reed Warblers, *Acrocephalus scirpaceus* and *A. baeticatus*: vocal and other evidence for a single species. *Bull. Brit. Orn. Club* 107: 74-85.

Dowsett-Lemaire F. & Dowsett R.J. 1987b. European Reed and Marsh Warblers in Africa: migration patterns, moult and habitat. *Ostrich* 58: 65-85.

Dowsett-Lemaire F. & Dowsett R.J. 1988. Vocalisations of the green turacos (*Tauraco* species) and their systematic status. *Tauraco* 1: 64-71.

Dowsett-Lemaire F. & Dowsett R.J. 1989. Zoogeography and taxonomic relationships of the forest birds of the Cameroon Afromontane region. *Tauraco Res. Rep.* 1: 48-56.

Dowsett-Lemaire F. & Dowsett R.J. 1998. Parallels between F. White's phytochoria and avian zoochoria in tropical Africa: an analysis of the forest elements. *In* Huxley C.R., Lock J.M. & Cutler D.F. (Eds). *Chorology, taxonomy and ecology of the floras of Africa and Madagascar*: 87-96. Kew: Royal Botanic Gardens.

Dowsett-Lemaire F. & Dowsett R.J. 2001. African forest birds. Patterns of endemism and species richness. *In* Weber W., White L.J.T., Vedder A. & Naughton-Treves L. (Eds). *African rain forest. Ecology and conservation*: 233-262. New Haven & London: Yale Univ. Press.

Dowsett-Lemaire F. & Dowsett R.J. 2005. On Rufous-naped Lark *Mirafra africana* 'flappeting' display. *Bull. Afr. Bird Club* 12: 76.

Dowsett-Lemaire F. & Dowsett R.J. 2006. *The Birds of Malawi*. Liège: Tauraco Press & Aves.

Duval C.T. 1969. Recent ornithological records from the Southern Province. *Puku* 5: 223-226.

Dyer M. 1992. Observations on Wattled Cranes nesting on Nyika Plateau, Malawi. *Nyala* 15: 57-62.

Engelmoer M. & Roselaar C.S. 1998. *Geographical variation in waders*. Dordrecht: Kluwer Acad. Publ.

Everett G.V. 1971. Sampling fish stocks in the Kafue River. *Fish. Res. Bull. Zambia* 5: 297-304.

Fanshawe D.B. 1960. "Mist" forests of the Bwingimfumu Hills. *N. Rhod. J.* 4: 147-152.

Fanshawe D.B. 1969. *The Vegetation of Zambia*. (Forest Research Bull. N° 7). Lusaka: Govt Printer.

Farmer L. 1992. *A visitor's guide to the Kasanka National Park*. London: Kasanka Trust.

Feather P.J. 1997. Carmine Bee-Eater nesting colonies in Zimbabwe. *Honeyguide* 43: 188-210.

Feely J.M. 1964. Heron and stork breeding colonies in the Luangwa Valley. *Puku* 2: 76-77.

Feely J.M. 1965. Observations on *Acacia albida* in the Luangwa Valley. *Puku* 3: 67-70.

Fellowes E.C. 1971. House Martins apparently roosting in nests of Striped Swallows. *Brit. Birds* 64: 460.

Fishpool L.D.C. & Evans M.I. (Eds) 2001. *Important Bird Areas in Africa and associated islands: Priority sites for conservation*. Newbury & Cambridge: Pisces Publications & BirdLife International.

Fleming P.D. 1999. Some notes on birds and seasonality at Hippo Camp, Kafue National Park. *Zambia Bird Rep.* 1998: 74-79.

Fosbrooke H.A. 1968. Brown-necked Parrots. *Black Lechwe* 7 (1): 24-25.

Francis D.M. 1975. A possible hybrid *Uraeginthus angolensis* x *U. bengalus. Bull. Zambian Orn. Soc.* 7: 26-27.

Francis D.M. 1980. Moult of European Swallows in Central Zambia. *Ringing & Migr.* 3: 4-8.

Franzmann N.-E. 1983. A new subspecies of the Usambara Weaver *Ploceus nicolli. Bull. Brit. Orn. Club* 103: 49-51.

Friedmann H. 1955. The honeyguides. *Bull. U.S. Nat. Mus.* 208: 1-292.

Fry C.H. & Keith S. (Eds) 2004. *The Birds of Africa.* Vol. 7. London: Christopher Helm.

Fry C.H., Keith S. & Urban E.K. (Eds) 1988. *The Birds of Africa.* Vol. 3. London & New York: Academic Press.

Fry C.H., Keith S. & Urban E.K. (Eds) 2000. *The Birds of Africa.* Vol. 6. London: Academic Press.

Fuchs J., Bowie R.C.K., Fjeldså J. & Pasquet E. 2004. Phylogenetic relationships of the African bush-shrikes and helmet-shrikes (Passeriformes: Malaconotidae). *Mol. Phylogenet. Evol.* 33: 428-439.

Fuchs J., Fjeldså J., Bowie R.C.K., Voelker G. & Pasquet E. 2006. The African warbler genus *Hyliota* as a lost lineage in the Oscine songbird tree: Molecular support for an African origin of the Passerida. *Mol. Phylogenet. Evol.* 39: 186-197.

Garcia E.F.J. 1975. Ornithological observations at Chassa, Petauke District. *Bull. Zambian Orn. Soc.* 7: 68-87.

Gargett V. & Grobler J.H. 1976. Prey of the Cape Eagle Owl *Bubo capensis mackinderi* Sharpe 1899, in the Matopos, Rhodesia. *Arnoldia Rhod.* 8 (7): 1-7.

Gill F. & Wright M. 2006. *Birds of the World: Recommended English Names.* London: Christopher Helm.

Ginn H.B. & Melville D.S. 1983. *Moult in birds.* Tring: B.T.O.

Goodwin D. 1964. Some aspects of taxonomy and relationships of barbets (Capitonidae). *Ibis* 106: 198-220.

Gore-Browne S. 1953. "Bobo" Young. Shiwa Ngandu. *N. Rhod. J.* 2 (1): 74-76.

Grant C.H.B. 1915a. [New subspecies]. *Bull. Brit. Orn. Club* 35: 54-55.

Grant C.H.B. 1915b. [New subspecies of birds from Africa]. *Bull. Brit. Orn. Club* 35: 99-102.

Grant C.H.B. & Mackworth-Praed C.W. 1934. [Descriptions of some new races]. *Bull. Brit. Orn. Club* 55: 15-19.

Grant C.H.B. & Mackworth-Praed C.W. 1944. A new race of Quelea from Northern Rhodesia. *Bull. Brit. Orn. Club* 64: 65.

Grant C.H.B. & Mackworth-Praed C.W. 1958. A new race of serin from Northern Rhodesia. *Bull. Brit. Orn. Club* 78: 17.

Greenberg D.A. 1976. Observations at Sefula, Mongu District. *Bull. Zambian Orn. Soc.* 8: 24-25.

Greenberg D.A. & Colebrook-Robjent J.F.R. 1976. First Zambian breeding record of Great Spotted Cuckoo (*Clamator glandarius*). *Bull. Zambian Orn. Soc.* 8: 69-70.

Grimes L.G. 2002. Observations of the breeding and social behaviour of the Long-tailed Shrike in the vicinity of Bulawayo. *Honeyguide* 48: 5-27.

Grimwood I.R. 1957. Movements of ducks and geese in Northern Rhodesia. *Black Lechwe* 1 (2): 21-23.

Grimwood I.R. & Benson C.W. 1960. [Letter: Bird-life of Lochinvar ranch]. *Black Lechwe* 2 (4): 142.

Groombridge J.J., Jones C.G., Bayes M.K., Van Zyl A.J., Carillo J., Nichols R.A. & Bruford M.W. 2002. A molecular phylogeny of African kestrels with reference to divergence across the Indian Ocean. *Mol. Phylogenet. Evol.* 25: 267–277.

Guernsey T.D. 1954. Bibliography of Northern Rhodesia. Part III. – Geology. *N. Rhod. J.* 2 (3): 26-33.

Guhrs P. & Osborne T. 1988. Prey selectivity of the Red-necked Falcon *Falco chicquera* in Luangwa Valley, Zambia. *Proc. 6th Pan-Afr. Orn. Congr.*: 307-314.

Gurney M., Cope N. & Cope D. 2001. New to Zambia: Northern Carmine Bee-eater *Merops nubicus. Zambia Bird Rep.* 1999: 77-80.

Haagner A. 1910. A note on the Black-faced Love-Bird (*Agapornis nigrigenis* W.L. Sclater). *J. S. Afr. Orn. Union* 5 (1909): 16-19.

Hall B.P. 1960. The ecology and taxonomy of some Angola birds (based on a collection made in 1957). *Bull. Brit. Mus. (N.H.). Zool.* 6 (7): 367-453.

Hall B.P. & Moreau R.E. 1970. *An atlas of speciation in African Passerine birds.* London: Brit. Mus. (Nat. Hist.).

Harrison J.A., Allan D.G., Underhill L.G., Herremans M., Tree A.J., Parker V. & Brown C.J. 1997. *The Atlas of Southern African Birds.* (2 vols). Johannesburg: BirdLife South Africa.

Hartley R.R. & Douthwaite R.J. 1994. Effects of DDT treatments applied for tsetse fly control on the African goshawk in north-west Zimbabwe. *Afr. J. Ecol.* 32: 265-272.

Harwin R.M. & Irwin M.P.S. 1966. The spread of the House Sparrow, *Passer domesticus*, in south-central Africa. *Arnoldia (Rhod.)* 2 (24): 1-17.

Harwin R.M. & Rockingham-Gill D.V. 1981. Aspects of the biology of the southern races of the Swallow-tailed Bee-eater. *Honeyguide* 106: 4-10.

Haydock E.L. 1949a. Field notes on Northern Rhodesian birds. *Ibis* 91: 656-659.

Haydock E.L. 1949b. A study of the Cinnamon-breasted Rock Bunting *Fringillaria tahapisi tahapisi. Ostrich* 20: 126-130.

Haydock E.L. 1951. Bee-eaters and kingfishers at Luanshya. *Bokmakierie* 3: 89-90.

Haydock E.L. 1956. Breeding record of *Phalacrocorax carbo lucidus* in Central Province of Northern Rhodesia. *Ostrich* 27: 87-88.

Heery S. 1974. Notes on the water birds of Tondwa Lake. *Bull. Zambian Orn. Soc.* 6: 44-48.

Helbig A.J., Seibold I., Kocum A., Liebers D., Irwin J., Bergmanis U., Meyburg B.U., Scheller W., Stubbe M. & Bensch S. 2005. Genetic differentiation and hybridization between Greater and Lesser Spotted Eagles (Accipitriformes: *Aquila clanga, A. pomarina*). *J. Orn.* 146: 226-234.

Hockey P.A.R., Dean W.R.J. & Ryan P.G. (Eds) 2005. *Roberts – Birds of Southern Africa* (7th ed.). Cape Town: John Voelcker Bird Book Fund.

Hole A.M. 1905. Some interesting birds of the Zambezi Valley. *Proc. Rhod. Sci. Assoc.* 5 (3): 99-105.

Holliday C.S. 1965a. A new record of the Red-eyed Bulbul *Pycnonotus nigricans* Vieillot, in Zambia. *Ostrich* 36: 39.

Holliday C.S. 1965b. A note on the Teita Falcon. *Puku* 3: 71-73.

Hopkinson G. & Masterson A. 1984. The occurrence and ecological preferences of certain Rallidae near Salisbury. *Proc. 5th Pan-Afr. Ornithol. Congr.*: 425-440.

Howard G.W. 1989. Recent counts of Wattled Cranes *Bugeranus carunculatus* on the Kafue Flats, Zambia – November 1987. *Scopus* 12: 69-72.

Howard G.W. & Aspinwall D.R. 1984. Aerial censuses of Shoebills, Saddlebilled Storks and Wattled Cranes at the Bangweulu Swamps and Kafue Flats, Zambia. *Ostrich* 55: 207-212.

Howells W.W. 1985. The birds of the Dande Communal Lands, Middle Zambezi Valley, Zimbabwe. *Honeyguide* 31: 26-48.

Hunter N.D. 1990. An overview of the larks of Botswana. Part 1. *Babbler* 20: 12-21.

Hustler K. 1985a. Barred Long-tailed Cuckoo in Mana Pools National Park. *Honeyguide* 31: 171.

Hustler K. 1985b. Status of the Collared Palm Thrush in the Middle Zambesi Valley. *Honeyguide* 31: 219-220.

Hustler K. 1987. Notes on Kariba birds. *Honeyguide* 33: 146-149.

Hustler K. 1989. First report of the OAZ Rarities Committee. *Honeyguide* 35: 63-68.

Hustler K. 1996. Ross's Turaco on the Upper Zambezi. *Honeyguide* 42: 104-106.

Hustler K. 1998. Review: *The Atlas of Southern African Birds.* (Harrison *et al.* 1997). *Honeyguide* 44: 169-180.

Hustler K. 1999. New to Zambia: Kori Bustard *Ardeotis kori. Zambia Bird Rep.* 1998: 87-88.

Hustler K. 2000. Namaqua Sandgrouse in Hwange National Park. *Honeyguide* 46: 28.

Hustler K. 2001. The breeding biology of the Black-backed Cisticola in north-west Zimbabwe with notes on song and specific status. *Honeyguide* 47: 25-36.

Hustler K. & Eriksson M. 1985. Notes on Kariba birds. *Honeyguide* 31: 111-113.

Hustler K. & Irwin M.P.S. 1995. Fifth report of the OAZ Rarities Committee. *Honeyguide* 41: 103-106.

Hustler K., Eriksson M.O.G. & Skarpe C. 1986. Status of the White-breasted Cormorant in the Middle Zambesi Valley. *Honeyguide* 32: 42.

Irwin M.P.S. 1960. Relationships within the *Camaroptera fasciolata-stierlingi-simplex* complex of warblers. *Durban Mus. Novit.* 6 (3): 47-60.

Irwin M.P.S. 1974. The Pintail *Anas acuta* in Rhodesia. *Bull. Brit. Orn. Club* 94: 56-57.

Irwin M.P.S. 1978. On the status and distribution of the Brown-throated Golden Weaver *Ploceus xanthopterus* in Rhodesia. *Honeyguide* 94: 17-18.

Irwin M.P.S. 1981a. *The Birds of Zimbabwe.* Salisbury (Harare): Quest Publ.

Irwin M.P.S. 1981b. The status of the Crowned Plover in the Middle Zambezi Valley. *Honeyguide* 107/108: 49.

Irwin M.P.S. 1982a. Seasonal range overlap between Bradfield's and Crowned Hornbills in the Hwange (Wankie) National Park. *Honeyguide* 111/112: 18-19.

Irwin M.P.S. 1982b. On the status of the Chestnut-backed Finch Lark in the Middle Zambezi and Luangwa Valleys. *Honeyguide* 111/112: 20-21.

Irwin M.P.S. 1982c. The status of the Desert Cisticola in the Middle Zambezi Valley, with notes on geographical variation. *Honeyguide* 111/112: 67-68.

Irwin M.P.S. 1983a. The status of the Groundscraper Thrush in the Middle Zambezi Valley. *Honeyguide* 114/115: 55.

Irwin M.P.S. 1983b. Obituary: Constantine Walter Benson O.B.E. *Ibis* 125: 421-422.

Irwin M.P.S. 1984. The status of Ross's Violet Lourie in the Okavango Region of northern Botswana. *Honeyguide* 30: 76.

Irwin M.P.S. 1987. Earliest record of the Barred Long-tailed Cuckoo from the Middle Zambezi Valley. *Honeyguide* 33: 150.

Irwin M.P.S. 1988. Obituary: Reay Henry Noble Smithers 1907-1987. *Tauraco* 1: 158-159.

Irwin M.P.S. 1993. Further remarks on the grass warblers *Cisticola melanura, angusticauda* and *fulvicapilla*. *Honeyguide* 39: 36-38.

Irwin M.P.S. 1996. Obituary: Jali Makawa. *Honeyguide* 42: 191-192.

Irwin M.P.S. 2002. The origins and spread of the Northern and Southern Grey-headed Sparrows in Zambia. *Honeyguide* 48: 41-46.

Irwin M.P.S. & Benson C.W. 1966a. Notes on the birds of Zambia, Part I. *Arnoldia (Rhod.)* 2 (32): 1-19.

Irwin M.P.S. & Benson C.W. 1966b. Notes on the birds of Zambia, Part II. *Arnoldia (Rhod.)* 2 (37): 1-21.

Irwin M.P.S. & Benson C.W. 1967a. Notes on the birds of Zambia, Part III. *Arnoldia (Rhod.)* 3 (4): 1-30.

Irwin M.P.S. & Benson C.W. 1967b. Notes on the birds of Zambia, Part IV. *Arnoldia (Rhod.)* 3 (8): 1-27.

Irwin M.P.S. & Benson C.W. 1981. The status of the Golden Bishop in the Middle Zambezi Valley. *Honeyguide* 107/108: 41.

Irwin M.P.S., Niven P.N.F. & Winterbottom J.M. 1969. Some birds of the lower Chobe River area, Botswana. *Arnoldia (Rhod.)* 4 (21): 1-40.

Irwin M.P.S., Benson C.W. & Steyn P. 1982. The identification of the Ovambo and Red-breasted Sparrow Hawks in South Central Africa. *Honeyguide* 111/112: 28-44.

Jackson P.B.N. 1961. *The fishes of Northern Rhodesia*. Lusaka: Govt Printer.

Jackson H.D. 1972. The status of the Pied Mannikin, *Lonchura fringilloides* (Lafresnaye) in Rhodesia and its association with the bamboo *Oxytenanthera abyssinica* (A. Richard) Munro. *Rhod. Sci. News* 6: 342-348.

James H.W. 1970. *Catalogue of the birds eggs in the collection of the National Museums of Rhodesia*. Salisbury: National Museums of Rhodesia.

Jensen R.A.C. 1965. Interesting sight records from the Victoria Falls National Park S.R. *Ostrich* 36: 95.

Johansson U.S., Fjeldså J., Lokugalappatti L.G.S. & Bowie R.C.K. 2007. A nuclear DNA phylogeny and proposed taxonomic revision of African greenbuls (Aves, Passeriformes, Pycnonotidae). *Zoologica Scripta* 36: 417-427.

Johnson J.A., Watson R.T. & Mindell D.P. 2005. Prioritizing species conservation: does the Cape Verde kite exist? *Proc. Roy. Soc.* B 272: 1365-1371.

Jones H. 1945. Notes on some birds of the Northern Rhodesia Copperbelt. *Ostrich* 16: 176-183.

Jones H. 1946. Marabou Storks at the Kalambo Falls. *Ostrich* 17: 190-191.

Jones E.A. 1964. Abandoned bomas in North-eastern Rhodesia. A few notes from memory only. *N. Rhod. J.* 5: 606.

Jones B.W. 1974a. Sight record of a Grey Kestrel (*Falco ardosiaceus*) in Sumbu National Park. *Bull. Zambian Orn. Soc.* 6: 25.

Jones B.W. 1974b. Additions to the Ndola list by Madge. *Bull. Zambian Orn. Soc.* 6: 51-52.

Jones J.M.B. 1994. Concentration of Larklike Buntings in Kuburi Wilderness, Kariba. *Honeyguide* 40: 31.

Jones J.M.B. 1997. Sabota Lark at Gache Gache, Kariba. *Honeyguide* 43: 219-220.

Kamweneshe B. & Beilfuss R. 2002. Population and distribution of Wattled Cranes and other large waterbirds on the Kafue Flats, Zambia. *Zambia Crane and Wetland Conservation Project, Working Paper* 1: 31 pp.

Kamweneshe B., Beilfuss R. & Morrison K. 2003. Population and distribution of Wattled Cranes and other large waterbirds and large mammals on the Liuwa Plains National Park, Zambia. *Zambia Crane and Wetland Conservation Project, Working Paper* 4: 19 pp.

Keay R.W.J. 1959. *Vegetation map of Africa*. London: Oxford Univ. Press.

Keith S. & Vernon C. 1966. Notes on African warblers of the genus *Chloropeta* Smith. *Bull. Brit. Orn. Club* 86: 115-120.

Keith G.S. & Vernon C.J. 1969. Bird notes from northern and eastern Zambia. *Puku* 5: 131-139.

Keith S., Benson C.W. & Irwin M.P.S. 1970. The genus *Sarothrura* (Aves, Rallidae). *Bull. Amer. Mus. Nat. Hist.* 143: 1-84.

Keith S., Urban E.K. & Fry C.H. (Eds) 1992. *The Birds of Africa*. Vol. 4. London & San Diego: Academic Press.

Kelsey M.G. 1989. A comparison of the song and territorial behaviour of a long-distance migrant, the Marsh Warbler *Acrocephalus palustris*, in summer and winter. *Ibis* 131: 403-414.

Kelsey M. & Barnard P. 1988. Scarlet facial feathering of *Uraeginthus angolensis*: a phenotypic throwback? *Ibis* 130: 444-445.

Kinnear N.B. 1938. [Cape Bittern in Northern Rhodesia]. *Bull. Brit. Orn. Club* 58: 77.

Kirk J. 1864. On the birds of the Zambesi region of Eastern Tropical Africa. *Ibis* (1) 6: 307-339.

Knox A.G., Collinson M., Helbig A.J., Parkin D.T. & Sangster G. 2002. Taxonomic recommendations for British birds. *Ibis* 144: 707-710.

König C., Weick F. & Becking J.-H. 1999. *Owls. A guide to the owls of the World.* Robertsbridge: Pica Press.

Lack D. 1958. *Apus pallidus* in Northern Rhodesia. *Ostrich* 29: 86.

Lahti D.C. & Payne R.B. 2003. Morphological and behavioural evidence of relationships of the Cuckoo Finch *Anomalospiza imberbis*. *Bull. Brit. Orn. Club* 123: 113-125.

Lawson W.J. 1962. A new race of warbler *Apalis flavida* (Strickland) from Central Africa. *Bull. Brit. Orn. Club* 82: 133-134.

Lawson W.J. 1964a. Systematic notes on African birds 2. *Durban Mus. Novit.* 7 (6): 141-155.

Lawson W.J. 1964b. Geographical variation in the Cape Batis *Batis capensis* (Linnaeus). *Durban Mus. Novit.* 7 (8): 189-200.

Lawton R.M. 1964. The ecology of the *Marquesia acuminata* (Gilg) R.E. Fr. evergreen forests and the related chipya vegetation types of north-eastern Rhodesia. *J. Ecol.* 52: 467-479.

Lees R.H. 1932. Nesting habits of the Marsh Whydah (*Coliuspasser hartlaubi*). *Ostrich* 3: 64.

Lees R.H. 1935. *Glaucidium perlatum* (Vieill.) preying on eggs of *Eurystomus afer suahelicus* Neum. in the Ndola Dist. N. Rhodesia. *Ostrich* 6: 51-52.

Lees R.H. 1938. Further bird notes from Northern Rhodesia. *Ostrich* 9: 13-19.

Leonard P.M. 1995. A Blue Swallow near Kitwe. *Zambia Orn. Soc. Newsl.* 25: 3-4.

Leonard P.M. 1998a. New to Zambia: Greater Spotted Eagle *Aquila clanga*. *Zambia Bird Rep.* 1997: 3-5.

Leonard P.M. 1998b. Forest birds in western Zambezi District. *Zambia Bird Rep.* 1997: 12-22.

Leonard P.M. 1998c. Notes on Afrotropical bird movements and seasonality near Kafue. *Zambia Bird Rep.* 1997: 23-45.

Leonard P.M. 1998d. Distributional records from Nchelenge District. *Zambia Bird Rep.* 1997: 52-53.

Leonard P.M. 1998e. Sombre Bulbul *Andropadus importunus* – a range extension and some observations of juveniles. *Zambia Bird Rep.* 1997: 56-57.

Leonard P.M. 1998f. Concentration of Emerald Cuckoos. *Zambia Bird Rep.* 1997: 57.

Leonard P.M. 1999a. Afrotropical bird movements in Zambia – part 1: grebes to nightjars. *Zambia Bird Rep.* 1998: 15-73.

Leonard P.M. 1999b. Some singing seasons in Kafue. *Zambia Bird Rep.* 1998: 80-84.

Leonard P. 1999c. Birds of Lechwe Lodge and surrounding areas. *ZOS Checklist* 1: 1-34.

Leonard P.M. 2001a. A Mallard *Anas platyrhynchos* in the Luangwa Valley. *Zambia Bird Rep.* 1999: 90-91.

Leonard P.M. (Ed.) 2001b. Pacific Golden Plovers *Pluvialis fulva* in Lochinvar and a review of Zambian records. *Zambia Bird Rep.* 1999: 92-95.

Leonard P.M. 2001c. Cape Wagtail *Motacilla capensis* movements. *Zambia Bird Rep.* 1999: 96-97.

Leonard P.M. (Ed.) 2001d. New atlas records. *Zambia Bird Rep.* 1999: 194-196.

Leonard P. 2005. *Important Bird Areas in Zambia. Priority sites for conservation.* Lusaka: Zambian Orn. Soc.

Leonard P.M. 2006. The Curlew Sandpiper *Calidris ferruginea* in Zambia. *Intern. Wader Studies* 19: 160-162.

Leonard P. 2007. Birds of Lusenga Plain National Park, Zambia. *Bull. Afr. Bird Club* 14: 38-44.

Leonard P.M. & Beel C. ["Anon."] 1996. Lake Lufira Weaver (*Ploceus reichardi*) – new to Zambia. *Zambia Orn. Soc. Newsl.* 26: 3-4.

Leonard P. & Beel C. 1999. Two new resident birds in northern Zambia. *Bull. Afr. Bird Club* 6: 56-58.

Leonard P.M. & Colebrook-Robjent J.F.R. 2001. A review of Sooty Falcon *Falco concolor* records in Zambia. *Zambia Bird Rep.* 1999: 47-53.

Leonard P. & Peters W. (Eds) 1998. 1997 species records. *Zambia Bird Rep.* 1997: 59-139.

Leonard P.M. & Peters W. (Eds) 1999. 1998 species records. *Zambia Bird Rep.* 1998: 116-188.

Leonard P.M. & Van Daele P. 1999a. Mwinilunga's marginal forests. *Zambia Bird Rep.* 1998: 1-11.

Leonard P.M. & Van Daele P. 1999b. New to Zambia: Shrike-Flycatcher *Megabyas flammulatus*. *Zambia Bird Rep.* 1998: 89-92.

Leonard P.M. & Van Daele P. 2001a. Palearctic migrants at Chozi, Isoka D. *Zambia Bird Rep.* 1999: 85-86.

Leonard P.M. & Van Daele P. 2001b. Baglafecht Weavers *Ploceus baglafecht* near Mbala. *Zambia Bird Rep.* 1999: 98.

Leonard P.M., Kaholo H. & Wishcote B. 1998. New to Zambia: Franklin's Gull *Larus pipixcan. Zambia Bird Rep.* 1997: 5-9.

Leonard P.M., Van Daele P. & Beel C. 2001a. Birds of the Mafinga Mountains. *Zambia Bird Rep.* 1999: 6-15.

Leonard P.M., Van Daele P. & Beel C. 2001b. New to Zambia: White-throated Bee-eater *Merops albicollis. Zambia Bird Rep.* 1999: 73-76.

Leonard P.M., Beel C. & Peters W. (Eds) 2001c. 1999 species records. *Zambia Bird Rep.* 1999: 100-193.

Lewis D.M. 1982a. Dispersal in a population of White-browed Sparrow Weavers. *Condor* 84: 306-312.

Lewis D.M. 1982b. Cooperative breeding in a population of White-browed Sparrow Weavers *Plocepasser mahali. Ibis* 124: 511-522.

Lister C. 1998. Ten thousand storks on the Zambezi. *Honeyguide* 44: 139.

Louette M. 1986. Geographical contacts between the taxa of *Centropus* in Zaïre, with the description of a new race. *Bull. Brit. Orn. Club* 106: 126-133.

Louette M. 1987. Additions and corrections to the avifauna of Zaïre (1). *Bull. Brit. Orn. Club* 107: 137-143.

Louette M. 1988a. Additions and corrections to the avifauna of Zaïre (2). *Bull. Brit. Orn. Club* 108: 43-50.

Louette M. 1988b. Additions and corrections to the avifauna of Zaïre (3). *Bull. Brit. Orn. Club* 108: 112-120.

Louette M. 1989. Additions and corrections to the avifauna of Zaïre (4). *Bull. Brit. Orn. Club* 109: 217-225.

Louette M. 1990. The nightjars of Zaïre. *Bull. Brit. Orn. Club* 110: 71-77.

Louette M. & Benson C.W. 1982. Swamp-dwelling weavers of the *Ploceus velatus/vitellinus* complex, with the description of a new species. *Bull. Brit. Orn. Club* 102: 24-31.

Lovette I.J. & Rubenstein D.R. 2007. A comprehensive molecular phylogeny of the starlings (Aves: Sturnidae) and mockingbirds (Aves: Mimidae): congruent mtDNA and nuclear trees for a cosmopolitan avian radiation. *Mol. Phylogenet. Evol.* 44: 1031–1056.

Lowe P.R. 1932. [*Fringillaria capensis vincenti*, subsp. nov.] *Bull. Brit. Orn. Club* 52: 144-145.

Lynes H. 1930. Review of the genus *Cisticola. Ibis* (12) 6 suppl.: 1-673.

Lynes H. 1933. [Descriptions of three new subspecies of *Cisticola*]. *Bull. Brit. Orn. Club* 53: 168-171.

Lynes H. 1938. Contribution to the ornithology of the southern Congo basin. *Rev. Zool. Bot. Afr.* 31: 1-129.

Lynes H. & Sclater W.L. 1933-34. Lynes-Vincent tour in Central and West Africa in 1930-31. *Ibis* (13) 3: 694-729; 4: 1-51.

Maasdorp L. 1995. Fig tree with a thousand birds. *Honeyguide* 41: 28-29.

Macartney P. 1968. Wattled Cranes in Zambia. *Bokmakierie* 20: 38-41.

Mackworth-Praed C.W. 1920. [Five new races of African francolins]. *Bull. Brit. Orn. Club* 40: 139-142.

Mackworth-Praed C.W. & Grant C.H.B. 1945. On the plumages and moults of males of the sunbirds occurring in Eastern Africa. *Ibis* 87: 145-158.

Mackworth-Praed C.W. & Grant C.H.B. 1949. On the plumages of Eastern African weavers. *Ibis* 91: 299-304.

Mackworth-Praed C.W. & Grant C.H.B. 1957-60. *Birds of Eastern and North-eastern Africa.* (2nd edition). 2 vols. London: Longmans.

Maclaren P.I.R. 1955. Behaviour of Ruffs in Northern Rhodesia. *Bull. Brit. Orn. Club* 75: 81.

Maclean G.L. (Ed.) 1993. *Roberts' birds of southern Africa.* Cape Town: John Voelcker Bird Book Fund.

Macrae F.B. 1956. Mweru wa ntipa: more about water levels. *N. Rhod. J.* 3: 127-130.

Madge S.G. 1971a. Uningi Pans, Mbala. *Bull. Zambian Orn. Soc.* 3: 19-20.

Madge S.G. 1971b. Great Crested Grebes breeding near Mbala. *Bull. Zambian Orn. Soc.* 3: 20-21.

Madge S.G. 1971c. Shoebill Stork at Ndola. *Bull. Zambian Orn. Soc.* 3: 21-22.

Madge S.G. 1971d. Cuckoo Falcon's nest near Livingstone. *Bull. Zambian Orn. Soc.* 3: 22-23.

Madge S.G. 1971e. Albino Stonechat at Ndola. *Bull. Zambian Orn. Soc.* 3: 61.

Madge S.G. 1972a. Western Banded Snake-Eagle breeding near Ndola. *Bull. Zambian Orn. Soc.* 4: 25-26.

Madge S.G. 1972b. Notes on some bird species in Forestry Experimental Plots at Ndola. *Bull. Zambian Orn. Soc.* 4: 47-51.

Madge S.G. 1972c. Observations at a Bat Hawk's nest at Ndola. *Bull. Zambian Orn. Soc.* 4: 52-54.

Madge S.G. 1972d. Record of nest and eggs of Purple-throated Cuckoo Shrike near Ndola. *Bull. Zambian Orn. Soc.* 4: 55-56.

Madge S.G. 1972e. Eastern Golden Plover (*Pluvialis dominicus*) at Ndola: a species new to Zambia. *Bull. Zambian Orn. Soc.* 4: 59.

Madge S.G. 1972f. Scops Owl in the Luangwa Valley. *Bull. Zambian Orn. Soc.* 4: 59.

Madge S.G. 1972g. Nest of Spectacled Weaver made of pine needles. *Bull. Zambian Orn. Soc.* 4: 61.

Madge S.G. 1972h. Three species of the genus *Ortygospiza* feeding on the same ground at Ndola. *Bull. Zambian Orn. Soc.* 4: 61.

Madge S.G. 1972i. Brown Firefinch using old nests of weaver birds. *Bull. Zambian Orn. Soc.* 4: 62.

Madge S.G. & Sitters H.P. 1973. Great Crested Grebe and other species in Western Province. *Bull. Zambian Orn. Soc.* 5: 23-24.

Malambo C.H. & Chabwela H. 1992. Preliminary observations on the distribution and abundance of Wattled Cranes in Zambian wetlands. *Proc. 7th Pan-Afr. Orn. Congr.*: 71-74.

Mansfield D.N. 1963. The Cardinal Quelea in Nyasaland. *Bull. Brit. Orn. Club* 83: 119-120.

Marks S.A. 1996. Local hunters and wildlife surveys: an assessment and comparison of counts for 1989, 1990 and 1993. *Afr. J. Ecol.* 34: 237-257.

Masterson A.N.B. & Parkes D.A. 1998. Green Coucal in the Middle Zambezi Valley. *Honeyguide* 44: 89-90.

Mayr E. & Cottrell G.W. (Eds) 1986. (*Peters's*) *Check-list of birds of the world*. Vol. XI. Cambridge, Mass.: Mus. Compar. Zool.

Mees G.F. 1977. The subspecies of *Chlidonias hybridus* (Pallas), their breeding distributions and migrations (Aves, Laridae, Sterninae). *Zool. Verhand.* 157: 1-64.

Meiklejohn M.F.M. 1940. Notes on migratory birds from the southern shores of Lake Victoria, &c. December 22, 1939, to February 28, 1940. *Ostrich* 11: 33-40.

Melville R.V. & Smith J.D.D. (Eds) 1987. *Official Lists and Indexes of Names and Works in Zoology*. London: Int. Trust Zool. Nomencl.

Meyburg B.-U. & Meyburg C. 2005. Tracking the endangered Greater Spotted Eagle. http://microwavetelemetry.com/newsletters/winter_05page4.pdf.

Meyburg B.-U., Mendelsohn J.M., Ellis D.H., Smith D.G., Meyburg C. & Kemp A.C. 1995a. Year-round movements of a Wahlberg's Eagle *Aquila wahlbergi*, tracked by satellite. *Ostrich* 66: 135-140.

Meyburg B.-U., Scheller W. & Meyburg C. 1995b. Zug und Überwinterung des Schreiadlers *Aquila pomarina*: Satelliten-telemetrische Untersuchungen. *J. Orn.* 136: 401-422.

Meyburg B.-U., Ellis D.H., Meyburg C., Mendelsohn J.M. & Scheller W. 2001. Satellite tracking of two Lesser Spotted Eagles, *Aquila pomarina*, migrating from Namibia. *Ostrich* 72: 35-40.

Meyer de Schauensee R. 1951. Northern Rhodesian birds. *Proc. Acad. Nat. Sci. Philad.* 103: 23-63.

Miles M.J. 1977. Observations of Little Bitterns at Lusaka. *Bull. Zambian Orn. Soc.* 9: 16-20.

Mills M.S.L. 2006. First record of Pink-billed Lark *Spizocorys conirostris* for Angola. *Bull. Afr. Bird Club* 13: 212.

Mitchell B.L. 1963. A first list of plants collected in the Kafue National Park. *Puku* 1: 75-191.

Mitchell B.L. 1964. Owl prey. *Puku* 2: 129.

Mitchell B.L. 1966. Orientation of nests of the White-browed Sparrow-Weaver. *Puku* 4: 167-170.

Moltoni E. 1935. Ucelli raccolti dal Prof. Lidion Cipriani in Rhodesia nei 1929-30. *Atti della Soc. Ital. Sci. Nat. Milano* 74: 311-332.

Moreau R.E. 1944. Clutch-size: a comparative study, with special reference to African birds. *Ibis* 86: 286-347.

Moreau R.E. 1948. Aspects of evolution in the parrot genus *Agapornis*. *Ibis* 90: 206-239, 449-460.

Moreau R.E. 1958. Some aspects of the Musophagidae. *Ibis* 100: 67-112, 238-270.

Moreau R.E. 1966. *The bird faunas of Africa and its islands*. London & New York: Academic Press.

Morris A. 1981. The Mana experience. *Honeyguide* 107/108: 6-10.

Mouritz L.B. 1914. Notes on birds observed in Katanga, Belgian Congo. *Ibis* (10) 2: 26-38.

Moyle R.G. & Marks B.D. 2006. Phylogenetic relationships of the bulbuls (Aves: Pycnonotidae) based on mito-chondrial and nuclear DNA sequence data. *Mol. Phylogenet. Evol.* 40: 687–695.

Mundy P.J. 1998. Rüppell's Griffon in Zimbabwe – a third time. *Honeyguide* 44: 23-24.

Mundy P.J. & Maasdorp L. 1993. Possible Black Roughwing over Chirundu. *Honeyguide* 39: 195-196.

Mundy P.J., Maozeka F. & Couto J.T. 2001. An update on the status of Wattled Cranes in Zimbabwe. *Honeyguide* 47: 129-134.

Mwenya A.N. 1973. Ornithological notes from south east of Lake Bangweulu. *Puku* 7: 151-161.

Mwima H.K. 2001. A brief history of Kafue National Park, Zambia. *Koedoe* 44: 57-72.

Naylor R.T. 1974. A large roost of Black-breasted Snake Eagles. *Bull. Zambian Orn. Soc.* 6: 24.

Naylor E.G. 1975. European Golden Oriole eating a lizard. *Bull. Zambian Orn. Soc.* 7: 28.

Neave S.A. 1906. A journey to North-east Rhodesia during 1904 and 1905. *Manchester Memoirs* 51 (3): 1-7.

Neave S.A. 1907. On a collection of birds from N.E. Rhodesia. *Manchester Memoirs* 51 (10): 1-104.

Neave S.A. 1909. [New type of Weaver-Finch etc.] *Bull. Brit. Orn. Club* 25: 25-26.

Neave S.A. 1910. On the birds of Northern Rhodesia and the Katanga District of Congoland. *Ibis* (9) 4: 78-155,

225-262.

Neumann O. 1908. [New species and subspecies of African birds]. *Bull. Brit. Orn. Club* 21: 76-78.

Neunzig R. 1910. [*Amadina fasciata meridionalis* ssp. nov.] *J. Orn.* 58: 198.

Nhlane M.E.D. 1989. First record of Grey Kestrel *Falco ardosiaceus* in Malawi. *Vocifer* 12: 6-7.

Oatley T.B. 1969. Bird ecology in the evergreen forests of North Western Zambia. *Puku* 5: 141-180.

Oatley T.B., Oschadleus H.D., Navarro R.A. & Underhill L.G. 1998. *Review of ring recoveries of birds of prey in southern Africa: 1948-1998*. Johannesburg: Endangered Wildlife Trust.

Ogilvie-Grant W.R. 1896. Notes on some birds from the higher mountains of Nyika, west of Lake Nyasa, British Central Africa, with a description of a new species of francolin (*Francolinus crawshayi*). *Ibis* (7) 2: 482-489.

Ogilvie-Grant W.R. 1910. [A new species of crombec]. *Bull. Brit. Orn. Club* 27: 10-11.

Osborne T.O. 1975a. First breeding record of Mottled Swift in Zambia. *Bull. Zambian Orn. Soc.* 7: 28-29.

Osborne T.O. 1975b. A Black-breasted Snake Eagle roost at Blue Lagoon National Park. *Bull. Zambian Orn. Soc.* 7: 29.

Osborne T.O. 1975c. Sharpe's Akalat *Sheppardia sharpei*: a species new to Zambia. *Bull. Zambian Orn. Soc.* 7: 100-101.

Osborne T.O. 1975d. A sight record of Silvery-cheeked Hornbill (*Bycanistes brevis*) in Zambia. *Bull. Zambian Orn. Soc.* 7: 104.

Osborne T.O. 1978. Notes on the birds of Liuwa National Park and Preliminary Checklist. *Bull. Zambian Orn. Soc.* 10: 8-24.

Osborne T.O. 1981. Ecology of the Red-necked Falcon *Falco chicquera* in Zambia. *Ibis* 123: 289-297.

Osborne T.O. 1982a. Observations on the Tawny Eagle in southern Zambia. *Ostrich* 53: 107-111.

Osborne T.O. 1982b. Notes on breeding of the Bateleur in southern Zambia. *Ostrich* 53: 115-117.

Osborne T.O. 1984. Rednecked Falcon populations in Zambia. *Proc. 2 Symp. Afr. Predatory Birds*: 31-43.

Osborne T.O. 1987. Rock hyrax *Procavia capensis* new to Zambia. *Mammalia* 51: 327.

Osborne T.O. & Colebrook-Robjent J.F.R. 1975. Wahlberg's Eagle breeding success in the Southern Province of Zambia in 1974. *Bull. Zambian Orn. Soc.* 7: 30.

Osborne T.O. & Colebrook-Robjent J.F.R. 1982. Nesting of the Greater Kestrel *Falco rupicoloides* in Zambia. *Raptor Res.* 16: 71-76.

Osborne T.O. & Colebrook-Robjent J.F.R. 1984. Observations on the Lanner Falcon in eastern Zambia. *Proc. 2 Symp. Afr. Predatory Birds*:19-23.

Osborne T.O. & Scott P. 1976. First record of Cape Vulture (*Gyps coprotheres*) in Zambia. *Bull. Zambian Orn. Soc.* 8: 23.

Paget-Wilkes A.H. 1926. Birds of the upper tributaries of the Kafue River, N.W. Rhodesia. *S. Afr. J. Nat. Hist.* 6 (1): 61-69.

Parkin D.T., Collinson M., Helbig A.J., Knox A.G., Sangster G. & Svensson L. 2004. Species limits in *Acrocephalus* and *Hippolais* warblers from the Western Palearctic. *Brit. Birds* 97: 276-299.

Pasquet E., Cibois A., Baillon F. & Erard C. 2002. What are African monarchs (Aves, Passeriformes)? A phylogenetic analysis of mitochondrial genes. *C. R. Biologies* 325: 107-118.

Payne R.B. 1967. Nest and eggs of *Buccanodon anchietae*. *Bull. Brit. Orn. Club* 87: 34-35.

Payne R.B. 1969. Overlap of breeding and molting schedules in a collection of African birds. *Condor* 71: 140-145.

Payne R.B. 1971. Paradise Whydahs *Vidua paradisaea* and *V. obtusa* of southern and eastern Africa, with notes on differentiation of the females. *Bull. Brit. Orn. Club* 91: 66-76.

Payne R.B. 1973. Behavior, mimetic songs and song dialects, and relationships of the parasitic indigobirds (*Vidua*) of Africa. *Orn. Monogr.* 11: 1-333.

Payne R.B. 1977. Juvenile plumages of *Cuculus canorus* and *Cuculus gularis* in Africa. *Bull. Brit. Orn. Club* 97: 48-53.

Payne R.B. 1980a. Behavior and songs of hybrid parasitic finches. *Auk* 97: 118-134.

Payne R.B. 1980b. Seasonal incidence of breeding, moult and local dispersal of Red-billed Firefinches *Lagonosticta senegala* in Zambia. *Ibis* 122: 43-56.

Payne R.B. 1987. Song dialects and neighborhood habitats in the indigobirds *Vidua chalybeata* and *V. purpurascens* at Lochinvar National Park, Zambia. *J. Field Orn.* 58: 152-170.

Payne R.B. 2005. Nestling mouth markings and colors of Old World finches Estrildidae: mimicry and coevolution of nesting finches and their *Vidua* brood parasites. *Misc. Publ. Mus. Zool., Univ. Mich.* 194: 1-45.

Payne R.B. & Sorenson M.D. 2003. Museum collections as sources of genetic data. *Bonn. Zool. Beitr.* 51: 97-104.

Payne R.B., Hustler K., Stjernstedt R., Sefc K.M. & Sorenson M.D. 2002. Behavioural and genetic evidence of a recent population switch to a novel host species in brood-parasitic indigobirds *Vidua chalybeata. Ibis* 144: 373-383.

Payne R.B., Payne L.L. & Nhlane M.E.D. 1992. Song mimicry and species status of the Green Widowfinch *Vidua codringtoni. Ostrich* 63: 86-97.

Payne R.B., Payne L.L., Nhlane M.E.D. & Hustler K. 1993. Species status and distribution of the parasitic indigo-birds *Vidua* in East and southern Africa. *Proc. 8th Pan-Afr. Orn. Congr.*: 40-52.

Pearson D.J. 1983. A Blacksmith/Spur-winged Plover *Vanellus armatus* x *V. spinosus* hybrid? *Scopus* 7: 93-94.

Pearson D.J. & Backhurst G.C. 1976. The southward migration of Palaearctic birds over Ngulia, Kenya. *Ibis* 118: 78-105.

Penry E.H. 1975a. Palaearctic migrant ducks in Zambia. *Bull. Zambian Orn. Soc.* 7: 8-11.

Penry E.H. 1975b. Yellow-billed Kite (*Milvus migrans parasitus*): observations in a nest area. *Bull. Zambian Orn. Soc.* 7: 12-14.

Penry E.H. 1975c. Forbes's Plover (*Charadrius forbesi*) in Kitwe. *Bull. Zambian Orn. Soc.* 7: 30-31.

Penry E.H. 1975d. Terek Sandpiper (*Xenus terek*) in Zambia: a summary of recent records, 1971-74. *Bull. Zambian Orn. Soc.* 7: 88-90.

Penry E.H. 1975e. A year of Dabchick in Kitwe. *Bull. Zambian Orn. Soc.* 7: 91-98.

Penry E.H. 1976a. Highlights from the Kalilele Dambo and the borders of Copperbelt and North-Western Provinces. *Bull. Zambian Orn. Soc.* 8: 11-18.

Penry E.H. 1976b. Notes on Sooty Chat. *Bull. Zambian Orn. Soc.* 8: 27-28.

Penry E.H. 1976c. Grey phase Cattle Egret in Kitwe. *Bull. Zambian Orn. Soc.* 8: 70, 71.

Penry E.H. 1978a. The House Sparrow – a successful opportunist? *Bull. Zambian Orn. Soc.* 10: 25-27.

Penry E.H. 1978b. African Hobby attempting to breed in an African Fish Eagle's nest. *Bull. Zambian Orn. Soc.* 10: 36-37.

Penry E.H. 1979a. Sight records of the Sooty Falcon *Falco concolor* in Zambia. *Bull. Brit. Orn. Club* 99: 63-65.

Penry E.H. 1979b. White-headed Saw-wing (*Psalidoprocne albiceps*) in Chingola. *Bull. Zambian Orn. Soc.* 11 (1): 34.

Penry E.H. 1979c. Early and late dates for Splendid Starlings (*Lamprotornis splendidus*). *Bull. Zambian Orn. Soc.* 11 (1): 36-38.

Penry E.H. 1979d. The Rock Pratincole *Glareola nuchalis* at Greystone, Kitwe and a review of its migratory movements. *Bull. Zambian Orn. Soc.* 11 (2): 20-32.

Penry E.H. 1980. First record of Long-tailed Wagtail from Copperbelt Province. *Bull. Zambian Orn. Soc.* 12: 40-41.

Penry E.H. 1985. Notes on breeding of *Cisticola brunnescens* and *C. juncidis* in Zambia. *Ostrich* 56: 229-235.

Penry E.H. 1986. Notes on the biology of the Red-billed Quailfinch (*Ortygospiza gabonensis*) in Zambia. *Ostrich* 57: 193-202.

Penry H. 1994. *Bird Atlas of Botswana*. Pietermaritzburg: Univ. Natal Press.

Perennou C. (Ed.) 1992. *African waterfowl census 1992*. Slimbridge: I.W.R.B.

Peters D.U. 1953. A visit to Kilwa Island and the African Oil Palm. *N. Rhod. J.* 2 (1): 9-23.

Pinto A.A. da Rosa. 1983. *Ornitologia de Angola*. Vol. 1. Non-Passerines. Lisbon: Inst. Invest. Cient. Trop.

Pitman C.R.S. 1932a. Notes on Chaplin's Barbet (*Lybius chaplini*). *Ibis* (13) 2: 304-308.

Pitman C.R.S. 1932b. Notes on the breeding habits and eggs of *Rhinoptilus chalcopterus. Ool. Rec.* 12: 16-23.

Pitman C.R.S. 1932c. Notes on the breeding habits and eggs of *Rhynchops flavirostris* (Vieill.) – African Skimmer or Scissor-bill. *Ool. Rec.* 12: 51-54.

Pitman C.R.S. 1934. *Report on a faunal survey of Northern Rhodesia*. Livingstone: Govt Printer.

Pitman C.R.S. 1935a. The eggs of Wahlberg's Eagle – *Aquila wahlbergi* Sundevall. *Ool. Rec.* 15: 33-38.

Pitman C.R.S. 1935b. The eggs of *Bugeranus carunculatus* (Gmelin) – Wattled Crane. *Ool. Rec.* 15: 49-53.

Pitman C.R.S. 1965a. The nest and eggs of the Striped Crake, *Porzana marginalis* Hartlaub. *Bull. Brit. Orn. Club* 85: 32-40.

Pitman C.R.S. 1965b. The nesting, eggs and young of the Saddle-bill Stork, *Ephippiorhynchus senegalensis* (Shaw). *Bull. Brit. Orn. Club* 85: 70-80.

Pitman C.R.S. & Took J.M.E. 1973. The eggs of the African marsh grass-warbler, *Cisticola galactotes* (Temminck). *Arnoldia Rhod.* 6 (24):1-12.

Plowes D.C.H. 1951. A new race of Cape Bunting, from Mashonaland. *Ostrich* 22: 35.

Pollard C.J.W. 1980. A visual record of Chestnut-banded Sandplover at the Victoria Falls. *Honeyguide* 102: 37.

Pollard C.J.W. 1989a. Bar-tailed Godwit at Victoria Falls. *Honeyguide* 35: 70-71.

Pollard C.J.W. 1989b. Black-tailed Godwits at Victoria Falls. *Honeyguide* 35: 71.

Pollard C.J.W. 1991a. Additions and corrections to the Victoria Falls checklist. *Honeyguide* 37: 123-124.

Pollard C.J.W. 1991b. Greater Swamp Warbler in Zimbabwe. *Honeyguide* 37: 183.

Pollard C.J.W. 1992. Gull-billed Tern at Victoria Falls. *Honeyguide* 38: 24.

Pollard C.J.W. 2003. Yellow-bellied Hyliota at Victoria Falls. *Honeyguide* 49: 78-79.

Poole G. 2006. New to Zambia: Western Reef Heron. *Africa Birds & Birding* 11 (3): 21.

Pope R., Pope J. & Gurney M. 1999. New to Zambia: Rüppell's Vulture *Gyps rueppellii*. *Zambia Bird Rep.* 1998: 85-86.

Prigogine A. 1975. Les populations du Héron crabier, *Ardeola ralloides*, au Zaïre, au Rwanda et au Burundi. *Gerfaut* 65: 59-94.

Prigogine A. 1976. Occurrence of the Madagascar Squacco Heron *Ardeola idae* in Central Africa. *Bull. Brit. Orn. Club* 96: 96-97.

Prigogine A. 1983. Contribution aux migrations de *Lamprotornis splendidus bailundensis*. *Gerfaut* 73: 193-195.

Prigogine A. & Benson C.W. 1980. The mysterious movements of *Lamprotornis splendidus bailundensis*. *Gerfaut* 69 (1979): 437-445.

Reichenow A. 1902. [Neue Arten]. *Orn. Monatsb.* 10: 8.

Reichenow A. 1904. Neue Arten aus Ost-Afrika. *Orn. Monatsb.* 12: 95.

Reichenow A. 1916. Neue Arten. *Orn. Monatsb.* 24: 168-169.

Reichenow A. 1921. [Neue Arten]. *J. Orn.* 69: 263-266.

Renson G. 1998. Observations sur la reproduction du Bec-en-sabot *Balaeniceps rex* en Zambie de 1992 à 1997. *Alauda* 66: 81-96.

Richards D. 1974. Eastern Golden Plover (*Pluvialis dominica*) at Ndola. *Bull. Zambian Orn. Soc.* 6: 25.

Riddell I.C. 1990. Rare birds in the Ruckomechi Camp area of Mana Pools National Park. *Honeyguide* 36: 165-170.

Riddell I.C. 1991. Range extensions and movements at Mana Pools and Sengwa. *Honeyguide* 37: 110-115.

Riddell I.C. 1995. Forest Weaver in the Zambezi Valley. *Honeyguide* 41: 236-237.

Riddell I.C. 1999. Olive Bee-eater in Hwange National Park. *Honeyguide* 45: 141-142.

Riddell I.C. 2003. The Zimbabwe Rarities and National List Committee resurrected. *Honeyguide* 49: 87-89.

Riddell I.C. 2004a. Mana Pools, then and now. *Honeyguide* 50: 60-61.

Riddell I.C. 2004b. Eighth report of the BirdLife Zimbabwe Rarities Committee. *Honeyguide* 50: 230-232.

Roberts A. 1917. Ornithological notes. *Ann. Transv. Mus.* 5: 246-262.

Roberts A. 1932. Preliminary description of sixty-six new forms of South African birds. *Ann. Transv. Mus.* 15: 21-34.

Roberts A. 1941. Notes on some birds of the Cape Province. *Ostrich* 11: 112-135.

Roberts A. 1981. *A History of Zambia*. (Revised edition). London: Heinemann.

Robinson G.P. 1973a. Forbes's Plover near Ndola. *Bull. Zambian Orn. Soc.* 5: 33.

Robinson G.P. 1973b. African Hawk Eagle (*Hieraaetus spilogaster*) eating a squirrel. *Bull. Zambian Orn. Soc.* 5: 77.

Robinson G.P. 1973c. Notes on the prey of Dickinson's Grey Kestrel (*Falco dickinsoni*). *Bull. Zambian Orn. Soc.* 5: 77.

Robinson G.P. 1973d. Crowned Eagle (*Stephanoaetus coronatus*): a summary of recent records from Copperbelt Province. *Bull. Zambian Orn. Soc.* 5: 77-78.

Robinson G.P. 1975a. Observations of Peregrine Falcons in the Copperbelt Province. *Bull. Zambian Orn. Soc.* 7: 31-32.

Robinson G.P. 1975b. Breeding records for the Black-winged Stilt at Mufulira. *Bull. Zambian Orn. Soc.* 7: 32-33.

Robinson G.P. 1976. First record of Broad-billed Sandpiper (*Limicola falcinellus*) in Zambia. *Bull. Zambian Orn. Soc.* 8: 64-65.

Robinson G.P. & Casalis de Pury R.J. 1978. Bar-tailed Godwit (*Limosa lapponica*) at Luanshya. *Bull. Zambian Orn. Soc.* 10: 79.

Robinson G.B. & Robinson J.M. 1975. European Bee-eaters feeding young in Zambia. *Bull. Zambian Orn. Soc.* 7: 107.

Robinson S., Van Daele P. & Van De Woestijne C. 2001. New to Zambia: Spur-winged Plover *Vanellus spinosus*. *Zambia Bird Rep.* 1999: 69-72.

Rockingham-Gill D.V. 1988. Long-toed Plover at Mana Pools. *Honeyguide* 34: 124-125.

Rockingham-Gill D.V. & Tayler L.M. 1995. Grey-headed Gulls breed again at Lake Kariba. *Honeyguide* 41: 23-24.

Roxburgh L., Stjernstedt R., Mwizabi D. & Droppelmann K. 2006. Shoebill survey in Bangweulu Swamps, Zambia. Technical Report for Wetlands International: AEWA/BUWAL IWC 2006.

Roy M.S., Arctander P. & Fjeldså J. 1998. Speciation and taxonomy of montane greenbuls of the genus *Andropadus* (Aves: Pycnonotidae). *Steenstrupia* 24: 51-66.

Ryan P.G., Wright D., Oatley G., Wakeling J., Cohen C., Nowell T.L., Bowie R.C.K., Ward V. & Crowe T.M. 2004. Systematics of *Serinus* canaries and the status of Cape and Yellow-crowned Canaries inferred from mtDNA and morphology. *Ostrich* 75: 288-294.

Salewski V., Jones P. & Vickery J. 2001. Additions to the bird list of the Sengwa Wildlife Research Area. *Honeyguide* 47: 162-164.

Salvadori T. 1907. Collezione di uccelli nelle vicinanze del Lago Moero nell' Africa centrale, raccolti del Dott. Ascenso. *Boll. Mus. Zool. Torino* 22 (570): 1-9.

Sampson R. 1956. *They came to Northern Rhodesia*. Lusaka: published by the author.

Sandberg A. 1908. The fauna of the Barotse Valley. *Proc. Rhod. Sci. Assoc.* 7 (2): 31-42; 8 (1): 94-98.

Sangster G., Collinson J.M., Helbig A.J., Knox A.G. & Parkin D.T. 2005. Taxonomic recommendations for British birds: third report. *Ibis* 147: 821-826.

Sayer J.A. & van Lavieren L.P. 1975. The ecology of the Kafue lechwe population of Zambia before the operation of hydro-electric dams on the Kafue River. *E. Afr. Wildl. J.* 13: 9-37.

Schouteden H. 1971. La faune ornithologique de la Province du Katanga. *Mus. Roy. Afr. Centr., Doc. Zool.* 17: 1-248.

Sclater W.L. 1905. An ornithological excursion to the Victoria Falls of the Zambesi. *Ibis* (8) 5: 106-114.

Sclater W.L. 1906. *Agapornis nigrigenis*, sp. n. *Bull. Brit. Orn. Club* 16: 61-62.

Sclater W.L. 1932. [Some new and rare birds obtained by Rear-Admiral Hubert Lynes.] *Bull. Brit. Orn. Club* 52: 140-144.

Scott A.J. 1979. A Scarce Swift *Schoutedenapus myoptilus* on the Nyika Plateau. *Bull. Zambian Orn. Soc.* 11 (2): 46.

Scott A.J. 1983. A Lesser Black-winged Plover *Vanellus lugubris* at Chililabombwe. *Bull. Zambian Orn. Soc.* 13/15: 123-125.

Scott A.J. 1991. A revised and annotated checklist of the birds of the Luangwa Valley national parks and adjacent areas. *Occ. Pap. Zambian Orn. Soc.* 3: 1-40.

Serle W. 1955. Whinchats in Northern Rhodesia. *Ostrich* 26: 45-46.

Sharpe R.B. 1877. *Layard's Birds of South Africa*. (2nd edition). London: Quaritch.

Sharpe R.B. 1881. Birds pp. 294-328, Appendix in: **Oates F.** *Matabele Land and the Victoria Falls*. (1st edition). London: Keegan Paul, French.

Sharpe A. 1893. A journey from the Shire river to Lake Mweru and the upper Luapula. *Geogr. J.* (Feb.).

Sheldon F.H., Whittingham L.A., Moyle R.G., Slikas B. & Winkler D.W. 2005. Phylogeny of swallows (Aves: Hirundinidae) estimated from nuclear and mitochondrial DNA sequences. *Mol. Phylogenet. Evol.* 35: 254-270.

Shelley G.E. 1899a. [New forms] *Bull. Brit. Orn. Club* 8: 35.

Shelley G.E. 1899b. On a collection of birds from the Tanganyika Plateau, in British Central Africa. *Ibis* (7) 5: 364-380.

Shelley G.E. 1900. *The Birds of Africa*. Vol. 2, 348 pp. London: Porter.

Shelley G.E. 1903. On six new birds from Nyasa-land. *Bull. Brit. Orn. Club* 13: 60-61.

Shelley G.E. & Sclater P.L. 1897. On the birds collected by Mr. Alexander Whyte, F.Z.S., during his expedition to the Nyika Plateau in North Nyasaland. *Ibis* (7) 3: 518-554.

Shelley G.E. & Sclater P.L. 1901. On some collections of birds from the Protectorate of British Central Africa, received in 1899 and 1900. *Ibis* (8) 1: 161-177.

Shenton J.B. 1961. Nature note from Kafue National Park: elephant are rapidly on the increase. *Black Lechwe* 3 (1): 44-47.

Shenton J.B. 1963. Colour of nape in Crested Guineafowl (*Guttera e. edouardi*). *Puku* 1: 28.

Short L.L. 1982. On the status of *Lybius* (*minor*) *macclounii*. *Bull. Brit. Orn. Club* 102: 142-148.

Short L.L. & Horne J.F.M. 1985. Social behavior and systematics of African barbets (Aves: Capitonidae). *Proc. Intern. Symp. Afr. Vertebr.* (*Bonn*): 255-278.

Short L.L. & Horne J.F.M. 1988. Lesser Honeyguide *Indicator minor* interactions with its barbet hosts. *Proc. 6th Pan-Af. Orn. Congr.*: 65-75.

Short L.L., Horne J.F.M. & Muringo-Gichuki C. 1990. Annotated check-list of the birds of East Africa. *Proc. Western Found. Vert. Zool.* 4: 61-246.

Sibley C.G. & Monroe B.L. Jnr 1990. *Distribution and taxonomy of birds of the world*. New Haven: Yale Univ. Press.

Simpson C.D. 1961. The African Jacana *Actophilornis africanus* (Gmelin). *Bull. Brit. Orn. Club* 81: 82-85.

Sinclair I. & Ryan P. 2003. *Birds of Africa south of the Sahara. A comprehensive illustrated field guide.* Cape Town: Struik.

Skead C.J. 1967. *The sunbirds of southern Africa, also the sugarbirds, the white-eyes and the Spotted Creeper.* Cape Town: Balkema.

Smith K.D. 1950. The birds of Chirundu, Middle Zambesi. *Ostrich* 21: 62-71.

Smithers R.H.N. 1952. Some interesting Rhodesian records II. *Ostrich* 23: 97-108.

Smithers R.H.N. 1954. A new race of nightjar from Northern Rhodesia. *Bull. Brit. Orn. Club* 74: 84.

Smithers R.H.N. 1956. Some interesting Rhodesian and Bechuanaland records, III. *Ostrich* 27: 14-17.

Smithers R.H.N. 1984. Recollections of some great naturalists. *Transv. Mus. Bull.* 20: 5-15.

Smithers R.H.N. 1985. President's address, Southern African Ornithological Society (Annual General Meeting, June 1985).

Snow D.W. 1965. The Moult Enquiry. Fourth report, June 1965. *Bird Study* 12: 135-142.

Snow D.W. (Ed.) 1978. *An atlas of speciation in African Non-passerine birds*. London: Brit. Mus. (Nat. Hist.).

Sparrow A. 1993. Openbill Storks nesting at Senkwi river mouth, Kariba. *Honeyguide* 39: 22.

Spohr O.H. 1979. Emil Holub and August von Pelzeln look at the birdlife of South Africa in the 1870s. *Bokmakierie* 31: 37-39.

Spottiswoode C.N. & Colebrook-Robjent J.F.R. 2007. Egg puncturing by the brood parasitic Greater Honeyguide and potential host counteradaptations. *Behav. Ecol.* 18: 792-799.

Spottiswoode C., Leonard P. & Mills M. 2005. Little-known African bird: Chaplin's Barbet *Lybius chaplini*, Zambia's fig-loving endemic. *Bull. Afr. Bird Club* 12: 50-52.

Stewart D.R.M. 1959. The Red-billed Quelea in Northern Rhodesia. *N. Rhod. J.* 4: 55-62.

Stjernstedt B. 1975. Eagle attack. *Black Lechwe* 12 (1): 18, 22.

Stjernstedt R. 1984. First record of the Barred Long-tailed Cuckoo *Cercococcyx montanus* in Zambia. *Bull. Zambian Orn. Soc.* 16: 18-20.

Stjernstedt R. 1989. *Birdsong of Zambia*. (3 audio cassettes). Livingstone, Zambia: R. Stjernstedt.

Stjernstedt R. 1996. *Rare birds of Zambia*. (Audio cassette). Livingstone, Zambia: R. Stjernstedt.

Stjernstedt R. 1998a. Courtship feeding and other observations on Klaas's Cuckoo. *Honeyguide* 44: 204-207.

Stjernstedt R. 1998b. Kori Bustard *Ardeotis kori* sightings near Livingstone. *Zambia Bird Rep.* 1997: 52.

Stjernstedt R. 2003. Cloud Cisticola in Sesheke District. *Zambia Orn. Soc. Newsl.* 33 (4): 4.

Stjernstedt R. & Aspinwall D.R. 1979. The nest and eggs of the Bar-winged Weaver *Ploceus angolensis. Bull. Brit. Orn. Club* 99: 138-140.

Stoehr F.E. & Sclater W.L. 1906. Notes on a collection of birds made in North-east Rhodesia by Dr. F.E. Stoehr. *J. S. Afr. Orn. Union* 2 (2): 83-114.

Stowe T.J. & Becker D. 1992. Status and conservation of Corncrakes *Crex crex* outside the breeding grounds. *Tauraco* 2: 1-23.

Stowe T.J. & Green R.E. 1997. Threats to the Corncrake *Crex crex* on migration and in the winter quarters. *Die Vogelwelt* 118: 175-178.

Sweetman J.C. 1979. Klaas's Cuckoo laying an egg in a Yellow-bellied Eremomela nest. *Bull. Zambian Orn. Soc.* 11 (2): 47.

Symes C. 1999. The status, biology and conservation of the Grey-headed Parrot in southern Africa. *Honeyguide* 45: 10-12.

Symmes T.C.L. 1960a. Short notes on the Black Coucal in Northern Rhodesia. *J. E. Afr. Nat. Hist. Soc.* 23 (6) (103): 247.

Symmes T.C.L. 1960b. Notes on the Rufous-naped Lark (*Mirafra africana*) and the Red-capped Lark (*Calandrella cinerea*). *N. Rhod. J.* 4: 377-381.

Tapson W. 1955. Choma boma and Kalungwishi boma. *N. Rhod. J.* 2 (5): 89-90.

Tarboton W.R., Kemp M.I. & Kemp A.C. 1987. *Birds of the Transvaal.* Pretoria: Transvaal Museum.

Taylor P.B. 1977. Yellow-billed Kite taking Carmine Bee-eater. *Bull. Zambian Orn. Soc.* 9: 66-67.

Taylor P.B. 1978a. An albino Red-faced Cisticola (*Cisticola erythrops*). *Bull. Zambian Orn. Soc.* 10: 42.

Taylor P.B. 1978b. A melanistic Pied Wagtail (*Motacilla aguimp*) at Ndola. *Bull. Zambian Orn. Soc.* 10: 43.

Taylor P.B. 1978c. Observations from northern Zambia. *Bull. Zambian Orn. Soc.* 10: 62-70.

Taylor P.B. 1979a. Palearctic and intra-African migrant birds in Zambia: a report for the period May 1971 - December 1976. *Occ. Pap. Zambian Orn. Soc.* 1: 1-169.

Taylor P.B. 1979b. Red-throated Pipit *Anthus cervinus* at Ndola, Zambia. *Scopus* 3: 80.

Taylor P.B. 1980a. Pectoral Sandpiper *Calidris melanotos* and Lesser Yellowlegs *Tringa flavipes* in Zambia. *Bull. Brit. Orn. Club* 100: 233-235.

Taylor P.B. 1980b. Little Ringed Plover *Charadrius dubius* at Luanshya, Zambia. *Scopus* 4: 69.

Taylor P.B. 1980c. Common Tern *Sterna hirundo* at Luanshya, Zambia. *Scopus* 4: 70.

Taylor P.B. 1980d. Further occurrences of Red-throated Pipits *Anthus cervinus* at Ndola, Zambia. *Scopus* 4: 72.

Taylor P.B. 1980e. Little Crake *Porzana parva* at Ndola, Zambia. *Scopus* 4: 93-95.

Taylor P.B. 1981. A second Zambian record of the Little Ringed Plover *Charadrius dubius. Scopus* 5: 57.

Taylor P.B. 1982a. First Zambian records of Chestnut-banded Sandplover *Charadrius pallidus* and observations of White-fronted Sandplover *C. marginatus* and Cape Teal *Anas capensis* at the same locality. *Bull. Brit. Orn. Club* 102: 5-7.

Taylor P.B. 1982b. House Martins *Delichon urbica* associating with a breeding colony of Red-throated Cliff Swallows *Hirundo rufigula* in Zambia. *Scopus* 6: 43-45.

Taylor P.B. 1983. Jack Snipe *Lymnocryptes minimus*, Common Snipe *Gallinago gallinago* and Broad-billed Sandpiper *Limicola falcinellus* at Ndola, Zambia. *Scopus* 7: 20-21.

Taylor P.B. 1984. A field study of the Corncrake *Crex crex* at Ndola, Zambia. *Scopus* 8: 53-59.

Taylor P.B. 1985. Field studies of the African Crake *Crex egregia* in Zambia and Kenya. *Ostrich* 56: 170-185.

Taylor P.B. 1987. A field study of the Spotted Crake *Porzana porzana* at Ndola, Zambia. *Ostrich* 58: 107-117.

Taylor V. & Rose P.M. 1994. *African waterfowl census 1994.* Slimbridge: I.W.R.B.

Them P. 1984. At home in a wilderness. [*Agapornis nigrigenis*]. *Cage & Aviary Birds* 18 Aug.: 9-10.

Thompson B.R. 1969. Some bird records from Sesheke District. *Puku* 5: 235-236.

Thomson W.R. 1969. Taita Falcon *Falco fasciinucha*, in New distributional data: 2. *Ostrich* 40: 130.

Thomson W.R. 1983. On the Monotonous or White-tailed Bush Lark in Zimbabwe. *Honeyguide* 113: 21-22.

Tittle D. & Dowsett R.J. 2006. Mangrove Kingfisher *Halcyon senegaloides* inland in eastern Zambia. *Bull. Afr. Bird Club* 13: 194-196.

Tjomlid S.A. 1973. Food preferences and feeding habits of the Pied Kingfisher *Ceryle rudis. Ornis Scand.* 4: 145-151.

Took J.M.E. 1955. A trip down the Middle Zambesi. *Ool. Rec.* 29: 1-7.

Took J.M.E. 1966. The nest of Souza's Shrike, *Lanius souzae. Ostrich* 37: 155-156.

Trapnell C.G. 1959. Ecological results of woodland burning experiments in Northern Rhodesia. *J. Ecol.* 47: 129-168.

Trapnell C.G. & Clothier J.N. 1957. *The soils, vegetation, and agricultural systems of north-western Rhodesia.* Lusaka: Govt Printer.

Traylor M.A. 1960. Notes on the birds of Angola, non-passeres. *Publ. Cult. Comp. Cia. Diamant. Angola* 51: 129-186.

Traylor M.A. 1962a. New birds from Barotseland. *Fieldiana, Zool.* 44: 113-115.

Traylor M.A. 1962b. Notes on the birds of Angola, passeres. *Publ. Cult. Comp. Cia. Diamant. Angola* 58: 53-142.

Traylor M.A. 1963. Revision of the Quail Finch *Ortygospiza atricollis. Bull. Brit. Orn. Club* 83: 141-146.

Traylor M.A. 1964. Three new birds from Africa. *Bull. Brit. Orn. Club* 84: 81-84.

Traylor M.A. 1965a. First male of *Ploceus ocularis tenuirostris. Bull. Brit. Orn. Club* 85: 115-116.

Traylor M.A. 1965b. A collection of birds from Barotseland and Bechuanaland. *Ibis* 107: 137-172, 357-384.

Traylor M.A. 1966. The race of *Acrocephalus rufescens* in Zambia. *Bull. Brit. Orn. Club* 86: 161-162.

Traylor MA. 1971. Molt and migration in *Cinnyricinclus leucogaster. J. Orn.* 112: 1-20.

Traylor M.A. & Hart R.C. 1965. Some interesting birds from Barotseland. *Puku* 3: 133-141.

Tree A.J. 1961. Observations on migrating movements of some migratory birds in Northern Rhodesia. *Ostrich* 32: 86-89.

Tree A.J. 1962a. Black Sunbird ringing recovery. *Naturalist Soc. Centr. Afr.* 3: 18.

Tree A.J. 1962b. The birds of the Leopardshill area of the Zambesi escarpment. *Ostrich* 33 (4): 3-23.

Tree A.J. 1963a. Three cases of melanism and albinism. *Ostrich* 34: 178.

Tree A.J. 1963b. Brown-hooded Kingfisher *Halcyon albiventris* killing and eating a snake. *Ostrich* 34: 179.

Tree A.J. 1963c. Grey Hornbill *Tockus nasutus* as prey of the Lanner *Falco biarmicus*. *Ostrich* 34: 179.

Tree A.J. 1963d. Laughing Dove *Streptopelia senegalensis* passage on the Zambesi at Feira. *Ostrich* 34: 180.

Tree A.J. 1964. The occurrence of the Cliff Swallow (*Hirundo spilodera* (Sundevall)) on the Copperbelt. *Ostrich* 35: 113-114.

Tree A.J. 1965. On the Red-headed Quelea, *Quelea erythrops* (Hartlaub) in Zambia. *Bull. Brit. Orn. Club* 85: 159-161.

Tree A.J. 1966a. Some recent bird observations from the north Kafue basin. *Ostrich* 37: 30-36.

Tree A.J. 1966b. Notes on the Palaearctic migrants in the north Kafue basin, Zambia. *Ostrich* 37: 184-190.

Tree A.J. 1966c. Two recoveries of foreign banded European Swallows, *Hirundo rustica*, in Zambia. *Ostrich* 37: 191-192.

Tree A.J. 1967. Notes on the Caprimulgidae of the Kafue basin. *Ostrich* 38: 189-193 [corrected 42: 88].

Tree A.J. 1969. The status of Ethiopian waders in Zambia. *Puku* 5: 181-205.

Tree A.J. 1972. Black-throated forms of *Euplectes ardens* in Zambia and Rhodesia. *Ostrich* 43: 139-140.

Tree A.J. 1992. Some results of a ten day canoe trip along the Middle Zambezi – October 1991. *Honeyguide* 38: 12-17.

Trollope G. 1966. A Barotseland breeding record of the Half-collared Kingfisher (*Alcedo atthis semitorquata*). *Puku* 4: 193, 195-196.

Tucker J.J. 1971. Blue Swallow near Lusaka. *Bull. Zambian Orn. Soc.* 3: 59.

Tucker J.J. 1973. Baillon's Crake (*Porzana pusilla*) near Lusaka. *Bull. Zambian Orn. Soc.* 5: 78-79.

Tucker J.J. 1975a. Host record for the Greater Honeyguide (*Indicator indicator*). *Bull. Zambian Orn. Soc.* 7: 37.

Tucker J.J. 1975b. White-winged Black Tern biometrics from Zambia. *Bull. Zambian Orn. Soc.* 7: 99.

Tucker J.J. 1978. A River Warbler *Locustella fluviatilis* "wintering" and moulting in Zambia. *Bull. Brit. Orn. Club* 98: 2-4.

Tucker J.J. & Tucker E.A. 1975. June record of Jacobin Cuckoo near Lusaka. *Bull. Zambian Orn. Soc.* 7: 38.

Turner M.I.M. 1978. Ross's Violet Loerie (*Musophaga rossae*) in northern Malawi. *Bull. Zambian Orn. Soc.* 10: 82.

Tyler S.J. 2005. The Slaty Egret *Egretta vinaceigula* – a review, with special reference to Botswana. *Babbler* 46: 8-17.

Ulfstrand S. & Alerstam T. 1977. Bird communities of *Brachystegia* and *Acacia* woodlands in Zambia. A quantitative study with special reference to the significance of habitat modification for the Palaearctic migrants. *J. Orn.* 118: 156-174.

Underhill L.G., Tree A.J., Oschadleus H.D. & Parker V. 1999. *Review of ring recoveries of waterbirds in southern Africa*. Cape Town: Avian Demography Unit, U.C.T.

Urban E.K., Fry C.H. & Keith S. (Eds) 1997. *The Birds of Africa*. Vol. 5. London: Academic Press.

Uys J.M.C. & Clutton-Brock T.H. 1966. The breeding of the Rufous-bellied Heron (*Butorides rufiventris*) in Zambia. *Puku* 4: 171-180.

Van Daele P. 1999a. A confirmed Zambian record of Brown-chested Wattled Plover *Vanellus superciliosus*. *Zambia Bird Rep.* 1998: 93-97.

Van Daele P. 1999b. A sight record of Grey Kestrel *Falco ardosiaceus* in Mwinilunga District. *Zambia Bird Rep.* 1998: 98-102.

Van Daele P. 1999c. An active nest of Woolly-necked Stork *Ciconia episcopus*. *Zambia Bird Rep.* 1998: 107-108.

Van Daele P. 1999d. New breeding data for Red-throated Cliff Swallows *Hirundo rufigula* at Mutanda Bridge. *Zambia Bird Rep.* 1998: 112-113.

Van Daele P. 1999e. Habitat of Honeyguide Greenbul *Baeopogon indicator* and Bristlebill *Bleda syndactyla* in Zambia. *Zambia Bird Rep.* 1998: 113.

Van Daele P. 1999f. Range extension of Collared Palm Thrush *Cichladusa arquata* in North-Western Province. *Zambia Bird Rep.* 1998: 114-115.

Van Daele P. 2001. Presumed breeding of Avocet *Recurvirostra avosetta* on the Zambezi River in Western Province. *Zambia Bird Rep.* 1999: 91-92.

Van Daele P. & Leonard P.M. 2001. The status of Great Crested Grebes *Podiceps cristatus* in Zambia. *Zambia Bird Rep.* 1999: 88-90.

Van Daele P. & Stjernstedt R. 2001a. The Kori Bustard *Ardeotis kori* in Zambia. *Zambia Bird Rep.* 1999: 54-56.

Van Daele P. & Stjernstedt R. 2001b. Bird surveys of the Barotse floodplains. *Zambia Bird Rep.* 1999: 58-68.

van Lavieren L.P. 1973. Shoebill Stork (*Balaeniceps rex*) in Lukanga Swamp. *Bull. Zambian Orn. Soc.* 5: 79.

Varden D. 1991. Olive Woodpecker at Victoria Falls. *Honeyguide* 37: 182.

Varden J. 1999a. Cardinal Quelea in Mana Pools National Park: a record at last for southern Africa. *Honeyguide* 45: 129-130.

Varden J.G. 1999b. The Double-banded Courser in Hwange National Park. *Honeyguide* 45: 135-136.

Vaurie C. 1965. *The birds of the Palearctic fauna*. Non Passeriformes. London: H.F. & G. Witherby.

Verheyen R. 1953. *Exploration du Parc National de l'Upemba*. Fasc. 19. Oiseaux. Bruxelles: Inst. Parcs Nat. Congo Belge.

Vernon C.J. 1964. Observations on *Cisticola njombe* and *nigriloris*. *Bull. Brit. Orn. Club* 84: 124-131.

Vernon C.J. 1971 Notes on the biology of the Black Coucal. *Ostrich* 42: 242-258.

Vernon C.J. 1983. Notes on the Monotonous or White-tailed Bush Lark in Zimbabwe. *Honeyguide* 113: 19-21.

Vernon C.J. 1987. On the Eastern Green-backed Honeyguide. *Honeyguide* 33: 6-12.

Vernon C.J. 1993. Pied Mannikin as prey of Cat-eyed Snake. *Honeyguide* 39: 149-150.

Vernon C.J. 2004. A review of the Bronze-winged Courser in southern and south-central Africa. *Honeyguide* 50: 26-36.

Vesey-FitzGerald L.D.E.F. 1965. Lechwe pastures. *Puku* 3: 143-147.

Vincent J. 1934. Review of two African species, *Cyanomitra olivacea* (Olive Sunbird) and *Batis molitor* (Chinspot Flycatcher). *Ibis* (13) 4: 85-94.

Warburton L. 2000. First nesting records of the Black-cheeked Lovebird, *Agapornis nigrigenis*: an update on the lovebird project to ZOS. *Zambia Orn. Soc. Newsletter* 30 (11/12): 10-12.

Warburton L. 2002. Black-cheeked Lovebird. Africa's most threatened lovebird. *Africa Birds & Birding* 7 (1): 52-59.

Warburton L.S. & Perrin M.R. 2005. Conservation implications of the drinking habits of Black-cheeked Lovebirds *Agapornis nigrigenis* in Zambia. *Bird Conserv. Int.* 15: 383-396.

Warburton L.S. & Perrin M.R. 2006. The Black-cheeked Lovebird (*Agapornis nigrigenis*) as an agricultural pest in Zambia. *Emu Austral Ornithology* 106: 321-328.

Weaver J., Dunkley A. & Hartley R.R. 2002. Taita Falcon surveys in the 1980s. *Honeyguide* 48: 175-180.

White C.M.N. 1941. A new species of flycatcher from Northern Rhodesia. *Bull. Brit. Orn. Club* 61: 48-49.

White C.M.N. 1943a. A new race of Green Pigeon from Northern Rhodesia. *Bull. Brit. Orn. Club* 63: 63-64.

White C.M.N. 1943b. Three new races from Northern Rhodesia. *Bull. Brit. Orn. Club* 64: 19-22.

White C.M.N. 1943c. Field notes on some birds of Mwinilunga, Northern Rhodesia. *Ibis* 85: 127-131.

White C.M.N. 1943d. Notes on the birds of the Lusaka District, Northern Rhodesia. *Ibis* 85: 257-264.

White C.M.N. 1943e. Garganey in Northern Rhodesia. *Ibis* 85: 346.

White C.M.N. 1944a. A new race of *Serinus*. *Bull. Brit. Orn. Club* 64: 40-41.

White C.M.N. 1944b. A new race of Scrub Robin and a new race of Red-winged Francolin from Northern Rhodesia. *Bull. Brit. Orn. Club* 64: 49-50.

White C.M.N. 1944c. New races of lark, pipit, and cordon bleu from Northern Rhodesia, Angola, and the Belgian Congo. *Bull. Brit. Orn. Club* 65: 5-7.

White C.M.N. 1944d. A new race of francolin from Northern Rhodesia. *Bull. Brit. Orn. Club* 65: 7-8.

White C.M.N. 1944e. Miscellaneous notes on Northern Rhodesian birds. *Ibis* 86: 139-150.

White C.M.N. 1944f. Further notes on Palaearctic migrants in Northern Rhodesia. *Ostrich* 15: 49-55.

White C.M.N. 1944g. A new subspecies of sunbird. *Ostrich* 15: 137.

White C.M.N. 1945a. A new race of barbet from Northern Rhodesia. *Bull. Brit. Orn. Club* 65: 18-19.

White C.M.N. 1945b. On francolins from Angola and Northern Rhodesia. *Bull. Brit. Orn. Club* 65: 38-40.

White C.M.N. 1945c. A new race of bustard from Northern Rhodesia. *Bull. Brit. Orn. Club* 65: 47-48.

White C.M.N. 1945d. A note on the larks of the *Mirafra rufocinnamomea* group. *Bull. Brit. Orn. Club* 66: 13-15.

White C.M.N. 1945e. On the validity of *Gallinago angolensis* Bocage. *Ibis* 87: 465-466.

White C.M.N. 1945f. A new subspecies of *Cisticola*. *Ostrich* 16: 138-139.

White C.M.N. 1945-46. The ornithology of the Kaonde-Lunda Province, Northern Rhodesia. *Ibis* 87: 11-25, 185-202, 309-345; 88: 68-103, 206-224.

White C.M.N. 1946a. Notes on pipits of the *Anthus richardi* group and a new race of waxbill from Northern Rhodesia. *Bull. Brit. Orn. Club* 67: 8-10.

White C.M.N. 1946b. The ornithology of the Kaonde-Lunda Province, Northern Rhodesia: Supplementary notes. *Ibis* 88: 502-512.

White C.M.N. 1947a. A new race of warbler from Northern Rhodesia. *Bull. Brit. Orn. Club* 67: 55.

White C.M.N. 1947b. Two new races of francolins from Northern Rhodesia and some records from Lundazi. *Bull. Brit. Orn. Club* 67: 72-73.

White C.M.N. 1947c. Notes on Central African birds. *Bull. Brit. Orn. Club* 68: 34-36.

White C.M.N. 1947d. The Pearl-breasted Swallow in Northern Rhodesia. *Ibis* 89: 359-360.

White C.M.N. 1947e. Notes on some little-known birds from Northern Rhodesia. *Ostrich* 18: 166-174.

White C.M.N. 1948a. A new race of Lemon Dove from Northern Rhodesia. *Bull. Brit. Orn. Club* 69: 20-21.

White C.M.N. 1948b. *Mirafra angolensis* in Northern Rhodesia. *Ibis* 90: 137.

White C.M.N. 1948c. Additions to the ornithology of the Kaonde-Lunda Province, Northern Rhodesia. *Ibis* 90: 328.

White C.M.N. 1949a. A new race of thrush from Northern Rhodesia. *Bull. Brit. Orn. Club* 69: 57-58.

White C.M.N. 1949b. *Petrochelidon rufigula* in Northern Rhodesia. *Ibis* 91: 348.

White C.M.N. 1950. A revision of *Anthreptes collaris* (Vieillot), with descriptions of two new races. *Bull. Brit. Orn. Club* 70: 40-43.

White C.M.N. 1951a. New or unusual records from Northern Rhodesia. *Bull. Brit. Orn. Club* 71: 50.

White C.M.N. 1951b. Weaver birds at Lake Mweru. *Ibis* 93: 626-627.

White C.M.N. 1953a. A revision of *Sylvietta ruficapilla* Bocage. *Bull. Brit. Orn. Club* 73: 68-70.

White C.M.N. 1953b. Systematic and distributional notes on African birds. *Bull. Brit. Orn. Club* 73: 76-77.

White C.M.N. 1954a. A new race of grass warbler from Northern Rhodesia. *Ann. Mus. Congo Belge* sér. 4, Zool. 1: 106.

White C.M.N. 1954b. A revision of *Colius indicus* Latham. *Bull. Brit. Orn. Club* 74: 58-59.

White C.M.N. 1954c. A new race of *Cossypha polioptera* Reichenow. *Bull. Brit. Orn. Club* 74: 88.

White C.M.N. 1957. Taxonomic notes on Northern Rhodesian birds. *Bull. Brit. Orn. Club* 77: 34-36.

White C.M.N. 1958. A new lark from Northern Rhodesia. *Bull. Brit. Orn. Club* 78: 163-164.

White C.M.N. 1960a. A new form of *Cisticola textrix* Vieillot. *Bull. Brit. Orn. Club* 80: 146-147.

White C.M.N. 1960b. Further notes on African warblers. *Bull. Brit. Orn. Club* 80: 147-152.

White C.M.N. 1961a. Notes on *Eremomela icteropygialis* (Lafresnaye). *Bull. Brit. Orn. Club* 81: 90-92.

White C.M.N. 1961b. Notes on *Oenanthe pileata* (Gmelin). *Bull. Brit. Orn. Club* 81: 166-168.

White C.M.N. 1961c. *A revised check list of African broadbills, pittas, larks* etc. Lusaka: Govt Printer.

White C.M.N. 1963. *A revised check list of African flycatchers, tits, tree creepers* etc. Lusaka: Govt Printer.

White C.M.N. 1965. *A revised check list of African non-passerine birds*. Lusaka: Govt Printer.

White C.M.N. & Grimwood I.R. 1954. Four birds new to Northern Rhodesia. *Bull. Brit. Orn. Club* 74: 103.

White C.M.N. & White K.A.A. 1939. Some overlooked records of Northern Rhodesian birds. *Ibis* (14) 3: 766-768.

White C.M.N. & Winterbottom J.M. 1949. *A Check List of the Birds of Northern Rhodesia*. Lusaka: Govt Printer.

White F. 1962. *Forest Flora of Northern Rhodesia*. Oxford: Oxford Univ. Press.

White F. 1965. The savanna woodlands of the Zambezian and Sudanian domains. *Webbia* 19: 651-681.

White F. 1979. The Guineo-Congolian region and its relationship to other phytochoria. *Bull. Jard. Nat. Bot. Belg.* 49: 11-55.

White F. 1981. The history of the Afromontane archipelago and the scientific need for its conservation. *African J. Ecol.* 19: 33-54.

White F. 1983a. *The vegetation of Africa*. Paris: UNESCO. (With vegetation maps).

White F. 1983b. Long-distance dispersal and the origins of the Afromontane flora. *In* Kubitzki K. (Ed.). Dispersal and distribution. *Sonderb. Naturwiss. Vereins Hamburg* 7: 87-116.

White F., Dowsett-Lemaire F. & Chapman J.D. 2001. *Evergreen forest flora of Malawi*. Kew: Royal Botanic Gardens.

Williams J.G. 1953. *Cinnyris mediocris*. A revision of the species and description of a new race. *Bull. Brit. Orn. Club* 73: 8-11.

Williams J.G. 1955a. *Tringa totanus totanus* in Northern Rhodesia. *Bull. Brit. Orn. Club* 75: 79-80.

Williams J.G. 1955b. *Cinnyris oustaleti*: notes on plumages and habits. *Ibis* 97: 150-153.

Williams J.G. 1958. *Cyanomitra batesi* in Northern Rhodesia. *Bull. Brit. Orn. Club* 78: 30-31.

Williams J.G. 1959. On the status of the Northern Rhodesian population of *Cyanomitra batesi*. *Bull. Brit. Orn. Club* 79: 101.

Williams J. 1989. Red-knobbed Coot on Lake Kariba. *Honeyguide* 35: 114.

Williams J. & Varden D. 1994. Lemon-breasted Canary at Nyanga. *Honeyguide* 40: 30.

Williamson K. 1968. *Identification for ringers*. 3. The genus *Sylvia*. (Revised edn). Tring: B.T.O.

Willis E.O. 1983. Jays, mimids, icterids and bulbuls (Corvidae, Mimidae, Icteridae and Pycnonotidae) as ant followers. *Gerfaut* 73: 379-392.

Willis E.O. 1985. East African Turdidae as safari ant followers. *Gerfaut* 75: 140-153.

Wilson K.J. 1964. A note on the stomach contents of a Palm Thrush (*Cichladusa arquata* Peters). *Puku* 2: 130-131.

Wilson K.J. 1965. A note on the crop contents of two Crested Guinea-fowl *Guttera edouardi* (Hartlaub). *Ostrich* 36: 103-106.

Wilson V.J. 1972a. Observations on the effect of Dieldrin on wildlife during Tsetse Fly *Glossina morsitans* control operations in eastern Zambia. *Arnoldia* (*Rhod.*) 5 (34): 1-12.

Wilson V.J. 1972b. Notes on *Otis denhami jacksoni* from the Nyika Plateau. *Bull. Brit. Orn. Club* 92: 77-81.

Winterbottom J.M. 1932. Letter on Chaplin's Barbet. *Ibis* (13) 2: 722-723.

Winterbottom J.M. 1936. Distributional and other notes on some Northern Rhodesian birds. *Ibis* (13) 6: 763-791 (correction 1937, (14) 1: 913).

Winterbottom J.M. 1937. The birds of the dams in the Eastern Province of Northern Rhodesia. *Ostrich* 8: 68-83.

Winterbottom J.M. 1938a. Further notes on some Northern Rhodesian birds. *Ibis* (14) 2: 269-277.

Winterbottom J.M. 1938b. The birds of the Mupane woodlands of the Luangwa Valley, Northern Rhodesia. *Ostrich* 9: 61-73.

Winterbottom J.M. 1938c. On three bird censuses in woodland in Northern Rhodesia. *J. Anim. Ecol.* 7: 266-271.

Winterbottom J.M. 1939a. *Revised Check List of the Birds of Northern Rhodesia*. Lusaka: Govt Printer.

Winterbottom J.M. 1939b. Miscellaneous notes on some birds of Northern Rhodesia. *Ibis* (14) 3: 712-734.

Winterbottom J.M. 1941a. Bird population studies, XII. On the bird population of Lundazi boma, Northern Rhodesia. *Ostrich* 11: 101-107.

Winterbottom J.M. 1941b. On the birds of the Acacia thickets ("Lusaka") Northern Rhodesia. *Ostrich* 12: 86-91.

Winterbottom J.M. 1942a. A contribution to the ornithology of Barotseland. *Ibis* (14) 6: 18-27, 337-389.

Winterbottom J.M. 1942b. An ornithological reconnaissance of southern Namwala. *Ostrich* 13: 88-92.

Winterbottom J.M. 1944. The avifauna of the Old Jeanes School station, Mazabuka, Northern Rhodesia, 1941-42. *Ostrich* 15: 114-129.

Winterbottom J.M. 1951-52. Some notes on Northern Rhodesian birds. *N. Rhod. J.* 1 (4): 24-30; (6): 32-40.

Winterbottom J.M. 1952. Some birds of the Victoria Falls. *Bokmakierie* 4: 10-11.

Winterbottom J.M. 1953. On the bird population of the old Jeanes School station, Mazabuka, Northern Rhodesia, 1948-49. *Ostrich* 24: 174-181.

Winterbottom J.M. 1954. An expedition to western Sesheke. *Bokmakierie* 6: 39-41.

Winterbottom J.M. 1956a. The bird population of the Mupane woodland. *N. Rhod. J.* 3 (2): 124-126.

Winterbottom J.M. 1956b. The birds of Livingstone township, Northern Rhodesia, 1942-1950. *Ostrich* 27: 134-147.

Wood P.A. & Tree A.J. 1992. Zambezi River survey October 1991. *Honeyguide* 38: 54-63.

Wright P.J. 1963. Nesting behaviour of the Wattled Plover. *Puku* 1: 218.

Wyatt J.K. 1965. Verreaux Eagle. [Letter]. *Black Lechwe* 5 (1): 30, 32.

Zimmerman D.A., Turner D.A. & Pearson D.J. 1996. *Birds of Kenya and northern Tanzania*. London: Christopher Helm.

Index of scientific names
(page numbers in bold refer to the main species account)

Index of English names
(page numbers in bold refer to the main species account)

Also published by Tauraco Press:

The Birds of Malawi

by Françoise Dowsett-Lemaire & Robert J. Dowsett

556 pages,
softback, 2006